TEACHER'S EDITION

Addison-Wesley

Physical Science

Gordon P. Johnson
Northern Arizona University

Bonnie B. Barr
State University of New York at Cortland

Michael B. Leyden
Eastern Illinois University

Consultants and Contributors

Patricia Bennett
Science Editorial Consultant,
San Jose, California

Alan Gould
Science Editorial Consultant,
Berkeley, California

Marcile Hollingsworth
Former Science Superintendent
Houston, Texas

Candace Holts
Science Editorial Consultant,
Santa Barbara, California

Donald Inman
Former Teacher, Menlo Park,
California

Marilyn Linner
Former Teacher, Clinton, Iowa

Chelcie Liu
Instructor, City College of
San Francisco

Katherine Liu
Teacher, Pacifica, California

Iris Martinez Kane
Teacher, Watsonville, California

Pat Obenauf
Associate Professor,
West Virginia University

Nancy Straus
Science Editorial Consultant,
Oakland, California

Clive Tucceri
Educational Consultant,
Melrose, Massachusetts

Alison Wells
Science Editorial Consultant,
Cupertino, California

Project Development Staff

Project Editor
Maria Kent

Editors
John McClements
   (Student Edition)
Andrea Julian
Michael O'Neill

Design Coordinator
Joyce Chang

Photo Editor
Inge Kjemtrup

Indexer
Lois Oster

About the Authors

Gordon P. Johnson is a professor of physics at Northern Arizona University in Flagstaff. He taught science and mathematics at the junior and senior high school level in Minnesota for eleven years. He served as president of the Arizona Science Teachers Association and has been on the board of directors of the National Science Teachers Association. He received a Ph.D. in education with a chemistry minor from the University of Minnesota. He is coauthor of *The Third Planet: Physical Science for Survival on Planet Earth* (Kendall–Hunt, 1975).

Bonnie B. Barr is a professor of science education at State University of New York at Cortland. She has been a teacher, elementary science coordinator, and science supervisor in public schools in New York, Oregon, and Pennsylvania. She has conducted workshops at national, state, and regional science teachers' conventions. She received a Ph.D. in science education from Cornell University, where she was assistant author of the *Cornell Science Leaflets*. She is the author of *Addison-Wesley Life Science* and coauthor of *Science A* and *Science B,* a junior high science program for Canadian students.

Michael B. Leyden is a professor of elementary and junior high science education at Eastern Illinois University in Charleston. He has taught junior high science in New York. In 1982 he was awarded a Gustav Ohaus-NSTA Award for innovations in science teaching. He is active in local and national science teachers associations and has written many articles for *The Science Teacher* and *Science and Children*. He is coauthor of *Science A* and *Science B* and is a consulting author of *Addison-Wesley Life Science*. He holds an Ed.D. in science education from the University of Florida.

Cover photo: © Robert Arnold

ISBN 0-201-22207-8

ABCDEFGHIJKL-KR-8909876

Contents of the Teacher's Edition

Addison-Wesley Life Science, Earth Science, and Physical Science

- Student success and understanding.
- Teacher effectiveness and support.

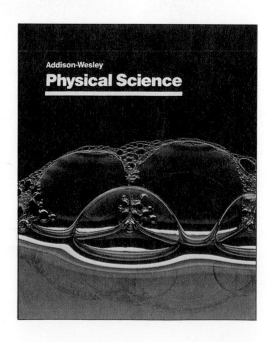

Discover excellence in
Addison-Wesley Physical Science

- Conceptually developed content.
- Skills and applications emphasized.
- Activities, investigations and laboratories.
- Supplements for teaching and supplements for learning.

In **Addison-Wesley Physical Science**

Conceptually developed lessons mean success.

- Lessons begin with familiar things in students' everyday life and build toward more complex science concepts.

- Students come to understand and comprehend concepts because they learn from their experiences and their environment.

- Concepts are defined in context and vocabulary is developed throughout the discussion.

- Students retain concepts and understanding.

In **Addison-Wesley Physical Science**

Conceptually developed lessons mean comprehension and longer retention of concepts and skills.

- Main ideas are explicit and well labeled.

- Problems are worked out in detail and immediately reinforced with practice exercises.

- Complete and balanced coverage of chemistry and physics topics.

- Applications provide the connection between textbook and real life.

Table 3-2.   **Periodic Table of the Elements**

Addison-Wesley Physical Science

has features developed to make learning and teaching easier.

What can iron filings show about a magnetic field?

Iron filings may be used to outline a magnetic field. A piece of paper, glass, or plastic is placed over the magnet. Iron filings are sprinkled on the paper. Each of the iron filings acts like a tiny, temporary magnet. The filings line up in the field like little compass needles. The positions of the filings show the direction of the magnetic field lines all around the magnet.

The iron filings are closest together where the magnetic field is the strongest. They are farthest apart where the magnetic field is the weakest. Thus, they show the positions of the magnetic field lines for the magnet.

The needle in a compass is a magnetized needle that is free to turn. It tends to point north because the earth itself has a magnetic field. A compass needle lines up with the magnetic field lines of the earth's own field.

The earth's magnetic field is nearly the same as that produced by a large bar magnet. The earth acts as though there were a bar magnet deep inside, near the earth's center.

Research Topic

Read about the hypotheses to explain what causes the earth's magnetic field. What seems to be the most widely accepted hypothesis?

Figure 11-4. *Iron filings outlining the magnetic field of a bar magnet (top) and horseshoe magnet (bottom). How can you tell where the poles of the magnets must be?*

Figure 11-5. *The earth's magnetic field is like that of a bar magnet near the earth's center. The imaginary bar magnet points toward the earth's magnetic poles, which are different from the true north and south poles.*

Geographic North Pole

Magnetic North Pole

Imaginary bar magnet

Direction of rotation of earth

Magnetic South Pole

Geographic South Pole

A compass needle does not point to the earth's true geographic north pole. This is because the imaginary bar magnet does not point directly north and south. Instead, it points northward to what is called the earth's magnetic north pole. The earth's magnetic north pole is in northern Canada, just north of the Arctic Circle. Similarly, the earth's magnetic south pole is right near the Antarctic Circle, south of Australia. The earth's magnetic poles slowly move. Studies indicate that there have been major changes in the earth's magnetic field over long time periods.

Pieces of iron can be magnetized with the help of the earth's field. A piece of iron is lined up with the earth's field. The iron is given a sharp blow with a hammer. The magnetic domains inside the iron are shaken by the blow. They realign in the direction of the earth's field. Now the entire piece of iron is a magnet.

Data Search

If you were standing on the Mexico-California border, how many degrees should you adjust your magnetic compass to find geographic north? Search pages 658–661.

Critical Thinking

If the magnetic field of the earth were to reverse, what would be the effects on navigation, on machinery and on animals such as bees and migrating birds?

Quick Review

1. How do magnetic field lines represent the strength of a magnetic field?
2. Explain why the magnetic north pole is in a different location from the geographic north pole.

Main Ideas spotlight the key concepts and help students understand the basic principles of chemistry and physics.

Research Topics provide opportunities to extend learning, explore sources of information and investigate related topics.

Critical Thinking develops students' skills in analysis and evaluation of Physical Science.

Safety Notes warn of hazards and suggest proper precautions to take to prevent accidents.

Data Search encourages students to locate and interpret data within and beyond the textbook.

Our Science Heritage spotlights the development of important ideas in science and the people who made contributions to the advancement of science.

Addison-Wesley Physical Science

means your students learn more and you don't have to work as hard.

Problem Solving exercises in the text include solutions worked out in detailed steps, immediately followed by additional problems for practice and maintenance of skills.

Problem Solving is emphasized to provide quantitative skills in measuring, processing data, and calculating results.

Unit, Chapter, and Section openers are designed to focus student attention and help them organize the content.

New science terms are defined in context, reviewed in Section and Chapter reviews, and included in the Glossary.

Frequent **Quick Review** questions assess student understanding of the basic concepts.

A perfect balance of chemistry and physics concepts to meet all curriculum needs.

Sample Problem

Suppose that incandescent light bulbs give off 3 J per second of light for every 100 watts of their rated power. What would you expect the rated power to be of a light bulb that gives off 4.5 J per second of light?

Solution

Set up a ratio between the power and light output of the unknown and known light bulbs.

$$\frac{? \text{ W}}{4.5 \text{ J/s}} = \frac{100 \text{ W}}{3 \text{ J/s}}$$

Multiply both sides by 4.5 J/s and cancel units as shown:

$$? \text{ W} = \frac{(4.5 \text{ J/s}) \times (100 \text{ W})}{3 \text{ J/s}}$$

Cancel the similar factors and divide out the numbers.

$$? \text{ W} = (1.5) \times (100 \text{ W}) = 150 \text{ W}$$

Practice Problem

Based on the assumption made in the example above, calculate the rated power of a light bulb that gives off 5.2 J per second of light. *Answer:* 173 W

Incandescent light bulbs use tungsten filaments. Tungsten filaments have a high resistance but do not melt at the high temperatures produced. Ordinary air is also removed from the bulb. The air is replaced by nitrogen and argon gases. These gases do not react with the metal filament. They also help to keep the filament from gradually wearing down and sticking to the inside of the bulb which would darken it. Oxygen, which is part of ordinary air, does react with metals at high temperatures. The presence of oxygen would reduce the life of the light bulb by causing the filament to burn up completely.

Main Idea

Why is tungsten used in incandescent light bulbs?

Quick Review

1. What kind of force makes something move in an electric motor?
2. What is the function of high-resistance wire in a circuit?
3. What prevents the filament of an incandescent light bulb from melting or wearing out quickly?
4. List at least three forms of energy that can be produced from electric energy.

11.2 Electric Energy   523

Addison-Wesley Physical Science

confronts the impact of science on society. Students see the effects of science and technology and apply the concepts they have learned to real-life issues.

Issues in Physical Science develop an awareness of the benefits and sometimes harmful side effects of modern technology and the social and political implications of scientific advances.

Trends in Technology provide students with up-to-date applications and advances of physical science concepts and principles and offer a glimpse into the developments of the future.

Careers offer students background information on two science-related occupations per chapter. Careers are related to the content of the chapter and reflect a variety of education and training requirements.

Addison-Wesley Physical Science

provides frequent reviews and evaluation for assessment.

Each **Section Review** measures student comprehension and vocabulary development, understanding higher level reasoning skills and recall of basic concepts.

The **Chapter Reviews** continue a strong emphasis on vocabulary development. **Critical Thinking** questions evaluate higher levels of reasoning—interpretation, application and analysis. **Individual Research** challenges motivated students with library projects and activities for extension of their learning. The **Bibliography** lists and briefly describes useful references for additional reading and study.

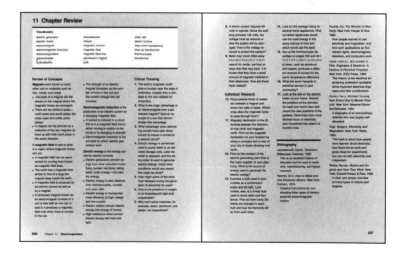

Addison-Wesley Physical Science

means you can depend on comprehensive planning and help in managing discussions and demonstrations.

Chapter Planning Guides provide a complete system for coordinating resources and meeting individual needs for each Section.

Developing Laboratory Skills helps you to manage activities, investigations and laboratories to meet your teaching style and requirements.

Getting Started in each section helps you with **Suggested Demonstrations** and **Ideas for Discussion** to capture student interest and motivate them with creative and stimulating demonstrations.

Activity outcomes and suggestions help you to prepare and direct hands-on science laboratory procedures.

Chapter 7   **Using Energy from Chemical Reactions**

Chapter 7 Planning Guide

Planning Your Classroom Lessons

	7.1 Carbon Chemistry 296–312	7.2 Using Fuels for Heat and Work 313–326	7.3 Using Fuels for Living Cells 327–341	Chapter 7 Review 342–343 Chapter 7 Supplements
Content Overview	An examination of the many kinds of organic compounds, which are the essential chemicals found in living beings Concept Summary T110 Learning Objectives T110	The absorption and release of energy in chemical changes, and the use of fuels to provide energy Concept Summary T112 Learning Objectives T112	Food, the fuel of living things, and the path taken by the energy in food from its origin in the sun to its release in the body Concept Summary T114 Learning Objectives T114	Science Background Information 294 Review of Concepts 342–343 Essential Ideas/ Chapter 7 Letter to Parents
Teaching Strategies	Getting Started: Ideas for Discussion and Suggested Demonstration T110	Getting Started: Ideas for Discussion and Suggested Demonstration T112	Getting Started: Ideas for Discussion and Suggested Demonstration T114	
Teaching Aids	Teaching Diagram 7-1A, 7-1B Overhead Transparency	Teaching Diagram 7-2A, 7-2B	Teaching Diagram 7-3A, 7-3B	Physical Science Software T00 Physical Science Films and Videos Video Lesson: Energy and Changes in Matter
Review and Evaluation*	Quick Review 297, 299, 303, 304, 305, 307, 308, 311 7.1 Review 312 Section Testsheet 7-1 TRB 217	Quick Review 315, 318, 319, 322, 325 7.2 Review 326 Section Testsheet 7-2 TRB 218	Quick Review 328, 330, 333, 335, 336, 337, 339 7.3 Review 341 Section Testsheet 7-3 TRB 219	Chapter Testsheets 7A and 7B TRB 253–254 Free Response Questions TRB 000 Semester Test 1 TRB 273–276 *Higher Level Evaluation* Critical Thinking 343

*TESTGEN can be used to prepare customized section and chapter testsheets

Meeting Individual Needs

Reinforcement	Reading Checksheet 7-1 TRB 97 Skillsheet 7-1 TRB 143 Essential Ideas 7.1	Reading Checksheet 7-2 TRB 98 Skillsheet 7-2 TRB 144 Essential Ideas 7.2	Reading Checksheet 7-3 TRB 99 Skillsheet 7-3 TRB 145 Essential Ideas 7.3	Information Library Software
Enrichment	Research Topic Data Search	Research Topic 320, 322 Data Search	Research Topic 333 Data Search	Individual Research 343 Bibliography 343 Issues in Physical Science: Use of Coal as Fuel 344 Trends in Technology: Solutions to Acid Rain 345
Critical Thinking and Problem Solving	Critical Thinking Practice Problem 303	Critical Thinking 317 Practice Problem 314	Critical Thinking	Chapter Testsheet 7B TRB 254 Problem-Solving Worksheets, Chapter 7

Addison-Wesley Physical Science

supports you every day. Annotations on fully reproduced student pages give you all the help you need for each and every lesson.

Learning Objectives identify key concepts to focus attention on expected outcomes, and are correlated to Section Review questions.

Complete cross-referencing to front-matter notes and **Teacher's Resource Book** activities are located at the start of each Chapter and Section.

Science Background Information and **Teaching Suggestions** help teachers of varying backgrounds prepare and conduct motivating and factual classes.

Complete Answers save you time in grading assignments and review questions.

For ideas for classroom demonstration and discussion, see Getting Started on page T00 in the front of this book.

11.1 Magnets

Supplemental materials: Teaching Diagram X-X (TRB page 00), Reading Checksheet X-X (TRB page 00), Skillsheet X-X (TRB page 00), Investigation X-X (Lab Manual pages 00–00)

Section Preview

- Magnetic poles and domains
- Magnetic fields
- Electromagnetism
- Electromagnets
- Galvanometers
- Electromagnetic induction

Learning Objectives

1. To describe the behavior of magnets and their interaction with other magnetic materials.
2. To define a magnetic field and explain the behavior of magnetic materials in a magnetic field.
3. To demonstrate the magnetic effects of an electric current.
4. To illustrate how a changing magnetic field can be used to produce an electric current.

Figure 11-1. *Iron tacks are attracted to the end of a bar magnet. The magnetic forces are strongest at the two ends of the magnet.*

Magnets are fascinating. A small magnet can pick up many paper clips or tacks. People have known about magnets for thousands of years. Yet, a real understanding of them has developed only in the last two centuries.

Magnetic poles and domains

Paper clips and tacks cluster at the ends of a straight, or bar, magnet. These places on a magnet where the magnetic forces are strongest are called the **poles.** The poles of a bar magnet are at either end. The poles of a horseshoe magnet are at the ends of the "legs."

The two poles of a magnet are different. If you bring them close to one of the poles of another magnet, they respond differently. One pole of the first magnet will attract the third pole and stick to it. The other pole of the first magnet will repel the third pole. This is evidence that the two poles are different.

Main Idea

What are the poles of a magnet?

496   *Chapter 11* **Electromagnetism**

Addison-Wesley Physical Science

provides flexibility for active learning. Activities are thoroughly integrated into the content and provide frequent opportunities for applying and verifying concepts.

Activities are easy to do in the classroom or laboratory.

Materials are simple, easy to obtain and inexpensive.

Activities reinforce concepts and develop observation and analysis skills.

Activities can be completed in one class period.

Activities of different levels allow hands-on learning by students of all ability levels.

Activities encourage development of oral and written communications skills.

Activity See also Activity Record Sheet 11-1B (Lab Manual page 150). Answers to Questions and Conclusion appear on page T151 in the front of this book.

11.1b The Magnetic Field of a Current-Carrying Wire

Materials
- 2 "D" cells
- masking tape
- 30-cm × 30-cm heavy cardboard
- at least 60-cm insulated wire with ends exposed
- 4 small compasses
- 5 thick books

Purpose

To map the magnetic field around a straight current-carrying wire.

Procedure

1. Tape together two "D" cells top to bottom to form a battery.
2. Punch a small hole in the center of a 30-cm by 30-cm piece of cardboard.
3. Push one end of the wire through the hole in the cardboard and tape it to the negative terminal (flat end) of your battery.
4. Place one side of the cardboard in the center of a stack of five books so that most of the cardboard sticks out.
5. Lay the upper end of the wire over the top book. Make sure the wire passes straight up and down through the cardboard.
6. Put four small compasses on the cardboard around the wire. Record the direction each needle points.
7. Close the circuit for a few seconds by touching the free end of the wire to the positive terminal of the battery. Record the direction each compass needle points when the current flows through the wire.
8. Reverse the direction of the current through the wire by reversing the connections to the battery. Again record the direction each compass needle points when current flows through the wire.

Questions

1. Do the compass needles point in the same direction when no current is flowing?
2. What happens to the compass needles when current flows through the wire?
3. What happens to the compass needles when current flows the opposite way?

Conclusion

What is the shape of the magnetic field lines around a straight current-carrying wire?

Step 3

Step 6

Addison-Wesley Physical Science

provides you with more options for lab work . . . how much you want when you want. Built-in **Activities** (p. T14) and a complete laboratory program give you all the choices you need.

The **Addison Wesley Physical Science Laboratory Manual** contains:

- **Investigations** to extend learning with in-depth experiments. Develop observation, recording and measuring skills.

- **Investigations** to build and improve problem-solving, critical thinking and process skills.

- **Activity Record Sheets** to record data and answer questions from text activities.

- **Research Labs** to challenge students to use their science skills in designing and performing experiments to broaden their knowledge and stimulate scientific thought. They also extend students' ability to apply skills to concepts and develop and prove hypotheses.

Teacher's Edition contains complete annotations with answers, setup instructions, safety tips, and suggestions for incorporating a flexible laboratory program into your course. Recommended group size and time are noted for each Investigation to help you plan further.

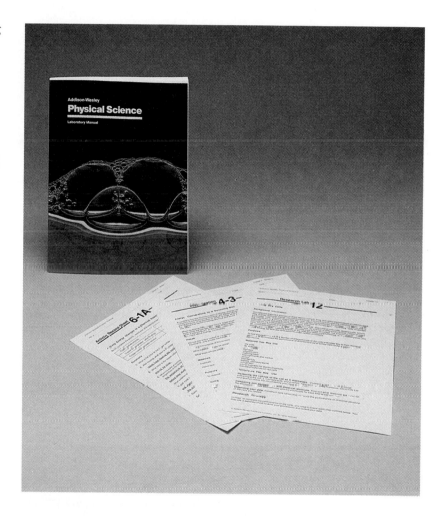

Addison-Wesley Physical Science

has a unique **Teacher's Resource Book:** It is a true resource—not filler to make it thick, and not a lot of excess practice.

The **Addison Wesley Physical Science Teacher's Resource Book** contains:

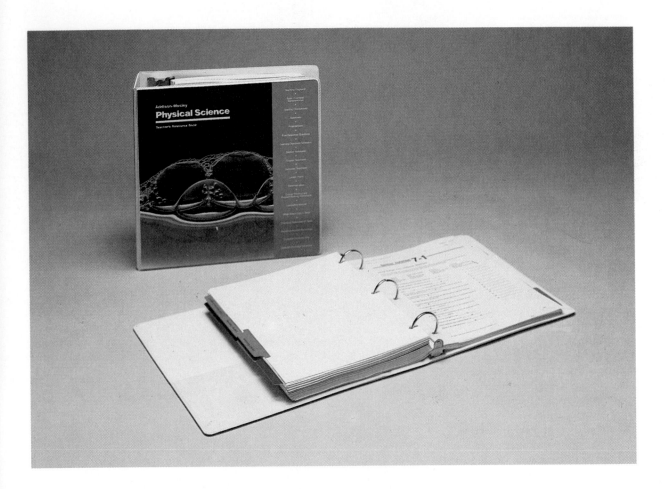

- Resources for meeting individual needs: remediation, maintenance, and extension.

- Skills and applications are developed and improved.

- Evaluation options for measuring student performance and progress.

- Total flexibility in designing a course to suit your needs.

Addison-Wesley Physical Science

builds, maintains, and extends skills and applications; a
science program you and your students can really use.

Reading Checksheets develop
science reading vocabulary
skills and help students improve
their ability to organize and analyze information.

Skillsheets develop science and
language skills with puzzles and
problems to reinforce student
understanding of basic concepts.

Projectsheets provide opportunities for additional lab work,
field investigations, and physical
science projects.

Tests for complete assessment
for each Section and Chapter,
and also for both semesters.
These tests measure recall and
ability to interpret data.

Daily Lesson Plans save teacher
preparation time by providing
you with detailed lessons for
every day of the school year.

Essential Ideas provide brief
summaries for each section; less
able students and poor readers
can access key concepts.

**Critical Thinking and Problem
Solving** worksheets develop
problem-solving skills in basic
chemistry and physics.

Addison-Wesley Physical Science

gives you more Supplemental Programs than any other text. You can choose software for students, software for testing, Video Lessons, overhead transparencies, and more.

Information Laboratory combines a comprehensive database of more than 600 topics with a built-in applications utility for solving problems.

A flexible software program for

- stimulating critical thinking
- meeting individual needs
- building problem-solving skills
- use with every text lesson

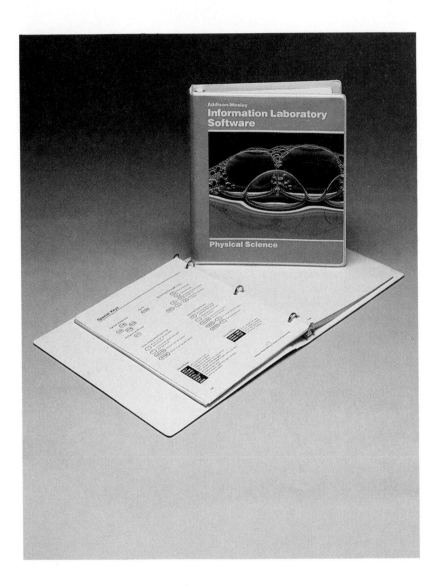

Addison-Wesley Physical Science

gives you access to a multimodal approach to teaching.

TESTGEN provides you with test generating software for creating customized tests to make multiple versions for meeting your own testing needs.

Video Lessons allow you to show topics economically and safely. Professionally produced to save time and money, they are closely correlated to each Unit.

Overhead Transparencies are in full color and allow you to teach more effectively using graphics from the textbook.

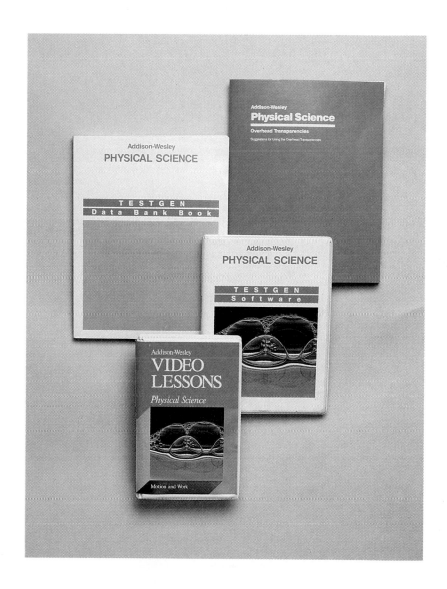

Scope and Sequence of Addison-Wesley Physical Science

Chapter & Sequence	Main Concepts	Skills
Chapter 1 Science and Measurement		
1.1 Scientific Methods	An **observation** is information gathered through the use of the senses or with the aid of instruments. The **scientific method** is a set of steps outlining a way of attacking problems in science. A **model** is a description of something unfamiliar in terms of familiar things.	To use direct and indirect observation to determine the properties of a solid object. To use the scientific method to determine the identity of a hidden object.
1.2 Measurement	A **measurement** is an observation that describes the amount of a property that includes both a number and a unit.	To discover how different measurements of the same object can have different values. To determine how the mass and volume of different size blocks of the same wood are related. To learn to make reasonable estimates.
1.3 Problem Solving	The **unknown** in a word problem is what is being asked for.	To determine how many 100-mL containerfuls of water will fit inside a cube 10 cm on a side.
Chapter 2 Properties of Matter		
2.1 Matter	**Matter** is anything that has mass and takes up space. The **classification of matter** is a grouping of matter according to its properties.	To determine the differences among substances that look very much alike. To learn the different ways in which objects can be classified. To demonstrate the separation of a solid from a liquid by the evaporation method.
2.2 Changes in Matter	A **physical change** is a change in which the properties of a substance change but no new substances are formed. A **chemical change** is a change in which one or more new substances are formed.	To show how temperature changes affect the volume of a sample of air. To determine when a chemical change has taken place.
Chapter 3 The Structure of Matter		
3.1 The Particle Model of Matter	**Processes of science** include making repeated observations, inferring relationships between sets of observations, and forming explanations that can be used to predict additional observations. A **scientific model** is a description in terms of familiar things and is used to explain observations and predict behaviors. The **particle model of matter** pictures matter as made of tiny particles with space between them.	To find out which can be compressed more easily—air or water. To show that there is space between the particles in a liquid or a solid.
3.2 Models of the Atom	The **periodic table of the elements** is an arrangement that is in order of increasing atomic number and in which elements with similar properties are in the same column. The **shell model of the atom** pictures an atom with a nucleus containing protons and neutrons, surrounded by shells of electrons.	To use models of atoms to learn about atomic structure. To use the periodic table to determine the identity of some mystery elements.
3.3 A Model for Chemical Change	**Electric charges** cause pushes and pulls between objects that do not have equal numbers of positive and negative charges. A **chemical bond** is a tie between two atoms that have transferred or shared electrons. **Acids** and **bases** are substances that furnish hydrogen ions and hydroxide ions, respectively.	To observe the behavior of charged objects. To test substances to determine if they are acidic or basic.

Chapter & Sequence	Main Concepts	Skills
Chapter 4 Motion		
4.1 Describing Motion	**Motion** is the movement or changing of position of an object with respect to a reference object. **Speed** is how fast an object changes its position with respect to a reference object. **Acceleration** is a change in the speed or in the direction of motion of an object.	To measure the speed of runners two ways. To recognize whether an object is moving at constant speed. To determine how changes in speed and direction can be detected.
4.2 Forces and Motion	A **force** is a push or pull. The **force of gravity** acts between any two objects.	To show that for an action force, there is an equal and opposite reaction force. To determine whether the mass of a ball affects the length of time it takes to roll down a ramp. To determine whether objects with different horizontal speeds fall at different rates.
4.3 Energy	**Energy** is the ability to cause change.	To determine whether the kinetic energy of a moving object depends on its mass. To determine when a pendulum has the most kinetic energy and when it has the most potential energy.
Chapter 5 Work and Heat		
5.1 Work and Machines	**Work** is energy that is transferred to an object when the object moves in the direction of a force acting on the object. A **machine** is something that changes the size and/or direction of a force used to do work. **Power** is a measure of how fast work is being done or how fast energy is being used.	To measure work with and without an inclined plane. To compare three kinds of levers. To determine the mechanical advantage of different pulleys.
5.2 Heat and Internal Energy	**Heat** is energy that is transferred as a result of differences in temperature. The **internal energy** of a substance is the energy inside it. **Forms of energy** are different kinds of energy, such as kinetic energy, potential energy, work, heat, and internal energy.	To predict the final temperature when hot and cold water are mixed. To determine how heat moves from one place to another.
5.3 The Kinetic Theory of Matter	The **kinetic theory of matter** is a model that pictures matter as made of particles that are in constant, random motion.	To determine if the speed of diffusion differs for solids dissolved in liquids at different temperatures. To show the temperature changes that occur during the melting of ice.
Chapter 6 Chemical Reactions		
6.1 Comparing Chemical Reactions	A **chemical change** is a change in matter that produces one or more new substances.	To show how the energy changes in a chemical reaction can be observed. To "count" the number of particles in a sample by weighing.
6.2 Controlling Chemical Reactions	The **reaction speed** of a chemical reaction is a measure of how fast the reactants are used up or how fast the products are formed. An **ore** is a compound that contains a metal in combination with other elements.	To observe the effect of steel wool on the decomposition of hydrogen peroxide. To observe the speed of chemical changes in hot and cold water.
Chapter 7 Using Energy from Chemical Reactions		
7.1 Carbon Chemistry	**Organic compounds** are compounds that contain carbon.	To make three-dimensional models of simple hydrocarbons. To compare the effect of organic solvents and water on the solubility of different pigments.

Chapter & Sequence	Main Concepts	Skills
7.2 Using Fuels for Heat and Work	A **chemical reaction** is a change in which one or more new substances are formed. A **fuel** is a substance that burns easily and is burned to supply energy.	To show how a steam turbine works. To show that coal contains natural gas or methane.
7.3 Energy and Living Things	**Cell respiration** is a process inside a cell in which glucose combines with oxygen to form carbon dioxide and water, and energy is released. **Fermentation** is a process inside a cell in which glucose is broken down in the absence of oxygen. **Photosynthesis** is a process in which the energy in sunlight is used to change carbon dioxide and water into glucose and oxygen.	To determine which kind of nut—a walnut, a cashew, or an almond—gives off the most energy per gram when it is burned. To find what factors affect the amount of heat released during fermentation.
Chapter 8 Waves and Sound		
8.1 Waves	A **wave** is a repeating pattern that moves through matter without moving the matter along with it.	To observe a wave traveling through matter without making the matter travel. To make a model of a compressional wave. To observe the behavior of water waves.
8.2 Properties of Sound	**Sound** is energy that is produced and transferred by vibrating matter.	To compare sound transmission in air to that in wood, metal, and string. To compare the length of a vibrating object with the pitch of the sound it makes.
8.3 The Wave Model of Sound	The **wave model of sound** is the theory that sound is energy that travels in a compressional wave.	To determine the relation between length and frequency for a pendulum. To make eight bottles play a musical scale.
Chapter 9 Light		
9.1 Properties of Light	**Light** is energy that can be detected by the eye.	To determine how the image distance is related to the object distance for a plane mirror. To measure the way light bends as it moves from one substance to another.
9.2 Color	**White light** is a combination of light of all colors.	*Part 1.* To see how colored light affects the color of colored objects. *Part 2.* To see what colors are produced when different colors of light are combined. To construct Benham's Disks and observe colors in the spinning black and white disks.
9.3 Models for Light	What is light? Is there a **model** that can explain the behavior of light?	To observe the diffraction of light through a diffraction grating; to compare the diffraction spectrum produced by an ordinary light bulb with that produced by a fluorescent light. To observe the effect polarizing filters have on light.
Chapter 10 Electric Charges and Currents		
10.1 Electric Charges	**Electric charges** cause pushes and pulls between objects that do not have equal numbers of positive and negative charges.	To demonstrate how the electric charge on an object can be identified. To observe the electric charge on an object with an electroscope.
10.2 Electric Currents	An **electric current** is created by the movement of electric charges. An **electric circuit** is a conducting path or set of paths through which current can flow.	To learn how to use an ammeter; to measure current in a circuit. To learn how to use a voltmeter; to measure the voltage drop across a conductor.

Chapter & Sequence	Main Concepts	Skills
10.3 Electric Circuits	An **electric current** is created by the movement of electric charges. An **electric circuit** is a conducting path or set of paths through which current can flow.	To study properties of a series circuit. To study properties of a parallel circuit.
Chapter 11 Electromagnetism		
11.1 Magnets	**Magnets** exert forces on each other and on materials such as iron, cobalt, and nickel. A **magnetic field** is said to exist in a region where magnetic forces can act. **Electromagnetic induction** is the production of an electric current by a changing magnetic field.	To map the magnetic field around a bar magnet. To map the magnetic field around a straight current-carrying wire. To make an electromagnet and determine how its strength can be changed. -
11.2 Electric Energy	**Electric energy** is the energy carried by electric currents.	To convert electrical energy to energy of motion. To make a model of an incandescent light bulb.
Chapter 12 Electrochemical Reactions		
12.1 Oxidation and Reduction	**Oxidation** is the loss of electrons in a chemical change; reduction is the gain of electrons in a chemical change.	To discover what factors slow down and speed up the process of corrosion. To identify the location of separate oxidation and reduction reactions in the corrosion of a metal object.
12.2 Electric Energy and Chemical Reactions	An **electrochemical cell** is made up of two metals that have different activities.	To construct a simple electrochemical cell. To find out how the voltage changes when different combinations of metals are used in a wet cell.
Chapter 13 Nuclear Reactions		
13.1 The Nuclear Structure of Atoms	**Radioactivity** is the release of particles and/or energy from the nucleus of an atom.	To model the half-life of a radioactive isotope. To investigate the effects of radiation on an electroscope.
13.2 Energy from Nuclear Changes	The **conservation of mass and energy principle** dictates that mass and energy must both be forms of the same thing. **Nuclear fission** is the breaking up of a nucleus into two or more smaller nuclei. **Nuclear fusion** is the joining together of two or more nuclei.	To illustrate a chain reaction by using dominoes. To construct a model of the fusion reaction between tritium and deuterium nuclei.
Chapter 14 Our Energy Needs		
14.1 Present Energy Resources	**Entropy** is a measure of the distribution of energy in a system. An **energy pathway** describes the set of changes energy goes through from its source, such as the sun, to its use by humans. A **nonrenewable energy resource** is a source of usable energy that is used much faster than it can be replaced.	To determine the difficulty of removing oil from a well. To determine how things increase exponentially.
14.2 Alternative Energy Resources	A **renewable energy resource** is a source of usable energy that can be replaced as fast as it is used.	To show how solar energy can be used to cook food. To determine whether the angle of sunlight affects the amount of energy absorbed by a sunlit surface.
14.3 Energy Conservation	**Conservation of energy** is the saving of energy by eliminating unnecessary uses and preventing waste of energy.	To find out if your family's driving habits are wasteful. To determine if a shower uses less hot water than a tub bath.

Philosophy and Approach

A CONCEPT-DEVELOPMENT APPROACH

Did you ever put together a do-it-yourself kit? At first glance, the vast number of parts can seem overwhelming. It is difficult to see how they all fit together.

This can also be true of a science program. The presentation of many isolated facts can distract from the understanding of scientific relationships. To remedy this situation, in Addison-Wesley Physical Science, the content is developed conceptually.

The application of science concepts to new situations, rather than rote memorization, allows students to draw their own logical conclusions about the world around them. It also provides a lasting context for future involvement. The students' own personal experiences strengthen the formation of science concepts.

LEARNING BY READING

The student text is written in concise language and structured to hold students' interest, continually motivating them to read further.

The reading level of this book has been analyzed with leading readability formulas and found to be at an appropriate level for intermediate grade students. The special science terms are carefully presented for maximum retention and understanding.

MOTIVATING STUDENTS TO READ

In addition to the activities, the photos and drawings are also designed to motivate reading. The captions frequently ask probing questions which can be answered by careful reading of the text.

Subheadings and Main Idea questions give students an idea of what they can expect to read in each subsection. These provide a focus for the student's interest before beginning to read.

BUILDING SCIENCE VOCABULARY

In Addison-Wesley Physical Science, each new science word is put in boldface type when first used. The word is then spelled phonetically, if necessary, and carefully defined in terms of the discussion at hand. This definition is reinforced by repeated use of the word in various contexts.

For further reinforcement, vocabulary tests are placed in every Section Review. A complete glossary lists all these new science words.

GROWTH IN READING TEXTBOOKS

Your students should read textbooks in a way that is very different from the way they read for recreational purposes. An effective method to help improve textbook reading skills is described as SQ3R by F. P. Robinson.* We recommend its use with these books as follows:

- **S—Survey.** Students should first glance over all the headings in a section and note the main points that are being developed.
- **Q—Question.** Students should mentally change each heading into a question which they intend to answer by reading the passage that follows it.
- **3R—Reading, Reciting, and Reviewing.** Students should read the passage for the purpose of answering the question. They should then look away from the page and recite the answer to the question. When they have finished reading the passage, they review their reading by doing the *Quick Review* questions.

LEARNING BY DOING

Students learn best when the content appears relevant and when hands-on experiences are integrated with text and illustrations. Addison-Wesley Physical Science provides many opportunities for active investigation on all levels. Informal activities are provided throughout the text. These activities are easy to perform and require only simple materials. They encourage further inquiry and motivate students to read the text and to do independent research. More formal investigations are included in the Laboratory Manual accompanying the text.

---

*Robinson, F. P. *Effective Reading*. New York: Harper & Row, 1962.

Student Edition Organization

The Student Edition has numerous features designed to enhance student success in learning about physical science. These features are described on this page. Page references for each feature are also given.

Unit openers provide an overview of the material covered in each of the six units. See page 1.

Chapter openers provide direction and motivation, making the content relevant to the students and giving a clear view of what is to come. See pages 2–3.

Section openers outline the major concepts of each section. Each chapter is divided into several sections. Each section takes about one week to complete. See page 4.

Critical Thinking questions develop students' skills in analysis and evaluation of information. See page 20.

Data Search questions encourage individual research and interpretation of tables, charts, and maps to gather data. See pages 5 and 24.

Safety Notes warn of hazards and suggest proper precautions to take to prevent accidents. See page 67.

Learning Objectives are listed at the beginning of each section to outline the major learning goals. See page 16.

Reading sections have built-in learning aids to stimulate students' interest in and understanding of what they read.

New science words are put in boldface type, spelled phonetically as needed, and defined. See page 1.

Main Idea questions focus attention on important topics. See page 13.

Stimulating illustrations include diagrams, drawings, maps, charts, photographs, and graphs. See pages 23, 67, and 424.

Captions provide information, focus attention, or pose self-testing questions. See page 385.

Research Topic suggestions encourage students to look further into certain topics. See page 7.

Quick Review questions are placed at the end of each important topic. See page 22.

Activities enable students to learn through their own experience and create student interest in reading further. See page 30.

Materials are inexpensive and easy to obtain.

Purpose focuses students' attention on the goal of the activity.

Procedure clearly outlines what to do, step by step.

Illustrations clearly demonstrate procedures or provide sample tables for recording data.

Safety Notes, when needed, encourage safe laboratory practices. See page 73.

Questions organize students' analysis of the data collected.

Conclusion questions lead students to draw conclusions about what they have observed and to suggest applications.

Problem-solving exercises in the text include solutions worked out in detailed steps, immediately followed by additional problems for practice. See page 39.

Problems to Solve are found in the Section Review to further reinforce problem-solving skills. See page 43.

Our Science Heritage sections in each chapter give students an idea of how scientists work. Students are made aware of how scientific advancements are built on earlier ones. See page 75.

Career pages located in every chapter make the student aware of significant physical science-related careers. A wide assortment of careers with various educational requirements are presented. See page 76.

Section Reviews test students' progress at the end of each week. Three types of questions are included. See page 15.

Vocabulary Review tests students' comprehension of all the new vocabulary in the section.

Review Questions presents multiple choice questions about principal concepts in each section.

Understanding the Concepts consists of questions requiring students to use higher levels of reasoning—interpretation, application, and analysis.

Chapter Reviews measure concept understanding and application, as well as provide suggestions for additional reading and investigation. See pages 44–45.

Review of Concepts reviews the main concepts of the chapter and lists supporting statements.

Critical Thinking questions are developed to encourage higher-level thinking skills of analysis and interpretation of ideas beyond the actual text.

Individual Research provides suggestions for out-of-class research projects.

The *Bibliography* offers carefully selected outside reading references.

Issues in Physical Science provide a refreshing look at current topics in physical science. These thought-provoking essays are located at the end of each unit. See page 132.

Trends in Technology provide students with up-to-date applications and advances of physical science principles and offer a glimpse into the developments of future technology. See page 133.

The **Glossary** provides a built-in vocabulary reference. All new science words introduced in the text and their definitions are included. Phonetic spellings, where needed, are also shown. See page 667.

The **Index** is a complete and useful tool for finding information quickly. See page 682.

Teacher's Edition Organization

The Teacher's Edition contains planning information, summaries, teaching objectives, teaching suggestions, answers, and information about software, audio-visual materials, and other resources. These teaching aids are described on this page. Page references are also included. The teaching aids fall into two categories: annotations on Student Edition pages and information at the beginning of the Teacher's Edition.

ANNOTATIONS ON STUDENT EDITION PAGES

Annotations on reading sections include answers to caption questions, *Quick Review* questions, *Critical Thinking,* and *Main Idea* questions (underlining of student text). Additional teaching suggestions and science background information are also given. See pages 21 and 59.

Annotations on activities indicate the approximate length of time the activity will take, suggested student group size, Preparation and Teaching Notes, and Answers to Questions and Conclusion or a reference to where the answers can be found. See page 62.

Annotations at the beginning of each chapter and section refer to supplementary worksheets in the Teacher's Resource Book and additional investigations in the Laboratory Manual. See pages 47 and 48.

Annotations on Section Reviews give answers to the Vocabulary Review and Review Questions, as well a reference to where answers to the Understanding the Concepts questions can be found. See page 77.

Annotations on Chapter Reviews indicate where the answers to the questions can be found. See page 78.

INFORMATION AT THE BEGINNING OF THE TEACHER'S EDITION

Chapter Teaching Information

Chapter Planning Guides give a complete overview of the content and resources in the program for each chapter. The planning guides include references to teaching aids, review and evaluation, advance preparation for activities and investigations, and skill-building and enrichment resources. See pages T56–T57.

Summary of Concepts reviews the main concepts in each section, as in the Chapter Review. See page T58.

Learning Objectives for each section list performance goals to be reached by students upon completion of the section. Each objective is correlated to Section Review questions. See page T58.

Getting Started includes Suggested Demonstrations and Ideas for Discussion for introducing each new section in class. See page T58.

Teaching information for Activities, including Preparation Notes, Teacher Notes, and Answers, appear in the T section of the Teacher's Edition when space on the student page is not available. See page T75.

Answers to Understanding the Concepts questions in the Section Reviews appear in the T section of the Teacher's Edition. See page T59.

Answers to Chapter Review questions includes answers for all questions of the Chapter Review. See page T64.

Additional Teacher Resources

Physical Science Software reviews up-to-date software that correlates to *Addison-Wesley Physical Science* and lists software publishers and distributors. See page T29.

Physical Science Films and Video provide an annotated list of selected high-quality films and videotapes. The information is organized by chapter. See page T37.

Physical Science Materials List shows the quantities of materials for the Activities in the Text and the Investigations in the Laboratory Manual. All quantities given are for a class size of 30. See page T46.

Suppliers of Laboratory Equipment and Supplies lists the names and addresses of suppliers of materials for use in the classroom and laboratory. See page T54.

Physical Science Software

The Addison-Wesley Information Laboratory: Physical Science

The Addison-Wesley Information Laboratory software is designed for use with this book. Through using this program, students become familiar with computer data search techniques. Search sheets are provided to accompany each chapter in the student book. Students search out the appropriate data and apply it to the solution of the problems presented on the search sheets.

Additional information on this product is available from your local Addison-Wesley representative.

Title of Program

Explorer Metros: A Metric Adventure

Correlates to Chapter

1

of *Addison-Wesley Physical Science*

Copyright 1982 **Price** $49.00
Producer/Distributor Sunburst Communications, 39 Washington Avenue, Pleasantville, NY 10570
Grade Levels 4–9
Compatible Hardware Apple (48K)
Subject Areas Metric Measurement, Mass, Capacity, Length, Temperature
Type of Program Simulation, Problem Solving
Features Graphics, Animation
Student Materials 1 record sheet
Documentation 27 pages—introduction, objectives, program description, suggestions for classroom use, student and teacher record sheets, information about Explorer Metros: Editor

Program Description This program gives students the opportunity to use their knowledge of the metric system, their decision-making skills, their mathematical skills, and their estimating skills. "Explorer Metros" is a rocket ship. It is on a journey to explore a space colony near Mars. The time is 1993. Once at the space colony, the student has eight hours in which to make decisions about twelve encounters. Dugan, a robot, is there to help out. Each encounter describes a problem. To solve the problem, students choose one of three possible actions. Choosing the action that is most appropriate depends on the student's correct understanding of the metric measurement given in that situation. Choosing the correct answer uses half an hour; an incorrect answer, one hour.

This program can be used over and over again because the values for the metric measurements in each encounter are changed every time the program is run. There are twenty-seven different encounters possible, too. The computer randomly chooses twelve encounters each time.

The graphics include snow-covered mountains, green trees, blue rivers, orange robots, orange creatures, etc.

The use of strange names to describe some of the monsters creates interest, too. Overall, a very motivating and interesting way for a student to review his or her knowledge of the metric system.

Title of Program

Chemicals of Life I: The Situation of Matter

Correlates to Chapters

2   3   6

of *Addison-Wesley Physical Science*

Copyright 1983 **Price** $65.00
Producer/Distributor IBM, P. O. Box 2150, Atlanta, GA 30055
Grade Levels 9–12
Compatible Hardware IBM
Subject Area Chemistry
Type of Program Tutorial
Features Graphics, Animation, Color
Student Materials None
Documentation Teacher's manual
Additional Software *Chemical of Life II: Water.*

Program Description This program provides the fundamentals of chemistry by use of interactive sequences, animations, and colorful graphics. It covers symbols; atomic mass; electrons, protons, and neutrons; and electron configuration. There are five concepts in the program. Each section is developed based on information from the previous lesson. One or two sentences are given at a time, followed by a question that ties in with a preceding section. Important words and concepts are in different colors ("Like charges repel"). Testing Your Knowledge is the final section, which allows the student to demonstrate what he or she has learned from the entire program. In this section, the student is given ten questions. If he or she doesn't score well, the student has the opportunity to repeat a section.

The menu consists of Molecules and Atoms, the Bohr Model, How to Draw an Atom, Ions and Charges, Ionic and Covalent Bonding, Testing Your Knowledge. The student moves through the sections at his or her own pace by pressing the arrow bar. The graphics are exciting. Pith balls move apart; the helium atom is shown with electrons in orbit.

The program uses repetition, questions, graphics, and color to keep your attention. To teach the Bohr Model, the program first shows the Bohr model of an atom, with the positions of the electrons, neutrons and protons. The student then has to put these in the correct places. A graph is given to show places for the electrons. Testing consists of matching.

General Chemistry

Correlates to Chapters

| 2 | 3 | 6 | 12 |

of *Addison-Wesley Physical Science*

Copyright 1984 **Price** $375.00
Producer/Distributor COMPress, P. O. Box 102, Wentworth, NH 03283
Grade Levels 3–12
Compatible Hardware Apple (48K)
Subject Area Chemistry
Type of Program Drill & Practice, Instructional Game
Features Graphics, Sound
Student Materials None
Documentation 4 pages—outline of program, operating instructions
Additional Software *Molecular Animation, Periodic Table,* and *Organic Chemistry.*

Program Description This program includes a thorough introduction to the nomenclature and concepts of chemistry. There are eight disks: Periodic Table, Nomenclature, Balancing Equations, Atomic Weights, Percent Composition, Chemaze, Organic Chemistry: Chemrain, and Ideal Gases. Each disk contains a varying number of lessons and takes about 25 minutes to complete. As an example, the lessons on Nomenclature are: Binary Salts, Variable Oxidation States, Nonmetals, Acids, Bases, Ternary Salts, and Review and Practice Problems. An outline is given in the documentation.

General Chemistry is a very comprehensive program. The instructions are easy to understand and graphic. The material is presented in clear sentences, in small doses, with many questions to enhance learning and retention. If a concept question is answered wrongly, a reason is given. The questions are posed in a straightforward manner. For example, "What is the name of this base? KOH."

Each lesson contains a brief paragraph discussing a concept or definition, followed by a question on the reading. At the end of each lesson is a review. For example, in the Binary Salts lesson, the student practices the names and the formulas. Each lesson integrates material from previous lessons. Tables and graphs are used for clarity. When answering questions, the program types "OK" or "NO, TRY AGAIN." Immediately after the second wrong answer, the correct answer is given, but the student cannot advance to another screen without typing the correct answer. Then the problem question is asked again. The student must answer all the questions correctly before moving on to the next lesson.

The Chemaze disk is a general chemistry game. The objective is to remove obstacles in a maze by hitting them with a flask. The obstacles are removed by the reagent in the flask reacting with the chemicals in the obstacle. This is a fast, fun, mind-boggling game that requires the students to have a firm grasp of reactivity (and his or her reflexes). The scores can be recorded and the student or teacher can see where the student stands in the class.

Chemrain is on organic chemistry. The premise of the game is to prevent the player's boxes from being destroyed by the organic compounds raining down on them. The student must type a compound in the box that does not react with the rain. The game does not demand the reflexes that Chemaze does, but requires an equivalent knowledge of chemistry.

Kinematics

Correlates to Chapter

| 4 |

of *Addison-Wesley Physical Science*

Copyright 1981 **Price** $24.95
Producer/Distributor Vernier Software, 2920 Southwest 89th St., Portland, OR 97225
Grade Levels 4–8, 9–12
Compatible Hardware Apple (48K)
Subject Area Motion
Type of Program Drill and Practice, Simlation, Educational Game
Features Graphics, Animation, Sound, Color
Student Materials None
Documentation 14-page user's manual

Program Description *Kinematics* familiarizes the student with quantities used in the study of motion: speed, acceleration, distance, and time. The student controls the motion of a truck that moves across the screen, painting a dot on the ground every 1.0 second, regardless of the truck's motion. Before each trip, the student is given an assignment. The student's job is to enter values (such as starting speed, acceleration, time for the acceleration to begin, total time for trip) in accordance with the specifications set. After each run, the results are shown.

There are eight possible assignments, but the program allows modification of the software, such as changing one or more of the assignments, reordering of the assignments or slowing the truck's motion.

This program is a good introduction to kinematics. It is easy to run and fun to play. The teacher may have to provide some help, however, because the program is not self-instructional.

Title of Program

Physics: Elementary Mechanics

Correlates to Chapters

4	5

of *Addison-Wesley Physical Science*

Copyright 1980–1981   **Price** $69.95
Producer/Distributor Control Data Publishing Co., Plato Educational Software, P. O. Box 261127, San Diego, CA 92126
Grade Levels 9–12
Compatible Hardware Apple (48K), Atari, Texas Instruments
Subject Area Elementary mechanics
Type of Program Drill and Practice
Features Animation, Sound
Student Materials None
Documentation 50-page manual, with five practice exercises.

Program Description This program provides nine "Phyquiz" exercises in elementary mechanics. The format is an animated physics situation with questions to be answered. The answers are also provided in the manual. The program is adapted from *Phyquiz: A Problem Solving Text in Elementary Mechanics*. The purpose of the program is to quiz the students in classical physics.

Each problem consists of four steps: description of the situation, questions about the situation, request for more help, and computation of the problem and evaluation of the answer. The student can choose the problem he or she wants to work from the index page.

The program is well thought out. Not all the information necessary to answer the questions is given in the situation, and the student must buy the information that he or she thinks necessary to answer the questions. The initial budget is $25. Information costs $2 each. A "formulas and constants" list can be bought for a steep price, and a calculator is also available. If the answer is incorrect, the student is charged. For example, a car is graphically driven across the screen from point A to point B. The student is asked, "How much time does it take for the car to drive from A to B?" That is all the information that is given, and the student must decide what information is necessary.

There is no instruction in this program. Computation, reasons, and explanations are outlined at the end of each problem. This program is *not* an introduction to physics. The problems are animated, basic, clear and a lot of fun to do.

Title of Program

The Physical Science Baseball Game— Physics Concepts

Correlates to Chapters

4	5	8	9	10	11

of *Addison-Wesley Physical Science*

Copyright 1980–1981   **Price** $55.00
Producer/Distributor J & S Software, 14 Vanderventer Avenue, Port Washington, NY 11050
Grade Levels 9–12
Compatible Hardware Apple (48K)
Subject Areas Motion, Energy, Waves, Light, Sound, and Electricity and Magnetism.
Type of Program Educational Activity, Logical Thinking, Problem Solving
Features Graphics, Animation, Sound
Student Materials None
Documentation Brochure with instructions
Additional Software *The Physical Science Baseball Game—Chemistry Concepts*

Program Description This program is designed for the review of physics concepts. Its objective is to increase a student's understanding of physics: concepts, definitions, and problem solving. The topics are: Motion, Energy, Waves, Light, Sound, and Electricity and Magnetism. The student has a choice of three games: a one-, two-, or three-inning game. If a player answers a question right, he or she gets a hit (a single, double, or triple). If the player answers the questions incorrectly, he or she gets a miss. Three misses and the player is out. The three highest scores are retained on the disk with the players' names. Additional copies of the disk can be obtained for $10. The names and scores of the previous record holders can be eliminated easily.

The graphics consist of a baseball diamond with three bases and homeplate and a runner. Questions are chosen at random. For example, "Ultrasonic waves are: light waves, radio waves, part of electromagnetic spectrum, soundwaves." Or, "A person who is farsighted needs a _____ lens to correct this problem: concave, convex, combination of concave and convex."

If the question is answered correctly, a buzzer goes off with the message, "You got a hit!" Also given is the present score. If the question is incorrect, the player is told that he or she struck out. Then the player is given the correct answer and an explanation. At the end of the game, the player can also request a review of the concepts missed. The review is presented in clear, easy-to-understand sentences, one concept at a time.

This program is highly recommended. The questions are of a broad spectrum and cover all the areas promised. The game is fun as well as academically useful.

Title of Program

Simple Machines

Correlates to Chapter

5

of *Addison-Wesley Physical Science*

Copyright 1984 **Price** $34.95
Producer/Distributor Micro-Ed, Inc., 8108 Eden Road, Eden Prairie, MN 55344
Grade Level 3–9
Compatible Hardware Commodore
Subject Areas Work, Levers
Type of Program Tutorial, Simulation
Features Graphics, Animation, Sound
Student Materials None
Documentation Teacher's booklet
Additional Software *Energy and Power*

Program Description The purpose of the program is to introduce the three types of levers (first-, second-, and third-class) and work. The menu consists of Balance Beam (Introduction of First-Class Lever), Bull's Eye (Second-Class Lever), Direct Hit (Third-Class Lever), and Block Stacker (Work). These lessons are highlighted by interesting graphics, animation, and sound. Each lesson takes 15 minutes to complete.

In each lesson the student can ask for information or for questions. The information is presented one sentence at a time. Questions are interspersed between information concerning the reading. At the end of each lesson, there are 20 questions. If a student answers the question wrong, he or she is told NO and the answer, but a reason is not given. This is sometimes frustrating as the student cannot proceed until the question is answered correctly.

The first three lessons consist of instructions that graphically introduce the lever, followed by a diagram of the parts of the lever. This is followed by instructions on answering the questions correctly. All the questions are mathematical. The last lesson, Block Stacker, discusses the principle of work. It introduces force and distance. The following test asks the student In how many seconds can you get six blocks to the top of stairs? The student gets the blocks to the top by multiplying correctly. Although the program may be too repetitive for some students, it is a good introduction to levers and work.

Title of Program

Physics Tutorial—Heat and Temperature Part A

Correlates to Chapters

5   7

of *Addison-Wesley Physical Science*

Copyright 1980 **Price** $14.50
Producer/Distributor The Teaching Assistant, Charles Levy, 22 Seward Drive, Huntington Station, NY 11746
Grade Levels 9–12
Compatible Hardware TRS 80
Subject Areas Heat, Temperature
Type of Program Tutorial
Features Graphics, Sound
Student Materials None
Documentation None
Additional Software *Physics Tutorial: Momentum, Physics Tutorial Program Set, Physics Tutorial—Dynamics—Newton's Laws, Physics Tutorial—Heat and Temperature Pt. B, Physics—Wave Motion*

Program Description This program is a good introduction to thermodynamics. Each time the program is run, the computer generates new problems and thus can be used for as much drill as the student cares to have, with the computer as his or her tireless teacher's assistant. The student can advance at his or her own pace.

The program starts with a paragraph on the kinetic molecular theory, and it is assumed that the student understands potential energy, equilibrium, and kinetic energy. Although the subject matter is fairly advanced, the information is presented in clear sentences and progresses along a logical path and would be engrossing to interested students. For example, the third paragraph ends, "As a consequence of the loss of kinetic energy the molecules have less motion and less energy on impact. This we interpret as being less hot—colder. Thus, the molecular kinetic energy is measured by temperature." There is a summary at the end of each lesson: "Temperature measures only the average kinetic energies of the molecules—their 'hotness' or 'coldness.'" The summary is followed by questions. Then the student may choose between four sets of problems: 1. Temperature Conversion, 2. Heat Content, 3. Heat of Fusion/Heat of Vaporization, 4. Method of Mixtures.

Each set of problems first gives instruction on the material. For example, the set of temperature conversions presents the formula to convert Fahrenheit to Celsius or Kelvin, as well as some other clues. All the questions are word problems: "A temperature of 77 degrees Celsius is equivalent to what temperature in Fahrenheit degrees?" The student is told if the answer is right or wrong. After three wrong answers to a question, the solution to the problem is presented—not just the answer, but the whole process. This is a very efficient program. It requires previous tutoring for some definitions, but it is a good introduction to heat and explains how to work conversion problems. Three problems are given for each of the four sections.

This is a very good program. Each of the four sections contain tutoring on a specific topic. The questions are all mathematical, but the tutoring is presented in clear, easy-to-understand language. The material holds the student's attention because of the mature, interesting way in which it is presented.

Title of Program

Waves

Correlates to Chapter

8

of *Addison-Wesley Physical Science*

Copyright 1981 **Price** $28.00
Producer/Distributor J & S Software, 14 Vanderventer
Avenue, Port Washington, NY 11050
Grade Levels 9–12
Compatible Hardware Apple (48K)
Subject Area Waves
Type of Program Tutorial, Logical Thinking, Problem
Solving
Feature Graphics
Student Materials None
Documentation Brochure
Additional Software *Circular Motion, Newton's Laws, Acceleration, Uniform Motion, Heat, Sound, Free Fall, Projectile Problems, Momentum, Work and Energy, Gas Laws*

Program Description Included is a program *Record,* which
is used by the teacher to obtain a listing of the student's progress. The program also contains pictures of experimental setups, formulas and graphs. The average program takes 30 to
45 minutes. The questions are slightly different each time the
program is run since the variables change.

The graphics are an exciting feature of this program. The
student analyzes graphs of various wave forms. The major
concepts covered include wave length, type of wave, frequency, amplitude, velocity, diffraction, refraction, reflection
and the propagation of waves. Questions answered incorrectly are repeated, but with different variables. There is a list
of equations and definitions. (For example, "Frequency—The
number of waves that leave the source each second," and
"Amplitude—The height of a crest of a wave above the undisturbed level of the wave medium.")

The student can exit at any time and get a grade percentage. A message about how many questions were not answered comes after the grade percentage and a request to
go back and try again.

The program is delightful. The questions are all different.
Some are mathematical, some are definition, some are recognition. The program is never boring and always instructional. The questions are elementary, but the program is not
an introduction. The student will be better equipped to interpret graphs and answer a variety of wave problems after
working with this program.

Title of Program

Standing Waves

Correlates to Chapter

8

of *Addison-Wesley Physical Science*

Copyright 1984 **Price** $75.00
Producer/Distributor Conduit, University of Iowa,
Oakdale Campus, Iowa City, IA 52242
Grade Levels 9–12
Compatible Hardware Apple (32K)
Subject Area Waves
Type of Program Drill & Practice, Simulation, Educational
Activity
Features Graphics, Animation
Student Materials None
Documentation User's guide
Additional Software *RKINET (Reaction Kinetics), Chemical Principals for the Introductory Laborator, Enzkin (Enzyme Kinetics), Haber (Production of Ammonia by the Haber Process), Newton, Interp (Wave Superposition), Scatter (Particle Scattering)*

Program Description This program presents the concepts, definitions, and physical properties of waves using the
computer's animated display. A simulation of standing waves
and pulses illustrates with real-time animation the properties
of transverse waves, including the superposition of traveling
waves. The documentation has detailed exercises for all the
basic wave concepts, with corresponding demonstrations on
the microcomputer. There is a special section for musicians,
a symbol table, and mathematical formulas.

This is a superb program for demonstrating waves—
material that is not easily presented. The waves are shown
oscillating on a graph. The student can change the frequency, momentum, height, period, and point of beginning of
the wave. The wave will oscillate until the student commands
the program to continue.

One part of the program enables the student to design his
or her own wave forms to see what they look like.

This is a very sophisticated program and should not be
used as an introduction to physics. Students should have a
firm background in basic mathematics, and the teacher may
elect to provide some instructions to enable the students to
complete the program satisfactorily. As a visual demonstration of waves, however, the program provides a very worthwhile experience.

Title of Program

Electricity and Magnetism

Correlates to Chapters

10   11

of *Addison-Wesley Physical Science*

Copyright 1986   **Price** $59.95
Producer/Distributor Educational Activities, Inc., P. O.
  Box 392, Freeport, NY 11520
Grade Levels 4–9
Compatible Hardware Apple (48K)
Subject Areas Electricity, Magnetism
Type of Program Tutorial
Features Animation, graphics
Student Materials Book of worksheets
Documentation Teacher's manual
Additional Software *Parts of Microscope, Heat and Light,*
  and *Introduction to Biochemistry.*

Program Description This delightful program is an elementary introduction to electricity and magnetism. There are four lessons: Magnets and Magnetism, Static Electricity, Electricity in Circuits, and More Circuits. Information is given in clear sentences and short paragraphs. Animation and graphics are used to present the material. Basic questions review the previous reading and lead into the next lesson. If a question is answered incorrectly, the computer types the correct answer.

The lessons are hands-on animation. For example, to demonstrate electromagnetism, a circuit is drawn. The student uses the space bar to close the circuit. When it is closed, a paper clip is attracted to the wire, moving to and from the circuit as the student opens and closes the circuit. This program is a delight to see and play. At the end of each lesson, there are review questions.

Although the program is juvenile in some aspects (it defines and gives pronunciation of such words as "compass" and "attraction"), the subject matter is not. The material is presented clearly and concisely.

Title of Program

Radioactive Decay

Correlates to Chapter

13

of *Addison-Wesley Physical Science*

Copyright 1980   **Price** $59.95
Producer/Distributor Longman Group, Ltd, 1900 East
  Lake Avenue, Glenview, IL 60025
Grade Levels 9–12
Compatible Hardware Apple (48K)
Subject Area Science
Type of Program Tutorial, Simulation
Student Materials Lab book, manual
Documentation Teacher's manual
Additional Software *Capacitor Discharge, Longitudinal
  Waves, Mass Spectrometer, Photoelectric Effect, Planetary Motion, Transverse Waves, Young's Slits, Lenses,
  Gravitational Fields, The Chemical Element Game, Gas
  Diffusion, Homogeneous Equilibrium, Rates of Reaction, Symbols to Moles, Hydrogen Spectrum, Gas
  Chromatography*

Program Description In this program the behavior of radioactive decay is demonstrated by the use of ten-sided dice and the computer's random number generator. The decay of radioactive material is simulated by the "decay" of the dice. The program gives the number of dice removed after each throw, the number of dice left, and the ln (natural log number).

The user has three options: Behavior, Decay, and Series. For each option the user inputs variables. For example, in the Behavior option, the user determines the number of dice to be used and how many sides the dice will have. Then the program computes the probability of the decay of the radioactive substance. The Series simulates a radioactive decay series. The initial number of "parents" and "daughter" atoms and their decay probability can be varied.

Questions are asked in sentence form. This program is not a tutorial, but provides an excellent demonstration of radioactive behavior and decay.

Title of Program

Energy House

Correlates to Chapter

14

of *Addison-Wesley Physical Science*

Copyright 1983 **Price** $40.00
Producer/Distributor TIES, 1925 West Country Road,
  St. Paul, MN 55113
Grade Levels 4–8
Compatible Hardware Apple (48K)
Subject Area(s) Energy Conservation
Type of Program Simulation, Problem Solving
Features Graphics, Sound, Animation
Student Materials 8 activity sheets
Documentation 56 pages—description, objectives, back-
  ground information, command list, sample run of the pro-
  gram, and other teacher resources

Program Description In *Energy House,* students move
through rooms of a house to find and correct energy wasters.
As the student corrects an energy waster, the energy efficiency of the house increases.

The student begins by getting directions and by choosing
the number of rooms he or she wants to visit. The HELP-
COMMAND list appears next. The commands include: TURN
OFF/ON, OPEN/CLOSE, TURN UP/DOWN, WRAP, GO BACK,
FIX, LEAVE, or STOP. As each room appears, the student
types the commands he or she wants to correct the energy
wasters (TURN OFF stereo). A thermometer shows the energy efficiency percentage in each room. Each command
uses up five minutes of time whether it is a correct answer or
not. The student has about two hours on the clock on the
screen to find all the energy wasters in the seven rooms. The
rooms shown may include a kitchen, a living room, a bath-
room, a bedroom, a recreation room, or a basement. The
computer randomly selects the rooms the student views. The
program has twelve possible options: two recreation rooms,
four bathrooms, three living rooms, seven bedrooms, one
basement, and three kitchens.

The graphics and animation are fun. Students get to see
windows close, lights turn off, fireplace doors close, water
turn off, stereos and televisions turn down, and so on.

At the end of the program, the student's success is stated
in terms of energy efficiency.

Selecting Physical Science Software

Educational software falls into many categories.

- Tutorial software teaches a concept step-by-step. Some relies heavily on graphics and animation, while some is basically a reading experience.
- Simulation software depicts a process or activity graphically.
- Instructional games use the motivation of fun and competition to teach concepts or pass on information.

Some software is interactive; that is, it requires the student to type in information and "work" with the computer. Other software is mainly looked at or read.

In evaluating software for your class, consider the following points.

- Is the software a tutorial, simulation, or instructional game?
- Is the software designed for remediation, reinforcement, or introduction of new material?
- Is there documentation (written material) to accompany the software?
- Are the instructions on the screen or in the documentation clear and easy to follow?
- Does the software do something that could not be done in a text or workbook?
- Is there too much emphasis on attractive graphics and animation and not enough on science content?
- Are there positive rewards for correct answers and nonjudgmental responses for incorrect answers?
- Are the readability and concept levels appropriate for your students?

Physical science software is distributed by equipment supply houses as well as exclusively software distributors. A general list of distributors and their addresses is given on page T37.

Sources of Software Reviews

Reviews of science software may be found in the following periodicals.

Booklist
50 East Huron Street
Chicago, IL 60611

Classroom Computer Learning
19 Davis Drive
Belmont, CA 94002

Curriculum Review
517 S. Jefferson
Chicago, IL 60607

Electronic Learning
902 Sylvan Avenue
Englewood Cliffs, NJ 07632

Epie Report
Epie Institute
PO Box 839
Water Mill, NY 11976

Media & Methods
1511 Walnut Street
Philadelphia, PA 19102

School Science & Mathematics
Science and Mathematics Assoc., Inc.
Arizona State University
Tempe, AZ 85287

Science and Children
National Science Teachers Association
1742 Connecticut Avenue, N.W.
Washington, DC 20009

The Science Teacher
National Science Teachers Association
1742 Connecticut Avenue, N.W.
Washington, DC 20009

Software Distributors

Berkshire Scientific
Astor Square
19 US Rt. 9
Rhinebeck, NY 12572

Cambridge Development Laboratory, Inc.
1696 Massachusetts Avenue
Cambridge, CA 02138

Carolina Biological Supply Co.
2700 York Road
Burlington, NC 27215

Central Scientific Co.
11222 Melrose Avenue
Franklin Park, IL 60131

COMPress
PO Box 102
Wentworth, NH 03283

Conduit
University of Iowa
Oakdale Campus
Iowa City, IA 52242

Control Data Publishing Co.
Plato Educational Software
PO Box 261127
San Diego, CA 92126

Cross Educational Software
PO Box 1536
Ruston, LA 71270

Educational Activities, Inc.
PO Box 392
Freeport, NY 11520

Educational Audio Visual Inc.
Pleasantville, NY 10570

Educational Images
3456 West Side Station
Elmira, NY 14905

Educational Materials and Equipment Co.
Old Mill Plain Road
PO Box 2805
Danbury, CN 06813-2805

Focus Media, Inc.
839 Stewart Avenue
PO Box 865
Garden City, NY 11530

Frey Scientific Co.
905 Hickory Lane
Mansfield, OH 44905

IBM
PO Box 2150
Atlanta, GA 30055

J & S Software
14 Vanderventer Avenue
Port Washington, NY 11050

Longman Group Ltd.
1900 East Lake Avenue
Glenview, IL 60025

Merlan Scientific
247 Armstrong Avenue
Georgetown, Ontario
Canada L7G 4X6

Micro-Ed, Inc.
8108 Eden Road
Eden Prairie, MN 55344

Nasco
901 Janesville Avenue
Fort Atkinson, WI 53538

Sargent-Welch Scientific Co.
7300 N. Linder Avenue
Skokie, IL 60077

Scholastic Inc.
2931 E. McCarty Street
PO Box 7501
Jefferson City, MO 65102

Science Kit and Boreal Laboratories
777 East Park Drive
Tonawanda, NY 14150

Science Software Systems
PO Box 555
Horseheads, NY 14845

Society for Visual Education, Inc.
Department VE
1345 Diversey Parkway
Chicago, IL 60614

Sunburst Communications
39 Washington Avenue
Pleasantville, NY 10570

TIES
1925 West Country Road
St. Paul, MN 55113

Vernier Software
2920 S.W. 89th Street
Portland, OR 97225

All the films listed on the next few pages are in color and are available in a 16-mm format unless otherwise specified. The major film suppliers also offer their films in a video format as well.

The films listed are at a level appropriate for high school physical science students. However, it is always a good idea to preview films yourself before showing them to the class. You are the best judge of what is suitable for— and what will hold the attention of—your own class.

New science films are reviewed in *Science Books & Films,* a magazine published five times per year by the American Association for the Advancement of Science, Washington, D.C.

Addresses of the distributors of the films listed are given on the following page. Before ordering from a distributor, check local film libraries for the film or video you wish to borrow.

Addison-Wesley Video Lessons for Physical Science

This set of seven video lessons has been developed and produced to accompany *Addison-Wesley Physical Science.* They are designed to allow you to present difficult concepts and skills effectively and provide flexibility in teaching. Each video lesson covers one class period and includes a teacher's guide with suggestions for follow-up activities.

- Particle Model of Matter
- Motion and Work
- Energy and Changes in Matter
- Sound and Light
- Electricity and Electromagnetism
- Nuclear Energy and Future Energy Needs
- Laboratory Safety

Film Distributors

Agency for Instructional Television
Box A
Bloomington, IN 47402

Barr Films
PO Box 5667
3490 E. Foothill Blvd.
Pasadena, CA 91107

BFA Educational Media
468 Park Avenue South
New York, NY 10016

Bullfrog Films, Inc.
Oley, PA 19547

Centron Films
Distributed by Coronet Films
& Video
(see below)

Churchill Films
662 N. Robertson Blvd.
Los Angeles, CA 90069-9970

The Cinema Guild
1697 Broadway
New York, NY 10019

Coronet Films & Video
100 Wilmot Road
Deerfield, IL 60015

Direct Cinema Limited
PO Box 69589
Los Angeles, CA 90069

Encyclopaedia Britannica Educational Corp.
425 N. Michigan Ave.
Chicago, IL 60611

Guidance Associates
Communications Park
Box 3000
Mt. Kisco, NY 10549

Handel Film Corp.
8730 Sunset Blvd.
West Hollywood, CA 90069

Innovative Communications
207 Coggins Drive
Pleasant Hill, CA 94523

International Film Bureau, Inc.
332 S. Michigan Ave.
Chicago, IL 60604-4382

Journal Films, Inc.
930 Pitner
Evanston, IL 60202

Lucerne Films, Inc.
37 Ground Pine Rd.
Morris Plains, NJ 07950

Macmillan Films
34 MacQuesten Pkwy. S.
Mount Vernon, NY 10550

The Media Guild
11722 Sorrento Valley Road
Suite E
San Diego, CA 92121

Modern Talking Picture Service
5000 Park Street
St. Petersburg, FL 33709

Moody Institute of Science
Educational Films Div.
12000 E. Washington Blvd.
Whittier, CA 90608

National Geographic Society
Educational Services
17th & M Sts., NW
Washington, DC 20036

Phoenix Films & Video, Inc.
468 Park Avenue South
New York, NY 10016

Pyramid Film & Video
PO Box 1048
Santa Monica, CA 90406-1048

Stuart Finley, Inc.
3428 Mansfield Rd.
Falls Church, VA 22041

Time-Life Video
1271 Avenue of the Americas
New York, NY 10020

Chapter 1   Science and Measurement

Buoyancy   (Coronet Films & Video; 1985; 15 min)
Uses questions about floating to show how experiments are conducted. Can be understood by students with no previous knowledge of density, specific gravity, or Archimedes' principle.

Living with Technology   (Agency for Instructional Television; 1983; 20 min; video only)
Follows a family for a day, showing the impact of technology on their lives.

Make Mine Metric   (Pyramid Film; 1975; 13 min)
Shows how metric measurement is easier to use than the English system. Emphasizes the need to learn only three prefixes (milli-, centi-, and kilo-).

Measuring Volumes of Liquids   (Lucerne Films, Inc.; 1981; 9 min)
Shows proper use of equipment in the measurement of liquid volume.

Metrics for Measure   (BFA Educational Media; 1975; 13 min)
Humorous animated film that presents a history of measurement, the three basic units of metric measure (meter, liter, and gram), the decimal basis of the metric system, and the prefixes.

The Pleasure of Finding Things Out   (Time-Life Video; 1983; 57 min; video only)
A conversation with down-to-earth Nobel Laureate physicist Richard Feynman, whose inquisitiveness and unwillingness to accept "authority" were important factors in his becoming a scientist. Originally shown on the *Nova* TV series.

Chapter 2   Properties of Matter

Chemistry: Elements, Compounds, and Mixtures (2nd ed.) (Coronet Films & Video; 1983; 20 min)
Distinguishes among elements, compounds, and mixtures; shows some ways of identifying and separating elements and compounds.

Crystal Gazing   (Moody Institute of Science; 1977; 14 min)
Discusses the natural occurrence of crystals and shows magnified crystals of salt, alum, and rock candy. Includes a spelunking trip to a cave to observe crystals.

Crystals and Their Growth   (Coronet Films & Video; 1985; 12 min)
Uses time-lapse photography and photomicrography to reveal how crystals grow.

Handling, Transferring and Filtering of Chemicals (Lucerne Films, Inc.; 1981; 10 min)
Demonstrates basic laboratory techniques for handling chemicals.

Chapter 3   The Structure of Matter

Elements Discovered   (The Media Guild; 1980; 25 min)
Examines how the development of certain experimental techniques (smelting, glassmaking, electrolysis) led to the discovery of various chemical elements.

Evidence for the Atomic-Molecular Theory   (2nd ed.) (Encyclopaedia Britannica Educational Corp.; 1982; 16 min)
Discusses classification of matter and the evidence that matter is made of atoms and molecules, including crystal shapes, electrolysis of water, and chemical reactions.

Explaining Matter; Chemical Change   (2nd ed.) (Encyclopaedia Britannica Educational Corp.; 1982; 13 min)
Explains chemical changes in terms of the rearrangement of atoms which join together because of electrostatic forces.

The Periodic Table   (The Media Guild; 1981; 24 min)
Introduces students to the periodic table, including its history, its terminology, and its structure.

Water: Why It Is What It Is   (Moody Institute of Science; 1975; 11 min)
Presents an overview of the structure and properties of water molecules.

Chapter 4   Motion

Attraction of Gravity   (BFA Educational Media; 1975; 9 min)
Illustrates the force of gravity with examples such as bricks falling in slow motion and astronauts bouncing around on the moon.

How Much Does the Earth Weigh? (Journal Films, Inc.; 1980; 12½ min)

Describes mass, volume, and density of four main constituents of the earth—sand, rocks, soil, and water. Explains differences between weight, mass, density, and force of gravity.

How We Know the Earth Moves (BFA Educational Media; 1977; 10 min)

Reviews the two basic motions of the earth—rotation and revolution. Uses the Foucault pendulum to demonstrate rotation.

Motion: Newton's Laws (The Media Guild; 1980; 25 min)

Effective demonstrations of all three of Newton's laws using scenes on earth and in Skylab.

Thonk! Science and Hitting a Ball (Centron Films; 1976; 20 min)

Explains energy and energy systems, such as how energy is transferred through various objects. Illustrates the formula for calculating the momentum of the object hit by its mass and velocity.

3-2-1 Contact: Forces and Motion (Guidance Associates; 1985; 60 min)

An excellent film from the *3-2-1 Contact* TV series; introduces gravity, force, motion, and buoyancy with real-life examples, simple demonstrations, and animation.

Levers (2nd ed.) (Coronet Films & Video; 1984; 12 min)

Effectively uses animation to present different kinds of levers logically and clearly.

Machines, Engines, and Motors (Journal Films, Inc.; 1980; 12 min)

Uses a model aircraft engine to introduce modern engines and machines. Shows how screws, screw drivers, door knobs, twig cutters, wheelbarrows are all examples of simple machines.

Pulleys (2nd ed.) (Coronet Films & Video; 1984; 12 min)

Animated skits show a weak but clever caveman using progressively more complicated pulleys to beat a brawny rival.

Simple Machines: Inclined Planes and Levers (3rd ed.) (Encyclopaedia Britannica Educational Corp.; 1982; 17 min)

Excellent and comprehensive coverage of inclined planes, wedges, screws, first- and second-class levers, pulleys, and the wheel and axle.

Simple Machines—Using Mechanical Advantage (Barr Films; 1979; 17 min)

Explores the advantages of simple machines. Illustrates the use of simple machines as subsystems of more complex machines. Describes the lever, the pulley, the wheel and axle, the inclined plane, the wedge, and the screw.

Chapter 5 **Work and Heat**

Heat and Energy Transfer (Coronet Films & Video; 1985; 13 min)

Explores the relation between heat and kinetic energy, and the transfer of heat by conduction, convection, and radiation.

Inclined Planes (2nd ed.) (Coronet Films & Video; 1984; 12 min)

The inclined plane and its derivatives, the wedge, chisel, hatchet, slicing knife, and screw are examined.

Learning About Heat (2nd ed.) (Encyclopaedia Britannica Educational Corp.; 1974; 15 min)

A combination of laboratory demonstrations and animation that illustrate the atomic and molecular basis for changes that occur in heating and cooling. Discusses the transfer of heat through conduction, convection, and radiation.

Chapter 6 **Chemical Reactions**

Alfred Nobel: The Merchant of Death? (Centron Films; 1978; 27 min)

The life and work of the inventor of dynamite, and the resistance he faced from a disapproving society because his invention was used in warfare.

Chemistry: Reaction Rates and Equilibrium (Coronet Films & Video; 1983; 23 min)

Excellent coverage of reaction rates, chemical equilibrium, and exothermic and endothermic reactions at a basic level.

Physical Science: Chemical Energy (Churchill Films; 1984; 16 min)

Good introduction to the energy changes that occur in chemical reactions, with aid of slow motion and time-lapse photography to show familiar processes in a new way.

Chapter 7   Using Energy from Chemical Reactions

Acid Rain   (Time-Life Video; 1985; 57 min; video only)
Comprehensive, yet cautious look at what is known about acid rain; from the *Nova* TV series.

Air Pollution: A First Film   (rev.) (Phoenix Films & Video, Inc.: 1984; 12 min)
Excellent introduction to air pollution, including strategies for reducing it.

Energy Sources   (International Film Bureau Inc.; 1982; 19 min)
Illustrates various sources of energy, including the production of fuel for heat and light through photosynthesis.

Food Chains—A Bond of Life   (Barr Films; 1981; 15½ min)
Describes the process of energy transfer from producer to consumer.

Food: Energy for Life   (Coronet Films & Video; 1978; 10 min)
Explores the flow of energy and materials through living systems, including the process of photosynthesis.

Modern Engines and Energy Conversion   (Centron Films; 1978; 12 min)
Explains the heat cycle of turbine and rocket engines and how these engines waste much of the energy they use for fuel.

Plants Make Food   (Churchill Films; 1981; 13 min)
Explains the nature and significance of photosynthesis.

Sun, Cities, and Smog   (The Media Guild; 1983; 24 min)
Shows how researchers determine the causes of air pollution and smog and its effects.

To Catch a Cloud: A Thoughtful Look at Acid Rain
(Modern Talking Picture Service; 1983; 30 min)
Illustrates the complexities of acid rain problems and the diversity of scientific research needed to document the nature and extent of them.

Chapter 8   Waves and Sound

Learning About Sound   (2nd ed.) (Encyclopaedia Britannica Educational Corp.; 1974; 17 min)
A useful introduction to sound that includes the response of a dog to a high-pitched whistle and the vanishing of sound when the air around a bell is removed.

The Sonic Boom: Sound Waves Through the Air
(Churchill Films; 1984; 6 min)
Excellent, short film that uses animation to show sound waves spreading out from a source and how a sonic boom is created when the source moves faster than the speed of sound.

Chapter 9   Light

Color from Light   (Churchill Films; 1976; 11 min)
Introduces the addition and subtraction of various wavelengths of light to produce color or lack of color. Includes a study guide with experiments for obtaining color from white light.

Color in Nature   (Encyclopaedia Britannica Educational Corp.; 1980; 12 min)
Explains the function of animal coloration. Shows animal adaptations according to color of the environment and prey–predator relationships.

Eyes—Seeing the Light   (Coronet Films & Video; 1982; 15 min)
Discusses the structure and function of the eye.

The Laser Beam   (2nd ed.) (Handel Film Corp.; 1982; 20 min)
Explains in lay language how lasers work, and shows their applications in surgery, industry, video disks, and measurements in space.

Light Is Many Things   (Barr Films; 1977; 12 min)
Shows the sun and its influence upon living creatures. Illustrates light as a form of energy and its importance in photosynthesis.

The Master of Light: A Biography of Albert A. Michelson   (The Cinema Guild; 1984; 30 min)
Superb short film about the first American to win a Nobel Prize in physics, narrated by his daughter Dorothy.

A Visit to Spectrum II   (Agency for Instructional Television; 1976; 20 min)
Introduces the electromagnetic spectrum by portraying a visit to an orbiting space laboratory.

Chapter 10   Electric Charges and Currents

Electric Currents and Circuits (Coronet Films & Video; 1985; 16 min)
  Well-paced film that explains the fundamentals of electric currents and circuits: voltage, current, resistance, series and parallel circuits.

Electricity—The Energy of Electrons (Barr Films; 1979; 14½ min)
  Explores static electricity, electric current, conductors and insulators, and the production of electricity by large generators.

Introduction to Electricity (2nd ed.) (Coronet Films & Video; 1971; 11 min)
  Demonstrations and animation explain resistance, voltage, parallel and series circuits.

Static and Current Electricity (Coronet Films & Video; 1985; 16 min)
  Makes good use of animation and photography to introduce charged objects and moving charges.

Story of Electricity—The Greeks to Franklin (Coronet Films & Video; 1968; 14 min)
  Reenactments of major discoveries about electricity.

Chapter 11   Electromagnetism

Arcs and Sparks (Journal Films, Inc.; 1980; 12 min)
  Introduces experiments in static electricity, magnetostatics, and magnetic fields induced by currents.

Electricity and Magnetism (Coronet Films & Video; 1985; 16 min)
  Fast-paced and well-organized film that explains the relationships between electricity and magnetism and illustrates the operational principles of motors, generators, solenoids, transformers, and electromagnets.

Electromagnets and Their Uses (Coronet Films & Video; 1972; 11 min)
  The effects of coiling a wire, adding a core, and passing a current through the wire in either direction; applications of electromagnets in electric motors and electronics.

Learning About Magnetism (2nd ed.) (Encyclopaedia Britannica Educational Corp.; 1975; 14 min)
  Magnetic fields, how magnets generate electricity, and how magnetism can be explained in terms of the nuclei and electrons of atoms.

L*I*G*H*T (Direct Cinema Limited; 1982; 15 min)
  Presents the invention of the electric light and the effects of the electric light on our society.

Chapter 12   Electrochemical Reactions

Learning About Electrical Current (2nd ed.) (Encyclopaedia Britannica Educational Corp.; 1974; 15 min)
  After an introduction to the generation of electric current, the film shows the conversion of chemical energy to electric energy in a dry cell, and the use of electric current in copper plating.

Chapter 13   Nuclear Reactions

Atomic Energy: Inside the Atom (2nd ed.) (Encyclopaedia Britannica Educational Corp.; 1982; 14 min)
  The release of energy in the processes of radioactivity, nuclear fission, and nuclear fusion, shown through a combination of demonstrations and animation.

Fusion: The Ultimate Fire (BFA Educational Media; 1976; 14 min)
  Presents thermonuclear fusion as an energy source. Depicts the fusion of hydrogen nuclei to release energy.

Learning About Nuclear Energy (2nd ed.) (Encyclopaedia Britannica Educational Corp.; 1975; 15 min)
  Introduces the production of energy from nuclear fission and fusion. Accounts for the apparent loss of mass. Emphasizes society's responsibility for the safe use of nuclear energy.

Nuclear Energy (National Geographic Society, Educational Services; 1981; 23 min)
  Raises the question of the future of fission nuclear power. Set in Wisconsin, a state with operating nuclear power plants.

Chapter 14 **Our Energy Needs**

After Oil What?   (International Film Bureau Inc.; 1982; 25 min)
   Presents the advantages and disadvantages of each nonfossil source of energy (solar, wind, wave, tidal, geothermal, hydroelectric, fission, breeder reactor, fusion), without trying to sell any particular one.

Backyard Alternative Energy   (Centron Films; 1980; 25 min)
   Presents alternate energy devices presently in use. Includes water mills, windmills, solar greenhouses, pedal power, and storage of electricity for use in golf carts.

Biogas in Fiji   (Bullfrog Films, Inc.; 1981; 6 min)
   Examines the use of pig manure for the production of methane gas for cooking and heating.

The Breeder   (Stuart Finley, Inc.; 1978; 23 min)
   Presents social, environmental, and scientific issues associated with the use of breeder reactors to generate nuclear power.

Decision: Energy for the Future   (Bullfrog Films, Inc.; 1980; 11 min)
   Focuses on fossil fuel limitations and alternative energy sources. Presents conservation measures.

Energy: New Sources   (Churchill Films; 1980; 24 min)
   Surveys new energy sources of greatest potential—solar, geothermal, nuclear fusion, and synthetic fuels from coal and shale.

Energy: The Alternatives   (The Media Guild; 1985; 24 min)
   Shows several renewable energy sources with present or imminent commercial use: geothermal steam, wind farm, tidal-powered electric generating plant, methanol for motor vehicles.

Energy: The Nuclear Alternative   (Churchill Films; 1980; 22 min)
   Presents both sides of the use of nuclear energy in the U.S.

Fields of Fuel: The Ethanol Debate   (International Film Bureau Inc.; 1980; 28 min)
   Presents the use of alcohol as an alternative fuel.

Generation on the Wind   (Churchill Films; 1980; 26 min)
   Portrays the cooperative efforts of a small island community to develop a windmill to generate power.

Geothermal: The Energy Within   (Barr Films; 1981; 17 min)
   Explores the heat below the earth's surface as a possible energy source.

Geysers, Lava and Hot Spots   (Journal Films, Inc.; 1982; 16 min)
   Shows the hidden workings of a geyser. Demonstrates clearly how water boils by a reduction in pressure. Portrays the generation of electricity in a steam turbine. Discusses sources of the earth's heat.

The Hottest Show on Earth   (Macmillan Films; 1980; 28 min)
   Shows the need for energy conservation and methods by which this goal can be achieved.

Toward the Sun   (Macmillan Films; 1981; 28 min)
   Gives practical applications of the use of solar energy—solar home heating, solar batteries, and a prototype solar steam generator.

Wind Power   (Innovative Communications; 1980; 18 min)
   Describes technical and scientific aspects of wind power. Gives the current status of wind energy systems.

Windows in Time: Research Today for Energy Tomorrow   (Innovative Communications; 1983; 30 min)
   Presents five scientists and their research projects, which include photovoltaic cells, wind power, fuel cells, and new ways of using coal. Gives insights into the research and development process, as well as the human side of the researchers.

Conducting a Safe Classroom and Lab

The materials recommended for use in the activities and investigations are generally safe and non-toxic. However, even everyday items such as candles, knives, and glass jars can be dangerous if not handled carefully. Be sure to caution your students about any possible danger whenever setting up or performing an activity. Safety notes have been placed in these books where necessary, but it is impossible for the author to know all the special hazards that might exist in an individual classroom.

Try to keep safety in mind at all times. Here are some good general precautions to follow:

- **Glassware.** Heat substances only in a heat-resistant glass container. (Pyrex® and Kimax® are the most common trademarks for such products.) Never handle broken glass with bare hands; use heavy gloves or a dustpan and brush. Try to avoid breakage by placing glass objects in secure places where they are not likely to fall or be knocked over.

- **Chemicals.** This program does not recommend that the students handle caustic or dangerous chemicals. However, all chemicals should be handled carefully. Read all caution labels on bottles and follow the directions strictly. Avoid keeping strong acids in your classroom. When diluting an acid, always add the acid to the water—very slowly, stirring constantly with a glass rod. And never allow students to taste a substance unless you know it is safe.

- **Heat and flames.** Never allow papers or other flammable substances anywhere near flames. Make sure students do not have loose clothing or hair near flames. Do not use a flame in an open draft. Keep an emergency supply of water and sand nearby to extinguish fires. Do not try to put out a fire from a leaking alcohol lamp with water; use sand or baking soda.

Do not let water get onto hot-plate coils. Do not heat any substance when the label cautions against it. *Anyone heating a liquid should wear safety goggles.*

Getting Started includes Suggested Demonstrations and Ideas for Discussion for introducing each new section in class. See page T58.

Teaching information for Activities, including Preparation Notes, Teacher Notes, and Answers, appear in the T section of the Teacher's Edition when space on the student page is not available. See page Txx.

Answers to Understanding the Concepts questions in the Section Reviews appear in the T section of the Teacher's Edition. See page T59.

Answers to Chapter Review questions includes answers for all questions of the Chapter Review. See page T64.

Additional Teacher Resources

Physical Science Software reviews up-to-date software that correlates to *Addison-Wesley Physical Science* and lists software publishers and distributors. See page T29.

Physical Science Films and Video provide an annotated list of selected high-quality films and videotapes. The information is organized by chapter. See page T37.

Physical Science Materials List shows the quantities of materials for the Activities in the Text and the Investigations in the Laboratory Manual. All quantities given are for a class size of 30. See page T46.

Suppliers of Laboratory Equipment and Supplies lists the names and addresses of suppliers of materials for use in the classroom and laboratory. See page T54.

Physical Science Materials List

The following list gives the quantities needed for a class of 30. Quantities for Activities and Investigations are listed separately. (Investigations are found in the *Laboratory Manual*). Activity numbers that are bold-faced indicate BASIC activities.

Material	Activities Quantity	Activity	Investigations Quantity	Investigation
agar mixture (contains phenolpthalein and potassium ferricyanide)	small amount	**12.1b**		
Alka-Seltzer or similar tablets	2	6.2b	3	2-2
alligator clips (optional)			4	12-2
almonds, shelled	10	**7.3a**		
alpha radiation, source of		**13.1a**	1	13-1
alum			small amount	2-1
aluminum foil	small amount	5.2b, **9.3a, 14.2**	small amount	5-3
15-cm square of	small amount	12.2a		
aluminum foil pie pans	2	**7.2a, 7.2b**		
aluminum nails			10	1-3
aluminum strip, 1 cm × 10 cm	small amount	**12.2b**		
ammeter, dc, range 0 to 1 A	1	**10.2a, 10.3a,** 10.3b	1	10-2, 10-3
ammonia, household	small amount	3.3b		
antacid tablets	4	3.3b	moderate amount	3-3
baking soda	small amount	3.3b		
balance			1	1-3, 12-2
balance with standard masses	1	**1.1a, 1.2b,** 6.1b, **7.3a,** 13.1b	1	7-3
balloons	12	**3.3a, 10.1a**	2	10-1
helium-filled, tied shut with			1	5-3
BB (shot)	small amount	3.2b		
beakers (numbered)	4	2.1c		
beaker, small, 50-mL or 100-mL	2	**1.1a, 6.1a, 6.2a**		
beakers, 100-mL	1 (3)	**7.3a,** 14.1a	3	9-3
beakers, 250-mL	3	3.1b	3	2-1, 2-2, 4-1, 5-2, 5-3
beakers, 400-mL	3	7.1b		
beaker, heat-resistant, 250-mL	2 (2)	5.2b, **5.3a,** 5.3b, 6.2b, 13.1b		
bean seeds	small amount	6.1b		
beans, jar of	moderate amount	1.2c		
birthday candles (small)			3 or 4	1-1, 7-2
blocks, rectangular, of the same kind of wood, but different sizes	5	**1.2b**		
blocks, same mass			3	4-2
blocks, wood, triangular, about 3 cm long			moderate amount	8-2
block, wood, with hook (approximately 0.5 kg)			1	4-2
board, about 2m in length	1	**5.1a**		
bolt			1	14-2
iron, long	1	11.1c		
book or magazine with shiny cover	1	9.3b		
books or blocks of wood	2	4.2b		
books	2 or 3 (2)	4.3a, **4.3b,** 8.1a, 11.2a		
books, thick	5	**11.1b**		

Material	Activities Quantity	Activity	Investigations Quantity	Investigation
books or other adjustable support	2	14.2b		
bottle, clear, soft plastic with cap	1	**3.1a**		
bottles, identical	8	8.3b		
bottle, plastic, with spray pump	1	14.1a		
bowl, small, or compass	1	9.2b		
box, sealed, containing an unknown object	1	1.1b		
box, small or plastic container, with lid			1	13-2
bromphenol blue or congro red indicator			small amount	3-3
bulb, flashlight, and socket	4 (4)	**10.2,** 10.2b, **10.3a,** 10.3b		
bulbs, light, clear incandescent of different wattages	several	**11.2b**		
can, small, with one end removed	1	**7.3a**		
car, family	1	**14.3a**		
cardboard, at least 10 cm longer and wider than container	small amount	9.1b		
cardboard boxes, small, identical (approximately 5 cm on a side) with one end open	2	4.3a		
cardboard circles (9 cm in diameter)	small amount	5.3b		
cardboard, heavy, 30 cm × 30 cm	small amount	**11.1b**		
cardboard, squares, covers for containers			5	5-2
cardboard tube	1	**9.3a**		
cart, small, or roller skate	1	4.1c		
cashew nuts, shelled	10	**7.3a**		
cell, dry, "D"	2 (2)	**10.2a,** 10.2b, **10.3a,** 10.3b, **11.1b,** 11.1c, 11.2a, **11.2b**	2	10-2, 10-3
cellophane or filters (red, green, blue)	small amount	**9.2a**		
10-cm wide squares, red			5	7-3
10-cm wide squares, green			3	7-3
10-cm wide squares, blue			3	7-3
10-cm wide squares, yellow			3	7-3
chair with straight back	1	**5.1a,** 5.1b		
chalk dust from eraser			small amount	3-1
coins, equal-size			64	13-2
clock, ticking, portable (or portable tape recorder, or portable radio)	1	8.2a, 8.2c		
cloth, porous, 10 cm × 10 cm	2	**12.1a**		
coal, soft	100 g	7.2b		
coffee filters	6	7.1b		
coins (same kind)	3	**4.2c**		
cola	small amount	3.3b		
comb, hard rubber	1	**10.1a**		
compass, small	4	11 1a, **11.1b**		
container, transparent, rectangular, at least 4 cm deep	1	9.1b		
container, transparent, 250-mL			1	12-2
containers, clear, each holding 100 mL of warm water and labeled "W," "X," "Y," "Z," and "M"	5	**2.1a**		
convex lenses of different shapes and thicknesses			several	9-1
copper chloride (CuCl$_2$) solution	10 mL	**2.2b**		
copper strip, 1 cm × 10 cm	small amount	**12.2b**		
2 cm × 10 cm			small amount	12-2
12 cm × 10 cm			small amount	12-2
copper sulfate, crystals (CuSO$_4$)	5 mL	**6.1a**		

Material	Activities Quantity	Activity	Investigations Quantity	Investigation
copper sulfate ($CuSO_4$) solution			small amount	12-1
saturated	small amount	**12.2b**	small amount	12-2
cord, about 1 m long	small amount	5.1c		
cork	small amount	**7.3a**		
corn syrup, pure			100 mL	4-1
cottonball (6 cm wide)	10	3.2b		
crayon			1	14-2
cups, plastic foam	3 (1)	**5.2a**, 14.3b	6	10-1
large			7	7-3
cups and tumblers of similar size and shape but of different materials, such as plastic, glass, plastic foam, metal, ceramic			5	5-2
cylindrical plastic or glass container with cover (approximately 8 cm in diameter and 4 cm high)			small amount	13-1
designs from activity page	1 each	9.2b		
desk, large, or table	1	1.2a	1	8-1
diffraction grating, 1 cm²	1	**9.3a**		
dishcloth	1	2.2a		
dominoes	15–20	**13.2a**		
dowel, wooden	1	**3.3a, 10.1a**	1	10-1
1 m long and about 2 cm in diameter	1	5.1b		
about 80 cm long	1	8.2a		
15 cm × 3 cm	1	11.2a		
drawing compass	10	3.2b		
drawing on activity page	1 each	8.1b		
drill			1	14-2
dry ice			small amount	13-1
electric fan			1	14-2
electromagnets with iron core, each connected to a battery of 2 "D" cells and a switch			2	11-1
electroscope		**13.1a**		
Erlenmeyer flask, 250-mL			1	3-3
eye dropper			small amount	13-1
eye screw			2	8-2
felt, black, 1-cm-wide strip of length 25 cm			small amount	13-1
felt-tip pen, broad-tip, black	1	7.1b, 9.2b		
fermentation tubes	3	7.3b		
ferric ammonium citrate			10 g	9-3
filters, polarizing, or sunglasses	2	9.3b		
flashlights or slide projectors	several	9.2b	several	9-2, 13-1
flashlight bulbs in sockets			3	10-2, 10-3
flowerpot, empty	1	**7.2a**		
fluorescent light	1	**9.3a**		
foil gum wrapper	1	10.1b		
food coloring	small amount	2.2a		
funnel, plastic or glass	1	7.2b		
galvanometer	1	12.2a		
glass jar or bottle			1	14-1
approximately 250-mL			1	1-1
glass marble			1	4-1
glass rod, solid	1	**10.1a**	1	10-1
glass slides, numbered	4	2.1c		
glass tubing, 1 cm in diameter and 30 in length			2 pieces	5-3
glue			small amount	13-1

Material	Activities Quantity	Activity	Investigations Quantity	Investigation
graduated cylinder			moderate amount	1-3, 2-2, 3-3, 6-1, 6-2, 12-1
50-mL			1	7-2, 9-3
100-mL	2 (1)	**1.3a**, 2.1c, 3.3b, **5.2a**, 14.1a	3	4-1
500-mL			1	8-2
granite			small amount	1-3
graph paper	moderate amount	**1.2b**, 13.1b	moderate amount	3-2
grease pencil	1	2.1c		
grass seeds			small amount	7-3
gumdrops of a different color	12	**7.1a**	moderate amount	7-1
gumdrops of one color	6	**7.1a**		
hamburger or liver, fresh			small piece	6-2
hammer	1	**7.3a**	1	14-2
home electric meter			1 per student	11-2
hot dog or marshmallow	1	**14.2a**		
hot pad	1	**6.1a**, 7.3a	1	5-2
hot plate	1	5.2b, 5.3b, **6.1a**, **7.2a**	1	2-1, 5-2
hydrochloric acid			1 N	3-3
hydrogen peroxide (3%)	small amount	**6.2a**	small amount	6-2
ice, crushed	small amount	5.3b		
ice cubes	small amount	2.2a		
incandescent light	1	**9.3a**		
index card	small amount	8.1b, **9.1a**		
index card, or small piece of paper	1 per student	1.2a		
insulating materials for testing, such as cotton, paper, plastic foam, fiberglass, aluminum foil			several	14-3
iron filings			small amount	11-1
iron nails, at least 4 cm long	2	**2.2b**		
iron strip	small amount	**12.2b**		
iron III chloride solution			small amount	12-1
jar or flask, narrow neck, that fits 2-hole rubber stopper	1	**11.2b**		
jar or beaker	1	2.2a, 7.2b		
jar, with cover, 500-mL			2	2-1
jar, with narrow neck	1	10.1b		
juice can, small, with one end removed			small amount	7-2
knife	1	**9.3a**		
lead ball with hole	1	**4.3b**		
lead shot			several	12-1
lead nitrate solution			small amount	12-1
lemon juice	small amount	3.3b		
liquid soap or detergent			small amount	3-1
litmus paper, red and blue	8 pieces	3.3b		
magic markers in spectrum colors			several	9-2
magnet, bar	1	11.1a	2	11-1
magnet, horseshoe	1	11.2a		
magnifying glass	several	**1.1a, 2.1a**, 2.1c		
manganese dioxide			small amount	6-2
marbles (enough to fill a 250-mL beaker)	4	**8.1a**	64	14-1
marking pencil			1	4-1

Material	Activities Quantity	Activity	Investigations Quantity	Investigation
masking tape	large amount	**1.3a**, 4.1b, 4.1c, 4.2a, **4.3b**, 7.3b, **8.3a**, **9.3a**, **10.2a**, 10.2b, **10.3a**, 10.3b, **11.1b**, 11.1c, **11.2b**, **14.2a**, 14.3b	large amount	1-2, 8-1, 10-2, 10-3
matches	several	7.2b, **7.3a**	several	1-1, 6-2, 7-2
material for making windmill, such as: foil pie tin, oak tag, balsa wood, acetate sheets, etc.			several	14-2
measuring spoons, metric	1	**6.1a**		
medicine droppers	4	2.1c	several	3-1, 3-3
metal baking pan			1	8-2
metal pie pan			1	1-1
methyl alcohol			small amount	13-1
metric ruler	several	**1.1a**, 1.2a, 3.1, **1.2b**, **1.3a**, 4.1b, 4.2b, **4.2c**, 4.3a, **4.3b**, **5.1a**, 5.1b, 5.1c, 8.1b, 8.2c, 8.3b, 9.1b, 9.2b, 13.1b, 14.3b	several	1-1, 1-2, 1-3, 3-2, 4-1, 4-3, 5-1, 7-2, 8-2, 9-1, 9-2, 10-2
metric tape measure at least 30 m long			1	8-3
milk jugs with caps, empty, 4-L, plastic			2	8-2
mirror, small, plane	1	**9.1a**		
modeling clay	moderate amount	2.2a, **7.2a**, **7.3a**, **9.1a**, 10.1b	moderate amount	1-1, 7-2
red	small amount	13.2b		
yellow	small amount	13.2b		
molasses solution, 10%	small amount	7.3b		
mortar and pestle or two large metal spoons			1	3-3
motor oil	100 mL	14.1a		
nail	small amount	**7.3a**	small amount	14-2
galvanized	2	12.1a		
iron, rust-free			small amount	12-1
ungalvanized	1	12.1a		
ungalvanized, painted	1	12.1a		
nail, steel, or screw	1	**12.1b**		
needle	1	**7.3a**		
nickel	1	1.2c		
notebook	1	**14.3a**		
nuts			3	14-2
object, solid, small	1	**1.1a**		
objects, random collection, different ones	10 or 12	2.1b		
paintbrush or paper towel			1	9-3
pan, clear (20 cm to 30 cm across and at least 3 cm deep)	1	8.1c		
paper	small amount	**6.1a**		
paper clip, large	1	**7.2a**	2	8-1
paper, colored, labeled "W," "X," "Y," "Z," and "M"	5 sheets	**2.1a**		
paper, construction, black	small amount	14.2b	small amount	13-1
paper, construction, or tagboard	moderate amount	**1.3a**		
8 cm × 8 cm	10	3.2b		

Material	Activities Quantity	Activity	Investigations Quantity	Investigation
paper, construction (white, black, red, green, blue)	moderate amount	**9.2a**		
paper, heavy or black posterboard			small amount	9-2
paper, lined	moderate amount	**9.1a**		
paper, small bits	small amount	8.1c		
paper, white	small amount	8.1c	moderate amount	9-1, 9-2, 9-3
paper towel	several	12.2a		
paper, unlined	small amount	11.1a		
pebbles, small (enough to half fill the plastic bottle)	moderate amount	14.1a		
pen or pencil, new, sharpened	several	1.3a, 5.3b, **8.1a,** 8.1c, 9.2b, 11.1c, 11.2a, 13.1b	several	3-2, 5-2, 9-2
3 different colors	several	3.2b	several	4-1, 5-2
pen cap	several	**7.2a,** 9.2b		
pennies, or other small objects such as paper clips, toothpicks, etc.	several	**14.1b**		
penny, copper	5	1.2c, 12.2a		
periodic table	1	3.2a	1	3-2
petri dish	1	12.1b		
pie pan, aluminum foil			several	7-2
pie pan, large, flat			several	3-1
pins	4	9.1b		
plastic, rigid squares, about 30 cm × 30 cm			2	11-1
plastic bag	several	**1.3a, 10.1a,** 10.1b	several	10-1
popcorn kernels, unpopped	small amount	6.1b		
poster board square (6 cm × 6 cm)	10	3.2b		
potassium ferricyanide			10 g	9-3
potassium hydroxide (KOH)	small amount	7.3b		
potassium permanganate (KMnO₄) or food coloring	small amount	**5.3a**		
potting soil (or Vermiculite)			moderate amount	7-3
powder, white, labeled "W," "X," "Y," and "Z"	4 vials	**2.1a**		
prism			1	9-2, 9-3
protractor	1	9.1b	1	9-2
pulley, with attachment points at both ends	1	5.1c		
ramps, grooved, of equal length, metal or wood, long, with a metal stop at one end	2	4.2b		
ramps, identically-grooved, or rulers	2	4.3a		
reading material			small amount	8-3
red cabbage leaf (or other colored leaf or flowers)	small amount	7.1b		
refrigerator			1	14-3
ringstand and clamp			1	9-3
ringstand with ring			1	7-2
rod, metal, about 80-cm long	1	8.2a		
roller skate or skateboard	1	**5.1a**		
rope with knot in center	3 m	4.2a		
rubber band	several	**8.2b**	7	7-3
identical			2	8-1
rubber stopper, 2-hole	1	**11.2b**		
or other supports for plastic			8	11-1
rubbing alcohol	small amount	7.1b		
ruler, plastic	1	**8.2b**		

Material	Activities Quantity	Activity	Investigations Quantity	Investigation
salt, chemically pure (or Kosher)	small amount	2.1c		
table salt	15 mL	3.3b		
saltwater solution	small amount	12.2a		
sand	small amount	3.1b, 13.1b		
sandpaper			small amount	12-1
fine	small amount	11.2a, 12.2a		
scissors	large amount	**1.3a**, 7.1b, **7.2a**, 8.1b, **8.3a**, **9.1a**, 9.2b, 10.1b	large amount	9-2, 14-2
screwdriver			1	10-2
shoebox			1	9-2
spring balance calibrated in N	1	**5.1a**, 5.1b, 5.1c		
screen, white, or wall	1	**9.2a**		
shower, home, with a tub	1	14.3b		
silk	1 piece	**10.1a**	1 piece	10-1
silver nitrate solution			10 mL	12-1
skateboards	2	4.2a		
sodium chloride			small amount	6-2
sodium hydroxide solution			1 N	3-3
solutions of:				
calcium nitrate			moderate amount	6-1
sodium carbonate			moderate amount	6-1
sodium nitrate			moderate amount	6-1
solution of 80% corn syrup in water			100 mL	4-1
solution of 90% corn syrup in water			100 mL	4-1
source of direct current (6-V or 9-V battery)			1	12-2
spatula or spoon (small)			1	6-2
spoon, metal	1	5.2b		
spoon, stainless steel	1	8.2a		
spring balance marked in newtons			1	4-2
splint			1	6-2
squares in a row, on tile floor or tabletop	10	**14.1b**		
stairs (2 to 3 flights)			1	5-1
stand, with clamp(s)	1	**3.3a**, 11.2a	1	5-3
standard mass, 500-g	1	5.1c		
standard mass, 1-Kg	1	5.1b		
steel ball and aluminum ball of same diameter but different mass	1	4.2b		
steel balls, with different masses	2	4.3a		
steel ball with hole (or large metal nut)			1	1-2
steel ball or bearing			1	1-3
steel wire, thin			1.5 m	8-2
thicker			1.5 m	8-2
steel wool	small amount	**6.2a, 12.1a**	small amount	6-2
stick, pointed	1	**14.2a**		
stirring rods	5 (8)	1.1a, **2.1a**, 2.1c, 3.3b, 5.2a, 5.2b, 5.3b		
stopwatch or watch that indicates seconds	1	**4.1a**, 4.1b	1	4-1, 5-1
straight pin	10	3.2b	1	5-3
straw, drinking, transparent	small amount	2.2a, 3.2b		
string, long (1m), or thread	moderate amount	**3.3a, 4.3b**, 8.2a	moderate amount	1-2, 1-3, 4-2, 8-1
ball of	1	**8.3a**		
superball			1	4-3
support, (ring stand, clamp, bar)	1	5.1c		
sweater or folded cloth			1	8-2

Material	Activities Quantity	Activity	Investigations Quantity	Investigation
switch	several	**10.2a**, 10.2b, **10.3a**, 10.3b, **11.2b**	several	10-3
table, more than 1 m in length	1	**5.1a**	1	4-2
tagboard, white, 15 cm × 15 cm	1 piece	9.2b		
tacks, iron, or brads	several	11.1c		
tape, double stick			small amount	9-2
tape, transparent	large amount	2.2a, 5.3b, **7.2a**, 8.1b, **9.2a**, 9.2b, 14.2b	large amount	5-3, 12-2, 14-3
tape measure	1	**4.1a**, 4.2a		
teakettle, with narrow spout	1	**7.2a**		
test tube	2 (8)	2.2a, **2.2b**, 3.3b, 7.2b	5	6-2, 12-1
test tube holder	1	**2.2b**		
test tube rack	1	**2.2b**, 3.3b	1	6-1, 12-1
test tube with cork stopper			1	6-1
thermometer	2	**5.2a**, 5.2b, 5.3b, **7.3a**, 7.3b, 14.2b, 14.3b	6	2-2, 5-2, 7-2, 14-3
thread	1 piece	**10.1a**	small amount	2-1, 10-2
thread spool			1	14-2
toothpicks, round	18	**7.1a**	moderate	7-1
toy tractor, battery-powered	1	4.1b		
tubing, plastic, to fit the spray pump nozzle	1 piece	14.1a		
tuning forks, identical, with base supports and rubber hammer			2	8-1
tweezers	several	**5.3a**		
umbrella, old	1	**14.2a**		
vial with cap or small test tube with stopper	1	4.1c		
vinegar	small amount	3.3b, 7.1b	4 to 5 mL	6-1
voltmeter, dc, range 0 to 5 V	1	10.2b, **10.3a**, 10.3b	1	10-3
walnut halves, shelled	10	**7.3a**		
washer, or paper clip	1 per student	**8.3a**	2	14-2
watch or clock with second hand	1	1.2c, **2.2b, 5.3a**, 5.3b, **8.3a, 13.2a**		
water	large amount	2.1c, 2.2a, **2.2b**, **3.1a**, 3.1b, 3.3b, 4.1c, 5.2b, 5.3b, 7.1b, **7.2a, 7.3a**, 7.3b, 8.1c, 8.3b, 9.1b	large amount	1-1, 1-3, 2-1, 2-2, 3-1, 5-2, 5-3, 7-2, 8-2, 9-3
at room temperature	moderate amount	**6.1a**		
cold	large amount	**5.2a, 5.3a**, 6.2b, 14.1a	moderate amount	2-2
distilled	moderate amount	2.1c, 3.3b	moderate amount	3-3
hot	large amount	**5.2a, 5.3a**, 6.2b, 14.1a	moderate amount	2-2
white powder, mystery	1 vial	**2.1a**		
wire, bell, 20-cm lengths	4 (5)	**10.2a**, 10.2b	4	10-2
10-cm lengths	7 (10)	**10.3a**, 10.3b		
wire, connecting			small amount	10-3
wire, copper,	3 pieces	**11.2b**	2 pieces	12-1
30-cm pieces			2	12-2

Material	Activities Quantity	Activity	Investigations Quantity	Investigation
wire, insulated, with ends exposed	60 cm (1 m)	**11.1b**, 11.1c		
wire, iron, picture	2 cm	**11.2b**		
wire, lacquered, #22–26	4 m	11.2a		
wire, long, loose, or plastic spring (such as a Slinky)	1 piece	**8.1a**		
wire, stiff, with uninsulated ends	15 cm	10.1b		
wire, uninsulated, same diameter, 60-cm lengths of				
copper			several pieces	10-2
iron			several pieces	10-2
nichrome			several pieces	10-2
wire or strong cord	1 piece	5.1b		
wire gauze			small amount	7-2
wire screens	1 (2)	5.3b, **6.1a**		
wood, scrap			1 piece	14-2
wood block (small)	1	**4.3b**		
wood block with screw eye hook	1	**5.1a**		
wood cube, small			1	13-1
wooden board, about 1 m × 15 cm × 2 cm			1	8-2
wooden board, 60-cm long (about 10-cm wide)			1	10-2
wooden cube or rectangle			1	1-3
wool flannel	small amount	**3.3a, 10.1a,** 10.1b	small amount	10-1
yarn, small piece	1	**8.1a**		
yeast, dry	small amount	7.3b		
zinc strip, 1 cm × 10 cm	1	**12.2b**		

Suppliers of Laboratory Equipment

Catalogs from distributors/suppliers will provide you with the most up-to-date information about sources, availability, costs, and alternative equipment that might better fit your needs. The following suppliers are frequently cited as sources of scientific supplies and equipment.

Calbiochem
3625 Medford Street
Los Angeles CA 90054

Carolina Biological Supply Company
2700 York Road
Burlington NC 27215

Central Scientific Company
11222 Melrose Avenue
Franklin Park IL 60131–1364

DAMON/Educational Division
115 Fourth Avenue
Needham MA 02194

Edmund Scientific Company
Edscorp Building
Barrington NJ 08007

Fisher Scientific Company
Educational Materials Division
4901 West Lemoyne Avenue
Chicago IL 60651

Frey Scientific Company
905 Hickory Lane
Mansfield OH 44905

Hubbard Scientific Company
P.O. Box 104
Northbrook IL 60062

Klinger Scientific Apparatus
83–45 Parsons Boulevard
Jamaica NY 11432

Lab Safety Supply
P.O. Box 1368
Janesville WI 53547

LaPine Scientific Company
6001 S. Knox Avenue
Chicago IL 60629

Nasco
901 Janesville Avenue
Fort Atkinson WI 53538

Sargent-Welch Scientific Company
7300 North Linder Avenue
Skokie IL 60077

Science Kit, Inc.
777 East Park Drive
Tonawanda NY 14150–6782

Scientific Glass Apparatus Company
737 Broad Street
Bloomfield NJ 07003

Scott Resources
P.O. Box 2121
Fort Collins CO 80522

Ward's Natural Science
Establishment, Inc.
P.O. Box 92912
Rochester NY 14692–9012

Teaching Notes

Chapter 1   Science and Measurement

Chapter 1 Planning Guide			
Planning Your Classroom Lessons			
	1.1 Scientific Methods 4–15	**1.2** Measurement 16–33	**1.3** Problem Solving 34–43	**Chapter 1 Review** 44–45 Chapter 1 Supplements
Content Overview	The processes used in science and the way theories and laws, though well established, can be refined Concept Summary T58 Learning Objectives T58	How measurements are made, and how graphs can be used to study measurements Concept Summary T60 Learning Objectives T60	How to solve a problem involving an unknown factor, and how to handle the units of measurements involved in a calculation, either directly or by converting them to a form necessary to perform the calculation Concept Summary T62 Learning Objectives T62	Science Background Information 2 Review of Concepts 44 Essential Ideas/ Chapter 1 Letter to Parents
Teaching Strategies	Getting Started: Ideas for Discussion and Suggested Demonstration T58	Getting Started: Ideas for Discussion and Suggested Demonstration T60	Getting Started: Ideas for Discussion and Suggested Demonstration T62	
Teaching Aids	Teaching Diagram 1-1A, 1-1B Overhead Transparency	Teaching Diagram 1-2A, 1-2B	Teaching Diagram 1-3A, 1-3B	Physical Science Software T29 Physical Science Films and Videos T37 Video Lesson: Particle Model of Matter
Review and Evaluation*	Quick Review 5, 9, 11, 13, 14 1.1 Review 15 Section Testsheet 1-1 TRB 201	Quick Review 17, 18, 20, 21, 22, 23, 26, 29, 31 1.2 Review 33 Section Testsheet 1-2 TRB 202	Quick Review 36, 38, 40 1.3 Review 43 Section Testsheet 1-3 TRB 203	Chapter Testsheets 1A and 1B TRB 241–242 Free Response Questions TRB 187 Semester Test 1 TRB 273–276 *Higher Level Evaluation* Critical Thinking 44–45

*TESTGEN can be used to prepare customized section and chapter testsheets.

Meeting Individual Needs			
Reinforcement	Reading Checksheet 1-1 TRB 81 Skillsheet 1-1 TRB 127 Essential Ideas 1.1	Reading Checksheet 1-2 TRB 82 Skillsheet 1-2 TRB 128 Essential Ideas 1.2	Reading Checksheet 1-3 TRB 83 Skillsheet 1-3 TRB 129 Essential Ideas 1.3	Information Library Software
Enrichment	Research Topic 7 Data Search 5	Research Topic 24, 31 Data Search 22	Research Topic 40 Data Search 42	Individual Research 45 Bibliography 45
Critical Thinking and Problem Solving	Critical Thinking 11, 13	Critical Thinking 20, 21, 27	Critical Thinking 35 Practice Problems 36, 38, 39	Chapter Testsheet 1B TRB 242 Problem-Solving Worksheets, Chapter 1

Chapter 1 Planning Guide

Developing Laboratory Skills

	1.1 Scientific Methods 4–15	1.2 Measurement 16–33	1.3 Problem Solving 34–43	Chapter 1 Supplements
Plan Ahead	For Activity, page 6: A wide variety of materials can be used, including metal wire, paper, fabric and rocks. For Activity, page 8: The object used for this activity should provide the students with some sensory clues as to its nature without being obvious.	For Activity, page 25: Set up the desk or table so that each student can make his or her measurement without others observing the result. For Activity, page 30: Fill a jar with a known number of beans for the activity.	For Activity, page 41: Have students smooth out the plastic bag inside the cube so that the space can hold as much water as possible.	

Basic Activities	Direct and Indirect
	  Observation 6
	  20 minutes
	  Groups of 3
	Activity Record Sheet
	  1-1A, LM 1
		Graphing Measurements
		  of Blocks 28
		  40 minutes
		  Individual work
		Activity Record Sheet
		  1-2B, LM 6
			Comparing Units 41
			  30 minutes
			  Groups of 3 or 4
			Activity Record Sheet
			  1-3A, LM 11	

Additional Activities	What Is in the Box? 8
	  15 to 25 minutes
	  Entire class
	Activity Record Sheet
	  1-1B, LM 2
		Differences in Length
		  Measurements 25
		  20 minutes
		  Entire class
		Activity Record Sheet
		  1-2A, LM 5
		
		Estimating 30
		  20 minutes
		  Individual work
		Activity Record Sheet
		  1-2C, LM 7
				Projectsheet 1 TRB 173

Investigations and Research Lab	Investigation 1-1,
	  Forming and Testing a
	  Hypothesis LM 3–4
	  30 minutes
	  Groups of 4
		Investigation 1-2,
		  Graphing Pendulum
		  Measurements
		  LM 9–10
		  30 minutes
		  Groups of 2
			Investigation 1-3,
			  Problem-Solving:
			  Working with Density
			  LM 13–14
			  50 minutes
			  Groups of 5 or 6
				Research Lab 1
				  LM 15–16

1.1 Scientific Methods

Concept Summary

An **observation** is information gathered through use of the senses or with the aid of instruments.
- Observations both initiate and verify the results of scientific investigation.

The **scientific method** is a set of steps outlining a way of attacking problems in science.
- The heart of the scientific method is the formation and testing of hypotheses.
- Hypotheses are tested by controlled experiments.

A **model** is a description of something unfamiliar in terms of familiar things.
- A scientific model is changed in order to agree with new observations and revised hypotheses.
- A theory in science is a well-tested model or set of hypotheses about some aspect of the natural world.
- Theories are revised and broadened as more observations are made.

Learning Objectives

1. To describe the characteristics of a scientific hypothesis and how hypotheses are used.
2. To identify the basic steps used in solving a problem in science.
3. To describe the characteristics of a controlled experiment.
4. To describe how scientists use and revise models.
5. To distinguish between a theory and a hypothesis.

Getting Started

Ideas for Discussion
Students will learn the process of finding the answer to a question using the scientific method.

Discuss the process of finding the answer to a question. Explain that this process is known as *research*. Usually research will provide the answer you need. Ask what happens if you research a problem and no one knows the answer. How can you go about finding out? Discuss the following example with the students. You are lost in the woods and you have no food. You find a tree bearing strange looking nut-like seeds.

You've never seen them before, and you do not know if they are safe to eat. What do you do?

Explain that you can look for evidence. You may see animals in the process of eating the seeds, or you may find piles of gnawed shells on the ground. You may try a tiny piece of seed yourself. If it tastes bitter, you may not want to eat it. If it tastes good, you can swallow the small piece and wait several hours. If it does not make you sick, you have found a new food supply. Explain that this process of gathering evidence by observation and direct experimentation involves the fundamentals of the scientific method. Tell the class that in Chapter 1, Section 1, they will learn how the scientific method is used to solve problems.

Suggested Demonstration
In this demonstration the students will learn the difference between an observation and a conclusion. For this experiment you will need a random collection of four or five small objects.

Write the words *observation* and *conclusion* on the board. Hold up one of the small objects (such as a tennis ball) and, without naming it, ask what observations can be made about this object. Tell the class that naming the object is not an observation. Write *tennis ball* in the conclusion column. Students should observe that the object is fuzzy, white, spherical, and compresses when you squeeze it. Write the class responses in the observation column. Repeat this process with the rest of the objects. When all the observations and conclusions about each object are on the board, ask what all the observations have in common. (They are all descriptions of some property of the object that is perceived through the senses.) What do all the conclusions have in common? (They are all based on observations.) Tell the students that making accurate observations is one of the most important skills in science, and it is a major part of the scientific method. This will be explained in Chapter 1, Section 1.

Activity 1.1a
Direct and Indirect Observation   page 6

Preparation Notes
Materials can include metal wire or strips, pieces of paper, fabric, or yarn, rocks, rubber band, cork, small plastic objects, sugar cube, antacid or aspirin tablets, scented items like bath oil beads or small soaps.

Answers to Questions

1. Surface features appear larger and can be seen in more detail. The magnifying glass may reveal features not seen with the naked eye.
2. Answers will vary but will probably include the object's shape, color, texture, flexibility, odor, and behavior when placed in water.
3. Indirect observations include the appearance under the magnifying glass and the object's mass and measured dimension(s).

Conclusion

Instruments make it possible to measure according to standard units of measurement. They also detect information our senses are unable to pick up.

Activity 1.1b
Formulating a Hypothesis:
What Is in the Box?   page 8

Teacher Note
The time required will vary with the size of the class.

Preparation Notes
Choose an object that will provide some sensory clues without being obvious. Allow each student to handle the box for only a few seconds. They may shake the box or move it back and forth. Students should think of questions they need to ask while the box is passed around. Limit each student to one question. Students should write down their guess before the box is opened.

Answers to Questions
1. Direct observation, collecting data, making inferences, forming a hypothesis.
2. Questions that provide specific data about characteristics of the object such as what it is made of, where or by whom it is used, and so on. Questions that eliminate a group of objects, those made of metal, for example, are also helpful.
3. Answers will vary. Students may suggest the use of X-rays to determine the shape of the object, heating or freezing to determine how properties change, or perhaps passing the box through a strong magnetic or electric field. Encourage students to think about different kinds of tests that do not destroy the box.

Conclusion
The scientific method is a systematic approach to problem-solving. It involves careful observation and uses available information to reach a logical solution or conclusion.

1.1 Section Review

Understanding the Concepts   page 15
19. Questions arise from observations. Hypotheses are formed and then tested by further observations. Even well-established theories and laws are changed if they are found to disagree with solid experimental evidence.
20. A model in science is usually verbal or mathematical. It may be described with the aid of drawings, but it need not be a three-dimensional object like an architect's model of a building.
21. Using a control test whether there really is only one variable being changed and whether it does have an effect. In fact, in experiments with living things, where it is hard to control all the variables, large numbers of controls may be involved in an experiment. (With many controls, random effects from uncontrolled variables tend to cancel each other.)

1.2 Measurement

Concept Summary

A **measurement** is an observation that describes the amount of a property and that includes both a number and a unit.

- Measured values always include some error.
- Graphing measurements can help reveal relationships between the quantities being measured.
- Estimation can provide approximate measurements when direct measurement is impractical.
- Very small or very large quantities can be measured indirectly.

Learning Objectives

1. To identify the SI units commonly used for length, mass, temperature, time, and certain other derived units.
2. To recognize the presence of some amount of error in every measurement that is made.
3. To determine if a relationship exists between two variables using graphical analyis.
4. To estimate the value of a large or small measurement using indirect procedures.

Getting Started

Ideas for Discussion
Students will learn to distinguish between quality and quantity and how these factors are important in science.

Write on the board the words, "To measure is to know." Discuss the meaning of these words with the class. Explain that measurement is a way of communicating observations so that they can be understood by everyone. Explain that the statement on the board was made by Johannes Kepler (1571–1630), a German astronomer who formulated the laws of planetary motion. Kepler had a great deal of trouble with his work because of a lack of an accurate and standardized method of measuring.

Write on the board the words *quantitative* and *qualitative*. Ask the class to give a definition of each word. Quantity means the number or amount of something. Quality means the basic nature of something. Explain that quantitative features are things that can be measured, such as length, mass, volume, and temperature. Qualitative features such as color are not easily

characterized. Give the example of an aqua or turquoise color. Some people perceive it as blue, and others perceive it as green. The exact color is not precisely described in a way that is understood by everyone, so the description of aqua is a qualitative one. Tell the class that in Chapter 1, Section 2, they will learn how to use the metric system of measurement and how to construct graphs.

Suggested Demonstration
Students will learn that measurement errors occur in coins. You will need an equal-arm balance and five nickels for this demonstration. The mass of each nickel should be determined and recorded in advance of the demonstration.

Have the class examine the five nickels and observe how they are different. For example, ask them to note where the coins were minted and how shiny the various coins are. Explain that the coins also differ in mass, which is a quantity measured in grams. The U.S. government standard for the mass of a nickel is five grams. However, when billions of nickels are produced annually, there is an error of measurement in the manufacturing process. Coins are produced that vary slightly from the five-gram standard.

Demonstrate the use of the equal-arm balance for measuring mass. Explain that mass is measured by comparing the mass of an unknown object with the mass of a known standard. Point out the parts of the balance. Explain that it must be treated gently and used on a level surface. The balance operates by balancing on a knifepoint that can be chipped or broken.

Demonstrate how to zero the scale. Explain why this is important. Measure the mass of each of the five nickels. Write the amount of mass of each nickel on the board. Round to two decimal places. Have the class calculate the average mass by adding all the masses together and dividing by five. Have the students determine if the average mass is close to five grams. What is the largest error of measurement made in the sample? What is the smallest error of measurement in the sample? What is the average error made by the mint? Explain that vending machines weigh coins and reject those that are very off-weight.

Activity 1.2a
Differences in Length Measurements
page 25

Teaching Hints
If you have the meter stick flat on the table some students will use it flat; others may put it on edge so that the marks on the meter stick are touching the table.

This second technique will give more accurate and more consistent readings because error due to parallax is reduced. Also, some students may have been taught to begin measuring from the first numbered division rather than from the end of the meter stick. This technique avoids measuring problems which come from irregularities on the worn end of a meter stick.

Answers to Questions
1. No, there will probably be a range of values.
2. Possible sources for variation in the values include parallax, alignment problems, movement of the meter stick, a "bad" end, different opinions on where the exact edge of the table is.
3. Answers will vary.
4. Students should suggest ways of reducing errors created by problems they list in Question 2. Also, see Teaching Hints.

Conclusion
The average is probably the best value because the low and high values cancel each other out.

Activity 1.2b
Graphing Measurements of Blocks
page 28

Teaching Hints
If all of the blocks are made of the same kind of wood, the plotted points should line up along a straight line. However, real life data will probably have some scatter due to variation in the wood samples and inconsistencies in measuring techniques. If the plotted points do not line up along a straight line, do one of the following. See if most of the points line up on a straight line or very nearly so. Draw a straight line through these points. Alternatively, you can see if a straight line can "average" the points. That is, if possible draw a straight line such that there are equal numbers of points on each side of the line.

Answers to Questions
1. Yes, they should. (Also, see Teaching Hints.)
2. As the volume of a block of wood increases, the mass also increases.
3. Yes, doubling the volume should double the mass.
4. The mass of a wood block of zero volume is zero. Of course, if this were actually the case, there would be no block of wood at all!

Conclusion
The mass of a wood block is proportional to its volume. As the volume increases or decreases, so does the mass.

Activity 1.2c
Estimating   page 30

Teaching Hints
Part 2. Pulse beats (while at rest) will range from about 50 to 90 in one minute.

Part 3. Two pennies have about the same mass as a nickel. Therefore, the mass of one penny is about 2.5 grams.

Answers to Questions
1. Most students probably had differences in all of their estimates.
2. The estimate based on the most information will probably be the most accurate.

Conclusion
Estimates can be improved by basing them on as much information as possible.

1.2 Section Review

Understanding the Concepts   page 33
31. When scientists all use the same system of measurement, they can compare the results of investigations and communicate more easily.
32. **a.** 100 cubes
    b. 100 rows
    c. 100 layers
    d. The total number of little cubes that fit inside the big cube is $100 \times 100 \times 100$, or 1 000 000. Thus, 1 000 000 cm^3 = 1 m^3.
33. **a.** A little finger is about 1 cm across. Mark off the height of the brick with your little fingers.
    b. Multiply the estimate of the height of one brick by the number of rows of bricks, as counted or estimated.

1.3 Problem Solving

Concept Summary

The **unknown** in a word problem is what is being asked for.

- The first step in solving a word problem is to identify the unknown.
- The unknown is determined by writing an equation that expresses it in terms of the known quantities, and performing calculations on the numbers and units.
- Dimensional analysis can help you decide whether an equation makes sense.
- Conversion factors are used to express a measurement in a different unit.

Learning Objectives

1. To learn a procedure for attacking a problem that involves solving for an unknown.
2. To learn procedures for handling the units of measurements involved in a calculation.
3. To learn a procedure for converting one kind of units to an equivalent kind, in order to perform calculations on quantities with the same units.

Getting Started

Ideas for Discussion
Students will learn that they can solve problems with greater facility when they know the units that comprise them.

Write the sentence on the board, "There are six . . ." Ask the students to finish the sentence with different endings. Explain that the number six is not a complete description of something. To complete the description, it is necessary to determine what there are six *of* (for example, six books, six pencils, or six pennies). These items are called the *units*. Explain that a numerical description has no meaning without units. Tell the students that knowing the units in a problem makes it easier for them to solve the problem. Chapter 1, Section 3 will describe how units are used in problem-solving.

Suggested Demonstration
In this demonstration the students will learn the interconvertibility of units of mass and volume in the metric system. For this experiment you will need the following items:

25-mL graduated cylinder
platform balance
test weights 1 g, others to total 25 g
water

Explain that the metric system was designed to make it easier to solve problems. The way this was done was to design the system of units in such a way that they all could be easily interconverted. Set up the platform balance. Ask: What does it measure, and in what units? (Answer: mass in grams.)

Show the class the graduated cylinder, and ask what it measures and in what unit. (The graduated cylinder measures volume of a liquid in mL.) Explain that you will demonstrate how the units of mass and volume are related. Zero the balance. Determine the mass of the empty graduated cylinder and write the mass on the board. Explain that you can now find the mass of any amount of liquid you put into the cylinder. Fill the cylinder and determine the combined mass of the cylinder and its contents, then subtract from the combined mass the known mass of the empty cylinder. Have the class perform the calculation for 25 mL of water and for 10 mL of water. The students should find that 25 mL of water has a mass of 25 g and 10 mL of water has a mass of 10 g. Ask the students what this tells them about the relationship of the units of mass and volume. 1 mL of water has a mass of 1 gram. Tell the class that in Chapter 1, Section 3 they will learn how to use this information to make word problems easier to solve.

Activity 1.3a
Comparing Units   page 41

Teaching Hints
1. Make sure students smooth out the plastic bag inside the cube so that the space can hold as much water as possible.
2. In Step 6, the volume of the cube in cm^3 is $1000\ cm^3$.
3. In Step 7, the volume of the cube in mL is

$$1000\ \cancel{cm}^3 \times \frac{1\ mL}{\cancel{cm}^3} = 1000\ mL$$

4. In Step 8, the solution to the problem is

$$number\ of\ volumes = \frac{volume\ of\ cube}{volume\ of\ cylinder}$$

$$= \frac{1000\ \cancel{mL}}{100\ \cancel{mL}} = 10$$

Answers to Questions
1. Answers will vary.
2. 10
3. They should be fairly close.

Conclusion
The volume of the cube is 1000 mL. This equals 1 L.

1.3 Section Review

Understanding the Concepts   page 43

8. 1) If there are different units for the same quantity (mass, length, etc.), use a conversion factor between that pair of units. 2) Following the rules for working with units, check that the units of the answer are appropriate.

9. You can use dimensional analysis to check that you have the right equation before you start doing any numerical calculations.

Problems to Solve   page 43

10. a. Unknown: mass of iron

b. Knowns: density of iron = 7.9 g/cm³
volume of iron = 20 cm³

c. $\text{density} = \dfrac{\text{mass}}{\text{volume}}$

d. mass = density × volume

e. mass = 7.9 g/cm³ × 20 cm³

f. mass = $7.9 \, \dfrac{g}{cm^3} \times 20 \, cm^3$

= 7.9(20) g

It is not necessary to use any conversion factors.

g. Yes, the unit g is appropriate for mass.

h. mass = 158 g

11. a. Unknown: volume of gold

b. Knowns: density of gold = 19.3 g/cm³
mass of gold = 1 kg

c. $\text{density} = \dfrac{\text{mass}}{\text{volume}}$

d. $\text{volume} = \dfrac{\text{mass}}{\text{density}}$

e. $\text{volume} = \dfrac{1 \, kg}{19.3 \, g/cm^3}$

f. $\text{volume} = \dfrac{1 \, kg \cdot cm^3}{19.3 \, g} \left(\dfrac{1000 \, g}{1 \, kg} \right)$

$= \dfrac{1(1000)}{19.3} \, cm^3$

Yes, you have to use the conversion factor

$$\dfrac{1000 \, g}{1 \, kg}$$

g. Yes, the units cm³ are appropriate for volume.

h. volume = 51.8 cm³

Chapter Review

Critical Thinking   page 44

1. A legislature can change a law however it wishes (subject to some limits, such as a constitution). A law in science must always fit the scientific evidence, and changes only as new, verified evidence that does not match the old law becomes available.

2. a. An ice cube has a greater volume when frozen. (For the same mass, the density can be less only if the volume is greater.)

b. When an ice cube floats, part of it is above the water level. The water level in the glass does not change because the volume of water from the melted ice cube exactly equals the volume of the *submerged* part of the frozen ice cube.

3. Accept values from 0.1 to 10 times the values given here. Be sure that the units given are appropriate.

a. 20 m

b. 300 mL

c. 100 g

d. 40°C

e. 40 cm

f. 60 L

Chapter 2   Properties of Matter

	Chapter 2 Planning Guide			
	Planning Your Classroom Lessons			
	2.1 Classes of Matter 48–63	**2.2** Changes in Matter 64–77		**Chapter 2 Review** 78–79 Chapter 2 Supplements
Content Overview	An examination of the properties most commonly used in classifying matter: phase, metal vs. nonmetal, solubility, conductivity, hardness, etc. Concept Summary T68 Learning Objectives T68	How matter can be changed, and the difference between physical and chemical changes. Concept Summary T69 Learning Objectives T69		Science Background Information 46 Review of Concepts 78 Essential Ideas/ Chapter 2 Letter to Parents
Teaching Strategies	Getting Started: Ideas for Discussion and Suggested Demonstration T68	Getting Started: Ideas for Discussion and Suggested Demonstration T69		
Teaching Aids	Teaching Diagram 2-1A, 2-1B Overhead Transparency	Teaching Diagram 2-2A, 2-2B		Physical Science Software T29 Physical Science Films and Videos T37 Video Lesson: Particle Model of Matter
Review and Evaluation*	Quick Review 51, 55, 57, 61 2.1 Review 63 Section Testsheet 2-1 TRB 204	Quick Review 67, 69, 71, 72, 74, 75 2.2 Review 77 Section Testsheet 2-2 TRB 205		Chapter Testsheets 2A and 2B TRB 243–244 Free Response Questions TRB 187 Semester Test 1 TRB 273–276 *Higher Level Evaluation* Critical Thinking 78–79

*TESTGEN can be used to prepare customized section and chapter testsheets.

	Meeting Individual Needs			
Reinforcement	Reading Checksheet 2-1 TRB 84 Skillsheet 2-1 TRB 130 Essential Ideas 2.1	Reading Checksheet 2-2 TRB 85 Skillsheet 2-2 TRB 131 Essential Ideas 2.2		Information Library Software
Enrichment	Research Topic 49, 57 Data Search 59	Research Topic 65, 74 Data Search 68		Individual Research 79 Bibliography 79
Critical Thinking and Problem Solving	Critical Thinking 50, 51, 55, 56, 59, 61	Critical Thinking 70, 72		Chapter Testsheet 2B TRB 244 Problem-Solving Worksheets, Chapter 2

Chapter 2 Planning Guide

Developing Laboratory Skills

	2.1 Classes of Matter 48–63	2.2 Changes in Matter 64–77		Chapter 2 Supplements
Plan Ahead	For Activity, page 52: Gather at least four white powders for the activity. Prepare the five vials for each group. For Activity, page 54: List the various properties the objects have in common and how they can be subdivided into groups. For Activity, page 62: Slides prepared in the activity must be left undisturbed overnight.	For Activity, page 66: Most indicative results will be obtained on days with mild temperatures. For Activity, page 73: Be sure there are safety goggles for every student conducting the experiment		

Basic Activities	Distinguishing Among
	   Substances 52
	   20 minutes
	   Groups of 4
	Activity Record Sheet
	   2-1A, LM 17
		Recognizing Chemical
		   Changes 73
		   15 minutes
		   Groups of 5 or 6
		Activity Record Sheet
		   2-2B, LM 24		

Additional Activities	Classifying Objects 54
	   30 minutes
	   Groups of 4 or 5
	Activity Record Sheet
	   2-1B, LM 18
	
	Preparing and Separating
	   Solutions 62
	   15 minutes and
	   overnight
	   Groups of 3 or 4
	Activity Record Sheet
	   2-1C, LM 19
		Temperature and Air
		   Volume 66
		   20 minutes
		   Groups of 2 or 3
		Activity Record Sheet
		   2-2A, LM 23
				Projectsheet 2 TRB 174

Investigations and Research Lab	Investigation 2-1
	   Growing Crystals
	   LM 21–22
	   30 minutes
	   Groups of 3
		Investigation 2-2,
		   Temperature and the
		   Speed of Chemical
		   Change LM 27–28
		   30 minutes
		   Groups of 3 or 4
				Research Lab 2
				LM 29–30

Chapter 2   Properties of Matter

2.1 Classifying Matter

Concept Summary

Matter is anything that has mass and takes up space.
- Each substance, or kind of matter, has properties by which it is recognized.

The **classification** of matter is a grouping of matter according to its properties.
- Substances can be put in order by differences in the same property.
- Substances are classified as solids, liquids, or gases at ordinary temperatures; as metals or nonmetals; or as elements, compounds, or mixtures.
- Elements are substances that cannot be broken down into other substances.
- Compounds are substances made of two or more elements according to a fixed formula and have properties very different from those of the elements.

Learning Objectives

1. To distinguish between substances on the basis of their differences in properties.
2. To group and to order substances using similarities and differences in the properties of the substances.
3. To describe the properties of each of the phases of matter—solid, liquid, and gas.
4. To differentiate among mixtures, solutions, compounds, and elements.

Getting Started

Ideas for Discussion
Students will learn that all matter has mass and takes up space.

Ask the students to name as many different common items as they can. Write the items on the board. A typical list may be:

house	bicycle
turnip	paper
piano	baseball bat
rock	

When a sufficiently large list is obtained, ask the students what property is common to all the items on the list. The students may suggest that all the items are made out of "stuff." Explain that the stuff things are made of is called matter. Emphasize that everything that is made up of matter has mass and takes up space. Discuss the meaning of the word *mass*. Care should be taken not to confuse mass with weight. An astronaut's body and space suit, although weightless in space, has the same mass in space that it has on earth. Ask the students to name some things that do not have mass or take up space.

Have the class re-examine the list. Emphasize that in order to know more about the items, we need to classify them into groups based on the properties of their matter. Scientists use classification to increase their understanding and draw conclusions. The students will learn more about classifying matter in Section 1 of Chapter 2.

Suggested Demonstration
Students will learn to classify objects according to their properties.

Have the students stand in a circle and remove their left shoe. Pile the shoes in the center of the circle. Instruct the students to classify the shoes into groups according to style, such as sneakers, pumps, loafers, and/or sandals. Put each group in order according to size and color. After the shoes are arranged, allow the class to examine the groups and to make observations about each group. What inferences can be made about the activities and preferences of the class from observing the shoes? For example, if most of the shoes are running shoes or sneakers, do most of the students walk to school? Discuss whether or not these inferences are correct.

Activity 2.1a
Distinguishing Among Substances   page 52

Advance Preparation
Collect and prepare the materials needed for the activity prior to the class session. Test all the substances you use for this activity. Keep a record showing if the substance does or does not dissolve, and if it makes the warm water cloudy. The record should also show

any variation, texture, and particle size that may occur in each substance. Prepare a set of vials for each group of students. Each vial is labeled "W," "X," "Y," and "Z," and each contains one teaspoon of the white powder to be tested. The mystery vial labeled "M" may or may not contain one of the substances in the other vials. However, all the vials labeled "M" should contain the same substance. Some substances suggested for testing are: granulated sugar, white flour, table salt, baking powder, garlic salt, baking soda, cornstarch, arrowroot, confectioners sugar, kosher salt, or onion salt. Select samples with some variation in color, smell, and texture.

Teacher Note
The sheets of colored paper and the containers used for warm water should be labeled by the students if time permits. Small envelopes can be used in place of the vials. Emphasis is placed on the importance of using a clean stirrer in each mixture to avoid contamination.

Answers to Questions
1. Answers will vary depending on substances tested. The students should observe properties such as color variation, the size and shape of individual particles, etc.
2. Answers will vary depending on substances selected for testing.
3. Answers will vary. The students should notice clumping of the substance, coarseness when rubbed between the fingers, variation in particle size within a sample, variation in color within a sample, etc.
4. Answer depends on the substance tested. Some substances, such as granulated sugar, kosher salt, and baking soda, will dissolve completely. Other substances, such as garlic powder or onion powder, will not dissolve at all.
5. Answer depends on the substance tested. Table salt gives water a cloudy appearance because of an additive to prevent sticking in hot weather. Kosher salt is chemically pure and dissolves completely in water. Additives are not necessarily soluble in water.
6. Answer depends on the selection of the substance for the mystery vial.

Conclusion
Different properties of substances that look very much alike can be determined by close observation through a magnifying glass, by feeling the substance with your fingers, by smelling the substance, and by putting the substance in warm water to test solubility.

Activity 2.1b
Classifying Objects   page 54

Teacher Suggestion
Almost any combinations of materials can be used for this activity, such as groups of buttons, coins, postage stamps, leaves, rocks, or an assortment of unrelated objects. Let each group exchange their collection and later compare results.

Answers to Questions
1. The students may select a property such as color, size, texture, shape, pliability, the kind of material used in manufacturing, or the objects' functions.
2. Answers will vary. The students are to explain their answer.
3. Answers will vary. The students may select a less obvious property; for example, the number of holes in buttons, the kind of picture that appears on postage stamps, the variation in branching patterns on leaves, or the presence of the magnetic property.
4. Answers will vary. Students are to explain their answer.
5. The students may choose to rank the objects by the degree of hardness, the degree of coarseness, the size variation, or the differences in mass.
6. The students are to compare lists and to explain any differences that occur between the ranking on their list and the ranking on the lists of the other students.
7. The students may choose a more subtle property when ranking a second time. Some properties that may be chosen are the intensity of color, the degree of magnetic quality, the fineness of texture, the degree of luster, or variations in height or mass of the object.
8. Answers will vary. Students are to explain how their ranking list differed from the ranking lists of the others in their group.

Conclusion
Substances can be classified by their properties and ranked by the degree to which the property occurs in the substance. Substances can be classified according to such properties as color, size, shape, texture, amount of mass, buoyancy in water, magnetic quality, function, material content, resiliency, or pliability.

Activity 2.1c
Preparing and Separating Solutions
page 62

Preparation Note

Assemble the materials needed before the class section. Put 15 mL of salt in packets to be distributed to each group of students. The students should label the beakers and slides. Ordinary table salt can be used for this activity, but solutions will be cloudy due to an additive, not to the salt itself.

Answers to Questions

1. Beaker 3 will have the saltiest solution.
2. All of the water should have evaporated from the solutions left overnight on the four slides.
3. The students should observe and note the amount, the color, and the size and shape of the particles of each residue. Slide 1 will probably have some residue because of the minerals in tap water. Slide 2 should have no residue. Slides 3 and 4 should have cubical salt crystals.
4. Slide 3 should have the most salt residue. This sample was taken from beaker 3 which has the most salt in solution.
5. The amount, the color, and the crystalline structure of the residue on slide 1 will vary according to the minerals in local tap water. Slide 3 should have more cubical salt crystals than slide 4. The color and the crystalline structure of the residue on slides 3 and 4 should be the same. The residue indicates the amount and the content of the solute contained in water.
6. There will probably be some residue on slide 1. The lack of residue on slide 2 indicates that there are no solids in solution in distilled water.

Conclusion

By evaporating the liquid from a solution, the solids present in the solution are separated out and can be studied.

2.1 Section Review

Understanding the Concepts   page 63

25. The properties of substances in a solution remain the same while the properties of substances in a compound are changed.

26. Answers will vary. Examples of classification: spices, saucepans. Examples of classification into groups: measuring devices, cooking devices, cleaning products. Example of classifying something in order: measures of ½ teaspoon, 1 teaspoon, 1 tablespoon, ¼ cup, ⅓ cup, ½ cup, 1 cup, etc.
27. It is a compound. It has the properties of neither carbon, a black solid, nor oxygen, a life-supporting gas. It cannot be broken down easily into these elements.
28. Many individual grains of salt will take the shape of the container, but each individual grain is a solid which does not change its shape. When water evaporates from a salt-water solution, the salt remains in the form of larger solid crystals.
29. A saturated solution contains more than the maximum amount of a given solute that will dissolve in a given volume of the solvent. An unsaturated solution contains less than this maximum amount of solute.

2.2 Changes in Matter

Concept Summary

A **physical change** is a change in which the properties of a substance change but no new substances are formed.
- Substances generally increase in volume as their temperature increases.
- The phase of a substance depends on the temperature of the substance.
- Most solids become more soluble in water as the water temperature increases.
- Breaking up a solid allows it to dissolve in a liquid more quickly.

A **chemical change** is a change in which one or more new substances are formed.
- The total mass of substances before and after a chemical change does not change.
- Burning is a chemical change that involves the combining of oxygen with another substance to produce new substances.

Learning Objectives

1. To distinguish between physical and chemical changes.
2. To predict the effect of changes in temperature on physical and chemical changes.
3. To recognize that even though substances are changed, mass remains unchanged in a chemical change.
4. To identify some common physical and chemical changes.

Getting Started

Ideas for Discussion
Students will learn the difference between the physical, chemical, and nuclear changes that can occur in matter. Explain that matter can undergo three types of changes; physical, chemical, and nuclear.

Inform the students that a physical change involves changing the characteristics of a substance without changing the substance itself. Ask the students to give examples of changes that are physical. Write the responses on the board under the heading *physical change*. The following are examples: wood, paper, or cloth being cut, broken, or torn; ice melting; water evaporating; and sugar or salt dissolving in water.

Explain to students that a chemical change is one that results in a new substance being formed. Ask the students to give some examples of a chemical change. Write the responses on the board under the heading *chemical change*. The following are some examples: iron rusting, smog combining with rainwater to form acid rain, bleach whitening clothes, silver tarnishing, wood burning, food cooking, and soap combining with grease.

Write the heading *nuclear change* on the board. Explain that a nuclear change occurs naturally in radioactive elements such as uranium. A nuclear change also occurs in nuclear reactors. Scientists can study nuclear particles with such machines as the two-mile-long Stanford Linear Accelerator and the cyclotron. These machines use photons to break the atom apart. List on the board the ways a nuclear change takes place.

Tell the students that in Chapter 2, Section 2 they will learn more about the types of changes that take place in matter.

Suggested Demonstration
This demonstration explains the effect of a change of phase on a given mass. You will need:
1 clean, dry 100-mL beaker (measure and record the mass ahead of time)
2 or 3 ice cubes
equal-arm balance

Explain that we will investigate what happens during the phase change that occurs when ice melts. Write the amount of the mass of the beaker on the board. Place the ice cubes in the beaker. Emphasize that the beaker is not packed with ice. Explain how to find the mass of the ice cubes by measuring the combined mass of the beaker and ice cubes and then subtracting the mass of the beaker. Follow the same procedure to find the mass of the water after the ice melts. Ask if the mass of the melted ice will be less than, more than, or equal to the mass of the ice cubes. Remind the class that the unit of mass is the gram.

Zero the balance. Emphasize the importance of this step. Dry the outside of the beaker and place the beaker filled with ice on the balance pan. Measure the combined mass and record it on the board. Ask the students why it is necessary to dry the outside of the beaker. Ask why water sometimes collects on the outside of the beaker. The outside of the beaker is dried to protect the balance pan, and to avoid measuring any additional mass of water which may condense on the beaker. Have the class calculate the mass of the ice cubes and record this value. Set the beaker and ice aside. Allow the ice to melt completely.

After the ice is melted, ask the class what prediction they made. Is the mass of the water greater than, less than, or equal to the mass of the ice cubes? Dry the outside of the beaker. Zero the balance. Place the beaker filled with water on the balance pan and measure the mass. The mass should measure the same as before the ice melted. Explain that you have just demonstrated a physical principle known as the *law of conservation of matter*, which states that matter can change from one state to another, but the total amount of matter remains unchanged.

Activity 2.2a
Temperature and Air Volume   page 66

Answers to Questions

1. The water level in the straw is the same as the water level in the jar.
2. When the test tube is lifted, the water level will remain the same within the straw.
3. When the air sample is cooled, the water level inside the straw will rise.
4. The volume of the air sample is decreasing. When cooled, the air contracts and the volume of air sample decreases. The water is then drawn higher into the straw.
5. The water level in the straw is higher than the water level in the jar.
6. As the air sample is warmed, the water level inside the straw goes down.
7. The volume of the air sample increases. As the water is warmed, the volume will increase, and the water is forced down inside the straw.

Conclusion

The volume of a sample of air will change as the temperature changes. Reducing the temperature will cause the air sample to contract and will reduce the volume of the sample. Increasing the temperature will cause the air sample to expand and will increase the volume of the sample.

Activity 2.2b
Recognizing Chemical Changes   page 73

Advance Preparation

The copper chloride solution for this activity should be prepared before the class session. Mix 1 gram of copper chloride crystals to each 10 mL of distilled water. Stir with a glass rod until the crystals dissolve. The crystals will dissolve faster in warm water. Have a large glass or plastic container filled with water available into which the students can dump the copper chloride solution when they finish the experiment.

SAFETY NOTE: *It is important to check with your local authorities for the proper disposal of copper chloride.*

Teacher Note

Copper sulfate ($CuSO_4$) can be used for this activity. The solution is a clear blue liquid. When left in the copper sulfate solution for 30 seconds, the nail has a shiny, copper-colored deposit on it. If the nail is left in the copper sulfate solution for 60 seconds, it will start to blacken. The safety precautions for copper sulfate are the same as those for copper chloride.

Answers to Questions

1. The copper chloride solution is a greenish-blue color. It is a clear liquid.
2. When dipped in the copper chloride solution for 30 seconds, the nail will have a dull, copper-colored deposit on it.
3. The copper deposit on the nail can be easily rubbed off with paper. The dark, copper-colored deposit is left on the paper. The nail will look as it did originally.
4. A chemical change took place. New substances were formed.
5. The nail put into plain water was not changed.
6. The change in the nail put in copper chloride is probably not rust because no rusting occurred on the nail put into plain water.

Conclusion

When a chemical change occurs, a new substance with different properties is formed.

2.2 Section Review

Understanding the Concepts   page 77

25. Answers will vary. Some examples are: air in a container, water boiling, bimetallic strip in a thermostat.
26. Evaporation of liquid occurs more slowly at lower temperatures than boiling.
27. An increase in temperature allows more solid but less gaseous material to remain in solution.
28. The formation of a new substance and the transfer of energy.

2 Chapter Review

Critical Thinking page 78

1. Mass is an unchanging property, while volume may change with the amount of packing down.

2. a. Color, shininess, hardness, melting and boiling temperatures, odor, shape of crystals, solubility, and conductivity
   b. Mass, volume, and temperature

3. Both involve a change of phase from solid to liquid, both are helped by an increase in temperature, and both require heat.

4. The specific properties of a particular substance may limit the number of ways in which that substance can be used. Slate, for example, cannot be used for windows because it is opaque. However, slate can be used for roofs because it can be easily formed into shingles and is very durable. Lead would not be a good material to be used in making a chisel because lead is relatively soft, as another example.

5. All are made of matter; all take up space; all have mass. In these ways the three substances are alike. In the following ways, they are different. Rock is a solid, gasoline is a liquid, and steam is a gas; rock does not flow, but gasoline and steam do; gasoline has a strong odor, but rock and steam do not.

6. Light, heat, and sound.

7. Possible groupings include organic and inorganic; bigger than a desk and smaller than a desk; animals, electrical appliances, food, and containers. Many other groupings are possible.

8. The hot water deep in the earth dissolves minerals in large quantities. The hot solution of minerals cools as it reaches the earth surface and minerals leave the solution because they are not as soluble at the lower temperatures.

9. KI; KNO_3; KNO_3

10. The solubility of oxygen gas decreases as the temperature increases. Therefore, the increase in temperature would cause some oxygen to leave solution, reducing the oxygen concentration and reducing the amount of oxygen available to aquatic organisms.

11. A thermostat contains a hybrid strip consisting of two different metals joined together. The metals expand at different rates, and as a consequence the hybrid strip bends when heated. As the strip bends it acts as a switch turning a heating or cooling system on or off.

12. Water boils at a lower temperature in the mountains because the air pressure is lower. Boiling water in the mountains is not as hot as boiling water at sea level, and therefore cooking in the mountains takes longer than cooking at sea level.

13. Gases tend to be less soluble as the temperature increases, whereas solids tend to be more soluble.

Chapter 3 Planning Guide

Planning Your Classroom Lessons

	3.1 The Particle Model of Matter 82–95	3.2 A Model of the Atom 96–112	3.3 A Model for Chemical Changes 113–129	Chapter 3 Review 130–131 Chapter 3 Supplements
Content Overview	Using a particle model of matter to explain how elements, compounds, and mixtures differ from each other Concept Summary T74 Learning Objectives T74	Explaining the properties of elements and the patterns within the periodic table by applying the shell model of the atom Concept Summary T76 Learning Objectives T76	Applying the shell model of the atom to the tendency of elements to combine in certain ways to form compounds Concept Summary T78 Learning Objectives T78	Science Background Information 80 Review of Concepts 130 Essential Ideas/ Chapter 3 Letter to Parents
Teaching Strategies	Getting Started: Ideas for Discussion and Suggested Demonstration T74	Getting Started: Ideas for Discussion and Suggested Demonstration T76	Getting Started: Ideas for Discussion and Suggested Demonstration T78	
Teaching Aids	Teaching Diagram 3-1A, 3-1B Overhead Transparency	Teaching Diagram 3-2A, 3-2B	Teaching Diagram 3-3A, 3-3B	Physical Science Software T30 Physical Science Films and Videos T38 Video Lesson: Particle Model of Matter
Review and Evaluation*	Quick Review 85, 86, 89, 92, 93, 94 3.1 Review 95 Section Testsheet 3-1 TRB 206	Quick Review 98, 99, 101, 107, 110 3.2 Review 112 Section Testsheet 3-2 TRB 207	Quick Review 116, 117, 119, 121, 123, 125 3.3 Review 129 Section Testsheet 3-3 TRB 208	Chapter Testsheets 3A and 3B TRB 245–246 Free Response Questions TRB 000 Semester Test 1 TRB 273–276 *Higher Level Evaluation* Critical Thinking 131

*TESTGEN can be used to prepare customized section and chapter testsheets.

Meeting Individual Needs

Reinforcement	Reading Checksheet 3-1 TRB 86 Skillsheet 3-1 TRB 132 Essential Ideas 3.1	Reading Checksheet 3-2 TRB 87 Skillsheet 3-2 TRB 133 Essential Ideas 3.2	Reading Checksheet 3-3 TRB 88 Skillsheet 3-3 TRB 134 Essential Ideas 3.3	Information Library Software
Enrichment	Research Topic 85, 88, 92 Data Search 90	Research Topic 101 Data Search 98, 103	Research Topic 115, 124, 125 Data Search 122	Individual Research 131 Bibliography 131 Issues in Physical Science: The Metric Controversy 132 Trends in Technology: Lasers and Measurement 133
Critical Thinking and Problem Solving	Critical Thinking 86, 91	Critical Thinking 102	Critical Thinking 116	Chapter Testsheet 3B TRB 246 Problem-Solving Worksheets, Chapter 3

Chapter 3 Planning Guide

Developing Laboratory Skills

	3.1 The Particle Model of Matter 82–95	3.2 A Model of the Atom 96–112	3.3 A Model for Chemical Changes 113–129	Chapter 3 Supplements
Plan Ahead	For Activity, page 84: Gather empty, clear plastic shampoo or detergent bottles that compress when squeezed. For Activity, page 87: Collect enough marbles so that each group will be able to fill a 250-mL beaker with them.	For Activity, page 111: Paper for the shell model must be stiff enough to allow the rings to be twisted to form a three-dimensional model but thin enough to cut easily. Lightweight poster board works best.	For Activity, page 126: Label all test tubes clearly.	
Basic Activities	Compressibility of Air and Water 84 15 minutes Groups of 4 or 5 Activity Record Sheet 3-1A, LM 31	Making Models of Atoms 111 20 minutes Groups of 3 Activity Record Sheet 3-2B, LM 36	Charged Objects 118 15 minutes Groups of 4 or teacher demonstration Activity Record Sheet 3-3A, LM 39	
Additional Activities	Spaces Between Particles 87 20 minutes Groups of 5 Activity Record Sheet 3-1B, LM 32	Using the Periodic Table 108 20 minutes Individual work Activity Record Sheet 3-2A, LM 35	Identifying Acids and Bases 126 20 minutes Groups of 3 or 4 Activity Record Sheet 3-3B, LM 40	Projectsheet 3 TRB 175
Investigations and Research Lab	Investigation 3-1, Measuring the Size of a Molecule LM 33–34 30 minutes Groups of 2 or 3	Investigation 3-2, Using the Periodic Table to Graph Atomic Size and Atomic Mass LM 37–38 40 minutes Groups of 3	Investigation 3-3, Comparing Effectiveness of Several Antacids LM 41–42 50 minutes Groups of 3 or 4	Research Lab 3 LM 43–44

Chapter 3
The Structure of Matter

3.1 The Particle Model of Matter

Concept Summary

Processes of science include making repeated observations, inferring relationships between sets of observations, and forming explanations that can be used to predict additional observations.

A **scientific model** is a description in terms of familiar things and is used to explain observations and predict behaviors.

The **particle model of matter** pictures matter as made of tiny particles with space between them.
- The particles of a gas are farther apart than those of a liquid or solid.
- An element is made of atoms, which are identical particles of that element.
- Compounds are made of two or more kinds of atoms joined in a fixed arrangement.
- In some elements and compounds, the atoms are grouped into particles known as molecules.
- Mixtures are made of two or more kinds of atoms that are not in a fixed arrangement.

Learning Objectives

1. To describe what a scientific model is and how it is developed and used.
2. To apply the particle model to the nature of matter.
3. To use the particle model of water to explain the differences in the properties of elements, compounds, and mixtures.

Getting Started

Ideas for Discussion
Students learn how the grains of sand on the beach inspired the scholar, Leucippos, to develop the theory that matter is made of atoms.

Ask your class how the beach looks from far away compared to the way it looks close up. From far away, a beach appears as a homogeneous, uniformly-colored stretch of land or group of mounds. Close up it appears to be composed of individual grains of sand. Explain that this observation inspired early Greek philosophers and scientists to theorize that all matter is made up of tiny particles.

Leucippos, who lived in Abdera in Thrace during the fifth century B.C., is said to have asked if the water of the sea, which seems continuous, might really be composed of separate, extremely tiny grains like a beach, which also seems continuous? Together with his student Democritos, Leucippos concluded that all material is made up of such tiny grains, which they called atoms. The word atom comes from the Greek word *atomes* which means indivisible. Tell the students that Chapter 3, Section 1 will describe how the existence of these tiny atoms explains the different kinds and the different phases of matter.

Suggested Demonstration
Students learn how the physical properties of elements change when they form a mixture or when they combine to form a chemical compound. For this demonstration, you will need the following items:

5.55 g iron powder or filings – Fe	50-mL beaker
	alcohol burner
5.32 g sulfur powder – S	stirring rod
large magnet	test tube tongs
100-mL test tube containing	safety glasses
0.55 g iron and 0.32 g sulfur	

Show the iron filings to the class. Explain that the chemical name for iron is written *Fe*. Write the chemical symbol on the board. Ask the class to name all the properties of iron. Iron is a silver-gray color, it rusts, and it is magnetic. List the properties of iron on the board. Show the sulfur to the class. Write the chemical symbol for sulfur on the board. Ask the class to give the properties of sulfur. It is bright yellow, soft, and odorless. Use the magnet to show the class that sulfur is not magnetic. List the properties of sulfur on the board.

Tell the class that the two elements can be combined to form a mixture. Pour 5 g of the powdered sulfur into the beaker. Add an equal amount of powdered iron and mix the two together. Tell the class that you now have a mixture of iron and sulfur. Pour the contents of the beaker onto a sheet of paper. Pass the magnet through the mixture. Show the class that the magnet picks up the iron filings and leaves the sulfur behind. Tell the class that the elements are not chemically combined with each other; therefore, they can be easily separated.

Tell the class a mixture of sulfur and iron can be chemically combined. Wear safety glasses for this part of the demonstration. Show the class the test tube containing the sulfur and the iron. Explain that there is 0.55 g of iron and 0.32 g of sulfur in the test tube.

Use the test tube tongs and point the test tube at an angle away from the students and yourself. Carefully heat the tube, shaking it slightly as it is heated. Ask the students to observe carefully. The sulfur will heat up and start to vaporize. Sulfur has an unpleasant odor when it burns. The whole mixture will turn brownish-black and become crumbly. Remove the test tube from the heat and turn off the alcohol burner. Hold the test tube so the students can see the results of the reaction. When the compound has cooled slightly pour it out of the test tube onto a piece of paper. It may be necessary to break the test tube to get the iron sulfide out of it. Ask the class if a new substance has been formed. Ferrous sulfide is formed. Does the substance look similar to the elements that were used to make it? What happens when you pass the magnet over the new substance? The ferrous sulfide is not magnetic.

Tell the students that the iron and sulfur combined to form the compound ferrous sulfide—FeS. Explain that in order to form this compound, the same number of atoms of iron and sulfur must be present. A chemical reaction requiring heat must occur. Tell the students that Chapter 2, Section 2 discusses elements, compounds, and mixtures.

Activity 3.1a
Compressibility of Air and Water   page 84

Advance Preparation
The activity calls for clear plastic bottles with a cap. Any clear plastic bottle that is pliable is suitable. Students will bring their own, but you should have several extra on hand.

Answers to Questions
1. The "empty" bottle was filled with air.
2. Yes. The sides of the bottle can be pushed in, showing that the air can be compressed easily.
3. No. The sides of the bottle cannot be pushed in. This shows that water cannot be compressed easily.
4. Squeezing below the water line causes the water level to rise. This happens because you are compressing the air above the water line.
5. The water level remains the same when you squeeze above the water line. You cannot make the water level go down by pushing on the air above it. The air and not the water is compressed.
6. Answers will vary.

Conclusion
Air can be more easily compressed than water. This occurs because air is a gas, and the particles are farther apart in a gas than in a liquid. In liquid water, the molecules are very close together, and there is less room for them to be squeezed together.

Activity 3.1b
Space Between Particles   page 87

Answers to Questions
1. About half of the space in the beaker is filled. The marbles fill the beaker so that no more marbles can be added. However, there is space between the marbles.
2. Students will find that about ⅓ of the sand measured into the second beaker can be added to the beaker containing the marbles.
3. No more sand can be added to the beaker. However, there are some small spaces around the sand particles. Therefore, all the space is not filled in the first beaker.
4. Students will be able to add about ¼ of the water measured into the third beaker to the marble-sand mixture.

Conclusion
Although no more water, sand, or marbles can be added to the beaker, it is still possible to add some material that will go into solution.

Going Further
Additional experimentation can be done by placing a small spoonful of sugar on top of the marble-sand-water mixture. At first the sugar makes a mound, but then it gradually disappears into the mixture. This provides further evidence of the space between molecules. If warm water and superfine sugar are used, more sugar will go into the solution. Ask the students to explain why the sugar disappeared.

3.1 Section Review

Understanding the Concepts   page 95
16. ■ Solids dissolve in liquids.
    ■ Even when a gas fills a space, more of the gas can be added.
    ■ Compounds always form according to a definite formula.
17. In liquid water, the molecules are very close together. In water vapor, the molecules are far apart.
18. In mixtures, the atoms or molecules of different substances are independent of each other. In compounds, the atoms of different elements are held together according to a definite formula.
19. Scientists use the same symbols for elements and measurements no matter what language is used in their country. The symbols are recognized by people who might not know the language.
20. The white circles are oxygen atoms. The black circle is a carbon atom.

21. The models showing Dalton's ideas are drawn with Dalton's symbols for oxygen and hydrogen (as shown in Figure 3-6 on p. 88).

a) oxygen

b) water vapor

c) mixture of hydrogen and oxygen gases

3.2 Models of the Atom

Concept Summary

The **periodic table of the elements** is an arrangement that is in order of increasing atomic number and in which elements with similar properties are in the same column.

The **electron cloud model of the atom** includes a nucleus containing protons and neutrons, surrounded by electrons at various energy levels.

- Within each row of the periodic table, all the elements have the same number of energy levels.
- Within each column of the periodic table, all the elements have the same number of electrons in the highest energy level.

Learning Objectives

1. To use the periodic table to identify elements with similar in properties.
2. To describe the arrangement of protons, neutrons, and electrons in the atoms of the elements.
3. To relate the properties of the elements to the arrangement of the electrons in the atoms of the different elements.

Getting Started

Ideas for Discussion
Students learn about the methods that were used to study the structure of the atom.

Ask the class what atoms look like. Ask various students to sketch their ideas on the board. These sketches may include solid spheres or a solar system model. Ask why it is difficult to be sure what atoms look like. The students may respond that atoms are too small to see. Ask how the shape and the structure of something too small to see can be determined. A possible response may include building a special microscope. Tell the class that the size, shape, and structure of the atom is a very difficult problem to solve. It is still being studied today.

Explain that early attempts to determine atomic size included hammering a sheet of gold as thin as possible and measuring the thickness of the sheet. The logic for this was that no layer of material could become less than one atom thick and remain the same material.

Scientists later studied the behavior of atoms and the results of combining chemicals to determine atomic structure. The study of electricity brought new approaches to scientific studies of atomic structure. Tell the students that in Chapter 3, Section 2 they will study the different models of the atom that were developed over the years.

Suggested Demonstration
Students learn how the electron of the hydrogen atom travels around the nucleus. You will need the following items for this demonstration:
white cardboard disk, 40 cm in diameter
pencil or thin dowel
thumb tack

Approximately 2 cm from the outside edge of the disk, draw a black dot 2 cm in diameter. Cut a small hole in the center of the disk. Loosely fasten the disk to the top of the pencil or dowel with the thumb tack. Allow the disk to spin freely.

Explain to the class that the currently accepted model of the atom is known as the *electron cloud model*. The simplest atom is the hydrogen atom which has a nucleus consisting of one proton and one electron. In the electron cloud model, an electron may appear anywhere on a spherical area surrounding the nucleus. Refer the students to the cloud model on page 107. Explain that the single electron is moving rapidly around the nucleus. This gives the atom a charge.

Show the model you constructed to the class and tell them that the black dot represents the electron. The center, where the pencil is located, represents the nucleus of the atom. Twirl the disk rapidly and ask the class to describe what they see. The rapidly moving dot will appear to form a circle as it revolves around the nucleus.

Explain that this model shows an effect similar to that of the single electron in the hydrogen atom. Explain that the electron moves in a three-dimensional sphere, instead of a flat circle as it does in your model. Tell the class that atoms containing more than one electron generate highly-complex electron clouds due to the movement of their electrons.

Activity 3.2a
Using the Periodic Table   page 108

Teacher Note
This activity can either be done in class or assigned as homework. A display-size periodic table of elements can be used in the classroom to assist the students in learning the periodic table.

Answers to Questions
1. ■ L - magnesium (Mg)
   ■ M - calcium   (Ca)
   ■ N - strontium   (Sr)
   ■ P - beryllium   (Be)
   ■ W - nitrogen   (Ni)
   ■ X - arsenic   (As)
   ■ Z - antimony   (Sb)

2.

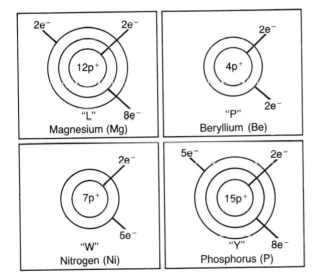

"L" Magnesium (Mg)

"P" Beryllium (Be)

"W" Nitrogen (Ni)

"Y" Phosphorus (P)

Conclusion
Students need to know and understand the following. The number of protons in an element is called the atomic number. In an element, the number of electrons equals the number of protons. The periodic table of elements is arranged by atomic number. Elements in the same family are arranged in vertical columns on the periodic table. The elements that have the same number of shells are arranged in rows across the periodic table.

Activity 3.2b
Making Models of Atoms   page 111

Preparation Notes
Paper for the shell model must be stiff enough to allow the rings to be twisted to form a three-dimensional model but thin enough to cut easily. Lightweight posterboard works best.

Allow 10 minutes for preparation of the models and pinwheel. Students should use the remaining time for observation.

Answers to Questions
1. An atomic model is a picture or object that helps to show what an atom "looks like."
2. The posterboard model represents the shell model. The cottonball model represents the electron cloud model.
3. The lithium nucleus contains 3 protons and 4 neutrons. The atom has 3 electrons. Two electrons occupy the first energy level and one electron the second energy level.
4. Electrons do not move in a circular orbit but occupy cloud-like regions (energy levels) around the nucleus. The nucleus of an atom is small compared to the size of the electron cloud.
5. No. The blades appear as a blur of motion.
6. The rapid movement of electrons forms a hazy cloud of negative electricity around the nucleus. The electron cloud gives an atom its size and shape.

Conclusion
The chemical properties of an element are closely related to the arrangement of its electrons. Because atoms are too small to be seen, models show what scientists know about atomic structure.

3.2 Section Review

Check Your Understanding   page 112
25. Elements in the halogen family have seven electrons in their outer shell and react strongly with metals. Elements in the alkali metal family have one electron in their outer shells and react strongly with nonmetals.
26. All have 4 electrons in the outer shell. Each element in the family has a different number of shells.
27. Third row: 3; fifth row: 5
28. Chlorine has 17 protons, which have a mass of about 17 u. The remainder of the isotope's mass (37 u − 17 u = 20 u) must come from 20 neutrons. (The mass of an atom is slightly less than the total mass of its individual parts. The "missing" mass can be explained in terms of the energy needed to split up a nucleus, using Einstein's mass and energy equivalence formula $E = mc^2$.)

29. When he bombarded a thin piece of gold foil with a stream of alpha particles, most of them passed through the foil. A few bounced back very strongly. He reasoned that the atom consisted of mostly empty space, with a heavy, positively charged nucleus at the center.

3.3 A Model for Chemical Changes

Concept Summary

Electric charges cause pushes and pulls between objects that do not have equal numbers of positive and negative charges.
- An electron has one negative charge.
- A proton has one positive charge.
- An atom that gives up electrons becomes a positive ion.
- An atom that accepts extra electrons becomes a negative ion.

A **chemical bond** is a tie between two atoms that have transferred or shared electrons.
- Chemical bonds result from the attraction between opposite charges.
- Chemical changes involve the forming and/or breaking of chemical bonds.

Acids and **bases** are substances that furnish hydrogen ions and hydroxide ions, respectively.
- The pH value of a substance is a measure of how acidic or basic the substance is.
- An acid and base can neutralize each other in a reaction that produces a salt and water.

Learning Objectives

1. To interpret chemical equations by identifying reactants and products.
2. To identify whether or not a chemical equation is balanced.
3. To describe chemical bonds within compounds in terms of the transfer or sharing of electrons.
4. To identify the properties of acids, bases, and salts.

Getting Started

Ideas for Discussion

Students will learn how atoms bond together to form compounds (that is, bond formation).

Write the word *bond* on the board. Ask the class to define it and write their suggestions underneath the word. Various definitions may include band or cord used to tie things, a uniting or binding element, or a

force. Ask what the sorts of things cause two people to have a bond of friendship. The students might suggest shared interests or activities. Explain that atoms also form bonds because they share something. Ask what it is that atoms share with another atom. You can help the students answer this question by recalling the fundamental parts of the atom. Ask what particles make up an atom. (Protons, neutrons, and electrons.) Ask what part of the atom is shared with other atoms. (Electrons are shared because they are not concentrated in the nucleus and they are more loosely bound to the atom.) Explain that sharing of electrons is one way that different atoms can join to form compounds. The joining of atoms is known as *bond formation*. Making and breaking chemical bonds is the basis of all chemical changes that occur in matter. Tell the class that chemical changes are the topic of Chapter 3, Section 3.

Suggested Demonstration

Students will learn to use the pH scale for testing the acidity of a substance. They will learn what effect an acid has on egg shells. You will need the following items for this demonstration:
egg shell
distilled white vinegar
1 roll pH paper, hydrion pH 1-7
500-mL beaker
tap water

Explain to the class that acids are highly reactive. Acids have a sour taste and can burn the skin. Warn the students that unknown substances should never be tested by touching or tasting them. The degree of acidity of a substance can be determined by dropping some of it onto pH paper to determine the pH. Water is neutral and has a pH of 7. The most acidic substances have a pH of 0 to 1. Included in the latter group are hydrochloric acid and concentrated sulfuric acid.

Tear off a piece of pH paper and put a drop of tap water on it. Show the students that tap water tests approximately pH 7. Test the pH of the soda water (it should be around pH 3). Pour 250 mL of vinegar in the beaker and test its pH. Vinegar should test about pH 3.

Ask the students to make a mental note of the size of the egg shell before you place it in the beaker of vinegar. Vinegar has about the same pH as carbonated soda. Tell them you will leave the egg shell immersed in the vinegar for several days so they can observe what takes place. The egg shell will dissolve as a result of being submerged in the acid. Tell the students that in Chapter 3, Section 3 the reactions caused by acids and bases will be discussed.

Activity 3.3a
Charged Objects   page 118

Teacher Note
Activities which involve charging work best on dry days. Dry winter days are best.

Answers to Questions
1. No, since they did not affect each other, they were both neutral.
2. Yes, if an objcct contains equal amounts of negative and positive charge it is neutral.
3. a) Yes, charges could have been transferred.
   b) The balloon and wool flannel would have opposite charges. For example, if one (in this case, the balloon) picks up electrons, it becomes negatively charged and the other (in this case, the wool flannel) is left positively charged.
4. The same. Since each was rubbed with the same material, you would expect them to have the same charge.

Conclusion
Like charged objects repel each other. Unlike charged objects attract each other.

Activity 3.3b
Identifying Acids and Bases   page 126

Answers to Questions
1. There is no color change in either the blue or red litmus paper in testing distilled water. The conclusion is that distilled water is neither an acid nor a base.
2. When the lemon juice is added to blue litmus paper, a red spot will develop. Adding a drop of ammonia to red litmus paper will cause a blue spot to develop.
3. Vinegar and cola are acids.
4. Baking soda and the antacid tablets are bases.
5. The table salt and tap water are neither acidic nor basic and therefore do not change the litmus papers. These are known as neutral substances.

Conclusion
Litmus paper can be used to test various substances to determine if they are acidic or basic. Red litmus paper turns blue when it is dipped into a basic solution. Blue litmus turns red when dipped into an acidic solution.

3.3 Section Review

Understanding the Concepts   page 129
25. **a.** left side: 3O, 1N   **d.** left side: 2S, 6O
        right side: 2O, 1N   right side: 2S, 6O
        not balanced   *balanced*

    b. left side: 2O, 1C   **e.** left side: 1C, 4H, 2O
        right side: 2O, 1C   right side: 1C, 4H, 4O
        balanced   *not balanced*

    c. left side: 1N, 3O
        right side: 2N, 4O
        not balanced

26. When a substance burns, if forms chemical bonds with oxygen. Inert gases have full outer shells (2 electrons for helium, 8 for the others), which makes them not likely to form chemical bonds by gaining, losing, or sharing electrons.
27. Some acids and bases are very dangerous to living tissue and are poisonous. Better ways to make a test are to use litmus, BTB, or other test substances.
28. NaOH: base—contains OH^-
    HNO_3:   acid—contains H^+
    $NaNO_3$:   salt—contains metal and nonmetal ions

Problems to Solve   page 129
29. $2C + O_2 \longrightarrow 2\ CO$
30. $2H_2O_2 \longrightarrow 2H_2O + O_2$
31. $2CH_4 + Cl_2 \longrightarrow 2CH_3Cl + 2HCl$
32. $Zn(OH)_2 + 2HCl \longrightarrow ZnCl_2 + 2H_2O$
33. $2K + 2H_2O \longrightarrow 2KOH + H_2$

3 Chapter Review

Critical Thinking   page 130

1. The atoms of different isotopes of an element have different numbers of neutrons and so are not identical. Atoms of the same element all have the same number of protons.

2. Potassium is in the same family as sodium, and bromine is in the same family as chlorine. The compound of potassium and bromine would be ionic. Bromine, like chlorine, accepts electrons easily from elements on the left-hand side of the periodic table.

3. Astatine has six energy levels of electrons, since it is in the sixth row. It has seven electrons in the highest energy level of these atoms, since it is in the same column as the halogens.

4. There would be 200 times the number of atoms of hydrogen in a gram of hydrogen compared to the number of atoms in a gram of lead.

5. The first liquid is a base, the second liquid is an acid. When they are mixed together in equal volumes they neutralize each other. Therefore, the strengths of the acid and base in the initial liquids must have been equal.

6. The number of protons in the nucleus is needed to assign the element a place in the periodic table.

Notes

Chapter 4   Motion

Chapter 4 Planning Guide			
Planning Your Classroom Lessons			
	4.1 Describing Motion 138–153	**4.2** Force and Motion 154–178	**4.3** Energy 179–191	**Chapter 4 Review** 192–193 Chapter 4 Supplements
Content Overview	How to determine the direction and speed of a moving object, and whether it is accelerating Concept Summary T84 Learning Objectives T84	How forces are related to motion, and how objects move under gravity Concept Summary T86 Learning Objectives T86	An introduction to kinetic energy—the energy of motion, and an introduction to potential energy—stored energy Concept Summary T88 Learning Objectives T88	Science Background Information 136 Review of Concepts 192 Essential Ideas/ Chapter 4 Letter to Parents
Teaching Strategies	Getting Started: Ideas for Discussion and Suggested Demonstration T84	Getting Started: Ideas for Discussion and Suggested Demonstration T86	Getting Started: Ideas for Discussion and Suggested Demonstration T88	
Teaching Aids	Teaching Diagram 4-1A, 4-1B Overhead Transparency	Teaching Diagram 4-2A, 4-2B	Teaching Diagram 4-3A, 4-3B	Physical Science Software T00 Physical Science Films and Videos T00 Video Lesson: Motion and Work
Review and Evaluation*	Quick Review 140, 144, 145, 148, 152 4.1 Review 00 Section Testsheet 4-1 TRB 209	Quick Review 155, 158, 161, 166, 167, 168, 170, 171, 174, 175, 177 4.2 Review 00 Section Testsheet 4-2 TRB 210	Quick Review 181, 184, 186, 188, 189 4.3 Review 00 Section Testsheet 4-3 TRB 211	Chapter Testsheets 4A and 4B TRB 247–248 Free Response Questions TRB 000 Semester Test 1 TRB 273–276 *Higher Level Evaluation* Critical Thinking 193

*TESTGEN can be used to prepare customized section and chapter testsheets

Meeting Individual Needs			
Reinforcement	Reading Checksheet 4-1 TRB 89 Skillsheet 4-1 TRB 135 Essential Ideas 4.1	Reading Checksheet 4-2 TRB 90 Skillsheet 4-2 TRB 136 Essential Ideas 4.2	Reading Checksheet 4-3 TRB 91 Skillsheet 4-3 TRB 137 Essential Ideas 4.3	Information Library Software
Enrichment	Research Topic 144 Data Search 141	Research Topic 157 Data Search 171	Research Topic 184 Data Search 183	Individual Research 193 Bibliography 193
Critical Thinking and Problem Solving	Critical Thinking 141, 147, 148 Practice Problems 143, 150	Critical Thinking 160, 173 Practice Problems 161, 174		Chapter Testsheet 4B TRB 248 Problem-Solving Worksheets, Chapter 4

Chapter 4 Planning Guide

Developing Laboratory Skills

	4.1 Describing Motion 138–153	4.2 Force and Motion 154–178	4.3 Energy 179–191	Chapter 4 Supplements
Plan Ahead	For Activity, page 142: Use a gymnasium or a flat, open area where 50 m can be measured off. For Activity, page 146: Locate a flat, smooth surface at least 2 m long. For Activity, page 151: Obtain a small cart or roller skate.	For Activity, page 164: Obtain two skateboards. For Activity, page 176: Roll out a carpet or rug on the floor to prevent the coins from scattering.	For Activity, page 180: Obtain small boxes, such as empty film boxes.	

Basic Activities	Measuring Speed 142
	  30 minutes
	  Entire class
	Activity Record Sheet
	  4-1A, LM 45
		Falling Coins 176
		  15 minutes
		  Groups of 2 to 4
		Activity Record Sheet
		  4-2C, LM 53
			Energy of a Pendulum
			  185
			  20 to 30 minutes
			  Groups of 4
			Activity Record Sheet
			  4-3B, LM 58	

Additional Activities	Recognizing Constant
	  Speed 146
	  30 minutes
	  Entire class
	Activity Record Sheet
	  4-1B, LM 46
	
	Detecting Changes in
	  Speed and Direction
	  151
	  20 minutes
	  Groups of 2 to 4
	Activity Record Sheet
	  4-1C, LM 47
		Action and Reaction 164
		  10 minutes
		  Student demonstration
		Activity Record Sheet
		  4-2A, LM 51
		
		Motion Down a Ramp
		  172
		  20 to 30 minutes
		  Groups of 2 to 4
		Activity Record Sheet
		  4-2B, LM 52
			Kinetic Energy 180
			  20 to 30 minutes
			  Groups of 2 to 4
			Activity Record Sheet
			  4-3A, LM 57
				Projectsheet 4 TRB 176

Investigations and Research Lab	Investigation 4-1,
	  Determining Constant
	  Speed LM 49–50
	  30 to 40 minutes
	  Groups of 4 or teacher
	  demonstration
		Investigation 4-2,
		  Changes in the Force of
		  Friction LM 55–56
		  30 minutes
		  Groups of 2 to 4
			Investigation 4-3,
			  Energy Conversions in
			  a Bouncing Ball
			  LM 59–60
			  30 minutes
			  Groups of 3 or 4
				Research Lab 4
				  LM 61–62

Chapter 4   Motion

4.1 Describing Motion

Concept Summary

Motion is the movement or changing of position of an object with respect to a reference object.

- The description of motion may change with a change in the reference object.

Speed is how fast an object changes its position with respect to a reference object.

- Speed is described in units of distance divided by units of time.
- Average speed is the total distance traveled divided by the total time taken to travel that distance.
- An object traveling at constant speed always travels equal distances in equal times.
- On a distance-time graph, a slanting straight line indicates constant speed.

Acceleration is a change in the speed or in the direction of motion of an object.

- On a distance-time graph, a curving line indicates changing speed and thus acceleration.

Learning Objectives

1. To describe the position and motion of an object with respect to a reference object.
2. To determine the speed of a moving object using time and distance measurements.
3. To recognize constant speed on a distance-time graph.
4. To differentiate between speed and acceleration.
5. To recognize changing speed on a distance-time graph.

Getting Started

Ideas for Discussion
Students will learn the importance of a reference object to determine movement and speed.

Have the class sit completely still for one minute. After one minute, ask the class how it felt to travel at 1666 km/hr. Explain to the students that in one minute they travel approximately 28 km east with the rotation of the earth. Explain that this is sixteen times faster than they move in a car traveling at 60 km/h.

Ask the class why they could not tell they were moving that fast. The students should observe that nothing around them is moving. Explain to the students that our perception of motion depends upon the use of reference objects. Write the term *reference object* on the board. In order to perceive speed, we must compare our motion to that of objects that are standing still. Ask the class to name some reference objects they see from a car. Some examples may include trees, roadsigns, and houses. Ask the class to explain why another car is not necessarily a reference object. The students should report that the other car may also be moving. Tell the students they will learn about motion, speed, and acceleration in Section 1 of Chapter 4.

Suggested Demonstration
Students will learn how the motion of an object can be described by using a reference point. You will need a stick or pole one to two meters in length with a bright scarf or ribbon tied at the top.

Select a student volunteer. Tell the rest of the class they are to act as observers. Have the volunteer hold the pole at arm's length in a vertical position. Tell the class that the back wall of the classroom will be the reference point. Have the student walk toward the front of the classroom holding the stick so all the students can see it. Ask the class what direction the pole is moving in relation to the back wall. The pole is moving away from the wall. What is the movement of the pole in relation to the student carrying it? The pole does not move in relation to the student carrying it.

Have the student volunteer return to the starting point. Instruct the student to hold the pole at arm's length in front of him or her. Have the volunteer walk slowly toward the front of the room. The pole is to be held at the same location. It should not move with the student. The student will be able to walk only a short distance. Ask the class which direction the pole is moving in relation to the wall. If the student keeps the pole stationary and moves around it, the pole will not move in relation to the wall. If the student moves the pole with him, it will move away from the wall. Ask in which direction the pole is moving in relation to the student carrying the pole. The student is moving away from the pole. Does the position of the pole change in relation to the student or in relation to the reference point? (The position of the pole changes in relation to the student.)

Activity 4.1a
Measuring Speed   page 142

Teaching Hints
If a metric tape measure is not available, either do this activity with the distance measured in yards, or use the conversion 50 m = 54.68 yards (about 54 yards and 2 feet).

For the first set of runs, it is probably easiest to have the timer stand at the finish line and start each runner with the drop of a hand or similar signal. For the second set, student spotters can be stationed at 5-m intervals along the edge of the track to estimate the location of each runner at the end of the time interval.

After returning to the classroom, the recorder's information can be shared. You may want each student to complete a chart such as the one shown, calculate individual speeds, then use the chart to answer the questions.

Answers to Questions
1. Runners with shorter times had higher speeds.
2. Runners with longer distances had higher speeds.
3. The five fastest runners the first time are likely to be among the five fastest runners the second time.

Conclusion
Speed is calculated by dividing the distance traveled by the time it took to travel that distance.

Activity 4.1b
Recognizing Constant Speed   page 146

Teaching Hints
Any relatively slow-moving battery-operated vehicle can be used.

You may wish to have each student make his or her own distance-time graph of the data.

If the tractor moved at constant speed, the plotted points should line up along a straight line. However, real-life data will probably have some scatter due to such things as irregularities in the speed of the tractor and measurement errors. If the plotted points do not line up along a straight line do one of the following. See if a number of the points lie on a straight line or very nearly so. Draw a straight line through these points. Alternatively, you can see if a straight line can "average" the points. That is, if possible draw a straight line through the points such that there are similar numbers of points on each side of the line.

Answer to Question
See Teaching Hints

Conclusion
See Teaching Hints.

Activity 4.1c
Detecting Changes in Speed and Direction   page 151

Teaching Hints
A small carpenter's level may be substituted for the cart-vial combination.

Answers to Questions
1. The cart was moving forward when the bubble moved forward. (The bubble moves in the opposite direction from the water in the vial. When you push the cart forward, the water tends to remain behind, so the bubble moves forward.) As soon as the cart is no longer accelerating, the bubble should move backward. In practice, the forward motion is followed immediately by the backward motion.
2. The cart was stopped when the bubble first moved backward and then forward.
3. If you twist the front end of the cart while it is moving forward, the bubble can move either toward the back or toward the front depending on whether the speed decreases or increases as the cart is twisted.
4. When the cart moves at constant speed, the bubble should not move.

Conclusion
The bubble changed position when the speed or direction of the cart was changed.

4.1 Section Review

Understanding the Concepts   page 153
11. Cyclist A was going the fastest because Cyclist A has the steepest distance-time line. More distance is covered (vertical squares) per time spent (horizontal squares).
12. Speed, acceleration
13. A straight line
14. **a.** Yes
    b. Yes. It is changing direction.

Problems to Solve   page 153
15. 45 km/1.0 hours
16. 24 km/hour
17. **a.** 300 km
    b. 15 days

4.2 Force and Motion

Concept Summary

A **force** is a push or pull.
- Balanced forces act on the same object without producing any changes in its motion.
- An unbalanced force acting on an object produces a change in the speed or direction of the object.
- Friction forces prevent or slow down the movement of objects.
- The greater the unbalanced force on an object is, the greater the acceleration of the object.
- The greater the mass of an object is, the smaller the acceleration of the object.
- When a force acts on an object, the object exerts a reaction force of equal strength but opposite in direction.

Momentum is the product of mass and speed, and depends on the direction of motion.
- When objects interact through forces, the total momentum of the objects does not change.

The **force of gravity** acts between any two objects.
- Weight is the pull of gravity on an object.
- The force of gravity increases as the masses of the objects increase.
- The force of gravity decreases as the distance between the objects increases.
- The acceleration of a falling object does not depend on the mass of the object.

Learning Objectives

1. To identify the forces acting on an object both when the forces are balanced and when the forces are unbalanced.
2. To describe the effects of friction on a moving object.
3. To relate the acceleration of an object to the force applied and to the mass of the object being accelerated.
4. To recognize that forces always come in pairs that are described as action and reaction forces.
5. To apply the law of gravitation to the motion of objects near the surface of the earth.

Getting Started

Ideas for Discussion
Students will discuss the effect of gravity on an object.

Ask your class to consider what would happen if all of a sudden their chairs disappeared. Have the students explain why everyone would fall on the floor. The students should already be aware of gravity. Discuss the concept of gravity with the class. Ask the class to decide on a definition of gravity. A sample definition might be, the earth pulling objects toward its surface. Ask if gravity is a force. Ask how a chair keeps them from falling on the floor. A chair exerts an upward force on the person sitting in it that is equal to the force of gravity; therefore, the person doesn't fall.

Explain that when an object is subjected to forces that are equal, or balanced, it does not move. When the forces are unequal, or unbalanced, motion results. For example, if you are sitting in a chair that breaks, there is no longer an upward force to balance the force of gravity, and you fall to the ground. The laws that affect these forces will be studied in Chapter 4, Section 2.

Suggested Demonstration
The students will learn the effect friction has on a moving object. You will need a small toy car and a sheet of sandpaper for this demonstration.

Place the toy car on a flat surface on the floor or a table where all the students can see it. Ask the class if the car will move by itself. Explain that the inability of the car to move by itself illustrates the first part of Newton's first law of motion. This law states that an object at rest tends to remain at rest unless acted upon by an outside force. This is called *inertia.* The car will not move unless a force is applied that is sufficient to overcome its inertia. Ask the class if the car will continue to roll forever if it is pushed. Ask what will cause the car to stop. The students should reply that it will stop when it runs into something, or it will slow down and stop by itself.

Introduce the second part of Newton's first law which states that an object that is moving continues in a straight line at constant speed unless acted upon by an outside force. Give the car a push and allow the class to watch it slow down. Ask the students what force caused the moving car to slow down and stop. Put the piece of sandpaper on the floor and allow the car to run over it. The car should slow down and stop sooner when rolled over sandpaper. Explain to the class that you increased the outside force that slows down the car. This force is friction. Explain that on the earth, friction has some effect on the movement of all objects. In outer space, where there is no atmosphere, friction is much less important.

Activity 4.2a
Action and Reaction   page 164

Teaching Hints
If skateboards aren't available, students can do the activity using roller skates.

This activity will work inside or out on any flat, smooth surface. The 3-m length for the rope is only a guideline. The longer the distance between students, the more dramatic the results.

For Steps 1 through 7, the more identical the masses of the students, the clearer the results. For Step 8, the greater the difference in masses, the clearer the results. A backpack filled with books can be used to add mass to the heavier student if necessary.

Answers to Questions
1. Yes. The direction of motion of Student A should have been opposite to that of Student B in all trials.
2. **a.** If the students had equal masses, they should have moved equal distances.
   b. The student with less mass will move a greater distance. For example, if Student A is half as heavy as Student B, he/she will move twice as far. (This relationship between distance and mass is what we would expect to happen *if the forces on the two students are equal.* Since "force equals mass times acceleration," if the mass is less for the same force, the acceleration and thus the distance traveled in the same time must be greater.)
3. No. Since the action force equals the reaction force, the students should have moved the same distance and the same direction regardless of which one did the pulling.
4. Yes

Conclusion
The reaction force was equal in size and opposite in direction to the action force.

Activity 4.2b
Motion Down a Ramp   page 172

Teaching Hints
If steel and aluminum balls are not available, other balls of similar size may be used as long as their masses are noticeably different.

Predictions may vary. Encourage students to give reasons for their predictions.

Answers to Questions
1. The steel ball has more mass than the aluminum ball.
2. If friction is negligible, both balls should reach the stop at the same time. Actual answers may vary. Students should base their conclusions about the relation between mass and time on their observations. Under ideal conditions, objects of different mass are given the same acceleration by the earth's gravitational pull.
3. Some sources of error might be 1) a failure to release the balls at exactly the same time; 2) a differ-

ence in the amount of friction between each ball and its ramp due to a difference in the smoothness of the ramps, a difference in the smoothness of the balls, or both; 3) a difference in the angles between the ramps and the horizontal.

Conclusion
The mass of the ball does not affect the length of time it takes to roll down the ramp.

Activity 4.2c
Falling Coins   page 176

Answers to Questions
1. All coins should not travel the same horizontal distance. The coin farthest from the fixed end of the ruler should be the furthest away.
2. The coin farthest from the fixed end of the ruler should have the greatest horizontal speed. The farther a coin lands from the table, the greater its horizontal speed.
3. All coins should reach the floor at the same time. You can tell that they reached the floor at the same time because you hear them hit simultaneously, not one after the other.
4. Yes, because they all started with no downward speed and they took the same time to fall the same distance.

Conclusion
Horizontal speed does not affect the acceleration downward due to gravity.

4.2 Section Review

Understanding the Concepts   page 178
21. The pull of gravity depends not only on the masses but on the distance between the centers of the two objects. The shorter the distance, the stronger the pull. You are so much closer to the center of the earth than to the center of the sun that the earth's pull is stronger than the sun's pull, despite the sun's far greater mass.
22. On the earth, the upward friction force due to the air affects the feather far more than the hammer, so the hammer accelerates more than the feather. On the moon, there is no air to produce a friction force.

Problems to Solve   page 178
23. ½ m/s
24. 12 N

4.3 Energy

Concept Summary

Energy is the ability to cause change.
- Kinetic energy is the energy of an object due to its motion.
- The kinetic energy of an object depends on both its mass and its speed.
- The kinetic energy of an object can be transferred to other objects.
- Potential energy is stored energy due to the position of an object that is acted on by a force.
- Energy can be converted from one form to another.

Learning Objectives

1. To relate the kinetic energy of an object to its mass and speed.
2. To relate the potential energy of an object to its position.
3. To describe changes in the kinetic energy and potential energy of an object as it changes position.
4. To associate increases in the temperature of moving objects with the presence of friction.

Getting Started

Ideas for Discussion
The students will learn the scientific meaning of energy and the difference between potential energy and kinetic energy.

Ask the class the meaning of the word energy. Explain that the scientific definition for the word energy is the ability of an object to cause change. Write the word *energy* on the board. Hold up an object and ask the class if the object has energy. The students should answer yes. It has potential energy that becomes kinetic energy if the object is allowed to fall.

Explain to the class that there are different kinds of energy. Ask the students what changes might occur if the object is thrown. The students should observe that the object could hit something and break it. Explain to the class that the energy of movement is known as kinetic energy. Write the words *kinetic energy* on the board. Hold the object above a student's head. Ask the class if the object has the ability to cause change. Explain that if you let go of the object, it will fall on the person beneath it. Explain that when the ability of an object to cause change is due to its position, the object has potential energy. Write the words *potential energy* on the board.

Ask the class if a burning object has the ability to cause change. Explain that the chemical energy released by fire is also a form of potential energy. In-

form the students that the interactions between kinetic and potential energy explain many everyday occurrences. Tell them they will learn more about the different forms of energy in Chapter 4, Section 3.

Suggested Demonstration
The students will learn to recognize the difference between potential and kinetic energy in this demonstration. You will need the following items:
oatmeal box with cover or similar cylindrical container
120-g lead sinker
large rubber band
string about 10 cm long
sharp knife or scissors
smooth board about 1 m long
2 paper clips

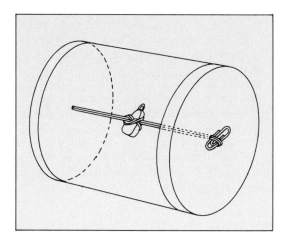

Before class, construct and test this device to demonstrate the interconversion of kinetic and potential energy. Use the string to tie the lead sinker to the middle of the rubber band. Cut a tiny opening in the center of the bottom end and in the center of the cover of the empty oatmeal box. Place the rubber band and sinker inside the box. Pull the ends of the rubber band through the opening, and secure them with paper clips on the outside. With the cover snugly in place and the rubber band stretched tightly, suspend the sinker in the center of the box. Place two or three books under one end of the board to make an inclined plane. Demonstrate the device for the class. Hold the box on its side at the top end of the incline. Ask the class what kind of energy the box has in this position. The box has potential energy. Ask the class what kind of energy the box will have when it rolls to the bottom of the inclined plane. The box will have kinetic energy.

Let the box roll down the incline. When the oatmeal box is allowed to roll down the ramp, it should slow down and stop before reaching the bottom. Then it should roll back up the ramp! Ask the class what kind of energy the box had to regain in order to go up the ramp. The box has to regain potential energy, because the top of the ramp is higher up.

Open the box. Show the class the rubber band and the sinker. Explain that as the box rolls down the inclined plane, kinetic energy is stored in the twisting rubber band. Tell the class the energy being stored is potential energy. Ask the class to help you write a sequence of steps on the board outlining what happened.

1. Box at top of ramp—potential energy is demonstrated.
2. Box rolling—kinetic energy is being demonstrated.
3. Box slowing down—kinetic energy is changing to potential energy. Rubber band is storing energy.
4. Box stopping—potential energy is stored in the twisted rubber band.
5. Box moving back up—potential energy in the twisted rubber band changes to kinetic energy as the box moves. The kinetic energy changes back to potential energy which is being stored in the rubber band as the box reaches the top of the inclined plane.

Activity 4.3a
Kinetic Energy   page 180

Teaching Hints

The boxes used must be large enough to hold the largest steel ball. The more difference there is in the masses of the two balls, the easier it will be to see that kinetic energy depends upon mass.

Answers to Questions

1. The kinetic energy of each ball was transferred to the box that caught it. (*Note:* During the collision some of the ball's kinetic energy was also converted into heat. When the boxes came to a stop, the kinetic energy of each box was converted into heat.)
2. Answers will vary.
3. Answers will vary, but this distance should be greater than that given in Question 2.
4. No, because the heavier ball moved its box farther than the lighter ball.
5. Yes, both balls should have had the same speed because they both rolled down ramps of the same length and of the same height. (*Note:* The acceleration of a solid ball rolling down a ramp does not depend on either the diameter or the mass of the ball.)

Conclusion

Yes, the kinetic energy of a moving object does depend upon its mass. Both balls had the same speed but different kinetic energies. Since the only significant difference between the two balls was their masses, the kinetic energy must also depend on their masses.

Activity 4.3b
Energy of a Pendulum   page 185

Teaching Hints

You may want to change the height of the release point. The release point which works best will depend upon the relative masses of the block and pendulum bob (lead ball). A fishing weight or similar dense object may be substituted for the lead ball.

Encourage your students to give their reasons for their predictions in Step 6. The pendulum should move the block farthest at the bottom of its swing because that is where it has the most kinetic energy. It gains kinetic energy as it loses potential energy while swinging downward.

Answers to Questions

1. When the pendulum hits the block at the bottom of its swing, it knocks the block off the book.
2. The pendulum gives the block kinetic energy.
3. The pendulum moves the block the farthest when it is at the bottom of its swing.
4. The pendulum has the least potential energy at the bottom of the swing because it is then that the pendulum is closest to earth.
5. The pendulum is highest above the ground at the beginning of its swing.

Conclusion

1. The kinetic energy of the pendulum is greatest at the bottom of its swing because it moves the block the farthest.
2. The potential energy of the pendulum is greatest at the beginning of its swing because it is farthest from the earth at this point.

4.3 Section Review

Understanding the Concepts   page 191

13. Yes, a moving object, which has kinetic energy, can also have potential energy due to its position. For example, a pencil rolling over the edge of a desk has both kinetic and potential energy. So does a ball as it moves away from the earth and as it falls back toward the earth.
14. a. The earth's potential energy is greatest in July when the earth is farthest from the sun.
    b. If the total amount of energy does not change, the earth's kinetic energy is greatest in January when its potential energy is the least.
    c. The earth moves the fastest in January when its kinetic energy is the greatest.
15. Friction between the tires and the road causes the tires to get hot.

4 Chapter Review

Critical Thinking   page 192

1. The sun would be a possible reference object. It could be considered stationary compared to the movements of Mars and the earth.

2. You would need to know the time needed for the ball to cover several short but equal distances.

3. You would be accelerating as you start upward and as you slow down before coming to a stop. You would feel the floor push up against you with a greater force as the elevator speeded up and with a decreased force as the elevator slowed down at the top.

4. The acceleration of the object doubles when the force on the object is doubled.

5. Friction

6. The weight of an object in this comparison is the gravitational force between the object and the earth or between the object and the moon. The two forces are different, so the weight of the object on the moon is different from its weight on the earth.

7. The path is like the right half of an arch (actually a parabola). The path starts out horizontally but curves downward more and more.

8. The air resistance results in a friction force equal in size to the gravitational force but in the opposite direction. The forces on the falling raindrop are balanced.

9. A greater force is needed to stop or change the direction of a car with greater mass.

10. **a.** The smaller gravitational force and the lack of air resistance
    b. The smaller gravitational force would allow the ball to remain in the air a longer time and so travel farther in a horizontal direction. The lack of air resistance would allow the ball to maintain its constant speed in the horizontal direction so it would move farther horizontally.

11. The kinetic energy of a moving object decreases as the object slows down.

Notes

Chapter 5   Work and Heat

	5.1 Work and Machines 196–215	5.2 Heat and Internal Energy 216–231	5.3 The Kinetic Theory of Matter 232–249	Chapter 5 Review 250–251 Chapter 5 Supplements
Content Overview	A study of work, which is a form of energy, and the simple machines which make it easier to do work Concept Summary T94 Learning Objectives T94	A study of heat, which is also a form of energy, and which—like work—can increase the temperature of a material Concept Summary T96 Learning Objectives T96	How the behavior of solids, liquids, and gases can be explained by the idea that the particles of matter are in constant motion Concept Summary T98 Learning Objectives T98	Science Background Information 194 Review of Concepts 250–251 Essential Ideas/ Chapter 5 Letter to Parents
Teaching Strategies	Getting Started: Ideas for Discussion and Suggested Demonstration T94	Getting Started: Ideas for Discussion and Suggested Demonstration T96	Getting Started: Ideas for Discussion and Suggested Demonstration T98	
Teaching Aids	Teaching Diagram 5-1A, 5-1B Overhead Transparency	Teaching Diagram 5-2A, 5-2B	Teaching Diagram 5-3A, 5-3B	Physical Science Software T00 Physical Science Films and Videos T00 Video Lesson: Motion and Work
Review and Evaluation*	Quick Review 199, 203, 205, 209, 211, 213, 214 5.1 Review 00 Section Testsheet 5-1 TRB 212	Quick Review 218, 222, 224, 225, 227, 229, 230 5.2 Review 00 Section Testsheet 5-2 TRB 213	Quick Review 234, 237, 240, 241, 242, 243, 244, 246, 247 5.3 Review 00 Section Testsheet 5-3 TRB 214	Chapter Testsheets 5A and 5B TRB 249–250 Free Response Questions TRB 000 Semester Test 1 TRB 273–276 *Higher Level Evaluation* Critical Thinking 251

*TESTGEN can be used to prepare customized section and chapter testsheets

Meeting Individual Needs

Reinforcement	Reading Checksheet 5-1 TRB 92 Skillsheet 5-1 TRB 138 Essential Ideas 5.1	Reading Checksheet 5-2 TRB 93 Skillsheet 5-2 TRB 139 Essential Ideas 5.2	Reading Checksheet 5-3 TRB 94 Skillsheet 5-3 TRB 140 Essential Ideas 5.3	Information Library Software
Enrichment	Research Topic 204, 210, 211	Research Topic 221, 225, 230 Data Search 221	Research Topic 233, 241 Data Search 247	Individual Research 251 Bibliography 251 Issues in Physical Science: The 55 Mile Per Hour Speed Limit 252 Trends in Technology: Aerospace Planes of the Future 253
Critical Thinking and Problem Solving	Critical Thinking 209, 214 Practice Problems 198, 201, 213	Critical Thinking 223 Practice Problems 221	Critical Thinking 239, 246	Chapter Testsheet 5B TRB 250 Problem-Solving Worksheets, Chapter 5

Chapter 5 Planning Guide				
Developing Laboratory Skills				
	5.1 Work and Machines 196–215	5.2 Heat and Internal Energy 216–231	5.3 The Kinetic Theory of Matter 232–249	**Chapter 5 Supplements**
Plan Ahead	For Activity, page 202: Obtain a roller skate or skateboard and a board about 2 m long.	For Activity, page 228: Students should be instructed on proper safety procedures regarding hot plate use.	For Investigation, LM 75–76: Obtain a helium tank for filling balloons.	
Basic Activities	Measuring Work with and without an Inclined Plane 202 20 minutes Groups of 2 or teacher demonstration Activity Record Sheet 5-1A, LM 63	Predicting Temperature Changes 220 20 minutes Groups of 2 to 4 Activity Record Sheet 5-2A, LM 69	Diffusion at Different Temperatures 235 15 minutes Groups of 4 Activity Record Sheet 5-3A, LM 73	
Additional Activities	Three Classes of Levers 208 40 minutes Groups of 4 or teacher demonstration Activity Record Sheet 5-1B, LM 64 Using Pulleys 212 40 minutes Groups of 2 to 4 or teacher demonstration Activity Record Sheet 5-1C, LM 65	Transfer of Heat 228 20 minutes Groups of 4 or teacher demonstration Activity Record Sheet 5-2B, LM 70	Melting Materials 245 30 minutes Groups of 4 or teacher demonstration Activity Record Sheet 5-3B, LM 74	Projectsheet 5 TRB 177
Investigations and Research Lab	Investigation 5-1, Your Stair-Climbing Power LM 67–68 20 minutes Groups of 2	Investigation 5-2, Preventing the Transfer of Heat LM 71–72 40 minutes Groups of 5 or entire class	Investigation 5-3, Comparing Diffusion of Different Gases LM 75–76 20 minutes Groups of 2 or teacher demonstration	Research Lab 5 LM 77–78

Chapter 5 Work and Heat

5.1 Work and Machines

Concept Summary

Work is energy that is transferred to an object when the object moves in the direction of a force acting on the object.

- The amount of work done is equal to the amount of force in the direction of motion multiplied by the distance moved.
- No work is done when the object does not move.

A **machine** is something that changes the size and/or direction of a force used to do work.

- Examples of machines are the inclined plane, wedge, screw, lever, wheel and axle, and pulley.
- The mechanical advantage of a machine equals the force needed to do the work directly divided by the force applied to the machine.
- The efficiency of a machine equals the work done by the machine divided by the work put into the machine, expressed as a percentage.
- The efficiency of any machine is always less than 100% because some of the work is used to overcome friction.

Power is a measure of how fast work is being done or how fast energy is being used.

Learning Objectives

1. To define work in terms of a force moving through a distance.
2. To explain how several simple machines assist in doing work.
3. To measure the mechanical advantage and efficiency of different machines.
4. To differentiate between work and power.
5. To relate work to energy.

Getting Started

Ideas for Discussion

The students will learn how work is measured and how the equation for work is written.

Ask your students to name some kinds of very hard work. Digging ditches, breaking rocks with a hammer, and carrying sacks of cement up a hill are all examples of hard work. Ask the students what it is about each type of work that makes it so hard. For example, digging ditches is hard because you have to pick up a shovelful of heavy dirt and move it to one side. Breaking rocks with a hammer is hard work because you have to swing the hammer with great force to hit the rocks hard enough to break them.

Explain to the students that when you perform work, you are exerting a force over some distance. Write the equation *work = force × distance* on the board. Inform the class that this equation is the scientific formula for work. Explain that in Chapter 5, Section 1 the students will learn more about work and about some simple machines that make work easier.

Suggested Demonstration

The students will learn how a bicycle uses simple machines. You will need to ask one of the students to bring a bicycle for this demonstration.

Explain to the class that a machine is used to do work. Machines make work easier by changing the direction and the amount of force needed. Ask the class if a bicycle is a machine. Ask the students what kind of work is made easier by a bicycle. Students should know moving a person from place to place is made easier with a bicycle. Point out that a bicycle is really a combination of simple machines that makes it easier to move from place to place.

Ask the class to name the different simple machines that are used on a bicycle. Some of the following things may be suggested by the students. Hand brakes are levers. Screws, which are spiral inclined planes, hold the bike together. The pedals are levers with the fulcrum at the center of the sprocket wheel. The large sprocket wheel moves a chain that turns a smaller sprocket wheel attached to the rear-wheel axle. The spokes attached to the rear-wheel axle act as levers to transfer force to the tire. The rider and the bike overcome friction with the road and move forward.

Activity 5.1a
Measuring Work with and without an Inclined Plane   page 202

Answers to Questions
1. The force of friction between the wood block and the table top balanced the horizontal force applied.
2. To find the work done in joules, multiply the force in newtons by the distance moved in meters.

3. No work would be done because the block did not move.
4. The work done should be the same in both cases, unless the skate does not roll easily and additional work is done to overcome friction between the skate and the inclined plane. A greater force is needed to lift the skate than to pull it up the inclined plane. The skate traveled a greater distance when pulled up the inclined plane.
5. It lessens.

Conclusion
An inclined plane reduces the amount of force needed to raise an object.

Activity 5.1b
Three Classes of Levers   page 208

Teaching Hints
Be sure that strong cord is used to hold the 1-kg mass. Have your students tape the cords holding the mass and balance to the dowel to help keep them from moving. SAFETY NOTE: *Also, be certain that students stand in such a way that the mass cannot fall on them if the string breaks. A sliding or falling mass is dangerous.*
- A straight-backed chair is best because one with a back which tilts will not be as stable.
- A meter stick can replace the dowel, but to prevent breaking, it MUST be used on edge.

You may also want to have students calculate the mechanical advantage (M.A.) of each lever. The M.A. is equal to the weight of the mass divided by the force needed to slowly lift the mass. The M.A. calculated in this way will be affected by the weight of the lever. In all second- and third-class levers, the force required will be greater than for a "weightless" lever. In first-class levers, the force required will be greater when the fulcrum is closer to the effort than to the resistance.

Another method used to calculate the M.A. of a lever is to divide the effort arm (distance from the fulcrum to the applied force) by the resistance arm (distance from the fulcrum to the weight). M.A. calculated in this manner gives the ideal M.A. This can differ from the M.A. calculated above because the weight of the lever changes the effort force.

Answers to Questions
1. The force went from less than the weight of the mass to more than the weight of the mass.
2. The force approached the weight of the mass, but was always less than the weight of the mass (if the weight of the dowel was small).
3. The force approached the weight of the mass, but was always greater than the weight of the mass.

Conclusion
The part indicated (*) should be moved in the direction of the arrow.

Activity 5.1c
Using Pulleys   page 212

Teaching Hints
Shorter pieces of cord may also be needed to attach the pulleys to the support and to the mass being lifted.

In Step 4, the force required to lift the mass should be equal to its weight. However, the force reading on the scale may be less than the weight of the mass because the weight of the scale helps lift the mass. If there is too much friction in the pulley, the scale reading will be greater than the weight of the mass.

Answers to Questions
1. The mechanical advantage of the attached pulley should be 1 if there is little friction. (The *M.A.* equals the weight lifted divided by the force needed.)
2. The attached pulley allows one to lift the mass by pulling down.

3. The mechanical advantage should be about 2. Because of friction, and the fact that some of the force is being used to lift the pulley, the mechanical advantage will probably be less than 2.
4. Should be about the same, but the ratio of distances will probably be closer to 2 than the answer in Question 3.
5. Should be about 2, but will probably be lower. (See answer to Question 3.)
6. Should be about the same, but the ratio of distances will probably be closer to 2 than the answer in Question 5.
7. The mechanical advantage of a pulley equals the number of lines supporting the load.

Conclusion
1. Divide the weight lifted by the force needed.
2. Divide the distance the balance moved by the distance the mass moved.
3. Count the number of lines supporting the load.

5.1 Section Review

Understanding the Concepts   page 215
25. In each lever, the fulcrum is at one end. In a second-class lever, you apply the force to the lever at the other end. In a third-class lever, the lever applies a force to something at the other end.
   A wheelbarrow is an example of a second-class lever. A rake, fishing pole, tennis racket (and playing arm), and baseball bat (and playing arms) are all examples of third-class levers.
26. One example of a machine with a mechanical advantage greater than 1 is a ramp. Another is a moving pulley. Each one reduces the force needed to do work, but the force must move through a greater distance.
27. The efficiency of a machine is the work output divided by the work input, expressed as a percentage. Efficiency is always less than 100% because some of the work input is used to overcome friction.

Problems to Solve   page 215
28. work = force × distance

$$= 600 \text{ N} \times 5 \text{ m}$$

$$= 3000 \text{ J}$$

$$\text{M.A.} = \frac{\text{length of inclined plane}}{\text{length of resistance arm}}$$

29. $\text{M.A.} = \dfrac{\text{length of effort arm}}{\text{length of resistance arm}}$

length of effort arm = M.A. × length of resistance arm

$$= 3 \times 2.5 \text{ m}$$

$$= 7.5 \text{ m}$$

5.2 Heat and Internal Energy

Concept Summary

Heat is energy that is transferred as a result of differences in temperature.
- Temperature is a measure of how hot or cold a substance is.
- Heat moves from a warmer to a cooler substance.
- Substances usually become warmer when they take in heat and cooler when they give it off.
- When a substance is changing phase, it gains or loses heat but remains at a constant temperature.
- The amount of heat gained or lost by a substance depends on the amount of substance, the type of substance, and the temperature change.
- Heat is transferred by conduction, convection, and radiation.
- Insulators are substances that are poor conductors of heat.

The **internal energy** of a substance is the energy inside it.
- A substance may gain internal energy either by taking in heat or by having work done on it.
- When a substance gains internal energy, either its temperature increases or it changes phase.

Forms of energy are different kinds of energy, such as kinetic energy, potential energy, work, heat, and internal energy.
- Energy can be changed from one form to another.
- Energy cannot be created or destroyed.

Learning Objectives

1. To relate heat to the energy transfer because of differences in temperature.
2. To recognize that the amount of heat gained or lost by a substance depends on the kind of substance, the amount of the substance, and the change in temperature of the substance.
3. To differentiate among temperature, heat, and internal energy.
4. To describe the different methods by which heat is transferred and how heat is prevented from being transferred.

Getting Started

Ideas for Discussion
The students will learn that heat is a form of energy.

Write the word *heat* on the board. Ask the students to name different sources of heat. A typical list may include the sun, fire, an electric heater, friction, and chemical reactions. List the students' suggestions on the board. Have the students examine the list. Ask what all the sources of heat have in common. Students should know that they all involve energy. Explain that heat is a form of energy that is known as thermal energy.

Explain that the internal energy of different substances and how it is manifested as heat will be discussed in Chapter 5, Section 2.

Suggested Demonstration
The students will learn that mechanical work done on water will change the internal kinetic energy of the water and will increase its temperature. For this experiment, you will need the following items:
100-mL graduated cylinder
plastic foam bowl large enough to hold 200 mL
hand-held beater
thermometer
watch or clock that indicates seconds

Explain to the class that temperature measures the internal kinetic energy of a substance. The temperature of a substance can be increased by adding energy in the form of work. Place 200 mL of water in the bowl. Measure the temperature of the water. Record the information on the board. Using a hand beater, rapidly beat the water for one minute. You may wish to ask a student volunteer to do this. Again measure and record the temperature of the water. Beat the water for a second full minute. Measure and record the temperature of the water again. Repeat this procedure a third time.

Ask the class if the temperature increases with the amount of work done. The temperature of the water should increase after each minute of beating. Explain that this is an example of the *law of conservation of energy* which states that energy is neither created nor destroyed, it only changes from one form to another. In this demonstration, the mechanical energy of work changes the internal kinetic energy of the water. This change is indicated by the increase in the temperature of the water.

Activity 5.2a
Predicting Temperature Changes   page 220

Answers to Questions
1. Answers will vary. Predictions are most likely to be correct for the trial in which volumes of hot and cold water are used.
2. For equal volumes of hot and cold water the temperature of the mixture should be halfway between the temperatures of the hot and cold water.
3. When the volumes are unequal, students should realize that the temperature of the mixture will be closer to the temperature of the larger sample.

When 30 mL of cold water is mixed with 60 mL of hot water, the final temperature should be two-thirds of the temperature difference above the lower temperature.

When 60 mL of cold water is mixed with 30 mL of hot water, the final temperature should be one-third of the temperature difference above the lower temperature.

Conclusion
The temperature of the mixture will be closer to the original temperature of the larger sample than to that of the smaller one. The larger the ratio of the volumes of the two samples of water, the closer the temperature of the mixture is to that of the larger sample.

Going Further
The temperature of the mixture is still proportionately determined by the amounts of hot and cold water mixed.

Activity 5.2b
Transfer of Heat   page 228

Answers to Questions
1. When holding their hands above and to the side of the hot plate, students will feel radiated heat. If they hold their hands directly above the hot plate, they will feel heat transferred by a combination of convection and radiation.
2. The water should be hotter near the bottom of the beaker.
3. As the water warms, the foil balls should circulate. The movements of the foil balls suggests that the water, too, is circulating.
4. Warm water moves up from the bottom and displaces the cooler water which then moves to the bottom where it is warmed. This process is called convection.
5. The metal spoon should transfer heat faster than the glass rod. Note: Many metal spoons are made of stainless steel which is a poor heat conductor. Thus, a piece of brass or copper, or real silverware, may work better. Metal is the better heat conductor.

Conclusion
The three ways heat can be transferred are conduction, convection and radiation. Examples will vary.

5.2 Section Review

Understanding the Concepts   page 231
19. The liquid takes in heat when it evaporates, cooling the food and air in the refrigerator.
20. The room will be cooled better if the vent is closer to the floor. This is because the heated air is pushed upward as the cooler air near the ceiling

moves downward. If the warm air entered near the ceiling, it would remain there because it is less dense than the cooler air.

21. The picnic cooler does not cool the food. The cooler is made of a good insulator that prevents heat from being transferred to the cold food.

22. The air between the two panes of glass is an insulator, so heat does not pass through it by conduction. Because air is trapped, heat is not carried away by convection either.

Problems to Solve   page 231

23. heat absorbed = specific heat × mass × increase in temperature

$$= 920 \, \frac{J}{kg \cdot °C} \times 15 \text{ kg} \times$$
$$(150°C - 28° C)$$
$$= \frac{920 \text{ J}}{kg \cdot ° C} \times 15 \text{ kg} \times 122° \text{ C}$$
$$= 920 \text{ J} \times 15 \times 122$$
$$= 303 \, 600 \text{ J}$$
$$= 303.6 \text{ kJ}$$

24. Heat of vaporization of water = 2260 kJ/kg

$$= \frac{2260 \text{ kJ}}{kg} \times 80 \text{ g} \times \frac{1 \text{ kg}}{1000 \text{ g}}$$
$$= 2260 \text{ kJ} \times .08$$
$$= 180.8 \text{ kJ}$$

5.3 The Kinetic Theory of Matter

Concept Summary

The **kinetic theory of matter** is a model that pictures matter as made of particles that are in constant, random motion.

- The temperature of a substance is related to the average kinetic energy of the particles.
- When a substance becomes hotter, its particles move faster, on the average.
- Models for solids, liquids, and gases picture the particles as having potential energy because of the forces between them.
- Changes in phase are explained by changes in the potential energy of the particles.
- The internal energy of a substance equals the sum of all the energies of the particles.

Learning Objectives

1. To apply the kinetic theory of matter to the behavior of gases, solids, and liquids.
2. To relate the internal energy of a substance to the potential and kinetic energy of its particles.
3. To use the kinetic theory of matter to explain phase changes, heat transfer, and specific heat.

Getting Started

Ideas for Discussion
Students will learn how the behavior of molecules differs in a solid, a liquid, and a gas.

Ask your class what they feel like doing when they have a lot of energy. They will probably say running, jumping, dancing, or some other vigorous activity. Ask the class what they feel like doing when they don't have a lot of energy. They will probably say sleeping, resting, or sitting around. Explain that molecules behave the same way.

Explain that the molecules of a gas have the most energy. They have so much energy that they move around in three different ways. Molecules vibrate. Demonstrate by pretending that you are a molecule and waving your arms around. Molecules rotate. Turn in a circle. Molecules move from one place to another. Walk across the front of the room. Ask the class why they think gas molecules have so much freedom of movement. The molecules of a gas move around because they are very far apart.

Explain that the molecules of a liquid are closer together than those of a gas, and they can only vibrate and rotate. The molecules of a solid are very close together. They are so close together they don't have room to turn around. The molecules of a solid can only vibrate. Tell the class that the ideas you just described are known as the *kinetic theory of matter*. It can be used to explain and to predict the behavior of solids, liquids, and gases. Tell the students that the kinetic theory of matter will be explained in Chapter 5, Section 3.

Suggested Demonstration
Students will learn that the molecules of a gas will move throughout and mix with another gas. You will need a bottle of strong-smelling perfume or cologne. SAFETY NOTE: *If you have any asthmatic or allergic students, seat them near a window or send them out of the room during this activity.*

Place the capped bottle of perfume on the front desk. Note the time. Explain to the class that this experiment demonstrates the motion of molecules. Open the bottle and ask the students in the front row to indicate when they can smell it. In the meantime, explain to the class that the fluid in the bottle is made up of molecules. Ask what happens to the molecules when you open the bottle. Some of the molecules can escape into the air. When the students in the front row tell you they can smell the perfume, explain to them that they are sensing the presence of a few perfume molecules inside their noses. Ask the class to estimate how much time passed since the bottle was opened. Explain to the class that it took that length of time for the molecules of perfume to leave the bottle, float through the air, and reach their noses. The longer you leave the bottle open, the more molecules of perfume can escape. Eventually, the molecules of perfume will disperse through the room, and all the students will be able to smell it. If enough time passes, all of the molecules of perfume will evaporate into the air. Explain to the class that this experiment shows that the molecules of matter are in motion.

Activity 5.3a
Diffusion at Different Temperatures
page 235

SAFETY NOTE: *Avoid sudden heating of potassium permanganate crystals. Care should be taken to avoid eye and skin contact.* See the student's safety note. Provide a large container half-filled with water for the students to dump the potassium permanganate solution when they finish the activity. It is important to dispose of all chemicals according to procedures required by local authorities.

Teacher Note
The particles in a substance do not all move at the same speed. Thus, some have more kinetic energy than others. Temperature is really related to the average kinetic energy of the particles. As the temperature increases, individual particles may lose kinetic energy. However, the average kinetic energy will increase.

Answers to Questions
1. The color will diffuse faster in hot water. Differences in temperature do affect the speed of diffusion.
2. Answers will vary. At each time interval, the color in the hot water should be more diffused than the color in the cold water.

Conclusion
A warm substance has more kinetic energy than a cold one. When a substance gains kinetic energy, its particles move faster. Diffusion of a solid in a liquid takes place faster at high temperatures than at low ones.

Activity 5.3b
Melting Materials   page 245

Answers to Questions
1. At the start, the ice water and the crushed ice should be at the same temperature—0°C.
2. The same amount of heat will be added to both beakers, since they are on the same hot plate. At the end of five minutes the temperature will not be the same in both beakers.
3. At the end of 5 minutes, the temperature of the water that started as ice water will be higher than that of the water that started as crushed ice.
4. Answers will vary according to the amount of heat given off by the hot plate.

Conclusion
As the crushed ice melts, its temperature will remain at 0°C until it is fully melted. Meanwhile, the temperature of the ice water will rise.

5.3 Section Review

Understanding the Concepts   page 249
12. Because spaces between particles in a gas are larger than they are between particles in a liquid, particles in a gas can move farther between collisions. Thus they spread out, or diffuse, more quickly.
13. An increase in the temperature of a substance results in an increase in the average speed of its particles.
14. Particles in a solid and in a liquid vibrate. Particles in a solid, however, do not move past each other as they do in a liquid.
15. In a solid or liquid, some of the energy is converted into potential energy of the particles. If the substance is melting or boiling, however, when it absorbs heat, all of the energy is converted into potential energy. Also, if there are molecules of two or more atoms, some of the energy may make the atoms vibrate or rotate faster without affecting the kinetic energy of the molecules themselves.
16. Particles making up the heated pot collide at the surface with particles in the soup and transfer kinetic energy to them.
17. A puddle in the sun receives more heat than one in the shade. The additional heat increases the kinetic energy of the particles in the puddle. As some particles escape and cool the water remaining in the puddle, the sun's energy replaces the lost energy. Thus, particles continue to have enough energy to escape.
18. The specific heat of helium should be five times that of neon. (There are five times as many atoms in a gram of helium as in a gram of neon.)

5 Chapter Review

Critical Thinking   *page 250*

1. When you pushed on the center of the door, your push would be closer to the fulcrum. Your force would have to be greater in order to do the same amount of work opening the swinging door.

2. Evaporation rates depend upon the amount of moisture already in the air. The drier the air, the more evaporation and more cooling that occurs as a result.

3. Plastic foam has many tiny air spaces. These air spaces allow very little transfer of heat either by conduction or by convection currents.

Notes

Chapter 6   Chemical Reactions

	Chapter 6 Planning Guide			
	Planning Your Classroom Lessons			
	6.1 Comparing Chemical Reactions 258–277	**6.2** Controlling Chemical Reactions 278–291		**Chapter 6 Review** 292–293 Chapter 6 Supplements
Content Overview	The various chemical reactions that produce chemical changes in substances, as well as changes in energy Concept Summary T104 Learning Objectives T104	How chemical properties, temperature and concentration affect the course of reactions, and how reactions must be controlled to be useful Concept Summary T105 Learning Objectives T105		Science Background Information 256 Review of Concepts 292 Essential Ideas/ Chapter 6 Letter to Parents
Teaching Strategies	Getting Started: Ideas for Discussion and Suggested Demonstration T104	Getting Started: Ideas for Discussion and Suggested Demonstration T105		
Teaching Aids	Teaching Diagram 6-1A, 6-1B Overhead Transparency	Teaching Diagram 6-2A, 6-2B		Physical Science Software T00 Physical Science Films and Videos T00 Video Lesson: Energy and Changes in Matter
Review and Evaluation*	Quick Review 261, 262, 263, 266, 267, 271, 272, 276 6.1 Review 277 Section Testsheet 6-1 TRB 215	Quick Review 280, 281, 282, 283, 286, 289 6.2 Review 291 Section Testsheet 6-2 TRB 216		Chapter Testsheets 6A and 6B TRB 251–252 Free Response Questions TRB 000 Semester Test 1 TRB 273–276 *Higher Level Evaluation* Critical Thinking 292

*TESTGEN can be used to prepare customized section and chapter testsheets

	Meeting Individual Needs			
Reinforcement	Reading Checksheet 6-1 TRB 95 Skillsheet 6-1 TRB 141 Essential Ideas 6.1	Reading Checksheet 6-2 TRB 96 Skillsheet 6-2 TRB 142 Essential Ideas 6.2		Information Library Software
Enrichment	Research Topic 266, 268 Data Search 000	Research Topic 287 Data Search 000		Individual Research 293 Bibliography 293
Critical Thinking and Problem Solving	Critical Thinking 264, 267, 269 Practice Problems 269	Critical Thinking 000, 000		Chapter Testsheet 6B TRB 252 Problem-Solving Worksheets, Chapter 6

Chapter 6 Planning Guide

Developing Laboratory Skills

	6.1 Comparing Chemical Reactions 258–277	6.2 Controlling Chemical Reactions 278–291		Chapter 6 Supplements
Plan Ahead	For Activity, page 260: Contact local health authorities for advice on how to dispose of chemicals after activity. For Activity, page 270: Have 300 kernels of popcorn, 300 beans, and a balance for each group of students.	For Activity, page 284: Use fresh hydrogen peroxide solution to get the most effective reaction. For Activity, page 288: Additional time may be needed to heat water if hot water is not available.		

Basic Activities	Energy Changes in a
	  Reaction 260
	  30 minutes
	  Groups of 2 or teacher
	  demonstration
	Activity Record Sheet
	6-1A, LM 79
		Comparing Speeds of a
		  Reaction 284
		  15 minutes
		  Groups of 2 to 4
		Activity Record Sheet
		6-2A, LM 83		

Additional Activities	Counting by Weighing
	  270
	  30 minutes
	  Groups of 2 to 4
	Activity Record Sheet
	6-1B, LM 80
		Temperature and
		  Reaction Speed 288
		  10 minutes
		  Groups of 2 or 3
		Activity Record Sheet
		6-2B, LM 84
				Projectsheet 6 TRB 178

Investigations and Research Lab	Investigation 6-1,
	  Reaction of Ions
	  LM 81–82
	  30 minutes
	  Groups of 2 or 3
		Investigation 6-2,
		  Catalysts LM 85–86
		  30 minutes
		  Groups of 4 or 5
				Research Lab 6
				LM 87–88

6.1 Comparing Chemical Reactions

Concept Summary

A **chemical change** is a change in matter that produces one or more new substances.

- Chemical reactions can be classified according to whether they give off more energy than they absorb or whether they must absorb energy continuously for the reaction to keep going.
- Different chemical bonds require different amounts of energy to break them apart.
- Chemical reactions are considered complete if one or more of the reactants is used up in the reaction. They are incomplete if some of each of the reactants remains.
- The formation of a solid or a gas in a reaction is a clue that the reaction will continue until at least one of the reactants is used up.
- Chemical reactions can be classified according to whether the product is a single compound; the reactant is a single compound; one element replaces another in a compound; or two elements switch places.
- Mass is conserved in a chemical reaction.
- A quantity called the mole is used to compare numbers of atoms involved in chemical reactions. The mole represents a fixed number of particles.
- A balanced chemical equation can be used to predict the masses of the products and the amount of energy released or required, given the masses of the reactants.
- Chemical changes are involved in everyday processes in our lives such as baking and cleaning. Vital elements are supplied to plants by fertilizers.

Learning Objectives

1. To distinguish between exothermic and endothermic reactions.
2. To compare complete and incomplete chemical reactions.
3. To describe four types of chemical reactions.
4. To relate the law of the conservation of mass to chemical reactions.
5. To relate defined quantities of particles to the amount of energy released in some chemical reactions.

Getting Started

Ideas for Discussion
Students will learn that many of their everyday activities involve chemical reactions.

Ask your class how many of them have conducted a chemical reaction. (You are likely to get few responses. Discuss the few that come up with the class.) Tell the class that every one of them has conducted many chemical reactions. Explain that when you cook breakfast you denature proteins by heat. This is why raw egg white is clear and runny and cooked egg white is firm and opaque white. Explain that when toasting bread you are performing what is known as the *browning reaction.* When you bathe, shower or wash clothes you are making a soap emulsion of the dirt and grease. Discuss with the class other possible everyday chemical reactions. Tell the students that Chapter 6, Section 1 will explain the various types of chemical reactions to increase their understanding of everyday chemistry.

Suggested Demonstration
In this demonstration the students will observe an *endothermic reaction,* the electrolysis of water. They will learn to compare molar ratios of products and reactants. For this demonstration you will need:

500-mL beaker
two test tubes
6-V dry cell
15-cm × 15-cm piece of cardboard with two small holes cut in it to serve as test tube holder
two 30-cm pieces insulated copper wire, No. 18, 20, or 22
two platinum electrodes
two wood splints
5-mL of sulphuric acid or sodium sulfate
tongs
water
matches
rubber gloves

To set up the electrolysis apparatus, insert the test tubes into the holes in the cardboard, making sure the test tubes are held snugly when they are inverted. Prepare a solution of 400 mL of water containing 5 mL of sulphuric acid or sodium sulfate, and set it aside. Attach one wire to each electrode and arrange the electrodes in the bottom of the beaker. Make sure the electrodes are submerged. Carefully invert the test tubes so that they are positioned over the top of each electrode. There should be no air space inside each tube. Place the dry cell into position to connect the wires leading to the electrodes. SAFETY NOTE: *If sulphuric acid is used, use tongs to adjust the submerged electrodes. Be careful not to spill any of the solution on your skin or clothing.* Ask the class if they know the chemical formula for water. Write the formula H_2O on the board. Ask what the letters H and O mean in the formula (hydrogen and oxygen). Explain to the class that hydrogen and oxygen are colorless gases, but when they combine chemically, the compound water is formed and energy is released. Explain that adding electrical energy to water reverses the reaction, and water is converted into its component gases, hydrogen and oxygen.

Start the reaction by connecting the ends of the wires to the terminals of the dry cell. The electrodes will bubble and gas begins to collect in each tube. The gas displaces the water and forces down the water level. Point out the negative and positive electrodes to the class. Ask them to observe at which electrode gas is accumulating faster. Hydrogen gas is generated at the negative electrode twice as fast as oxygen is generated at the positive electrode. Ask what will happen to the reaction if you disconnect the wires. Disconnect one wire from the dry cell and have the class observe that the electrodes stop bubbling. Explain that a reaction that requires energy to keep going is known as an *endothermic reaction*. Reconnect the wires. When the tube above the negative electrode is full, disconnect the dry cell and stop the reaction. Ask the class to predict which of the tubes contains hydrogen. The one that is nearly full. Explain that you will now test their prediction. Remove the test tube with the tongs. Explain that you must keep the test tube inverted because hydrogen is lighter than air and it will escape into the air. Hold a lighted match or wood splint near the mouth of the test tube. The students will hear a small pop. Explain that this is a hydrogen explosion. Ask why they predicted that this tube was hydrogen. They should know that there is twice as much gas as in the tube containing oxygen since the formula is H_2O.

You may wish to test for oxygen using a smoldering splint. Light one end of a wooden split, blow it out, and immediately insert it into the tube containing oxygen. The oxygen should cause the splint to burst into flame. This test is not as dramatic as the test for hydrogen. Tell the class that in Chapter 5, Section 1 they will learn what takes place in many different types of chemical reactions.

Activity 6.1a
Precipitation from Solutions   page 260

Preparation Notes
Use distilled water to make up solutions, if it is available.

The following stock solutions are made up for 25 groups of students, and allow for waste and repeats.

0.05M NaOH (sodium hydroxide): Dissolve 1 gm of NaOH in 400 mL of water with cooling and stirring. Dilute with water to 500 mL. Store in a plastic bottle.

0.05M K_2CO_3 (potassium carbonate): Dissolve 3.45 gm of K_2CO_3 in 400 mL of water with stirring. Dilute with water to 500 mL and store in a plastic bottle.

$CoCl_2$ (cobalt chloride): Dissolve enough cobalt chloride in 200 mL of water to make a wine-red solution. The exact amount of cobalt chloride in the solution does not matter. Store in a plastic bottle.

Teacher Notes
To dispose of the materials in the test tubes, have students pour them into a large beaker or bucket. Add sodium bicarbonate to the solution to neutralize it. Then it is safe to dump down the drain and flush it with water.

Before beginning this activity, consult safety procedures for working with sodium hydroxide in a chemistry book. Review emergency procedures with each class. The sodium hydroxide solution is relatively dilute, but treat it carefully.

Warn students not to ingest any of the chemicals in this activity. Remind them to wash their hands after doing this activity.

The expected results of this activity are as follows. A blue or blue-green precipitate ought to form when cobalt chloride is dropped into sodium hydroxide. A pinkish precipitate ought to be formed when cobalt chloride is dropped into potassium carbonate. After being swirled, the precipitate in the sodium hydroxide solution may remain the same or turn more green. After being swirled, the precipitate in the potassium carbonate solution should turn violet blue.

The chemical reactions can be summarized as follows:
$$2\,NaOH + CoCl_2 \rightarrow 2\,NaCl + Co(OH)_2$$
$$\text{blue ppt.}$$
$$K_2CO_3 + CoCl_2 \rightarrow 2\,KCl + CoCO_3$$
$$\text{red ppt.}$$

The second color change in the solution of potassium carbonate is due to the formation of a complex between cobalt carbonate and cobalt hydroxide that is formed from excess hydroxide ions.

Answers to Questions
1. The evidence for chemical changes was the formation of a precipitate in the test tubes when cobalt chloride was added.
2. Yes, in the potassium carbonate solution. Maybe, in the sodium hydroxide solution. Color changes signaled the chemical changes.
3. An insoluble substance that forms in a solution.
4. Yes, they dropped to the bottom of the test tubes initially and again after being swirled.

Conclusion
The precipitation of a new substance from a solution is evidence of a chemical change.

Activity 6.1b
Counting by Weighing   page 270

Advance Preparation
Make certain to have about 300 kernels of popcorn, about 300 beans, and a balance for each group of students.

Answers to Questions
1. Four "bowls" in 1000 g; 40 "bowls" in 10,000 g.
2. Four "bowls" in 1000 g; 40 "bowls" in 10,000 g.
3. The masses of a "bowl" of popcorn and a "bowl" of beans are different.
4. The number of kernels in a "bowl" of popcorn should equal the number of seeds in a "bowl" of beans.
5. "Bowls" of popcorn refers to a fixed number of kernels of popcorn, 250 in this case. "Bowls" of beans refers to a fixed number of beans: 250. There is a difference in the masses of "bowls" of each of these materials. For that reason, the number of "bowls" of each in an unmeasured amount of popcorn or beans can be determined by measuring the masses of each. Moles of a substance refer to a fixed number of particles of that substance: 6.02×10^{23}. The number of moles of different substances can be determined by measuring the masses of each.

Conclusion
Chemists count and compare the number of particles taking part in reactions by weighing the masses of the reacting substances. Knowing the number of particles in a given mass of a substance makes it possible to determine the number of particles in any amount of mass of the substance.

6.1 Section Review

Understanding the Concepts   page 277
18. A synthesis reaction is any chemical reaction in which a single compound is formed from the combination of two or more elements or compounds. A decomposition reaction is a reaction in which a compound is broken down into two or more elements or compounds.
    Synthesis: $2Mg + O_2 \longrightarrow 2MgO$
    Decomposition: $2H_2O \longrightarrow 2H_2 + O_2$
19. Hard water is water in which soap will not suds up because of the presence of certain positive metal ions. The metal ions bind to the soap molecules, preventing them from interacting with the water. Soap loses its cleaning power in hard water.
20. Baking powder contains baking soda, $NaHCO_3$, and a weak acid such as tartaric acid. In the presence of water, the weak acid reacts with the baking soda to produce carbon dioxide. The bubbles of carbon dioxide gas cause the dough in bread or cake to rise.

Problems to Solve   page 277
21. mass of 4 moles aluminum atoms
    = 4 mol $\times$ 27 g/mol = 108 g

    mass of 3 moles O_2 molecules
    = 3 mol $\times$ 2 atoms/molecule $\times$ 16 g/mol of atoms = 96 g

    mass of reactants = mass of products
    108 g Al + 96 g O_2 = 204 g Al_2O_3
22. $$\frac{284 \text{ kJ}}{18 \text{ g}} = \frac{\text{energy used}}{72 \text{g}}$$

    $$\text{energy used} = \frac{284 \text{ kJ} \times 72 \text{ g}}{18 \text{ g}}$$

    $$= \frac{20\ 448 \text{ kJ}}{18} \qquad = 1136 \text{ kJ}$$

6.2 Controlling Chemical Reactions

Concept Summary

The **reaction speed** of a chemical reaction is a measure of how fast the reactants are used up or how fast the products are formed.
- Different combinations of reactants have different reaction speeds.
- For solid reactants, the amount of exposed surface affects the reaction speed.
- Increasing the temperature of the reactants increases the reaction speed.
- Concentration is a measure of how much of a substance is present in a solution.
- Increasing the concentration of the reactants increases the reaction speed.
- Activation energy is the energy required to get a chemical reaction going.
- A catalyst speeds up a reaction without being changed itself by the reaction.
- An inhibitor slows down a reaction.

An **ore** is a compound that contains a metal in combination with other elements.
- Metals can be removed from their ores by refining.

Learning Objectives

1. To compare two methods for describing the speed of chemical reactions.
2. To describe the effect of temperature changes on chemical reactions.
3. To identify differences in concentration and relate them to their effect on the speed of reactions.
4. To define catalysts and relate their effect on activation energy to reaction speed.
5. To describe two important industrial chemical processes.

Getting Started

Ideas for Discussion
The students will be introduced to some of the ways chemical reactions can be controlled.

Ask the students to name some chemical reactions with which they are familiar and write their suggestions on the board. Some examples might be rusting, burning fuels, and cooking. Ask the class if all the reactions they listed occur at the same rate of speed. Write the words *fast* and *slow* on the board. Ask the students to classify the reactions they named into these two categories.

Review aloud the various reactions mentioned by the students and ask how the speed at which each occurs can be changed. Examples might be painting the car so it won't rust, adding more wood to a fire, and turning the heat down to slow the cooking time. Tell the students that they suggested a few of the major ways in which chemical reactions can be controlled. They are changing temperature and altering the amount of a reactant.

Explain that there are many ways of controlling chemical reactions. Reactions can be speeded up and slowed down so that we may take advantage of them. Some of the ways of controlling chemical reactions are discussed in Section 2 of Chapter 6.

Suggested Demonstration
Students will learn the effect the concentration of a chemical has on the time that is required for a reaction to take place. For this demonstration you will need:
20 mL 0.3M formaldehyde
20 mL 0.1M sodium hydrogen sulfite—NaHSO$_3$—
   (sodium bisulfite)
phenolphthalein
two 50-mL beakers
watch or clock with second hand
10 mL distilled water

SAFETY NOTE: *Avoid breathing formaldehyde vapors. Use in a well-ventilated room. Care should be taken not to get sodium hydrogen sulfite on the skin or clothing. If the chemical should be spilled, flush the area with large amounts of water. For disposal, neutralize the material with sodium bicarbonate before flushing it down the drain.*

Add 10 mL 0.1M sodium hydrogen sulfite and one drop of phenolphthalein to one of the beakers. Set it aside. Students should observe that there is no apparent change. To the other beaker, add 10 mL of 0.3M formaldehyde. Time the reaction with the watch. In approximately 30 seconds, the solution should turn a brilliant pink. Record on the board the amount and the concentration of all the reactants used. Record the time of the reaction.

Rinse the second beaker thoroughly. Put 10 mL of 0.1M sodium hydrogen sulfite, 10 mL of distilled water, and one drop of phenolphthalein into the beaker. Add 10 mL of formaldehyde. Time the reaction with the watch. This time the reaction should take approximately twice as long. Record on the board the amount and concentration of the chemicals that were used. Discuss with the students how the second reaction differs from the first. Ask why it was slower. In the second reaction, the sodium hydrogen sulfite is more dilute, and the molecules of formaldehyde must search harder for the reactant; therefore, the reaction time is longer.

Activity 6.2a
Comparing Speeds of a Reaction   page 284

Advance Preparation
Use fresh hydrogen peroxide solution to get the most effective reaction.

Answers to Questions
1. The hydrogen peroxide solution very slowly forms tiny bubbles before the steel wool is added.
2. After the steel wool is added, the bubbling reaction proceeds much faster. The solution bubbles vigorously.
3. During the reaction, the steel wool had small bubbles of gas forming on its surface. When the reaction was finished, the steel wool seemed the same as at the start of the reaction.
4. There was only a little reaction in the beaker before the sand was added.
5. There was a slight increase in the rate of reaction after sand was added.
6. Steel wool provides a surface on which the hydrogen peroxide molecules can decompose into oxygen and water.
7. Much less effectively than steel wool.

Conclusion
A catalyst speeds up a chemical reaction. The catalyst itself is not changed during the course of the reaction.

Activity 6.2b
Temperature and Reaction Speed   page 288

Teacher Suggestions
If hot water is not available, have the students heat the water in one beaker to about 50°C on a hot plate. Allow additional time for heating the water.

If graduated flasks are not available, students can measure the volume of water with a graduated cylinder or beaker before they add the water to the flasks.

Have students wet the rubber stoppers before they put them into the flasks to make tighter seals.

Encourage students to put the stoppers into the flasks as soon as they can after adding the Alka-Seltzer tablets so that not much gas escapes.

Students may need to hold the stoppers in the flasks after adding the Alka-Seltzer tablets to the water to keep the balloons or stoppers from popping out.

Answers to Questions
1. Bubbling indicates the formation of a new substance, a gas.
2. The reaction is more vigorous and takes less time in hot water.
3. Yes.
4. Some of the variables include the size of the flasks, the number of tablets, the size of the balloons, the amount of water in each flask, and the temperature of the water. The variables that remain constant are the size of the flasks, the number of tablets, the amount of water in each flask. The variable that is being manipulated is the temperature of the water. The variable that is responding is the speed with which the balloons fill, or the size of the balloons after a fixed time.

Conclusion
Increasing the temperature increases the rate of a chemical change.

6.2 Section Review

Understanding the Concepts   page 291
16. a. Sulfur dioxide and oxygen are reacted in the presence of a catalyst (an oxide of platinum or vanadium) to form sulfur trioxide
$2SO_2 + O_2 \longrightarrow 2SO_3 + heat$;
    b. Sulfur trioxide is reacted with sulfuric acid to form the reaction intermediate $H_2SO_4 \cdot SO_3$
$SO_3 + H_2SO_4 \longrightarrow H_2SO_4 \cdot SO_3$;
    c. The reaction intermediate is reacted with water to form two molecules of sulfuric acid (a net gain of one H_2SO_4)
$H_2SO_4 \cdot SO_3 + H_2O \longrightarrow 2H_2SO_4$.

17. The dissolving of sulfuric acid in water is a very exothermic reaction. If water is added to the acid the heat released can be sufficient to cause the water to boil and spatter, carrying corrosive sulfuric acid with it. (Note that sulfuric acid is denser than water and that if water is added to sulfuric acid, the water will form a layer on top of the acid. The heat produced in the dissolution would be localized in the area between the two layers and can be great enough to explosively boil off water containing sulfuric acid.)

18. Ores are the naturally-occurring compounds in which useful metals are commonly bound up. Fe_2O_3, Cu_2O, and $PbCO_3$ are examples of ores.
19. a. Iron ore, limestone, and coke are fed in at the top of a blast furnace;
    b. A blast of hot air is forced upward from the bottom of the furnace;
    c. The hot air reacts with coke to produce carbon monoxide;
    d. The carbon monoxide reacts with iron ore to produce pig iron (molten);
    e. Pig iron is treated to lower its carbon content, to remove impurities of phosphorus and sulfur, and to add desired elements such as chromium;
    f. Steel is treated with heat to give it the specific characteristics desired by the steelmaker.
20. Meat tenderizers contain an enzyme that speeds up the breakdown of protein molecules. As with all enzymes, the enzyme in meat tenderizers increases the reaction rate by lowering the activation energy of the reaction.
21. The greater exposed surface area of the finely-divided coal provides for more contact with reactant molecules in the air. The more opportunities for contact between reactants, the faster is the reaction.
22. An increase in temperature generally increases the rate of a reaction. A rule of thumb is that for every 10°C rise in temperature the reaction rate will be doubled. As the temperature increases the average kinetic energy of the particles in the reaction mixture also increases. As a result of this faster movement, on average, the frequency of collisions and the force of the collisions also increase. Both these latter factors contribute to an increase in the speed of the reaction.
23. A catalyst reduces the activation energy of a reaction. At any given temperature, more particles have the energy necessary for reaction in the presence of a catalyst than in the absence of a catalyst.
24. An increase in the concentrations of the reactants tends to increase the rate of reaction. This is because the increased concentration permits more frequent collisions between reactants.

Problems to Solve   page 291
25. The rate of reaction will likely be increased by a factor of 4.

6 Chapter Review

Critical Thinking   page 292

1. A reaction that requires energy to get started is exothermic if the amount of energy released is greater than the amount required to get started.

2. Yes, the breaking of bonds requires energy.

3. A decomposition reaction is more likely to be endothermic. The bonds in the compound that is decomposed must be broken, and the breaking of bonds requires energy. In a synthesis reaction, bonds are formed and energy is released.

4. No, there are exactly the same number of particles in a mole of *any* kind of particles. A mole of anything is 6.02×10^{23} of that thing.

5. ■ Desirable to decrease reaction speed: burning of gasoline vapor; rusting of iron.
   ■ Desirable to increase reaction speed: burning of wood; reactions helped by enzymes in the body.

6. The coal dust found in coal mines ignites very easily because there is more surface area than if it were collected in a single lump.

7. The reaction speed would be about double what it was for a 10°C increase, or about 4 times as great altogether.

8. Reducing the concentration to half should reduce the reaction rate to about half, since doubling the concentration would double the rate.

9. The activation energy needed to burn wood is greater, since the wood must be raised to a certain temperature, whereas cement hardens without the addition of energy.

10. Lead $2 \text{ PbS} + 3 \text{O}_2 \longrightarrow 2 \text{ PbO} + 2 \text{ SO}_2$
             double replacement
             $2 \text{ PbO} + \text{C} \longrightarrow 2 \text{ Pb} + \text{CO}_2$
             single replacement

    Iron $\text{Fe}_2\text{O}_3 + 3\text{CO} \longrightarrow 3 \text{ CO}_2 + 2\text{Fe}$
             single replacement (oxygen moves from Fe_2O_3 to CO)

    Zinc $\text{Zn CO}_3 \longrightarrow \text{ZnO} + \text{CO}_2$
             decomposition

Chapter 7   Using Energy from Chemical Reactions

	Chapter 7 Planning Guide			
	Planning Your Classroom Lessons			
	7.1 Carbon Chemistry 296–312	**7.2** Using Fuels for Heat and Work 313–326	**7.3** Using Fuels for Living Cells 327–341	**Chapter 7 Review** 342–343 Chapter 7 Supplements
Content Overview	An examination of the many kinds of organic compounds, which are the essential chemicals found in living beings Concept Summary T110 Learning Objectives T110	The absorption and release of energy in chemical changes, and the use of fuels to provide energy Concept Summary T112 Learning Objectives T112	Food, the fuel of living things, and the path taken by the energy in food from its origin in the sun to its release in the body Concept Summary T114 Learning Objectives T114	Science Background Information 294 Review of Concepts 342–343 Essential Ideas/ Chapter 7 Letter to Parents
Teaching Strategies	Getting Started: Ideas for Discussion and Suggested Demonstration T110	Getting Started: Ideas for Discussion and Suggested Demonstration T112	Getting Started: Ideas for Discussion and Suggested Demonstration T114	
Teaching Aids	Teaching Diagram 7-1A, 7-1B Overhead Transparency	Teaching Diagram 7-2A, 7-2B	Teaching Diagram 7-3A, 7-3B	Physical Science Software T00 Physical Science Films and Videos T00 Video Lesson: Energy and Changes in Matter
Review and Evaluation*	Quick Review 297, 299, 303, 304, 305, 307, 308, 311 7.1 Review 312 Section Testsheet 7-1 TRB 217	Quick Review 315, 318, 319, 322, 325 7.2 Review 326 Section Testsheet 7-2 TRB 218	Quick Review 328, 330, 333, 335, 336, 337, 339 7.3 Review 341 Section Testsheet 7-3 TRB 219	Chapter Testsheets 7A and 7B TRB 253–254 Free Response Questions TRB 000 Semester Test 1 TRB 273–276 *Higher Level Evaluation* Critical Thinking 343

*TESTGEN can be used to prepare customized section and chapter testsheets

	Meeting Individual Needs			
Reinforcement	Reading Checksheet 7-1 TRB 97 Skillsheet 7-1 TRB 143 Essential Ideas 7.1	Reading Checksheet 7-2 TRB 98 Skillsheet 7-2 TRB 144 Essential Ideas 7.2	Reading Checksheet 7-3 TRB 99 Skillsheet 7-3 TRB 145 Essential Ideas 7.3	Information Library Software
Enrichment	Research Topic 000 Data Search 000	Research Topic 320, 322 Data Search 000	Research Topic 333 Data Search 000	Individual Research 343 Bibliography 343 Issues in Physical Science: Use of Coal as Fuel 344 Trends in Technology: Solutions to Acid Rain 345
Critical Thinking and Problem Solving	Critical Thinking 000 Practice Problem 303	Critical Thinking 317 Practice Problem 314	Critical Thinking 000, 000	Chapter Testsheet 7B TRB 254 Problem-Solving Worksheets, Chapter 7

Chapter 7 Planning Guide

Developing Laboratory Skills

	7.1 Carbon Chemistry 296–312	7.2 Using Fuels for Heat and Work 313–326	7.3 Using Fuels for Living Cells 327–341	Chapter 7 Supplements
Plan Ahead	For Activity, page 300: Wrapping gumdrops in plastic sandwich bags with twister seals will discourage students from eating them.	For Activity, page 323: Gather a tea kettle and an empty flour pot. For Investigation, LM 95–96: Gather small juice cans.	For Activity, page 331: Gather small juice cans, hammer, and nuts. For Activity, page 334: Fermentation tubes are needed. Obtain dry yeast. Prepare molasses solution ahead of time. For Investigation, LM 99–100: Allow up to 2 weeks for grass seeds to sprout and grow.	
Basic Activities	Making Hydrocarbon Models 300 20 minutes Groups of 2 to 4 Activity Record Sheet 7-1A, LM 89	Making a Steam Turbine 323 20 minutes Groups of 4 or teacher demonstration Activity Record Sheet 7-2A, LM 93	Energy from Burning Nuts 331 30 minutes Groups of 4 or teacher demonstration Activity Record Sheet 7-3A, LM 97	
Additional Activities	Comparing Solvents 310 25 minutes Groups of 3 or 4 Activity Record Sheet 7-1B, LM 90	Methane from Coal 316 20 minutes, plus 2 to 3 days Groups of 3 to 4 Activity Record Sheet 7-2B, LM 94	Heat Release in Fermentation 334 2 days Groups of 4 or teacher demonstration Activity Record Sheet 7-3B, LM 98	Projectsheet 7 TRB 179
Investigations and Research Lab	Investigation 7-1, Polymers: Giant Molecules LM 91–92 30 minutes Groups of 3 or 4	Investigation 7-2, Energy from a Burning Candle LM 95–96 20 minutes Groups of 2 or teacher demonstration	Investigation 7-3, Plant Growth and Colored Light LM 99–100 8 to 12 days Groups of 4 or entire class	Research Lab 7 LM 101–102

Chapter 7 Using Energy from Chemical Reactions

7.1 Carbon Chemistry

Concept Summary

An **organic compound** is a compound that contains carbon.

- Carbon atoms can form chemical bonds with carbon atoms as well as with other kinds of atoms.
- Many different compounds can be formed from only the elements hydrogen and carbon.
- Hydrocarbons can be classified according to the types of bonds that connect the carbon atoms to each other within the compound.
- Carbon can form compounds with single, double, or triple carbon-carbon bonds.
- Carbon can form compounds with closed ring structures.
- Two compounds may have the same molecular formula but different structures.
- Carbon compounds have different chemical reaction rates that depend on their structures.
- Many compounds can be formed from hydrocarbons by replacing one or more hydrogen atoms with other atoms or groups of atoms.
- Organic compounds that are especially important to living things include those that are classified as carbohydrates, fats, proteins, or vitamins.

Learning Objectives

1. To understand why carbon can form so many compounds.
2. To recognize several important groups of carbon compounds.
3. To recognize different kinds of carbon bonds.
4. To relate some chemical properties to different kinds of carbon atoms.
5. To identify classes of organic compounds that are essential for living beings.

Getting Started

Ideas for Discussion

Students will learn that carbon and the classes of compounds formed by it are the essential chemicals found in living beings.

Write the following list on the board, and as you do so ask the class to try and think of what all these substances have in common: food, coal, candles, cosmetics, paper, plastic, pesticides, petroleum, rubber, wood, a person.

Explain to the class that each one of these substances contains carbon. Ask them to find carbon in the Periodic Table on pp. 104–105. Ask: What can we tell about carbon? (Answer: It is a non-metallic solid with atomic number 6 and an atomic mass of 12.011.) Ask: How many electrons does it have in its outer shell? (Answer: four) Explain that because carbon has four electrons available for bonding it is able to form many different types of bonds with many different types of atoms. Tell the class that in Chapter 7, Section 1 they will learn about the chemistry of carbon and the classes of compounds formed by it.

Suggested Demonstration

In this demonstration the students will compare what happens when several inorganic and organic compounds are burned. For this experiment you will need the following items:

Bunsen burner or propane torch
ring stand with wire gauze
lid cut from a tin can (unpainted)
small (pea-size) samples of: sugar, salt, paraffin, calcium carbonate, petroleum jelly (there are many possible substitutions)

Distribute the samples along the outer edge of the tin can lid. Place the lid carefully on top of the wire gauze and set it on the ring stand. Ask the class: What do all organic compounds have in common? (Answer: They all contain carbon.) Explain that when some organic compounds are burned, they give off a great deal of heat and light and a black residue of carbon can be seen to remain. Show the class the samples you have prepared. Write the samples' names on the board. Ask the class to predict which of them are organic compounds. Light the Bunsen burner and place the flame directly on each material in turn. Ask the class to observe carefully what happens to each one. For each of the substances ask: Did it burn? (Answer: Everything except the salt and $CaCO_3$ will burn.) Ask: From the data, which of the substances would you expect to be organic? (Answer: sugar, paraffin, petroleum jelly.)

Activity 7.1a
Making Hydrocarbon Models   page 300

Preparation Note

Put the gumdrops for each group in plastic sandwich bags with twister seals for ease in dispensing and to discourage students from eating them (at least until the activity is completed).

Answers to Questions

1. The molecules contain only carbon and hydrogen atoms.
2. All of the molecules have two carbon atoms. The number of hydrogen atoms is different for each molecule.
3. Each toothpick represents a single covalent bond.
4. The carbon atoms in ethane are joined by a single covalent bond. In ethene, they are joined by a double covalent bond. The carbon-carbon bond in ethyne is a triple covalent bond.
5. When carbon atoms are joined by a single covalent bond, they can bond with more hydrogen atoms. The molecule having the triple bond contains the smallest number of hydrogen atoms.
6. Ethane is a saturated hydrocarbon. Ethene and ethyne are unsaturated hydrocarbons.

Conclusion

Carbon atoms can be joined by single, double, or triple covalent bonds. The kind of bond formed determines how many other atoms can bond with the carbon atoms. Many different combinations are possible.

Activity 7.1b
Comparing Solvents   page 310

Teacher Note
The outcome of this activity will depend a lot on the kind of marking pen used. That is why the answers to the questions are not definite.

Answers to Questions

1. This answer depends on what kind of felt tip marker was used and whether or not the ink is water soluble.
2. This answer depends on the kind of leaves that are used and on the substances that give color to the leaves.
3. Answers may vary.

Conclusion
Students should be able to conclude that there are differences in the dissolving effects between organic liquids and water.

7.1 Section Review

Understanding the Concepts   page 312
25. The molecule bonds more strongly to the hemoglobin in the blood than does oxygen.
26. Butane, propane, methane.
27. Isomer: compounds with the same molecular formulas but with different structures. Butane and methyl propane are examples.
28. Alkane series: saturated hydrocarbons which only have single covalent bonds between the carbon atoms.

Alkene series: unsaturated hydrocarbons with at least 1 double bond between 2 carbon atoms.
Alkyne series: unsaturated hydrocarbons with at least 1 triple bond between 2 carbon atoms.
Benzene series: hydrocarbons based on compounds with the benzene ring structure.
29. A functional group contains atoms or groups of atoms that replace one or more of the hydrogens in hydrocarbons to form compounds. =OH group, -OH group.
30. Composed of carbon, hydrogen and oxygen atoms. They have twice as many hydrogen atoms as oxygen atoms.

Problems to Solve   page 312
31.

32. The number of hydrogen atoms is always two more than twice the number of carbon atoms in the chain.
C_7H_{16}—16 hydrogens

7.2 Using Fuels for Heat and Work

Concept Summary

A **fuel** is a substance that burns easily and is burned to supply energy.
- The most widely used fuels are hydrocarbons.
- Most of the energy released when a fuel burns is in the form of heat.
- The amount of heat released can be controlled by changing the amount of fuel, the amount of oxygen, the length of time that burning takes place, or the surface area of solid and liquid fuels.
- The heat released by burning can be used to do work in an engine.
- The burning of fuels adds substances to the atmosphere, some of which are responsible for pollution problems.

Learning Objectives

1. To relate the amount of energy obtained from burning a fuel to the quantity of the fuel.
2. To compare the amount of energy obtained from burning natural gas, coal, and gasoline.
3. To recognize the factors that control the rate of burning.
4. To contrast internal and external combustion engines.

Getting Started

Ideas for Discussion

Students discuss the uses and properties of natural fuels.

Ask the class to make a list of different kinds of fuels used in their community. Ask them to classify each kind according to whether the fuel occurs naturally or is the product of a refining process. Naturally-occurring fuels include coal, crude oil, natural gas, and wood. Refined or conversion products include gasoline, kerosene, coal gas, fuel oil, diesel fuel, cola, charcoal, propane, butane, paper, and wax.

Discuss with the class the uses and properties of each fuel. Explain that in Chapter 7, Section 2 they will learn what happens chemically when the various fuels are burned.

Suggested Demonstration

In this demonstration the students will be shown some of the products of incomplete burning: carbon, carbon dioxide and water. For this experiment you will need the following items:

500-mL pyrex beaker
white china saucer
candle (short enough to fit completely inside the beaker)
matches
100 mL limewater

Seat the candle in the bottom of the beaker by lighting it, dripping some melted wax on the bottom of the beaker and firmly pushing the candle into it. Let it harden. Explain to the class that a candle burns because the molecules of the wax, which are long chain alkanes with 20–30 carbons, combine chemically with the oxygen in the air to produce carbon dioxide and water. However, because the oxygen in the air is limited, the reaction does not proceed completely, and unreacted carbon is released in pure form. Light the candle and hold the saucer over the flame near the top of the beaker, but not closing it off.

After a minute or so, carefully tilt the plate up and show it to the class. A black sooty spot of carbon as well as some droplets of water vapor should be clearly visible. Explain that we can test for the formation of carbon dioxide by using the limewater. It will turn from clear to milky white in the presence of carbon dioxide. Pour the limewater into the bottom of the beaker along one side. (It is a good idea to put a little bit of limewater aside in another beaker or test tube to serve as the control.) Cover the beaker with the saucer. Ask the class to observe carefully.

Ask: As the candle goes out, what happens? (Answer: The amount of soot and smoke increases.) When the candle is out, pick up the beaker and swirl it, taking care that it stays covered. The limewater should turn

milky, indicating the presence of carbon dioxide. Review with the class the three combustion products they have observed: Soot (carbon), water vapor and carbon dioxide. Tell the students that in Chapter 7, Section 2 they will compare the combustion processes of many kinds of fuels.

Activity 7.2a
Methane from Coal   page 316

Advance Preparation

If you cannot obtain soft coal from a local source, you can order small quantities from Scott Resources, Inc., P.O. Box 2121, Fort Collins, Colorado 80522.

Teacher Note

In Step 9 of the Procedure, the students may or may not be able to get the gas that they have collected to ignite. Other gases that are trapped in coal, such as nitrogen, are not flammable.

Answers to Questions

1. The water level in the test tube should get lower as gas displaces the water.
2. The evidence that the gas came from the coal is that there should be no gas collected in the test tube from the jar that had no coal.
3. Methane is less dense than air. The purpose of holding the test tube upside down until it was ready to ignite was to keep the lighter gas from escaping upward.

Conclusion

Coal does contain a flammable gas that can be used for fuel.

Activity 7.2b
Making a Steam Turbine   page 323

SAFETY NOTE: *The teacher should supervise the testing of the students' turbines. To prevent scalding by the steam, care should be taken that the spout is pointed away from the flower pot until the apparatus is completely assembled.*

Preparation Notes

Fill the teakettle half full of water and set it on the hot plate to boil. Place the inverted flower pot next to the hot plate. Turn the spout away from the flower pot. When the kettle is boiling and after the "turbine" has been placed on the flower pot, slowly turn the steaming spout toward the turbine. This introduces the steam to the turbine slowly and keeps it from tipping.

Answers to Questions

1. The steam turbine rotates.
2. The blades move away from the steam, causing the turbine to rotate in the same direction as the steam.

Conclusion

When steam is directed at the blades of a turbine, it pushes against the blades and causes the turbine to rotate.

7.2 Section Review

Understanding the Concepts   page 326

14. Fuel in a fireplace burns incompletely, producing some carbon monoxide, which is a poisonous gas. It is dangerous to close the chimney opening to prevent hot gases from escaping up the chimney, for then the carbon monoxide will enter the room instead.

15. The air in a diesel engine is compressed more than the fuel and air mixture in a gasoline engine. Accordingly, a thicker wall is needed in a diesel engine than in a gasoline engine to withstand the additional pressure.

16. Hydrocarbon fuels often contain sulfur as an impurity. Sulfuric acid can be formed, which washes down in the next rain. Also, nitrogen from the air may form nitrogen oxides inside an auto engine. These may then form acids that contribute to acid rain.

    Acid rain can be controlled by cutting down on the use of hydrocarbon fuels, by using purer fuels, and by using antismog devices and catalytic converters.

17. New bonds are formed and more energy is released.
$$CH_4 + 2O_2 \longrightarrow CO_2 + 2H_2O \text{ (Methane)}$$

Problems to Solve   page 326

18. Propane, acetylene.

7.3 Using Fuels for Living Cells

Concept Summary

Biochemistry is the study of the chemical reactions of living organisms.
- All living organisms require a supply of energy.
- Energy is supplied by chemical reactions in the cells.

Cell respiration is a process inside a cell in which glucose combines with oxygen to form carbon dioxide and water, and energy is released.
- The energy released in cell respiration is not used directly by the cell; some is used to form ATP from ADP, and some is given off as heat.
- When a cell needs energy, it gets it from the reaction of ATP and water.

Fermentation is a process inside a cell in which glucose is broken down in the absence of oxygen.
- Smaller amounts of ATP are formed in fermentation than in cell respiration.
- More energy is given off as heat in fermentation than in cell respiration.

Photosynthesis is a process in which the energy in sunlight is used to change carbon dioxide and water into glucose and oxygen.
- Food-making organisms include plants and other green organisms that contain chlorophyll, the green substance that can absorb energy from sunlight.
- Animals that eat food-making organisms gain the energy stored in the food.
- Plant eaters are eaten by other animals, which may be eaten in turn by still other animals.
- A food energy pyramid shows that when animals eat their food, they eat less than the total food available; thus, less energy is available in food to those that eat them in turn.

Learning Objectives

1. To explain how cell respiration releases energy to carry on the body functions and growth.
2. To explain how the fermentation process supplies the body with energy and how fermentation differs from respiration.
3. To describe the process of photosynthesis and its importance.
4. To use a pyramid to illustrate the energy relationships in a natural community of plants and animals.

Getting Started

Idea for Discussion

Students will learn that expending greater energy to perform a given task faster does not amount to more work performed than if the task were done at a slower pace.

Ask the class: How would you feel after running up ten flights of stairs? Get them to be descriptive. (Panting, out of breath, legs hurt, maybe they couldn't make it all the way without stopping to rest, etc.)

Ask: How would you feel after walking at your own pace up the same ten flights of stairs? (Answer: Also tired but not quite as bad.) Ask: Is getting your body up to the top of the stairs work? (Answer: Yes, you are applying a force to your body to move it up ten flights of stairs.) Ask: In scientific terms, are you doing more work when you run up the stairs than when you walk? (Answer: No, work equals force times distance.) Ask: Why is it then, that you feel so much worse when you run up the stairs than when you walk? Explain that there are two ways for your muscles to change the energy from the food you eat into the energy you need to climb the stairs. Explain that it is the difference between these two chemical processes that causes you to feel worse after running up the stairs than you do after walking up. Chapter 7, Section 3 will explain these processes.

In this demonstration the students will observe an increase in photosynthetic rate as demonstrated by the bubbling of oxygen produced by aquatic plants placed in a strong light. For this experiment you will need the following items:

2 large beakers or jars
several sprigs *Elodea* or other aquatic plant
water (may use 0.5% sodium bicarbonate solution)
strong light source (lamp or sunny window)

Fill each beaker or jar with water and place 1–2 plants into each. Place one in a shady area, the other in bright light. Tell the class that in 1772, Joseph Priestly discovered that plants could make "restored air." He placed a mouse under a large glass jar. It subsequently died. He placed a sprig of mint in water under another jar. To his surprise it lived several months, but then it too died. However, when he put the mouse and the plant in the jar together, they both lived.

In another experiment he placed a burning candle under the jar until it went out. He then placed another mint sprig in the same jar and found that after a few days, a candle would again burn in the jar.

Ask: From this experimental evidence, what was the "restored air" described by Priestly? (Answer: Oxygen gas.) Tell the class that if they observe the jars with the aquatic plants closely, they can observe the production of oxygen gas. (Small bubbles of the gas are produced near the leaves and eventually float to the surface, after the water is fully oxygenated.) Ask them to observe carefully the oxygen production in both the jar in the shade and in the light. Ask: What differences do you observe? (Answer: The plant in the jar in the light is producing bubbles of oxygen much more rapidly than in the other jar.) Explain that the process by which plants produce oxygen is known as photosynthesis, a word that means "made from light." Write the word on the board. Explain that plants trap light from the sun and in the process of photosynthesis, use carbon dioxide and water to make glucose and oxygen. Tell the class that in Chapter 7, Section 3 they will learn how the energy trapped by plants in photosynthesis is the ultimate source of food on earth.

Activity 7.3a
Energy from Burning Nuts   page 331

Advance Preparation
Use raw nuts for this activity. If one of the nuts has been roasted in oil, then all of the nuts should be roasted in oil. There should be an ample number of holes in the can to provide oxygen to the burning nut.

Answers to Questions
1. It will probably be the walnut. The nut that raises the temperature of the water the most is the one that releases the most energy.
2. It will probably be the walnut. The nut that produces the greatest temperature change divided by nut mass is the one that releases the most energy per gram.
3. The walnuts will probably have the most food energy. The cashews will probably have the least.

Conclusion
The walnut will probably release the most energy per gram, followed by the almond and then the cashew.

Activity 7.3b
Heat Release in Fermentation   page 334

Advance Preparation
Prepare the molasses solution ahead of time. To make a 10% solution, add enough water to 10 mL of molasses to make 100 mL of solution.

Teacher Note
Demonstrate the reaction of potassium hydroxide in the fermentation tube for the students. Be sure to use tongs to handle this chemical.
SAFETY NOTE: *Potassium hydroxide, KOH, can cause severe burns. Neutralize any spill with $NaHCO_3$ before cleaning it up with paper towels and water.*

Answers to Questions
1. The temperature should change the most in tube A and the least in tube C.
2. Tube A should have the most gas in the closed end and tube C should have the least.
3. Students should realize that the greatest temperature change indicates that the most fermentation took place.
4. Yes, the presence of molasses did affect the heat given off. More heat was given off in tube B than in tube C.
5. Yes, the amount of yeast affected the amount of heat given off, since more heat was given off in tube A than in tube B.
6. Tube A should have the highest temperature change.
7. The more heat that was given off, the greater was the amount of gas in the closed end.
8. The potassium hydroxide should absorb the gas, indicating that the gas is carbon dioxide. The carbon dioxide was given off as a product of the fermentation.

Conclusion
The amount of heat and gas released during fermentation are affected by the amount of yeast added to the tubes containing a 10% molasses solution. The

control used is tube C, which contains water and yeast. The amount of heat and gas released in tube C is compared to the amount of heat and gas that occurs during fermentation of the molasses in the other tubes.

7.3 Section Review

Understanding the Concepts   page 341

19. Cell respiration will take place at a lower temperature than burning. The temperature is low enough not to destroy the cells, as the starting temperature of burning would. Cell respiration stores energy in ATP molecules, from which cells can obtain energy as they need it. Burning produces heat, which cells cannot use to do their work.

20. In both processes, glucose is used to start a series of reactions in which carbon dioxide is formed and energy is released. Cell respiration requires oxygen; much more ATP is formed; and water is formed also. Fermentation takes place without oxygen. In fermentation with yeast, carbon dioxide is formed; in muscle cells, an acid is formed.

21. A wheat plant, a tomato plant, and grass used sunlight in making their food. The wheat plant stored some of its food in its seed; the tomato plant, in its fruit (the tomato); and the grass, in its leaves.

    A steer ate the grass to obtain food, some of which it stored in its muscles. You ate a spaghetti dinner made from wheat seeds, tomatoes, and beef. In your muscle cells, respiration released energy in the digested food, which was stored in ATP molecules. These molecules reacted with water to release energy in your muscle cells.

7 Chapter Review

Critical Thinking   page 342

1. Silicon can form chemical bonds both with carbon atoms and with other kinds of atoms.

2. A window or chimney damper should be kept open, so that the fuel has a sufficient oxygen supply to burn completely.

3. a. Butane has more chemical bonds since each molecule has 4 times as many carbon atoms and 2.5 times as many hydrogen atoms.

   b. Butane would need more energy—because of the greater number of bonds to be broken.

4. a. 2 carbon atoms.

   b. -ane: only has single covalent bonds between carbon atoms. -ene: at least 1 double bond between 2 carbon atoms. -yne: at least 1 triple bond between 2 carbon atoms.

   c. No. Once a double or triple bond were introduced, the compound would change to an *eth-* formula.

Chapter 8   Waves, Sound, and Light

Chapter 8 Planning Guide				
Planning Your Classroom Lessons				
	8.1 Waves 350–366	**8.2** Properties of Sound 367–380	**8.3** The Wave Model of Sound 381–391	**Chapter 8 Review** 392–393 Chapter 8 Supplements
Content Overview	What waves are, and how they can move through materials such as springs, air, and the surface of water Concept Summary T120 Learning Objectives T120	How sound is produced, how it travels, and the properties that make one sound different from another Concept Summary T121 Learning Objectives T121	The use of a wave model of sound to explain how the properties of sound can be changed, and how sound behaves as it travels through matter Concept Summary T124 Learning Objectives T124	Science Background Information 348 Review of Concepts 392 Essential Ideas/ Chapter 8 Letter to Parents
Teaching Strategies	Getting Started: Ideas for Discussion and Suggested Demonstration T120	Getting Started: Ideas for Discussion and Suggested Demonstration T121	Getting Started: Ideas for Discussion and Suggested Demonstration T124	
Teaching Aids	Teaching Diagram 8-1A, 8-1B Overhead Transparency	Teaching Diagram 8-2A, 8-2B	Teaching Diagram 8-3A, 8-3B	Physical Science Software T00 Physical Science Films and Videos T00 Video Lesson: Sound and Light
Review and Evaluation*	Quick Review 353, 356, 359, 361, 362, 364, 365 8.1 Review 366 Section Testsheet 8-1 TRB 220	Quick Review 368, 370, 372, 374, 375, 377, 378, 379 8.2 Review 380 Section Testsheet 8-2 TRB 221	Quick Review 382, 383, 387, 388, 389 8.3 Review 391 Section Testsheet 8-3 TRB 222	Chapter Testsheets 8A and 8B TRB 255–256 Free Response Questions TRB 000 Semester Test 1 TRB 273–276 *Higher Level Evaluation* Critical Thinking 393

*TESTGEN can be used to prepare customized section and chapter testsheets

Meeting Individual Needs				
Reinforcement	Reading Checksheet 8-1 TRB 100 Skillsheet 8-1 TRB 146 Essential Ideas 8.1	Reading Checksheet 8-2 TRB 101 Skillsheet 8-2 TRB 147 Essential Ideas 8.2	Reading Checksheet 8-3 TRB 102 Skillsheet 8-3 TRB 148 Essential Ideas 8.3	Information Library Software
Enrichment	Research Topic 000 Data Search 362	Research Topic 370, 374, 378 Data Search 371	Research Topic 382, 388 Data Search 385	Individual Research 393 Bibliography 393
Critical Thinking and Problem Solving	Critical Thinking 361 Practice Problems 362 Problems to Solve 366	Critical Thinking 375	Critical Thinking 388	Chapter Testsheet 8B TRB 256 Problem-Solving Worksheets, Chapter 8

Chapter 8 Planning Guide

Developing Laboratory Skills

	8.1 Waves 350–366	8.2 Properties of Sound 367–380	8.3 The Wave Model of Sound 381–391	Chapter 8 Supplements
Plan Ahead	For Activity, page 352: If possible, arrange for the students to perform the activity on slightly sloped surfaces.	For Activity, page 373: Perform the activity yourself to your students unless they have the maturity to use the rubber bands safely. For Investigation, LM 113–114: Gather empty 4-L (gallon) plastic milk jugs, metal baking pans, and sweaters.	For Activity, page 386: Having a spare bottle or two will insure against an accidentally broken one.	
Basic Activities	Travel Through Matter 352 20 minutes Entire class Activity Record Sheet 8-1A, LM 103	Pitch and Length 373 15 minutes Teacher demonstration or groups of 2 Activity Record Sheet 8-2B, LM 110	Length and Frequency 384 20 to 30 minutes Entire class Activity Record Sheet 8-3A, LM 115	
Additional Activities	A Model for a Compressional Wave 355 20 minutes Groups of 2 Activity Record Sheet 8-1B, LM 104 Water Waves 358 20 minutes Groups of 4 Activity Record Sheet 8-1C, LM 105	Sands in Solids 369 10–15 minutes Groups of 2 Activity Record Sheet 8-2A, LM 109 Noisy Backgrounds 376 30–40 minutes Groups of 2 Activity Record Sheet 8-2C, LM 111	Musical Bottles 386 25 to 30 minutes Groups of 8 or demonstration Activity Record Sheet 8-3B, LM 116	Projectsheet 8 TRB 180
Investigations and Research Lab	Investigation 8-1, Beats LM 107–108 30 minutes Groups of 4 or teacher demonstration	Investigation 8-2, A Two-String Guitar LM 113–114 30 minutes Groups of 2 to 4	Investigation 8-3, Measuring Noise Pollution LM 117–118 20 to 30 minutes Groups of 2	Research Lab 8 LM 119–120

Chapter 8   Waves and Sound

8.1 Waves

Concept Summary

A **wave** carries energy from one place to another without transfer of matter.

- In a compressional wave, particles vibrate back and forth in the direction of the wave motion as a series of compressions and rarefactions travel from one place to another.
- In a transverse wave, particles vibrate perpendicular to the direction of the wave motion as a series of crests and troughs travel from one place to another.
- The wavelength of a wave is the distance between neighboring crests or compressions.
- The frequency of a wave is the number of crests or compressions that arrive at a place per second.
- The amplitude of a wave is the distance the particles move from their normal positions as the wave passes.
- The frequency of a wave is determined by the vibration frequency of whatever is producing it.
- The wavelength of a wave depends on both the frequency and the wave speed.
- A wave can be reflected, refracted, or diffracted.
- When two waves reach the same point, they reinforce or cancel each other at that point without change in their own frequency, wavelength, amplitude, or speed.

Learning Objectives

1. To distinguish between compressional and transverse waves.
2. To identify the frequency, wavelength, and amplitude of both compressional and transverse waves.
3. To relate the wavelength to the frequency and the wave speed.
4. To recognize reflection, refraction, diffraction, and interference of waves.

Getting Started

Ideas for Discussion

Students will learn that what they commonly call a wave of water is in fact a wave of energy passing *through* the water.

Ask the class: Have you ever observed the waves that form in the ocean or in a lake? What do you see happening? (Answer: The water appears to move up and down. Near the shore the waves break, or spill over.) Explain that the wave they see is actually a form of energy passing through the water. The individual water molecules do not move forward with the wave, except at the very end when the wave "breaks." Instead they are simply moved up and down by the passage of the wave of energy through the water. Ask them to recall that anything that moves has kinetic energy. A wave provides a way of transporting other forms of energy from one place to another. Light, heat and sound are examples of energy that is transported by waves.

Ask the class to recall ocean waves they have seen. Ask: How do they differ? (Answer: Some are bigger than others, some come in close together, sometimes two waves will collide, other miscellaneous observations.) Explain that all types of waves follow essentially the same rules. In Chapter 8 Section 1 they will learn about the different types of wave motion.

Suggested Demonstration

In this demonstration the students will learn two properties of waves. Energy can travel in a wave through matter without having the matter traveling with it. A wave originating at one point in space travels outward in all directions. For this experiment you will need:
1 set of dominos
rubber ball

Form a cross with the dominos, standing them on end so that as each domino falls, it knocks over the one next to it. An arrangement of four rows of seven works well. Leave a space at the center of the cross slightly smaller than the diameter of the rubber ball. Explain to the class that the rows of dominos represent matter and the rubber ball represents a disturbance that creates a wave of energy. Push the rubber ball into the center of the cross. All four rows of the dominos will topple simultaneously.

Explain that the energy traveled to the end of each row and would have continued if the rows were longer. Explain that waves travel through matter in a similar fashion. They are transmitted through matter without causing the matter itself to travel. To demonstrate that waves travel in all directions from the point of a disturbance, clap your hands loudly. Tell the class you created a sound wave with your hands that moved outward in all directions through the room. Tell the class that in Chapter 8, Section 1 they will study the properties of waves.

Activity 8.1a
Travel Through Matter   page 352

Teaching Hints
Part 1. If student desks are flat rather than sloping slightly toward the student, they may have difficulty keeping the marbles touching. If so, suggest that they put a pencil or small tablet under the top end of the book.

Part 2. Try compressing different numbers of coils and try different amounts of stretch on the spring to see which give the clearest results. Be careful not to stretch the spring so much that it is permanently damaged.

Answers to Questions
1. The fourth marble moved away from the other three.
2. The coil with the yarn moved a short distance in the direction of the compression, then moved back to its original position.
3. As the compression travels along the spring, one coil after the other first moves closer to the next coil and then returns to its original position.
4. Although each coil moved, the spring as a whole did not change its position.
5. Two compressions moved along the spring.
   (See Fig. 8-2)

Conclusion
Answers will vary, but should include energy and or waves (vibrations) or both traveling through both the spring and the marbles. Note: Each coil of the spring transfers energy to the next, just as each marble transfers the energy it received when it was hit to the next marble. However, compressions in the spring are visible, whereas those in the marbles cannot be observed because they occur on an atomic level.

Activity 8.1b
A Model for a Compressional Wave
page 355

Teaching Hints
Step 5. Five more compressions reach the center of the slit. The compressions travel upward in the slit.

Step 6. Students might predict that, when the slit is moved from right to left, the number of compressions reaching the center of the slit is the same as be-

fore. Or, they might predict the compressions will travel in the opposite direction. Both are correct.

Step 8. The short colored line moves up and down, but stays near the center of the slit.

Answers to Questions
1. The compressions moved toward the *right*. There were *three* additional compressions.
2. The compressions moved toward the *left*.
3. The short colored line represents the motion of a single particle in the wave.
4. The frequency was *3* Hz.

Conclusion
One way is that as the wave moved through the short colored line, the line moved up and down but did not move with the wave. Another is that the compressions visibly reacted when the card was moved either top to bottom or bottom to top.

Activity 8.1c
Water Waves   page 358

Answers to Questions
1. The ripple was circular.
2. If the pan is square or rectangular, the reflected ripple will look like parts of circles curved the opposite way from the incoming ripples.
3. The reflected ripple moves back toward the center.
4. Dip the pencil eraser in the water at regular intervals.
5. The bits of paper moved up and down, indicating that the water surface moved up and down as the ripple passed.
6. The ripple moved right past the bits of paper. The paper did not move toward the edge of the pan.

Conclusion
One can infer from the answer to Question 6 that water does not move along with a wave—otherwise, the paper would have been swept to the sides of the pan.

8.1 Section Review

Understanding the Concepts   page 366
21. Both waves have a wavelength and an amplitude.

    In a compressional wave, particles move back and forth along the direction of the wave. In a transverse wave, particles move perpendicular, or crosswise, to the direction of the wave motion.
22. By alternating the frequency of the vibrating source.

Problems to Solve   page 366
23. 6 Hz
24. 3.5 m

8.2 Properties of Sound

Concept Summary

Sound is energy that is produced and transferred by vibrating matter.

- All sounds are caused by vibrations.
- Sound can travel through solids, liquids, and gases.
- Some materials transmit sound better than others do.
- Sound cannot travel where matter is absent.
- The speed of sound depends on the temperature and on the kind of matter carrying the sound.
- Pitch refers to how high or low a sound is.
- Loudness depends on the amount of energy used to make the sound, distance from the source, and pitch.
- Noise can be controlled by restricting the use of its sources and by using materials that absorb sound.
- Lecture halls and concert halls can be designed so that listeners can hear sounds the way they are most acceptable.
- Quality of sound refers to the difference in sounds from two sources even when the loudness and pitch are the same.

Learning Objectives

1. To recognize that sound is a form of energy produced by vibrations.
2. To compare the effect of different materials on the speed of sound.
3. To relate the pitch of sound to the length and thickness of the vibrating object.
4. To identify the conditions that affect the loudness of sound.
5. To recognize ways in which sound can be controlled.
6. To describe the sources of differences in the quality of sounds.

Getting Started

Ideas for Discussion
Students will discuss the effect sound vibrations have on the body.

Ask your students if they have ever been to a rock concert. Was the music so loud that they felt a thumping or vibrating in their chests in response to the rhythm of the music? Tell the students that the sound of the music produces vibrations. These vibrations are what produce a response in their chests and bodies. Explain that deaf people can enjoy music even though they can't hear it, because they can feel the vibrations sound produces.

Ask the class if after experiencing very loud noises, such as those of airplanes taking off or a jackhammer breaking concrete, they experience a temporary loss of hearing. They will probably answer yes. Ask why they think this happens. The ear is very sensitive to sound, and it is overwhelmed by very loud noises. Tell the students that they will learn more about the properties and characteristics of sound in Chapter 8, Section 2.

Suggested Demonstration
Students will learn to measure the distance sound travels and to calculate the speed of sound. You will need the following items for this demonstration:
two wooden blocks about 10 cm × 20 cm × 2 cm
metric tape measure or meter stick
a large outside wall

Take the class outside of the school building and find a wall that faces an open area. Have them form a line facing the wall. Stand in the middle of the line with the students. Tell the students that when you clap the blocks together, they are to listen for an echo. Start about 25 m from the wall. Clap the wooden blocks together. If the students hear an echo, have the entire line move a few meters closer to the wall. Clap the blocks again. Repeat this procedure until the line formed by you and the class agrees that an echo can no longer be heard.

Use the metric tape measure or meter stick to measure the distance between the wall and the place where the echo is no longer heard. Tell the class that the time needed for sound to travel from this point to the wall and back is about 0.10 second. Ask the students to calculate the total distance the sound traveled during this time. The total distance is twice the distance from the wall to the line of students. For example, 17 m × 2 equals 34 m. Ask the students to determine the speed of sound. Example, 34m/0.10s equals 340 m/s. Tell the students that the speed of sound in air is a property of sound.

Activity 8.2a
Sounds in Solids   page 369

Answers to Questions
1. Students probably will not hear the ticking of the watch when it is held at arm's length.
2. Students should be able to hear the ticking of the watch through a wooden dowel. With some watches, the sound of the balance-wheel spring can also be heard.
3. The ticking and spring noises should also be heard through a metal rod.
4. The metal rod should be the best carrier of sound, and wood second best.
5. The ringing should be louder and deeper when the string is pressed against their ear.
6. The ringing can be heard through the string when it cannot be heard through the air.
7. The taut string is a better carrier of sound than air is.

Conclusion
Of the materials tested, the solids were the best sound conductors (and metal was better than wood).

Activity 8.2b
Pitch and Length   page 373

Teaching Hints
STRETCHED RUBBER BANDS CAN BE DANGEROUS. We recommend that this activity be done as a demonstration unless your class has the maturity to use the rubber bands safely. Also, faces should be kept away from the vibrating rulers since they break very easily and if they do, they may send bits of plastic flying through the air.

This activity can be enhanced by repeating Steps 1 through 5 with other materials which you might have on hand, e.g., a wooden ruler, plastic knife, and chopstick.

Answers to Questions
1. The pitch of the sound produced rises as the length decreases.
2. The pitch of the sound produced falls as the length increases.
3. The pitch of the sound produced rises as the length decreases.

Conclusion
As the length of the vibrating portion of the ruler or rubber band decreased, the pitch of the sound rose. As the length of the vibrating portion increased, the pitch of the sound fell.

Activity 8.2c
Noisy Backgrounds   page 376

Teaching Hints
If portable tape recorders or radios are used, students should use talking rather than music for their sound comparisons because there will probably be less variation in loudness. Also, the volume control knob should be kept in one place during all of the trials.

Answers to Questions
1. The number of times farther away one can be and hear the clock against a quiet background rather than a noisy one will vary with the places chosen and the air stillness.
2. You raise your voice when you try to talk to someone against a noisy background and others around do the same thing, making the background still noisier.
3. Possible answers include irritation and fatigue.

Conclusion
It is harder to hear a particular sound against a noisy background than against a quiet background.

8.2 Section Review

Understanding the Concepts   page 380
15. The hand stops the sound because it stops the bell from vibrating.
16. The sound of the explosion would not reach the earth because the space between the sun and the earth is empty. Empty space does not carry sound.
17. The noise level near jet runways is above that of the loudest sound the ear can hear without pain. It is also above the noise level of sounds that can cause damage to the ear. The sound insulator in the ear muffs decreases the noise level near jet runways for those wearing the ear muffs.
18. The answer will depend on measures already taken to reduce noice. Some possible ways of reducing sound would be to install drapes, carpeting, and rough-textured ceiling tile. If one can hear from room to room, insulating materials in the walls will help to reduce noise.

8.3 The Wave Model of Sound

Concept Summary

The **wave model of sound** is the theory that sound is energy that travels in a compressional wave.
- Amplitude is related to loudness.
- Frequency is related to pitch.
- Combinations of frequencies are related to quality.
- The frequency of a sound wave appears to change when either the source or the listener is moving.

Learning Objectives

1. To use the wave model of sound to explain the behavior of sound.
2. To relate the pitch of a sound to the frequency of the compressional sound wave.
3. To relate the loudness of a sound to the amplitude of the compressional sound wave.
4. To use the wave model of sound to explain the Doppler effect.

Getting Started

Ideas for Discussion

The class will learn through demonstrations how different tones are created by musical instruments.

Ask members of your class who play musical instruments to talk to the class about how their instrument produces sound. (If possible have them bring them in to show the class.) Have them describe how different notes are produced, how to play louder and softer, short notes and long notes (staccato and legato). Have the class analyze and compare the way each type of instrument produces sound. Have them come up with a short description of each process and write it on the board. (Woodwinds; sound comes from a vibrating reed, then is passed through an air column of a length that can be closed or opened with keys. Brass and flute; sound comes from the player's vibrating lips, then is passed through an air column of an adjustable length similar to woodwinds. Stringed instruments; sound is produced by plucking, bowing or striking taut strings of varying thicknesses, the tension of which can be changed.)

Ask: Why does the same note played on different instruments sound different? Why can an electronic synthesizer produce a sound identical to the instruments above? Explain that the answers to these questions can be explained by the wave model of sound which is the subject of Chapter 8, Section 3.

Suggested Demonstration

In this demonstration the students will learn how sound can be amplified. For this experiment you will need the following items:

long, loose wire spring, such as a Slinky

cup hook

small block of wood (not thicker than 1 cm)

large paper cup, or cylindrical ice cream carton (32 oz size); be sure it is clean and dry; do not use plastic containers

pencil

Construct the apparatus by placing the block of wood inside the container, flush against the bottom. From the outside, screw the cup hook through the bottom of the container and into the block of wood. Slip the cup hook through one end of the wire coil. Place the wire coil on its side and pull it so it is loosely stretched out.

Ask the class: What are some ways to make a sound louder? (Likely response will be "turn it up.") Explain that putting more energy into production of the sound is one way. Ask: What are some other ways? Give the example of trying to call to a friend outside during lunch or passing period. Ask: What do you do if the friend doesn't hear you? (Answer: Yell louder and at some point cup your hands around your mouth while you yell in the direction of your friend.) Ask: What does cupping your hands around your mouth do? (Answer: It focuses the sound of your voice in the direction of your friend, so even though you are not yelling louder, you are more easily heard.)

Explain that there is yet another way to make sound louder or *amplified*. Show the class the device you have constructed. Tell them that it amplifies sound in a similar manner to any speaker found in a TV, radio, or stereo. Show them the coil and how it connects to the container, which in this case is analogous to the "horn" found in speakers. Review with the class how sound is initiated. (A column of air is set to vibrating by a vibrating source.) Explain that the larger the column of air set into vibration by a source, the louder the sound will be.

Detach the coil from the cup hook and tap a turn of it with a pencil. (A metallic tapping sound will be heard.) Reattach the coil and tap it with the pencil again. (This time a loud whining sound will come from the container.) Explain that this occurs because the container sets a great deal more air vibrating than does the wire alone. Thus the sound of the wire is amplified when it is connected to the container. Tell the class that all these behaviors of sound, as well as the others they have studied, can be explained by the wave model of sound. Chapter 8, Section 3 will explain the features of this model.

Activity 8.3a
Length and Frequency   page 384

Teaching Hints
Cut the strings so that the lengths are fairly evenly distributed (e.g. at 5-cm intervals) from 15 cm to 150 cm. Be sure to include both the 15 cm and 150 cm lengths.

Have students all start their pendulums at about the same relatively small angle (30° or less from the vertical).

Since you are essentially making a graph on the chalkboard, the numbers on the scale representing frequency should be uniformly spaced.

Answers to Questions
1. The pendulums should be in order of length. If any are out of place, students may wish to test them again.
2. The bottom of the pendulums should not be in a straight line. One can, however, connect the bottoms of the pendulums with a smooth line which turns out to be a hyperbolic curve.
3. Below 20 swings per minute the curve drops steeply. A pendulum that makes only one swing per minute would be about 900 m long!
4. The longest pendulums have the lowest frequencies.

Conclusion
The longer a pendulum is, the lower is its frequency, the shorter a pendulum is, the higher is its frequency. (For your information, the frequency of a pendulum is directly proportional to the square root of its length. The frequency is independent of the mass of the bob and, for small swings, of the length of the swing.)

Going Further
Obviously, students will be unable to make a pendulum long enough (900 m) to make only one swing per minute!

Activity 8.3b
Musical Bottles   page 386

Teaching Hints
A pitch pipe or a musical instrument brought in by a student can be used to help you to determine one octave.

Step 3. Encourage students to justify their predictions. If students hypothesize that the bottle is vibrating, they should predict that the bottle will not hum when one holds it, just as one cannot whistle while holding a finger on the center of one lip. In actuality, students should hear the hum whether or not they are holding the bottle.

Step 5. For notes that are one octave apart, the lengths of the air columns should differ by a factor of two.

Step 6. When students measure the height of the water column, have them measure from the bottom of the water and not from the bottom of the bottle. After the students have made the measurements, you may wish to suggest that each of eight students hold a different bottle. Have them blow across the mouths of the bottles to play a scale. HEALTH NOTE: Have enough bottles for each student to use one, or sterilize bottles between students with a thorough swabbing with rubbing alcohol.

Answers to Questions
1. The pitch rose as the water height increased.
2. The pitch rose as the height of the air column decreased.
3. The air column acted more like a vibrating string or rubber band; the longer the air column, the lower the pitch. The pitch changes in the opposite direction as the height of the water is increased.

Conclusion
The column of air inside the bottle was vibrating, not the bottle. If it had been the bottle, the humming sound would have disappeared when the bottle was held. Furthermore, the pitch rose as the air column was shortened, in keeping with the relationship between length and pitch for a vibrating string.

8.3 Section Review

Understanding the Concepts   page 391
13. The sound should be heard farther away through the pipe. Sound waves that move through the air spread out in all directions and decrease in amplitude fairly rapidly. Sound waves move through a pipe in basically one direction, so there is little decrease in amplitude. (There is some, because some of the energy is lost to the surrounding air.)
14. The frequency of the A used in tuning up an orchestra is 440 Hz. The frequency of the note one octave below the A used is 220 Hz. The frequency of the note one octave above the A used is 880 Hz.
15. The glass shattered because the sound waves from the stereo had a high frequency (resonance). This resonance, coupled with the ability of sound to travel through solids, was enough to cause the fine crystal glass to shatter.

8 Chapter Review

Critical Thinking   *page 392*

1. Changes in composition could change the speed and direction of these waves.
2. The particles in the material vibrate as the sound waves move through the material but do not travel with the wave.
3. The intensity or amplitude of the sound wave is reduced as the wave moves away from the source.
4. Yes, singers must produce overtones when they sing, because two people sound different even when they try to sing exactly the same thing. The overtones give the voice its own identity.
5. Highway noises could be reduced by using sound-absorbing materials in the office buildings and by keeping the windows closed. Trees and shrubbery between the highway and the office building could also reduce the sound.
6. The frequency of sound waves reaching your ear when the source moves away from you is lower than when the source is stationary.

Notes

Chapter 9   Light

	Chapter 9 Planning Guide
	Planning Your Classroom Lessons
	9.1 Properties of Light 396–421	**9.2** Color 422–432	**9.3** Models for Light 433–443	**Chapter 9 Review** 444–445 Chapter 9 Supplements
Content Overview	Familiar behavior of light, including reflection by mirrors and refraction by lenses Concept Summary T130 Learning Objectives T130	The behavior of colored light, and how colors are perceived by humans and animals Concept Summary T132 Learning Objectives T132	Light as the energy carried by a transverse wave; also, light as a stream of energy particles (photons) Concept Summary T134 Learning Objectives T134	Science Background Information 394 Review of Concepts 444 Essential Ideas/ Chapter 9 Letter to Parents
Teaching Strategies	Getting Started: Ideas for Discussion and Suggested Demonstration T130	Getting Started: Ideas for Discussion and Suggested Demonstration T132	Getting Started: Ideas for Discussion and Suggested Demonstration T134	
Teaching Aids	Teaching Diagram 9-1A, 9-1B Overhead Transparency	Teaching Diagram 9-2A, 9-2B	Teaching Diagram 9-3A, 9-3B	Physical Science Software T00 Physical Science Films and Videos T00 Video Lesson: Sound and Light
Review and Evaluation*	Quick Review 397, 403, 407, 410, 414, 419 9.1 Review 00 Section Testsheet 9-1 TRB 223	Quick Review 423, 425, 427, 429, 430 9.2 Review 00 Section Testsheet 9-2 TRB 224	Quick Review 434, 439, 442 9.3 Review 00 Section Testsheet 9-3 TRB 225	Chapter Testsheets 9A and 9B TRB 257–258 Free Response Questions TRB 000 Semester Test 1 TRB 273–276 *Higher Level Evaluation* Critical Thinking 444–445

*TESTGEN can be used to prepare customized section and chapter testsheets

	Meeting Individual Needs
Reinforcement	Reading Checksheet 9-1 TRB 103 Skillsheet 9-1 TRB 149 Essential Ideas 9.1	Reading Checksheet 9-2 TRB 104 Skillsheet 9-2 TRB 150 Essential Ideas 9.2	Reading Checksheet 9-3 TRB 105 Skillsheet 9-3 TRB 151 Essential Ideas 9.3	Information Library Software
Enrichment	Research Topic 396, 419 Data Search 397, 418, 419	Research Topic 425, 426	Research Topic 436, 437, 442	Individual Research 445 Bibliography 445 Issues in Physical Science: Better Vision Through Radial Keratotomy 446 Trends in Technology: Holography and its Applications 447
Critical Thinking and Problem Solving	Critical Thinking 397, 400, 404, 410, 411 Practice Problems 406, 407, 414		Critical Thinking 442	Chapter Testsheet 9B TRB 258 Problem-Solving Worksheets, Chapter 9

Chapter 9 Planning Guide

Developing Laboratory Skills

	9.1 Properties of Light 396–421	9.2 Color 422–432	9.3 Models for Light 433–443	Chapter 9 Supplements
Plan Ahead	For Activity, page 402: Gather small, flat mirrors. For Activity, page 408: Obtain a transparent rectangular waterproof container.	For Activity, page 428: Gather colored cellophane and construction paper.	For Activity, page 440: Obtain polarizing filters or polarizing sunglasses.	

Basic Activities	Mirror Images 402
	  20 minutes
	  Groups of 2 or 3
	Activity Record Sheet
	  9-1A, LM 121
		Using Colored Light/
		  Combining Colors 428
		  30 minutes
		  Groups of 4 or teacher demonstration
		Activity Record Sheet
		  9-2A, LM 125
			Diffraction 437
			  20 minutes
			  Groups of 2 or 3
			Activity Record Sheet
			  9-3A, LM 129	

Additional Activities	Bending of Light 408
	  15 minutes
	  Groups of 4
	Activity Record Sheet
	  9-1B, LM 122
		Benham's Disks 431
		  30 to 40 minutes
		  Groups of 2 or 3
		Activity Record Sheet
		  9-2B, LM 126
			Polarizing Filters 440
			  15 minutes
			  Groups of 3 or 4
			Activity Record Sheet
			  9-3B, LM 130
				Projectsheet 9 TRB 181

Investigations and Research Lab	Investigation 9-1,
	  Focal Length of Convex Lenses LM 123–124
	  30 minutes
	  Groups of 4
		Investigation 9-2,
		  The Color Spectrum LM 127–128
		  40 minutes
		  Groups of 4 or 5
			Investigation 9-3,
			  Energy and the Colors of Light LM 131–132
			  30 minutes
			  Groups of 4
				Research Lab 9 LM 133–134

Chapter 9   Light

9.1 Properties of Light

Concept Summary

Light is energy that can be detected by the eye.
- Matter may be a source of light, or it may transmit, reflect, or absorb light.
- Light is reflected from a mirror or shiny surface at an angle equal to the angle at which the light strikes the surface.
- The path of light bends as light moves from one substance to another. The degree of bending is different for different substances and is indicated by the index of refraction.
- Light travels at extremely high speed—close to 3×10^8 m/s in empty space.
- Light generally appears dimmer as the observer moves away from the source. An exception is laser light.

Electromagnetic radiation is any kind of energy that behaves as light does and travels at the speed of light, but which may have a frequency higher or lower than visible light.
- Electromagnetic radiation includes gamma radiation, X-rays, ultraviolet light, visible light, infrared radiation, microwaves, and radio waves.

Learning Objectives

1. To identify the different ways in which light interacts with matter.
2. To describe how images are formed by mirrored surfaces.
3. To describe how images are formed by lenses, including the lens of the human eye.
4. To recognize that the bending of light (refraction) is the result of the changing of the speed of light in different substances.
5. To relate the brightness of a light source to its distance from a light source.
6. To identify the types of radiation that are a part of the electromagnetic spectrum.

Getting Started

Ideas for Discussion
Students learn to recognize the ways light sources interact with matter.

Ask your students to name as many sources of light as they can. They might name such sources as the sun, the moon, the stars, a light bulb, or the reflections in a mirror or in a lake. List these light sources on the board. Tell the students that there are three ways light can interact with matter. Matter can transmit light, or it may be transparent. Matter can reflect light, in which case the matter is visible. Light can be absorbed by matter. This would cause objects to appear dark. Ask the students to classify the light sources listed on the board into one of these three categories. Ask why the brightest moonlight is dark compared to sunlight. The moon reflects the light of the sun. The moon does not create its own light. Tell the students that in Chapter 9, Section 1 they will study the behavior of light.

Suggested Demonstration
Students learn the law of reflection and how it relates to the angle of incidence and the angle of reflection. You will need the following items for this demonstration:
large rectangular mirror
large protractor
pencil or popsicle stick
black construction paper
flashlight or slide projector

Mask the lens of the light with black paper into which a 5 mm hole has been cut. This creates a more intense beam. Ask the students to explain how to bounce a ball off a wall so that it will come straight back to them. They should explain that the best way is to stand facing the wall and throw the ball straight at it. What happens if you don't throw the ball straight? It bounces off the wall at an angle.

Tell the students that light behaves in a similar manner when it bounces off a flat surface. The way light behaves is summarized in the *law of reflection*. Explain that you will demonstrate the law of reflection. Ask a student to hold the mirror on a table in an upright position. Lay the protractor flat on the table along the bottom edge of the mirror. Explain to the students that the protractor is used to measure angles. Darken the room and shine the beam of light on the mirror at an angle. Ask the students to observe the path of the light beam before and after it strikes the mirror. Place the pencil or popsicle stick at the point where the light beam strikes the mirror. The stick should be perpendicular to the mirror, that is, 90° on the protractor. Measure the angle between the perpendicular stick and the beam of light that strikes the mirror. Write the angle on the board. Explain that this is called the *angle of incidence*. Measure the angle between the perpendicular stick and the beam of light that comes from the mirror. Explain that this is the *angle of reflection*. Ask what the relationship is between these two angles. They are the same. Would you expect the two angles to differ from each other if you move the light source to a different angle? The students should answer that the angle of the incoming light beam will be the same as the angle of the outgoing light beam.

Move the light source and measure the angles again to verify the class's prediction. Ask the class to state the law of reflection. *The angle of incidence is equal to the angle of reflection.* Tell the class that the law of reflection is one of the rules that govern the behavior of light. In Chapter 7, Section 1 they will be introduced to these rules.

Activity 9.1a
Mirror Images   page 402

Teaching Hints
Step 6. The reflecting surface is usually the back surface of a mirror.

Step 9. When the cards are properly aligned, the image should look like a continuation of the rear card.

Step 11. The image and rear card remain the same size as you move away from the mirror.

Answers to Questions
1. The image position does not depend on the position of the observer.
2. As the object is moved farther from the mirror, the position of the image moves farther from the mirror. Students can relate the position of their images in a mirror to their distances from the mirror. When they move farther away, their images appear to be farther behind the mirror.

Conclusion
The position of the image is the same distance from the mirror as the position of the object.

Activity 9.1b
Bending of Light   page 408

Answers to Questions
1. The light bent away from the side of the container as it entered the water.
2. The light bent toward the side of the container as it left the water.
3. The angles measured in Steps 10 and 11 should have been equal.
4. The light was traveling the same direction when it left the water as it was when it entered the water.

Conclusion
No. The light bent in one direction (away from the side of the container) when it went from air to water and in the other direction (toward the side of the container) when it went from water back to air.

9.1 Section Review

Understanding the Concepts   page 421

27. Unlike air, glass is not completely transparent. About 8% of the light striking glass is reflected rather than transmitted. On a sunny day, the reflected light is bright enough to be seen against the dimmer light coming through the window from inside.
28. The wheel that rolls onto the linoleum first moves faster than the wheels remaining on the carpet. The stroller turns so that it is moving more parallel to the edge of the carpet. It behaves like light that moves from water or glass into air.
29. Metal pans are not used because metal reflects microwaves. Dishes made of paper or china are used. These materials transmit microwaves, but absorb little of their energy and so do not get hot.

Problems to Solve   page 421

30.
$$\frac{1}{10 \text{ cm}} + \frac{1}{d_i} = \frac{1}{6 \text{ cm}}$$

$$\frac{1}{d_i} = \frac{1}{6 \text{ cm}} - \frac{1}{10 \text{ cm}}$$

$$\frac{1}{d_i} = \frac{5}{30 \text{ cm}} - \frac{3}{30 \text{ cm}}$$

$$\frac{1}{d_i} = \frac{2}{30 \text{ cm}}$$

$$\frac{1}{d_i} = \frac{1}{15 \text{ cm}}$$

$$d_i = 15 \text{ cm}$$

$$\frac{10 \text{ cm}}{15 \text{ cm}} = \frac{4 \text{ cm}}{s_i}$$

$$\frac{10 \text{ cm}}{15 \times 4 \text{ cm}} = \frac{1}{s_i}$$

$$\frac{1}{s_i} = \frac{10}{60}$$

$$s_i = \frac{60}{10}$$

$$s_i = 6$$

31. Index of refraction in substance = $\dfrac{\text{speed of light in vacuum}}{\text{speed of light in substance}}$

$$= \frac{3.0 \times 10^8 \text{ m/s}}{1.5 \times 10^8 \text{ m/s}}$$

$$= 2.0$$

9.2 Color

Concept Summary

White light is a combination of light of all colors.

- The color of an object depends on both the object itself and on the colors of the light striking the object.
- The ability to distinguish among colors of light is limited to humans and only a few other animals.
- White light can be dispersed into colors because different colors are diffracted to different degrees.

Learning Objectives

1. To recognize that an object's color, in most cases, is due to the light reflected by the object.
2. To understand how white light is dispersed into a color spectrum.
3. To explain how the eye "sees" colored objects.
4. To describe how the blue appearances of the sky and water are produced.

Getting Started

Ideas for Discussion
Students learn that the colors they perceive depend on the kind of light that is present.

Ask your class if they ever purchased an article of clothing and found that it was not the same color in the daylight as it appeared to be in the store. Allow the students to discuss their experiences. Ask if the clothing actually changed color. Color would change only if it faded. What changed that made the color seem different? The light in the store is different than daylight. The students may be familiar with many examples of this type of color change. For example, makeup that appears flattering in candle light may appear garish and clown-like outdoors. Some grocery stores have special lighting at their meat counters to make the meat appear bright red. Photos and paintings sometimes show the tropics in colors that appear unnatural to people living in temperate zones.

Explain that the colors we perceive are dependent on the light an object reflects. If the light changes, we perceive a different color than we observed previously. Tell the students that in Chapter 9, Section 2 they will learn how white light is separated into colors. They will learn how humans and animals perceive color.

Suggested Demonstration
Students will learn how the amount and kind of light changes their perception of color. They will learn how flowers in sunlight look to a bee. You will need the following items:
black light or flashlight with lens covered with dark blue or deep purple cellophane
multi-colored bouquet of flowers

Separate the flowers by color and type. Set them where all the students can see them. Have the class determine the color of each one. On the board, write the name of each flower and its color. This provides an opportunity to discuss color-blindness and the different color-vision that occurs in people. Tell the class that in order for our eyes to perceive color, we need light. Darken the room as much as possible. When the students' eyes have adjusted to the dark, ask what changes took place in the colors. The color will fade considerably. If the room is dark enough the students will be able to perceive only shades of gray.

Tell the class that the receptors in our eyes that perceive color are called *cones* and they work only in bright light. Explain that in dim light, receptors called *rods* take over. Rods perceive black and white. Explain that most mammals have only rods and see everything in shades of black, white, and grey. Tell the class you are going to show them how flowers look to a bee. Turn on the black light and shine it on each flower. Ask the class how the colors under black light compare to the colors they perceived in bright light. The colors will look different. In some flowers, particularly the white ones, unseen patterns will appear.

Write the comparisons on the board that the students mention. Explain to the class that bees perceive the ultraviolet radiation reflected by these flowes in normal sunlight, and they are attracted to them. Turn the lights on and ask the students to re-evaluate their initial observations of the colors of the flowers. Tell them that in Chapter 9, Section 2 they will learn more about color and color perception.

Activity 9.2a
Using Colored Light and Combining
Colors   page 428

Teaching Hints

Part 1. The activity provides an opportunity to relate the color of the light striking an object to the colors of light absorbed and reflected by the object.

The red cellophane transmits red light. Under this light, the red paper appears more like the white paper. The green and blue papers will probably appear more like the black paper. The exact appearance of the papers will depend on how effectively the cellophane filters out light of the colors normally reflected by the paper.

Part 2. By moving the three sources back and forth, students should be able to combine red, green, and blue light to form white light.

Answers to Questions.
1. White paper reflects all colors. Black absorbs all colors.
2. Red paper reflects red light and absorbs all other colors. Green paper reflects green light and absorbs the others. Likewise, blue paper reflects blue light and absorbs all others.
3. Yes, red, green, and blue light can be combined to form white light.
4. Blue and green light produce cyan (blue-green). Blue and red light produce magenta (purple-pink). Red and green light produce yellow. Orange can be produced by the right proportions of red and green light. Purple is produced from blue and red light.

Conclusion

White light contains all colors of light. Therefore, the color an object appears will depend on the colors which it reflects and the colors it absorbs.

Activity 9.2b
Benham's Disks   page 431

Teaching Hints

Allow 20 to 30 minutes for the preparation of the disks. The remaining time should be sufficient to observe the color patterns produced by the spinning disks.

Perceptions will vary from person to person. The most common responses are given in *Answers to Questions.*

Answers to Questions
1. During a clockwise spin, red is on the inner circle and dark green or blue is on the outer circle. The colors reverse when the spin direction is reversed.
2. During a clockwise spin, the colors seen in order from the edge to the center are dark blue, green, yellow, and red. The colors are in reverse order when the spin direction is reversed.

Conclusion

Answers will vary, but should include the idea that human color vision is actually very complex.

9.2 Section Review

Understanding the Concepts   page 432
15. The produce will appear more green, and the meat will appear more red.
16. No, you cannot get sunburned through a closed window. Sunburn is caused by ultraviolet radiation, which cannot reach you.
17. The absence of particles above the earth's atmosphere prevents any scattering of the sun's light.

9.3 Models for Light

Concept Summary

The **wave model of light** describes light as energy that travels as a transverse wave.

- The pattern produced when light passes through a tiny double slit is evidence for light as a wave.
- The polarization of light is evidence for light as a transverse wave.
- The colors of light can be explained by the hypothesis that each color in white light has a different wavelength and, therefore, a different frequency.

The **particle model of light** is the theory that light consists of energy particles called photons.

- The photoelectric effect is evidence for light as particles.
- The colors of light can be explained by the hypothesis that each color corresponds to photons of a different energy.
- Neither the wave model alone, nor the particle model alone, can explain all the known behaviors of light.

Learning Objectives

1. To recognize that light is a form of energy and travels from place to place.
2. To compare the particle and wave models of light and the properties of light that support each model.
3. To gain an appreciation of the dual, wave-particle nature of light.

Ideas for Discussion
Students will learn how released energy can take the form of heat and light.

Discuss with your class the question: Why does a fire give off light? The students may recall seeing films of torchlight processions, or may have had occasion to try and read by candlelight or the light of a campfire. Review with the class the chemical reaction of burning, or combustion. Burning wood combines with oxygen in the air to produce carbon dioxide, water vapor and a few other products. In so doing it releases the energy that was stored in the chemical bonds of the wood. This released energy takes the form of heat and light. Ask: What other type of energy can give off light? (Answer: Electric energy, for example, when an electric plug is pulled from its plug a bright spark leaps out.) Tell the class that Chapter 9, Section 3 will explain the ways light energy travels through space and interacts with matter.

Suggested Demonstration
In this demonstration the students will observe a light-induced chemical reaction as an example of the absorption of light energy by matter. For this experiment you will need the following items:

several sheets blueprint paper

If not readily available, blue print paper may be prepared in the following manner: Prepare a 20% solution of ferric ammonium citrate and a 16% (w/v) solution of potassium ferricyanide. These solutions are very light sensitive and must be prepared in low light. Mix equal parts of each solution together and, using a paintbrush, coat several pieces of duplicator or typing paper (any nonabsorbent paper will do). Paint each paper twice, once in each direction, and let dry in a dark place. SAFETY NOTE: *Be sure to wash hands afterwards.*

Materials to image: buttons, coins, keys, cut-out letters and shapes, old black and white photo negatives, wire jewelry, etc. Light source: sunny window, or incandescent bulb.

Tell the class that the behaviors of light they have observed so far are examples of light behaving as a wave. Ask: What are these behaviors? (Answers: reflection, refraction and diffraction.) Explain that you are going to demonstrate a situation in which light behaves as a particle. Light behaves as a particle when it is absorbed by matter. Pull out the blueprint paper and explain that it is coated with a solution of a chemical that absorbs and reacts to light. When it absorbs light energy, it undergoes a chemical change that causes it to turn bright blue and become insoluble in water. Place the materials you wish to image on the paper and place it under the light source. After a few seconds it will change color. Remove the paper from the light source and take off the items you placed on it. Then rinse the entire paper in clear water and show it to the class. The area of the paper that was covered by the items, or the dark parts of the photo negative, will remain white so that an image of each item will be produced.

Tell the class that this process is analogous to what happens on photographic film. Explain that the absorption of light energy by chemical compounds is one illustration of the existence of light particles or *photons*. Tell the class that Chapter 9, Section 3 will compare the behavior of light as predicted by the wave model and the particle model.

Activity 9.3a
Diffraction   page 437

Answers to Questions

1. The spectrum produced by a normal light bulb is brighter in the longer wavelength regions—the red and yellow. The spectrum produced by a fluorescent light source is brighter at the shorter wavelength end of the visible spectrum—blue and violet. The spectrum of the fluorescent source may contain bright discrete lines in the yellow, green, and purple ranges.

2. The spectra will now be oriented vertically and will be very narrow. The width of the spectrum band will correspond to the width of the slit. In the other orientation, this dimension corresponded to the length of the slit.

Conclusion

The bright discrete lines in the fluorescent spectrum indicate that the fluorescent light contains a significant amount of light in particular, discrete wavelengths. This, in fact, is the case and is a function of the way in which fluorescent light is produced.

Activity 9.3b
Polarizing Filters   page 440

Teaching Hints

The brightness of the light source is reduced by about half by the polarizing filter. Rotating the single filter does not further change the brightness if the source is not polarized.

The use of two filters turned in the right positions (with their transmission axes at right angles to each other) should block out nearly all of the light from the source. Turning one filter a quarter turn should make the light nearly as bright as it appears through only one filter.

A single polarizing filter will block out much of the shine from a horizontal reflecting surface when the transmission axis of the filter is vertical. The reflected light in glare is largely polarized in the horizontal direction. As they rotate the filter, students should find one position for which the shine just about disappears. If they then rotate the filter a quarter turn (so that the transmission axis is horizontal), the maximum amount of shine will pass through the filter.

Answers to Questions

1. No, because the brightness did not change as the polarizing filter was rotated.

2. Yes, because the brightness changed as the polarizing filter was rotated.

3. Yes, the polarizing material in sunglasses should be placed so that it reduces glare from horizontal surfaces since the surfaces of roads and water are basically horizontal. If the material were turned one quarter turn, it would have little effect on road or water glare.

Conclusion

Light can be polarized with a polarizing filter or by reflection.

Going Further

Yes. Light is transmitted through the three-filter combination.

9.3 Section Review

Understanding the Concepts   *page 443*

16. Light behaves as a water wave when it reflects, refracts, and interferes with itself after passing through a double slit.

17. Radio waves and light waves travel at the same speed, but they have different frequencies and wave lengths.

18. The photons of ultraviolet light have more energy than the photons of infrared radiation because ultraviolet light has the higher frequency

19. The photoelectric effect is the release of electrons from a metal surface in response to incident light. The maximum energy of the released electrons was found to be independent of the intensity of the incident light. The maximum intensity depended only on the frequency of the incident light. These findings were not consistent with the wave model of light which predicted that the maximum energy of the released electrons should depend on the intensity of the incident light, just as the maximum energy imparted to a pebble on the beach would depend on the intensity of the water wave that struck it. An explanation of the photoelectric effect depended on the development of the particle model of light.

20. Not all the properties of light can be explained by either the wave model alone or the particle model alone. Both models of light have to be used at present to explain all the behaviors of light.

9 Chapter Review

Critical Thinking   page 444

1. No, light does not always travel in a straight line. Light changes direction when it moves from one substance to another, when it bounces off a surface, when it passes through a tiny opening, and when it is scattered by molecules in air.

2. The apparent brightness of a star does change with distance, but stars also vary in their actual brightness. A very bright star could be farther away than a star of very low brightness if its actual brightness is greater.

3. The lighting in the store may emphasize different colors than sunlight or the lights in your home. As a result, the clothing will reflect different amounts of the different colors under the different lights. (Store lighting has a higher proportion of orange and yellow light than sunlight does.)

4. Accept any answer that shows an understanding of how polarizing filters work. If the windshields of automobiles are made of a polarizing material, 50% of the light from oncoming headlights would be filtered out. Light reflected back from the road by the driver's own headlights must be reflected from tiny, almost vertical surfaces on the rough surface of the road. (More horizontal surfaces would not send the light back to the driver.) Thus, the reflected light will be somewhat polarized in the vertical direction. If the transmission axis of the windshield is vertical, this light can pass through.

5. White material reflects all colors of available light. By wearing white you maximize the amount of light that will be reflected from you to any oncoming traffic.

6. If the eyeball is too long, images are focused in front of the retina—nearsightedness. If the eyeball is too short, images are focused behind the retina—farsightedness.

7. The ability to distinguish color makes it easier to find food and to detect the presence of danger. Other answers are possible.

8. The fuzziness is the result of diffraction.

9. Black. Because black absorbs all colors of light, it will seem "invisible" hanging in the air.

Notes

Chapter 10   Electric Charges and Currents

	Chapter 10 Planning Guide			
	Planning Your Classroom Lessons			
	10.1 Electric Charges 452–462	**10.2** Electric Currents 463–476	**10.3** Electric Circuits 477–491	**Chapter 10 Review** 492–493 Chapter 10 Supplements
Content Overview	The different ways that charged objects are produced and the nature of the forces that exist between them Concept Summary T140 Learning Objectives T140	The types of electric currents and the measurements used to compare amounts of current, voltage, resistance, and power Concept Summary T142 Learning Objectives T142	The effects of changing the arrangement of circuit elements and the use of safety devices in circuits Concept Summary T144 Learning Objectives T144	Science Background Information 450 Review of Concepts 492 Essential Ideas/ Chapter 10 Letter to Parents
Teaching Strategies	Getting Started: Ideas for Discussion and Suggested Demonstration T140	Getting Started: Ideas for Discussion and Suggested Demonstration T142	Getting Started: Ideas for Discussion and Suggested Demonstration T144	
Teaching Aids	Teaching Diagram 10-1A, 10-1B Overhead Transparency	Teaching Diagram 10-2A, 10-2B	Teaching Diagram 10-3A, 10-3B	Physical Science Software T00 Physical Science Films and Videos T00 Video Lesson: Electricity and Electromagnetism
Review and Evaluation*	Quick Review 453, 457, 458, 460, 461 10.1 Review 00 Section Testsheet 10-1 TRB 226	Quick Review 465, 467, 468, 471, 475 10.2 Review 00 Section Testsheet 10-2 TRB 227	Quick Review 479, 482, 484, 487 10.3 Review 00 Section Testsheet 10-3 TRB 228	Chapter Testsheets 10A and 10B TRB 259–260 Free Response Questions TRB 000 Semester Test 1 TRB 273–276 *Higher Level Evaluation* Critical Thinking 492–493

*TESTGEN can be used to prepare customized section and chapter testsheets

	Meeting Individual Needs			
Reinforcement	Reading Checksheet 10-1 TRB 106 Skillsheet 10-1 TRB 152 Essential Ideas 10.1	Reading Checksheet 10-2 TRB 107 Skillsheet 10-2 TRB 153 Essential Ideas 10.2	Reading Checksheet 10-3 TRB 108 Skillsheet 10-3 TRB 154 Essential Ideas 10.3	Information Library Software
Enrichment	Research Topic 460, 461 Data Search 455	Research Topic 464, 466, 474 Data Search 470	Research Topic 478, 484, 488 Data Search 487	Individual Research 493 Bibliography 493
Critical Thinking and Problem Solving	Critical Thinking 457	Critical Thinking 468, 471 Practice Problems 475	Critical Thinking 481, 489	Chapter Testsheet 10B TRB 260 Problem-Solving Worksheets, Chapter 10

T138   **10   Electric Charges and Currents**

Chapter 10 Planning Guide

Developing Laboratory Skills

	10.1 Electric Charges 452–462	10.2 Electric Currents 463–476	10.3 Electric Circuits 477–491	Chapter 10 Supplements
Plan Ahead	For Activity, page 456: Be certain that the person doing the test is not carrying a charge. For example, a sweater or other piece of clothing may be already charged and will mask any effects of charges on other objects. For Activity, page 459: Gather foil gum wrappers and jars with narrow necks.	For Activity, page 469: Borrow a dc ammeter (range 0 to 1 A) if necessary. For Activity, page 472: Borrow a dc voltmeter (range 0 to 5 V) if necessary.	For Activity, page 480: The dc ammeter and voltmeter used earlier are needed again. For Activity, page 483: The dc ammeter and voltmeter used earlier are needed again.	
Basic Activities	Identifying Positively and Negatively Charged Objects 456 20 minutes Groups of 3 or 4 Activity Record Sheet 10-1A, LM 135	Using an Ammeter 469 20 minutes Groups of 4 or teacher demonstration Activity Record Sheet 10-2A, LM 139	Bulbs in Series 480 40 minutes Groups of 4 or teacher demonstration Activity Record Sheet 10-3A, LM 143	
Additional Activities	Observing Charges with an Electroscope 459 20 minutes Groups of 2 or 3 Activity Record Sheet 10-1B, LM 136	Using a Voltmeter 472 20 minutes Groups of 4 or teacher demonstration Activity Record Sheet 10-2B, LM 140	Bulbs in Parallel 483 40 minutes Groups of 4 or teacher demonstration Activity Record Sheet 10-3B, LM 144	Projectsheet 10 TRB 182
Investigations and Research Lab	Investigation 10-1, Measuring the Tendency to Gain Electrons LM 137–138 40 minutes Groups of 3 or 4	Investigation 10-2, Making a Model of a Rheostat LM 141–142 40 minutes Groups of 4	Investigation 10-3, Resistance in Series and in Parallel LM 145–146 50 minutes Groups of 4	Research Lab 10 LM 147–148

Chapter 10 Electric Charges and Currents

10.1 Electric Charges

Concept Summary

Electric charges cause pushes and pulls between objects that do not have equal numbers of positive and negative charges.

- Neutral objects have equal numbers of protons and electrons.
- Objects that gain electrons are negatively charged.
- Objects that lose electrons are positively charged.
- Opposite charges attract; like charges repel.
- Electrons move easily through conductors of electric charge but do not move through insulators.
- Objects can be charged by friction, contact, and induction.
- The force between charged objects depends on the amount of charge on each object and the distance between them.
- Energy is required to separate opposite charges or to bring together like charges.

Learning Objectives

1. To explain the charging of objects by friction, by contact, and by induction.
2. To describe how lightning and thunder occur in clouds.
3. To relate the electric force between charged objects to the kinds of charges, to the amount of charge, and to the distance between the charges.

Getting Started

Ideas for Discussion
Students will learn the precautions to take when using electrical appliances to avoid getting shocked.

Ask the students if they have ever gotten a shock from touching a doorknob, from folding clothes, or from using an electrical appliance. Ask the individual students who volunteer to explain the circumstances. Ask if the shock lasted a long time, or if it was of short duration. Generally, the shock will be of short duration. Ask the students to tell you what basic rules they know about handling electricity. Write the rules on the board as the students suggest them. Some of the rules the students suggest should include the following things: Never handle an electrical appliance while in the shower or bathtub or with wet hands. Do not use an electrical appliance with a broken or frayed cord. Tell the students that Chapter 8, Section 1 will explain what electric charges are and how they behave. This will help them understand the behavior of electricity.

Suggested Demonstration
Students will learn to collect and to discharge static electricity. You will need the following items:
aluminum pie pan with a wooden or plastic handle securely cemented on the center back
inflatable plastic pillow or other inflatable plastic object 2 mL thick.

Tell the class that this demonstration illustrates static electricity. Explain that experiments demonstrating static electricity work best in cold and dry weather or in a heated room. On humid days, a microscopic film of moisture forms on the objects and disperses the static charges into the moist air. This prevents any accumulation of static electric charge. Place the pie pan face down on a dry flat surface. Hold it by the handle and rub it vigorously with the plastic pillow. The pillow or plastic object should be partially inflated and folded over many times. While you are rubbing the pie pan, ask a student to darken the room. Explain to the class that as you are rubbing, the electric charges are being transferred from the plastic onto the pie pan. When a sufficient amount of charge collects, lift the pan and bring your knuckle close to it. A bright spark results.

Explain that friction causes electrons from the plastic to rub off onto the pie pan. Many electrons build up so that when the pan is held near the knuckle, electrons jump onto your hand.

Activity 10.1a
Identifying Positively and Negatively Charged Objects   page 456

Teacher Notes
(Activities that involve charging work best on dry winter days.)

When the glass rod is rubbed with silk, the silk should repel, and the glass rod should attract the negatively-charged balloon. This implies that the silk acquired a negative charge and the glass rod a positive charge.

Charges on the other objects used can be inferred in the same way. A rubber comb will repel the balloon and therefore must have a negative charge. The wool flannel will attract the balloon and must have a positive charge.

In all of these trials, be certain that the person doing the test is not carrying a charge. If a sweater or other piece of clothing is already charged it could mask any effects of charges on other objects. Objects can be discharged by rubbing them against a water pipe or other grounded metal.

If objects are used more than once, they should be discharged between trials. The hanging balloon may gradually lose its charge and have to be recharged with the wool flannel during the activity.

Answers to Questions
1. Negative.
2. Negative.
3. Positive.
4. Balloon (−); wool flannel (+); glass rod (+); silk (−); comb (−); hair (+).

Conclusion
The balloon is given a known charge, in this case a negative charge. Then the charge on the other charged objects can be inferred depending upon whether they attract or repel the balloon.

Activity 10.1b
Observing Charges with an
Electroscope   page 459

Teacher Notes
A small piece of thin aluminum foil may be substituted for the foil gum wrapper. A balloon may be substituted for the plastic bag. The wire hook and foil strips must be small enough to fit through the neck of the bottle.

The ends of the foil separate when the wool flannel is brought close to the top end of the wire. The ends of the foil go back together when the flannel is removed. The same results will occur when the plastic bag is used instead of the flannel.

Answers to Questions
1. The wool flannel is positive. The plastic bag is negative.
2. Positive. As the positively charged wool flannel is brought close, electrons move off the foil toward the top of the wire.
3. Negative. As the negatively charged plastic is brought close, electrons move from the wire onto the foil.

Conclusion
Hypotheses may vary but should suggest that the two ends of the foil take on the same charge and thus repel each other when a charged object is brought near the top of the electroscope. When the charged object is removed, the induced charges leave the foil ends and the ends fall back down.

10.1 Section Review

Understanding the Concepts   page 462
15. Electrons are relatively free to move in conductors but not in insulators.
16. A charge is induced on the hair as the charged balloon is brought near. Since the charge on a balloon is negative, electrons must move from the hair to your arm. The positively charged hairs then reach toward the negatively charged balloon.
17. If the objects have the same kind of charge, the potential energy is increased by moving them closer together. If the objects have opposite kinds of charge, the potential energy is increased by moving them apart. In either case, moving the objects *against* the force increases the potential energy.

10.2 Electric Currents

Concept Summary

An **electric current** is created by the movement of electric charges.

- Electric charges move only when energy is supplied.
- A current will flow when there is an unbroken path of conductors connected between the negative and positive terminals of an energy source such as a cell.
- The size of a current is measured as the amount of charge that passes a point per second.
- In a direct current, electrons move in only one direction.
- In an alternating current, electrons move back and forth in a regular cycle.
- Resistance is a measure of how hard it is for charge to move through a conductor.
- The amount of energy removed per unit of charge passing through a conductor is the voltage drop across the conductor.
- The voltage drop across a conductor equals the resistance times the current through it.
- The amount of electric energy used per second by an electric appliance is its power.

Learning Objectives

1. To know the necessary conditions for an electric current to exist.
2. To know the differences between direct and alternating current.
3. To describe the measures of current, voltage drop, and resistance.
4. To relate the power rating of an electric appliance to the energy used.

Getting Started

Ideas for Discussion
The students will learn that electrical current is the flow of electrons and that voltage measures the force of the flow of electrons.

Ask your class for the meaning of the word *current*. Most students will equate it with a river or ocean current. Point out that the word current implies that something is flowing. Ask the students what it is that flows in a river or ocean current. They should answer that water flows in these currents. Explain to the class that there are other kinds of currents; for example, electric current.

Ask the students what flows in an electric current. They should answer that electrons flow in this current. Explain that the strength of an electric current is defined by the number of electrons that pass a given point in one second. Tell the class that the force electricity exerts when it moves is similar to the force produced by moving water. This electric force is called *voltage*. Tell the students that they will learn how to measure current and voltage in Chapter 10, Section 2.

Suggested Demonstration
Students will learn that electricity flows through metals. They will learn to predict which materials will conduct electricity. You will need the following items for this demonstration:

"D" cell	iron nail
three 10-cm copper wires	wood
flashlight bulb and holder	coins
masking tape	paper
aluminum foil	string

Explain to the students that electric current cannot exist unless the electrons in a given substance are relatively free to move around. The moving electrons make up the electric current. Have the students study the periodic table on pages 104 and 105 and the electron shell diagrams of the first 18 elements shown on page 109. Ask the students to predict in which elements the electrons are the least tightly-bound. Are these metals or nonmetals? The students should predict that the elements with the least tightly-bound electrons are those on the left side of the periodic table. They are the metals. It may be necessary to review the periodic table and atomic structure with the class. Tell the class you will test their predictions.

Connect a copper wire to the top of the "D" cell. Connect a second wire to the bottom of the "D" cell. Use masking tape to hold the wires in place. Connect the bulb to one of the wires. Connect the third wire to the other side of the bulb holder. You should have two free ends of wire. Explain to the class that you constructed a device to test for the flow of electric current through various materials. Explain that you wish to determine whether or not the materials are *conductors* of electricity. Show them that when you touch the ends of the two wires together, the bulb lights up. Proceed to test the various materials you have on hand. Before you test each one, ask the class to predict if the material conducts electricity. Ask the class if the results match their predictions. The class should predict that metals are better conductors than non-metals. The test results will support this prediction.

Activity 10.2a
Using an Ammeter   page 468

Teacher Note
The bulbs used should be those for a 2-cell flashlight. Tell students to open the switch in the circuit after recording the data to conserve the life of the batteries. Alkaline "D" cells are recommended because they last significantly longer.

Answers to Questions
1. The current reading was 0.
2. Answers will vary depending upon the bulb and the condition of the "D" cells. (Fig. 10−14 shows 0.15A.)
3. No.
4. Yes. Brightness increased.
5. Answers will vary, but should be about twice the value in Question 3.
6. The current is proportional to the voltage. That is, if the voltage doubles, the current will double.

Conclusion
The ammeter should be connected in line (in series) with the light bulb. The positive terminal of the ammeter must be toward the positive terminal of the voltage source ("D" cell or battery) and the negative terminal of the ammeter must be toward the negative terminal of the voltage source.

Activity 10.2b
Using a Voltmeter   page 472

Teacher Note
The bulbs used should be those for a 2-cell flashlight. Tell students to open the switch in the circuit after recording the data to conserve the life of the cells. Alkaline "D" cells are recommended because they last significantly longer.

Answers to Questions
1. Zero V
2. 1.5 V
3. About the same, perhaps a little less than the cell voltage. May be much less than cell voltage if the cell is in poor condition.
4. Voltmeter reading should about double.
5. The voltage drop is proportional to the total voltage of the cells in the circuit. As the total voltage of the cells increases, so does the voltage drop.
6. The voltage drop across the wire will be very small, much less than that of the bulb.

Conclusion
The voltmeter should be connected across (in parallel with) the part of the circuit for which the voltage drop is being measured. The positive terminal of the voltmeter must be toward the positive terminal of the voltage source ("D" cell or battery) and the negative terminal of the voltmeter toward the negative terminal of the voltage source.

10.2 Section Review

Understanding the Concepts   page 476
22. Since aluminum is a poorer conductor than silver, the aluminum wire will have the greater resistance to the flow of electrons.

Problems to Solve   page 476
23. Energy = power × time
$$= (100 \text{ W}) \times (24 \text{ h})$$
$$= (100 \text{ W}) \times \frac{1 \text{ kW}}{1000 \text{ W}} \times (24 \text{ h})$$
$$= 2.4 \text{ kilowatt-hours}$$
24. 54 000 joules
25. 50.4 kilowatt hours
26. $2.52

10.3 Electric Circuits

Concept Summary

An **electric current** is created by the movement of electric charges.

- Electric charges move only when energy is supplied.
- A current will flow when there is an unbroken path of conductors connected between the negative and positive terminals of an energy source such as a cell.
- The size of a current is measured as the amount of charge that passes a point per second.
- In a direct current, electrons move in only one direction.
- In an alternating current, electrons move back and forth in a regular cycle.
- Resistance is a measure of how hard it is for charge to move through a conductor.
- The amount of energy removed per unit of charge passing through a conductor is the voltage drop across the conductor.
- The voltage drop across a conductor equals the resistance times the current through it.
- The amount of electric energy used per second by an electric appliance is its power.

An **electric circuit** is a conducting path or set of paths through which current can flow.

- A closed circuit is an unbroken loop, while an open circuit has a break in the path.
- A series circuit provides only one path for all the charges moving through the circuit.
- A parallel circuit provides branches, or alternate paths, so that the moving charges divide up among the branches.
- Fuses, circuit breakers, and ground-fault interrupters open a circuit when the current becomes too high for safety.

A **computer** is an electronic machine that handles data and does calculations using complex circuits.

- Components of complex circuits include capacitors, resistors, vacuum tubes, and transistors.
- Two classes of computers—analog and digital—handle information differently.
- Computers perform three functions with information: input, processing, and output.

Learning Objectives

1. To apply Ohm's law to simple electric circuits.
2. To describe the characteristics of series circuits.
3. To describe the characteristics of parallel circuits.
4. To explain how safety devices for circuits work.
5. To recognize some components of complex circuits and computers.

Getting Started

Ideas for Discussion

Students will learn about electrical circuits and their function. They will learn that a load and a source are necessary for circuits to work.

Ask the students to define the word *circuit*. If they have difficulty, ask them to think of a word that sounds like *circle* or *circular*. Explain that a circuit is like a circle in that it provides a round trip path in which the electrons travel. If an electric current cannot make a round trip, it cannot go at all. Ask the students for some examples of how electrical circuits are useful in the home. Students might suggest that circuits move electricity through the home and make appliances work. Some examples are: doorbells, light bulbs, electric space heaters, and appliances. Ask what these appliances do. A space heater radiates heat, a doorbell rings or buzzes, and light bulbs radiate light. Tell the class that a part of the circuit that performs an important function is known as the *load*. Without a load, there would be no reason for a circuit.

Ask the class what else is essential to make the circuit work. The students should be aware that a source of energy or current is needed. Explain that some sources of electric energy for circuits are generators that produce electricity for homes. Without a source of energy, a circuit does not operate. Explain that every electric circuit must have a source and a load. There are many kinds of electric circuits. Chapter 10, Section 3 describes different types of electric circuits and how they are used.

Suggested Demonstration

In this demonstration the student will learn how circuit overloads in a home can be prevented. Explain that every electrical outlet in the home is part of a large, complex circuit. Each of the circuits in a home is rated at a certain number of amperes or amps. An ampere is the unit used to measure the amount of electric current in a circuit. Each circuit's amp rating is clearly labeled in the circuit panel or "fuse box." The rating means that that circuit can carry no more than the specific number of amps it is rated for. If you try to get more current through than is allowed, the circuit will begin to heat up. This could cause a fire, except that the circuit is protected by a fuse or circuit breaker. When the circuit is overloaded the fuse will burn out, or the circuit breaker will open, breaking the circuit and preventing damage to the wiring.

Ask the students to examine the appliances shown in Figure 10–17, page 474. Explain that the number next to each item is known as the power rating. It describes the amount of power drawn by each appliance. Explain that the amount of power drawn by an appliance is directly related to the current in a circuit. Power is measured in watts. Current is measured in amperes. The relationship can be expressed as:

$$\text{amperes} = \frac{\text{watts}}{\text{volts}}$$

Given:
Household Voltage in
N. America is 110 volts

Tell the class that they can use this formula to figure out how much current is required to run each appliance. Ask the class to choose from Fig. 10–17 the items they would most like to have in the kitchen and living room. Write these on the board. Ask them to calculate the current used by each one, using the relationship above. (Answers: Lamp 0.9 A; TV 1.8 A; Blender 2.7 A; Toaster 10 A; Dishwasher 10.9 A; Refrigerator 1.8 A; Washer 4.5 A; Dryer 43.6 A; Stereo 1 A; Microwave 12.7 A.) When they have calculated the amperage and you have recorded it on the board, tell them it is time to try to "plug in" their appliances. For example, on the sample kitchen circuit (rated at 20 A), the lights and refrigerator are always on. Ask: What will happen to the circuit if you then run the dishwasher and turn on the microwave oven? (Answer: The current in the circuit will be 27.2 A. It is only rated for 20 A. The circuit will overload.)

Have them try several combinations in the kitchen, and then work out the living room. Ask: Why is it less likely for a living room circuit to overload? (Answer: Because most appliances used in the living room do not heat or cool things. Heating and cooling requires more power than motion does.) Tell the class that in Chapter 10, Section 3 they will learn more about the behavior of circuits.

Fuse Box or Circuit Panel

15A 20A

Kitchen

Living Room

Electrical outlet

Light switch

Activity 10.3a
Bulbs in Series   page 480

Teacher Note

All three bulbs should be identical. Tell students to open the switch in the circuit after recording the data to conserve the life of the cells. Alkaline "D" cells are recommended because they last significantly longer.

Answers to Questions

1. Yes, the current through each part of a series circuit is the same.
2. The voltage drop across two bulbs is double the voltage drop across one bulb (assuming that the bulbs are the same). The voltage drop across all three bulbs is three times the drop across one bulb; it should be nearly equal to the voltage of the battery.
3. No. Removing one of the bulbs breaks the circuit. (The other two bulbs will not be lit. The ammeter will read zero. When there is a break in a series circuit, there is no closed path for the current.)
4. When the circuit is complete, with only two bulbs in series, the current and voltage drop are greater than before. Using fewer bulbs in series decreases the total resistance in the circuit, so the current increases.

Conclusion

The current is the same in any part of a series circuit. The sum of the voltage drops across components connected in series is equal to the total voltage drop.

Activity 10.3b
Bulbs in Parallel   page 483

Teacher Notes

Use three identical light bulbs in the circuit. Alkaline "D" cells are recommended because they last significantly longer.

The ammeter reading for the path through the battery will be greater than for the series circuit. The bulbs in the parallel circuit will be brighter than in the series circuit.

Answers to Questions

1. The brightness should stay the same, but may brighten a little.
2. The current in one branch is less than the current in the main part of the circuit. (Also, see answer to conclusion below.)
3. No, because the remaining parallel circuits are still complete.
4. Voltage drops across bulbs in different branches are the same.
5. The voltage drop in a branch is equal to the voltage of the battery. (May be slightly less.)

Conclusion

The total current is equal to the sum of the currents in each branch. The voltage drop in each branch of a parallel circuit is the same.

10.3 Section Review

Understanding the Concepts   *page 491*

22. Too large a current was present in the circuit, and a safety device opened the circuit.

23. The two cells are in series. They supply a greater voltage than a single cell.

Problem to Solve   *page 491*

24. 10 A

10 Chapter Review

Critical Thinking   *page 492*

1. The balloon gains electrons at the expense of the flannel, so the balloon has the greater ability to attract electrons.

2. Rubbing the vinyl plastic record with a cloth increases the charge on it, so it attracts lint and dust particles to it.

3. The resistance of the voltmeter is large compared to the resistance of the ammeter. The ammeter measures the current passing through it; it must have a very small resistance or it would greatly reduce the current. The voltmeter is connected in parallel with the circuit element and should carry little current through it or it would greatly increase the total current.

4. The random motion of the particles in the wire increases with temperature. As a result, more resistance is offered to the orderly flow of electric charge.

5. Gravity seems stronger because the earth is so large that it has a very strong gravitational attraction.

6. Connect them in parallel.

7. The one with the lowest resistance will conduct the most current when it is being used.

Notes

Chapter 11 Electromagnetism

	Chapter 11 Planning Guide			
	Planning Your Classroom Lessons			
	11.1 Magnets 496–511	**11.2** Electric Energy 512–525		**Chapter 11 Review** 526–527 Chapter 11 Supplements
Content Overview	Magnetism—bar magnets, magnetic fields, the magnetic effects of electric currents, and the electric effects of magnetism Concept Summary T150 Learning Objectives T150	How some of the principles of electromagnetism are put to use in generating, transporting, and using electric energy Concept Summary T151 Learning Objectives T151		Science Background Information 494 Review of Concepts 526 Essential Ideas/ Chapter 11 Letter to Parents
Teaching Strategies	Getting Started: Ideas for Discussion and Suggested Demonstration T150	Getting Started: Ideas for Discussion and Suggested Demonstration T151		
Teaching Aids	Teaching Diagram 11-1A, 11-1B Overhead Transparency B16: The Earth's Magnetic Field	Teaching Diagram 11-2A, 11-2B		Physical Science Software T34 Physical Science Films and Videos T42 Video Lesson: Electricity and Electromagnetism
Review and Evaluation*	Quick Review 498, 501, 503, 505, 509 11.1 Review 511 Section Testsheet 11-1 TRB 229	Quick Review 514, 516, 521, 523 11.2 Review 525 Section Testsheet 11-2 TRB 230		Chapter Testsheets 11A and 11B TRB 261–262 Free Response Questions TRB 189 Semester Test 1 TRB 273–276 *Higher Level Evaluation* Critical Thinking 526–527

*TESTGEN can be used to prepare customized section and chapter testsheets

	Meeting Individual Needs			
Reinforcement	Reading Checksheet 11-1 TRB 109 Skillsheet 11-1 TRB 155 Essential Ideas 11.1	Reading Checksheet 11-2 TRB 110 Skillsheet 11-2 TRB 156 Essential Ideas 11.2		Information Library Software
Enrichment	Research Topic 500, 506 Data Search 501	Research Topic 512, 522 Data Search 514		Individual Research 527 Bibliography 527 Issues in Physical Science: Everyday Use of Microwaves 528 Trends in Technology: Communications Satellites 529
Critical Thinking and Problem Solving	Critical Thinking 501, 505, 513, 516	Practice Problems 518, 523 Problems to Solve 525		Chapter Testsheet 11B TRB 262 Problem-Solving Worksheets, Chapter 11

Chapter 11 Planning Guide

Developing Laboratory Skills

	11.1 Magnets 496–511	11.2 Electric Energy 512–525		Chapter 11 Supplements
Plan Ahead	For Activity, page 499: The activity calls for a sheet of unlined paper, a bar magnet and a small compass. For Activity, page 504: Note that four compasses are required. For Activity, page 508: Having a small compass available will allow the students to demonstrate the presence of a magnetic field when there is no bolt in the coil.	For Activity, page 519: 4 m lacquered wire (#22–26) is required. For Activity, page 524: Test all light bulbs beforehand to insure that all are functioning.		
Basic Activities	The Magnetic Field of a Current-Carrying Wire 504 20 minutes Groups of 4 Activity Record Sheet 11-1B, LM 150	Making a Model of an Incandescent Light Bulb 524 20 minutes Groups of 6 or teacher demonstration Activity Record Sheet 11-2B, LM 156		
Additional Activities	Mapping a Magnetic Field 499 30 minutes Groups of 2 to 4 Activity Record Sheet 11-1A, LM 149 Making an Electromagnet 508 20 minutes Groups of 2 Activity Record Sheet 11-1C, LM 151	Converting Electrical Energy to Energy of Motion 519 20 minutes Groups of 4 to 6 or teacher demonstration Activity Record Sheet 11-2A, LM 155		Projectsheet 11 TRB 183
Investigations and Research Lab	Investigation 11-1, Comparing Electromagnets and Bar Magnets LM 153–154 30 minutes Groups of 2	Investigation 11-2, Using Electric Energy LM 157–158 2 weeks Individual work		Research Lab 11 LM 159–160

11.1 Magnets

Concept Summary

Magnets exert forces on each other and on materials such as iron, cobalt, and nickel.

- The poles of a magnet are the places on the magnet where the magnetic forces are strongest.
- There are two kinds of poles—north poles and south poles; like poles repel and unlike poles attract.
- A magnet can be pictured as a collection of tiny bar magnets all lined up with their north poles in the same direction.

A **magnetic field** is said to exist in a region where magnetic forces can act.

- A magnetic field can be represented by curving lines known as magnetic field lines.
- The earth has a magnetic field similar to that of a large bar magnet deep inside the earth.
- A magnetic field is produced by an electric current as well as by a magnet.
- A temporary magnet known as an electromagnet consists of a coil of wire with an iron bar inside it; it produces a magnetic field only when there is current in the coil.
- The strength of an electromagnet increases as the number of turns in the coil and the current through the coil increase.

Electromagnetic induction is the production of an electric current by a changing magnetic field.

- A current is induced in a circuit that is in a magnetic field that is either moving in relation to the circuit or is changing in strength.
- Electromagnetic induction is the principle by which electric generators work.

Learning Objectives

1. To describe the behavior of magnets and their interaction with other magnetic materials.
2. To define a magnetic field and explain the behavior of magnetic materials in a magnetic field.
3. To demonstrate the magnetic effects of an electric current.
4. To illustrate how a changing magnetic field can be used to produce an electric current.

Getting Started

Ideas for Discussion
Students learn to define magnetism, and discuss the various uses of magnets.

Write the word *magnetism* on the board. Ask the students what it means. Write down the definitions the class suggests. Explain that the word magnetism means the ability to attract. A scientific definition of a magnet is a metal, usually iron or steel, that has the ability to attract other metals.

Ask how magnets are used. Have the class develop a list of the possible uses of magnets. Discuss such practical uses as separating metals, using magnets in motors, and other applications with which your students may be familiar.

Suggested Demonstration
Students learn how to magnetize an iron nail with a strong magnet. They learn to demagnetize the nail with heat. You will need the following items:

strong alnico magnet   alcohol or Bunsen burner
small tongs   hammer
iron nail   iron filings or small tacks

Tell the class you will demonstrate how to make a magnet. Explain that to make a magnet, the crystals in a metal, such as iron or nickel, are arranged in a particular alignment. One way to cause this alignment is to stroke the piece of iron or nickel with a magnet. The metal is stroked in only one direction to induce the crystals to line up in the same direction.

Show the class that the iron nail will not pick up any filings. Demonstrate that the magnet picks up the filings. Stroke the nail with the magnet in one direction at least 40 times. Ask a student volunteer to do this. Again test the nail with the iron filings. The nail should be magnetized and should pick up the filings. Explain that the nail is magnetized, but that the magnetism can be reduced by disrupting the alignment of the crystals of iron. Heat disrupts the alignment and demagnetizes the nail. Heat the nail in a flame until the nail is hot. Let the nail cool and test its magnetism with the iron filings. The magnetic ability of the nail should be markedly reduced. Next hit the nail with the hammer. Test the magnetism of the nail with the iron filings. The remaining magnetic property of the nail should be reduced still more.

Activity 11.1a
Mapping a Magnetic Field   page 499

Answers to Questions
1. Poles.
2. The field lines are parallel to the magnet near its center at points equidistant from the poles.
3. Near the poles.

Conclusion

The direction of the field is defined as the direction that the north pole of a compass would point. The field lines are parallel to the magnet near the center of the magnet. They are directly toward the magnet at the south pole and directly away from the magnet at the north pole. In other words, the lines extend from the north pole of the magnet around the magnet to the south pole of the magnet. The lines converge near the poles of the magnet and spread out near the center of the magnet. The relative strength of the field is indicated by the relative packing of the lines.

Activity 11.1b
The Magnetic Field of a Current-Carrying Wire   page 504

Teacher Notes

Since the wire has a small resistance, the battery is essentially being shorted out when both ends of the wire are connected to the battery. If the connection is made for more than a few seconds, the battery may be damaged and the wire may get hot.

Place the compasses as near to the wire as possible without having them so close that they interact with each other. If they all point in the same direction, they are not interacting.

Teaching Suggestion

For interested students, you may want to add two more steps to the activity, the left- and right-hand rules.

9. Assume that electrons were moving from the negative terminal of the battery to the positive terminal when current was flowing through the wire. Place your left hand around the wire so that your thumb points in the direction that the electrons were moving. Compare the direction your fingers are pointing to the direction the compass needles pointed.

10. Assume that positive charges had been flowing from the positive to the negative terminal. Place your right hand around the wire so that the thumb points in the direction of this imaginary positive charge flow. Compare the direction your fingers point to the direction the compass needles pointed.

Two more questions can be added to the activity.

4. What was your thumb indicating when the fingers of your left hand were pointing around the wire in the direction of the magnetic field?

5 What was your thumb indicating when the fingers of your right hand were pointing around the wire in the direction of the magnetic field?

Answers to Questions

1. Yes.

2. The needles point in a circle.

3. The needles of the compasses point in a circle, but the needles point in the opposite direction from the first time.

Answers to Supplementary Questions

4. The direction electrons are flowing.

5. The direction of an imaginary positive charge flow.

Conclusion

Magnetic field lines around a straight wire that is carrying current are circles with centers on the wire.

Activity 11.1c
Making an Electromagnet   page 508

Teacher Notes

Since the wire has a small resistance, the battery is essentially being shorted out by the wire when both of its ends are connected to the battery. If the connection is made for more than a few seconds, the battery may be damaged and the wire may get hot.

In Step 4 you may want to have the students use a small compass to demonstrate the presence of a magnetic field when there is no bolt in the coil.

Answers to Questions

1. Yes, the tacks should have moved a little. A compass placed near one end should have been deflected if the coil was at right angles to the natural direction of the compass needle.

2. The field is reduced, but it may not go to zero because the bolt may have been magnetized.

3. It increased the strength of the field.

4. It increased the strength of the field.

5. It increased the strength of the field.

6. The strength can be changed by changing the current flowing through the wire, so that the magnet can be turned on and off. (Depending on the core material, the electromagnet may not turn completely off when the circuit is broken.)

Conclusion

The strength of an electromagnet can be changed by adding an iron core, increasing the number of turns in the coil, and increasing the current in the wire.

11.1 Section Review

Understanding the Concepts   page 511

18. The magnet would be attracted to the brass-coated steel bed and not to the solid brass bed.

19. In the Arctic region the compass would point toward magnetic north and would, most of the time, not indicate true north.

20. The core of an electromagnet should respond quickly to the turning on and off of the current. The core should be able to be easily magnetized or de-magnetized.

11.2 Electric Energy

Concept Summary

Electric energy is the energy carried by electric currents.

- Electric generators convert energy from other sources—fossil fuels, nuclear reactions, falling water, solar energy—into electric energy.
- Electric energy is also obtained from thermocouples, crystals, and solar cells.
- Electric energy is transported most efficiently at high voltage and low current.
- Electric motors convert electric energy into energy of motion.
- High-resistance wires convert electric energy into heat and light.

Learning Objectives

1. To identify the various sources of electric energy.
2. To describe the procedures used to transfer electric energy over large distances.
3. To identify and describe the ways in which electric energy is put to use.

Getting Started

Ideas for Discussion
Students will learn how the conversion of electric energy is accomplished.

Ask the class to make a list of the electrical appliances they know. Explain that most electrical appliances convert electric energy to some other form of energy, such as heat, light, sound or motion. Ask them to categorize the appliances by the type of energy produced.

Ask: How is the electric energy converted to these other forms? Explain that the conversion of electric energy is accomplished by taking advantage of the natural interconversion of electricity and magnetism, or by the properties of various electrical conductors. Tell the class that Chapter 11, Section 2 will explain how electrical energy is created and utilized.

Suggested Demonstration
In this demonstration the student will learn how electrical energy can be produced from mechanical energy. For this demonstration you will need:

1 bicycle with attached generator light

Turn the bicycle upside down so you or a volunteer may operate the pedals by hand and the wheels may turn freely. Ask: What is providing the energy that is making the wheels turn? (Answer: Chemical energy from food gives your arms power to turn the pedals and is being changed into the mechanical energy of the spinning wheels.) Point out the generator assembly and attached light. Explain that the top of the generator is a small wheel with a rough surface so that friction between it and the side of the tire will cause it to turn. Place the generator in position against the tire and turn the pedals again. Ask: What happens? (Answer: The light turned on.) Stop turning the pedals. Ask: What happens now? (Answer: As soon as the wheels stop turning, the light goes out.) Ask: What kind of energy conversion is taking place? (Answer: Mechanical energy is being changed into electrical.)

Explain that the generator converts mechanical energy to electrical energy by using the principle of electromagnetic induction explained in Section 1 of this chapter. The spinning tire uses friction to turn a wheel on the outside of the generator. The wheel turns a wire loop between the poles of a magnet. As the loop turns, a current is induced in the wire by the magnetic field. The current is carried by wires to the bulb and the bulb lights up.

Activity 11.2a
Converting Electric Energy to Energy of Motion   page 519

Teacher Notes
The 3-cm diameter wooden dowel is used just as a form on which to wind the coil. You can replace it with any cylinder of about the same diameter. It must be large enough to give the coil a larger diameter than the magnet, but small enough so that you can make at least a 30 turn coil with about 40 cm of wire left at each end.

The direction that the coil moves in Step 9 will depend upon the direction that the current flows around the coil. If the coil moves in different directions for different groups of students, challenge the students to discover the reason for the difference. For some, the current will be moving clockwise in the coil, for others it will be moving counterclockwise.

Answers to Questions
1. Yes, the direction is reversed.
2. Yes, the direction is reversed.
3. The direction that the coil moves will be the same if both the magnet and the direction of the current are reversed. In other words, the coil will move the same direction when it is around the S pole with the "B" wire at the bottom of the cell, as it will when it is around the N pole with wire "A" at the bottom of the cell.

Conclusion
Yes, this is how an electric motor works. Examples are an electric mixer, drill, toothbrush, razor, fan, lawnmower, hedgetrimmer, and vacuum cleaner.

Activity 11.2b
Making a Model of an Incandescent Light Bulb   page 524

Teacher Notes
For students who want to know more about why light bulbs glow, explain that it is because electrons in the filament are energized by the electric field. These electrons bounce off the atoms in the wire, causing the atoms to vibrate and give off heat and light.

Have students compare the wattages and filaments in light bulbs to the wattages and heating elements in toasters and hair dryers. These comparisons will help to answer Questions 3 and 4.

The copper wire must be thicker than the strands of iron (steel) picture wire. Use a magnet to test the picture wire.

Answers to Questions
1. The strand of picture wire has a smaller diameter than the copper wire.
2. Probably (after it glowed).
3. In general, the light bulbs with higher wattages should have thicker filaments.
4. The bulbs with the highest wattage should have filaments with the lowest resistance.
5. The air inside has been replaced by argon or nitrogen. The filament is made of tungsten instead of iron. Tungsten filaments can be heated to a higher temperature than an iron filament without melting. Argon and nitrogen do not react with metals at high temperatures as oxygen does, so the filament lasts longer.

Conclusion
The picture wire glowed when the circuit was closed so that current could flow.

11.2 Section Review

Understanding the Concepts   page 525
16. Examples of possible answers:

Energy source	Advantage	Disadvantage
coal	inexpensive	pollution
natural gas	clean	costly
falling water	inexpensive	low availability
nuclear reaction	clean	radioactive wastes
solar	abundant	maintenance problems

17. Examples of answers: Availability of power during interruption from a single source, balancing of demand, lowering of cost.
18. Student answers will vary.
19. The electric energy that is not converted to light in an incandescent bulb escapes as heat. When many incandescent bulbs are used to light a room, the temperature of the room will rise.

Problems to Solve   page 525
20. Set up a ratio between the voltage and number of turns in the two coils.

$$\frac{110 \text{ V}}{1200 \text{ V}} = \frac{40 \text{ turns}}{? \text{ turns}} \qquad \text{Cancel out the Vs.}$$

Multiply both sides by (1200) (? turns).
(? *turns*) (110) = (1200) (40 turns) = 48 000 turns
Divide both sides by (110).

$$? \text{ } turns = \frac{48\ 000 \text{ turns}}{110} = \text{about 436 turns}$$

21. The ratios between the numbers of turns in the first and second coils can be found by setting up the ratios of the voltages in each transformer.

$$\frac{300\ 000 \text{ V}}{9000 \text{ V}} = \frac{\text{turns in first coil}}{\text{turns in second coil}}$$

Cancel out the Vs and reduce the fraction.   Ratio $= \dfrac{300}{9} = $ about $\dfrac{33}{1}$

$$\frac{9000 \text{ V}}{110 \text{ V}} = \frac{\text{turns in first coil}}{\text{turns in second coil}}$$

Cancel out the Vs and reduce the fraction.   Ratio $= \dfrac{900}{11} = $ about $\dfrac{81}{1}$

11 Chapter Review

Critical Thinking   page 526
1. The south-seeking pole of the compass will point toward the magnetic south pole, not toward the true south pole. On Antarctica, the south-seeking pole would point north, east, or west, but not south.
2. The electromagnet is a temporary magnet. The magnetic effect is present only while a current is present in the coil. Large steel objects can be lifted and carried to a new location with an electromagnet. The object can be dropped at the desired location by shutting off the current.
3. A changing magnetic field is needed to induce a current. The direct current would have to be turned on and off to induce a current, while the changing strength and direction of the alternating current provides the changing magnetic field needed.
4. The falling water from the elevated storage area can be used to generate electricity at times of peak usage, and the water can be pumped to the area during periods of low demand.
5. The "excess" heat could be used to supply heat for commercial and residential buildings rather than simply dumped or wasted.
6. The metal wire filament could combine with the oxygen at the high temperatures produced and lead to a very short lifetime for the bulb.
7. Their atoms cannot be formed into magnetic domains and therefore cannot be magnetized.
8. The voltage is reduced to one-half its former strength by putting it through a transformer with twice as many turns on its second coil as on its first.
9. Bees can use their internal magnets as compasses and find their way using the earth's magnetic field.

Chapter 12   Electrochemical Reactions

Chapter 12 Planning Guide			
Planning Your Classroom Lessons			
	12.1 Oxidation and Reduction 534–549	**12.2** Electrical Energy and Chemical Reactions 550–563		**Chapter 12 Review** 564–565 Chapter 12 Supplements

Content Overview	The loss and gain of electrons, oxidation numbers, and the corrosion and activity of metals; also oxidizing and reducing agents
	
	Concept Summary T156
	Learning Objectives T156
		The use of chemical changes to produce electric energy, and the use of electric energy to produce chemical changes
		
		Concept Summary T157
		Learning Objectives T157
				Science Background
				  Information 532
				
				Review of Concepts 564
				
				Essential Ideas/
				  Chapter 12 Letter to
				  Parents

Teaching Strategies	Getting Started: Ideas for
	  Discussion and
	  Suggested
	  Demonstration T156
		Getting Started: Ideas for
		  Discussion and
		  Suggested
		  Demonstration T157		

Teaching Aids	Teaching Diagram 12-1A,
	  12-1B
	
	Overhead Transparency
		Teaching Diagram 12-2A,
		  12-2B
				Physical Science Software
				  T00
				
				Physical Science Films
				  and Videos T00
				
				Video Lesson: Nuclear
				  Energy and Future
				  Energy Needs

Review and Evaluation*	Quick Review 536, 541,
	  543, 545, 548
	
	12.1 Review 549
	
	Section Testsheet 12-1
	  TRB 231
		Quick Review 553, 556,
		  560, 561
		
		12.2 Review 563
		
		Section Testsheet 12-2
		  TRB 232
				Chapter Testsheets
				  12A and 12B
				  TRB 263–264
				
				Free Response Questions
				  TRB 000
				
				Semester Test 1
				  TRB 273–276
				
				Higher Level Evaluation
				
				Critical Thinking 564–565

*TESTGEN can be used to prepare customized section and chapter testsheets

Meeting Individual Needs			

Reinforcement	Reading Checksheet 12-1
	  TRB 111
	
	Skillsheet 12-1 TRB 157
	
	Essential Ideas 12.1
		Reading Checksheet 12-2
		  TRB 112
		
		Skillsheet 12-2 TRB 158
		
		Essential Ideas 12.2
				Information Library
				  Software

Enrichment	Research Topic 548 Data Search 548	Research Topic 551, 555, 560 Data Search 561		Individual Research 565 Bibliography 565

Critical Thinking and Problem Solving	Critical Thinking 535,
	  540, 541, 543
	
	Practice Problem 540
		Critical Thinking 000,
		  000
				Chapter Testsheet 12B
				  TRB 264
				
				Problem-Solving
				  Worksheets, Chapter 12

Chapter 12 Planning Guide				
Developing Laboratory Skills				
	12.1 Oxidation and Reduction 534–549	**12.2** Electrical Energy and Chemical Reactions 550–563		**Chapter 12 Supplements**
Plan Ahead	For Activity, page 542: Two days before performing activity, paint one ungalvanized nail with rust-resistant paint for each group. For Activity, page 546: A number of solutions need to be prepared (see *Preparation Notes*).	For Activity, page 552: A salt water solution is required (to prepare, dissolve a teaspoonful of sodium chloride in 500 mL of tap water). For Activity, page 557: A few drops of I*M* sulfuric acid will keep the copper sulfate solution clear should it become cloudy.		
Basic Activities	Corrosion of Metals 542 20 minutes plus later observation time Groups of 3 or 4 Activity Record Sheet 12-1A, LM 161	A Wet Cell 557 30 minutes Groups of 3 or 4 Activity Record Sheet 12-2B, LM 166		
Additional Activities	Oxidation and Reduction on the Same Metal 546 20 minutes Groups of 3 or 4 Activity Record Sheet 12-1B, LM 162	Making a Simple Electrochemical Cell 552 20 minutes Groups of 3 or 4 or teacher demonstration Activity Record Sheet 12-2A, LM 165		Projectsheet 12 TRB 184
Investigations and Research Lab	Investigation 12-1, Activity of Metals LM 163–164 40 minutes plus later observation time Groups of 4 or 5	Investigation 12-2, Electroplating Copper LM 167–168 50 minutes Groups of 3 or 4		Research Lab 12 LM 169–170

Chapter 12 Electrochemical Reactions

12.1 Oxidation and Reduction

Concept Summary

Oxidation is the loss of electrons in a chemical change; **reduction** is the gain of electrons in a chemical change.
- Oxidation and reduction always occur simultaneously; neither can take place without the other.
- If the oxidation number of an element has increased, the element has been oxidized; if the oxidation number has decreased, the element has been reduced.

Corrosion is the combining of a metal with water, air, or other materials in the atmosphere.
- When a metal corrodes, it loses electrons.
- Metals differ in their tendency to give up electrons.

The activity of a metal refers to its tendency to give up electrons. The most active metals are those that are most easily oxidized.
- The activity series ranks metals with respect to their tendency to give up electrons. A metal above another metal in the activity series will give up electrons to ions of any of the metals below it in the series.
- Differences in the activities of metals are used to protect some metals against corrosion; an important metal (e.g. iron) that is vulnerable to corrosion is coated with or electrically connected to a more active metal (e.g. zinc or magnesium) that will be corroded preferentially.
- Different activities can exist in different places on the same piece of metal. Locations under the greatest stress tend to give up electrons most easily; these areas will corrode most easily.

Oxidizing agents accept electrons. **Reducing agents** give up electrons.
- The strongest oxidizing agents have the greatest attraction for electrons; the strongest reducing agents give up electrons most easily.
- The development of film involves the use of a weak reducing agent, the developer, to reduce light-sensitized crystals of silver bromide.
- Antioxidants retard the deterioration of some foods by combining preferentially with oxygen.

Learning Objectives

1. To relate oxidation and reduction to the loss and gain of electrons.
2. To use oxidation numbers to keep track of electrons transferred in oxidation-reduction reactions.
3. To relate oxidation and reduction to four types of chemical reactions.
4. To relate oxidation and reduction to the activity of metals.
5. To relate oxidation and reduction to some everyday chemical process.

Getting Started

Ideas for Discussion
Students will learn how and why oxidation occurs.

Ask the class to find oxygen in the periodic table on pages 104–105. Ask: What can we tell about the atomic structure of oxygen from the periodic table? (Answer: There are six electrons in its outer shell.) Draw an electron shell diagram of oxygen on the board. Ask: How many electrons does oxygen need to complete its outer shell? (Answer: 2) Explain that because oxygen needs these two electrons to have a complete shell of eight, it readily forms compounds with all elements except some of the noble gases. It participates in the reactions of combustion, corrosion, fermentation and decomposition. It is oxygen that is responsible for the bleaching and antiseptic action of peroxide and laundry bleach.

Oxygen can be thought of as an electron-grabber that picks up electrons wherever and whenever it can. For this reason, the word oxidation has come to be associated with all reactions involving the loss of electrons. Oxidation and its associated process, the reduction or gain of electrons, is the subject of Chapter 12, Section 1.

Suggested Demonstration
In this demonstration the students will observe the production of household bleach (sodium hypochlorite) from the electrolysis of brine. They will then observe the bleaching action of the product on an ink solution. For this experiment you will need the following items:
electrolysis apparatus (identical to that used for electrolysis of water in Chapter 6) and cardboard wedge cut to fit inside, dividing beaker into two compartments.

300–400 mL water
150–200 g table salt
container for mixing
red litmus or pH paper
test tube containing water with 1 drop ink for testing product
eye dropper or pasteur pipette

Set up the electrolysis apparatus as for the electrolysis of water described on page 558. Fit the cardboard wedge in between the electrodes so that separate compartments are created. Prepare a saturated salt solution by dissolving as much salt as possible in the water. Pour the saturated solution in the apparatus and get it ready to connect to the dry cell. (Note: Gloves or tongs are not required as the saturated salt solution is not dangerous.) Hang a folded piece of litmus or pH paper into each compartment so that the progress of the reaction can be monitored.

Tell the class that ordinary table salt can be broken into its component elements, sodium and chlorine, by passing an electric current through a salt solution. This process is used on an industrial scale to produce chlorine, hydrogen, sodium hydroxide, and sodium hypochlorite or bleach. Connect the current and let the reaction proceed. The students will see bubbles forming in the tube over the negative electrode almost immediately. Explain that these are bubbles of hydrogen gas. Ask: Where did they come from? (Answer: The water.) Explain that the sodium in the form Na^+ is being changed to sodium metal Na which reacts immediately with the OH^- in water liberating hydrogen. Explain that because this represents a gain in electrons by sodium, the sodium is said to have been reduced. In an electrolytic cell, reduction always takes place at the negative electrode. As the reaction proceeds, the build-up of NaOH will make the liquid in this compartment very basic, turning the litmus or pH paper dark blue. Examine the other compartment and explain that it contains the positive electrode. At this electrode the greenish-yellow chlorine gas is being produced.

Explain that the chlorine cannot be seen immediately because it is much more soluble than hydrogen gas; therefore, we must wait until the solution is saturated before we will see any of it in the tube. (Takes about 20 minutes.) Explain that in the formation of chlorine gas, electrons must be taken away from chlorine ion (Cl^-). The process of taking electrons away from an atom is known as oxidation. In an electrolytic cell, oxidation always occurs at the positive electrode. When greenish-yellow gas begins to be visible in the tube,

stop the reaction. The class may be able to smell the characteristic chlorine odor. The litmus or pH paper in this compartment will most likely have bleached. Remove the cardboard separating the two compartments and mix the solutions. Explain that you are mixing NaOH and Cl_2 from the reaction in the presence of water and producing NaClO, or sodium hypochlorite. This is the main component of commercial bleach. Using an eyedropper, transfer a little bit of the solution to the test tube containing the ink solution. It will lighten it instantly. Explain that this reaction as well as the reactions in the electrolytic cell all involve processes of oxidation and reduction. Chapter 12, Section 1 will explain these processes.

Activity 12.1a
Corrosion of Metals   page 542

Preparation Notes
Two days before the activity is scheduled, paint one ungalvanized nail for each group that will do this activity. Use rust-resistant metal paint.

Try to use nails that are all the same size. Ungalvanized nails are also called plain nails. Porous cloth is one made with a loose fabric, like cheesecloth, that allows air to enter and leave the nails freely.

Expected Results
The steel wool should rust the most because it has the greatest surface area exposed to air and water. The ungalvanized nail should rust second most because it has no protective coating. The galvanized and painted nails should not show signs of rust. The scratched ungalvanized nail may or may not show signs of rusting. That depends on whether or not the scratches went through the coating on the nail.

Answers to Questions
1. **a.** Should have rusted most and fastest.
   b. Should have rusted second most.
   c. Should not have rusted.
   d. Should not have rusted.
   e. May have rusted, but should have rusted less than the ungalvanized nail.
2. Student observations of changes in the properties of the nails should be used as evidence to support the inferences that chemical changes have taken place.
3. Students are likely to suggest covering the container or objects to keep out air and moisture. They may also suggest painting metals or using alloys to prevent rusting.

Conclusion
The presence of water and air should indicate to the students that these substances play a role in the corrosion of metals.

Going Further
You may wish to have the students observe the objects after one, two, or three weeks. The student can record the amount of corrosion on each object each week. The data can be compared and the changes recorded.

Activity 12.1b
Oxidation and Reduction on the Same Metal   page 546

Preparation Notes
Prepare the agar mixture just before it is to be used. The agar mixture contains phenolphthalein and $0.1M$ potassium ferricyanide. To prepare the phenolphthalein solution, dissolve 1.0 g of phenolphthalein in 200 mL of 95% ethanol. (Since the quantities needed are very small, you could instead dissolve 0.1 g of phenolphthalein in 20 mL of 95% ethanol.) To prepare the potassium ferricyanide solution dissolve 3.4 g of potassium ferricyanide in 100 mL of water.

The following procedure will give enough agar mixture for two 50-mL petri dishes. To prepare the agar mixture, heat 100 mL of water to boiling in a 250-mL beaker. Remove the beaker from the heating apparatus. While stirring, add 1 g of powdered agar to the hot water. Then heat and stir the mixture until the agar makes a suspension. Once the suspension has formed, remove the beaker from the heat. Add 5 drops of the $0.1M$ potassium ferricyanide solution and 3 drops of the phenolphthalein solution to the agar mixture while it is still hot. Stir the agar to mix in the potassium ferricyanide and phenolphthalein thoroughly. The agar mixture is now ready to be poured into the petri dishes.

Hint: Use plastic petri dishes and discard them after the activity is finished.

Note: After pouring the first batch of agar into the petri dishes, keep the remaining mixture warm enough so that it does not solidify and can be poured on top of the nails in the petri dishes.

Expected Results
The central section of the nail should become darkened. The agar around the central portion should become dark blue. There should be a pink color in the agar around the nail head. This color change should begin to be observed after 5 to 10 minutes.

Answers to Questions
1. The dissolving of iron, or oxidation, appears to be taking place where the nail is darkened and a blue color forms in the agar.
2. Reduction appears to be taking place where the nail is not darkened and where a pink color appears in the agar.
3. The nail is darkened where the blue color is and is shiny where the pink color is.

Conclusion
Oxidation and reduction can take place on the same metal object at the same time as is indicated by changes in the appearance of the nail and by different color changes in the agar.

12.1 Section Review

Understanding the Concepts   page 549
15. The compound of iron formed by corrosion (iron oxide, or rust) is very soft and crumbles easily, exposing more surface of iron to further corrosion. Aluminum corrodes but the compound formed (aluminum oxide) serves to protect the underlying aluminum.
16. An active metal, for example chromium, can be coated on a less active metal like iron to protect it from reaction with the oxygen of the air. Chromium itself will react with oxygen to form a thin layer of chromium oxide. This layer prevents any further reaction of chromium with oxygen, and it protects the iron from rusting.
17. The reaction would stop, as neither oxidation nor reduction can take place by itself.
18. Bleach releases oxygen, which as an oxidizing agent breaks down and dissolves the food substances in stains.
19. Yes. A double-replacement reaction is an example.

Problem to Solve   page 549
20. a.
$$2SO_2 \;+\; O_2 \longrightarrow 2SO_3$$
(reduction; oxidation)

b.
$$2H_2 \;+\; O_2 \longrightarrow 2H_2O$$
(reduction; oxidation)

c.

$$Zn \;+\; H_2SO_4 \longrightarrow ZnSO_4 \; H_2$$
(reduction; oxidation)

d.

$$\overset{+1\ -1}{HCl} + \overset{+1\ -2\ +1}{NaOH} \longrightarrow \overset{+1\ -1}{NaCl}\ \overset{+1\ -2}{H_2O}$$

no oxidation/reduction occurs in this reaction

12.2 Electric Energy and Chemical Reactions

Concept Summary

An **electrochemical cell** uses a chemical change involving oxidation and reduction to produce electric energy.

- Two metals that have different activities can be used to make an electrochemical cell.
- The chemical reactions that take place in electrochemical cells are spontaneous.
- A storage battery can be recharged by using electric energy to run a current through it in the reverse direction.
- In a fuel cell, the materials that react are supplied from outside the cell.
- Electric energy can be used to produce chemical changes such as the separation of metals from their ores and the electroplating of metals.

Learning Objectives

1. To relate the production of electric energy to chemical changes.
2. To compare different kinds of electrochemical cells.
3. To compare two processes in which electricity is used to produce chemical changes.
4. To relate the processes of electroplating to corrosion.

Getting Started

Ideas for Discussion
Students will learn how electrochemical cells function as a power source.

Ask your class: What are some battery-powered appliances that you use? Write the class's list on the board. (Lists will vary.) Ask: Do all these items use the same type of batteries? (Answer: No.) Why? (Answer: Power needs are different.) Ask: Have you observed that "alkaline" batteries last longer than other batteries? (Answer: Yes.) Ask: What happens to your appliance when a battery accidentally breaks open or leaks? (Answer: The connections are usually damaged by chemicals.)

Explain that what is commonly called a battery is usually a dry cell. This is because the chemicals inside are in paste, rather than liquid form. The chemicals in a cell may vary depending on the voltage that the cell needs to generate. Every set of chemical reactions that is used to produce electricity involves oxidation and reduction and gives off its own characteristic voltage. Sometimes several cells are linked together. The combined unit of cells is a true battery. Tell the class that in Chapter 12, Section 2 they will learn how chemical reactions are used to produce electric power in electrochemical cells.

Suggested Demonstration
In this demonstration the students will observe the operation of a lead storage cell. For the experiment you will need the following items:

1 6 V dry cell	flashlight bulb and
sodium sulfate (Glauber's salt, enough to saturate water.)	socket
	bell wire, 2 pieces 20–30 cm long
2 pieces of lead, approximately 4 cm × 10 cm any thickness.	sandpaper
	masking tape
	500-mL beaker
	water

Prepare a saturated solution of sodium sulfate by dissolving as much as possible in 400–500 mL water at room temperature. Pour 400 mL of this solution into the beaker. Clean the pieces of lead by sandpapering them well. Bend the ends of the lead strips into a "J" so they will hang over the sides of the beaker. Strip the insulation from the ends of the wire so that several turns of bare wire can be wrapped around the upper end of each strip. When the wire is tightly wrapped around the ends, secure it in place with the masking tape. Hang the lead strips in the beaker and run the other end of the wires to the dry cell.

Begin by telling the class that they have observed in Section 1 that many chemical reactions involve the movement of electrons. Ask: What do moving electrons produce? (Answer: An electric current.) Explain that electricity is produced by chemical reactions that occur in what are called electrochemical cells. They have already observed one type of electrochemical cell previously, the electrolytic cell used to separate the components of water or brine. In the electrolytic cell electricity was used to create a chemical reaction. However, there are other types of cells that do the opposite: use chemical reactions to create electric current. For this demonstration, you have built one that does both.

Show the class the lead storage cell. Explain that this type of cell is in every auto battery. Ask: How are auto batteries different than most other household batteries? (Answer: They can be recharged.) This is possible because the chemical reactions involved are easily reversible. Connect the lead storage cell to the dry cell and let the class observe the reaction. Ask: What do you observe? (Answer: Bubbles of gas appear at both lead strips and the lead strip connected to the positive terminal of the dry cell develops a brownish deposit.) After the cell has charged for approximately 5 minutes, disconnect it from the dry cell, and hook it up to the light bulb. The bulb should shine brightly. (Note: The lead storage cell provides 2 V.) Explain that the chemical reactions that took place while it was charging are taking place in reverse now while it is discharging. Explain that every electrochemical cell depends on coupled chemical reactions, and while this one is easily reversible, others are not. Tell the class that Chapter 12, Section 2 will explain the workings of the lead storage cell and other types of electrochemical cells.

Note: Many classes like to see it charged and discharged several times.

Activity 12.2a
Making a Simple Electrochemical Cell   page 552

Preparation Notes
To prepare the salt water solution, dissolve a teaspoonful of sodium chloride in 500 mL of tap water.

Answers to Questions
1. The electrodes must differ in their ability to furnish electrons.
2. The coating on the surface may prevent contact with the copper metal.
3. The salt water solution serves as the electrolyte.
4. The direction the needle is deflected shows the direction the charges are moving. In this cell, they move from the aluminum to the copper.
5. Aluminum is a more active metal than copper.
6. Electrons would flow from the magnesium to the aluminum.

Conclusion
An electrochemical cell converts chemical energy into electrical energy. In the cell, a chemical change takes place in which electrons are transferred from one substance (aluminum) to another (copper). The flow of electrons is an electric current.

Activity 12.2b
The Wet Cell   page 556

SAFETY NOTE: *Copper sulfate solution may be irritating to the skin. See the student safety note. Reuse the copper sulfate solution throughout the school day. Then save it in a labeled container for use next year. If it becomes cloudy, add a few drops of 1M sulfuric acid until it clears.*

Advance Preparation
To prepare a saturated copper sulfate solution, start with enough water to fill all the beakers that will be used about two-thirds full. Dissolve as much copper sulfate as possible in the water. Some solid copper sulfate should be visible at the bottom. The saturated (but clear) solution can then be poured into the beakers. The activity may be done even if only two or three different metal strips are available. The voltmeter should be set to read voltages between zero and two volts. The metal strips should be clean to insure good contacts. Prepare a container half filled with water and large enough to hold all the copper sulfate solution the students use. Instruct the students to dump the solution into the container when they finish the activity.

Answers to Questions
1. Readings of voltage should be the highest for the aluminum-copper combination.
2. Readings of voltage should be the lowest for the iron-copper combination.
3. If the aluminum-copper combination is not enough to light a 1.5-V bulb, use a bulb of smaller voltage.

Conclusion
The readings of voltage should be the highest for the aluminum-copper combination, followed by zinc-copper, and iron-copper.

12.2 Section Review

Understanding the Concepts   page 563
18. Normally, two different metals along with a conducting liquid or paste are all that is needed.
19. In a fuel cell, the gaseous fuels are continuously supplied from outside the cell. In other electrochemical cells, the energy is released when materials already inside the cell react.
20. To allow more copper to plate on a piece of iron, increase the current or the amount of time it is on.
21. A storage battery can be recharged rather than discarded when it is weak.

12 Chapter Review

Critical Thinking   *page 564*

1. Usually hydrogen forms bonds with elements that attract electrons more strongly than does the hydrogen itself (i.e. elements that are more electronegative than hydrogen itself). In these cases, hydrogen has a positive oxidation number and the elements it bonds to have negative oxidation numbers (e.g. H_2O H = +1 O = -2; HCl H = +1 Cl = -1). In the case of hydrides, the elements bonded to hydrogen are actually less electronegative than hydrogen. Consequently, the hydrogen in these compounds is given a negative oxidation number (e.g. LiH Li = +1 H = -1).

2. $3Ca^0 \rightarrow 3Ca^{+2} + 6e^-$
   $2Al^{+3} + 6e^- \rightarrow 2Al^0$
   $3Ca + 2Al^{+3} \rightarrow 2Al + 3Ca^{+2}$

3. Yes. Zinc is also more active than iron and will protect it from corrosion in the same way as the magnesium. Note that zinc is significantly less active than magnesium.

4. Theoretically, the corrosion resistance afforded by magnesium should be similar to that provided by zinc. Magnesium would also form a protective oxide layer and would also resist corrosion due to scratching because of its higher activity relative to iron.

5. Theoretically, no. The black insoluble solid that appears as a dark tarnish on the surface of silver is silver sulfide, Ag_2S, formed in the following reaction.
   $4Ag(s) + 2H_2S + O_2 \rightarrow 2Ag_2S(s) + 2H_2O$
   (N.B. It is still possible that the black oxide of silver, Ag_2O, would be formed in the sulfur-depleted air sample.)

6. A variety of answers are possible. Antioxidants used in food should certainly have the following characteristics. They should be stable, they should not be distasteful, and they should not be poisonous.

7. It would not work at all because the water is a critical element of the electric circuit in these batteries. Ions must be able to move through the water in order for the battery circuit to be complete. If there is no water, the ions cannot move, the circuit is not closed, and the battery will not function.

8. A direct current is passed through the battery in the reverse direction. This drives the battery's electrochemical reaction in reverse, regenerating the reactants consumed in the discharge of the battery.

9. At the cathode. The metal ion would be reduced at the cathode.

10. The galvanized nail will continue to resist corrosion after its surface is scratched. This is because the zinc coating will give up electrons to any Fe^{+2} ions that are formed. The painted nail will begin to corrode after its surface is scratched.

Chapter 13   Nuclear Reactions

	Chapter 13 Planning Guide			
	Planning Your Classroom Lessons			
	13.1 A Model of the Nucleus of Atoms 568–583	**13.2** Energy from Nuclear Changes 584–597		**Chapter 13 Review** 598–599 Chapter 13 Supplements
Content Overview	How alpha, beta, and gamma radiation is detected, and the nuclear change that accompanies each kind of radiation; also, the concept of half-life, and nuclear models Concept Summary T162 Learning Objectives T162	Radioactivity, nuclear fission, and nuclear fusion—nuclear changes in which energy is released Concept Summary T163 Learning Objectives T163		Science Background Information 566 Review of Concepts 598–599 Essential Ideas/ Chapter 13 Letter to Parents
Teaching Strategies	Getting Started: Ideas for Discussion and Suggested Demonstration T162	Getting Started: Ideas for Discussion and Suggested Demonstration T163		
Teaching Aids	Teaching Diagram 13-1A, 13-1B Overhead Transparency	Teaching Diagram 13-2A, 13-2B		Physical Science Software T00 Physical Science Films and Videos T00 Video Lesson: Nuclear Energy and Future Energy Needs
Review and Evaluation*	Quick Review 569, 571, 573, 577, 579, 581, 582 13.1 Review 583 Section Testsheet 13-1 TRB 233	Quick Review 586, 587, 588, 593, 595 13.2 Review 597 Section Testsheet 13-2 TRB 234		Chapter Testsheets 13A and 13B TRB 265–266 Free Response Questions TRB 000 Semester Test 1 TRB 273–276 *Higher Level Evaluation* Critical Thinking 599

*TESTGEN can be used to prepare customized section and chapter testsheets

	Meeting Individual Needs			
Reinforcement	Reading Checksheet 13-1 TRB 113 Skillsheet 13-1 TRB 159 Essential Ideas 13.1	Reading Checksheet 13-2 TRB 114 Skillsheet 13-2 TRB 160 Essential Ideas 13.2		Information Library Software
Enrichment	Research Topic 569, 579 Data Search 580	Research Topic 591, 593 Data Search 000		Individual Research 599 Bibliography 599 Issues in Physical Science: Hazards of Producing Nuclear Power 600 Trends in Technology: Diagnosing Illness with MRI 601
Critical Thinking and Problem Solving	Critical Thinking 000, 000	Critical Thinking 000 Practice Problems 588		Chapter Testsheet 13B TRB 266 Problem-Solving Worksheets, Chapter 13

Chapter 13 Planning Guide

Developing Laboratory Skills

	13.1 A Model of the Nucleus of Atoms 568–583	13.2 Energy from Nuclear Changes 584–597		Chapter 13 Supplements
Plan Ahead	For Activity, page 575: (TO COME) For Activity, page 578: Explain to students why they need to determine the mass of the empty beaker and how to calculate the mass of the sand.	For Activity, page 590: Obtain dominoes or similar wood blocks.		

Basic Activities	Model of Half-Life 578
	   25 minutes
	   Groups of 2 or 3 and
	   time to plot graph
	Activity Record Sheet
	   13-1B, LM 172
		Model of a Chain
		   Reaction 590
		   10 minutes
		   Groups of 3 or 4
		Activity Record Sheet
		   13-2A, LM 175		

Additional Activities	Radiation and an
	   Electroscope 575
	   (TO COME)
		Modeling Nuclear Fusion
		   594
		   15 minutes
		   Groups of 2 or 3
		Activity Record Sheet
		   13-2B, LM 176
				Projectsheet 13 TRB 185

Investigations and Research Lab	Investigation 13-1,
	   Detecting Radiation
	   LM 173–174
	   50 minutes
	   Groups of 3 or 4
		Investigation 13-2,
		   Approximating Half-Life
		   Decay LM 177–178
		   30 minutes
		   Groups of 4
				Research Lab 13
				   LM 179–180

Chapter 13   Nuclear Reactions

13.1 The Nuclear Structure of Atoms

Concept Summary

Radioactivity is the release of particles and/or energy from the nucleus of an atom.

- Three kinds of radiation can be given off by radioactive atoms: alpha radiation, beta radiation, and gamma radiation.
- Gamma radiation is the most penetrating of the three common types of nuclear radiation; gamma radiation can penetrate several centimeters of lead. Beta particles cannot penetrate skin or thin sheets of metal, and alpha particles can be stopped by a thin sheet of paper.
- In alpha radiation, a particle having the mass and charge of a helium nucleus is released.
- In beta radiation, a particle with the mass number and charge of an electron is released.
- Radioactivity cannot be detected with the senses, but it can be detected by a variety of devices, including dosimeters, cloud chambers, bubble chambers, and Geiger counters.
- Atoms in which there are more neutrons than protons are more likely to be radioactive than are atoms that have the same number of protons and neutrons; atoms in which there are fewer neutrons than protons may also tend to be radioactive.
- The number of nuclei in a sample of a radioactive isotope that may decay per second depends only on the type and amount of the sample.
- The half-life of a radioactive isotope is the time required for half of the nuclei in a sample of that isotope to decay.
- Radioisotopes have many practical uses. They are used as tracers in biological research as anticancer agents, for example.
- There are two models of how nucleons are arranged in the nucleus. In the liquid drop model, nucleons are closely packed in the nucleus and are in constant motion; in the nuclear shell model, the nucleons are arranged in discrete shells of different energies within the nucleus.

Learning Objectives

1. To compare the properties of alpha, beta, and gamma radiation.
2. To explain different methods for detecting various kinds of radiation.
3. To identify the nuclear change that accompanies each kind of radiation.
4. To illustrate the concept of half-life used in describing the rate of decay of a radioactive substance.
5. To compare two models of the nucleus of atoms.

Getting Started

Ideas for Discussion
Students will learn why atomic radiation is dangerous.

Write the word "radioactivity" on the board. Ask the class: What does this word make you think of? (Class will most likely respond "nuclear bombs") Ask: Why do nuclear bombs give off radioactivity? Where does the radioactivity come from? Explain that radioactivity occurs naturally as well as a product of nuclear explosions. Ask the class to recall what the nuclei of atoms are made of. (Answer: Neutrons and protons). As atoms get larger, with greater numbers of protons and neutrons their nuclei naturally become more unstable because the positively charged protons repel each other. These atoms with unstable nuclei readily fall apart. When they fall apart they release particles and energy, known as atomic radiation.

Ask the class: Is atomic radiation dangerous? (Answer: Yes.) Why? Explain that because the forces involved in holding together atomic nuclei are so strong, the radiation given off by disintegrating nuclei has very high energy. This means that the radiation can cause atoms inside living cells to change into ions. These ions can disrupt the cells normal functioning. Also radiation has a direct effect on the genetic material inside cells, causing mutations and changes that can lead to cancer. Explain that despite the dangerous properties of radiation, it can be useful if properly handled. Tell the class that Chapter 13, Section 1 will explain the properties and uses of the various types of radioactivity.

Suggested Demonstration
In this demonstration the students will observe the use of a Geiger counter to measure radioactivity, and to differentiate between beta and gamma radiation. For this experiment you will need the following items:

Geiger counter (Can be borrowed from instructor of physics lab course)

radioactive source (Luminous watch dials contain radium, and the mantles used to light gasoline lanterns contain thorium oxide. Both make good radioactive sources.)

sheet of aluminum, such as a cookie sheet

Show the Geiger counter to the class and explain that it measures the amount of radiation striking the counting tube. When radiation is present audible clicks are heard. Turn it on and ask the class: Why does it click occasionally? Explain that it is measuring what is known as the background radiation. Background radiation includes cosmic rays and radiation being emitted by rocks in the vicinity. Granite, which makes up most of the earth's crust, always contains small amounts of radioactive elements. Count the number of clicks for three separate 1 minute intervals. Have the class note them and calculate the average value. Write the average background count on the board for use in later calculations. Hold the counting tube near the radioactive source and measure the counts per minute (cpm). It may be necessary to change the scale to get an accurate reading, if so explain this process. Write this count on the board and explain that it represents the sum of both the gamma and beta radiation striking the tube. (Most Geiger counters do not detect alpha radiation.)

Ask: How can we separate the reading for gamma rays from the total? (Answer: Beta radiation cannot pass through metal, so if a piece of metal is placed between the source and the counter, only the gamma radiation will be measured.) Place the metal in between the source and the tube and measure the gamma count. Write this on the board. Ask: Is all of this just radiation from the source we are measuring? (Answer: No, some of it is due to background radiation.) Explain that whatever the reading, the background must always be subtracted to get a true measurement of the radioactivity of the sample. Do this for both the total count and the gamma count.

Ask the class: How can we use the information we have to calculate the beta count? (Answer: Subtract the gamma count from the total count.) Hold the counting tube 2–3 cm away from the source and measure the total count and the gamma count again. (The total count may decrease slightly, the gamma count will remain the same. If the total count does not decrease, try moving the counter still further away.) Emphasize that gamma rays can travel great distances and through almost any material. Tell the class that in Chapter 13, Section 1 they will study the changes in the nuclear structure of atoms that produce the different kinds of radioactivity.

Activity 13.1a
Radiation and an Electroscope   page 575

Preparation Notes

It takes time to get an electroscope ready for this activity. Making the leaves properly is crucial. The foil is very fragile. Handle it carefully. Make the leaves as long as possible. Make sure that they hang straight. The ones shown in this activity are each about 3.5 cm long.

Test the setup before you do the demonstration. The electroscope is very sensitive and a little difficult to use until you have had some practice.

Teacher Notes

SAFETY NOTE: *Follow the directions for handling and storage given by the supplier of whatever radiation source you use. Handle the radiation source with care.*

You may want to assign a student to time each of the trials with a stopwatch. With the apparatus shown, it took about 8 minutes for the leaves to collapse when no radiation source was near. When the radiation source was within 3 mm of the electroscope ball, it took about 2¼ minutes for the leaves to collapse. These times will vary according to conditions.

To expand this activity, you may want to compare the effect of other radioactive sources, such as beta and gamma emitters. You can also try moving the alpha source further away from the electroscope to see what effect that will have on the time for the leaves to collapse.

In this activity, the electroscope was charged by induction. The leaves were negatively charged. You may want to try to charge the electroscope directly by touching it with the plastic ruler. Then compare the effect of a radiation source on the collapse of leaves with a different charge.

Answers to Questions

1. An electroscope detects a static electric charge.
2. The leaves collapse because the electric charge gradually discharges into the surrounding air.
3. It took less time for the leaves to collapse when a radiation source was present.
4. From these observations, you can infer that an electroscope can be used to detect alpha radiation.

Conclusion

An electroscope is a useful device for detecting some kinds of radiation.

Activity 13.1b
Model of Half-life   page 578

Preparation Notes

Before the students begin, make sure they understand why they need to determine the mass of the empty beaker and how to calculate the mass of the sand. With some groups, it might also be a good idea to have the students determine beforehand how much sand they will need to pour off each turn.

Answers to Questions

1. The sand grains represent the nuclei of a radioactive isotope.
2. The time between trials represents the half-life of the isotope.
3. Half of the sand is poured off because half of the nuclei decays and becomes another kind of atom during each half-life period.
4. Theoretically, the beaker would never become completely empty. In reality, it would take a long time as the fraction of original nuclei remaining becomes smaller and smaller with each turn.

Conclusion

The half-life of a radioactive isotope is the time required for half of the nuclei in a sample of the isotope to decay.

13.1 Section Review

Understanding the Concepts   page 583

22. The property of uranium ore making images on covered photographic plates led to the discovery of radioactivity by Henri Becquerel.
23. Treatment of diseases such as cancer, tracing the use of various elements by plants and animals, and finding leaks in pipes are some possible answers.
24. The amount of the radioactive material at the initial time and the half-life of the radioactive material determine the rate of decay.
25. Gamma radiation. Gamma radiation is not charged and is not deflected by an electric field.
26. A Geiger tube detects radiation by measuring the electric current that flows when radiation ionizes gas particles in the detector tube. An electroscope detects radiation by the speed of collapse of charged leaves inside the vessel.

13.2 Energy from Nuclear Changes

Concept Summary

Mass and **energy** are different forms of each other.
- The mass of a helium nucleus is slightly less than the sum of the masses of two protons and two neutrons; the missing mass has been converted to energy according to the formula $E = mc^2$.
- The sum of the mass and energy is conserved in a nuclear reaction; this is the conservation of mass and energy principle.
- The binding energy is the energy holding the nucleus together; the binding energy comes from the mass lost when the nucleus is made from its particles.
- The magnitude of the binding energy is greatest for elements close to iron in the periodic table; the elements with the greatest binding energy are the most stable.
- The conversion of one element into another element in a nuclear reaction is called transmutation.
- Alpha particles are of limited usefulness in the production of nuclear changes. This is because the positive charge of these particles causes them to be electrically repelled by the nucleus which is also positively charged; neutrons, which are neutral, do not suffer from this limitation.

Nuclear fission is the breaking up of a nucleus into two or more smaller nuclei.
- Uranium-235 is commonly used for fission.
- A chain reaction is a series of fission reactions that occur when the neutrons released in one fission reaction cause another fission reaction.
- Einstein explained the energy released in a nuclear change by saying it was the equivalent of the mass that is given up in the reaction.
- Fission reactions can be controlled, and the energy can be used to generate electricity.
- Safety considerations and the production of radioactive waste materials have restricted the use of nuclear fission for generating electricity.

Nuclear fusion is the joining together of two or more nuclei.
- Fusion most commonly involves the joining of hydrogen nuclei to form helium nuclei.
- Fusion occurs only where the temperatures are very high, such as in stars.
- The heat released by fusion may someday be used to generate electricity.
- The use of nuclear fusion to supply energy has many potential advantages over nuclear fission.

Learning Objectives

1. To relate the energy involved in nuclear reactions to the change in mass of the substances.
2. To relate nuclear changes to changes of elements.
3. To compare the changes taking place in nuclear fission and nuclear fusion.
4. To explain how energy from nuclear changes can be harnessed as an energy resource for people.

Getting Started

Ideas for Discussion

Students will learn that the direct conversion of matter to energy is the source of nuclear energy.

Ask the class: What is the law of conservation of energy? (Answer: Energy cannot be created or destroyed. It can only change from one form to another.) Write it on the board. Ask: What are some of the forms we have seen energy take throughout the course? List the class's responses on the board. (kinetic energy, thermal energy, internal energy, chemical energy, electrical energy, mechanical energy, wave energy.)

After the list is completed, ask: Where does nuclear energy come from? Is it made from any of these other types of energy? (Answer: No.) Explain that the understanding of nuclear energy required a whole new concept of what energy was. Write the equation $E = mc^2$ on the board and ask the class to study it. Explain that in 1905 Albert Einstein proposed that matter itself could be transformed into energy. This meant that matter itself is really only another form of energy. Explain that the direct conversion of matter to energy is the source of what we call nuclear energy. Tell the class that in Chapter 13, Section 2 they will learn how this is accomplished.

Suggested Demonstration

In this demonstration students will observe simulated nuclear fission and transmutation of elements using a liquid drop model of the nucleus. For this experiment you will need the following items:

flat-sided jar or bottle (16-oz size)
1 bottle rubbing alcohol (isopropyl)
water
eyedropper or pasteur pipette
vegetable oil ⎫
castor oil   ⎬ enough for several droppersful

Fill each bottle approximately two-thirds full with alcohol. Add a little water to each but be sure to leave room to adjust the density later. Fill the eyedropper with vegetable oil. With the dropper tip below the surface of the alcohol-water mixture, squeeze out a small amount of oil. Adjust the density of the supporting solution until the drop remains suspended near the middle. If it floats add more water. If it sinks add more alcohol. When the drop is suitably suspended, inject more oil into it until it is approximately 1–1½ cm across. (Do this for both bottles.) Each bottle will now contain a pale yellow sphere suspended in the middle of the bottle.

Tell the class that the sphere represents the nucleus of a uranium atom. According to the liquid drop model, the nucleus will behave very much like one of these drops. When isolated from outside influences, a perfect sphere is formed. However, it is flexible, and may assume shapes more like a football or hamburger bun. Pick up one of the bottles and move it gently from side to side so the students will see the drop collide with one of the walls. The drop will flatten out. Explain that the drop behaves as if there is an elastic film around it holding it together. In a liquid this is caused by surface tension. It is not known what causes it but the nucleus has a similar "skin."

Ask: In our model, the molecules of the liquid correspond to what parts of the nucleus? (Answer: The protons and neutrons.) Remind the class that a molecule may escape the surface of a liquid by evaporation. Protons and neutrons may escape a heavy nucleus in a similar fashion. Explain that although the sphere-like nucleus appears very stable, it can also be unstable and simply split apart. Fill another eyedropper with castor oil. Inject some of this denser oil into one of the vegetable oil drops. The difference in density will cause the drop to bulge on its underside. Tell the class that this represents an unstable uranium nucleus. Because it is unstable, it easily splits apart. Insert the tip of the eyedropper into the drop and wiggle it. The bottom part of the drop will split off. This represents the process of nuclear fission.

Tell the class that it is possible, although difficult, to add particles to the nuclei of atoms. Ask: When the particle added is a proton, what happens to the atom? (Answer: It changes into a different atom, the next higher one in the periodic table.) Explain that this process is called transmutation of elements and can also be demonstrated with your oil drop. Fill an eyedropper with castor oil and "bombard" the oil drop in the other bottle with small drops of castor oil released just beneath the surface of the supporting liquid. The students will see many of the drops be bounced off, but an occasional one will be absorbed. This is similar to a nucleus undergoing bombardment in a cyclotron or linear accelerator. Tell the class that in Chapter 13, Section 2 they will learn about the energy changes associated with the processes they have just observed.

Activity 13.2a
Model of a Chain Reaction   page 590

Answers to Questions
1. Knocking over the first domino should result in the other dominoes being knocked over in rapid succession. Answers will vary.
2. The reaction time is faster when the dominoes are arranged so that each one falls onto two other dominoes. Answers will vary.
3. Students should compare the data they collected for the two timed trials. Answers will vary.
4. If each domino were set up to knock down three others, the reaction would be even faster.

Conclusion
A series of repeated reactions that occurs very quickly is illustrated when a number of dominoes are set up close to each other, and each domino falls onto the others in rapid succession.

Activity 13.2b
Modeling Nuclear Fusion   page 594

Preparation Notes
Any two colors of modeling clay can be substituted for the red and yellow clay. If students separate the balls at the end of the activity, the clay can be reused.

Answers to Questions
1. The red balls represent protons. The yellow balls represent neutrons.
2. Deuterium and tritium nuclei contain neutrons; hydrogen nuclei do not. Because neutrons are present, deuterium and tritium nuclei are heavier than ordinary hydrogen nuclei.
3. The main product formed was a helium nucleus.
4. Fusion reactions release energy.
5. Fusion occurs in the sun and other stars.
6. The products are tritium and a proton.

Conclusion
Nuclear fusion is the joining together of two or more atomic nuclei. Usually the nuclei of two hydrogen isotopes fuse to form a helium nucleus.

13.2 Section Review

Understanding the Concepts   page 597
16. The source of energy released in a nuclear reaction is the mass of particles that is converted into energy during the reaction.
17. Nuclear fusion has these advantages over nuclear fission. There is almost an unlimited supply of fuel in the oceans. The reaction can be controlled more easily by removing the fuel. Also, fusion does not produce as many dangerous waste products as fission.
18. The conversion of mass to energy is expressed by the formula $E = mc^2$, where E is energy, m is mass, and c is the speed of light. The conversion of 1 gm of mass to energy produces 9×10^{13} joules.
19. It is difficult to produce the right conditions for fusion in a laboratory because very high temperatures—several million degrees Celsius—are needed to start the reaction.
20. Theoretically it is possible to turn lead into gold by atomic transmutation. The important thing for students to realize is that three protons must be removed from the nucleus of lead to transmute it into gold. You may want to challenge students to devise a pathway for the transmutation. One possible pathway is the following series.

$${}^{188}_{82}\text{Pb} \rightarrow {}^{4}_{2}\alpha + {}^{184}_{80}\text{Hg} \qquad \text{(alpha decay)}$$

$${}^{184}_{80}\text{Hg} + {}^{1}_{1}\text{p} \rightarrow {}^{185}_{81}\text{Tl} \qquad \text{(proton bombardment)}$$

$${}^{185}_{81}\text{Tl} \rightarrow {}^{4}_{2}\alpha + {}^{181}_{79}\text{Au} \qquad \text{(alpha decay)}$$

Incidentally, this isotope of gold is radioactive and has a half-life of 11.4 seconds.

Problems to Solve   page 597
21. **a.** Charge: 92; mass: 238
    b. Charge: 47; mass: 107
    c. Charge: 11; mass: 23
    d. Charge: 98; mass: 250
    e. Charge: 0; mass: 1
22. **a.** ${}^{133}_{53}\text{I} \rightarrow {}^{0}_{-1}\text{e} + {}^{133}_{54}\text{Xe}$
    b. ${}^{222}_{86}\text{Rn} \rightarrow {}^{4}_{2}\text{He} + {}^{218}_{84}\text{Po}$
    c. ${}^{2}_{1}\text{H} + {}^{3}_{1}\text{H} \rightarrow {}^{4}_{2}\text{He} + {}^{1}_{0}\text{n}$
    d. ${}^{6}_{3}\text{Li} + {}^{1}_{0}\text{n} \rightarrow {}^{3}_{1}\text{H} + {}^{4}_{2}\text{He}$

13 Chapter Review

Critical Thinking page 597

1. Gamma radiation travels at the speed of light because it is a form of electromagnetic radiation. Alpha and beta particles would travel much slower than the speed of light because they have mass. Alpha particles would travel much slower than beta particles because their mass is so much greater than the mass of beta particles.

2. No, gamma radiation is a form of electromagnetic radiation and has no mass.

3. A cloud chamber can be used to detect any kind of radiation that ionizes the gas particles in the chamber. A cloud chamber shows the path of ionizing radiation as a track of water or alcohol droplets. These droplets condense around ionized gas particles along the path that the radiation traveled.

4. The loss of an electron from a nucleus does not have much effect on the total mass of a nucleus because an electron has only $\frac{1}{1837}$th of the mass of a proton.

5. Carbon-14 would not be as useful for dating purposes if its half-life were only two weeks. It would decay so rapidly that in 10 weeks less than one millionth of the initial amount would remain.

6. Carbon-14 dating depends on comparing the amount of carbon-14 remaining in a sample of organic material from the past to the amount of carbon-14 present on the earth at this time. It is necessary to clean the samples carefully so that no carbon-containing matter that is younger than the sample contaminates the sample. Otherwise, the age of the sample material will appear to be too young.

7. If the amount of carbon-14 in the atmosphere has been increasing, then the ages of the materials that have already been dated would appear to be older than they actually are.

8. The rate of decay is the amount of a radioactive element that breaks down in a given amount of time. The rate of decay is proportional to the amount of the radioactive element present at any time. As the element breaks down, there is less of it remaining. This means that the rate of decay also diminishes with time.

The half-life of a radioactive element is the amount of time for half of the sample to break down. The half-life is a property of each particular radioactive isotope. The half-life does not depend on the amount of the radioactive elements present, so it does not change with time.

9. The beta particle is given off by the nucleus when a neutron splits into a proton and an electron, or beta particle. The beta particle leaves, and the proton remains, so the nucleus increases in protons by one.

10. Electrons would have limited usefulness in transmuting elements by bombardment. Because they have a negative charge they would not be repelled by the nucleus. It is also relatively easy to produce them and to get them moving at high speeds. However, because their mass is so small, they would not be effective in adding mass to the nucleus. They could only bring about transmutation if they combined with protons in the nucleus and thereby made neutrons. In that process, the nucleus would lose one proton for every neutron it gained.

11. The reaction in a nuclear reactor is controlled by the amount of radioactive fuel in place and by the control rods which slow the reaction. If the reaction gets out of control, it can produce too much heat which could cause the reactor to burn or melt releasing radioactive materials into the environment. The radioactive contaminants would be the greatest hazard in the long term.

Chapter 14   Our Energy Needs

	Chapter 14 Planning Guide			
	Planning Your Classroom Lessons			
	14.1 Present Energy Resources 606–623	**14.2** Alternative Energy Resources 624–640	**14.3** Energy Conservation 641–653	**Chapter 14 Review** 654–655 Chapter 14 Supplements
Content Overview	Fossil fuels and nuclear fission, and the supply and environmental problems related to them Concept Summary T168 Learning Objectives T168	The use of alternative energy sources, including energy directly from the sun Concept Summary T170 Learning Objectives T170	How energy resources can be made to last longer Concept Summary T172 Learning Objectives T172	Science Background Information 604 Review of Concepts 654 Essential Ideas/ Chapter 14 Letter to Parents
Teaching Strategies	Getting Started: Ideas for Discussion and Suggested Demonstration T168	Getting Started: Ideas for Discussion and Suggested Demonstration T170	Getting Started: Ideas for Discussion and Suggested Demonstration T172	
Teaching Aids	Teaching Diagram 14-1A, 14-1B Overhead Transparency	Teaching Diagram 14-2A, 14-2B	Teaching Diagram 14-3A, 14-3B	Physical Science Software T00 Physical Science Films and Videos T00 Video Lesson: Nuclear Energy and Future Energy Needs
Review and Evaluation*	Quick Review 607, 608, 610, 613, 617, 620, 622 14.1 Review 00 Section Testsheet 14-1 TRB 235	Quick Review 629, 635, 638, 639 14.2 Review 00 Section Testsheet 14-2 TRB 236	Quick Review 644, 649, 650, 651 14.3 Review 00 Section Testsheet 14-3 TRB 237	Chapter Testsheets 14A and 14B TRB 267–268 Free Response Questions TRB 000 Semester Test 1 TRB 273–276 *Higher Level Evaluation* Critical Thinking 654–655

*TESTGEN can be used to prepare customized section and chapter testsheets

	Meeting Individual Needs			
Reinforcement	Reading Checksheet 14-1 TRB 115 Skillsheet 14-1 TRB 161 Essential Ideas 14.1	Reading Checksheet 14-2 TRB 116 Skillsheet 14-2 TRB 162 Essential Ideas 14.2	Reading Checksheet 14-3 TRB 117 Skillsheet 14-3 TRB 163 Essential Ideas 14.3	Information Library Software
Enrichment	Research Topic 613, 616, 620, 621 Data Search 611	Research Topic 625, 630, 639, 642 Data Search 635	Research Topic 648, 650 Data Search 641	Individual Research 655 Bibliography 655 Issues in Physical Science: Hydroelectric Power Plants and Wild Rivers 656 Trends in Technology: The Gasoline-Powered Car of Tomorrow 657
Critical Thinking and Problem Solving	Critical Thinking 609	Critical Thinking 629		Chapter Testsheet 14B TRB 268 Problem-Solving Worksheets, Chapter 14

Chapter 14 Planning Guide			
Developing Laboratory Skills			
	14.1 Present Energy Resources 606–623	**14.2** Alternative Energy Resources 624–640	**14.3** Energy Conservation 641–653	**Chapter 14 Supplements**
Plan Ahead	For Activity, page 618: Obtain plastic bottles with spray pumps.	For Activity, page 631: Ask students to bring in old umbrellas, even torn or tattered ones. Have hot dogs or marshmallows available.	For Activity, page 643: Allow two weeks for students to collect data. For Activity, page 646: Allow two or three days for students to collect data.	
Basic Activities	Exponential Growth 618 20 minutes Groups of 2 or 3 Activity Record Sheet 14-1B, LM 182	A Solar Cooker 631 1 hour Groups of 4 or teacher demonstration Activity Record Sheet 14-2A, LM 185	Surveying Your Car Usage 643 2 weeks Individual work Activity Record Sheet 14-3A, LM 189	
Additional Activities	Oil Recovery 614 20 minutes Groups of 2 or 3 Activity Record Sheet 14-1A, LM 181	Angle for Maximum Solar Energy 634 20 minutes Groups of 2 or 3 Activity Record Sheet 14-2B, LM 186	Your Shower Usage 646 2–3 days Individual work Activity Record Sheet 14-3B, LM 190	Projectsheet 14 TRB 186
Investigations and Research Lab	Investigation 14-1, Depletion of a Resource LM 183–184 50 minutes Groups of 3 or 4	Investigation 14-2, Designing a Windmill LM 187–188 45 minutes Individual work	Investigation 14-3, Testing Various Insulating Materials LM 191–192 35 minutes Groups of 4 or 5	Research Lab 14 LM 193–194

14.1 Present Energy Resources

Concept Summary

Entropy is a measure of the distribution of energy in a system.

- Energy flows from places of high concentration to places of low concentration.
- Entropy increases as energy becomes more evenly distributed.
- When entropy increases, the total amount of energy remains the same, but the energy becomes less available to use.

An **energy pathway** describes the set of changes energy goes through from its source, such as the sun, to its use by humans.

- Each time energy changes form, some of it becomes unusable.
- In a fossil fuel energy pathway, energy from the sun is stored for a very long time in the remains of organisms that slowly turn into coal, oil, and natural gas, the fossil fuels.

A **nonrenewable energy resource** is a source of usable energy that is used much faster than it can be replaced.

- Examples of nonrenewable energy resources are coal, oil, natural gas, oil shale, and tar sands.
- The demand for fossil fuels is increasing at a much higher rate than that at which the world population is growing.
- The supply of fossil fuels will run out sooner or later.

Learning Objectives

1. To recognize that we depend on energy and that energy supplies are limited.
2. To recognize that changes in the form of energy reduce the amount of available energy.
3. To identify the steps in several energy pathways.
4. To describe the rate of growth of energy usage.
5. To relate energy usage to our current and future environmental problems.

Ideas for Discussion
Students learn that because of our dependency on fossil fuels, we must manage our resources carefully.

Ask the class to name as many products as they can think of that are made from the fossil fuels oil, coal and natural gas. (They will probably come up with gasoline and related fuels.) Write their list on the board. Explain that the number of products made from fossil fuels is much larger than the list they have started, and that we are dependent on fossil fuels not only for energy but also for a great many other things. Ask them to study the "family tree" in Figure 14-8 on page 612. Using the "family tree" as a guide, ask the class to revise the list.

Suggested Demonstration
In this demonstration students will learn to calculate the energy lost between two levels of an energy pathway. For this demonstration you will need the following items:
hamburger patty (uncooked)
5 lb. sack of rice or other grain
scale or balance, 2000g capacity

Explain that an energy pathway is a sequence of steps by which energy is converted into different forms. Tell the class that the hamburger patty and the sack of grain represent two different steps on the same energy pathway. Ask: Where did the energy required to produce the sack of grain come from? (Answer: The sun.) Ask: Where did the energy required to produce the hamburger patty come from? (Answer: The grain eaten by cattle.) Explain that because the hamburger patty was produced from energy that came from grain, we can calculate the amount of energy that was lost in the conversion. Explain that a steer needs to consume approximately 16 kg of grain to produce 1 kg of usable meat. Ask: How does this relate to the amount of energy involved? Explain that we can calculate this.

The first step is to find the mass of the hamburger patty. Place it on the balance and find the mass in grams. (A 1/4-lb patty will have a mass of 113.5 g.) Write the mass of the hamburger patty on the board. Ask: What will be the mass of the grain that was required to produce that amount of meat? (Answer: The mass of the hamburger patty multiplied by 16, or 1816 g for a 1/4-lb patty.) Weigh out that amount of grain from the sack and show it to the class. Explain that we can compare the amount of energy lost by comparing the food value of the hamburger patty and the grain. Ask: Which would be more fattening? Eating the hamburger or eating all the grain? (Answer: Eating all the grain.)

Explain that we can calculate the food value of the hamburger and the grain by using a few simple facts. Hamburger is mostly protein, which is known to have a food value of 16.72 kJ/g*, and some fat which is known to have a food value of 37.62 kJ/g. Grain is mostly carbohydrate, which is known to have a food value of 16.72 kJ/g. Ask the class to calculate the food value (number of kilojoules) in the hamburger and in the grain. This would be 16.72 kJ/g × 113.5 g equals 1897.72 kJ for the hamburger; 16.72 kJ/g × 1816 g equals 30 363.52 kJ for the grain. Write the values determined by the class on the board. Ask: How much food value was lost in the conversion of grain to meat? (Answer: 30 363.52−1897.72 equals 28 465 kJ lost.) Discuss with the class what happened to those lost kilojoules. (They were used by the cattle to keep warm, move around, or to produce tissues that are not edible, such as hair and bone.) Tell the class that in Chapter 14, Section 1 they will learn about other energy pathways and forms of energy conversion.

*The food Calorie is equivalent to 4.18 kJ/g.

Activity 14.1a
Oil Recovery   page 614

Teacher Note
Students' notes will vary, but additional amounts of oil should be removed at each step. Emphasis should be placed on the increased difficulty and expense involved in obtaining greater percentages of oil. Recovery will never be complete.

Answers to Questions
1. Students should measure the amount they pumped into the beaker and calculate the percentage. The amount recovered divided by 100 equals the percentage. Answers will vary.
2. The oil will rise to the top of the recovered liquid. The amount of oil is determined by subtracting the amount of water at the bottom of the beaker from the total amount of liquid recovered. Answers will vary.
3. Use the method in Answer 2 to determine the amount of oil recovered. Answers will vary.
4. The amount of oil left in the bottle is calculated by subtracting the total amount recovered from 100 mL. Answers will vary.
5. The total amount recovered divided by 100 equals the percentage of the oil recovered.

Conclusion
Much of the oil in the earth is trapped in reservoirs filled with rock. The oil mixes with the rock and cannot be drawn into the well.

Activity 14.1b
Exponential Growth   page 618

Background Notes
You may wish to explain to the students how an exponent is expressed and what it means. Starting with the first square containing one penny, explain that $2^0 = 1$, $2^1 = 2$, $2^2 = 4$, $2^3 = 8$, and so forth. You may also wish to label each square. For example, square 1 is labeled 2^0, square 2 is labeled 2^1, square 3 is labeled 2^2, and so forth.

Answers to Questions
1. Squares 1 through 3 have 7 pennies.
2. There is one more penny on square 4 than on squares 1 through 3.
3. There are 64 pennies on square 7.
4. Square 7 has 64 pennies, one more than the first six squares.
5. Students will run out of pennies on square 9, since only five pennies will remain after square 8 is filled with 128 pennies.
6. Square 10 would have 512 pennies.

Conclusion
When the number of objects is doubled repeatedly, a very large number quickly results.

14.1 Section Review

Understanding the Concepts   page 623
17. Energy from the burning of fossil fuels, from falling water, or from nuclear reactions is used to heat water, which forms steam, which turns the turbines generating the electricity that runs the washing machine and may even heat the water.
18. Usable energy is being changed to other forms which are less usable as sources of energy.
19. Fossil fuels can cause air and water pollution along with destruction of land surfaces and plant and animal life.

14.2 Alternative Energy Resources

Concept Summary

A **renewable energy resource** is a source of usable energy that can be replaced as fast as it is used.
- Renewable energy resources will have to be used more and more to keep up with the world demand for energy.

Learning Objectives

1. To distinguish between renewable and nonrenewable energy resources.
2. To identify some alternative energy sources that may find use in the immediate future.
3. To describe different ways in which the sun's energy can be put to use.
4. To identify sources of energy that are the result of other natural causes.

Ideas for Discussion

Students will learn that because the supply of fossil fuels is limited, alternate sources of power will be needed in the next century.

Ask the class to imagine what their world would be like with no electricity. Ask: Which of your favorite activities would no longer be possible? (List the class's responses on the board.) Explain to the class that most electric power plants operate by burning fossil fuels and that the U.S. Department of Energy estimates that by the year 2050, the U.S. oil resources will be depleted. Ask: Will people in the future be willing to do without electric power? (Answer: Probably not.)

Tell the class that other sources of power are beginning to be explored and developed, but that much more work needs to be done before they will be ready to take the place of the fossil fuels we use now. Chapter 14, Section 2 describes the alternatives currently available to our present dependence on fossil fuels.

Suggested Demonstration

In this demonstration the students will learn how flat plate solar collectors trap and store solar energy. For this experiment you will need the following items:

shallow cardboard box, approximately 50 cm × 70 cm, lined with black paper or painted black on the inside.
3–4 m black rubber tubing, 2 cm diameter
2 tubing clamps
2 large buckets
2 thermometers
water

Tell the class that you are going to build a simple flat plate solar collector. Show them the box and the tubing. Ask: Why is black the color of choice for a solar collector? (Answer: Black absorbs light and radiation better than any other color.) To construct the solar collector, fill one bucket and the tubing with water.

When you are sure the tubing is filled, clamp both ends shut and arrange the tubing in a series of "s" curves inside the box one layer thick. Tell the class that the water inside the tubing will be heated by the solar radiation absorbed by the box and tubing.

We will use the thermometers to measure how much the sun has heated the water. Place the solar collector and the bucket of water in the sun on a counter or table. Submerge one end of the tubing in the bucket of water and remove the clamp. Place the other bucket on the floor and arrange the other end of the tubing so that it will fill the empty bucket. Adjust the clamp to a flow rate of 3–4 drops/second. Measure the temperature of the water in the top bucket. When the lower bucket begins to fill up, measure the temperature of its water. Record the two temperatures and calculate the difference. Explain that this type of solar collector is used to heat homes and provide hot water, and can be used in conjunction with previously existing systems to save on the use of fossil fuels. Tell the class that in Chapter 14, Section 2 they will explore the use of energy resources that do not involve fossil fuels or nuclear reactors.

Activity 14.2a
A Solar Cooker   page 631

Alternate Note

You may wish the students to try different types of foods. Thinly-sliced foods cook faster than thickly-sliced ones. Different kinds of meat can be used.

Answers to Questions

1. Answer will depend on the size of the umbrella. Some trial and error adjustment will be necessary.
2. The food should get hot at some locations in the solar cooker and not at others.
3. Answer will depend on the size of the umbrella, the air temperature, the time of day, and the size of the piece of meat or marshmallow.
4. Students may suggest a variety of improvements, from using better reflecting material to ways of orienting the cooker to obtain the best angle for collecting the sunlight.

Conclusion

If the sun's energy is concentrated at a point in a curved solar mirror, the heat that is generated is sufficient to cook food.

Activity 14.2b
Angle for Maximum Solar Energy   page 634

Teacher Note
If the sun is very high in the sky when this activity is done, two books may be needed to prop the envelope in the first position. When the envelope is in the correct position, it will cast the smallest possible shadow.

Answers to Questions
1. In the first position, sunlight hit the envelope at the smallest angle. In the third position, sunlight hit the envelope at the largest angle, about 90°.
2. The envelope warmed up the most at 90°. The envelope warmed up the least at the smallest angle.
3. A painted surface will dry fastest if it faces the sun directly.
4. Your nose faces the sun more directly than does the rest of your face.

Conclusion
The greater the angle of sunlight on an object, the more solar energy the object will absorb. Maximum solar energy is absorbed by a surface that is directly facing the sun (at an angle of 90°).

14.2 Section Review

Understanding the Concepts   page 640
22. Renewable energy resources are replaced rather quickly—as fast as they are used. Nonrenewable resources are used much faster than they can be replaced.
23. ▪ Direct-gain solar—the energy is stored in the construction materials that make up the building.
    ▪ Indirect solar—heat-storage materials collect energy behind large south-facing windows.
    ▪ Convection loop solar—the living space is enclosed within a second building that collects and circulates the heat.
    None of the passive solar homes uses fans or pumps to circulate the heat, although active solar homes do.
24. a. Locations on the coast of Maine might be able to use tidal energy, since they have access to the ocean tides.
    b. Southern California locations might use solar energy because of the high percentage of days with sunshine.
    (Accept other reasonable suggestions.)
25. 1) The shape of the shoreline; 2) adverse weather conditions; 3) the range of tidal differences; 4) the flow of water between the canal (or river) and the ocean.

14.3 Energy Conservation

Concept Summary

Conservation of energy is the saving of energy by eliminating its unnecessary uses and by preventing its waste.
- Conservation of fossil fuels will make them available for a longer time.
- Large amounts of energy can be saved through wiser use of the automobile.
- In the home, much energy can be saved by making the heating and cooling of space more efficient.
- Recycling of materials can reduce the energy used in manufacturing.

Learning Objectives
1. To recognize that energy conservation is needed to provide time to develop alternative energy sources.
2. To identify ways in which energy can be conserved.
3. To describe needs and practices for the future that would assist in conserving energy.

Ideas for Discussion
Students will learn how they as individuals can preserve the remaining supply of fossil fuel.

Explain to the class that because the fossil fuel supply is limited, it is important to use the remaining supply carefully, in order to make the most of what we have. Ask: What can we as individuals do right away to save energy? Discuss this question with the class and write their answers on the board. (Possible answers include dressing warmly indoors in order to keep the thermostate at a lower setting; turning off lights when not in use; etc.) Ask the students to start taking these measures at home, and to compare power bills before and after. Tell the class that in Chapter 14, Section 3 they will learn further ways to conserve energy.

Suggested Demonstration
In this demonstration the students will learn how power to their homes is measured and billed. For this demonstration you will need:
several copies of power bills, preferably from different homes
an opaque projector

Project the copy of the power bill on the screen for the class. Discuss with the class its various parts, and make them take note of the units used to bill usage. (Discussion will vary depending on the local power company and the type of energy involved.) Explain that electricity is measured in kilowatt hours. To give them an idea of how much electricity that is, explain that one kilowatt hour is enough to operate ten 100-watt light bulbs for one hour. Ask: How many kilowatt hours would it take to operate ten 60-watt light bulbs for one hour? (Answer: 0.6)

Using the information on the bill, have them calculate the price difference between operating the ten 100-watt bulbs for one hour and operating the ten 60-watt bulbs. (Answer: Based on a price of 7¢/kwh, the ten 60-watt bulbs would cost 4.2¢/kwh, a savings of 2.8¢.) Discuss the other parts of the bill, and compare the various bills. Tell the class that in Chapter 14, Section 3 they will learn ways to conserve energy and reduce their power bills.

Activity 14.3a
Surveying Your Car Usage   page 643

Answers to Questions
1. Answers will vary. Collect and compare the L/km. or gal/mi. data collected for the students' family cars.
2. Answers will vary. You may wish to discuss any differences in fuel-efficiency that may occur among the same kind of cars that were driven by different families.
3. Cars that did mostly freeway driving should be the most fuel-efficient.
4. Answers will vary. You may wish to use this question to help the students to become more aware of wasteful car usage.
5. The students should list any suggestions they have that might be effective in reducing car usage.

Conclusion
Examining the type of driving, the kind of trips taken, the fuel-efficiency, and the fuel costs of the family automobile can be used to determine if a family's driving habits are wasteful.

Activity 14.3b
Your Shower Usage   page 646

Teacher Note
You may wish to have some of the students measure the difference in the amount of warm water used for a 5-minute shower and a 15-minute shower.

Answers to Questions
1. Answers will vary among the students.
2. The difference equals the temperature of the warm water minus the temperature of the cold tap water.
3. Answers will vary with the length of the shower and the students' choice of bath water depth. A short shower should use less hot water than the average bath.

4. Answers will vary with the length of shower time and the students' choice of bath water depth. If the shower takes less than five minutes, more hot water is used for a tub bath.
5. Results will vary but should clearly indicate that a short shower uses less hot water than the average tub bath.
6. Students may suggest taking short showers, using cooler water for showering, or using less water for a tub bath.

Conclusion
A short shower should use less hot water than the average tub bath. However, if the shower takes longer than five minutes, more hot water is used than for a tub bath.

14.3 Section Review

Understanding the Concepts   page 653
13. Fossil fuels are nonrenewable energy resources. Additionally, they have many important uses apart from energy. Petroleum, for instance, is used to make fertilizers, insecticides, plastics, synthetic fibers, and many other products used worldwide.
14. More energy is required to freeze and package the food initially and to store it in frozen food sections and in home freezers.
15. A person can select the minimum brightness needed for each task.
16. Answers will vary.

14 Chapter Review

Critical Thinking   page 654
1. The energy is in a form that cannot be used.
2. Coal is used quickly but requires millions of years to be produced, while wood, with proper practices, can be replenished at the rate at which it is being used.
3. The increase in energy use in agriculture is due to population growth, reduction in soil fertility with use, and increased mechanization of farm practices.
4. The energy pathway is: Sun by photosynthesis to plant life, by fermentation to methane, by burning to heat, by turbines to electricity.
5. The roof overhang lets in sunlight in the winter when the angle of sun is low and blocks out sunlight in the summer when the sun is at a higher angle.
6. Reducing the amount of energy used means that the remaining resources will be available over a longer period of time.

Addison-Wesley

Physical Science

Gordon P. Johnson
Northern Arizona University

Bonnie B. Barr
State University of New York at Cortland

Michael B. Leyden
Eastern Illinois University

⚠ Addison Wesley Publishing Company, Inc.
Menlo Park, California ▪ Reading, Massachusetts ▪ Don Mills, Ontario
Wokingham, England ▪ Amsterdam ▪ Sydney ▪ Singapore ▪ Tokyo
Madrid ▪ Bogotá ▪ Santiago ▪ San Juan

Elaine Barrett
Teacher, Bellevue, Washington

Pat Obenauf
Associate Professor,
West Virginia University

Daniel Peterson
Teacher, Palo Alto, California

Cover photo: © Robert Arnold

ISBN 0-201-22206-X

ABCDEFGHIJKL-KR-8909876

Table of Contents

Chapter 5
194 Work and Heat

Activities and Special Interest Topics

Activities

Activities are listed by page number, chapter-section, and title.

Careers

Our Science Heritage

Working Safely in the Science Classroom

In studying physical science you will be doing various activities in your classroom or in the field. There are some important things to keep in mind when working on science activities. These things have to do with **safety.** There are safe ways to handle equipment and chemicals you will be using.

The first step to take in working safely is to read carefully the description of the activity or investigation you are about to do. Look for SAFETY NOTE cautions and read them before starting the activity or investigation. Some cautions will warn you about being careful to handle hot things with oven mitts or to avoid spilling or splashing hot liquids. Other cautions will remind you to be careful not to touch edges of knives or other sharp objects, or to avoid spilling certain chemicals on your skin or inhaling chemicals.

Find out where the fire extinguisher, first aid kit, and eyewash are located. Also learn how to use these in an emergency.

Some pieces of equipment that you will be using are easy to damage if they are not used properly. Be sure to notice how your teacher handles such equipment.

A few good rules to remember when working on physical science activities and investigations are:

1. Always *ask before doing* if you are uncertain about how to do any part of an activity or investigation.
2. Always make sure that a teacher or other supervisor is present when you are working with special equipment or using new techniques.
3. Notify your teacher or supervisor *immediately* in case of injury to yourself or others, or if equipment is damaged.

Being mindful of safe procedures while working in your science classroom will help you form good working habits as a student of science.

1 Building a Particle Model of Matter

Learning Objectives

■ **Process**

1. To identify basic steps in solving problems in science
2. To estimate the value of a measurement indirectly
3. To plot a graph and infer relationships from graph data
4. To classify data on the basis of similarities and differences
5. To predict the effects of changing variables in an experiment
6. To identify a balanced chemical equation

■ **Content**

1. To describe the characteristics of a controlled experiment
2. To distinguish among theories, hypotheses, and facts
3. To distinguish between observations and inferences
4. To compare substances on the basis of their different properties
5. To apply the particle model in explaining the nature of matter
6. To interpret chemical equations by identifying reactants and products

As rock breaks down from weathering, it reaveals smaller and smaller particles that made up the entire mass of rock. This is a scene from Monument Valley in Arizona.

Chapter 1
Science and Measurement

The tall, thin buret above the flask is marked with volume measurements so that the amount of liquid dropped into the flask can be determined. A dye called phenolphthalein is in the flask. This dye is colorless when the flask contains an acid. It turns purplish pink in a base. The photo shows the color change of the dye just after enough base was added from the buret to make the whole solution in the flask basic.

Science background information:
Science must be recognized as an ongoing process as well as a body of knowledge. Because of the everchanging state of scientific knowledge, it is important for every person to understand the criteria by which scientific knowledge is validated. What is accepted as a scientific fact is actually a consensus of what is most likely to be true based on the information available at the present time. The truth of a scientific fact is established by attempting to disprove it by all possible means. If it has not been disproved, then it is accepted as a fact until new evidence becomes available that disproves it. Thus, the nature of all scientific knowledge is provisional. The most fundamental principle in science, the law of conservation of energy, is accepted only because it has never been violated in any reproducible experiment. If that were to occur, the concept would have to be discarded and a new one sought.

The most important skill in science is that of observation. An observation is information, including measurements, that is gathered directly with the senses or indirectly by using instruments. In learning to observe one must give up preconceived ideas and "see what is there." Full-scale drawing

For detailed information about teaching this chapter, see Chapter 1 Planning Guide on pages T56–T57 in the front of this book.

Projectsheet 1 (TRB page 173) and Research Lab 1 (Lab Manual pages 15–16) may be used at any point in this chapter.

Chapter Preview

1.1 Scientific Methods

- **Observations**
- **The scientific method**
- **Controlled experiments**
- **Using models**
- **Scientific theories and laws**

Scientific investigations are carried out according to certain standards. Explanations must always be testable. They are revised as new information becomes known.

1.2 Measurement

- **Measurements and SI**
- **Length**
- **Area and volume**
- **Mass**
- **Density**
- **Temperature**
- **Time**
- **Measurement errors**
- **Graphing measured values**
- **Estimating and indirect measurement**

Scientists all over the world use the same system of measurement. One way of studying measurements is to graph them. Measurements that cannot be obtained directly can be obtained through other means.

is a good exercise for practicing observation as it requires that the features of an object be seen and recorded as they are. Systems of measurement exist to facilitate the recording and communication of observations.

Once observations have been accumulated, they can be examined for possible relationships. Often, mathematical manipulations of measured data, such as graphing, can point out hidden relationships. These relationships can be stated in the form of hypotheses and tested by controlled experiment. If the experimental evidence supports the predictions of the hypothesis, and these results are independently repeated by other scientists, the hypothesis is considered provisionally true. The scientific thinker becomes accustomed to withholding judgement and remaining in doubt when the evidence is insufficient.

1.3 Problem Solving

- **Steps in problem solving**
- **Calculating with units**
- **Dimensional analysis**
- **Converting between units**

The ability to solve word problems is a skill that can be improved through practice and by following good techniques.

For ideas for classroom demonstration and discussion, see Getting Started on page T58 in the front of this book.

1.1 Scientific Methods

Supplemental materials: Teaching Diagram 1-1 (TRB page 3), Reading Checksheet 1-1 (TRB page 81), Skillsheet 1-1 (TRB page 127), Investigation 1-1 (Lab Manual pages 3–4)

Section Preview

- Observations
- The scientific method
- Controlled experiments
- Using models
- Scientific theories and laws

Bracketed numbers are Section Review numbers correlated to that objective.

Learning Objectives

1. To describe the characteristics of a scientific hypothesis and how hypotheses are used. [4, 14, 15]
2. To identify the basic steps used in solving a problem in science. [3, 5, 6, 7, 8, 19]
3. To describe the characteristics of a controlled experiment. [1, 9, 10, 11, 17, 21]
4. To describe how scientists use and revise models. [13, 18, 20]
5. To distinguish between a theory and a hypothesis. [4, 13, 14, 15, 16]

Figure 1-1. *Explanations in science must agree with observations, or they will be discarded.*

Main Idea

What is physical science?

Science background information: All of science is indebted to the work of hundreds of men and women who spent their lives investigating and discussing the phenomena of the natural world. According to some estimates, about 90 percent of all of the scientists who ever lived are alive at this time.

What is science? You can think of it as a way of gathering and organizing information about the natural world. In this section, you will learn more about the methods used in science.

Physical science, the subject of this course, is the study of the nonliving part of the natural world. It includes the fields known as physics and chemistry. The fields of astronomy and geology, while also concerned with nonliving things, are really specialized applications of basic physical science.

Life science, on the other hand, is the study of the living part of the natural world. A good understanding of what happens to living things requires a knowledge of chemistry. Thus, physical science is a good background course for *all* further study in science.

Observations

New vocabulary: observation, direct observation, indirect observation

Scientific knowledge is based on **observations** of the natural world. An observation is information gathered through the use of the senses or with the aid of instruments.

Figure 1-2. *Telescopes are used in making observations of distant objects, such as stars and galaxies.*

Data Search

Donald Glaser received the Nobel Prize in physics for inventing a piece of equipment that could be used to study subatomic particles. What was this piece of equipment? Search pages 658–661.

The bubble chamber

Observations form the core of what is done in science. Investigation begins with observations. Questions arise and are pursued by further observations. These observations lead to new questions and new investigations. Scientific advances depend on observations.

You use your senses for many observations. You see the changing shape of the moon. You hear the thunder following a flash of lightning. You feel the heat from a burning candle. You smell the odor of ammonia gas as it escapes from a container. Observations made directly with your senses are called **direct observations.**

Your ability to observe can be extended through the use of instruments. Microscopes and telescopes enhance your "seeing." Electronic equipment detects sound too quiet or too high-pitched for you to hear. Thermometers and thermocouples detect small changes in temperature. Your senses of taste and smell might even be improved upon with the use of instruments. Observations made indirectly with the use of instruments are called **indirect observations.**

Main Idea

What are direct observations?

Main Idea

What are indirect observations?

Quick Review

1. How can observations lead to the need for new observations?
2. How does a direct observation differ from an indirect observation?

Quick Review answers:
1. When questions arise as a result of observations, they are pursued by further observations.
2. ■ Direct: Made directly with senses.
   ■ Indirect: Made with instruments.

1.1a   Direct and Indirect Observation

Science Processes: Observing, recording data, measuring

Materials   BASIC   20 minutes   Groups of 3

- **small solid object**
- **magnifying glass**
- **balance**
- **centimeter ruler**
- **beaker**
- **stirring rod**

Purpose

To use direct and indirect observation to determine the properties of a solid object.

Procedure

1. Use a data table like the one shown.
2. Examine the object using your senses. In your data table make a list of the properties you observe. SAFETY NOTE: *Do not taste the object. Unknown substances may be poisonous.*
3. Observe the object with a magnifying glass. Record what you see.
4. Use a balance to determine the mass of the object. Add the mass to your list of properties.
5. Use a centimeter ruler to measure at least one of the object's dimensions (length, width, height, or diameter). Add to your list of properties.
6. Place the object in a beaker of water. Stir and record your observations.

Questions

1. How did the appearance of the object differ under the magnifying glass?
2. Which data were obtained by direct observation?
3. Which data were obtained by indirect observation?

Conclusion

How do instruments extend your senses?

Step 5

Properties of a Solid Object
Observed with senses:
Observed with magnifying glass:
Mass:
Dimension (specify which):
Behavior in water:

The scientific method

New vocabulary: hypothesis, scientific method

In studying some problem in science, a scientist first has to assume that the events in the natural world are predictable. The scientist also assumes that there must be some laws of nature that these events depend upon. Even further, the scientist must assume that it is possible to uncover these laws through observations. These assumptions are basic to everything a scientist does. There is no purpose in conducting a scientific investigation unless these assumptions are made. The success of scientists in predicting events in the natural world gives credibility and builds confidence in these assumptions.

The steps followed by a scientist in conducting an investigation may not always be clear. However, there are certain activities that invariably occur. One of these activities is observation. Observations both initiate and verify the results of scientific investigation.

A **hypothesis** (hī-POTH′-uh-sis) is a tentative explanation for an event and is usually based on a number of observations. To be a good scientific hypothesis, the hypothesis has to be capable of being tested. Hypotheses are more than guesses as to the cause of an event. They provide direction for further investigation.

Sometimes competing or multiple hypotheses are used. For example, at one time materials that burned easily were thought to contain a special substance. Those materials that

Additional information:
The word *hypothesis* in Greek means groundwork, foundation, or supposition. This last meaning is close to its scientific use.

Figure 1-3. *When a jar is placed over a burning candle, the flame goes out. What hypothesis explains this?* The candle has used up all the oxygen in the air in the jar.

Activity

See also Activity Record Sheet 1-1B (Lab Manual page 2). Preparation Notes, Answers to Questions, and Conclusion appear on page T59 in the front of this book.

1.1b Formulating a Hypothesis: What Is in the Box?

Science Processes: Observing, hypothesizing, predicting

Materials 15 to 25 minutes Entire class

- **sealed box containing an unknown object**

Purpose

To use the scientific method to determine the identity of a hidden object.

Procedure

1. Use a data table like the one shown.
2. Observe some of the properties of an unknown object sealed in a box by briefly handling the box. Record the properties you have observed. Pass the box around the classroom so that everyone can handle it.
3. Ask your teacher one question that will reveal more information about the object. Word the question so that it can be answered a chance to ask a question. Record each answer and its question.
4. Use the information from your observations and the answers to the questions asked by the students to make an "educated guess," or hypothesis, about the identity of the object. Write down your guess.

Questions

1. Which processes in the scientific method were used to identify the object?
2. What kinds of questions were most helpful in identifying the object?
3. What other kinds of tests or experiments could you use to determine what is in a box?

Conclusion

Why is the scientific method a good approach to problem-solving?

Step 2

Properties of Object Sealed in Box		
Observed by handling box:		
Question	Yes	No

did not burn easily were thought not to contain the special substance. According to this hypothesis, burning was the giving off of this special substance.

An alternate hypothesis that was advanced later was that burning was the combining of the material with a part of air–oxygen. For a time, both of these hypotheses were used. Both could be tested.

Both hypotheses about burning explain why a candle will burn down completely. According to the first hypothesis, the candle has enough of the substance that allows it to burn. According to the second hypothesis, there is enough oxygen in the air for the candle to burn completely.

Predictions result from and are based on hypotheses. As long as a hypothesis suggests correct predictions, it is useful. If it leads to any incorrect predictions, it must be changed or discarded.

What do the two hypotheses about burning predict will happen to a burning candle when a jar is placed over it? The first predicts that the candle will still burn down completely. The second predicts that the candle will go out when the oxygen in the air inside the jar has been used up.

Predictions lead to more observations. When you place a jar over a burning candle, does the flame go out? Yes, it does. The first hypothesis must be incorrect. This observation does not prove that the second hypothesis is correct. You can tell only that a hypothesis is *not* correct, and that is when it leads to an incorrect prediction.

The process a scientist actually uses in solving a problem in science can vary. However, it is based on the following.

1. State the problem.
2. Make observations.
3. Make one or more testable hypotheses.
4. Make predictions that test the hypotheses.
5. Check the predictions against more observations.
6. Change or discard a hypothesis that leads to incorrect predictions.

These steps form what is known as the **scientific method.**

Quick Review

1. What are the important characteristics of a scientific hypothesis?
2. How does a scientist tell whether a hypothesis is incorrect?

Main Idea

What are predictions based on?

Main Idea

Does an observation prove that a hypothesis is correct?

Controlled experiments
New vocabulary: controlled experiment, variable, manipulated variable, data

Hypotheses and the predictions suggested by these hypotheses are tested by **controlled experiments.** A controlled experiment is an investigation in which the factors that influence the outcome are kept the same except for the one whose effect is being studied.

The factors that influence the outcome of an experiment are called **variables** (VAYR'-ee-uh-bulz). All the variables should be kept the same throughout the experiment except the one whose effect is being studied. The variable that is intentionally changed or manipulated is called the **manipulated variable.** The outcome is sometimes called the *responding variable.*

As an example, suppose you make a hypothesis that the number of swings per second of a pendulum is determined by the mass of the pendulum. A prediction follows that this swing rate should change as you change the mass of the pendulum.

An experiment to test the prediction is easily set up. Pendulum balls of different mass are attached in turn to a string

Main Idea

What are variables?

Figure 1-4. *In a controlled experiment to test the effect of mass on the swing rate of a pendulum, balls of different mass are used. What should be kept the same?*

Length of string, position of ball before release, shape of ball in order to compare their swing rates. The number of swings in a given time interval for each mass tried is counted. The number of swings and the mass of each pendulum are recorded.

These collected and recorded observations are **data.** One way to look for patterns in data is to plot the data on a graph. The interpretation of the results gives evidence to either support or reject the hypothesis.

There are other factors that might affect the swing rate of a pendulum. For example, the length of the string, the position of the ball before release, and the shape of the pendulum ball might also affect the swing rate. For this to be a controlled experiment, those factors must not change during the experiment. The mass of the pendulum is being varied intentionally, so it is the manipulated variable. The swing rate can be considered the responding variable.

The experiment could be changed so that a different variable—for instance, length—was the manipulated variable. Then the mass of the pendulum would be one of the variables that would have to be constant. How would you test to see whether the initial position of the ball has an effect on the swing rate of the pendulum?

It is difficult to be sure that all the variables really are being controlled. Thus, scientists insist that an experiment be repeatable. That is, someone else must be able to repeat the experiment and obtain the same results. If an experiment contradicts a hypothesis that has survived many previous tests, scientists look for some variable that may not have been controlled.

One way to determine whether all variables are being controlled is to include one or more **controls** in the experiment. A control is something used as a standard. It should be like what is being used in the experiment except that *none* of its variables are manipulated. For example, suppose you want to find out whether a new process for making steel will produce steel rods that are stronger. As controls you should use steel rods made under the old process, and run the same tests on both sets of rods.

Quick Review

1. What is the relationship of an experiment to a hypothesis?
2. How do you recognize whether an experiment is controlled?
3. Why should an experiment be repeatable?

Main Idea

What is another name for recorded observations?

Keep everything the same except the initial position of the ball.

Critical Thinking

Suppose that scientists in two different laboratories do the same experiment but get different results. What should they do to reconcile these differences?
They should carefully compare the procedures they used, the experimental conditions in their laboratories, and any other factors that might affect the results. What they should try to find is variables that have not been adequately controlled.

Quick Review answers:
1. An experiment is a test of a hypothesis.
2. In a controlled experiment all variables but the one whose effect is being studied are kept the same throughout the experiment.
3. If someone else can repeat an experiment and obtain the same results, there is less chance that some unknown variables were affecting the results.

Using models

New vocabulary: inference, model

A good part of what goes on in science involves thinking about the data that have been collected. Scientists look for patterns in the data and try to draw conclusions. An **inference** (IN'-fer-uns) is a logical conclusion drawn from information that is available.

Scientists usually use many inferences to try to put together an overall picture of what is taking place. They often try to describe something unfamiliar in terms of familiar things. Such descriptions are called **models.**

Models are helpful when it is not possible to observe the object or event directly or completely. For example, the sun, moon and five planets were familiar to early observers of the heavens. Yet, it is not possible to observe the relationship of these seven objects to each other directly. Early scientists suggested a model of the solar system with the earth at the center. According to this model, the sun, moon, and five visible planets moved around the earth in circular paths. This model was used to both explain and predict the changing positions of these objects.

As it was adjusted to agree with more observations, the earth-centered model became more complicated. Copernicus (1473–1543), a Polish astronomer, proposed an alternate model with the sun at the center and the earth and other planets moving around the sun. The only thing moving

Science background information:
Ptolemy is given credit for developing the model for the solar system with the earth at the center. The model was sufficiently good to enable astronomers to predict the positions of the planets for many centuries.

Science background information:
One reason that Copernicus had for developing a new model of the solar system was that the astronomical observations of Tycho Brahe were more accurate than any observations that had been made before. His careful observations could not be fitted into the model of the solar system developed by Ptolemy.

Figure 1-5. *This drawing from a book by Copernicus shows the sun ("Sol") at the center. The earth ("Terra") has a circular path beyond those of the planets Mercury and Venus. The moon is shown with a circular path around the earth.*

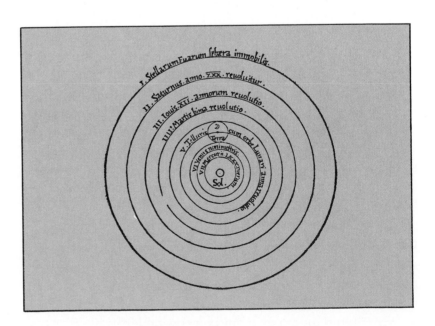

around the earth was the moon. This model made it easier to explain the observed changes in position of the planets, sun, and moon. The model met with great resistance from people who believed that the earth *must* be the center of everything, but finally received general acceptance.

A scientific model develops as the result of many observations, inferences, and hypotheses. The hypotheses are tested and revised or discarded. The model is then changed in order to agree with the new observations and revised hypotheses.

As long as the model can be used to explain observations and make good predictions, it is used. Like a hypothesis, a model can never be proved correct. However, when it contradicts observations, it may be revised or discarded for a new or better model. In Chapter 3 you will learn about several different models of the atom that have been used to explain what was known at the time.

Quick Review

1. What is meant by a model in science?
2. What is required of a good scientific model?

Scientific theories and laws

New vocabulary: theory, law

The word *theory* in science means something different from its everyday meaning. In everyday speech, a theory is like a hypothesis a tentative explanation that may or may not be correct. However, to a scientist, a **theory** is a well-tested model or set of hypotheses about some aspect of the natural world. For example, physical science covers the theory of the atom; life science covers the cell theory. Once something has become a theory, it is well accepted by scientists because it agrees with many observations and experiments.

Even so, a theory in science is not fixed. It is changed as new evidence is gathered. For example, the theory of the atom has changed greatly in the last hundred years as scientists have learned more about the inside of atoms.

A **law** in science is a general statement that describes relationships accurately, as tested by many experiments. For example, Newton's laws of motion describe how forces affect the motion of objects. Coulomb's law states how the forces between electrically charged particles changes as the distance between them changes. Laws are often summarized in the form of mathematical equations.

Critical Thinking

If there are two different models to explain a set of observations about the natural world, why do scientists often prefer to use the simpler model rather than the more complex one?
The simpler model is usually thought to be more valid. (Read about William of Ockham to learn more about the reasoning behind this.)

Quick Review answers:
1. A scientific model is a description of something unfamiliar in terms of something familiar.
2. A good scientific model should be based on hypotheses that have stood up against many experimental tests.

Main Idea

How does the use of the word *theory* by a scientist differ from the ordinary use of the word?

Critical Thinking

Suppose that in the laboratory you do an experiment whose results seem to contradict a law of physical science? Why should you be cautious about announcing that the law has been proven inadequate or wrong?
A law of physical science has a great number of tests and experiments to support it. An experiment that gets different results from a generally accepted law needs to be repeated many times.

A law can provide predictions of behavior without necessarily explaining the behavior. Coulomb's law, for example, does not answer the question of what electric charge is, only how it behaves.

Scientific laws, like theories and models, must be consistent with observations. A law must provide accurate predictions. A law will be refined when it is determined that it is not true under all conditions.

Quick Review

1. Describe the difference between a hypothesis and a theory.
2. In what form are scientific laws usually expressed?

Our Science Heritage

SI: The Metric System

This cylinder is a copy of the one-kilogram standard mass kept in France. This copy is kept at the Bureau of Standards in Washington, D.C.

The international metric system has been known officially as SI since 1960. The initials SI come from the French title *Le Système International d'Unités* (the International System of Units).

The metric system was invented in France about 200 years ago. Before then, the French had many confusing and different ways to measure lengths and masses. French scientists wanted an easy, simple system of measurement. They decided to base the measurements for length and mass on decimal numbers.

The French scientists began with a standard measurement for length, the meter. It represented one ten-millionth of the measured distance from the North Pole to the Equator. A platinum bar was made to represent this length. The centimeter was then one hundredth of this meter.

The gram was chosen to be the mass of one cubic centimeter of pure water. A platinum cylinder of mass 1000 g, or one kilogram, was made to represent the kilogram.

In 1840 the metric system became the official measuring system in France. Other countries soon adopted it. Of all the measuring systems in use, metric was the easiest to learn. When different countries used the same system, they could be sure they were measuring things in exactly the same way.

The SI standards for length and other units—even time— are now defined in such a way that laboratories all over the world can recreate them. An international committee occasionally refines the definitions.

1.1 Section Review

Answers to Understanding the Concepts appear on page T59 in the front of this book. Blackline master test for this section: Section Testsheet 1-1 (TRB page 201)

Vocabulary

11 control
9 controlled experiment
8 data
7 direct observation
4 hypothesis
6 indirect observation
2 inference
12 law
1 manipulated variable
14 model
5 observation
3 scientific method
13 theory
10 variable

Vocabulary Review

Match each term above with the numbered phrase that best describes it.

1. Variable that is intentionally changed
2. Logical conclusion drawn from available information
3. Set of several steps that outline how a scientist attacks a problem
4. Tentative explanation for an event
5. Information gathered through the senses or with instruments
6. Information gathered with instruments
7. Information gathered directly with the senses
8. Collected and recorded observations
9. Investigation in which all variables are kept the same except one
10. Factor that influences the outcome of an experiment
11. Standard used for comparison in an experiment
12. General statement that describes relationships
13. Well-tested model or set of hypotheses
14. Description of something unfamiliar in terms of something familiar

Review Questions

Multiple Choice: Choose the answer that best completes each of the following sentences.

15. To be useful, a hypothesis should be _?_.
    a. in mathematical form
    b. able to be proved correct
    c. able to be proved incorrect
    d. a creative guess made without regard to known observations
16. A theory in science is _?_.
    a. a reasonable guess
    b. well tested and generally accepted
    c. a mathematical equation
    d. an unchanging statement of scientific truth
17. An experiment must _?_.
    a. be repeatable
    b. prove a hypothesis incorrect
    c. prove a hypothesis correct
    d. involve at least two variables that are manipulated
18. In general, a model in science _?_.
    a. is a reduced physical representation of the real thing
    b. describes something unfamiliar in terms of mathematical symbols
    c. describes something unfamiliar in terms of familiar things
    d. is accepted only after it has been proved correct

Understanding the Concepts

19. Explain why observations are considered the core of all activity in science.
20. How is a model in science different from an architect's model of a proposed new building?
21. What information can be obtained by using a control in an experiment?

For ideas for classroom demonstration and discussion, see Getting Started on page T60 in the front of this book.

1.2 Measurement

Supplemental materials: Teaching Diagrams 1-2A, 1-2B, 1-2C, (TRB pages 4, 5, 6), Reading Checksheet 1-2 (TRB page 82), Skillsheet 1-2 (TRB page 128), Investigation 1-2 (Lab Manual pages 9–10)

Section Preview

- **Measurements and SI**
- **Length**
- **Area and volume**
- **Mass**
- **Density**
- **Temperature**

- **Time**
- **Measurement errors**
- **Graphing measured values**
- **Estimating and indirect measurement**

Bracketed numbers are Section Review questions correlated to that objective.

Learning Objectives

1. To identify the SI units commonly used for length, mass, temperature, time, and certain other derived units. [1–19, 26, 28–30, 3
2. To recognize the presence of some amount of error in every measurement that is made. [33]
3. To plot a graph of data and infer from the graph whether a relationship exists between the two variables plotted. [20, 21, 22]
4. To estimate the value of a large or small measurement using indirect procedures. [25, 33]

Figure 1-6. *The calipers (top) and the micrometer (bottom) are both instruments used for measuring small distances more precisely than can be done with a ruler.*

Some properties are described with words alone. For example, chlorine is an element that is a yellowish-green gas. Three properties of chlorine have just been described in words. Other properties are described with numbers. In Section 1.2 you will learn more about how numbers are used to answer "how" questions—"how much," "how hot," "how long," etc.

Measurements and SI

New vocabulary: measurement, SI

When you observe a property that is described with numbers, you are making a **measurement.** Suppose you find that a certain amount of salt balances a 50-gram piece. You have measured the mass of the salt. Your measurement answers the question, How much salt is there?

Mass, length, and volume are three properties often measured in science. Another property often measured is temperature. Temperature describes the hotness or coldness of a substance. It doesn't depend on the amount of substance. A glass of water and a bathtub of water can be at the same temperature.

Something else is often measured in science, but it is not a property of matter. That something is time. In science, you may measure how long it takes for some event to happen.

Measurements have two parts. There is a number followed by a unit. A mass cannot be simply 50. Rather, it is 50 grams or 50 kilograms or perhaps 50 metric tons. The modern metric system, known as **SI,** contains all the units scientists have agreed to use for all their measurements. The letters *SI* come from the French name for *international system*. SI has units for measurements of all sizes—from very large to very small. In this course, you will be using SI units. You will also use a few older metric units convenient for everyday use.

Quick Review

1. What are the two parts of a measurement?
2. Are SI units metric?

Length

New vocabulary: meter, kilometer, millimeter, centimeter

The basic SI unit of length is the **meter.** One meter is about the distance from the floor to the knob of a door. The short form, or symbol, for the name *meter* is m. Most doors are about 2 m in height. Try holding your hands a distance of 1 m apart. Now compare the distance between your hands to the length of a meter stick. How close were you?

Large distances are described and measured in **kilometers** (KIL'-uh-meet'-erz). The prefix *kilo-* means *one thousand*. One

Figure 1-8. *How well can you estimate a distance of 1 m?*

Teaching suggestion:
Many educators feel that it is better for students to first associate metric (SI) units with the sizes of everyday objects, familiar to them, instead of learning the relationship of metric to English units. For example, students should be able to conceptualize a meter as the distance from the floor to their waist, or the width of a certain window, before trying to define it as 1.1 yards, or 39.37 inches.

kilometer (symbol km) is one thousand meters. A fast runner can run a distance of 1 km in just under three minutes.

Smaller distances may be measured in **millimeters** (mm). The prefix *milli-* means *one thousandth*. A millimeter is 1/1000 of a meter. A dime is about 1 mm in thickness.

Another unit for measuring small distances is the **centimeter** (cm). The prefix *centi-* means *one hundredth*. A centimeter is 1/100 of a meter. A centimeter is equal to 10 mm. Your little finger is about 1 cm across.

Examine a meter stick. Identify the marks indicating the length of a centimeter and a millimeter. How many centimeters are in a meter? With a little practice it is easy to change from one unit to another.

Meter, kilometer, centimeter, and millimeter are the common units used to describe length. Other units of length are also used. They have different prefixes but all end in *-meter*. Even very large and very small distances can be described with appropriate prefixes.

Quick Review answers:
1. millimeter, mm
   centimeter, cm
   meter, m
   kilometer, km
2. a. 1000
   b. 1/100
   c. 1/1000

Quick Review

1. Give the name and symbol for four SI length units.

2. State the meaning of each of the following prefixes.

   a. kilo-

   b. centi-

   c. milli-

Area and volume
New vocabulary: area, square meter, square centimeter, square millimeter, volume, cubic meter, cubic centimeter, liter, milliliter

The amount of space on a surface is called **area.** For example, a rug covers a certain area of a floor. The top of your desk has a certain area. A tennis court has a definite play area.

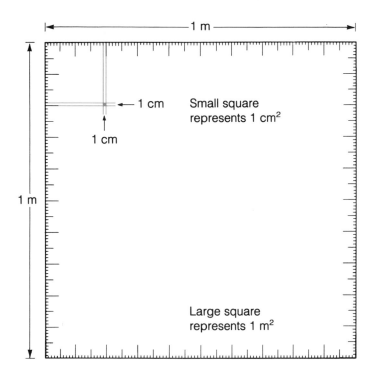

1 m

← 1 cm

Small square represents 1 cm²

1 cm

1 m

Large square represents 1 m²

A square that is 1 m on each side has an area of one **square meter.** The basic SI unit of area is the square meter (symbol m²). An open newspaper covers an area of about 1 m². The surface of an ordinary door is about 2 m².

Smaller areas can be described in square centimeters or square millimeters. A **square centimeter** (cm²) is the area of a square 1 cm on each side. A **square millimeter** (mm²) is the area of a square 1 mm on each side.

What units would you use to describe the area of the top of your desk? The area of a sheet of writing paper? The area of the floor in your classroom?

- Desk: square centimeters
- Paper: square centimeters
- Floor: square meters

The amount of space something fills up is its **volume.** A cube that is 1 m on each side has a volume of one **cubic meter.** The basic SI unit of volume is the cubic meter (symbol m³). The volume of a refrigerator is a little over 1 m³. The volume of a bedroom is about 40 m³.

A cubic meter is quite a large volume. You often need to measure much smaller volumes. A **cubic centimeter** (cm³) is the volume of a cube that is 1 cm on each side. A small die has a volume of about 1 cm³.

For everyday use, a metric volume unit between a cubic centimeter and a cubic meter is convenient. A **liter** (LEE′-ter) is the volume of a cube 10 cm on each side. The symbol capital L has come to be used for liter, although you may see lower case l used sometimes.

Figure 1-10. *A person sitting on the floor fits inside a space of one cubic meter.*

Figure 1-11. *How many little cubes of volume 1 cm³ fit inside a bigger cube of volume 1 L?*
10 × 10 × 10, or 1000

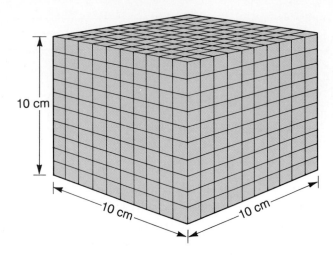

10 cm

10 cm

10 cm

Critical Thinking

If the cube in Figure 1-11 were 6 cm on a side, how many cubes of volume 1 cm³ would fit inside it?
6 × 6 × 6, or 216

Quick Review answers:
1. Square meter, m²
2. 1000
3. 1
4. 1 mL, 10 cm³, 100 mL, 1 L, 1 m³

How many cubic centimeters equal a liter? Ten small cubes 1 cm on a side fit along one side of a bigger cube 10 cm on a side. Ten rows of small cubes would cover the bottom of the bigger cube. And ten layers of small cubes would fill up the bigger cube. Altogether, it takes 10 × 10 × 10, or 1000, small cubes to fill the bigger cube. Each small cube has a volume of 1 cm³. So a liter (L) equals 1000 cm³.

The prefix *milli-* means *one thousandth*. A **milliliter** (mL) is equal to 1/1000 of a liter. One thousandth of a liter is also equal to 1 cm³. So 1 mL equals 1 cm³. This is a useful relationship to remember. The two separate volume units can be substituted for one another. Containers for measuring the volume of liquids are usually marked in milliliters.

Quick Review

1. Give the name and symbol for the basic SI unit of area.
2. How many cubic centimeters are there in one liter?
3. How many cubic centimeters are there in one milliliter?
4. List the following volume measurements in order from smallest to largest: 1 L, 1 mL, 1 m³, 10 cm³, 100 mL.

Mass

New vocabulary: kilogram, gram, milligram

The **kilogram** (kg) is the basic SI unit for mass. A liter of water has a mass of one kilogram, or 1 kg. One kilogram equals one thousand **grams** (g). A large paper clip has a mass of about 1 g.

You know that 1 L equals 1000 mL. So 1 mL of water has a mass of 1 g. If you know the volume of some water, you can calculate its mass from this relationship. For example, the

Figure 1-12. *What is the mass of 500 mL of water? Of a paper clip? Of a straight pin?*
- water: 500 g
- paper clip: 1 g
- straight pin: 120 mg

mass of 15 mL of water is 15 g. What is the mass of 175 mL of water?

175 g

For masses of less than 1 g, the **milligram** (mg) is a convenient unit. From the prefix, can you tell how many milligrams are in a gram? A straight pin has a mass of about 120 mg.

1000 mg

Quick Review

1. What is the mass of 1 L of water?
2. Which has a greater mass—a large paper clip or 10 mL of water? Explain how you know.

Quick Review answers:
1. 1000 g or 1 kg
2. The water has the greater mass— 10 g. The paper clip has a mass of 1 g.

Density

New vocabulary: density

If you saw a piece of wood in half, the smaller pieces will have less mass *and* less volume than the original piece. However, if you divide the mass by the volume, the value of this quotient remains the same. The mass of anything divided by the volume of that thing is called the **density.**

$$\text{density} = \frac{\text{mass}}{\text{volume}}$$

Critical Thinking

Suppose two balls, A and B, have the same mass, but A has a greater volume. Which ball has the greater density?

B has the greater density.

The density of a piece of wood does not change when you cut it up into smaller pieces. The density of a material does not depend on the amount of the material.

The units of density are a mass unit divided by a volume unit, such as grams per cubic centimeter. The word "per" means "divided by." When density units are written with symbols, a slash (/) is used for the word "per":

$$\text{grams per cubic centimeter} = \text{g/cm}^3$$

Figure 1-13. *The density of aluminum is always 2.7 g/cm³ whether the aluminum is in a piece of foil or in a cheese slicer.*

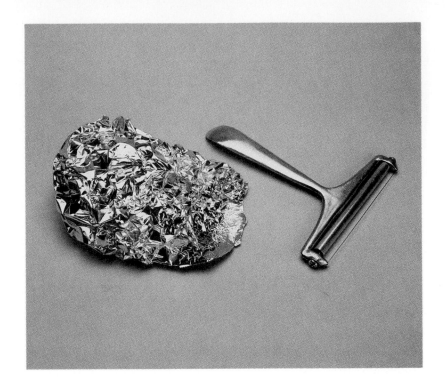

Substance	Density (in g/cm³)
Gold	19.3
Mercury	13.6
Lead	11.3
Silver	10.5
Copper	8.9
Steel	7.9
Iron	7.9
Aluminum	2.7
Sea water	1.03
Water at 4°C	1.00
Ice	0.92
Pine wood	0.50
Balsa wood	0.12
Oxygen	0.0013
Hydrogen	0.00009

Table 1-1. *Densities of some common substances.*

For example, water has a density of 1.0 g/cm³. Aluminum has a density of 2.7 g/cm³. This means that if you had one cubic centimeter each of water and aluminum, the water would have a mass of 1.0 g and the aluminum would have a mass of 2.7 g. Two cubic centimeters of water would have twice as much mass, or 2.0 g. What would be the mass of 2 cm³ of aluminum?

Another way of saying "mass divided by volume" is "mass per unit volume." When density is expressed in units of g/cm³, one *unit volume* is one cubic centimeter. The value of the density states the mass per unit volume.

Density can be used to identify a substance. Polished aluminum and steel look alike, but their densities are different. Table 1-1 gives the densities of a few common substances. Note that lead has a higher density than all but two substances on the list. When you think of lead as being heavy, you really mean "heavy for its size," that is, dense.

Quick Review
1. How does the density of a substance depend on the amount of the substance?
2. Which has the greater density—200 g of lead or 500 g of aluminum?

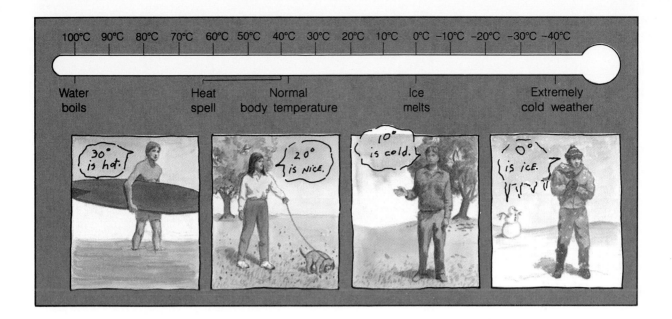

Figure 1-14. *Some important Celsius temperatures.*

Temperature

New vocabulary: Celsius

The everyday temperature scale used with SI units is the **Celsius** scale. On the Celsius scale, the melting temperature of ice is 0°C. Liquid water boils at 100°C (at sea level). Normal room temperature is about 20°C. Normal body temperature is 37°C. On a very warm day the temperature may surpass 40°C. Some of the coldest temperatures during winter may reach below −40°C.

Quick Review

1. What change takes place at 0°C?
2. What change takes place at 100°C?

Quick Review answers:
1. Ice melts.
2. Water boils.

Time

New vocabulary: second, millisecond

The basic SI unit of time, the **second** (s), is very familiar to you. In scientific work, only the second and the appropriate prefixes are used. For example, many time intervals are measured in **milliseconds** (ms). A millisecond is 1/1000 of a second. In everyday measurements, the minute (min) and hour (h) are also used.

Table 1-2 lists units for length, area, volume, mass, temperature, and time. The common SI units are included along with some everyday units that can be used with SI but are not part of the SI system of units.

Main Idea

Why has the second become a most important unit of time?

Table 1-2. *Some common SI units.*

Used for	Name	Symbol
1000	kilo-	k-
1/100	centi-	c-
1/1000	milli-	m-
length	meter	m
	kilometer	km
	centimeter	cm
	millimeter	mm
area	square meter	m²
	square centimeter	cm²
	square millimeter	mm²
volume	cubic meter	m³
	cubic centimeter	cm³
	* liter	L
	* milliliter	mL
mass	kilogram	kg
	gram	g
	milligram	mg
temperature	* degree Celsius	°C
time	second	s
	millisecond	ms
	* minute	min
	* hour	h

* Not an SI unit but may be used along with SI units.

Research Topic

Table 1-2 lists only three prefixes. Find out what other prefixes are used with SI units, and give examples of quantities measured in units that have these prefixes.

Quick Review answer:
The second(s)

Quick Review

What is the name and symbol of the basic SI unit of time?

Measurement errors

Different observers using the same measuring device often find different values. Also, different instruments used for measurement give different values. For example, a student using different meter sticks may report different values for the same length. Measurements can never be exact. Some error in measured values is always present.

An average value can be calculated if the same measurement is repeated. The average is usually better than a single

Activity

1.2a Differences in Length Measurements

Science Processes: Measuring, recording data, reading a table, using numbers

Materials   20 minutes   Entire class

- **meter stick**
- **large desk or table**
- **index card or small piece of paper (one per student)**

Purpose

To discover how different measurements of the same object can have different values.

Procedure

In the following procedure, each student will make the same measurement with the same meter stick.

1. Measure the length of a large desk or table with a meter stick. Read the meter stick to the nearest tenth of a centimeter.
2. Record the measurement on the card or paper. (Do not tell anyone the value of the measurement you made.)
3. Give the card with your name and measurement on it to your teacher. (When everyone has finished, your teacher will write each value on the board.)
4. Calculate the sum of all the measurements. Find the average value of these measurements by dividing the sum by the number of measurements made.
5. Find the largest measurement made. Calculate the difference between the largest measurement and the average.
6. Find the smallest measurement made. Calculate the difference between the smallest measurement and the average. The larger of the two differences found here and in Step 5 is an estimate of the possible error.

Questions

1. Were all the values the same?
2. Why do you think there were different values for the same measurement? List at least three different reasons.
3. What is the possible error in the measurement of the desk?
4. How could the error in the measurement be reduced?

Conclusion

Why is the average value probably the best value for the size of the desk?

Step 1

Step 1

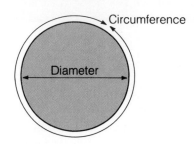

Figure 1-15. *Is the circumference of a circle always larger than the diameter?*
Yes

Diameter	Circumference
5.0 cm	15.7 cm
4.0 cm	12.6 cm
3.0 cm	9.4 cm
2.0 cm	6.3 cm
1.0 cm	3.1 cm

Table 1-3. *Measurements of five circles.*

measurement. Values that are too large are cancelled out by values that are too small. Measurements in science are repeated to reduce the amount of possible error in the measurement.

Quick Review

Why is it better to use the average of several measurements rather than a single measurement?

Graphing measured values
New vocabulary: diameter, circumference, origin, vertical axis, horizontal axis

Graphing is a way of looking for possible relationships between two measurements. For example, two different measurements of a circle can be made. The **diameter** (dī-AM′-uh-ter) of a circle is the straight-line distance across the circle through the center of the circle. The **circumference** (ser-KUM′-fer-ens) of a circle is the distance around the circle. The diameter and circumference of several different size circles can be measured. Suppose the results shown in Table 1-3 are obtained.

The measurements can be plotted on a graph. A simple graph is made as follows. On a piece of graph paper, draw a horizontal line along one of the printed lines near the left. The intersection, or meeting point, of the two lines is called the **origin.** The vertical line is the **vertical axis.** The horizontal line is the **horizontal axis.** The other lines on the graph paper divide the axes into equal-length sections.

Assign each of the two measured quantities to one of the two axes. Label each axis with the quantity and the units used to measure it.

Study Figure 1-17. Notice that the value of each quantity is represented by a certain distance from the origin. For each quantity, a scale was chosen that included all the values measured. For example, all the circumference values fall between 0.0 cm and 16.0 cm. Each small space along the vertical axis represents 1.0 cm. Values are marked every 2.0 cm to avoid cluttering the axis. What does each small space along the horizontal axis represent? Each space represents 0.5 cm of the diameter.

Notice the five points on the graph. Each point marks the intersection of the diameter and circumference values for one circle. For example, for the first circle, the dashed vertical line for diameter 5.0 cm intersects the dashed horizontal line for circumference 15.7 cm. The position of 15.7 cm is found by reading to the nearest tenth of a space.

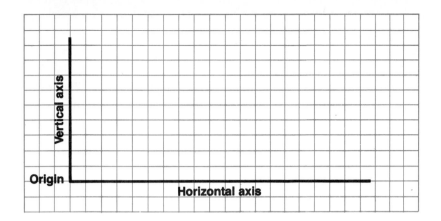

Figure 1-16. *On a graph, what point is the origin?*
The origin is where the vertical axis and horizontal axis meet.

Notice that the five points for the five circles happen to lie along a straight line. This line shows how the two measurements of a circle are related. The line can be used to predict the circumference of any other circle if the diameter is known. For example, a circle with a diameter of 3.5 cm would be expected to have a circumference of 11.0 cm. (See where the dashed vertical line for diameter 3.5 cm meets the slanted graph line.) What is the circumference of a circle of diameter 0.0 cm? Is this answer what you would expect?

Critical Thinking

What is the diameter of a circle of circumference 8.0 cm?
The diameter is a little over 2.5 cm.

The circumference would be 0.0 cm—there would be no circle at all!

Figure 1-17. *Graph of the measurements in Table 1-3.*

1.2b Graphing Measurements of Blocks

Science Processes: Measuring, recording data, using numbers, making a graph, predicting

Materials   BASIC   40 minutes   Individual work

- **5 rectangular blocks of the same kind of wood (different sizes)**
- **graph paper**
- **balance**
- **meter stick**

Purpose

To determine how the mass and volume of different size blocks of the same wood are related.

Procedure

1. Use a table like the one shown to record your data.
2. Measure and record the mass in grams of one wooden block.
3. Measure and record the length, width, and thickness in centimeters of the same block.
4. Calculate and record the volume in cubic centimeters. (*Hint:* The volume is equal to the length times the width times the thickness.)
5. Make and record the same measurements (mass, length, width, and thickness) for three more blocks. Save the fifth block for Step 7.
6. Calculate the volume for each block. Record your results.
7. Measure *only* the length, width, and thickness of the fifth block. DO NOT measure the mass of this block at this time. Record your measurements and calculate the volume.
8. Prepare a graph like the one shown to plot the mass and volume of the four blocks.
9. Plot your mass and volume values for each block of wood. Draw a straight line through your points.
10. Using your graph, predict the mass of the fifth block of wood. Record your prediction. Check your prediction by measuring the mass of the block on the balance.

Questions

1. Do the points on your graph lie on a straight line?
2. What happens to the mass of a wood block as the volume is increased?
3. According to your graph, does doubling the volume double the mass?
4. What is the mass of a wood block of zero volume? Is this the answer you would expect?

Conclusion

How is the mass of a wood block related to its volume?

Mass (in grams)

Volume (in cubic centimeters)

Block	1	2	3	4	5
Mass					
Length					
Width					
Thickness					
Volume					

Estimating and indirect measurement

New vocabulary: estimate

You measure the length of a table by comparing it to a meter stick. You measure the volume of a liquid by comparing it to the space in a marked container. You measure mass by comparing it to marked standard masses. Direct measurements are made by comparing something with marked objects.

How could you measure the height of a friend without a meter stick or measuring tape? If you knew your own height, you could **estimate** (ES′-tuh-mayt) your friend's height. That is, you could make a rough measurement by guessing how much taller or shorter your friend is than you.

Similarly, you can use the known height of a door to estimate the height of a ceiling. Knowing the width of a section of the chalkboard helps you estimate the width of your classroom. Estimate the height of the ceiling in your classroom. Estimate the width of the classroom. Estimate the length of the classroom. How close are your estimates to the measured values?

Direct measurement may often take too much time. It may not always be convenient or even possible. Estimating is a valuable skill that improves with practice.

Direct measurement of very small distances or very small amounts may not be possible. But the measurements may be made indirectly. Suppose you wanted to measure the thickness of a sheet of paper. A measurement instrument of the right size may not be available. You could, however, measure the thickness of a ream (500 sheets) of paper. Suppose the thickness of the ream is 5 cm. Then the thickness of each sheet is 5 cm ÷ 500, or 0.01 cm.

The mass of a light object such as a rubber band is hard to measure directly. You can count out 100 rubber bands. Then measure the total mass of the rubber bands. Divide the total mass by 100. This method gives an average mass for the rubber bands and assumes that individual masses do not vary much.

Small time intervals are also difficult to measure directly. Suppose you wanted to measure the time between pulse beats.

Figure 1-18. *What is the thickness of a single sheet of typing paper?* 0.01 cm

1.2c   Estimating

Science Processes: Estimating, using numbers

Materials   20 minutes   Individual work

- jar of beans
- clock or watch that indicates seconds
- nickel
- 5 pennies

Purpose

To learn to make reasonable estimates.

Procedure

PART 1
Estimating the number of beans in a jar.

1. Record the number of beans you think are in the jar.
2. Determine about how many beans touch the bottom of the jar. Record your answer.
3. Determine about how many beans fit in a straight line from top to bottom along the side of the jar. Record your answer.
4. Multiply the number of beans touching the bottom by the number that fit from top to bottom.
5. Find out from your teacher how many beans are actually in the jar.

PART 2
Estimating how long it takes for one minute to pass.

1. While a partner watches a clock or watch, estimate how long it takes for one minute to pass. Record how much time had actually passed during that time.
2. Determine how many seconds away from one minute your estimate was. Record your answer.
3. Use the clock or watch to measure how many times your pulse beats in 30 seconds. Record your answer.
4. While your partner watches the clock, use your pulse count to estimate one minute. Record the length of time you estimated.

5. How many seconds were you off this time?

PART 3
Estimating the mass of a penny.

1. Guess the mass of a penny in grams. Record your guess.
2. The mass of a nickel is 5 grams. Decide how many pennies have about the same total mass as a nickel. Record your answer.
3. Using the information in Step 2, estimate the mass of one penny. Record your answer.

Questions

1. Was there a difference between your first and second estimates in Part 1? in Part 2? in Part 3?
2. Which estimate was closest to the correct value, your first one, or the second one based on additional information?

Conclusion

How can you improve the accuracy of your estimates?

Step 1

Figure 1-19. *How could you estimate the height of the building?* Each story is about 3 m. Count the number of stories and multiply this number by 3 m to get the height estimate.

You could measure the time for fifty pulse beats. The time between pulse beats would be the time for 50 beats divided by 50.

Large distances and large amounts can also be measured indirectly. You can compare the large distances to smaller distances that can be measured. For example, suppose you wanted to find the height of a 50-story building. You can use the height of one story. The floor-to-ceiling height in most buildings is close to 3 m. To get the building height, multiply the height of one story by 50. The height of the building is about 3 m × 50, or 150 m.

Suppose you want to measure the mass of a carton of textbooks. The carton is too big to fit on your balance. How can you measure the mass indirectly?

Quick Review

1. What is the difference between a direct measurement and an estimate?
2. What is the difference between a direct measurement and an indirect measurement?

Research Topic

The distances to the stars cannot be measured directly. Find out how astronomers measure these large distances indirectly.

Quick Review answers:
1. Direct measurements are made by comparing something with a marked object. Estimates are guesses made by comparing something with an object whose measurements are known.
2. Very large or small measurements are often made indirectly by multiplying or dividing a measurement that can be made directly.

A pharmacist must carefully measure ingredients when preparing a prescription medication.

Pharmacist

A pharmacist provides an essential service in the medical and health fields by dispensing medicines and medical supplies. This is usually done according to a doctor's prescription for a particular medicine and dosage. The pharmacist may also suggest medicines and advise people directly in the proper use of medicines available without a prescription. Although most pharmacists work in drugstores, about twenty percent work in hospital pharmacies.

Pharmacists must have an understanding of the physical and chemical properties of the ingredients found in medicines and drugs as well as how various combinations of drugs may interact. They must insure that prescribed medicines are prepared in the right dosage amounts and must see to the purity and freshness of the ingredients.

A bachelor's degree in pharmacy is required. Most colleges of pharmacy now require prepharmacy studies in mathematics, chemistry, biology, and physics as well as courses in social science and business administration. These courses are offered in two- and four-year colleges.

Many pharmacists are in business for themselves. They must be able to manage employees and run their business profitably. Qualities of honesty, precision, and orderliness are important in this occupation.

For more information, write to: American Pharmaceutical Association, 2215 Constitution Ave. N.W., Washington, D.C. 20037.

Surveyors use instruments that help them to measure long distances accurately.

Surveyor

Surveyors make measurements. They may prepare specialized surveys for government agencies, real estate developers, construction companies, or engineering and industrial firms.

Training for a career in surveying is usually obtained through special courses beyond high school, community college programs, or even on the job. High school courses in mathematics, science, and drafting are good background preparation.

Surveying requires work with tools and instruments, attention to detail, and physical stamina. Surveyors often work as members of a team. Much of the work is outdoors, in a variety of locations.

For more information write to: American Congress on Surveying and Mapping, 210 Little Falls Street, Falls Church, Virginia 22046.

1.2 Section Review

Answers to Understanding the Concepts appear on page T61 in the front of this book. Blackline master test for this section: Section Testsheet 1-2 (TRB page 202)

Vocabulary

17 area
4 Celsius
10 centimeter
24 circumference
8 cubic centimeter
7 cubic meter
19 density
23 diameter
25 estimate
13 gram
21 horizontal axis
2 kilogram
12 kilometer
9 liter

16 measurement
3 meter
14 milligram
8 milliliter
11 millimeter
15 millisecond
22 origin
1 second
26 SI
6 square centimeter
5 square meter
20 vertical axis
18 volume

Vocabulary Review

Match each term above with the numbered phrase that best describes it.

1. Basic SI unit of time
2. Basic SI unit of mass
3. Basic SI unit of length
4. Everyday temperature scale used with SI units
5. Area of a square 1 m on a side
6. Area of a square 1 cm on a side
7. Volume of a cube 1 m on a side
8. Volume of a cube 1 cm on a side (two correct answers)
9. Volume of a cube 10 cm on a side
10. 1/100 of a meter
11. 1/1000 of a meter
12. 1000 meters
13. 1/1000 of a kilogram
14. 1/1000 of a gram
15. 1/1000 of a second
16. A number followed by a unit
17. Amount of space on a surface
18. Amount of space something fills up

19. Mass divided by volume
20. Vertical line on graph labeled with one of the measured quantities
21. Horizontal line on graph labeled with one of the measured quantities
22. Point on graph where two axes cross and both measurements have value of zero
23. Distance across a circle
24. Distance around a circle
25. To make a rough measurement by guessing
26. Modern metric system

Review Questions

Multiple Choice: Choose the answer that best completes each of the following sentences.

27. The mass of 50 mL of water is _?_.
   a. 50 kg
   b. 50 km
   c. 50 mg
   d. 50 g

28. In the SI symbol km, the "m" stands for _?_.
   a. minute
   b. meter
   c. milli-
   d. metric

29. The SI unit for power is the watt (W). The symbol kW stands for _?_.
   a. 1000 watts
   b. 1000 meters
   c. 1/1000 of a watt
   d. 1/1000 of a meter

30. The SI symbol for cubic centimeter is _?_.
   a. cc
   b. cu cc
   c. cm^2
   d. cm^3

Understanding the Concepts

31. Why is it important for scientists in all countries to use the same system of measurements?
32. a. How many small cubes 1 cm on a side fit along the side of a big cube 1 m on a side?
   b. How many rows of the small cubes fit along the bottom of the big cube?
   c. How many layers of the small cubes will fill up the big cube?
   d. How many cubic centimeters equal one cubic meter?
33. You are standing beside a high brick wall. You have no measuring instruments with you.
   a. How could you estimate the height of a brick?
   b. How could you measure the height of the wall indirectly?

1.2 Measurement   33

For ideas for classroom demonstration and discussion, see Getting Started on page T62 in the front of this book.

1.3 Problem Solving

Supplemental materials: Teaching Diagram 1-3 (TRB page 7), Reading Checksheet 1-3 (TRB page 83), Skillsheet 1-3 (TRB page 129), Investigation 1-3 (Lab Manual pages 13–14)

Section Preview

- Steps in problem solving
- Calculating with units
- Dimensional analysis
- Converting between units

Bracketed numbers are Section Review questions correlated to that objective.

Learning Objectives

1. To learn a procedure for attacking a problem that involves solving for an unknown. [2, 3, 8, 10, 11]
2. To learn procedures for handling the units of measurements involved in a calculation. [4, 9, 10, 11]
3. To learn a procedure for converting one kind of unit to an equivalent kind, in order to perform calculations on quantities with the same units. [1, 5, 6, 7]

Figure 1-20. *Word problems in science become easier to solve when you are methodical in your work and when you have had some practice.*

Do you like word problems? You know the kind: Lincoln High School's basketball team won 5 of their first 6 games. If they have 14 more games in their schedule, how many of the remaining games must they win in order to finish the season with a win record of 60%? (The answer is 7 games.) Some people feel overwhelmed by word problems. If you are one of them, consider the following analogy.

People who like playing basketball generally fall into one of two categories. Either they feel they are already good basketball players, or they feel they are getting better through practice. People who try basketball and then give up are generally not good players. They do not want to put in the time needed to become a good player.

In much the same way, if you like word problems, you are probably already a fairly proficient problem solver. Most students who dislike word problems have not yet become good problem solvers. If you dislike word problems, do not be like someone who tries basketball and quits. Just as a basketball player gets better with practice, you can become a better problem solver by doing problems and learning from your mistakes.

Main Idea

How can you become a better problem solver?

Steps in problem solving

New vocabulary: unknown, known

After you have read a word problem, your first thought is likely to be "Where do I begin?" Often there are several ways to solve a problem. No one method will work in every situation. Nevertheless, most word problems can be solved by using the following guidelines.

1. *Identify the unknown.* The **unknown** in a problem is what is being asked for. Be certain that you know what that is. Read the problem carefully. If it is long, you might need to reread it. When you determine what is being asked for, be aware of whether the answer will have units of measurement, and what those are likely to be.

2. *Identify the knowns.* The **knowns** in a problem are the necessary facts that are stated. These usually include one or more measurements and one or more relationships between measurements. The problem may also state some unnecessary facts. Learn to ignore information that is not needed.

3. *Plan a solution.* Think of an equation that relates the knowns and the unknown. Sketching a picture often helps you see a relationship between the knowns and the unknown.

4. *Do the calculations.* If the unknown is not on one side of the equation by itself, solve the equation for the unknown. (See the math review in the appendix if you need help in solving equations.) Substitute the knowns (with their units of measurement) into the equation, and do the arithmetic.

5. *Check your answer.* The numerical value of your answer should be a decimal number, not a fraction. Check that the answer has units of measurement that make sense. For example, if you are asked for the length of time it takes for something to happen, your answer should not be in meters. Finally, check that the numerical value makes sense. A car may travel at 50 kilometers per hour but not 500 kilometers per hour.

Teaching suggestion:
Emphasize that the answer should be a decimal number, not a fraction, and that it will normally contain units of measurement.

Figure 1-21. *Sketching a picture of the situation described in the problem can help you plan a solution.*

Sample Problem

For the following problem, state (1) the unknown, (2) the knowns, and (3) the appropriate equation to use in solving the problem.

The density of iron is 7.9 g/cm³. What is the volume, in cm³, of a piece of iron of mass 500 g?

Solution

1. The unknown is:

   volume of piece of iron (in cm^3)

2. The knowns are:

   density of iron = 7.9 g/cm^3
   mass of piece of iron = 500 g

3. The equation that relates volume, density, and mass is:

   $$density = \frac{mass}{volume}$$

Practice Problem

For the following problem, state (1) the unknown, (2) the knowns, and (3) the appropriate equation to use in solving the problem.

A piece of ice of volume 10.0 cm^3 melts. The water from the melted ice has a volume of 9.2 cm^3. By how much did the volume change during melting?

Answer:

1. Unknown:

   change in volume (in cm^3)

2. Knowns:

   initial volume = 10.0 cm^3
   final volume = 9.2 cm^3

3. Equation to use:

   change in volume = initial volume − final volume

Critical Thinking

What key words and phrases act as clues that point out the unknown in word problems?

Clues include:
- What is
- How much
- How long
- Determine
- Find

Quick Review answers:
1. Identify the unknown.
2. Identify the knowns.

Quick Review

1. What is the first step in attacking a word problem?
2. What is the second step in attacking a word problem?

Calculating with units

The best way to keep track of what you are doing when you solve problems in science is to include the units of measurement in your calculations. You can use the following rules when calculating with units.

1. When one unit is divided by a different unit, a slash (/) is used in the result.

$$\frac{10\ m}{5\ s} = 2\frac{m}{s} = 2\ m/s$$

Figure 1-22. *When you calculate with measurements, there are rules that determine the units of the answer.*

$$\frac{m}{s} = m/s$$

$$\frac{g}{cm^3} = g/cm^3$$

2. When you are multiplying by units with a slash, write those units as a fraction that has the units after the slash in the denominator.

$$s \times m/s = s \times \frac{m}{s}$$

3. When you are multiplying a fraction by a unit that is identical to a unit in the denominator of the fraction, cancel the identical units.

$$\frac{g}{mL} \times mL = g$$

4. When one unit (with or without an exponent) is multiplied or divided by the exact same unit (with or without an exponent), use the rules for exponents (see the Math Review appendix) to write the result. (An exponent is a small number written at the upper right corner of a symbol. It is used to indicate the square or cube of the unit, as in cm^2 or cm^3.)

$$cm \times cm = cm^2$$

$$cm \times cm^2 = cm^3$$

$$\frac{cm^2}{cm} = cm$$

$$\frac{cm^3}{cm^2} = cm$$

5. When you are multiplying two different units by each other, use a raised dot between them in the result.

$$g \times {}^\circ C = g \cdot {}^\circ C$$

6. When units with a slash appear in the denominator of a fraction, move the unit after the slash up to the numerator.

$$\frac{kg}{g/cm^3} = \frac{kg \cdot cm^3}{g}$$

7. When the numerator and denominator of a fraction have the same units, cancel them.

$$\frac{m \cdot s}{m} = s$$

Figure 1-23. *What is wrong with this calculation?*
You cannot cancel the "g" in "kg"; the unit "kg" can be cancelled only by another unit "kg."

Sample Problem

Simplify the units in the following equation, and then perform the arithmetic with the numbers.

$$\text{volume} = \frac{\text{mass}}{\text{density}} = \frac{500 \text{ g}}{7.9 \text{ g/cm}^3}$$

Solution

$$\frac{500 \text{ g}}{7.9 \text{ g/cm}^3} = \frac{500 \text{ g·cm}^3}{7.9 \text{ g}} = \frac{500}{7.9} \text{ cm}^3 = 64 \text{ cm}^3$$

Practice Problems

Complete the following calculations.

1. volume = area × height = 34 m² × 10 m
   Answer: 340 m³
2. distance = speed × time = 45 km/h × 3 h
   Answer: 135 km
3. time = $\frac{\text{distance}}{\text{speed}}$ = $\frac{120 \text{ m}}{6 \text{ m/s}}$
   Answer: 20 s

Quick Review

1. What is the meaning of a slash between two units of measurement?
2. What is the meaning of a raised dot between two units of measurement?

Dimensional analysis

New vocabulary: dimensional analysis

One of the best techniques to use in solving science problems is to use the stated units of measurement to help analyze and solve the problem. This technique is called **dimensional analysis.**

The technique of dimensional analysis is based on the rules for calculation with units of measurement. For example, suppose you were trying to solve a problem where the time was the unknown and the distance and speed were the knowns. You knew that there was an equation relating distance, time, and speed, but you were not sure of the exact equation. If you wrote down

$$\text{time} = \text{distance} \times \text{speed} = 50 \text{ m} \times 2.5 \frac{\text{m}}{\text{s}}$$

you could see, even before you did any calculations with the numerical values, that this must be incorrect. There is no way that the product of these two measurements can be in s (seconds), the units of time. By paying attention to the units of measurement, you can tell whether you seem to be on the right track. That is the advantage of dimensional analysis.

$$time = distance \times speed \ ?$$
$$time = \frac{distance}{speed} \ ?$$
$$time = \frac{speed}{distance} \ ?$$

Figure 1-24. *You can use dimensional analysis to help you decide which equation is correct.*

Sample Problem

Use dimensional analysis to tell whether the following equations make sense.

a. density $= \dfrac{7.1 \text{ g}}{3.2 \text{ cm}^3}$

b. mass $= 4.5 \text{ cm}^3 \times 2.8 \text{ g/cm}^3$

c. distance $= \dfrac{60 \text{ h}}{35 \text{ km/h}}$

Solution

a. density $= \dfrac{7.1 \text{ g}}{3.2 \text{ cm}^3} = \dfrac{7.1}{3.2} \text{ g/cm}^3$

The units g/cm^3 are appropriate for density, so the equation makes sense.

b. mass $= 4.5 \text{ cm}^3 \times 2.8 \text{ g/cm}^3 = (4.5 \times 2.8) \, \cancel{\text{cm}^3} \cdot \dfrac{\text{g}}{\cancel{\text{cm}^3}}$

$$= (4.5 \times 2.8) \text{ g}$$

The unit g is appropriate for mass, so the equation makes sense.

c. distance $= \dfrac{60 \text{ h}}{35 \text{ km/h}} = \dfrac{60 \text{ h·h}}{35 \text{ km}} = \dfrac{60 \text{ h}^2}{35 \text{ km}} = \dfrac{60}{35} \text{ h}^2/\text{km}$

The units h^2/km make no sense for distance, so this equation must be incorrect.

Practice Problems

Use dimensional analysis to tell whether the following equations make sense.

1. volume $= \dfrac{15 \text{ g}}{4.6 \text{ mL}}$

   Answer: No

2. area $= \dfrac{7.8 \text{ cm}^3}{1.2 \text{ cm}}$

   Answer: Yes

Solutions:
1. The units g/mL are units of density, not volume.
2. The answer is in units of cm², which are units of area.

Quick Review answer:
Determine the units that the answer
will be in, and check that they are
appropriate for the unknown.

Main Idea

What is a conversion factor?

Quick Review

What is one way you can tell whether you have used an incorrect equation to solve a word problem?

Converting between units

New vocabulary: conversion factor

In physical science it is often necessary to express a measurement in a different unit. To do this, you need to use **conversion factors.** A conversion factor is a ratio between two equivalent measurements.

For example, you know that 1 kilogram equals 1000 grams.

$$1 \text{ kg} = 1000 \text{ g}$$

You can form two different conversion factors from this information:

$$\frac{1 \text{ kg}}{1000 \text{ g}} \qquad \text{and} \qquad \frac{1000 \text{ g}}{1 \text{ kg}}$$

In each ratio, the measurement on the top equals the measurement on the bottom. Thus, *each ratio is equal to one.* You can multiply anything by one without changing its value. So you can multiply a measurement by one of these ratios without changing its value.

A conversion factor can be formed from *any* two measurements that are equal. With the aid of dimensional analysis you can tell what conversion factor you need to use.

Figure 1-25. *Before you can compare two quantities with different units, you must convert one to the other kind. Which is a bigger volume—1.0 L or 750 mL?*
1.0 L

See also Activity Record Sheet 1-3A (Lab Manual page 11). Teaching Hints, Answers to Questions, and Conclusion appear on page T63 in the front of this book.

Activity

1.3a   Comparing Units

Science Processes: Measuring, making models, estimating, using numbers

Materials   BASIC   30 minutes   Groups of 3 or 4

- construction paper or tagboard
- pencil
- metric ruler
- scissors
- masking tape
- plastic bag
- 100-mL graduated cylinder

Purpose

To determine how many 100-mL containerfuls of water will fit inside a cube 10 cm on a side.

Procedure

1. On construction paper or tagboard draw a full-size enlargement of the pattern shown in the drawing.
2. Cut out your drawing, and fold it to make a cube 10 cm on a side. Use masking tape to hold the sides together.
3. Line the inside of the cube with a small plastic bag. Spread the bag out inside the cube so that it is against the sides and bottom.
4. Study the space inside a 100-mL cylinder, and compare it to the space inside the cube. Estimate how many cylinders of water would fill the cube, and record your estimate.
5. Now fill the lined cube with water, using the 100-mL cylinder. Record how many cylinders of water you need to fill the cube.
6. The volume of the cube equals 10 cm × 10 cm × 10 cm. Calculate the volume in cm^3.
7. Convert the volume of the cube to a value in mL. *Hint:* Choose a conversion factor that will allow you to cancel cm^3 and end up with an answer in mL.
8. Solve the following problem: How many volumes of 100 mL equal the volume inside a cube 10 cm on a side?

Questions

1. How did your estimate in Step 4 compare to your measurement in Step 5 of the number of cylinders of water needed to fill the space inside the cube?
2. According to your calculation in Step 8, how many cylinders of water should fill the space inside the cube?
3. How did the value you calculated in Step 8 compare to the one you measured in Step 5?

Conclusion

What is the volume of a cube 10 cm on a side in milliliters and in liters?

Step 1

10 cm

10 cm

Step 2

Data Search

Find out the speed of sound (in air at 0°C) in meters per second and express it in kilometers per hour by using appropriate conversion factors. Search pages 658–661.

The speed of sound in air at 0°C is

$$331 \, \frac{\cancel{m}}{\cancel{s}} \left(\frac{1 \text{ km}}{1000 \, \cancel{m}} \right) \left(\frac{60 \, \cancel{s}}{1 \, \cancel{min}} \right) \left(\frac{60 \, \cancel{min}}{1 \text{ h}} \right)$$

$$= 1192 \, \frac{\text{km}}{\text{h}}$$

Solutions:

1. $1 \, \cancel{h} \left(\dfrac{60 \, \cancel{min}}{1 \, \cancel{h}} \right) \left(\dfrac{60 \text{ s}}{1 \, \cancel{min}} \right) = 3600 \text{ s}$

2. $1 \, \cancel{year} \left(\dfrac{365 \, \cancel{days}}{1 \, \cancel{year}} \right) \left(\dfrac{24 \text{ h}}{1 \, \cancel{day}} \right) = 8760 \text{ h}$

Quick Review answers:
1. The value of the measurement does not change; the old value equals the new value.
2. Use the form that allows you to cancel the original units and end up with the desired units.

Sample Problem

A snail crawls at a speed of 3 cm/s. How long would it take to cross a path 1.5 m wide?

Solution

To solve this problem, you need to have the same distance units in the speed and the path width. Suppose you decide to express the path width in cm.

$$1.5 \text{ m} = ? \text{ cm}$$

The relationship between m and cm is

$$1 \text{ m} = 100 \text{ cm}.$$

To change 1.5 m into a measurement in cm, you must multiply by cm and divide by m. That way, the m units would cancel and the result would be in cm. You should use the conversion factor that has cm on top and m on the bottom. Multiply the path width by this conversion factor and cancel similar units.

$$1.5 \, \cancel{m} \times \frac{100 \text{ cm}}{1 \, \cancel{m}} = 150 \text{ cm}$$

The time it takes the snail to cross the path is

$$\text{time} = \frac{\text{distance}}{\text{speed}} = \frac{150 \text{ cm}}{3 \text{ cm/s}} = \frac{150 \, \cancel{cm} \cdot \text{s}}{3 \, \cancel{cm}} = 50 \text{ s}$$

You can also write the equation and multiply by the conversion factor in one step:

$$\text{time} = \frac{\text{distance}}{\text{speed}} = \frac{1.5 \text{ m}}{3 \text{ cm/s}} \left(\frac{100 \text{ cm}}{1 \text{ m}} \right)$$

$$\frac{1.5(100) \, \cancel{m} \cdot \cancel{cm} \cdot \text{s}}{3 \, \cancel{cm} \cdot \cancel{m}} = 50 \text{ s}$$

Practice Problems

1. Find the equivalent of 1 hour in seconds, using two conversion factors. *Answer:* 3600 s
2. Find the equivalent of 1 year in hours, using two conversion factors. *Answer:* 8760 h

Quick Review

1. When you multiply by a conversion factor, how is the value of the measurement affected?
2. How can you tell which form of a conversion factor to use?

1.3 Section Review

Vocabulary

1 conversion factor
4 dimensional analysis
2 known
3 unknown

Vocabulary Review

Match each term above with the numbered phrase that best describes it.

1. Can be multiplied by a measurement without changing its value
2. What is stated in a problem
3. What you are asked to find in a problem
4. Helps you tell whether you are using the correct equation in solving a problem

Review Questions

Multiple Choice: Choose the answer that best completes each of the following sentences.

5. Which of the following is correct?
   a. kg·m/s = kg·m·s
   b. kg·m/s = kg·s/m
   c. $\dfrac{km}{km/h} = \dfrac{km·h}{km}$
   d. $\dfrac{km/h}{km} = km^2/h$

6. To convert 2.6 km to m, you should multiply by ? .
   a. $\dfrac{1\ km}{1000\ m}$
   b. $\dfrac{1000\ m}{1\ km}$
   c. $\dfrac{1\ m}{100\ cm}$
   d. $\dfrac{100\ cm}{1\ m}$

7. To convert a time of 3 weeks to hours, you should multiply by ? .
   a. $\dfrac{7\ days}{1\ week}$
   b. $\dfrac{1\ day}{24\ hours}$
   c. $\dfrac{7\ days}{1\ week} \times \dfrac{1\ day}{24\ hours}$
   d. $\dfrac{7\ days}{1\ week} \times \dfrac{24\ hours}{1\ day}$

Understanding the Concepts

8. Once you have reached the point in solving a problem at which you have written down an equation for the unknown in terms of the values of the knowns, what two things should you check for before completing the calculation?
9. What are some advantages of including the units of measurement when you substitute values into an equation?

Problems to Solve

10. Read this problem: The density of iron is 7.9 g/cm³. What is the mass of 20 cm³ of iron?
    a. State the unknown.
    b. State the knowns.
    c. Write an equation that relates the unknown and the knowns.
    d. Rearrange the equation so that the unknown is by itself on one side of the equation.
    e. Substitute the values of the knowns into the equations.
    f. Use the rules for calculating with units to determine the units of the answer. Do you have to use any conversion factors to convert units before you can proceed?
    g. Are the units of the answer appropriate for the unknown?
    h. Complete the calculation to determine the value of the unknown.
11. Repeat Steps a through h of Question 10 for the following problem: The density of gold is 19.3 g/cm³. What is the volume of gold that has a mass of 1 kg?

1 Chapter Review

Vocabulary

area	gram	millimeter
Celsius	horizontal axis	millisecond
centimeter	hypothesis	model
circumference	indirect observation	observation
control	inference	origin
controlled experiment	kilogram	scientific method
conversion factor	kilometer	second
cubic centimeter	known	SI
cubic meter	law	square centimeter
data	liter	square meter
density	manipulated variable	theory
diameter	measurement	unknown
dimensional analysis	meter	variable
direct observation	milligram	vertical axis
estimate	milliliter	volume

Review of Concepts

An **observation** is information gathered through use of the senses or with the aid of instruments.

- Observations both initiate and verify the results of scientific investigation.

The **scientific method** is a set of steps outlining a way of attacking problems in science.

- The heart of the scientific method is the formation and testing of hypotheses.
- Hypotheses are tested by controlled experiments.

A **model** is a description of something unfamiliar in terms of familiar things.

- A scientific model is changed in order to agree with new observations and revised hypotheses.

- A theory in science is a well-tested model or set of hypotheses about some aspect of the natural world.
- Theories are revised and broadened as more observations are made.

A **measurement** is an observation that describes the amount of a property and that includes both a number and a unit.

- SI is an international metric system of measurement.
- Measured values always include some error.
- Graphing measurements can help reveal relationships between the quantities being measured.
- Estimation can provide approximate measurements when direct measurement is impractical.
- Very small or very large quantities can be measured indirectly.

The **unknown** in a word problem is what is being asked for.

- The first step in solving a word problem is to identify the unknown.
- The unknown is determined by writing an equation that expresses it in terms of the known quantities, and performing calculations on the numbers and units.
- Dimensional analysis can help you decide whether an equation makes sense.
- Conversion factors are used to express a measurement in a different unit.

Critical Thinking

1. How is a law in science different from a law that a legislature might pass?

2. Ice has a smaller density than water.
   a. Which has a greater volume—an ice cube when frozen or the water from that ice cube when it has melted?
   b. When an ice cube floating in a glass of water melts, the water level in the glass does not change. How is this possible?
3. Estimate the following measurements, using appropriate metric units.
   a. Length of a swimming pool
   b. Space inside a drinking glass
   c. Mass of an apple
   d. Temperature of a hot bath
   e. Height of a seat
   f. Volume of gasoline a car tank can hold
4. A tank of water is being drained. The table shows the volume of water remaining after different times. Make a graph showing how the volume of water changes as time passes.
   a. How long does it take for half the water to drain out?
   b. How long does it take altogether for the tank to empty?

Time (in s)	Volume of Water Remaining (in L)
0	100
1	95
2	90
3	85
4	80
5	75
6	70

5. Estimate the number of basketballs that would be required to fill your classroom. Describe how you made your estimate.
6. The units W, J, s, V, C, and A are related as follows.
$$1\ W = 1\ J/s$$
$$1\ V = 1\ J/C$$
$$1\ A = 1\ C/s$$
Use dimensional analysis to determine whether the following equations make sense.
   a. power in $W = 10\ V \times 6\ A$
   b. current in $A = \dfrac{120\ V}{60\ W}$

Individual Research

7. Observe how long it takes for different pieces of paper to fall to the ground. Form a hypothesis that explains the different times. Then perform a controlled experiment to test your hypothesis. Write a report that summarizes what you did and what conclusions you drew.
8. In your kitchen, look for metric measurements on the boxes and cans of food. Record the measurements of at least ten different foods. Are they all mass measurements, or are any volume measurements?
9. Interview some business people in your community to find out how they feel about the metric system. Do they use it in their own business? Would they like it to be used more widely?

10. Look up the definitions of hectare and acre as units of area. Compare the ease of calculating 1) the area of a 30-m by 50-m rectangular lot in hectares and 2) the area of a 300-foot by 500-foot lot in acres. Which calculation is simpler?

Bibliography

Gardner, Robert. *Kitchen Chemistry; Science Experiments to Do at Home.* New York: Messner, 1982
   Nicely outlined experiments using the stove, refrigerator, counter, sink, and materials commonly found in the kitchen.

Goodstein, Madeline P. *Numbers in Science.* Menlo Park, CA: Addison-Wesley, 1987
   Helps develop the mathematical skills used in science: calculations with exponents, scientific notation, significant figures, estimation of the size of an answer.

Moore, William. *Metric Is Here!* New York: Putnam, 1974
   The history of the metric system and its use in sports, at the pharmacy, and in science and industry. Has clear explanations.

Smith, Norman F. *How Fast Do Your Oysters Grow? Investigate and Discover through Science Projects.* New York: Messner, 1982
   Introduces the scientific method by describing the stages of a well-planned investigation. Explains how to do a science project that is based on scientific investigation.

Chapter 2
Properties of Matter

In this chapter you will learn how matter can be described and compared to other matter. In the photo at the right you can see matter in two phases—solid and liquid (as water in the form of clouds). You can also see some of the properties of different substances. For instance, metals are shiny, strong and bendable. Glass sometimes appears shiny and sometimes transparent, depending on its composition and where the light source is located. Water becomes visible when it condenses into a liquid in clouds.

Science background information:
The earliest known attempts at understanding and classifying matter came from ancient Egypt and Mesopotamia. These societies had highly skilled craftsmen with the ability to smelt metals and perform other sophisticated manipulations of matter.

The ancients believed that to understand the nature of matter, you must first account for its existence. Was it created from nothing or did it arise from some other primal material? They reasoned that matter probably came from some known substance such as water. They coupled this idea with the observation that throughout the natural world one finds opposite or contrary factors: light and dark, hot and cold, wet and dry. Therefore, they thought that the primal material must be changed so that two opposite and contrary substances are formed. A third substance, serving as a buffer or mediator of the two extremes, would also be formed. These three substances would then unite in various combinations to form all known types of matter.

The early Greek philosopher, Thales of Miletos (c. 640–546 B.C.) pursued this idea further. If the primal material

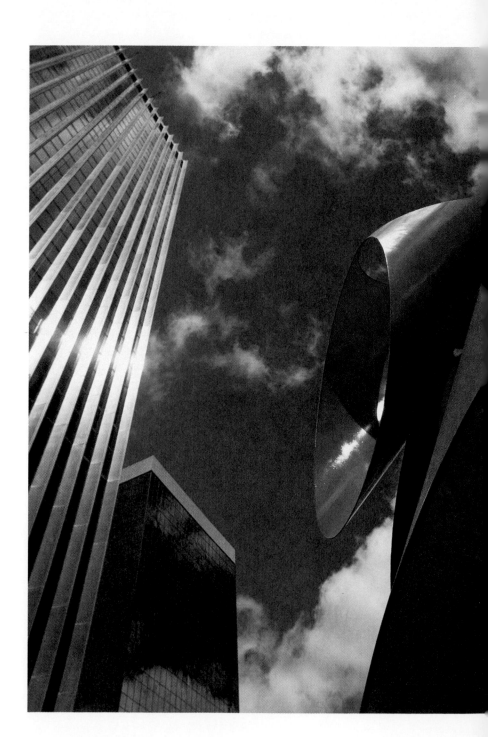

For detailed information about teaching this chapter, see Chapter 2 Planning Guide on pages T64–T65 in the front of this book.

Chapter Preview

2.1 Classifying Matter

- **Properties of matter**
- **Properties of substances**
- **Classifying into groups**
- **Classifying in order**
- **Solids, liquids and gases**
- **Metals and nonmetals**
- **Mixtures, compounds and elements**

Matter can be described in different ways. Different kinds of matter that are similar in some ways can be grouped together. If you know something about some members of the group, you can expect other members of the group to be similar.

2.2 Changes in Matter

- **Volume changes**
- **Phase changes**
- **Solubility changes**
- **Chemical changes**
- **Mass and volume changes**
- **Combustion**

Some changes in matter do not change the matter from one kind to another. Other changes can form a different kind of matter. During a change, certain clues indicate whether a different kind of matter has been formed.

could take on three forms, why couldn't everything in the world be regarded as a single reality, appearing in different forms? He affirmed the ancient idea of water as the primal material because it was observed to easily convert to air (evaporate) or congeal into a solid (ice). Later Greek philosophers variously proposed air, fire, and a mysterious substance called *apeiron* "the indefinite and infinite," as candidates for the primal material. In all cases, the explanation of the whole natural world was based on the supposition that primal material could be converted into other physical forms such as solids, liquids, and gases. The entire range of known substances was believed to be produced by the manipulation of qualities such as brilliance, ductility, etc., imposed on the primal matter. There was no concept of a group of immutable elements with different properties as there is today.

We know now that the "primal material" sought by the ancients is actually pure energy. The process by which matter, which has mass and takes up space, is created from energy, which has no mass and takes up no space, has been observed but is not understood. The properties of matter we observe are a result of the fact that energy has been turned into basic particles. In turn, these basic particles have been arranged into the more or less stable structures we call atoms. Different atomic structures produce substances with different physical properties such as mass, hardness, conductivity and chemical reactivity. Because of the basic stability of most atoms, substances can undergo changes of state such as solid-liquid-gas, without changing their essential natures.

For ideas for classroom demonstration and discussion, see Getting Started on page T68 in the front of this book.

2.1 Classifying Matter

Supplemental materials: Teaching Diagram 2-1 (TRB page 8), Reading Checksheet 2-1 (TRB page 84), Skillsheet 2-1 (TRB page 130), Investigation 2-1 (Lab Manual pages 21–22)

Section Preview

- Properties of matter
- Properties of substances
- Classifying into groups
- Classifying in order
- Solids, liquids and gases
- Metals and nonmetals
- Mixtures, compounds and elements

Bracketed numbers are Section Review questions correlated to that objective.

Learning Objectives

1. To distinguish among substances on the basis of differences in their properties. [1, 11, 19]
2. To group and to order substances using similarities and differences in the properties of the substances. [19, 20, 23, 26]
3. To describe the properties of each of the phases of matter—solid, liquid, and gas. [3, 5, 9, 16, 20, 28]
4. To differentiate among mixtures, solutions, compounds, and elements. [2, 4, 6, 7, 12, 13, 14, 15, 17, 18, 22, 24, 25, 27, 29]

Figure 2-1. *What different kinds of matter are pictured here?*

Metal, glass, wood, china, etc. Details are in first four paragraphs.

Main Idea

What is meant by properties of matter?

The forks look like metal because they are gray and shiny.

Water is a liquid at room temperature, glass and wood are solid. One can see through water and glass but not wood.

Many kinds of matter are shown in the photo at left. The utensils are made of one kind of matter. The dishes are made of another kind. The glass is made of a different kind. The ice is floating in still a different kind of matter.

The ice is floating in a clear, colorless liquid. You might guess that the liquid is water, because you know that water is clear and colorless. You recognize water by its **properties**—things that describe how it is different from other kinds of matter. Of what kind of matter are the forks made? What properties helped you decide?

Glass is a kind of matter. It has many properties that help you identify it. You can see through glass. Glass breaks easily, leaving sharp edges. Glass does not bend unless it is very hot. The surface of glass is hard. Glass has no odor.

Each kind of matter is called a **substance** (SUB′-stuns). Water, wood, and glass are examples of different substances. What properties make these three substances different from each other? What properties do some of them share?

Properties of matter

New vocabulary: property, substance

There are two properties that all kinds of matter share. The first property of all matter is that it takes up space. The second property of all matter is that it has mass. Consider the first property. Suppose a drinking glass is filled to the very top with water. An ice cube is gently lowered into the water. What will happen? Does the ice cube take up space? Does the water take up space? Can the ice cube and water take up the same space at the same time?

Look at Figure 2-2. Someone is trying to pour water into the flask. The water will not go in. Why not?

Did you realize the flask was not really empty? If so, you were right. The flask contained air. Even air takes up space. There was no way for the air to get out of the flask. The water could not take up the same space as the air. How could you get the water into the flask?

Consider now the second property of all matter, namely that it has mass. As you will recall from Chapter 1, mass is the property of matter that causes it to be pulled toward the earth. All matter has mass, but some matter has more

Main Idea

What two properties does all matter share?

Some water will spill out. Water and ice both take up space, but never the same space.

Loosen the stopper to allow the air to escape.

Figure 2-2. *What prevents the water from going from the funnel into the flask?*
Air in the flask is taking up all the space.

mass than other matter. The more mass something has, the stronger is the earth's pull on it. Two samples of matter have the same mass if they balance each other on an equal arm balance.

Figure 2-3 shows how the masses of an empty balloon and a balloon full of air can be compared. A meter stick is suspended from its center with a string. A balloon filled with air is attached to each end of the meter stick. The meter stick balances. It is an equal-arm balance with equal masses at each end. Then a pin is used to poke a hole in one of the balloons. The meter stick is no longer balanced. Which has more mass—the balloon filled with air or the empty balloon? Is it correct to say that air is matter? Explain.

All matter takes up space and has mass. These two properties define matter. That is, anything with both properties is matter. Anything without both properties is not matter. Do you think sunlight is matter? Explain.

You will also recall from Chapter 1 that the amount of space a sample of matter takes up is called its volume. Sometimes volume and mass are confused. Different kinds of matter may take up the same amount of space. They have the same volume. Yet, they may have different masses. For example, a baseball and a plastic foam ball can have the same volume. Which would you expect to have more mass? Suppose a steel ball had the volume of a baseball. Which would you expect to have more mass—the baseball or the steel ball?

A small shovel is used to move sand. A much larger shovel is used to move snow. A small shovel of sand may have the same mass as a large shovel of snow. Yet, the snow takes up much more space. Why wouldn't you use a snow shovel to move sand?

A balloon filled with air has more mass than an empty balloon. Air is matter because it has mass and takes up space.

Sunlight is classified as energy, not matter, since ordinary measuring devices have not detected that it has mass. However, in modern physical theory, it is thought to consist of particles called photons, which do have mass, but can exist only while moving at the speed of light. Ordinary matter can exist at rest.

Critical Thinking

Explain how two objects can have the same volume but different masses.

Different amounts and kinds of matter can take up the same amount of space.

The volume of sand the shovel would hold is too heavy for many people to lift.

Figure 2-3. *An equal-arm balance shows that air has mass. At left, the balloons are balanced. At right, an air-filled balloon is heavier than an empty one.*

Quick Review

1. What two properties do all kinds of matter share?
2. Do substances occupying the same volume necessarily have the same mass?

Quick Review answers:
1. All matter has mass and takes up space.
2. No. They will have different masses if their densities are different.

Properties of substances

Metal is a different substance from plastic. Yet, either one can be used to make things such as forks, rulers, or bowls. How do you know if a material is metal or plastic? What properties are different for the two substances?

These questions are answered in the text that follows.

For example, do metal and plastic make the same sound when you tap them? Is a plastic bowl as heavy as a metal bowl? Are metal and plastic both shiny? Do they both bend easily? Can you scratch both substances with your fingernail? Do they smell the same? Do they rust or tarnish?

You probably recognize a metal by its shininess. It is usually silvery gray or golden yellow. Metals also make a ringing sound when they drop to the floor. Thin strips of metal bend easily. Metals are hard and are quite heavy for their size. Some metals rust. Some forms of plastic may have some of these properties. But plastics do not have all the properties of metals. You are able to distinguish metal from plastic because they have some properties that are different.

Other substances have different properties. Paper is quite different from plastic or metal. Most forms of paper bend easily. Paper burns quickly. It is not very heavy for its size. What properties do you use to identify paper?

Substances are identified by their different properties. Still, many different substances have similar properties. Both paper and plastic bend easily. Thin sheets of metal also bend easily. Plastic wrap, paper, and aluminum foil can all be used for packaging of foods. Before you can decide what a substance is, you need to know several of its properties.

Critical Thinking

What properties do paper and plastic share? What properties of paper and plastic are different?
Both paper and some plastics bend easily. They may differ in the amount of light they allow to pass through and in their strength.

Quick Review

1. Describe two ways in which paper and metal differ.
2. Describe two common properties of paper and metal.

Quick Review answers:
1. Metal is shiny, usually silver gray, and rings when dropped. Paper tears, burns easily, and is not shiny.
2. Both bend easily, are solid, and can be rolled in thin sheets.

Classifying into groups

Identifying every substance by its many properties is difficult. A lot of information about each substance must be remembered. It is much easier to group similar substances

Activity

See also Activity Record Sheet 2-1A (Lab Manual page 17). Answers to Questions and Conclusion appear on page T69 in the front of this book.

2.1a   Distinguishing Among Substances

Science processes: Observing, inferring, interpreting

Materials   BASIC   20 minutes   Groups of 4

- **4 vials of white powder labeled "W," "X," "Y," and "Z"**
- **5 sheets of colored paper labeled "W," "X," "Y," "Z," and "M"**
- **magnifying glass**
- **5 clear containers each holding 100 mL of warm water and labeled "W," "X," "Y," "Z," and "M"**
- **5 stirring rods**
- **mystery vial of white powder**

Purpose

To determine the differences among substances that look very much alike.

Procedure

SAFETY NOTE: *Wear safety goggles when conducting this activity.*

1. Pour a small amount of the substance from the vial marked "W" onto the sheet of colored paper labeled "W."
2. Examine the substance with a magnifying glass. Note the size and shape of particles.
3. Rub a small amount of the substance between your fingers. Observe the texture.
   SAFETY NOTE: *Do not taste any of the substances. Unknown substances may be poisonous.*
4. Using the same procedure, test each of the other substances. Note carefully all your observations about each substance in the table on the activity record sheet.
5. Pour about half of the substance out of vial "W" into 100 mL of warm water. Stir with a *clean* stirring rod.
6. Carefully note the color, odor, and clarity of the liquid.
7. Use the same procedure to test the other three substances. Be careful to match the labels on the paper, vials, and beakers with each other. Use *clean* water each time for each test. Carefully note your observations.
8. Repeat the entire testing procedure with the mystery substance. Carefully note the results of each test. Compare these results with the results for the other substances you tested.

Questions

1. Describe what each substance looks like when it is magnified.
2. Which of the substances has a noticeable odor when dry? When mixed with water?
3. What other properties describe each of the substances?
4. Which of the substances disappears when put in water and stirred?
5. Which of the substances causes the water to become cloudy? Why do you think this happens?
6. In which of the vials are the test results the same as in the mystery vial?

Conclusion

What are some of the methods you can use to determine the different properties of substances that look very much alike?

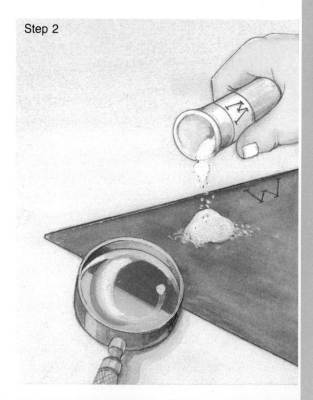

Step 2

together. Then you can remember properties for the whole group. People organize all kinds of things into groups. Books are in groups in the library. Groceries are in groups in the supermarket. Businesses are in groups in the telephone directory. Objects for sale are in groups in the want ads.

The same things may be organized into different groups, based on different properties. For example, school children are put in grades based on age and educational background. People may be put into groups based on their occupation. Sales people may make up one group, teachers another, and so on. People may be put into groups based on where they live. They may also be grouped by ethnic background. What are some ways you could group your classmates?

You put familiar substances into groups, perhaps without thinking about it. You group foods by their taste. Some are sweet, others sour, and others bitter. You may group other substances by their texture. Substances can be smooth or rough. They can be shiny or dull. Some substances have a definite shape. Others change their shape. Substances can be organized into groups using any of these properties. Other properties might also be used to group substances.

The process of organizing information is called **classification** (klas-ih-fuh-KAY'-shun). Putting things into groups based on shared properties is one example of classification. As you have learned, this process is widely used outside of science as well as in science.

Quick Review

1. What properties are used to group school children in grades?
2. Name three taste sensations that can be used to group different foods.

Classifying in order

Putting things into groups is not the only way of classifying them. For example, names in a telephone directory are put in alphabetical order. Singers in a choir may be put in order by height. Baseball players may be listed in order of batting average. Mail is sorted in order of location along the mail route. In other words, things can be classified in order according to the order of one property.

Substances, also, are classified by putting them in order according to one property. For example, solid substances can

Teaching suggestion: Your students are probably familiar with classification methods described in previous science courses. A review of biological classification in an earlier life science course or classification of minerals in an earth science course would probably be helpful here.

Main Idea

What is meant by the classification of things?

Quick Review answers:
1. Age and educational background.
2. Sweet, sour, and bitter.

Activity

2.1b Classifying Objects

Science processes: Observing, clarifying, inferring, communicating

Materials   30 minutes   Groups of 4 or 5

- **random collection of 10 to 12 different objects**

Purpose

To learn the different ways in which objects can be classified.

Procedure

1. After examining the collection of objects, select a property that some, but not all, of the objects have.
2. Now separate the objects into two groups. One group will have the property you just selected, the other group will not.
3. Have the other students in your group decide what property you selected to classify the objects.
4. Now select a second property and repeat steps 2 and 3.
5. Select a property that can be used to rank the objects in order, such as the degree to which the objects change shape by bending or stretching. On a sheet of paper, arrange the objects in order according to the increasing degree to which the property applies.

6. Now ask the other students to identify the property you used and to rank the objects in order.
7. Repeat steps 5 and 6 with a second property.

Questions

1. What property was used in the first trial?
2. Were the other students able to identify the property you chose? If not, why not?
3. What property was used in the second trial?
4. Were the students able to identify the second property you chose? Why or why not?
5. What was the first property you used to arrange the objects in rank order?
6. How did the way you ranked the objects compare to the way the other students in your group ranked them?
7. What was the second property you used to arrange the objects in order?
8. How did the way you ranked the objects compare to the way the other students in your group ranked them?

Conclusion

What can you conclude about the different ways in which substances can be classified into groups and ranked within a group?

Step 1

Step 2

be put in order by hardness. Diamond is the hardest natural substance known. It is placed at one end of the list. Talc, the white substance used in bath powder, is very soft. It would go at the other end of the list.

Another way to put solid substances in order is by how easily they change their shape. Some substances are very rigid. Others bend easily. The most rigid would be at one end of a list, the least rigid at the other end.

Classification is widely used in all branches of science. For example, in astronomy stars are classified. In health science, diseases are classified. When things are put into groups, all the things in one group must have one property in common. When things are put in order, all the things have different amounts of one property. They are put in order of amount of that property.

The classification skills you learn in science can be applied outside of science. These skills can help you organize any kind of information. The information may be about the physical world. It may be about how people behave. It may be about activities you enjoy doing. Organizing information by classifying often leads to understanding. Some examples from physical science will show the importance of classifying.

Research Topic

Find out about the Mohs scale of hardness of minerals. How are samples of minerals tested for hardness?

Critical Thinking

How is classifying into groups different from classifying in order?

All substances classified into a group have at least one property in common. Substances classified in order have the same property but in different amounts or to a different degree.

Quick Review

1. Give three examples of classifying things according to the order of one property they all share.
2. Name two substances at opposite ends of the hardness scale.

Quick Review answers:
1. Many answers are possible. For example, the violin family ranges in order from high to low pitch; violin, viola, cello, bass viol.
2. Diamond and talc.

Solids, liquids and gases

New vocabulary: phase, solid, liquid, gas, plasma

Scientists use several classification systems for matter. One very useful system classifies matter as solid, liquid, or gas at ordinary temperatures. Solids, liquids, and gases are referred to as the three common **phases** (FAY'-zuz) of matter.

A **solid** has a definite shape. That is, a solid keeps its original shape when put in a container of another shape. It is difficult for other matter to penetrate, or pass into, a solid. You hear the phrase "solid as a rock." Rocks are good examples of solids. Some other common examples of solids include wood, plastic, iron, copper, and cardboard.

A **liquid,** on the other hand, does not have a definite shape. A liquid takes the shape of the container it is in. The shape of a liquid changes with the shape of the container. But even when its shape changes, a liquid still fills the same amount of space. Like a solid, a liquid has a definite volume.

Water is the most familiar liquid. The properties of liquids are illustrated well by the behavior of water. Vinegar, alcohol, cooking oil, gasoline, syrup, and mercury are some other familiar liquids.

Liquids can be poured from one container to another. Other matter can penetrate a liquid easily.

Like a liquid, a **gas** has no definite shape. It takes the shape of its container. Unlike a liquid, a gas has no definite volume, either. Instead, it tends to fill whatever space is available to it. For instance, a small amount of gas will expand to fill a large, empty space.

Figure 2-5. *What property do solids and liquids have in common? Liquids and gases?*

Solids and liquids have definite volumes. Liquids and gases are fluids and have no definite shape.

The air that we breathe includes several gases. Nitrogen and oxygen are the most abundant. Smaller amounts of carbon dioxide, water vapor, and other gases are also present. In addition to the gases in air, common gases include hydrogen, ammonia, helium, and natural gas. Some gases are becoming familiar because of the threat they pose to health. Sulfur dioxide, nitrogen dioxide, and carbon monoxide are some examples. Ozone, too, is a gas that currently attracts attention.

At very high temperatures, a fourth phase of matter can exist. This phase of matter is called **plasma** (PLAZ'-muh). Plasma exists inside stars, where temperatures reach several thousand degrees Celsius.

Examples of solids, liquids, and gases surround you. In most cases, you would have little trouble deciding the phase of a substance. But you have also seen substances change from one phase to another. For example, a solid ice cube will melt and become a liquid. Classifying substances as solid, liquid, or gas may not always be useful.

Quick Review

1. How do solids differ from liquids?
2. How do gases differ from liquids?
3. How do gases differ from solids?

Metals and nonmetals

New vocabulary: conductor

Substances are often classified as metals or nonmetals. Copper, tin, iron, aluminum, silver, and gold are all familiar examples of metals. What do metals have in common?

Metals are shiny. They can be formed into thin wires or flattened into thin sheets of foil. Metals are good **conductors,** or carriers, of heat and electricity. Copper and silver are especially good conductors.

As a general rule, nonmetals are poor conductors of heat or electricity. Nonmetals vary in appearance. Glass, plastic, and polished wood are shiny. Most nonmetals, however, have a dull appearance. Common nonmetals include carbon, sulfur, silicon, arsenic, and iodine.

Quick Review

1. List three properties metals have in common.
2. Name two metals that are especially good conductors.
3. Name two properties that most nonmetals have.

Research Topic

The properties of matter change at very low temperatures. Cryogenics is the study of low temperature conditions. Read about some of the unusual properties of matter at low temperatures and write a report.

Quick Review answers:
1. Solids have a definite shape. Liquids do not; they assume the shape of whatever container they are poured into.
2. Liquids have a definite volume. Gases do not. Gases expand to fill the available space.
3. Gases have no definite shape and expand to fill the available space. Solids have a definite shape and definite volume.

Additional information: The term *ductile* is used to describe the property of being able to be formed into wires. The term *malleable* is used to describe the property of being able to be flattened into thin sheets.

Quick Review answers:
1. Most metals are shiny, make a clanging sound when dropped, can be formed into thin wires and flat sheets, and will conduct electricity.
2. Copper and silver.
3. Most non-metals are poor conductors of heat and electricity.

Figure 2-6. *The elements copper (reddish wire) and sulfur (yellow powder) combine chemically to make a compound, copper sulfate (blue granules). Copper sulfate is a substance with different properties from either of the elements that compose it. If copper and sulfur are separated chemically from copper sulfate, will they still be the same elements?*
Yes

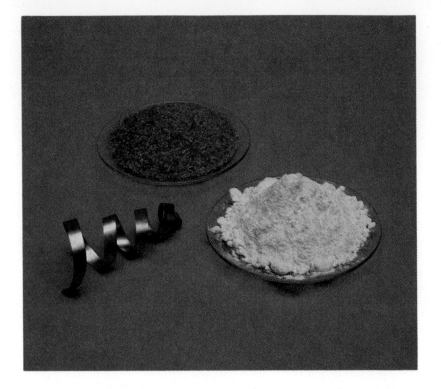

New vocabulary: mixture, solution, dissolve, solute, solvent, saturated solution, unsaturated solution, chemical formula, compound, element

Science background information: A mixture contains two or more substances that are not chemically combined. Often the substances in a mixture are unevenly mixed throughout. On the other hand, a solution is an evenly mixed, or *homogeneous,* mixture of two or more substances.

Main Idea

What is a solution?

Mixtures, compounds and elements

In a third classification system, substances are grouped by whether they can be separated into other substances. A **mixture** contains two or more substances. Sometimes both substances remain visible. For example, if you drop sand into water, the sand and water both can be seen.

You can mix just a little sand with water. Or you can add a lot of sand to the water. The mixture can contain varying amounts of sand. The amounts of the substances in a mixture can be changed. This is an important characteristic of all mixtures.

Air is a mixture of several invisible gases. It contains oxygen, nitrogen, carbon dioxide, and several other substances. The amounts of some of the substances in air change. When it is very humid, there is a lot of water present in the air as a gas.

A **solution** (suh-LOO′-shun) is a special kind of mixture. The substances are spread evenly throughout each other in a solution. Samples taken from different parts of the solution will be completely identical.

The most common solutions are mixtures of water and something else. For example, suppose sugar is added to water in a beaker. The water is stirred. The grains of sugar are no longer visible. The solution of sugar in water is as clear as the water alone. You know the sugar is present in the water when you taste a small sample. Tasting samples of the solution from different parts of the solution confirms that the sugar is spread evenly through the water. The sugar remains spread evenly through the water even after a few days. It does not settle out. The sugar is said to have **dissolved** (duh-ZOLVD') in the water.

Food coloring dissolves in water. A drop of food coloring added to a beaker of water will spread evenly through the water. You can see the color in all parts of the solution. The solution is colored but clear. No particles, however, can be seen in the solution.

You can add a second drop of food coloring to the solution. The second drop will spread through the original solution. The solution appears more deeply colored. Different amounts of food coloring can be mixed with the water. Solutions can vary in the amount of substance that is dissolved.

The substance that dissolves is the **solute** (SOL'-yoot). The substance in which the solute dissolves is the **solvent** (SOL'-vent). In a sugar water solution, sugar is the solute. Water is the solvent.

Water is the most common solvent. More substances dissolve in water than in anything else. Tap water contains many dissolved substances. Alcohol is another good solvent. Not all substances dissolve in water or alcohol. Special cleaning fluids must be used to dissolve substances such as tar, oil, and grease.

Data Search

Two solid metals can be mixed together if they are both liquids. They become liquids at a temperature above the higher melting point of the two. How hot would a mixture of iron and chromium have to be heated in order to mix them together as liquids? Search pages 658–661.

Above 1857°C, the melting point of chromium.

Main Idea

What is the difference between a solute and a solvent?

Figure 2-7. *Both beakers contain mixtures. Which mixture is a solution? How can you tell?*
The beaker on the right contains a solution. The material in the water is mixed evenly, and the liquid is clear.

Additional information: Metal solutions are called alloys, and are formed by mixing molten metals together, and then allowing them to cool and harden.

Solutions can be classified by the phases of the solute and solvent. Both solutes and solvents may be solids, liquids, or gases. For example, carbon dioxide (gas) dissolves readily in water (liquid). Carbonated beverages are solutions of carbon dioxide in water. A solid can be dissolved in another solid. Sterling silver is a solution of silver and copper.

Solutions may also be classified according to the amount of solute they contain. Solutions can be either saturated or unsaturated with respect to a particular solute. A **saturated solution** contains the maximum amount of solute that will dissolve in a given amount of solvent, at a given temperature. An **unsaturated solution** contains less than the maximum amount of solute that a given amount of solvent will hold at a given temperature. Additional solute can be dissolved in an unsaturated solution. Additional solute will not dissolve in a saturated solution.

Mixtures can be made in many proportions, and are easily separated.

Compounds are chemically joined, always in the same proportion, and not normally easy to break apart. Compounds have different properties from substances they contain.

Elements are made up of only one substance, and are sometimes called the building blocks of matter.

Figure 2-8. *How are mixtures, compounds, and elements different?*

The substances in a mixture can often be separated quite easily. For example, sand can be strained out of water. Likewise, the substances in many simple solutions can be separated easily. When water in a solution evaporates, it leaves the solute behind.

Water itself can be broken down into other substances. Yet it is not a mixture. The two substances into which water can

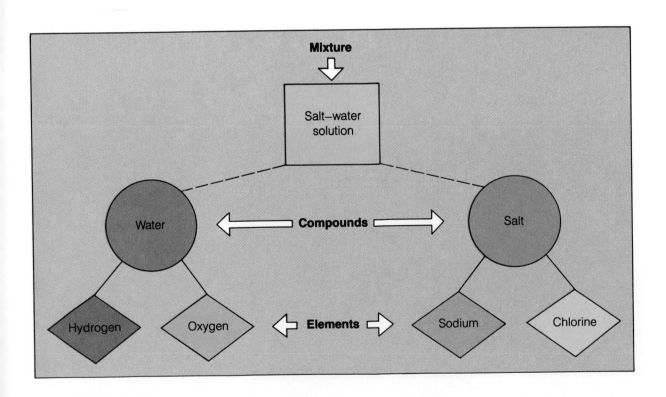

be broken down are hydrogen and oxygen. They are both gases. A mixture made of two gases, on the other hand, will always be a gas.

There is another important difference between water and a mixture. When two substances are mixed together, the amount of each can be changed. There will still be a mixture. The chemical recipe, or **chemical formula** (FORM'-yoo-luh), for water is always the same, on the other hand. For a certain amount of hydrogen, there is only one amount of oxygen that will combine to form water. When water is broken down, the amounts of hydrogen and oxygen fit the same formula.

A third difference between water and a mixture is that it is harder to break down water. Boiling water or freezing it does not break it down.

Table salt, too, is formed from two other totally different substances, sodium and chlorine. Sodium is a soft, silvery metallic solid. Chlorine is a greenish-yellow gas. Again, the amounts of chlorine and sodium are fixed. The formula never changes.

Substances such as water and table salt are called **compounds** (KOM'-powndz). All compounds are combinations of two or more substances. Unlike mixtures, compounds always have the same formula. It is normally hard to break them down. And compounds have very different properties from those of the substances that make them.

Hydrogen and oxygen, the substances that form water, cannot be broken down into other substances. They are examples of **elements** (EL'-uh-ments). Sodium and chlorine are also elements.

Only about one hundred substances have been identified as elements. All other substances can be thought of as different combinations of those elements. The elements are sometimes referred to as building blocks. They are rearranged in different ways to form many different substances.

Quick Review

1. How does a solution differ from a mixture that is not a solution? Give an example of each.
2. What is the difference between a saturated solution and an unsaturated solution?
3. How does a solution differ from a compound? Give an example of each.
4. How does a compound differ from an element?

Teaching suggestion: The chemical formula for water is H_2O. You may want to mention this now. You can also wait until the idea is more fully developed in Chapter 3.

Critical Thinking

What three important properties does a compound have that a mixture does not have?

Compounds always have the same formula. They are difficult to break down or separate, and they have very different properties from the substances making them up.

Quick Review answers:
1. A solution is a mixture in which the substances are spread evenly. The particles of the solution cannot be seen. A mixture that is not a solution usually is not clear and may not be mixed evenly. It is usually easier to separate the parts of a mixture.
2. Additional solute will dissolve in an unsaturated solution, but not in a saturated solution.
3. In a compound, the substances are chemically combined in a definite proportion. The compound has different properties from the substance it contains, while a solution usually does not.
4. An element is a single substance; a compound is a chemical combination of two or more elements.

Activity

See also Activity Record Sheet 2-1C (Lab Manual page 19). Answers to Questions and Conclusion appear on page T69 in the front of this book.

2.1c Preparing and Separating Solutions

Science processes: Observing, measuring, inferring, interpreting, using time relations

Materials 15 minutes and overnight Groups of 3 or 4

- 100-mL graduated cylinder
- grease pencil
- distilled water
- tap water
- magnifying glass
- 15-mL chemically pure (or kosher) table salt
- 4 beakers (numbered)
- 4 glass slides (numbered)
- 4 medicine droppers
- stirring rod

Purpose

To demonstrate the separation of a solid from a liquid by the evaporation method.

Procedure

1. Put the amount of water specified below into the four numbered beakers as follows:
   beaker 1: 75 mL of tap water
   beaker 2: 75 mL of distilled water
   beaker 3: 100 mL of distilled water
   beaker 4: 50 mL of distilled water
2. Add 15 mL of table salt to beaker 3 and mix with a *clean* stirring rod until the salt has dissolved.
3. Measure 25 mL of the salt-water solution from beaker 3 and add it to beaker 4. Mix with a clean stirring rod.
4. Using a clean medicine dropper, put five drops of the water from beaker 1 onto slide 1.
5. Use a medicine dropper to place five drops of solution from each of the other three beakers onto the slide with the same number as the beaker.
6. Place the four slides in a warm location where they will not be disturbed. Leave overnight.
7. On the next day, examine the residue on each of the four slides under the magnifying glass. Record your observations in the table on the activity record sheet.

Questions

1. Which of the beakers has the saltiest solution?
2. How did the five drops of solution change on the slides when left overnight?
3. Describe the amount and the properties of the residue on each of the numbered slides.
4. Which of the slides has the most salt residue? Why?
5. How do the residues found on slides 1, 3, and 4 differ from one another? How are these differences related to the solutions in the beakers with corresponding numbers? Explain your answer.
6. What does the presence of residues on slides 1 and 2 tell you about the difference between tap water and distilled water?

Conclusion

How does the evaporation method allow us to study a solid?

Step 4

2.1 Section Review

Answers to Understanding the Concepts appear on page T69 in the front of this book. Blackline master test for this section: Section Testsheet 2-1 (TRB page 204).

Vocabulary

6 chemical formula
12 compound
10 conductor
2 dissolve
15 element
5 gas
9 liquid
18 mixture
16 phase

3 plasma
11 property
7 saturated solution
1 solid
13 solute
17 solution
14 solvent
8 substance
4 unsaturated solution

Vocabulary Review

Match each term above with the numbered phrase that best describes it.

1. A piece of wood is in this phase
2. Become mixed into a liquid
3. A very hot gas
4. More of a substance will dissolve in this
5. Will expand to fill all of the available space
6. A recipe for a compound
7. No more of a particular substance can dissolve in this
8. Each kind of matter
9. Has a definite volume, but no definite shape
10. Will carry heat or electricity
11. A characteristic by which you tell how one thing is different from another
12. Made of other substances according to a specific formula
13. Dissolves when mixed with a solvent
14. What dissolves a solute
15. Substances that cannot be broken down into different substances
16. A way of looking at matter according to whether it is a solid, liquid, or a gas

17. A mixture with one substance evenly spread out through another
18. Two or more substances together, like sand and water

Review Questions

Multiple Choice: Choose the answer that best completes each of the following sentences.

19. All matter takes up space and ? .
    a. dissolves in water
    b. has mass
    c. has a definite shape
    d. is visible
20. The three common phases of matter used to group substances are ? .
    a. solids, liquids, and gases
    b. elements, compounds, and mixtures
    c. solvents, solutes, and solutions
    d. metals, plastics, and wood
21. The number of elements now known is about ? .
    a. 30
    b. 100
    c. 1000
    d. 100,000

22. Salty water is best classified as a(n) ? .
    a. element
    b. compound
    c. mixture
    d. plasma
23. A property metals have in common is that they ? .
    a. conduct electricity
    b. take the shape of their container
    c. dissolve in water
    d. can be broken down into other substances
24. When sugar dissolves in water ? .
    a. it becomes a solid
    b. it forms a mixture known as a solution
    c. it forms a mixture known as a plasma
    d. it evaporates quickly

Understanding the Concepts

25. Explain why a solution is classified as a mixture rather than as a compound.
26. In your own kitchen, find three examples of classification. Try to find at least one example of classification into groups and one in order.
27. Carbon dioxide is one of the invisible gases in air. It can be broken down into carbon, a black solid, and oxygen, another invisible gas. Is carbon dioxide an element, compound, or mixture? Explain your choice.
28. When salt is poured into a salt shaker, it takes the shape of the salt shaker. Explain why salt is classified as a solid rather than a liquid.
29. Explain the difference between a saturated and an unsaturated solution.

For ideas for classroom demonstration and discussion, see Getting Starting on page T69 in the front of this book.

2.2 Changes in Matter

Supplemental materials: Teaching Diagram 2-2 (TRB on page 9), Reading Check-sheet 2-2 (TRB page 85), Skillsheet 2-2 (TRB page 131), Investigation 2-2 (Lab Manual pages 27–28)

Section Preview

- **Volume changes**
- **Phase changes**
- **Solubility changes**
- **Chemical changes**
- **Mass and volume changes**
- **Combustion**

Bracketed numbers are Section Review questions correlated to that objective.

Learning Objectives

1. To distinguish between physical and chemical changes. [6, 13, 16, 19, 2̲]
2. To predict the effect of changes in temperature on physical and chemical changes. [2, 10, 11, 18, 21, 24]
3. To recognize that even though substances are changed, mass remains unchanged in a chemical change. [20]
4. To identify some common physical and chemical changes. [1, 4, 5, 8, 14, 15, 17, 21, 23, 25]

Figure 2-9. *What is most likely the reason that the ice is melting at the tip of this icicle?*
Because the temperature of the air around it is above the melting point of ice.

Substances change. **Physical changes** are the changes in properties of a substance without a change in the substance. For example, ice melts and becomes liquid water. The ice and water are different forms of the same substance. When dry ice seems to disappear, it is changing directly to a gas. The dry ice and the gas formed are both the same substance, carbon dioxide. A balloon filled with air expands, or increases in volume, when heated. Salt and sugar seem to disappear when stirred into water. These are all physical changes.

Volume changes

New vocabulary: physical change, thermostat

A change in the volume of a substance is a physical change. The volume can be changed by changing the temperature.

The volume of a sample of air increases when its temperature increases. A decrease in temperature causes a decrease in volume. The results of temperature changes in air are shown in Figure 2-10. The flask is fitted with a one-hole rubber stopper. One end of a piece of glass tubing is inserted through the hole. The flask is turned upside down. The

Main Idea

How can you cause a physical change in the volume of a substance?

other end of the glass tubing is in a beaker of water. Air is trapped in the flask and in the glass tube. Then the air in the flask is warmed. The air expands, and some air is forced from the glass tube. Bubbles of air can be seen escaping into the water.

Cooling the flask with a few ice cubes reverses the result. The air contracts, or decreases in volume. Water moves up into the glass tube to fill the space left by the air.

You may have seen a hot air balloon rising when the air inside is heated. The air inside the balloon expands. The volume of the balloon does not change. Instead, some of the heated air is forced from the balloon. How does the mass of the air in the balloon change? Try to explain why the balloon rises.

Other gases also change volume with temperature change. They change in the same way as air does.

Liquids and solids also increase in volume when the temperature is increased. The changes in volume are not as easy to see as in gases. These changes, however, can be observed if you look carefully. Telephone and electric power lines sag on hot days. Cold temperatures cause them to tighten up. Concrete is poured in sections to allow for expansion and contraction. Even so, sidewalks and concrete pavement crack and crumble with changes in temperature.

Steel, too, changes in size as the temperature changes. You may have seen metal plates covering expansion joints on large bridges. The metal plates cover the openings that appear when the joints expand. Even though the volume

Research Topic

How do engineers design a bridge for expansion and contraction? Look up the subjects of engineering and bridge design and write a brief report on the answer.

Figure 2-10. *What causes the water level to move up and down in the glass tube?*

When the air in the flask is heated, it expands and pushes the water level down.

When the air in the flask is cooled, it contracts. Pressure of the outside air forces the water up in the tube.

2.2a Temperature and Air Volume

Science processes: Observing, communicating, measuring, inferring, interpreting, formulating

Materials   20 minutes   Groups of 2 or 3

- jar or beaker
- water
- food coloring
- transparent drinking straw
- modeling clay
- transparent tape
- test tube
- dishcloth
- ice cubes

Purpose

To show how temperature changes affect the volume of a sample of air.

Procedure

1. Fill the jar about halfway with water. Add several drops of food coloring and stir with the straw.
2. Let the straw rest on the bottom of the jar. Compare the water level in the straw with the water level in the jar. Make a table like the one below and record the data as you collect it.
3. Hold a test tube upside down over the top 4 to 5 cm of the straw. Keep the straw in the water to maintain the same water level and pack modeling clay tightly around the mouth of the test tube. Be sure to form an airtight seal. A sample of air is now trapped between the water in the straw and the end of the test tube.
4. Keep the bottom of the straw in the water and lift the test tube. Note the water level in the straw.

5. Now mark the water level in the straw by wrapping a piece of transparent tape around the straw. Place the top edge of the tape along the water level in the straw.
6. Put some ice in the dishcloth and press the cloth against the test tube to chill the air inside. Observe what happens to the water level in the straw.
7. Now let the straw rest on the bottom of the jar. On the table, record the water level in the straw.
8. Put your hands around the test tube and warm the air sample. Record the water level in the straw.

Questions

1. How does the water level in the straw compare to the water level in the jar when the straw is resting on the bottom of the jar?
2. After you form an airtight seal in the test tube, what happens to the water level in the straw when you lift the test tube?
3. What happens to the water level inside the straw when the air sample is cooled?
4. Considering your answer to question 3, what is happening to the volume of the air sample? Why?
5. Immediately after the air sample is cooled and the straw is lowered to the bottom of the jar, how does the water level inside the straw compare to the water level in the jar?
6. When you warm the air sample with your hands, what happens to the water level inside the straw?
7. Considering your answer to question 6, what is happening to the volume of the air sample? Why?

Conclusion

Explain how temperature changes affect the volume of an air sample.

	Comparison of Water Levels in the Straw and the Jar	Change in Volume of Air Sample
When straw is resting on bottom of jar		
When air is cooled		
When air is warmed		

changes in solids and liquids are small compared to gases, the changes are important. Engineers must plan for these changes or serious problems result.

Thermometers work because the volume of a substance changes when the temperature changes. The flask and tubing in Figure 2-10 could be used as a thermometer. The level of the water in the glass tubing could be marked with a temperature scale. In common thermometers, liquids such as mercury and alcohol are used to indicate temperature changes.

Some thermometers use the expansion and contraction of different metals. For example, devices to control heating and cooling are called **thermostats.** They consist of two strips of metal fastened together. The metals expand by different amounts for the same temperature change. As a result, the strips bend. As they bend, the strips act as a switch to turn on or off a heating or cooling unit.

Quick Review

1. What happens to the volume of gases, liquids, and solids that are cooled?
2. Name two devices that work because a temperature change causes a change in volume.

Figure 2-11. *Two metals are fastened together in a strip. What causes the strip to bend?*

The strips are made of different metals. Both expand when heated, but at different rates. The metal that expands more is kept from going all the way by the other metal. This causes it to bend toward the other metal, making it and the entire bar bend.

■ Safety Note

Thermometers should always be handled with care. They often contain mercury, which is very toxic. If a thermometer is broken in class, do not touch any mercury that spills and notify the teacher immediately so that mercury can be disposed of safely.

Quick Review answers:
1. It decreases.
2. Thermometers, thermostats, etc.

Phase changes
New vocabulary: water vapor, freezing, melting, melting point, evaporation, condensation, boiling, boiling point, sublimation

A substance is classified as a solid, liquid, or gas at ordinary temperatures (around 20°C). It can change phase when its temperature changes. For example, water is a liquid at ordinary temperatures. When the temperature is lowered to 0°C, liquid water freezes, or changes to a solid (ice). When the temperature is increased to 100°C, liquid water boils, or changes to a gas. Water in the gas phase is known as **water vapor** (VAH′-per).

Other substances also change from one phase to another when their temperatures change. The phase of a substance depends on the temperature.

For any substance, **freezing** is the change in phase from liquid to solid. **Melting** is the reverse change, from solid to liquid. A pure substance will melt at a specific temperature. Water (ice) melts at 0°C. Lead melts at 327°C. Copper melts at 1083°C. The temperature at which a substance begins to melt is called its **melting point.** The melting point does not change with the amount of the substance. Small amounts of ice melt at the same temperature as large amounts of ice. The melting temperature of a substance is a useful property in identifying the substance.

Evaporation (ih-vap′-uh-RAY′-shun) is the change in phase from liquid to gas. Some evaporation of a liquid takes place at any temperature. Water spilled on a desk top in an open room will soon dry up. The water changes from the liquid phase to the gas phase (water vapor). Warming a liquid speeds up evaporation.

Condensation (kon′-den-SAY′-shun) is the reverse change, from gas to liquid. Droplets of liquid water collect on a glass containing a cold drink. Where did these droplets come from? Water vapor in the air has condensed to a liquid on the cold surface. The cooling of a gas leads to condensation.

When a liquid is heated to a high enough temperature, bubbles of gas of the same substance begin to form within the liquid itself. This process is called **boiling.** The **boiling point** is the temperature at which boiling begins. The boiling point, like the melting point, does not depend on the amount of the substance. Small amounts of a liquid boil at the same temperature as large amounts.

The boiling point of water is 100°C. Other pure substances also have definite boiling points. Alcohol boils at 78°C. Mercury boils at 357°C. Boiling points are affected by altitude, or

Main Idea

What is the reverse of freezing?

Data Search

What is the melting point of sodium? What is its boiling point? Search pages 658–661.

Sodium melts at 98°C and boils at 883°C.

Water vapor from the air condensed on the cold surface of the glass.

Figure 2-12. *Condensation caused the droplets of water to form on the outside of the cold glass.*

height above sea level. The boiling temperature of a substance is usually given for locations at or near sea level.

Sublimation (sub'-lih-MAY'-shun) is the change from solid to gas or gas to solid without going through the liquid phase. Dry ice (solid carbon dioxide) is a familiar solid that sublimes. In the hottest weather, dry ice does not melt. Instead, it just seems to disappear. The solid carbon dioxide changes directly into a gas. Solid water in the form of ice and snow also sublimes. In cold, clear weather, snow banks will slowly disappear without melting. The snow changes directly into water vapor. The frost inside a freezer forms in the reverse kind of sublimation. Water vapor in the air sublimes and becomes ice.

Quick Review

1. What change is the reverse of melting?
2. What change is the reverse of condensation?
3. Explain why the melting and boiling points of a pure substance can be considered properties of the substance.

Solubility changes

New vocabulary: soluble

Gases dissolve in water in varying amounts. The amount of a gas that dissolves depends on the kind of gas. Large amounts of carbon dioxide dissolve in water. Carbon dioxide is said to be very **soluble** (SOL'-yoo-bul) in water. Ammonia is also

Name three properties of a substance that can change when the temperature of the substance is changed.

Volume, phase and solubility are properties of a substance that change with temperature.

A soft drink left at room temperature tastes flat because there are no more bubbles. All the dissolved carbon dioxide has gone. The bubbles give a prickly sensation to the tongue.

There is less dissolved oxygen in warmed water. Some fish that need lots of oxygen may die.

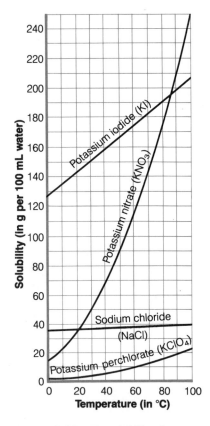

Figure 2-14. *The solubility of some substances changes greatly with increasing temperature.*

very soluble in water. Much smaller amounts of oxygen dissolve in water. Nevertheless, the small amounts of oxygen dissolved are important. Fish depend on the oxygen dissolved in water just as land animals depend on oxygen from the atmosphere.

The amount of a gas that dissolves in water depends on the water temperature, also. Fill a glass with water taken from the cold water faucet. Let the glass stand in the warmer room air for a few minutes. Notice the bubbles that form in the water. The bubbles are formed from gases that had been dissolved in the water. These gases slowly escape from solution as the water is warmed. This shows that warm water cannot hold as much dissolved gas as cold water.

Carbonated beverages contain dissolved carbon dioxide gas. You may have tasted a carbonated beverage from a bottle left open in a warm room. How would you describe its taste? What has happened that affects the taste?

In some places water in streams and lakes is warmed by excess heat discarded by electric power plants. How does the warming of the water affect the amount of oxygen that remains dissolved? How might this change in temperature of the water affect the fish that live in the water?

The amount of a solid that dissolves in water depends both on the solid and on the water temperature. Unlike gases, most solids increase in solubility as the temperature increases.

The graph at the left compares the changes in solubility with temperature for several substances. Sodium chloride (table salt) is not much more soluble in hot water than in cold water. Potassium nitrate, on the other hand, is far more soluble in hot water than in cold water.

Deposits of minerals are found around geysers and hot springs. You might have visited locations where these are found. The hot water below the surface of the earth dissolves minerals in large quantities. The hot solution cools as it reaches the surface. The minerals are not as soluble in the cooler water. Some of the dissolved minerals leave the solution. More minerals are deposited as the water evaporates.

Sometimes you want to know not how much solid will dissolve but how fast it will. Suppose you were making iced tea for some people who liked sugar in it. To dissolve the sugar faster, you should put it in while the tea is still hot, rather than after the ice cubes have cooled the tea.

The temperature of a liquid affects how fast a solid dissolves in it. At higher temperatures, most solids dissolve

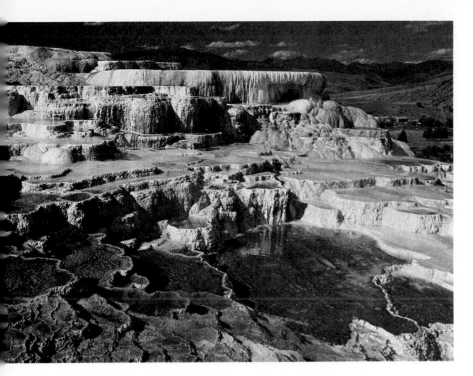

Figure 2-15. *What causes the build-up of mineral deposits around the edge of this hot spring?*
See text on facing page.

faster, as well as in greater amounts. Increasing the temperature increases the speed of dissolving of a solid.

Another way to increase the speed of dissolving is to break up the solid into smaller pieces. Granulated sugar will dissolve faster than a sugar cube. Superfine sugar will dissolve even faster. The smaller the particles, the more surface area is exposed to the liquid. Why does stirring the liquid speed up the dissolving process? Which kind of sugar would you choose for sweetening a cold drink?

Additional information: Each solid acts somewhat differently, but in general, the hotter the water, the more of the solid dissolves.

Stirring the liquid allows more contact between particles of liquid and solid. Superfine sugar is good for sweetening a drink.

Quick Review

1. Name two gases that are more soluble than oxygen is in water.
2. What effect does an increase in temperature have on the solubility of a gas in water?
3. Name two ways of making a solid dissolve more quickly in water.

Quick Review answers:
1. Carbon dioxide, ammonia.
2. An increase in temperature causes a decrease in the solubility of a gas in water.
3. Increasing the temperature and breaking up the solid into finer pieces.

Chemical changes

New vocabulary: chemical change

The changes discussed so far have been physical changes. In physical changes, no new substances are formed.

Chemical changes are changes that produce new substances. For example, gasoline burns easily in air to form

Main Idea

How do chemical changes differ from physical changes?

Figure 2-16. *Why is it incorrect to say that this tablet is dissolving in the water?*
Because the formation of bubbles indicates that a chemical change is taking place.

Critical Thinking

What property remains unchanged in all chemical changes?
The total mass of the substances in chemical changes is unchanged.

Quick Review answers:
1. A chemical change is taking place causing a new, gaseous substance to be formed.
2. A chemical change is taking place, causing an insoluble solid to be formed.
3. Chemical changes produce new substances. Physical changes do not.

water and carbon dioxide. The properties of water and carbon dioxide are much different from those of gasoline. New substances have been formed. Iron rusts in air. The rust formed from iron crumbles and breaks apart. It no longer has the strength of the iron. A new substance has been formed. The change in cake batter as it bakes is a chemical change. The flour and other ingredients have been changed into new substances.

Sometimes it is hard to tell whether a change is physical or chemical. Changes in properties accompany both kinds of change. When the changes in properties indicate that a new substance has been formed, a chemical change has taken place.

When paper burns, it gives off heat. The formation of new substances is often accompanied by the release of heat. The release of heat is sometimes used to help decide if a chemical change has taken place. However, some physical changes also release heat. Even in some chemical changes, the release of heat is slow and hard to detect. The heat released in the rusting of iron is not noticed. Also, some chemical changes produce a cooling effect rather than a release of heat.

Other clues indicate that a chemical change is happening. Suppose a solid or liquid is added to another liquid, and bubbles are produced. The bubbles indicate that a new substance, a gas, has formed. Another clue is the appearance of cloudiness when two clear liquids are mixed together. The cloudiness indicates that a new substance, a solid, has formed. You will learn more about these clues for chemical changes in Chapter 6.

We make use of chemical changes in many ways. Much of our food is prepared using chemical changes. The frying of an egg, the toasting of bread, and the cooking of meat all involve chemical changes. Our digestive system produces other chemical changes in the foods we eat. New cells for body growth and energy for body activities result from these chemical changes.

Quick Review

1. If two liquids are mixed together and bubbles are produced, what is happening?
2. If two clear liquids are mixed together and the mixture turns cloudy, what is happening?
3. What is an important difference between physical and chemical changes?

See also Activity Record Sheet 2-2B (Lab Manual page 24).

Answers to Questions and Conclusion appear on page T70 in the front of this book.

Activity

2.2b Recognizing Chemical Changes

Science processes: Observing, communicating through data, experimenting, controlling variables

Materials   BASIC   15 minutes   Groups of 5 or 6

- 2 test tubes
- water
- 10 mL copper chloride ($CuCl_2$) solution
- 2 20-cm sections of wire

- 2 iron nails at least 4 cm long
- test tube rack
- test tube holder
- watch or clock with second hand

Purpose

To determine when a chemical change has taken place.

Procedure

SAFETY NOTE: *Wear safety goggles when conducting this activity.*

1. Label one test tube "$CuCl_2$" and the other "water." Make a table like the one below.
2. Fill one labeled test tube with 10 mL of the copper chloride solution. Fill the second labeled test tube three-quarters full of water. SAFETY NOTE: *Avoid touching or inhaling the copper chloride. If you get any on your skin, wash the affected skin area with soap and water. If you get any in your eyes, flush them with large amounts of water.*
3. Wind a section of the wire securely around the nail as shown in the diagram. Leave enough wire to allow you to raise and lower the nail in the test tube.
4. Holding each nail by the wire, put the first nail halfway into the copper chloride solution for 30 seconds. Put the second nail halfway into the water for 30 seconds.
5. Remove the nails and record on the table any changes that took place on the two nails.

Questions

1. What is the color of the copper chloride solution? What other properties describe the solution?
2. What happened to the nail dipped in the copper chloride solution for 30 seconds?
3. What evidence is there to show that new substances were formed when the nail was held in the copper chloride solution?
4. What kind of a change took place on the nail?
5. What happened to the second nail that was put in plain water?
6. How do you know that the change in the first nail was not the rusting of wet iron?

Conclusion

Explain how you can recognize when a chemical change takes place in a substance.

Step 3

	Description at start	Description after 30 s
Nail in water		
Nail in $CuCl_2$ solution		

Mass and volume changes

New substances are formed as a result of chemical changes. Is the volume of the new substances the same as that of the original substances? Is the mass the same?

The volume of the new substances formed in a chemical change may be different from the volume of the original substances. When the chemical change results in the forming of a substance in a different phase, such as a gas, this is particularly true. The volume of the new substances may also be unchanged. Where the substances formed are in the same phase as the original substances, no change in volume may be noticed.

For a long time, scientists were not sure whether or not mass changes during a chemical change. Collecting the new substances formed was often a problem. Not until late in the eighteenth century was an acceptable answer found. Mass remains unchanged in a chemical change. New substances with new properties can be formed. But no gain or loss of mass can be detected.

Additional information: The total mass does not change in a chemical reaction. There may or may not be changes in volume in a chemical reaction. The only trustworthy sign of a chemical change is the production of new substances.

Quick Review

1. What is always produced as a result of any chemical change?
2. In a chemical change, how does the volume of the new substances compare to the volume of the original substances?
3. In a chemical change, how does the mass of the new substances compare to the mass of the original substances?

Quick Review answers:
1. A new substance.
2. If the new substance is in a different phase, there is probably a noticeable change in volume. If there is no phase change, the volume may not change.
3. The total mass does not change.

Research Topic

Find out the meaning of *spontaneous combustion*. Under what conditions does it occur? How can it be prevented?

■ **Safety Note**
A small kitchen fire can be stopped by covering it with baking soda. This works because baking soda releases carbon dioxide when heated. The carbon dioxide surrounds the fire, keeping oxygen from getting to it. Without oxygen, the fire goes out.

Combustion

New vocabulary: combustion, combustible

Burning, or **combustion** (kum-BUS′-tyun), is a chemical change. Substances that will burn are said to be **combustible** (kum-BUS′-tih-bul). Some familiar combustible substances are paper, wood, coal, natural gas, and petroleum.

What changes accompany burning? Think about wood being burned in a fireplace or stove. Heat and light are released. Smoke is usually observed. The wood turns into ash. Only a small amount of ash is produced from a large supply of wood. These and other observations once led scientists to believe that a substance was released during burning. Substances that would burn were thought to contain this special substance. When burning took place, the special substance was thought to be released.

Today burning is viewed as a combining of substances. The combustible substance combines with oxygen that is a part of the air. They combine in a chemical change that releases heat. Additional new substances are produced as a result of the burning. Some of them are released into the air. When wood burns, ashes are only one of many new substances produced.

Quick Review

In burning, what substance combines with the combustible substance?

Our Science Heritage

The Father of Modern Chemistry

The French scientist Antoine Lavoisier (1743–1794) changed the direction of chemical investigation. Unlike many chemists of his time, he used measurements to support his conclusions. He repeated his experiments many times with many different substances.

Prior to Lavoisier's work, it was believed that all burning things gave off something called *phlogiston*. Supposedly, only substances containing phlogiston would burn. The phlogiston that left a burning substance was absorbed by the surrounding air.

When burned, most substances lost mass. Some gained mass, however. Lavoisier wondered how a loss of phlogiston could cause a loss of mass sometimes and a gain in mass other times.

Lavoisier experimented with the burning of substances in air inside a closed container. He found that the change in mass of a substance after burning was always equal and opposite to the change in mass of the surrounding air. Lavoisier's explanation was that the burning substance combined with oxygen from the air. At the same time, if other gases were given off, they became part of the air.

Lavoisier did experiments that convinced others that the total mass of all the substances in a chemical reaction did not change. This result became the principle of conservation of mass.

Lavoisier's many contributions led to his being called the Father of Modern Chemistry.

Antoine Lavoisier is observing mercury rise in the domed container. Air in the container is combining with the mercury being heated at his left.

A metallurgical engineer may examine an ore sample under the microscope.

Metallurgical Engineer

The job of a metallurgical engineer involves studying the properties of metals, designing ways to extract metals from their ores, and finding uses for the metals. Most metallurgical engineers are employed by the mining industries. Others may work for mining equipment manufacturers, for colleges and universities, or for government.

Metallurgical engineers must have a bachelor's degree in metallurgical engineering. Many have higher degrees as well. High school students planning for a college engineering program should take chemistry, physics, and as much math as their high school offers.

Metallurgical engineers are expected to be able to work with detail and precision. They are also expected to be creative and to demonstrate problem-solving ability.

For further information write to: The Metallurgical Society of AIME, 420 Commonwealth Dr., Warrendale, Pennsylvania 15086, or the American Society for Metals, Metals Park, Ohio 43214.

Machinists must be skillful with many kinds of tools and be able to follow blueprint instructions.

Machinist

A machinist is someone who operates power-driven tools to cut, shape, or finish particular products. Typically, a person employed as a machinist follows specific guidelines in cutting and shaping metal to a certain size in order to produce metal parts. Parts produced by machinists are commonly used in transportation equipment and in a wide range of manufacturing machinery.

Most machinists work in factories where parts are mass-produced. A machinist may have any of a variety of job titles depending upon the type of machine being operated. A machinist can be called a metal lathe operator, a milling machine operator, a drill press operator, or a grinding machine operator, for example.

The work environment of a machinist can present hazards and often machinists must wear safety goggles to protect their eyes from flying metal particles. Machinists who operate noisy machinery must wear ear plugs.

Training of machinists generally takes place on the job, often through formal apprenticeship programs. Useful high school courses that can be taken to prepare for a career as a machinist include mathematics, machine shop, and blueprint reading.

For further information write to: The National Tooling and Machining Association, 9300 Livingston Rd., Ft. Washington, Maryland 20744.

2.2 Section Review

Answers to Understanding the Concepts appear on page T70 in the front of this book. Blackline master test for this section: Section Testsheet 2-1 (TRB page 204).

Vocabulary

- 5 boiling
- 11 boiling point
- 13 chemical change
- 2 combustible
- 4 combustion
- 15 condensation
- 8 evaporation
- 14 freezing
- 1 melting
- 10 melting point
- 6 physical change
- 9 soluble
- 3 sublimation
- 12 thermostat
- 7 water vapor

Vocabulary Review

Match each term above with the numbered phrase that best describes it.

1. A physical change in which a liquid is formed from a solid
2. Can be burned
3. The disappearance of dry ice
4. The burning of natural gas in a kitchen stove burner
5. Water starts to do this at 100°C
6. Results in different properties, but not new substances
7. Another name for steam
8. The drying up of water on a counter
9. Can be dissolved in a liquid
10. The temperature at which a solid substance begins to melt
11. The temperature at which a liquid becomes a gas
12. Controls heating and cooling
13. Produces new substances
14. When a liquid becomes a solid

15. What happens when drops of water appear on the outside of a cold glass in a warm room

Review Questions

Multiple choice: Choose the answer that best completes each of the following sentences.

16. __?__ is a physical change.
    a. The burning of paper
    b. The freezing of water
    c. The baking of bread
    d. The rusting of iron
17. The change of phase from gas to liquid is known as __?__.
    a. sublimation
    b. freezing
    c. evaporation
    d. condensation
18. As the temperature of water is increased, the solubility of __?__.
    a. both gases and solids increases
    b. both gases and solids decreases
    c. gases increases, while that of solids decreases
    d. gases decreases, while that of solids increases
19. Most chemical changes are accompanied by __?__.
    a. a cooling effect
    b. a heating effect
    c. explosions
    d. harmful effects
20. During all chemical changes, the __?__ remain(s) the same.
    a. temperature
    b. total volume
    c. total mass
    d. kinds of substances present
21. The volume of __?__ is most affected by temperature changes.
    a. gases
    b. liquids
    c. solids
    d. metals

22. Combustion results in __?__.
    a. a decrease of heat in the surroundings
    b. the condensation of water vapor on a hot surface
    c. only a physical change in the substance that is burned
    d. a chemical change in substances
23. Chemical and physical changes __?__.
    a. both produce changes in properties
    b. both produce new substances
    c. both increase the amount of heat in a room
    d. do not result in the production of new substances
24. Evaporation and condensation __?__.
    a. are chemical changes
    b. both result in the production of a liquid from a gas
    c. involve a change of phase
    d. are identical processes

Understanding the Concepts

25. Give three examples of changes in the volume of a substance that are caused by a temperature change.
26. How is the boiling of a liquid different from the evaporation of a liquid?
27. How does an increase in temperature affect the speed of dissolving?
28. What are some things to look for that will help you decide if a chemical change has taken place?

2 Chapter Review

Vocabulary

boiling	evaporation	saturated solution
boiling point	freezing	solid
chemical change	gas	soluble
chemical formula	liquid	solute
combustible	melting	solution
combustion	melting point	solvent
compound	mixture	sublimation
condensation	phase	substance
conductor	physical change	thermostat
dissolve	plasma	unsaturated solution
element	property	water vapor

Review of Concepts

Matter is anything that has mass and takes up space.

- Each substance, or kind of matter, has properties by which it is recognized.

The **classification of matter** is a grouping of matter according to its properties.

- Substances can be put in order by differences in the same property.
- Substances are classified as solids, liquids, or gases at ordinary temperatures; as metals or nonmetals; or as elements, compounds, or mixtures.
- Elements are substances that cannot be broken down into other substances.
- Compounds are substances made of two or more elements according to a fixed formula and have properties very different from those of the elements.

A **physical change** is a change in which the properties of a substance change but no new substances are formed.

- Substances generally increase in volume as their temperature increases.
- The phase of a substance depends on the temperature of the substance.
- Most solids become more soluble in water as the water temperature increases.
- Breaking up a solid allows it to dissolve in a liquid more quickly.

A **chemical change** is a change in which one or more new substances are formed.

- The total mass of substances before and after a chemical change does not change.
- Burning is a chemical change that involves the combining of oxygen with another substance to produce new substances.

Critical Thinking

1. Flour is sold by mass, not volume, even in the U.S., where recipes call for certain volume amounts of flour. Why is it fairer to sell flour by mass, rather than by volume?
2. Suppose you were given two unidentified samples and were asked to test whether they were made of the same substance.
   a. Name as many properties as you can that would have to be the same if the samples were of the same substance.
   b. Name as many properties as you can that could be different even if the samples were of the same substance.
3. Name three similarities between the dissolving of a solid in water and the melting of a solid.
4. How do the properties of a substance determine how it can be used? Give two examples.

5. In what ways are a rock, gasoline, and steam alike? Name at least two ways in which they are different.

6. We know that matter takes up space and has mass. What are some things you can think of that do not take up space or have mass?

7. Devise at least three different ways of grouping the following items: bear, electric razor, TV antenna, mailbox, chest of drawers, lunch box, drinking glass, stereo, dog, banana, telephone, cow, book, cake, fish.

8. What does solubility have to do with the fact that there are generally extensive mineral deposits around hot springs?

9. Examine the graph in Figure 2-14 on p. 70. According to the graph, which compound is more soluble in water at 60°C, potassium iodide or potassium nitrate? Which of these two compounds is more soluble at 100°C? Which of the four compounds in the graph shows the greatest change in solubility as a function of temperature?

10. Explain how an increase in temperature, such as might be caused by the release of heat from electric power plants, can affect oxygen concentration and of excess fish life in a body of water.

11. Describe how the different expansion characteristics of different metals are used in thermostats.

12. When boiling water is used for cooking, the process takes longer in the mountains than at sea level. Why is this?

13. How do gases and solids differ as to how their solubilities in water are affected by temperature?

Individual Research

14. Interview a librarian in your school or public library. Find out what different systems are used to classify and locate books.

15. Examine a classification key used in biology or geology to identify plants, animals, or minerals. Describe the system used. What skills would you need to use such a key?

16. In a supermarket, make a list of the different sizes of bottles and/or cans of a single soft drink product. Record the stated volume (in L or mL) and the price for each size. Use your data to calculate the cost per milliliter for each size. (*Hint:* Divide the price by the volume of soft drink received for that price.)

17. Trap a soap bubble on the top of a flask or bottle. Warm the flask with your hands. What happens to the soap bubble? Cool the flask by placing it in cold water. What happens to the soap bubble?

18. An explosion is a very rapid chemical change. Conduct an interview with a firefighter or safety officer. Find out what precautions are taken to prevent the occurrence of an explosion.

Bibliography

Arnov, Boris. *Water: Experiments to Understand It.* New York: Lothrop/Morrow, 1980
   Experiments to investigate 13 properties of water, including its ability as a solvent and the effects of evaporation.

O'Donnell, James J. *Fire! Its Many Faces and Moods.* New York: Messner, 1980
   The role of fire in ancient civilizations; how magicians use fire; how to deal with forest fires and house fires.

Paterson, Alan J. *How Glass Is Made.* New York: Facts on File, 1985
   This well-illustrated text detailing the history of glassmaking provides descriptions of many different methods of making glass.

Perrins, Lesley. *How Paper Is Made.* New York: Facts on File, 1985
   The many uses of paper and the different processes for producing it are clearly described. Historical perspective is provided.

Chapter 3
The Structure of Matter

Snowflakes show diversity and order at the same time. Each snowflake is unique, and yet each one is based on an orderly pattern. The fact that there is a pattern suggests that there is order in the components of the snowflake and that there is order in the process by which snowflakes are formed. In this chapter you will learn something about the basis for the order in the things we see.

Science background information:
The particle nature of matter is multi-level. One way to understand the many levels of organization in the visible world is to envision a series of boxes inside one another. The smallest box contains pure energy. The next largest box represents a fundamental particle formed by the conversion of energy to mass. Each successively larger box represents a higher level of organization that requires more energy—in the form of both particles with mass and energy itself—in order to exist.

Fundamental particles join together to make atoms. More than thirty sub-atomic particles have been isolated from atoms. However, the chemical behavior of atoms can be explained in terms of only three subatomic particles: protons, neutrons, and electrons.

Atoms are highly organized. The protons and neutrons, which contain most of the mass of the atom, are found clumped together in the nucleus. The nucleus has a diameter which is only 1/10 000th of the diameter of the atom itself. The protons, which are positively charged, can be concentrated in this small space because of their interactions with neutrons, which carry no charge. The negatively charged electrons are attracted to the positively charged nucleus, but re-

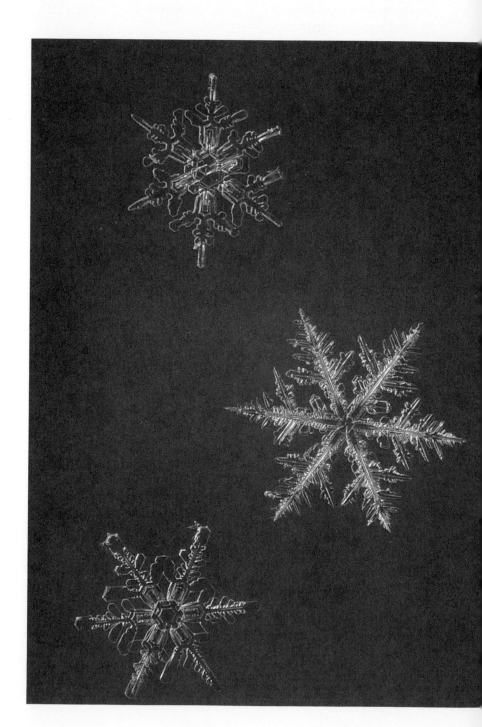

For detailed information about teaching this chapter, see Chapter 3 Planning Guide on pages T72–T73 in the front of this book.

Projectsheet 3 (TRB page 175) and Research Lab 3 (Lab Manual pages 43–44) may be used at any point in this chapter.

Chapter Preview

3.1 The Particle Model of Matter

- **Particles of matter**
- **Atoms**
- **Element names and symbols**
- **A model for elements**
- **A model for compounds**
- **A model for mixtures**

The idea that all matter is made of very small particles can explain many observations of the behavior of matter. It can explain how elements, compounds, and mixtures differ from each other.

3.2 Models of the Atom

- **Atomic mass**
- **The periodic table of Mendeleev**
- **Particles within the atom**
- **The modern periodic table**
- **Atomic models**

The difference among elements can be explained by the idea that each element is made of a unique kind of particle. The uniqueness of each kind of particle can be explained by the idea that the particles are made of even smaller particles.

3.3 A Model for Chemical Changes

- **Chemical equations**
- **Electric charges**
- **Ions**
- **Shared electrons**
- **Chemical bonds**
- **Acids and bases**
- **Neutralization and salts**

The idea that matter is made of particles can be used to explain how elements combine to form compounds. It can also explain the behavior of certain groups of compounds known as acids and bases.

pelled by each other. As a result, the electrons occupy regions of space around the nucleus known as energy levels. Large atoms, containing many electrons, have highly complex systems of energy levels.

The number of protons in an atomic nucleus determines which element it is. For instance, all atoms which have six protons in their nucleus are carbon atoms. Gold, which has 79 protons, could be converted to mercury with the addition of a single proton. However, this does not occur even under the most extreme conditions of chemical reactions. Atoms of elements do not exchange protons with one another during chemical reactions. Atoms retain their nuclear characteristics, or their essential identities through all chemical reactions.

Chemical reactions involve the electrons in the outer part of the atom. Chemical reactions result from the gain or loss or sharing of electrons. Some configurations of electrons are more stable than others. In chemical reactions, atoms tend to acquire more stable configurations of electrons.

An atom that can easily attain a stable electron configuration by losing or gaining one electron will readily do so, forming an ion. The alkali metals each can lose one electron to form an ion. The halogens each can gain an electron to form an ion. The alkaline earth elements form ions by losing two electrons. These elements mostly participate in ionic bonding. Ionic bonding is the result of electrostatic attraction between oppositely charged ions. Ionic solids or salts have a crystal lattice structure in which the different ions alternate.

Other groups of elements participate in covalent or electron-sharing bonds. In covalent bonds, atoms share electrons. A hybrid orbital is formed so that the electrons can move about two or more nuclei. Forming a hybrid orbital stabilizes the newly formed molecule.

The molecule is the next highest level of organization in matter above the atom. Molecules are chemically bonded groups of atoms that act as a unit. They range in size from the simplest diatomic gas, hydrogen, with a molecular mass of two daltons, to biological macromolecules, with molecular masses of more than 500 000 daltons.

For ideas for classroom demonstration and discussion, see Getting Started on page T74 in the front of this book.

3.1 The Particle Model of Matter

Supplemental materials: Teaching Diagram 3-1 (TRB page XX), Reading Check-sheet 3-1 (TRB page 86), Skillsheet 3-1 (TRB page 132), Investigation 3-1 (Lab Manual, pages 33–34)

Section Preview

- **Particles of matter**
- **Atoms**
- **Element names and symbols**
- **A model for elements**
- **A model for compounds**
- **A model for mixtures**

Bracketed numbers are Section Review questions correlated to that objective.

Learning Objectives

1. To describe what a scientific model is and how it is developed and used. [5, 11]
2. To apply the particle model to the nature of matter. [2, 4, 6, 7, 8, 10, 12, 13, 14, 16, 19]
3. To use the particle model of water to explain the differences in the properties of elements, compounds, and mixtures. [1, 3, 9, 15, 17, 18, 20, 21]

Figure 3-1. *Oranges are packed together like atoms in a solid.*

Additional information:
The oranges in the picture are representative of the particles in solid matter. The oranges are arranged in rows, and form an orderly pattern. The particles in solid elements and compounds arrange themselves in a similar fashion, though the pattern may differ, depending on the substance.

Figure 3-2. *Use the hypothesis that sugar and water are made of tiny particles to explain how sugar dissolves.*
The sugar breaks into tiny particles that fit in between the particles of water. The particles become mixed so evenly that you can taste sugar in any part of the solution even though none can be seen.

You can observe sugar disappearing when it is stirred into water. If the water evaporates away, you can observe grains of sugar remaining in the container. You infer that the sugar was in the water the entire time. How can the dissolving of sugar in water be explained?

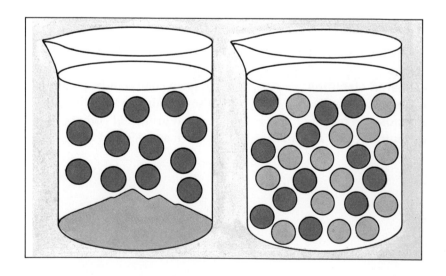

Scientists may guess at explanations, but the explanations must fit the facts. For example, a good explanation is that both sugar and water are made of very tiny particles. The particles are much too small to be seen even under a microscope. When sugar dissolves, it breaks up into particles. The sugar particles fit in between the water particles. So the solution can taste sweet even though the sugar cannot be seen.

Particles of matter

New vocabulary: compressibility

The hypothesis that matter is made of particles just begins to explain how matter behaves. The hypothesis must be expanded. It must explain how there can be different phases of matter and how there can be elements, compounds, and mixtures. It must explain physical and chemical changes.

A hypothesis is expanded by making more inferences from further observations. Observations of gases are helpful. For example, add air to a balloon. Keep adding air until the balloon seems ready to burst. Release the air from the balloon. You can get some idea of how much air was inside. A lot of air can be forced into a small space.

Large amounts of gas can be forced into a small space. This property of gases is called **compressibility.** Gases are very compressible. Liquids and solids cannot be compressed easily. They strongly resist being pushed into smaller spaces.

From these observations, you can infer that there is empty space between the tiny particles of gas. When a gas is compressed, the particles move closer together. You can infer that the particles in liquids and solids must be much closer together than in gases.

Alcohol and water can be mixed together. The volume of the alcohol-water mixture is less than the sum of the individual volumes. For instance, if 50 mL of alcohol is mixed with 100 mL of water, the volume of the mixture is less than 150 mL. You can infer that there must be some space between the particles in a liquid. The dissolving of a solid in a liquid adds additional evidence. The particles of the solid must be able to move between the particles of the liquid.

A particle picture of matter seems consistent with observations. The particles must be very tiny. They cannot be seen with a microscope and can move through tiny openings.

Have you ever tried to save a filled balloon? The balloon eventually deflates. The air finds its way out through tiny openings in the material of the balloon.

Figure 3-3. *What can be inferred about the spacing between particles in gases and in liquids?*

The particles in liquids must be much closer together than particles in gases.

Main Idea

What can you infer about the spaces between particles of gases, liquids, and solids from observations on compressibility?

Science background information: Water molecules are smaller than alcohol molecules. Some of the water molecules fit into open spaces between the alcohol molecules. That is why the volume of a mixture of alcohol and water is less than volumes of the two components separately.

3.1a Compressibility of Air and Water

Science Processes: Observing, inferring, predicting

Materials   BASIC   15 minutes   Groups of 4 or 5

- clear soft plastic bottle with cap
- water

Purpose

To find which can be compressed more easily–air or water.

Procedure

1. Put the cap tightly on the "empty" plastic bottle.
2. Squeeze the bottle with your hands. Note whether or not it takes up less space (compresses).
3. Fill the bottle to the top with water and replace the cap tightly.
4. Squeeze the bottle and note the ease or difficulty with which it compresses.

Steps 2 and 6

Water level

Squeeze bottle

5. Now pour out half of the water and replace the cap tightly.
6. Hold the bottle upright and predict what will happen if you squeeze the bottle below the water line. Then squeeze it and record your observation on the table below.
7. Now predict what will happen if you squeeze the bottle above the water line. Then squeeze it and write down your observations on the table below.

Questions

1. What filled the bottle before you put water in it?
2. Could you compress the "empty" bottle after you put the cap on? Why?
3. Could you compress the bottle when it was filled with water and tightly capped? Why?
4. What happened to the water level of the half-filled bottle when you squeezed below the water line? Why?
5. What happened to the water level of the half-filled bottle when you squeezed above the water line? Why is there a difference?
6. In what way did your predictions about what would happen to the water level of the half-filled bottle differ from what you actually observed?

Conclusion

In what ways do the compressibility of air and water differ from each other?

Half-filled Bottle	Your Prediction	What Was Observed
squeezed below water line		
squeezed above water line		

When water is added to a clay flowerpot, the outside of the pot becomes wet. Water inside the clay pot moves to the outside through tiny openings in the clay.

There must be space between the particles of matter. The amount of space between particles must be greater in gases than in liquids and solids. This part of the hypothesis explains how gases are more easily compressed.

Quick Review

1. Give two examples of evidence that supports the inference that there is space between the particles of matter.
2. Give two examples of evidence that supports the inference that the particles of matter are very tiny.

Atoms

New vocabulary: atom

Matter can be classified as belonging to one of the following groups: elements, compounds, or mixtures. Elements are substances that cannot be broken down any further. Compounds are formed from elements and can be broken down into elements. The elements that form a compound have different properties from the compound. Also, the elements in a compound are combined according to a definite formula. Mixtures include two or more substances with the amounts of each varying. Substances in a mixture are more easily separated than the substances in a compound. How can a particle picture of matter explain these differences in substances?

John Dalton (1766–1844) was a British teacher who thought of a hypothesis that explained how particles formed elements, compounds, and mixtures. The idea that matter was made of particles had been introduced over 2000 years earlier by the Greeks. Dalton called his particles **atoms** (AT′-umz) after the Greek word for *indivisible*. In other words, Dalton believed that atoms were the smallest particles of matter possible and could not be broken up.

Dalton suggested that each element consists of only one kind of atom. All the atoms of one element are alike. But the atoms of one element are different from the atoms of another element. Each element is made of its own kind of atom. And an element is a substance made of a single kind of atom.

Dalton explained how compounds were formed from atoms. He said that atoms of one element combined with atoms of one or more other elements. For example, he said that water was made of particles that were combinations of

Figure 3-4. *Explain why it is not a good idea to put a clay flowerpot and saucer directly on a wood floor.*
Water particles can pass through tiny openings in the clay and make water stains on the floor.

Quick Review answers:
1. (1) Gases can be compressed.
   (2) When alcohol is mixed with water, the resulting mixtures does not have as great a volume as the alcohol and water separately.
2. (1) Particles of air can escape through tiny openings in a balloon.
   (2) Particles of water can pass through tiny openings in a clay flowerpot.

Research Topic

Read about the life of John Dalton. Write a report about him, and present it to the class.

Science background information:
Evidence for the existence of atoms can be seen in a microscope. Using a microscope, in 1827 English botanist Robert Brown discovered that pollen grains in water move around in an irregular way. This motion, caused by the random impact of water molecules on pollen grains, is called "Brownian motion."

Oxygen atom   Hydrogen atom

Oxygen (element)   Water vapor (compound)   Mixture of hydrogen and oxygen gas

Figure 3-5. *The atoms in an element, compound, and mixture. What is the difference between the particles in an element and in a compound? In a compound and in a mixture?*

An element is made of a single kind of atom. A compound consists of two or more different kinds of atoms, tightly joined, according to a definite formula.

A mixture, too, is made up of different kinds of atoms, but not tightly joined. The number of one kind of atom can be changed without affecting other atoms.

Quick Review answers:
Dalton suggested that each element consists of only one kind of atom. Compounds consist of more than one kind of atom, tightly joined, according to a definite formula.

Critical Thinking

If some of the details of Dalton's hypothesis were incorrect, why is the hypothesis still accepted?
Because, on the whole, Dalton's hypothesis gives a better explanation for the observations that scientists have made than any other hypothesis.

hydrogen atoms and oxygen atoms. All water particles were the same. This explained why a compound always formed according to a definite formula.

According to Dalton, a mixture, too, was made of two or more kinds of atoms. But the different kinds of atoms were not joined tightly together as in a compound. The number of one kind of atom could be changed without affecting the other atoms. This explained how varying amounts of substances could form a mixture. It also explained what made it easier to separate mixtures.

Dalton developed his hypothesis after making many observations of the behavior of gases in physical and chemical changes. Observations made since Dalton's time have shown that some of his details were incorrect. But his overall picture of particles of matter is still used today.

Quick Review

How did Dalton explain the difference between elements and compounds?

Element names and symbols

More than twenty elements had been identified when Dalton proposed his hypothesis. Just over a hundred elements are now known. The names of the elements have many different origins. Some elements are named for their properties. For example, hydrogen means *water former*. Hydrogen gas burns in air to form water. Bromine means *stench*. Bromine has a very disagreeable odor.

Other elements are named for a location. Most often they are named for the location where they were discovered. Some elements discovered after Dalton's time include germanium, californium, europium, and indium. Do you recognize the lo-

Activity

3.1b Space between Particles

recording
Materials 20 minutes Groups of 5

- **marbles (enough to fill a 250-mL beaker)**
- **sand**
- **water**
- **3 250-mL beakers**

Purpose

To show that there is space between the particles in a liquid or a solid.

Procedure

1. Fill one beaker with marbles.
2. Fill a second beaker with sand.

Step 5

3. Fill a third beaker with water.
4. Observe how much of the space is taken up by measuring the volume of material in each of the three beakers.
5. Add sand from the second beaker to the beaker of marbles. Mix the sand and marbles carefully to get as much sand as possible into the first beaker. Measure the volume of sand left in the second beaker and record the data on the table below.
6. Now slowly add water from the third beaker to the beaker containing the sand and marbles. Measure the volume of water left in the third beaker and record the data on the table below.

Questions

1. Before adding other materials, how much of the space is filled in the first beaker? Explain your answer.
2. How much sand did you add to the first beaker?
3. Explain how you can determine whether or not there is space in the first beaker after adding sand to the marbles.
4. How much water did you add to the first beaker?

Conclusion

Explain how you can determine if there is space between the particles of a liquid or a solid.

	Beaker of Marbles	Beaker of Sand	Beaker of Water
Amount at start of experiment	mL	mL	mL
Amount after adding sand to first beaker	mL	mL	mL
Amount after adding water to first beaker	mL	mL	mL

Science background information:
Elements named after locations:
- germanium—Germany
- californium—California
- europium—Europe
- indium—India

Elements named after Roman gods and planets):
- mercury—Mercury
- neptunium—Neptune
- plutonium—Pluto

Figure 3-6. *Some of Dalton's symbols for the elements known during his time. Would such symbols be convenient today? Explain.*

We know of many more elements today, and therefore need many more symbols than Dalton used. It is more convenient for us to use letter symbols, which can be easily reproduced by typewriters and other printing machines. They are recognized by all nations, and they are based on either the modern or ancient (Latin) names of the elements.

cations they are named after? Helium was first discovered by studying sunlight. Its name comes from the Greek word *helios*, meaning *sun*.

Some elements are named after scientists. Einsteinium, mendelevium, nobelium, and curium are examples. Often, the person discovering the element was allowed the privilege of naming it. What objects are the names of the elements mercury, neptunium, and plutonium taken from?

Dalton represented the different kinds of atoms by symbols he invented. He used circles filled in with different designs or letters. Some of Dalton's symbols for the elements are shown in Figure 3-6.

The number of known elements increased. The names for some of the elements were different in different countries. It became important that everyone agree on at least a common symbol for each element.

The symbols in use today are accepted by all countries. An element is represented by one or two letters. The first letter used is always capitalized. The second letter (when used) is always a lower-case letter.

Name	Symbol	Name	Symbol
aluminum	Al	mercury	Hg
arsenic	As	neon	Ne
bromine	Br	nickel	Ni
calcium	Ca	nitrogen	N
carbon	C	oxygen	O
chlorine	Cl	phosphorus	P
chromium	Cr	platinum	Pt
copper	Cu	potassium	K
fluorine	F	radium	Ra
gold	Au	silicon	Si
helium	He	silver	Ag
hydrogen	H	sodium	Na
iodine	I	sulfur	S
iron	Fe	tin	Sn
lead	Pb	tungsten	W
lithium	Li	uranium	U
magnesium	Mg	zinc	Z

Table 3-1. *Names and symbols of some common elements.*

Science background information:
Symbols based on Latin names are:
- Cu—cuprium (copper)
- Au—aurum (gold)
- Fe—ferrum (iron)
- Pb—plumbum (lead)
- Hg—hydrargyrum (mercury)
- K—kalium (potassium)
- Ag—argentum (silver)
- Na—natrium (sodium)
- Sn—stannum (tin)

The symbol W stands for wolfram, which is the internationally accepted name for the metal commonly called tungsten in English-speaking countries.

The letters are chosen from the name of the element. The symbol for the element hydrogen is H. The symbol for the element helium is He. The element sodium takes its symbol, Na, from its Latin name, natrium.

The names and symbols of some common elements are given in Table 3-1. Which symbols do you think are based on the Latin name of the element?

Quick Review

How do some elements happen to have symbols that are not the first letter of the name of the element?

Quick Review answers:
Except for W (mentioned above), all symbols whose first letters differ from those of the English names are based on the Latin names of the elements.

A model for elements

New vocabulary: model, molecule, diatomic, monatomic, ozone

Scientists often use **models** to describe unfamiliar things in terms of familiar objects. We can picture atoms as behaving much like tiny balls or marbles. This model of atoms can be used to explain the differences between solids, liquids, and gases. However, remember that the model that scientists use today to represent the atoms is more complex than simple balls.

Main Idea

How do scientists use models?

Figure 3-7. *Model of the arrangement of atoms in a solid element.*

Main Idea

What are the differences in the atoms in solids, liquids, and gases?

Data Search

Name four elements that melt between 0°C and 100°C. Search pages 658–661.

Iodine, phosphorus, potassium, and sulfur.

If we consider all atoms to be like tiny balls, then the differences we find between solids, liquids, and gases are due to the arrangements of the atoms in these different states of matter. Solids will have one arrangement of atoms, liquids another, and gases yet another arrangement. The changes of a substance between one phase and another can be pictured as changes in the arrangements of the atoms of that substance.

Iron, copper, and lead are among the elements that are solids at normal temperatures. A model for the arrangement of atoms in a solid element is shown in Figure 3-7. The atoms are represented by balls. The balls are very close together in a regular pattern.

Other elements in the solid phase would be represented in much the same way. The atoms might be different in size. They might be packed together in a slightly different pattern. But the general picture would be similar.

Mercury is among the elements that are liquids at normal temperatures. A model for the arrangement of atoms in a liquid element is shown in Figure 3-8. Although the balls are close together, they are not arranged in a regular pattern. In a liquid element, the atoms are free to move past each other. Thus, a liquid can take the shape of its container and can be poured. In a solid element, on the other hand, the atoms stay in the same location. This allows a solid to keep its shape.

Helium, neon, and oxygen are among the elements that are gases at normal temperatures. Figure 3-9 shows a model

Figure 3-8. *Model of the arrangement of atoms in a liquid element.*

for the arrangement of atoms in a gas like helium. The spaces between the balls are much bigger than the balls themselves. The balls are free to move in all directions.

This simple model of solid, liquid and gaseous elements does not fit all elements. Some elements seem to be made of particles consisting of more than one atom each. So instead of each ball representing a single atom, it can also represent a conglomeration of two or more atoms.

Regardless of the number of atoms it consists of, the smallest particle of a substance that still retains the characteristic properties of that substance is called a **molecule** (MOL'-uh-kyool). For example, a molecule of oxygen gas consists of two identical oxygen atoms held together by a chemical bond. A molecule which is made up of two like atoms is called a **diatomic** (dī-uh-TOM'-ik) molecule. The gaseous elements hydrogen, nitrogen, fluorine, and chlorine are made up of diatomic molecules. So are the liquid element bromine and the solid element iodine. A molecule made up of only one atom is called **monatomic.** Helium is a monatomic element, as are neon, argon, krypton, xenon, and radon. All are gases. With a few exceptions, which we will study later, all matter is made up of molecules.

The number of atoms in one molecule of a substance is indicated in its chemical formula. The formula for oxygen gas is written O_2. The small number to the lower right indicates that there are two atoms of oxygen in every oxygen molecule. The symbol for helium gas is written He. The absence of a number on the lower right means that there is only 1 helium atom per molecule of helium. You know that nitrogen and hydrogen are diatomic. How would you write the symbol for nitrogen gas? Hydrogen gas?

Some elements are made of molecules of more than two atoms. There is a special form of oxygen found in small amounts in the outer layer of the earth's atmosphere. It is made of molecules that have three oxygen atoms each. The

Main Idea

What is a molecule?

Critical Thinking

Density is related to mass and volume. Would you expect the solid or the liquid state of a substance to be less dense? Why?

The liquid. Because the atoms would occupy more space in a liquid, there would be less mass for a set volume, hence, the liquid would be less dense. This is true for most substances.

Figure 3-10. *The label on this can lets consumers know that this product will not destroy the ozone in the atmosphere.*

Quick Review answers:

1. A helium molecule contains only one atom, while an oxygen molecule contains two or even three (ozone).
2. Molecules of ordinary oxygen (O_2) contain two oxygen atoms. Molecules of ozone (O_3) contain three oxygen atoms.
3. A molecule of oxygen contains two oxygen atoms.

Additional information:

Elements are combined chemically in a compound. Elements and/or compounds may be components of a mixture, but in a mixture the components are not linked chemically to one another.

formula is O_3. This form of oxygen is given the special name of **ozone** (Ō-zōn). Ozone can absorb many dangerous ultraviolet rays from the sun. These rays can cause skin cancer. Without the ozone in the earth's atmosphere, many more ultraviolet rays would reach the earth, causing an increase in skin cancer. The chemicals that were once used widely in spray cans, called fluorocarbons, react strongly with the ozone in the atmosphere and destroy it. Scientists were concerned that the release of these chemicals into the air by millions of spray cans would decrease the amount of ozone. Because of this concern, restrictions were placed on the use of fluorocarbons in spray cans. Some scientists think that high altitude jet airplanes may also affect the amount of ozone. This effect is currently being studied.

Other elements that consist of molecules made up of more than two atoms include phosphorus and sulfur. Solid phosphorus is made of molecules that have four atoms each. The chemical formula for solid phosphorus is P_4. Elemental sulfur, a yellow crumbly solid, is composed of molecules formed of eight sulfur atoms connected in a ring. The chemical formula for solid sulfur is S_8.

Quick Review

1. How do the molecules of helium differ from the molecules of oxygen?
2. What is the difference in the way the atoms are grouped in ordinary oxygen and in ozone?
3. What does the number mean in the formula O_2?

A model for compounds

So far you have seen only molecules made up of all the same type of atom, such as O_2, S_8, and P_4. In fact, most molecules are made up of various combinations of different types of atoms. These combination molecules are called compounds.

In a compound, there is a special combination of two or more different kinds of elements. Water is a compound formed from a particular combination of the elements hydrogen and oxygen. One water molecule, the smallest particle of water, consists of two atoms of hydrogen and one atom of oxygen. Thus the formula for water is written H_2O. The three atoms in a molecule of water are held together by chemical bonds. Carbon dioxide, a gaseous compound that is exhaled in every breath, has the formula CO_2. Sugar (su-

Sodium

Chlorine

crose) is a larger, more complicated molecule. The formula for sucrose is $C_{12}H_{22}O_{11}$. How many atoms of hydrogen are in a molecule of sucrose? 22

Molecules of a single compound are all alike. Molecules of carbon dioxide are all alike whether they come from auto exhaust or human respiration. Molecules do not change when a compound changes phase. The molecules of solid water (ice) are the same as molecules of liquid water or of water vapor. Only the arrangement of the molecules changes.

There are also compounds which are not made up of molecules. These are known as ionic compounds. Sodium chloride (table salt) is one example. This compound is made from ions of the elements sodium and chlorine. We will study ions in section 3. For every atom of sodium there is one atom of chlorine but they are not bound together into a molecule. Instead, the atoms of sodium and chlorine are locked together into an alternating pattern.

Whether compounds are made of molecules or ions, compounds are always made up of elements combined in definite proportions. This is known as the *law of definite proportions*. The proportions are determined by experimentally measuring the masses of the elements in the compounds.

Figure 3-11. *Compounds such as sodium chloride are not made of molecules.*

Additional information:
The sodium and chlorine atoms in table salt are always arranged alternatingly in a *crystal lattice*. The shape of the lattice is cubical, as shown in the illustration. There is almost no limit to the number of sodium and chlorine atoms that can join and become part of this lattice. The lattice may get much larger, but it always keeps the same shape. When it gets large enough for us to see, we call it a salt crystal. Other substances form crystals of various shapes, depending on the arrangement of the particles.

Main Idea

What is the law of definite proportions?

Quick Review

1. How many atoms of carbon are in one molecule of sucrose?
2. Give an example of a compound that is not made of molecules.

Quick Review answers:
1. 12
2. Sodium chloride (table salt)

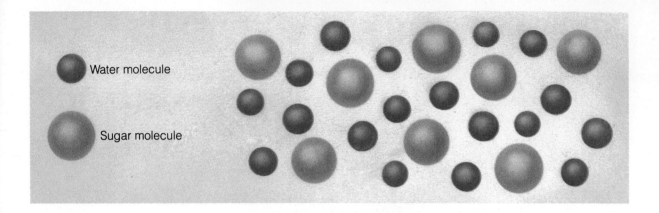

Water molecule

Sugar molecule

Figure 3-12. *How is the model for a mixture different from that of a compound?*

In a mixture, the atoms or molecules are not tightly joined, and more of one kind can be added. In a compound, the atoms are tightly joined together and the formula is fixed.

A model for mixtures

New vocabulary: alloy

In a mixture, the numbers of particles of each of the different substances can vary. The different particles are not held together tightly as in a compound. A mixture of sugar and water is pictured in Figure 3-12. The molecules of sugar are scattered among the molecules of water. More molecules of sugar can easily be added.

Clean air is a mixture. Molecules of oxygen and nitrogen make up most of this mixture. Molecules of water vapor are there in varying amounts. There are also molecules of carbon dioxide and several other gases.

Solids, liquids, and other gases can all mix with clean air and pollute it. For example, smoke consists mostly of bits of solid carbon. The carbon bits are collections of carbon atoms. Car engines give off gases such as carbon monoxide and nitrogen dioxide. These gases contribute to the haze in the air known as smog.

In a solid mixture, atoms or molecules of two different substances are mixed together. Even though they are not free to move about, as in a gas or liquid, there is no fixed recipe. This is what makes a solid mixture different from a compound. For example, in carbon steel, carbon atoms are mixed among iron atoms. In stainless steel, chromium and manganese atoms are mixed among iron atoms. Mixtures of metals are called **alloys** (AL′-oyz). Brass is another common alloy. It is a mixture of copper atoms and zinc atoms.

Main Idea

What are mixtures of metals called?

Quick Review answers:
Possible answers: air, sugar-water solution, steel, brass

Quick Review

Give two examples of mixtures that contain different kinds of molecules.

94   *Chapter 3*   **The Structure of Matter**

3.1 Section Review

Answers to Understanding the Concepts appear on page T75 in the front of this book. Blackline master test for this section: Section Testsheet 3-1 (TRB page 206).

Vocabulary

3 alloy
6 atom
4 compressible
8 diatomic
5 model
2 molecule
7 monatomic
1 ozone

Vocabulary Review

Match each term above with the numbered phrase that best describes it.

1. An element that has three atoms in each molecule.
2. The smallest particle of sugar.
3. Stainless steel.
4. Able to be squeezed into a small space.
5. A description of something unfamiliar in familiar terms.
6. Once believed to be the smallest indivisible particle of matter.
7. A molecule made up of only one atom.
8. A molecule made up of two atoms.

Review Questions

Multiple Choice: Choose the answer that best completes each of the following sentences.

9. A substance made up of only one kind of atom is a(n) ? .
   a. mixture
   b. element
   c. compound
   d. alloy
10. The present-day international symbols for the elements are made up of ? .
    a. circles with designs or letters inside
    b. the first letter of the name of the element
    c. two letters for every element
    d. either one or two letters
11. A scientific model ? .
    a. has been proved correct
    b. can be proved correct
    c. can never be proved correct
    d. may or may not be proved correct
12. A molecule ? .
    a. is sometimes made of matter
    b. is made of three or more atoms
    c. is always made of only one element
    d. is the smallest particle that retains the properties of a substance
13. A gas is compressible because ? .
    a. it is colorless
    b. it is odorless
    c. it is squeezable into a small space
    d. it is a mixture
14. According to the atomic theory ? .
    a. all matter is made up of larger particles
    b. all matter is made up of tiny particles
    c. no substances are made of tiny particles
    d. all tiny particles are compressible
15. To make an alloy, you must ? .
    a. blend together two or more metals when they are liquids
    b. blend together two or more liquids
    c. rub together two solids
    d. compress two solids together

Understanding the Concepts

16. List three observations that support the hypothesis that matter is made of tiny particles.
17. Use the particle model to explain the difference between liquid water and water vapor.
18. Use the particle model to explain how mixtures are different from compounds.
19. The Spanish word for silver is *plata,* while the French word is *argent.* How is the use of the symbol Ag in all countries like the use of SI symbols of measurement?
20. The formula for carbon dioxide is CO_2. Draw a model of a carbon dioxide molecule. Use different colored circles for each kind of atom. Be sure to explain your color scheme.
21. Dalton thought that hydrogen and oxygen were made of individual atoms not joined together. He also thought that a water molecule had one atom each of hydrogen and oxygen. Draw a model that shows Dalton's idea of a) the element oxygen; b) the compound water vapor; and c) a mixture of hydrogen and oxygen gases.

For ideas for classroom demonstration and discussion, see Getting Started on page T76 in the front of this book.

3.2 Models of the Atom

Supplemental materials: Teaching Diagram 3-2 , Reading Check sheet 3-2 (TRB page 87), Skillsheet 3-2 (TRB page 133), Investigation 3-2 (Lab Manual pages 37–38)

Section Preview

- **Atomic mass**
- **The periodic table of Mendeleev**
- **Particles within the atom**
- **The modern periodic table**
- **Atomic models**

Bracketed numbers are Section Review questions correlated to that objective.

Learning Objectives

1. To use the periodic table to identify elements with similar properties. [1, 2, 5, 6, 9, 11, 12, 16, 17, 18, 20, 22, 24, 25]
2. To describe the arrangement of protons, neutrons, and electrons in the atoms of elements. [7, 8, 10, 13, 14, 23, 28, 29]
3. To relate the properties of the elements to the arrangement of the electrons in the atoms of the different elements. [3, 4, 15, 19, 21, 26, 27]

Figure 3-13. *Tracks in a bubble chamber are caused by particles of matter that are smaller than an atom. The existence of particles that are smaller than atoms helps to explain some of the properties of atoms.*

Elements differ in their properties. At room temperature, some are gases, while others are solids or liquids. Some, such as oxygen, combine with many other elements to form compounds. Others, such as helium, rarely form compounds. Some, such as copper, conduct electricity. Others, such as sulfur, do not.

If the elements differ in properties, it is likely that their atoms differ also. A study of the properties of the elements has led to mental pictures of what the atoms are like.

Main Idea
What property must all atoms have?

Atomic mass

New vocabulary: atomic mass

A property of all matter is mass. Matter is made up of atoms. Therefore, all atoms must have mass.

Oxygen combines with many other elements. For example, oxygen combines with hydrogen. Eight grams of oxygen combines with one gram of hydrogen to form water. Oxygen combines with carbon to form carbon dioxide. Eight grams

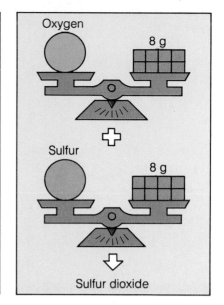

of oxygen combines with three grams of carbon. Oxygen combines with sulfur to form sulfur dioxide. Eight grams of oxygen combines with eight grams of sulfur. The same mass of oxygen combines with different masses of other elements.

Suppose all atoms have the same mass. In water, the mass of the oxygen is eight times the mass of the hydrogen. There would have to be eight oxygen atoms for each hydrogen atom in a water molecule. Similarly, in carbon dioxide, there would have to be eight oxygen atoms for every *three* carbon atoms. And in sulfur dioxide, there would be equal numbers of oxygen and sulfur atoms.

Dalton thought that each molecule had the smallest possible number of atoms. He rejected the idea that a water molecule had eight atoms of oxygen and one of hydrogen. Instead, he assumed it had one atom each of oxygen and hydrogen. Then the atoms would have to have different masses.

Evidence discovered after Dalton's time showed he was right about different masses for different kinds of atoms. But he was not completely right about water molecules. Each molecule actually has two hydrogen atoms and one oxygen atom. So the mass of an oxygen atom is 16 times the mass of a hydrogen atom.

Many measurements were made of the masses of elements that combine with each other to form compounds. The results of these measurements led to a table of masses for an atom of each different element. The mass of one atom of an element is called the **atomic mass** of the element.

Figure 3-14. *In these compounds containing oxygen, the same mass of oxygen is combined with different masses of other elements.*

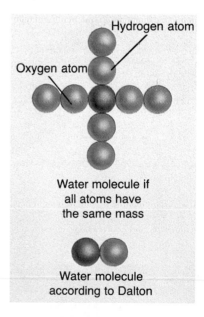

Water molecule if
all atoms have
the same mass

Water molecule
according to Dalton

Figure 3-15. *If all atoms had the same mass, a water molecule would have eight oxygen atoms and one hydrogen atom. Dalton assumed a water molecule had one atom each of oxygen and hydrogen.*

Quick Review answer:
Dalton

Quick Review

Who developed the hypothesis that different kinds of atoms each have different masses?

The periodic table of Mendeleev

New vocabulary: family, periodic table

As scientists became more familiar with the elements, they began to look for similarities. They noticed groups of elements that had similar properties. For example, fluorine, chlorine, bromine, and iodine all react very easily with metals. The compounds they form with each metal have similar formulas. The formulas for the compounds of the metal magnesium are MgF_2, $MgCl_2$, $MgBr_2$ and MgI_2. The formulas for the compounds of the metal sodium are NaF, NaCl, NaBr, and NaI. Groups of elements with similar properties are called **families.** Fluorine, chlorine, bromine, and iodine are in the same family.

Scientists tried many different arrangements to classify all the elements in one system. Dmitri Mendeleev (1834–1907), a Russian scientist, developed a classification system in 1869 that, with some changes, is still used today.

Mendeleev first arranged all the known elements in order of increasing atomic mass. Hydrogen had the smallest atomic mass, so it was first. He compared additional properties of each of the elements. Then he made a chart that looked something like a monthly calendar.

On a calendar, the days of the month are in numerical order. But dates for the same day of the week are in the same column. In Mendeleev's chart, the elements in the same family were in the same column.

Every seventh day on a calendar falls on the same day of the week. Mendeleev found a pattern of repeating properties in the elements. Things that repeat according to a pattern are said to be periodic. Mendeleev's chart is called the **periodic table** because it shows a periodic pattern for the elements.

Mendeleev based his table on the idea that the properties of an element are related to the mass of the atoms that make up that element. The properties of the elements repeat in a regular way with increasing atomic mass. Mendeleev was so convinced of the periodic properties of the elements that he left a few empty spaces in his table. He felt that none of the known elements belonged in those spaces. But he predicted the existence of elements with the correct properties to fit in

Main Idea

What are groups of elements with similar properties called?

Science background information:
Mendeleev's periodic table was based on sixty-three known elements. One periodic property of the elements that Mendeleev used in making his table was valence. The theory of valence had been developed by English chemist Sir Edward Frankland in 1852.

Data Search

Which element has the greater atomic mass, magnesium or sodium? Search pages 658–661.

Magnesium.

APRIL						
S	M	T	W	TH	F	S
					1	2
3	4	5	6	7	8	9
10	11	12	13	14	15	16
17	18	19	20	21	22	23
24	25	26	27	28	29	30

Figure 3-16. *What do the dates April 5, 12, 19, and 26 have in common?*

They all fall on the same day of the week (Tuesday), and therefore are all listed in the same vertical column.

the empty places. His convictions were confirmed when these elements were discovered.

More elements were discovered and atomic masses were measured more accurately. A few elements seemed to fit in the table out of order. For example, argon seems to be in the same family as helium. Yet argon's atomic mass is greater than potassium's. The reason for these "misfits" became clear as more was learned about atoms.

Main Idea

What problem did there seem to be about argon's position in the periodic table?

Quick Review

1. How did Mendeleev arrange the elements in his periodic table?
2. Why did Mendeleev leave some empty spaces in his periodic table?

Quick Review answers:
1. He arranged them in order of increasing mass, with elements of the same family in the same vertical column.
2. He could not find elements to fill certain spaces where he expected properties to be repeated. He left spaces because he predicted that these elements existed and would be discovered someday.

Particles within the atom
New vocabulary: electron, nucleus, proton, neutron, atomic number, isotope

Dalton had assumed that atoms could not be broken apart. But in 1897, the British scientist J. J. Thomson observed, in an experiment with gas tubes, that all matter gives off small, negatively charged particles. Thus, atoms must be made up of even smaller particles of matter. He named these particles **electrons** (uh-LEK'-trons). All electrons are identical no matter from which type of element they come.

It became important to determine the relationship of the electron to the rest of the atom. Ernest Rutherford continued Thomson's experiments. In 1911 he conducted a now-famous experiment. He bombarded a very thin piece of gold

Additional information:
Electrons have a mass that is equal to $\frac{1}{1837}$ the mass of a proton.

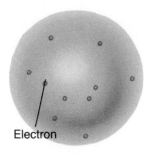

Figure 3-17. *Thomson's model of the atom had the electrons stuck to a lump of positively charged protons. It was called the "plum pudding model."*

foil with a stream of positively charged alpha particles. Alpha particles are helium atoms without any electrons. He reasoned that if atoms were solid, the bombarding particles should bounce right off. He found, to his surprise, that most of the alpha particles went straight through the gold foil as if there was nothing there. A few alpha particles bounced back very strongly. From the fact that most of the alpha particles passed through the foil, he concluded that an atom is mostly empty space. From the fact that some of the alpha particles bounced back, he concluded that the center of an atom has a heavy positively charged core, which is called the **nucleus.**

The nucleus is very small compared to the whole atom. Yet, it has almost all the mass of the atom. Suppose a nucleus were as big as a tiny flea. Then the whole atom would be the size of

Our Science Heritage

The Discovery of the Periodic Relationship

Mendeleev's periodic arrangement of the elements enabled him to predict the existence of unknown elements.

The periodic table was suggested independently by two different people at about the same time. Dmitri Mendeleev (1834–1907), a professor of chemistry in St. Petersburg, Russia, is generally given credit for discovering the periodic relationship among the elements. He published the first version of his table in 1869. Julius Lothar Meyer (1830–1895), a professor of chemistry in Tuebingen, Germany, prepared a table relating atomic mass to properties in 1868 but did not publish it until 1870. Meyer's publication probably influenced Mendeleev's revision of his table published in 1871.

At the time Mendeleev and Meyer discovered the periodic relationship, each was trying to write a chemistry textbook. There existed a large amount of information about the more than 60 elements known at that time. In trying to organize this information for students, each professor discovered the periodic relationship that relates the elements.

Unlike Meyer, Mendeleev left spaces in his table and predicted that elements with certain properties would be discovered. When gallium, scandium, and germanium were found, their properties matched his predictions.

a large baseball park. The individual electrons would be too small to be seen at all.

The nucleus was found to be made of two kinds of particles. One kind, with a positive charge, was called the **proton** (PRŌ'-ton). The other, with no charge, was called the **neutron** (NEW'-tron). All protons are identical, no matter from which kind of element they come. Similarly, all neutrons are identical. A neutron has slightly more mass than a proton. Each has almost 2000 times the mass of an electron.

All atoms, then, are made of three basic particles: electrons, protons, and neutrons. What makes atoms of different elements different? Evidence from experiments led to the following model for the atoms of different elements.

Each element has a specific number of protons in its atoms. A hydrogen atom always has one proton. A helium atom always has two protons. A lithium atom always has three protons, and so on. The number of protons in the nucleus of an atom determines the element. The number of protons in the atom came to be called the **atomic number** of the element.

In the modern periodic table, the elements are arranged in the order of their atomic number. Argon may have a greater atomic mass than potassium, but it has a lower atomic number. The families line up in perfect columns when atomic number is used instead of atomic mass.

Most atoms have roughly as many neutrons as protons. A helium atom normally has two of each. An oxygen atom normally has eight of each. However, a hydrogen atom normally has one proton and no neutrons at all.

All atoms of one element have the same number of protons. Yet, they do not all have the same mass. Different numbers of neutrons cause the differences in mass. For example, most oxygen atoms have eight neutrons. But some have nine or even ten neutrons. Atoms of the same element with different numbers of neutrons are called **isotopes** (Ī'-suh-tōps).

When an atom is not combined with other atoms, it has the same number of electrons as protons. An oxygen atom would have eight electrons, no matter which isotope it is. In a chemical change, an atom may gain or lose electrons. However, the nucleus is not affected by a chemical change.

Figure 3-18. *Rutherford's model of the atom had the protons clumped into a tiny nucleus. The nucleus is shown here much larger than it is in proportion to the whole atom. If the atom were really this size, the nucleus would be too small to be seen.*

Research Topic

Read about Maria Goeppert Mayer (1906–1972), who won a Nobel Prize in physics in 1963. Write a report about her life and her work on the nucleus.

Main Idea

What is the term for atoms of the same element with different numbers of neutrons?

Quick Review

1. Atoms are made of what three basic particles?
2. In the modern periodic table, the elements are in what order?

Quick Review answers:
1. Atoms are made of electrons, protons, and neutrons.
2. The elements are in order of increasing atomic number.

The modern periodic table

New vocabulary: atomic mass unit, inert gas, halogen, alkali metal

A modern periodic table of the elements is shown in Table 3-2. It is based on Mendeleev's original periodic table, but the elements in the modern version are arranged in order of increasing atomic number rather than increasing atomic mass.

Examine the table. The large number in dark print above the symbol for each element is that element's atomic number. Recall that the atomic number tells the number of protons in the nucleus of one atom of the element. This is what makes each element unique.

Notice the number in light print underneath the name of each element. This is the average atomic mass of the element. The mass of atoms is measured in **atomic mass units** (symbol amu). Atoms are so tiny that it would take 6×10^{23} atomic mass units to make one gram.

If you add a proton to the nucleus of an atom, that element changes into the next element in the table. In 1919, Ernest Rutherford changed nitrogen into oxygen by bombarding nitrogen with a stream of alpha particles. This is called the transmutation of elements. It is difficult to accomplish because the nucleus of an atom is positively charged and naturally repels another positively charged proton.

The elements to the right of uranium at the bottom of the periodic table were prepared in the laboratory by transmutation and do not exist in nature. They have so many protons that the concentration of positive charge in their nucleus is too great. These atoms are unstable and spontaneously fall apart. When unstable atoms fall apart, they give off excess protons and neutrons. This is called radioactivity and will be discussed in Chapter 13.

The naturally occurring elements in the periodic table fall into two large groups. These are the metals and the non-metals. Near the right side of the periodic table you will see a heavy zig-zag line. All of the elements above and to the right of this line are non-metals. All other elements, except hydrogen, are considered to be metals. About eighty percent of all known elements are metals.

Metals have many properties in common. They are all good conductors of heat and electricity. They are malleable, meaning that they can be pressed or bent into different shapes. For example, silver bars are hammered into jewelry. Finally, most metals have what is called a **metallic luster** or shine. Often a coating will be present on a metal, such as rust

Main Idea

What is the unit for measuring the mass of atoms?

Critical Thinking

If you examine the periodic table on page 104, you may notice that, for most elements, the average atomic mass is at least twice as large as the atomic number. What does that tell you about the average number of protons and neutrons in each element?

Remember that the atomic number is equal to the number of protons. That means, on the average, that there are at least as many neutrons in the nucleus as protons.

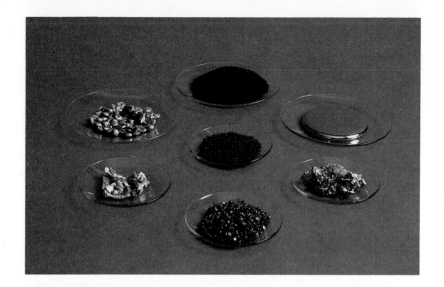

Figure 3-19. *Five metals and one non-metal include, starting clockwise from the bottom of the circle, copper, aluminum, zinc, iron, mercury, and silicon (the non-metal). Most of the metals, except for the iron in powdered form, are shiny. What other properties do metals have in common?* They are good conductors of heat and electricity and they can be hammered or bent into different shapes.

or tarnish. When the coating is scraped away, the luster underneath will be revealed.

The **alkali** (AL'-kuh-li) **metals** are the elements in the left hand column of the periodic table. These are lithium (Li), sodium (Na), potassium (K), rubidium (Rb), cesium (Cs), and francium (Fr). They have all the properties associated with metals. They are also the most chemically reactive metals. They are so reactive that they are never found in their pure state in nature. When they are purified, they must be stored under oil so they will not react with oxygen or water vapor in the air. All the alkali metals form ionic rather than molecular compounds. The alkali metals can be identified by means of a flame test. When heated in a flame, they give off light of characteristic colors. Sodium's light is bright yellow, while potassium gives off a pale pink light.

The next column is occupied by the **alkaline earth metals.** Which elements are they? They are also very reactive and are not found in their pure form in nature. Most tend to form ionic rather than molecular compounds. Some react with water. The alkaline earth elements include two of the most biologically important metals. Magnesium is a main component of the plant pigment chlorophyll. Chlorophyll enables plants to capture light energy for growth. This capture of light energy is the ultimate source of energy for life on earth. Calcium is an important part of your bones and teeth. It is also essential for muscle contraction and nerve function.

The rest of the metals in the periodic table are called **transition metals.** These include what we consider to be the most

Data Search

Compare the melting points of alkali metals, such as lithium, sodium, and potassium, with the melting points of the alkaline earth metals, such as magnesium and calcium.

Lithium (181°C), sodium (98°C), and potassium (63°C) melt at lower temperatures than the alkaline earth metals magnesium (649°C) and calcium (839°C).

Table 3-2.

Periodic Table of the Elements

1	1
H	
Hydrogen	
1.008	

Metals

Transition Elements

3 2/1	4 2/2							
Li Lithium 6.941	**Be** Beryllium 9.012							
11 2/8/1	12 2/8/2							
Na Sodium 22.990	**Mg** Magnesium 24.305							
19 2/8/8/1	20 2/8/8/2	21 2/8/9/2	22 2/8/10/2	23 2/8/11/2	24 2/8/13/1	25 2/8/13/2	26 2/8/14/2	27 2/8/15/2
K Potassium 39.098	**Ca** Calcium 40.08	**Sc** Scandium 44.956	**Ti** Titanium 47.90	**V** Vanadium 50.942	**Cr** Chromium 51.996	**Mn** Manganese 54.938	**Fe** Iron 55.847	**Co** Cobalt 58.933
37 2/8/18/8/1	38 2/8/18/8/2	39 2/8/18/9/2	40 2/8/18/10/2	41 2/8/18/12/1	42 2/8/18/13/1	43 2/8/18/14/1	44 2/8/18/15/1	45 2/8/18/16/1
Rb Rubidium 85.468	**Sr** Strontium 87.62	**Y** Yttrium 88.906	**Zr** Zirconium 91.22	**Nb** Niobium 92.906	**Mo** Molybdenum 95.94	**Tc** Technetium 98.906	**Ru** Ruthenium 101.07	**Rh** Rhodium 102.906
55 2/8/18/18/8/1	56 2/8/18/18/8/2	71 2/8/18/32/9/2	72 2/8/18/32/10/2	73 2/8/18/32/11/2	74 2/8/18/32/12/2	75 2/8/18/32/13/2	76 2/8/18/32/14/2	77 2/8/18/32/15/2
Cs Cesium 132.905	**Ba** Barium 137.33	**Lu** Lutetium 174.967	**Hf** Hafnium 178.49	**Ta** Tantalum 180.948	**W** Tungsten 183.85	**Re** Rhenium 186.2	**Os** Osmium 190.2	**Ir** Iridium 192.22
87 2/8/18/32/18/8/1	88 2/8/18/32/18/8/2	103 2/8/18/32/32/9/2	104 2/8/18/32/32/10/2	105 2/8/18/32/32/?/?	106 2/8/18/32/32/?/?			
Fr Francium 223	**Ra** Radium 226.025	**Lr** Lawrencium 257	---- ~ 257	---- ~ 260	---- ~ 263			

Rare Earth Elements

Lanthanide Series

57 2/8/18/18/9/2	58 2/8/18/20/8/2	59 2/8/18/21/8/2	60 2/8/18/22/8/2	61 2/8/18/23/8/2	62 2/8/18/24/8/2
La Lanthanum 138.906	**Ce** Cerium 140.12	**Pr** Praseodymium 140.908	**Nd** Neodymium 144.24	**Pm** Promethium ~ 147	**Sm** Samarium 150.4

Actinide Series

89 2/8/18/32/18/9/2	90 2/8/18/32/18/10/2	91 2/8/18/32/20/9/2	92 2/8/18/32/21/9/2	93 2/8/18/32/22/9/2	94 2/8/18/32/24/8/2
Ac Actinium 227	**Th** Thorium 232.038	**Pa** Protactinium 231.036	**U** Uranium 238.029	**Np** Neptunium 237.048	**Pu** Plutonium ~239

Electrons in each energy level

11 / 2 8 1
Na
Sodium
22.990

Atomic number
Element symbol
Average atomic mass

Legend: ☐ Not found in nature ☐ Solid ☐ Gas ☐ Liquid

Nonmetals

Noble Gases

| 2 / 2 **He** Helium 4.003 |

| 5 / 2 3 **B** Boron 10.81 | 6 / 2 4 **C** Carbon 12.011 | 7 / 2 5 **N** Nitrogen 14.007 | 8 / 2 6 **O** Oxygen 15.999 | 9 / 2 7 **F** Fluorine 18.998 | 10 / 2 8 **Ne** Neon 20.179 |

| 13 / 2 8 3 **Al** Aluminum 26.982 | 14 / 2 8 4 **Si** Silicon 28.086 | 15 / 2 8 5 **P** Phosphorus 30.974 | 16 / 2 8 6 **S** Sulfur 32.06 | 17 / 2 8 7 **Cl** Chlorine 35.453 | 18 / 2 8 8 **Ar** Argon 39.948 |

| 28 / 2 8 16 2 **Ni** Nickel 58.71 | 29 / 2 8 18 1 **Cu** Copper 63.546 | 30 / 2 8 18 2 **Zn** Zinc 65.38 | 31 / 2 8 18 3 **Ga** Gallium 69.74 | 32 / 2 8 18 4 **Ge** Germanium 72.59 | 33 / 2 8 18 5 **As** Arsenic 74.922 | 34 / 2 8 18 6 **Se** Selenium 78.96 | 35 / 2 8 18 7 **Br** Bromine 79.904 | 36 / 2 8 18 8 **Kr** Krypton 83.80 |

| 46 / 2 8 10 18 **Pd** Palladium 106.4 | 47 / 2 8 10 18 1 **Ag** Silver 107.868 | 48 / 2 8 10 18 2 **Cd** Cadmium 112.41 | 49 / 2 8 10 18 3 **In** Indium 114.82 | 50 / 2 8 10 18 4 **Sn** Tin 118.69 | 51 / 2 8 10 18 5 **Sb** Antimony 121.75 | 52 / 2 8 10 18 6 **Te** Tellurium 127.60 | 53 / 2 8 10 18 7 **I** Iodine 126.904 | 54 / 2 8 10 18 8 **Xe** Xenon 131.30 |

| 78 / 2 8 18 32 17 1 **Pt** Platinum 195.09 | 79 / 2 8 18 32 18 1 **Au** Gold 196.966 | 80 / 2 8 18 32 18 2 **Hg** Mercury 200.59 | 81 / 2 8 18 32 18 3 **Tl** Thallium 204.37 | 82 / 2 8 18 32 18 4 **Pb** Lead 207.2 | 83 / 2 8 18 32 18 5 **Bi** Bismuth 208.980 | 84 / 2 8 18 32 18 6 **Po** Polonium ~209 | 85 / 2 8 18 32 18 7 **At** Astatine ~210 | 86 / 2 8 18 32 18 8 **Rn** Radon ~222 |

| 63 / 2 8 18 25 8 2 **Eu** Europium 151.96 | 64 / 2 8 18 25 9 2 **Gd** Gadolinium 157.25 | 65 / 2 8 18 27 8 2 **Tb** Terbium 158.925 | 66 / 2 8 18 28 8 2 **Dy** Dysprosium 162.50 | 67 / 2 8 18 29 8 2 **Ho** Holmium 164.930 | 68 / 2 8 18 30 8 2 **Er** Erbium 167.26 | 69 / 2 8 18 31 8 2 **Tm** Thulium 168.934 | 70 / 2 8 18 32 8 2 **Yb** Ytterbium 173.04 |

| 95 / 2 8 18 32 25 8 2 **Am** Americium 243 | 96 / 2 8 18 32 25 9 2 **Cm** Curium 247 | 97 / 2 8 18 32 27 8 2 **Bk** Berkelium 247 | 98 / 2 8 18 32 28 8 2 **Cf** Californium 251 | 99 / 2 8 18 32 29 8 2 **Es** Einsteinium 254 | 100 / 2 8 18 32 30 8 2 **Fm** Fermium 257 | 101 / 2 8 18 32 31 8 2 **Md** Mendelevium 257 | 102 / 2 8 18 32 32 8 2 **No** Nobilium ~254 |

What is a common characteristic of nonmetals?

useful of metals. They are hard and have a high melting point. They form useful alloys with each other. The properties of a transition metal and its nearest neighbors in the periodic table are often very similar. Iron, cobalt, and nickel have similar properties as do copper, silver, and gold.

As you continue from left to right in the periodic table, elements become less metallic. Elements along the zig-zag line, such as boron, silicon, and germanium, are known as **metalloids** and have some but not all of the properties of metals.

The **nonmetals** have an important characteristic in common, namely, that they are *not* metals. For one thing, the nonmetals are not shiny. Also, nonmetals are good insulators and do not conduct heat or electricity well. Many are gases at room temperature.

At the far right of the periodic table are the **noble** gases. This family of elements was unknown in Mendeleev's time and it is to his credit that they fit right into the basic periodic table he designed. They form very few compounds and are not likely to react with other elements. For this reason they have also been called the **inert** gases. The word inert means unreactive. They do not even react with themselves, so they are monatomic gases. The noble gas helium is used to fill "lighter than air" craft such as dirigibles or blimps. Other noble gases such as neon and argon are used to make brightly colored lighted signs for advertising.

Just to the left of the noble gases are the **halogens.** The word halogen means "salt former." The elements in this family form compounds known as salts when they combine ionically with a metal. Sodium chloride, or table salt, is a familiar example. Many other salts can also be formed. Which elements are elements of the halogen family?

The remaining nonmetals, carbon, oxygen, nitrogen, sulfur, phosphorus and hydrogen, are neither as highly reactive as the metals nor as unreactive as the noble gases. Their "in-betweenness" makes them the most useful and important in the building of living systems. All life on earth is based on the chemistry of carbon and these other elements. Their interactions make up what is known as organic chemistry.

The periodic chemical properties shown by the elements can be explained as a result of similarities and differences in atomic structure. To understand this we must take yet a closer look at the atom.

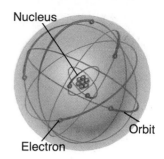

Figure 3-21. *Bohr's model of the atom had electrons travelling around the nucleus in definite orbits. This model explained some of the observations that scientists had made about atoms when they gave off light.*

Quick Review

1. How is the modern periodic table arranged?
2. Name three properties of metals.
3. What is unusual about the noble gases?
4. Using the periodic table, name at least two salts other than sodium chloride.

Atomic models

New vocabulary: planetary model, electron cloud model, energy levels

The electrons of an atom play a major role in chemical changes. The chemical properties of an element are closely linked to the arrangement of its electrons.

In 1913, Niels Bohr proposed a model that described the arrangement of electrons in atoms. In the Bohr **planetary model,** the electrons move in orbits at different distances from the nucleus. In this way the electrons are like planets which move around the sun. This model was very successful in explaining many of the characteristics of the hydrogen atom. However, it was difficult to apply this model to more complex atoms.

A more recent and useful model of atomic structure can be described as the electron cloud model. In the **electron cloud model** only the likely location, but not the exact location, of electrons can be described. In this model, electrons with a certain energy can likely be found in a particular region of space surrounding the nucleus. We can picture their location over a period of time with cloud-like shapes. This effect is similar to one produced by an electric fan. When the fan is

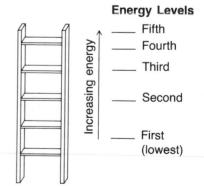

Figure 3-22. *The rungs of a ladder are like the energy levels in an atom. The higher the energy level occupied by an electron, the further it usually is from the nucleus and the more energetic it is.*

3.2a Using the Periodic Table

Science Processes: Observing, interpreting data, communicating, formulating models

Materials   BASIC   20 minutes   Individual work
- **periodic table**

Purpose

To use the periodic table to determine the identity of some mystery elements.

Procedure

1. Make a table like the one shown below. From the description given of each mystery element, use the periodic table to determine which element is being described. Write the name and the symbol of the element corresponding to each mystery element on your table.

Family 1
- Element "L" has 12 protons and 12 neutrons in the nucleus of each of its atoms.
- An atom of element "M" has two more electrons than an atom of argon.
- Element "N" has a total of 38 electrons in each normal atom.
- Element "P" has electrons in only two energy levels in each of its atoms.

Family 2
- Element "W" makes up the largest portion of the atmosphere.
- Element "X" has 33 protons and 42 neutrons in each of its nuclei.

- An atom of element "Y" has electrons in three shells.
- An atom of element "Z" has 15 more electrons than an atom of krypton.

2. Draw a model of mystery elements "L," "P," "W," and "Y." Show the number of protons in the nucleus and the number of electrons in each shell. Give the name and the symbol of each mystery element you drew.

Conclusion

What kinds of information are useful in identifying elements?

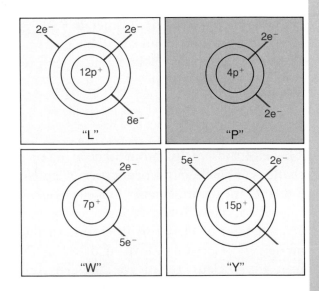

Family 1		Family 2	
Letter representing mystery element	Element identified from periodic table	Letter representing mystery element	Element identified from periodic table
"L"		"W"	
"M"		"X"	
"N"		"Y"	
"P"		"Z"	

turned off, you can see that it has distinct blades. When it is turned on, you see only a cloud-like blur.

The electron cloud model is based on complex mathematical equations. These equations predict that electrons can only be at certain **energy levels** in atoms. Electrons at low energy levels tend to be close to the nucleus most of the time. Electrons at higher energy levels spend more time further from the nucleus.

There is a limit to how many electrons can be in each energy level. The lowest energy level can never hold more than two electrons. The second energy level can hold up to eight electrons. The third energy level can hold up to 18 electrons. The fourth energy level can hold up to 32 electrons.

There are two more restrictions on the number of electrons in energy levels. First, the number of electrons in a neutral atom is the same as the number of protons in its nucleus. This limits the total number of electrons. Second, there are usually just eight electrons in the highest occupied energy level. Energy levels without electrons are not counted.

The arrangement of the electrons in energy levels matches the arrangement of the periodic table. Look at Figure 3-24.

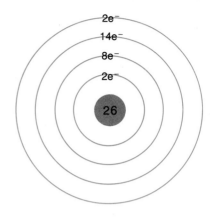

Figure 3-23. *In this energy level model of the atoms, how many electrons are in the third energy level?*

Figure 3-24. *Energy level models of the first 18 elements in the periodic table. The number in the center circle is the number of protons in the nucleus.*

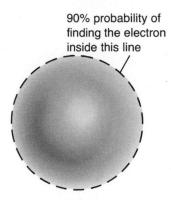

90% probability of finding the electron inside this line

Figure 3-25. *Electron cloud model of the atom shows electrons as fuzzy clouds. In this model, no one can say exactly where an electron is at any time, but rather that it is travelling somewhere in a defined volume of space.*

Science background information:
Elements in the second column all have two electrons in their highest energy level.

Elements in the third column from the right (the oxygen family) all have six electrons in their highest energy level.

Science background information:
As the text states on page 101, it is really the number of protons (atomic number) that is used to determine the order of the elements in the periodic table. However, in electrically neutral atoms, the number of electrons is always equal to the number of protons. Nonneutral atoms (ions) will be discussed in the next section.

Quick Review answers:
1. Anywhere within a sphere of space surrounding the nucleus.
2. The outer energy levels of elements in the same family have the same number of electrons. (There are a few exceptions among the transition elements.)

It shows the arrangement of electrons in energy levels for the first 18 elements. There are two elements in the first row: hydrogen and helium. Both have electrons in the first energy level. Hydrogen has one electron and helium has two.

All the elements in the second row have electrons in the first two energy levels. The first energy level has two electrons. The second energy level has from one to eight electrons as you go to the right along the row.

All the elements in the third row have electrons in the first three energy levels. All have two electrons in the first energy level and eight in the second. How many electrons does each element have in its third energy level?

Consider the noble gases at the right-hand end of each row in the periodic table. Helium has two electrons, the maximum that the first energy level can hold. Neon's second energy level has eight electrons, the maximum it can hold. Argon's third energy level has eight. This is the maximum number of electrons that this atom's highest energy level can hold. Thus, the outer energy level of each of the noble gases is full. This fact seems to be related to the non-reactive properties of these elements.

Now look at the highest occupied energy levels of the halogens, just to the left of the noble gases. They each have one fewer electron than the noble gases to their right. The family of elements in the first column is the alkali metal family. They each have only one electron in their highest occupied energy level. The elements in the second column are members of the alkaline earth metal family. What similarities can you see in the highest energy level of these elements in the second column? What similarities can you see in the highest energy level of the elements in the third column from the right?

The electron cloud model is able to explain the arrangement of the elements in the periodic table. Each element is in order of the total number of electrons in one atom. Elements with similar electron arrangements are in the same column of the table.

Quick Review

1. According to the electron cloud model where can the electrons of an atom be found?
2. What property do the highest occupied energy levels of the atoms of all the elements of a family have in common?

3.2b Making Models of Atoms

Science Processes: Making models, observing, inferring

Materials   20 minutes   Groups of 3

- posterboard square (6 cm by 6 cm)
- drawing compass
- colored pencils or markers
- cottonball (6 cm wide)
- B·B
- construction paper square (8 cm by 8 cm)
- common straight pin
- plastic soda straw

Purpose

To construct and compare planetary and electron cloud models of a lithium atom.

Procedure

1. Using the compass, draw three circles on the posterboard square with the same center and radii of 1, 2 and 3 cm.
2. Draw three large red dots and four large blue dots in the center circle.
3. Draw two large black dots on the middle ring and one large black dot on the outer ring.
4. Carefully cut out the three circles. Put them together to make a three-dimensional model of the atom.
5. Place a B·B in the center of the cottonball. Fluff the cotton out until the ball is the same size as the posterboard model.
6. Make 4 diagonal cuts to within 1 cm of the center of the construction paper square. Bend the paper and make into a pinwheel as shown. Use the pin to fasten the pinwheel to the straw.

   SAFETY NOTE: *Watch for the sharp pin point sticking through the straw.*
7. Blow on the pinwheel and observe its motion.

Questions

1. What is an atomic model?
2. Which atomic model does the posterboard model represent? the cottonball model?
3. What does the planetary model reveal about the structure of a lithium atom?
4. What does the electron cloud model show about the structure of a lithium atom?
5. Can you see the blades of the pinwheel when it spins rapidly? Explain.
6. What is the relationship between the spinning pinwheel and the electron cloud model?

Conclusion

Why are atomic models useful in the study of the elements?

Step 4

Cut   Cut

Cut   Cut

Bend

Bend

Step 6

3.2 Section Review

Answers to Understanding the Concepts appear on page T77 in the front of this book. Blackline master test for this section: Section Testsheet 3-2 (TRB page 207)

Vocabulary

9 alkali metal
16 alkaline earth metal
13 atomic mass
2 atomic number
3 electron
15 electron cloud model
21 energy level
1 family
4 halogen
6 inert gas
14 isotope
12 metallic luster
18 metalloid
7 neutron
11 noble gas
17 nonmetal
8 nucleus
5 periodic table
19 planetary model
10 proton
20 transition metal

Vocabulary Review

Match each term above with the numbered phrase that best describes it.

1. Any group of elements with similar properties
2. Determines order of elements in modern periodic table
3. Negatively charged particle in an atom
4. Element that reacts very easily with metals
5. Arrangement of elements according to repeated pattern of properties
6. Element that tends not to react with others
7. Neutral particle in an atom
8. Has almost all the mass, but occupies hardly any of the space of an atom
9. Most reactive metals
10. Particle whose number is always the same for a particular element
11. Another name for unreactive elements
12. Shiny property of some elements
13. Property of atom that relates to its total number of particles
14. Atom that has different mass from another atom of the same element
15. Picture of atom with a fuzzy shape
16. Elements with one more electron than alkali metals
17. Element that is not shiny and that is a poor conductor of electricity
18. Element with the properties both of metals and nonmetals
19. Picture of atom with electrons in orbits around the nucleus
20. Elements in the middle of the periodic table
21. For an electron, related to the time spent close to or far from the nucleus

Review Questions

Multiple Choice: Choose the answer that best completes each of the following sentences.

22. In his periodic table, Mendeleev put the elements in order of _?_.
   a. atomic mass
   b. atomic number
   c. number of neutrons
   d. boiling temperature
23. Two atoms must belong to the same element if they have the same number of _?_.
   a. energy levels
   b. electrons
   c. protons
   d. neutrons
24. In the periodic table, all the gases except hydrogen are _?_.
   a. in the first row
   b. in the first column
   c. in the same family
   d. on the right-hand side

Understanding the Concepts

25. Compare the properties of elements in the halogen family with the properties of elements in the alkali metal family.
26. Compare the arrangement of the electrons in an atom of silicon with those of another element in the same family.
27. How many energy levels of electrons does every element in the third row of the periodic table have? How many energy levels would you expect every element in the fifth row to have?
28. The masses of both the proton and the neutron are approximately 1 u. One isotope of chlorine has an atomic mass of 36.97 u. How many neutrons does it have?
29. How did Ernest Rutherford determine that the atom had a nucleus?

For ideas for classroom demonstration and discussion, see Getting Started on page T78 in the front of this book.

3.3 A Model for Chemical Changes

Teaching Diagram 3-3 (TRB page   ), Reading Checksheet 3-3 (TRB page 88), Skillsheet 3-3 (TRB page 134), Investigation 3-3 (Lab Manual pages 41–42)

Section Preview

- **Chemical equations**
- **Electric charges**
- **Ions**
- **Electron sharing**

- **Chemical bonds**
- **Acids and bases**
- **Neutralization and salts**

Bracketed numbers are Section Review questions correlated to that objective.

Learning Objectives

1. To interpret chemical equations by identifying reactants and products. [1, 2, 12]
2. To identify whether or not a chemical equation is balanced. [19, 25, 29, 30, 31, 32, 33]
3. To describe chemical bonds in compounds as the transfer or sharing of electrons. [4, 9, 10, 11, 13, 15, 16, 17, 20, 22, 23, 24, 26]
4. To identify the properties of acids, bases, and salts. [3, 5, 6, 7, 8, 14, 18, 21, 27, 28]

Figure 3-26. *Potassium metal reacts strongly with water. When the fire goes out, the potassium has disappeared. Can you infer that a chemical change has occurred?*
Yes, purely physical changes do not involve combustion.

A good model explains a large number of observations. Dalton was able to explain how new substances are formed in chemical changes. According to his model, different substances are made from different combinations of atoms. In a chemical change, old combinations break up and new combinations form.

Chemical equations

In one common chemical change, carbon combines with oxygen to form carbon dioxide. A short way to write this is with the following expression.

$$\text{carbon} + \text{oxygen} \rightarrow \text{carbon dioxide}$$

The substances on the left are called **reactants.** They are the substances that exist before the change. The substance on the right is the **product.** It is formed during the change. More than one product can be formed in a chemical change. The arrow indicates the direction of the change.

Main Idea

What are reactants and what are products?

Figure 3-27. *The red compound in the test tube is mercury oxide. When heated, it breaks down into mercury and oxygen. You can see tiny drops of mercury on the inside of the test tube.*

Main Idea

How are the atoms in the reactants and products related in a balanced equation?

Additional information:
Balanced equations are important because they represent chemical changes accurately. In chemical changes, matter is neither created nor destroyed. Another way of saying this is that mass is conserved in a chemical reaction.

A chemical change can be described even more briefly using formulas instead of names. The same chemical change would appear in this form as

$$C + O_2 \rightarrow CO_2.$$

This is a **chemical equation.** Chemical equations are a way of summarizing a chemical change.

Another example of a chemical change is what happens when mercury oxide is heated. It breaks down into mercury and oxygen. The chemical equation for this reaction is

$$2HgO \xrightarrow{\text{heat}} 2Hg + O_2.$$

In this equation, mercury oxide is the reactant, and mercury and oxygen are the products.

In a chemical change, the total number of atoms of each element does not change. Only the arrangement of the atoms changes. Look at the chemical reaction in the first paragraph. There is one carbon atom before the change. There is one carbon atom after the change. There are two oxygen atoms before the change and there are two oxygen atoms after the change. The equation is said to be **balanced** because the same number of atoms of each element are on the left and right sides.

Look at the chemical reaction in the second paragraph. There are two mercury atoms in the reactant, on the left, and two mercury atoms in the products, on the right. Also there are two oxygen atoms in the reactant and two oxygen atoms in the products. This equation is said to be balanced because there are the same number of atoms of each element in the reactant and in the products.

To write balanced equations, you need to know the reactants and the products of a chemical change. You also need to know the correct ratios of the reactants and products. For example, hydrogen and oxygen gases combine to form water. The balanced chemical equation that summarizes this change is

$$2H_2 + O_2 \longrightarrow 2H_2O.$$

The 2s in front of the formulas for hydrogen and water are needed to balance the equation. In words, two molecules of hydrogen combine with one molecule of oxygen. The product of the reaction is two molecules of water. This reaction is illustrated in Figure 3-28.

2H₂
Hydrogen

O₂
Oxygen

2H₂O
Water

If you know the formulas for the reactants and products of a chemical reaction, you can find their proper ratio. To do this, use the process of balancing the number of atoms on each side of the equation. For instance, under pressure and heat, nitrogen gas reacts with hydrogen gas to produce ammonia. The basic equation for this reaction is

$$N_2 + H_2 \longrightarrow NH_3.$$

Look carefully at this equation. Is it balanced?

Compare the number of nitrogen atoms on the left with the number of nitrogen atoms on the right. There are two on the left, but only one on the right. To get the equation closer to balancing, you must put a 2 in front of the ammonia on the right. The partially balanced equation now is

$$N_2 + H_2 \longrightarrow 2NH_3.$$

Now compare the number of hydrogen atoms on the left and on the right. There are two on the left, but six on the right. To get the equation in better balance, put a 3 in front of the hydrogen on the left. The equation now is

$$N_2 + 3H_2 \longrightarrow 2NH_3.$$

Compare the number of nitrogen atoms on the left with the number on the right. Compare the number of hydrogen atoms on the left with those on the right. Are they now in balance? If so, the equation is said to be balanced. Yes

To summarize the process of balancing equations, start with the proper formulas for the reactants and the products. Put the reactants on the left side of the arrow and the products on the right. Count the number of atoms of each element in the reactants and products. Balance the equation by using small whole numbers in front of the reactants and products. Work at balancing one element at a time. Don't change the subscript numbers, the ones below the line, when

Research Topic

It is not easy to make ammonia from hydrogen and nitrogen. Read about the German chemist Fritz Haber and write a report on the process he developed for making ammonia.

Figure 3-29. *Ammonia plant produces an essential ingredient for most fertilizers from nitrogen and hydrogen gases. The reaction requires great heat and pressure.*

you balance equations. Overall, use the smallest whole number ratios possible to balance the equation. Finally, check the numbers of each kind of atom in the reactants and products to make sure that there are equal numbers in the reactants and products. Then the equation should be balanced.

Sample Problem
Balance the equation.

$$CS_2 + Cl_2 \longrightarrow CCl_4 + S_2Cl_2$$

Solution
Start with carbon. There is a balance already, one on each side. Next, count the sulfur atoms. They also balance. Then, check on chlorine. There are two chlorine atoms on the left, but 6 on the right. Put a 3 in front of the chlorine on the left. That balances the equation.

$$CS_2 + 3Cl_2 \longrightarrow CCl_4 + S_2Cl_2$$

Practice Problems
Balance these equations.
1. $FeS + HCl \longrightarrow FeCl_2 + H_2S$
2. $Fe_3O_4 + H_2 \longrightarrow Fe + H_2O$
3. $P + O_2 \longrightarrow P_2O_5$
4. $C + O_2 \longrightarrow CO$
5. $NO_2 \longrightarrow NO + O_2$

Answers:
1. $FeS + 2HCl \longrightarrow FeCl_2 + H_2S$
2. $Fe_3O_4 + 4H_2 \longrightarrow 3Fe + 4H_2O$
3. $4P + 5O_2 \longrightarrow 2P_2O_5$
4. $2C + O_2 \longrightarrow 2CO$
5. $2NO_2 \longrightarrow 2NO + O_2$

Quick Review
For the chemical equation

$$Zn + 2HCl \rightarrow ZnCl_2 + H_2$$

answer each of the following.
1. List each element involved in this chemical change.
2. For each element, tell how many atoms of it appear on each side of the equation.
3. Is this equation balanced? How can you tell?

Electric charges

New vocabulary: electric charge, charged, neutral

Clothes stick together in a dryer. A sweater and a pillowcase crackle when they are pulled apart. Bits of paper will stick to a rubber comb that has been run through someone's hair a few times.

The sticking and crackling are due to **electric charges.** Two different kinds of electric charges have been identified. Normally, an object has the same number of each kind. But charges can be removed by rubbing. When an object has unequal numbers of charges, it may push or pull on other objects.

For example, suppose a glass rod is rubbed with silk. The rod and the silk will then stick together. They pull on each other because of their electric charges. After the rubbing, the rod was left with more of one kind and the silk was left with more of the other kind. On the other hand, suppose the rod is rubbed with two pieces of silk. Then, the pieces of silk will push each other apart. Both pieces have more of the same kind of electric charges.

In general, an object with more of one kind of charge than another is said to be **charged.** Two charged objects pull each other together if they are each charged with a different kind of charge. Two charged objects push each other apart if they are each charged with the same kind of charge. In short, opposites attract and likes repel. Charged objects act much like the ends of bar magnets.

The charges on objects can be traced to the particles that make up matter. The two kinds of charge are labeled positive and negative. A proton has a positive charge. An electron has a negative charge. The amount of charge on the proton and electron is the same. The positive charge on a proton balances the negative charge on an electron.

Objects that have equal numbers of protons and electrons seem to have no charge. They are **neutral** (NEW'-trul). Objects that have more electrons than protons have a negative charge. Objects that have more protons than electrons have a positive charge.

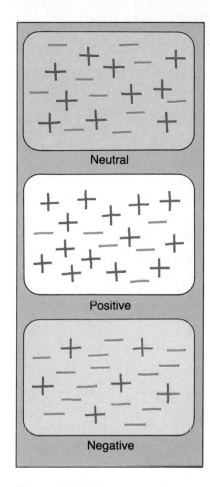

Figure 3-30. *How can an object with both kinds of charges be neutral?*

A neutral object is one with equal numbers of protons and electrons. The positive charges balance the negative charges.

Science background information:
Once electrons had been discovered, and after scientists were satisfied that electrons were small, negatively charged particles, they began to look for corresponding particles with positive charges. The alpha-particle scattering experiments by Ernest Rutherford helped to clarify the nature of protons.

Quick Review

1. What causes an object to have a negative charge?
2. What effect do two positively charged objects have on each other?
3. How many kinds of electric charges have been found?

Quick Review answers:
1. The object contains more electrons than protons.
2. Two positively charged objects repel each other.
3. Two.

3.3a Charged Objects

Science Processes. Observing, recording, inferring

BASIC   15 minutes   Groups of 4 or teacher demonstration

Materials

- 2 balloons
- string or thread
- wool flannel
- support stand with clamp
- wood dowel

Purpose

To observe the behavior of charged objects.

Procedure

1. Clamp the wood dowel to the support stand.
2. Hang an inflated balloon from the dowel by thread. Check to be sure the balloon is not touching anything.
3. Hold a piece of wool flannel close to, but not touching the balloon. Record whether the balloon is attracted, repelled, or unaffected by the flannel.
4. Rub the whole balloon with the piece of wool flannel.
5. Hold the piece of wool flannel away from the balloon. Then slowly bring it close to the balloon.
6. Record whether the balloon is attracted, repelled, or unaffected by the flannel.
7. Rub the whole surface of a second inflated balloon with the wool flannel.
8. Bring the second balloon close to the first balloon.
9. Record whether the first balloon is attracted, repelled, or unaffected by the second balloon.

Questions

1. Were the balloon and wool flannel charged before they were rubbed together?
2. Can an uncharged (neutral) object be made up of charged particles?
3. Was it possible that when the balloon and wool flannel were rubbed together, one picked up charges from the other? If this happened, would the wool flannel and balloon have the same or opposite charges?
4. Would you expect the charges on the two balloons to be the same or different after each was rubbed with the wool flannel? Explain.

Step 2

Step 4

Ions

New vocabulary: valence electrons, positive ion, negative ion

In a chemical change, the number of protons in an atom cannot change. If it did, the atom would become another element. However, the number of electrons can change.

In a chemical reaction, only some of the electrons of an atom are involved. The electrons that take part in a chemical reaction are the ones that belong to the highest energy level. Electrons that belong to the highest energy level are known as **valence electrons.** Valence electrons are the electrons of an atom that take part in a chemical change. For the most part, the chemical properties of the different elements depend on their number of valence electrons.

Atoms of some elements give up electrons easily. The elements in the left and middle portions of the periodic table have only one, two, or three valence electrons. These are the same elements that have metallic properties. So, metals are elements that give up electrons easily.

When atoms give up electrons, they become positively charged. The positively charged atoms are called **positive ions** (Ī'-unz). Atoms of elements in the alkali metal family have a single valence electron. If they lose this electron, they have one uncancelled positive charge. They become positive ions with a charge of 1+. An example is the sodium atom. The symbol for the sodium ion is Na⁺. (Note that the 1 is understood but not written.)

Atoms of elements in the second family have two valence electrons. These atoms lose two electrons quite easily. They become positive ions with a charge of 2+. An example is the magnesium atom. The symbol for the magnesium ion is Mg^{2+}.

Atoms of elements in the halogen family accept extra electrons. The halogens have seven valence electrons. The atoms of these elements accept one extra electron easily. They then have one extra negative charge. Atoms with a negative charge are called **negative ions.**

Chlorine, for example, forms a negative ion. The symbol for the negative chlorine ion is Cl⁻. Iodine is another element in the same family as chlorine. The symbol for its ion is I⁻.

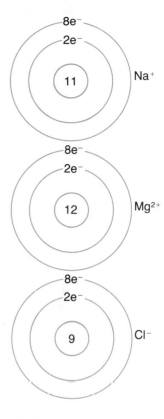

Figure 3-31. *How many protons and electrons does each of these ions have?*

Na⁺: 11 protons, 10 electrons
Mg^{2+}: 12 protons, 10 electrons
Cl⁻: 9 protons, 10 electrons

Quick Review

1. What is the meaning of the symbol H⁺?
2. What is the meaning of the symbol Br⁻?

Quick Review answers:
1. H⁺ is the symbol for a hydrogen atom that has lost its one electron and has a positive charge. (It is also a hydrogen nucleus, or a proton.)
2. Br⁻ is the symbol for a bromine atom that has gained an electron and therefore has a negative charge. This ion has 35 protons and 36 electrons.

Shared electrons

New vocabulary: electron dot structure

Atoms with four, five, and six valence electrons do not gain or lose electrons easily. Instead, they tend to share electrons with other atoms. They often share electrons with atoms of the same element. For example, nitrogen forms the diatomic molecule N_2. In this molecule, each atom shares three of its own electrons with the other atom.

Oxygen shares electrons with atoms of many other elements. For example, oxygen shares electrons with hydrogen in the compound water and with carbon in the compound carbon dioxide.

Many ions have the same electron structure as inert gases. For example, Na^+ and Mg^{2+} ions both have the same electron structure as neon. So does F^-. Similarly, K^+, Ca^{2+}, and Cl^- ions have the same electron structure as argon.

By sharing electrons, atoms may also acquire an electron structure of an inert gas. When an oxygen atom shares the electrons of two hydrogen atoms, it has as many electrons as neon.

Thus, many atoms that lose, gain, or share electrons become more like inert gases. Inert gases, on the other hand, have very little tendency to lose, gain, or share electrons.

There are different ways to picture what happens to the electrons when they are being shared between atoms. One of the simpler ways to illustrate what is happening to electrons is with symbols that show only the valence electrons. An **electron dot structure** shows the valence electrons of an atom as dots. The inner electrons of the atom are represented by the atomic symbol of the element. The electron dot structures for various atoms are shown in Table 3-3. The electron dot structures for some of the molecules that have been mentioned are shown in Figure 3-32.

Science background information:
In the formation of ions, electrons leave or join an atom indefinitely, while shared electrons are not lost or gained completely but shared with a neighboring atom.

Teaching suggestion:
Point out to students that a maximum of eight electrons around an atom is shown in the electron dot structure. That is because, according to valence theory, only eight electrons can be found in the outermost energy level. Note also that the electrons are spread apart until there are more than four valence electrons. At that point they can be represented in pairs.

Main Idea

How does the electron dot structure represent electrons?

Table 3-3. *The electron dot structures of some common elements.*

Electron dot structures of some Group A elements							
1 H·						H·	He:
2 Li·	·Be·	·B·	·C·	·N·	:O·	:F·	:Ne:
3 Na·	·Mg·	·Al·	·Si·	·P·	:S·	:Cl·	:Ar:
4 K·	·Ca·	·Ga·	·Ge·	·As·	:Se·	:Br·	:Kr:

Figure 3-32. *Electron dot structures of two molecules show what happens to valence electrons in covalent bonding.*

Quick Review

1. What is the difference between electron sharing and the formation of ions?
2. What are electron dot structures?

Quick Review answers:
1. In the formation of ions, electrons leave or join an atom indefinitely, while shared electrons are not lost or gained completely but shared with a neighboring atom.
2. These are structures that picture the valence electrons of an atom as dots.

Chemical bonds

New vocabulary: chemical bond, ionic compound, ionic bond, covalent bond

Dalton pictured compounds as made from atoms of different elements that had joined together. However, his theory did not explain what held atoms together. Nor did it explain why some combinations were more likely to occur than others.

As more became known about the atom, the theory behind combinations developed. Atoms that have lost electrons are positive ions. Atoms that have gained electrons are negative ions. Positive and negative ions pull on each other because of their opposite charges. The pull keeps the positive and negative ions together in a compound.

When atoms share electrons, there is also a pull between opposite charges. The positive nucleus of each atom pulls on the negative electrons being shared by the other atom. Again, the pull between positive and negative charges keeps the atoms together.

Thus, there is a sort of invisible tie between two atoms that have transferred or shared electrons. The tie is called a **chemical bond.** When elements combine and form compounds, their atoms form chemical bonds. The bonds exist because of the pulls between opposite charges.

Sodium chloride (salt) is an example of a compound held together by bonds between oppositely charged ions. Such a compound is called an **ionic (ī-ON′-ik) compound.** When the compound forms, sodium atoms give up their outer electrons to chlorine atoms. Look at Figure 3-33. Each positive sodium ion (Na^+) in the compound is surrounded by six

Science background information:
The ionic theory is a good explanation for the bonding of many kinds of compounds. However, it cannot explain the bonding of molecules such as H_2 and N_2 where there is no reason for one atom to be a positive ion and the other atom a negative ion.

Main Idea

What is a chemical bond?

Figure 3-33. *Sodium chloride is an ionic compound. The straight lines between the ions represent ionic bonds.*

Science background information: Ionic compounds, such as sodium chloride, form crystals. The crystal shape is based on the repeating arrangement of the ions in the crystal.

The arrangement shown here forms a cubic crystal. If very salty water were allowed to evaporate slowly, large cubic crystals would form.

The shapes of crystals of other substances vary, depending on the ionic arrangement. Have some students research different crystal shapes in a chemistry book and show them to the class.

Cl⁻   Na⁺

Data Search

In what year and to whom was a Nobel prize in physics given for research on the movement of electrons within the atom? Search pages 658–661.

James Franck and Gustav Hertz of Germany in 1925

Science background information: Covalent bonding is used to explain the kinds of bonds that occur in diatomic molecules such as H_2 and N_2 and in most organic, or carbon-containing, compounds.

negative chlorine ions (Cl^-). And each Cl^- ion is surrounded by six Na^+ ions. There are bonds between each ion and its neighbors. Since the bonds are between ions, they are called **ionic bonds.**

Elements of the alkali metals form ionic compounds with elements of the halogen family. Potassium bromide (KBr), magnesium chloride ($MgCl_2$), and lithium chloride (LiCl) are some additional examples of ionic compounds. Ionic compounds are usually formed by a metal and a nonmetal.

Methane (CH_4) is an example of a compound formed of molecules. Within each molecule, one carbon atom shares electrons with four hydrogen atoms. There is a bond between each hydrogen atom and the carbon atom, as shown in Figure 3-30. Bonds like these, due to shared electrons, are called **covalent** (kō-VAYL′-unt) **bonds.** Covalent bonds usually form between atoms of nonmetals.

In diatomic gases such as oxygen, there are covalent bonds between the two atoms in the molecule. Each nucleus is exactly the same, so each pulls with the same strength on the shared electrons. In a compound, on the other hand, the covalent bonds are usually between two different kinds of atoms. The nucleus of one kind will pull more strongly on the shared electrons. The electrons will still be shared but they will be closer to the nucleus with the stronger pull.

Some compounds contain both ionic and covalent bonds. Silver nitrate, for example, is made of Ag^+ and NO_3^- ions. The nitrate ion, NO_3^-, acts like a single atom that has gained one electron. But within the ion, the nitrogen and oxygen atoms share electrons and form covalent bonds. In chemical changes, the nitrate ion usually stays together. However,

Methane molecule, CH$_4$

Hydrogen atom   Carbon atom

Nitrogen atom

plants are able to take in nitrate ions from the soil and break them down. Ions, like nitrate, which are composed of more than two atoms, but which act like one atom in chemical changes, are known as polyatomic ions.

The compound calcium nitrate contains Ca^{2+} and NO$_3^-$ ions. Since the calcium ion has given up two electrons, there must be two nitrate ions for every calcium ion in the compound. The formula for calcium nitrate is Ca(NO$_3$)$_2$. The numeral 2 after the second parenthesis indicates that there are two of everything inside the parentheses. In other words, there are two nitrate ions for every calcium ion. If the formula were written CaN$_2$O$_6$, you would not realize the compound contained nitrate ions.

The formation of new substances always involves making and/or breaking chemical bonds. Thus, chemical changes are changes in chemical bonds. These changes occur when electrons are transferred from one atom to another. They also occur when electrons stop or start being shared between atoms.

Quick Review

1. How can the pull between atoms in a compound be explained?
2. Describe the difference between an ionic bond and a covalent bond.
3. The structure of potassium nitrate, KNO$_3$, is like that of silver nitrate. What ions make up potassium nitrate?

Figure 3-34. *Two different ways to represent covalent bonds are as straight lines or by pairs of electrons. Notice that methane is actually a three-dimensional molecule and that nitrogen is linear. The use of dots to show electrons is called an electron dot structure.*

Science background information:
The methane molecule is three-dimensional. The four hydrogen atoms are at the vertices (corners) of a tetrahedron. The carbon atom is at the center of the tetrahedron. The nitrogen molecule is linear.

Main Idea

What effect do chemical changes have on chemical bonds?

Quick Review answers:
1. Atoms in a compound are held together because of the attraction between opposite electric charges.
2. An ionic bond is formed by the attraction between two oppositely charged ions. A covalent bond is formed between atoms that share electrons.
3. The ions in KNO$_3$ are K$^+$ and NO$_3^-$. (The nitrate ion consists of atoms held together by covalent bonds.)

Acids and bases

New vocabulary: acid, acid indicator, neutralize, base, pH, hydroxide ion

Citrus fruits such as oranges, grapefruit, and lemons have a sour taste. So do vinegar and tomatoes. These foods have something in common with the liquid inside an automobile battery. They will all make a substance known as litmus dye turn from blue to red. They all make another substance, bromthymol blue (BTB), turn from blue to yellow.

Citrus fruits and tomatoes contain citric acid. Vinegar contains acetic acid. A battery contains sulfuric acid. An **acid** (AS'-id) is a substance that makes litmus dye or BTB change color as described. Although edible acids can be recognized by their sour taste, it is very dangerous to taste unknown substances.

Substances that are changed in color by acids are called **acid indicators.** Tea, as well as litmus dye and BTB, is an acid indicator. It turns lighter in color when lemon juice or any other acid is added.

There is another group of substances that can cancel, or **neutralize** (NEW'-truh-līz), an acid. That is, when one of them is added to an acid, it can prevent an acid indicator from turning the color for an acid. These substances are called **bases.** By themselves, bases have the opposite effect from acids on indicators. They turn litmus dye from red to blue and BTB from yellow to blue. Bases have a bitter taste and feel slippery. Again, however, it is dangerous to taste unknown substances. Many bases destroy skin and should not be felt.

Some substances will be more acidic or more basic than others. A scale of acidity has been set up to rank substances. A measure of the acidity of a substance is known as **pH.** The pH scale is from 0 to 14. A substance with a pH value of 7 is neither acidic nor basic. It can be called neutral. Substances with pH values less than 7 are acidic. Substances with pH values greater than 7 are basic. The lower the pH value, the more acidic the substance is. The higher the pH value, the more basic the substance is.

If you studied the chemical formulas of different acids, you would notice that they all contain hydrogen. Common laboratory acids, as well as household acids, are in water solutions. In water solutions, acids break up into positive and negative ions. The positive ion is always a **hydrogen ion,** H^+. For example, vinegar is a solution of acetic acid ($HC_2H_3O_2$) and water. The acetic acid breaks up into H^+ and $C_2H_3O_2^-$ ions. Hydrochloric acid (HCl) breaks up into H^+ and Cl^-

---

Main Idea

What are some common acid indicators?

Research Topic

Find out what besides litmus and BTB are commonly used as acid indicators and at what pH value they each change in color.

Science background information:
The pH scale is based on the hydrogen ion concentration of a solution. The scale ranges from 0 to 14. pH 7 is neutral, pH values of less than 7 are acidic, pH values of greater than 7 are basic.

0 — Hydrochloric acid
1 —
2 —
3 — Vinegar
4 — Grape juice
5 —
6 —
7 — Milk
    — Blood
8 — Sea water
9 —
10 — Milk of magnesia
11 —
12 — Ammonia
13 —
14 — Sodium hydroxide

ions. The strength of an acid depends on the amount of the hydrogen ions in solution.

Similarly, formulas for bases contain both oxygen and hydrogen. In water solutions, bases break up into ions. The negative ion is OH⁻, which is known as the **hydroxide** (hī-DROK'-sīd) **ion.** Many bases have the word *hydroxide* in their names. The base sodium hydroxide (NaOH) breaks up into Na⁺ and OH⁻ ions. The base potassium hydroxide (KOH) breaks up into K⁺ and OH⁻ ions. The strength of a base depends on the amount of hydroxide ions in solution.

Pure water (such as distilled water) is not made up strictly of H_2O molecules. Some of the H_2O molecules have broken up into H⁺ and OH⁻ ions. There are always equal numbers of these ions in pure water. When an acid is added to pure water, there will be more H⁺ ions than OH⁻ ions. When a base is added to pure water, there will be more OH⁻ ions than H⁺ ions.

Figure 3-35. *Substances are ranked for acidity on a pH scale from 0 to 14. Would a substance with a pH value of 2 be very acidic or very basic?*

Research Topic

Two common household cleaning substances are ammonia (in a water solution) and liquid bleach. Find out why they should never be used together.

Quick Review

1. Name three foods that contain an acid.
2. Which is more acidic—something with a pH of 3 or something with a pH of 5?
3. What ion can be found in water solutions of bases?

Quick Review answers:
1. Oranges, grapefruit, lemons, tomatoes, etc. (most fruits)
2. Something with a pH of 3 is more acidic.
3. The hydroxide ion (OH⁻).

3.3b Identifying Acids and Bases

Science Processes: Observing, recording data, inferring, communicating

Materials 15 minutes Groups of 3 to 4
- **distilled water**
- **household ammonia**
- **vinegar**
- **lemon juice**
- **tap water**
- **4 antacid tablets**
- **cola**
- **baking soda**
- **table salt**
- **graduated cylinder**
- **8 test tubes**
- **test tube rack**

- **8 pieces each of red and blue litmus paper**
- **8 stirring rods**
- **masking tape/labels or grease pencil**

Purpose

To develop a system for the identification of acids and bases.

Procedure

1. Place 3 mL of distilled water in a test tube. Place one end of a stirring rod in the test tube and pick up a drop of water.
2. Touch the drop of water to a piece of blue litmus paper. Note any color change in the litmus paper. Touch another drop to a piece of red litmus paper. Note any color change.
3. Place the test tubes in the test tube rack.
4. Use a grease pencil or label to mark the test tubes with the identity of the substances to be tested from the list above.
5. Place 2 mL of the liquids to be tested into the labeled test tubes.
6. Place an amount of each solid to be tested equal to the size of a pea into the labeled test tubes. Dissolve the solid by adding 2 mL of distilled water; stir if needed.
7. Test the lemon juice with a piece of blue litmus. Dip the stirring rod into the juice and transfer a drop to the litmus paper. Observe the results. Lemon juice is an acid.
8. Rinse the stirring rod, and test the household ammonia in a similar manner, using red litmus paper. Observe the results. Ammonia is a base.
9. Continue to test the remaining liquids in a similar manner, being certain to use a different stirring rod for each trial. Use separate pieces of litmus paper for each test.
10. When you have finished, wash and dry the test tubes and the stirring rod and return them to the supply area.

Questions

1. What color changes in the litmus papers did you observe in testing the distilled water? What can you conclude about distilled water from this test?
2. What color changes did you observe in litmus paper in testing the lemon juice? in testing the ammonia?
3. Which of the solutions tested to be acids?
4. Which solutions tested to be bases?
5. Did any solutions test to be neither acid nor base? List them, if any. What term might be used to describe these solutions?

Conclusion

How can litmus paper be used to identify the acid-base properties of a solution?

Step 2

Litmus paper

Neutralization and salts

New vocabulary: salt

Your stomach normally contains hydrochloric acid. Some people take drugs known as antacids when they feel discomfort due to too much acid in the stomach. Antacids contain a base. The base neutralizes some of the acid.

When a base neutralizes an acid, hydroxide ions from the base combine with hydrogen ions from the acid. Water is formed. The chemical equation is

$$OH^- + H^+ \rightarrow H_2O.$$

Another product is formed as well when an acid and base neutralize each other. This product is formed from the negative ion of the acid and the positive ion of the base. For example, suppose HCl in the stomach is neutralized by an antacid containing magnesium hydroxide, $Mg(OH)_2$. The complete chemical equation is

$$2HCl + Mg(OH)_2 \rightarrow 2H_2O + MgCl_2.$$

The product magnesium chloride, $MgCl_2$, is formed from the positive ion Mg^{2+} of the base and the negative ion Cl^- of the acid. This kind of compound is known as a **salt**. Salts are always formed from the positive ion of a base and the negative ion of an acid. A salt usually contains a metal and a nonmetal.

Common table salt, NaCl, is formed in the same way. Its sodium ion Na^+ comes from the base sodium hydroxide, NaOH. Its chloride ion Cl^- comes from the acid hydrochloric acid, HCl. The complete equation is

$$HCl + NaOH \rightarrow H_2O + NaCl.$$

All neutralization reactions between an acid and a base produce a salt and water.

$$acid + base \rightarrow salt + water$$

Although salts are all formed in the same standard way, they do not have the same properties. Some, but not all, are white like table salt. Some, but not all, dissolve in water. Some, but not all, taste salty.

Quick Review

1. What products are formed when an acid and a base neutralize each other?
2. What acid and what base form sodium chloride, NaCl, when they neutralize each other?

Figure 3-36. *Table salt, sodium chloride, can be produced by the reaction between an acid, hydrochloric acid, and a base, sodium hydroxide.*

Main Idea

How can we recognize that a certain chemical is a salt?

Science background information:
A pure salt and water mixture will result only if the neutralization reaction is complete—that is, if the quantities and strengths of acid and base are the same. Otherwise, a surplus of either a strong acid or base can remain in the solution with the salt that formed.

Even though salts are similar in some ways, they can also differ. While some salts are harmless, others are deadly poisons, and still others are explosives.

■ Safety Note
Don't taste unknown substances.

Quick Review answers:
1. Water and salt
2. Hydrochloric acid (HCl) and sodium hydroxide (NaOH)

Chemist

Most chemists perform some kind of research. They are employed by industry, by government agencies, and by universities and colleges. Some may investigate the basic properties and behaviors of matter. Other chemists strive to improve existing products or to develop new products that can be used by industry or by the public.

Today some chemists are employed in police work. Police use the evidence that chemists uncover to identify both substances and persons involved in crimes.

The petroleum and fuel industries make use of chemists in the search for and refinement of some of our energy sources. Chemists also play a significant role in agriculture and in the clothing industry.

In all areas, chemists are expected to be able to demonstrate creativity and problem-solving ability. While many chemists work as members of a team, some have great independence and plan their own work.

In general, chemists have college degrees. Employment is possible with a bachelor's degree, but specialized areas may require advanced degrees. College professors of chemistry usually have a Ph.D.

For more information, write to: American Chemical Society, 1155 16th St. N.W., Washington, D.C. 20036.

In the laboratory, a chemist may make tests to try to identify the substances in a mixture.

Medical Technologist

The job of the medical technologist includes the analysis of blood, fluids, and tissues from the human body. The technologist relies on sensitive instruments and microscopes in making these analyses. The results of the technologist's work is helpful in the diagnosis and treatment of disease. Technologists may be employed in hospitals, independent laboratories, physician's offices, public health agencies, or in research institutions.

Accuracy, ability to work under pressure, manual dexterity, and normal color vision are important attributes of the medical technologist.

Medical technologists are usually trained in community colleges, trade schools, technical institutes, or in the armed forces. They must receive a professional license. High school biology, chemistry, and math courses provide a good preparation for training as a medical technologist.

For more information write to: American Medical Technologists, 710 Higgins Road, Park Ridge, IL 60068.

A medical technologist uses sensitive instruments to analyze blood, fluid, and tissues.

3.3 Section Review

Answers to Understanding the Concepts and solutions to Practice Problems appear on page T79 in the front of this book. Blackline master test for this section: Section Testsheet 3-3 (TRB page 208)

Vocabulary

18 acid
6 acid indicator
19 balanced equation
8 base
11 charged
16 chemical bond
1 chemical equation
9 covalent bond
10 electrical charges
21 hydrogen ion
14 hydroxide ion
15 ionic bond
17 ionic compound
20 negative ion
4 neutral
8 neutralize
5 pH
13 positive ion
2 product
12 reactant
3 salt

Vocabulary Review

Match each term above with the numbered phrase that best describes it.

1. A way to summarize a chemical change
2. The substance(s) formed during a chemical change
3. One product of a reaction between an acid and a base
4. Having an equal number of positive and negative charges
5. A measure of acidity
6. A substance that shows an acid is present
7. What a base does to an equal amount of acid
8. A substance that has the opposite effect on litmus paper from an acid

9. A chemical bond that results from the sharing of electrons
10. Two kinds of these have been identified, positive and negative
11. Not electrically neutral
12. The substance(s) which will undergo a chemical change
13. An atom that has fewer electrons than protons
14. An ion that you will find in bases
15. A kind of chemical link that occurs between positive and negative ions
16. What occurs when atoms share or transfer electrons
17. A substance which is formed when positive and negative ions are linked chemically
18. A substance which will turn litmus paper from blue to red
19. When the same numbers of atoms of each element are on the left and right sides of a chemical equation
20. An atom that has more electrons than protons
21. What makes an acid an acid

Review Questions

Multiple Choice: Choose the answer that best completes each of the following sentences.

22. Positive ions are formed when neutral atoms ? .
    a. gain protons
    b. gain electrons
    c. lose protons
    d. lose electrons
23. Elements whose atoms are likely to form negative ions can be found in ? .
    a. the alkali metal family
    b. the halogen family
    c. the inert gas family
    d. all families in the periodic table

24. Ionic compounds are a result of the ? .
    a. transfer of electrons
    b. sharing of one electron by atoms in a molecule
    c. sharing of a pair of electrons by atoms in a molecule
    d. presence of more OH^- ions than H^+ ions

Understanding the Concepts

25. For each of the following chemical equations, tell how many atoms of each element appear on each side and whether the equation is balanced.
    a. $O_2 + NO \rightarrow NO_2$
    b. $O_2 + C \rightarrow CO_2$
    c. $NO + O_2 \rightarrow 2NO_2$
    d. $2SO_2 + O_2 \rightarrow 2SO_3$
    e. $CH_4 + O_2 \rightarrow CO_2 + 2H_2O$
26. Explain why inert gases do not burn.
27. Explain why it is not wise to taste a substance in order to tell whether it is an acid or base. Describe two better ways to make such a test.
28. In the chemical equation
    $NaOH + HNO_3 \rightarrow NaNO_3 + H_2O$
    identify the acid, base, and salt and explain what clues helped you identify them.

Problems to Solve

Balance the following equations.
29. $C + O_2 \rightarrow CO$
30. $H_2O_2 \rightarrow H_2O + O_2$
31. $CH_4 + Cl_2 \rightarrow CH_3Cl + HCl$
32. $Zn(OH)_2 + HCl \rightarrow ZnCl_2 + H_2O$
33. $K + H_2O \rightarrow KOH + H_2$

3 Chapter Review

Vocabulary

acid
acid indicator
alkali metals
alkaline earth metals
alloy
atom
atomic mass
atomic number
balanced equation
base
charged
chemical bond
chemical equation
compressibility
covalent bond
diatomic
electric charge

electron
electron cloud model
energy level
families
halogens
hydroxide ion
inert gases
ionic bond
ionic compound
isotopes
metallic luster
metalloids
model
molecule
monatomic
negative ion
neutral

neutralize
neutron
noble gases
nonmetals
nucleus
ozone
periodic table
pH
planetary model
positive ion
product
proton
reactant
salt
transition metals

Review of Concepts

A **scientific model** is a description in terms of familiar things and is used to explain observations and predict behaviors.

The **particle model of matter** pictures matter as made of tiny particles with space between them.
- The particles of a gas are farther apart than those of a liquid or solid.
- An element is made of atoms, which are identical particles of that element.
- Compounds are made of two or more kinds of atoms joined in a fixed arrangement.
- In some elements and compounds, the atoms are grouped into particles known as molecules.
- Mixtures are made of two or more kinds of atoms that are not in a fixed arrangement.

The **periodic table of the elements** is an arrangement that is in order of increasing atomic number and in which elements with similar properties are in the same column.

The **electron cloud model of the atom** includes a nucleus containing protons and neutrons, surrounded by electrons at various energy levels.
- The elements in each row of the periodic table all have the same number of energy levels.
- The elements in each column of the periodic table all have the same number of electrons in the highest energy level.

Electric charges cause pushes and pulls between objects that do not have equal numbers of positive and negative charges.
- An electron has one negative charge.

- A proton has one positive charge.
- An atom that gives up electrons becomes a positive ion.
- An atom that accepts extra electrons becomes a negative ion.

A **chemical bond** is a tie between two atoms that have transferred or shared electrons.
- Chemical bonds result from the attraction between opposite charges.
- Chemical changes involve the forming and/or breaking of chemical bonds.

Acids and **bases** are substances that furnish hydrogen ions and hydroxide ions, respectively.
- The pH value of a substance is a measure of how acidic or basic the substance is.
- An acid and base can neutralize each other in a reaction that produces a salt and water.

Critical Thinking

1. Dalton believed that all atoms of the same element were identical. How has the discovery of isotopes changed that view? In what way are atoms of the same element like each other?

2. Explain why a compound made of potassium and bromine is more likely to be like sodium chloride than like water. Would you expect the potassium-bromine compound to be molecular or ionic? Explain your reasoning.

3. The element astatine is in the sixth row down and the second column from the right of the periodic table. How many energy levels are occupied by electrons in an atom of this element? How many electrons are in the highest energy level of these atoms? How do you know?

4. The atomic mass of lead is approximately two hundred times that of hydrogen. How would the number of atoms in a gram of hydrogen compare to the number in a gram of lead?

5. A student tests two unknown liquids with litmus paper. The first liquid turns red litmus paper blue, the second turns blue litmus paper red. After the student mixes equal volumes of the two liquids together, the new mixture of liquids does not cause litmus to change color. How can you explain these results?

6. A chemist has discovered an unknown substance which acts chemically like a metal, and apparently has an atomic mass of 51. What will the chemist have to determine about the substance in order to assign the substance a place in the periodic chart?

7. The atomic number of an element is equal to the number of protons in the nucleus. The atomic mass reflects the sum of the masses of the protons and neutrons in the nucleus. When will the atomic number be the same as the atomic mass of an atom? For a given element, which number would you normally expect to be greater? Is it possible for atoms of two different elements to have the same atomic mass?

Individual Research

8. Different antacids are sold for neutralizing excess acid in the stomach. Design and carry out an experiment to compare the effectiveness of two or more antacids.

9. Compare the effectiveness of two or more antistatic products in preventing clothes that are removed from a dryer from clinging to one another.

10. Place about 6 uncooked popcorn kernels in a plastic tumbler of water. Add an Alka-Seltzer tablet to the water. Observe what happens to the popcorn kernels. Look for two kernels stuck together. Do the kernels seem to be sharing a bubble between them? How is the sharing of a bubble similar to a covalent bond?

11. The colored liquid obtained from boiling a few leaves of purple cabbage in water can be used as an indicator. Add a few drops of the liquid to vinegar. What color change takes place? Add a few drops of the indicator to a solution of baking soda in water. What color change takes place?

Bibliography

Asimov, Isaac. *How Did We Find Out About Atoms?* New York: Walker & Co., 1976
From the ideas of the Greeks to the actual "pictures" of atoms from a field-emission microscope.

Chester, Michael. *Particles; An Introduction to Particle Physics.* New York: Macmillan Pub. Co., 1978.
An introductory book on the structure of the atom and the atomic nucleus.

Cohen, Daniel. *Gold; The Fascinating Story of the Noble Metal Through the Ages.* New York: M. Evans & Co., 1976
The story of gold from its discovery in ancient times, through the alchemists' search for how to make it, to its modern use.

A metric ruler is divided into centimeters which are then divided into millimeters.

The Metric Controversy

All major countries of the world except the United States have adopted the metric system for measuring mass, volume and length. Even England, where our system of inches, feet, pounds, quarts, and other units was developed, has converted to metric. In the United States, only the scientific community has wholly embraced the metric system. This is true despite a strong, Congress-backed movement in the 1970s for nationwide adoption of the metric system.

Should the United States adopt the metric system?

PROS

- The metric system is based on tens, making it easy to convert from one unit to another within the system.
- Prefixes are used to distinguish between the values of units, making it easy to convert to scientific notation which is based on the exponential values of ten.
- The units of mass, volume and length use the same prefixes.
- Converting to the metric system would simplify world-wide trade since goods would no longer have to be packaged differently for the United States market.
- People in the United States already use milliliters and liters for soft drinks and liquor; they use metric tools for imported cars.

CONS

- The present, or English system, is well established in this country and people are reluctant to change.
- The English system is just as accurate as the metric system.
- Computers and calculators make conversion between systems quick and convenient.
- The United States is currently surveyed in miles and acres and resurveying would be time-consuming and expensive.
- Conversion of machinery, calibrated tools, signs, maps and other items would be very expensive.

Is a compromise possible in this situation? Should we learn to use both systems and then drop the English system when everyone feels comfortable with the metric system? Should we continue with the English system, even if it is different from the system used by the rest of the world? What is your solution?

Lasers and Measurement

Imagine being able to measure the distance to the moon accurately to within two and one half centimeters! Lasers are capable of this accuracy, making them particularly well suited as measurement tools. Whether measuring the distance to the moon or the diameter of an atom, lasers are able to do the job quickly and accurately.

The *laser,* which stands for "*l*ight *a*mplification by *s*timulated *e*mission of *r*adiation," works because of both the particle and wave nature of light. To make a laser, one must "excite" atoms in a gas, dye, or crystal. This is done by means of an electric current, a chemical reaction, radiowaves, or nuclear reactions An "excited" atom is one in which the electrons in the outermost energy level have been boosted up into another level by the absorption of energy. As these electrons fall back down into their original energy level, the excess energy is released as a photon or light particle. In a laser, these photons are trapped and then reflected back and forth between mirrors until they are all synchronized and have gained energy. The photons are then released as compact, parallel beams of coherent light. Coherent beams of light are all the same wavelength and travel in unison as a group. The substance that was originally excited determines the wavelength of these light beams. Because the beams are one wavelength, they are also the same single color.

Unlike light from the sun or a lightbulb, laser light travels with a specific frequency. The light is intense, pure, and directional. The laser's intensity or brightness makes it a powerful tool in medicine and industry. However, it is the laser's pure frequency that makes it an important measurement tool. A wave's frequency refers to the number of waves that pass a certain point in one second. In the case of lasers, this measurement can reach a high degree of accuracy. In using lasers to measure distance—for example, the distance to the moon—a scientist beams a laser of known frequency and wavelength at a reflector on the moon and times how long it takes the beam to get to the moon and back. The scientist then uses a simple equation relating the time and frequency to determine the distance in wavelengths. This distance can then be converted to the distance in centimeters.

This basic method of using reflected laser light to measure distance can also be used to measure the precise clearances of tunnels and bridges, depths of water and heights of mountains as well as the very small distances within atoms. The most common use of lasers as measurement tools is in surveying land. This application uses lasers to produce straight lines and measure accurate distances. Finally, by reflecting lasers off satellites, scientists are able to measure very slight movements of the continents. Such use of laser technology may help us to predict impending earthquakes and other natural disasters in the future.

A helium-neon laser atop this truck is used to make precise clearance measurements of a tunnel. These measurements will determine the highest and widest loads that can travel through the tunnel.

A laser's power is measured in watts, like that of a light bulb. Waves of laser light can be likened to a single musical tune.

2 *Motion and Heat*

Chapter 4
Motion

Chapter 5
Work and Heat

Learning Objectives

■ **Process**

1. To observe basic principles of motion
2. To calculate the speed of a moving object
3. To classify the forces acting on a given object
4. To measure the mechanical advantage and efficiency of different machines
5. To relate work and power to energy

■ **Content**

1. To distinguish between speed and acceleration
2. To analyze both balanced and unbalanced forces acting on an object
3. To apply the concept of energy to both kinetic and potential energy
4. To explain a variety of theories regarding heat and heat transfer
5. To compare the different forms of energy
6. To apply the kinetic theory of matter to explain the general behavior of gases, solids, and liquids

A time-lapse photograph captures the trail of lights left as evidence of vehicles moving along the Golden Gate Bridge in San Francisco.

135

Chapter 4
Motion

In this chapter you will learn how motion can be described and how it depends on forces.

Science background information:
Motion is one of the most fundamental problems of physics. Early explanations of motion came from intuition based on immediate observation. It is an intuitive conclusion that motion is connected with acts of pushing, lifting, or pulling. According to Aristotle (384–322 B.C.), whose conclusion was based on pure thought, a moving body comes to a standstill when the force that pushes it along stops.

The development of scientific reasoning by Galileo Galilei (1564–1642) was one of the most important achievements in the history of human thought. He reexamined the problem of motion and found the intuitive explanation lacking. Suppose that someone pushing a cart along a level road suddenly stops pushing. According to Aristotle, the cart should stop dead immediately. However, Galileo observed that the cart keeps on going a short distance. This distance can be reduced by reducing the friction within the wheels and between the wheels and the road.

It can be experimentally observed, then, that the cart is stopped by the action of friction, not by ending the action of pushing. Observations like these led to the formulation of what is now known as Newton's first law of motion.

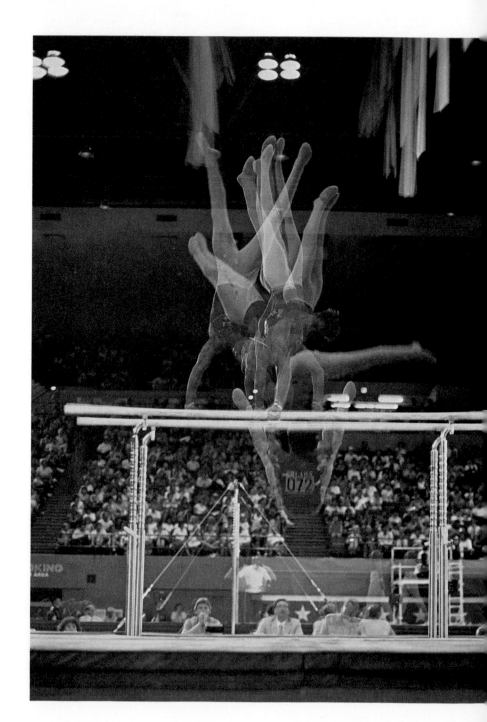

Projectsheet 4 (TRB page 176) and
Research Lab 4 (Lab Manual pages
61–62) may be used at any point in
this chapter.

For detailed information about teaching this chapter, see Chapter 4 Planning Guide on pages T82–T83 in the
front of this book.

Chapter Preview

4.1 Describing Motion

- **Reference objects**
- **Speed**
- **Average speed**
- **Constant speed**
- **Acceleration**

The speed of a moving object is related to how far it travels and how long it takes to travel that far. The speed of a moving object may change, or it may remain the same. An object may travel in a straight line, or its path may curve.

4.2 Forces and Motion

- **Forces**
- **Newton's first law of motion**
- **Newton's second law of motion**
- **Newton's third law of motion**
- **Momentum**
- **Curved motion**
- **The law of gravitation**
- **Weight and mass**
- **Motion under gravity**
- **Curved motion under gravity**

Isaac Newton was the first person who realized the rela-tion between forces and mo-tion. He understood that an unbalanced force causes a change in speed or direction or both.

4.3 Energy

- **Kinetic energy**
- **Potential energy**
- **Energy conversion**
- **Friction and mechanical energy**
- **Einstein's theory of relativity**

Moving objects have energy, or the ability to cause change. Nonmoving objects have en-ergy when they are in a posi-tion where a force can make them move. Each kind of en-ergy can be changed into the other.

For ideas for classroom demonstration and discussion, see Getting Started on page T84 in the front of this book.

4.1 Describing Motion

Supplemental materials: Teaching Diagram 4-1 (TRB page 00), Reading Checksheet 4-1 (TRB page 89), Skillsheet 4-1 (TRB page 135), Investigation 4-1 (Lab Manual pages 49–50)

Section Preview

- **Reference objects**
- **Speed**
- **Average speed**
- **Constant speed**
- **Acceleration**

Bracketed numbers are Section Review numbers correlated to that objective.

Learning Objectives

1. To describe the position and motion of an object with respect to a reference object. [2, 8]
2. To determine the speed of a moving object using time and distance measurements. [1, 3, 10, 15, 16, 17]
3. To recognize constant speed on a distance-time graph. [5, 7, 11, 12]
4. To differentiate between speed and acceleration. [3, 4, 9, 13, 14]
5. To recognize changing speed on a distance-time graph. [4]

Figure 4-1. *Is the cyclist moving or are the bushes moving? What helps you decide?*

The cyclist is moving. You know that bushes do not move.

Yes, the cyclist is moving. The photographer moved the camera to keep the cyclist in focus. That is why the bushes look blurred.

The car is coming toward the camera. Changes in the apparent size of the car and in its position in relation to the road help you answer the question.

Main Idea

How can you judge whether something is moving?

When something is moving, its position is changing. The motion can be described in terms of how fast the object is moving, in what direction, and whether the motion itself is steady or changing.

Reference objects

New vocabulary: reference object

Is the cyclist in Figure 4-1 moving? How do you explain the clear image of the cyclist? The blurred image of the bushes?

Now look at the three photos of a moving car in Figure 4-2. The photo on the left was taken first. The one on the right was taken last. The photos were taken with the same camera. Is the car coming toward or going away from the camera? What clues help you answer?

It is not always easy to decide which objects are moving. Clues are often found by looking at other objects in the surroundings. Normally, you think of signs or walls as stationary, not moving. You judge motion in relation to these apparently stationary objects. When you do this, you are using the signs or walls as **reference objects.**

When you are on a bus, you expect the bus to be moving and buildings to be still. You might see the wall of a building move by the window of the bus. Yet, you know it is the bus that is moving. You use the building as a reference object to judge the motion of the bus.

There are times you may be confused. Suppose your bus is parked close to a second bus. The bus next to you starts to move forward. You may think your bus is moving backward instead. You are fooled into thinking you are moving. This time your reference object is moving.

Imagine watching a beautiful sunset. The sun is slowly sinking below the horizon. But which is really moving—the sun or the earth? Even though the sun appears to move, you know it is really the earth that is moving. But wait! Is the sun perfectly still? Measurements made on distant stars indicate that the sun and all the planets are moving. The stars are also moving. In fact, there are no perfectly stationary objects to use as reference objects.

Figure 4-2. *Can you be sure that the car, rather than the camera, is moving? What helps you decide?*
Yes, you can. When the photographer moves the camera, fixed objects look blurred.

Figure 4-3. *Is the sun moving?*
The sun appears to move, but it is really the earth that is moving.

Even though buildings on the earth are moving, they can be perfectly good reference objects. Suppose you are studying a ball as it moves through the air. It makes sense to use a building as a reference object. It doesn't matter that the earth, to which the building is attached, is moving. On the other hand, suppose you were returning to the earth on a spacecraft. You would then find it important to consider the movement of the earth. You might choose stars as reference objects.

Generally, when you pick a reference object, you think of it as not moving. Then you compare the position of something else to that of the reference object. You study movement from the point of view of the reference object you choose.

Suppose you walk toward the rear of a moving bus. You are moving backward in relation to the bus. Yet, the bus is probably moving so fast that you are still moving forward in relation to the ground. The way you describe motion depends on the reference object you choose. Your description of motion will change as you change the reference object.

Quick Review

1. How can a reference object be used to study the motion of something else?
2. Can a moving object be selected as a reference object?

Speed

New vocabulary: speed, velocity

Speed describes how fast an object is moving in relation to a reference object. Objects in motion move at different speeds. That is, some objects move faster than others. You have also heard the word **velocity** (veh-LOS'-it-ee) used to describe how fast. In common speech, *velocity* and *speed* usually mean the same thing. However, in science *velocity* has a slightly different meaning. The velocity of an object describes not only how fast it is moving but in what direction. In other words, velocity is speed together with the direction of motion. Quantities that include both speed and direction are called *vector quantities*. This section will mostly focus on speed and not on direction, so the word *speed* will be used. Quantities that do not include any direction are called *scalar quantities*. Speed is a scalar quantity.

A car on a highway travels at about 90 kilometers per hour, or 25 meters per second. Light travels at 300 million meters per second. Other objects move at very slow speeds. A glacier may move only a few centimeters per year.

Main Idea

What is speed? How does velocity differ from speed?

Additional information:

To find the speed of a car in meters per second when its speed is given in kilometers per hour, first convert the kilometers to meters and the hours to seconds. Then divide the distance in meters by the time in seconds.

$$(90 \text{ km}) \times \left(\frac{1000 \text{ m}}{1 \text{ km}} \right) = 90\,000 \text{ m}$$

$$(1 \text{ h}) \times \left(\frac{3600 \text{ s}}{1 \text{ h}} \right) = 3600 \text{ s}$$

$$90 \text{ km/h} = \frac{90\,000 \text{ m}}{3600 \text{ s}} = 25 \text{ m/s}$$

Notice that speeds are described in units of distance *and* time. In the examples given, the distance units are kilometers, meters, or centimeters. The time units are years, hours, or seconds. Common units of speed are meters per second (m/s) and kilometers per hour (km/h). Note that when symbols are used for the distance and time units, the slash (/) means *per*.

You can measure the speed of a moving object. For example, you can measure how long it takes someone to bike a certain distance, such as 100 m. Or, you can measure how far the person can bike in a certain time, such as 10 s. In either case, the speed will be the distance traveled divided by the time it takes to travel that distance.

$$\text{speed} = \frac{\text{distance}}{\text{time}}$$

You can see that speed is both distance *per* unit of time and distance *divided by* time. The word *per* means *divided by*.

Critical Thinking

What clues tell you that 4 cm/s is a speed and not a distance or a time?

The unit cm/s is a distance unit (cm) divided by a time unit (s).

Sample Problem 1

Suppose it took a time of 4 s for a hiker to go a distance of 100 m. What was the speed?

Solution

To find the speed, divide the distance (100 m) by the time (4 s).

$$\text{speed} = \frac{\text{distance}}{\text{time}}$$

$$= \frac{100 \text{ m}}{4 \text{ s}} = 25 \text{ m/s}$$

Sample Problem 2

Suppose that in a time of 10 s the biker went a distance of 250 m. What was the speed?

Solution

To find the speed, divide the distance (250 m) by the time (10 s).

$$\text{speed} = \frac{\text{distance}}{\text{time}}$$

$$= \frac{250 \text{ m}}{10 \text{ s}} = 25 \text{ m/s}$$

Data Search

Between 1945 and 1955, by how much did the world record airspeed of aircraft increase? Search pages 658–661.

The world record increased by

1323 km/h. − 976 km/h = 347 km/h.

This represents an increase of

$$\frac{347 \text{ km/h}}{976 \text{ km/h}} \times 100\% = 35.6\%$$

over the 1945 value.

4.1a Measuring Speed

Science processes: Measuring, collecting data, using
numbers

Materials   BASIC   30 minutes   Entire class

- **stopwatch or watch that indicates seconds**
- **tape measure**

Purpose

To measure the speed of runners two ways.

Procedure

1. Draw a starting line out-of-doors or near one edge of a gymnasium or activity room.
2. Use the tape measure to measure off a distance of 50 m from the starting line. Draw a finish line at this point.
3. Select one student to be the timer and another to be the recorder. Prepare a data table like the one shown.
4. Have the timer measure how long it takes each person to run the 50 m. Have the recorder record each person's time.
5. Calculate the speed of each runner by dividing the distance (50 m) by the running time (number of seconds).
6. Mark off 5-m distances between the lines already drawn. Label these added lines 5 m, 10 m, 15 m, 20 m, etc. (These lines will be used to help estimate how far each person runs in a given time interval.)
7. Choose a time interval close to the shortest time measured in Step 4.

8. Measure and record the distance each person runs in the time interval chosen in Step 7.
9. Calculate the speed of each runner.

Questions

1. Who had the higher speeds for the 50-m runs—runners with shorter times or runners with longer times?
2. Who had the higher speeds for the fixed-time runs—runners with shorter distances or runners with longer distances?
3. Did the same five people have the fastest speeds each time?

Conclusion

How do you calculate the speed of an object?

Step 4

Student's name	Distance	Time	Speed	Distance	Time	Speed

Figure 4-4. *What two things must be known before the speed of an object can be known?*

The distance the object moved and the time it took the object to move that distance

Sample Problem 3

The biker in Sample Problem 1 traveled at a speed of 25 m/s for a time of 4 s. From the speed and time, determine the distance traveled.

Solution

$$distance = speed \times time$$
$$= 25 \text{ m/s} \times 4 \text{ s}$$
$$= 100 \text{ m}$$

Sample Problem 4

The biker in Sample Problem 2 traveled at 25 m/s for 10 s. What was the distance traveled?

Solution

$$distance = speed \times time$$
$$= 25 \text{ m/s} \times 10 \text{ s}$$
$$= 250 \text{ m}$$

Both answers agree with the measurements.

Practice Problems

1. A biker travels a distance of 150 m in a time of 5 s. What is the speed? *Answer:* 30 m/s
2. A biker travels at a speed of 22 m/s for a time of 5 s. What is the distance traveled? *Answer:* 110 m

Additional information:
Symbols can be used just like numbers. Having the same symbol in the numerator and denominator is like having a fraction with the same number in the numerator and denominator. Both equal 1.

Solutions to Practice Problems:

1. $speed = \dfrac{distance}{time}$

   $= \dfrac{150 \text{ m}}{5 \text{ s}} = 30 \text{ m/s}$

2. $distance = speed \times time$
   $= 22 \text{ m/s} \times 5 \text{ s}$
   $= 110 \text{ m}$

Quick Review answers:
1. A unit of distance and a unit of time
2. 21 m/s
3. 2600 m (or 2.6 km)

Quick Review

1. What two kinds of units make up all units of speed?
2. What is the speed of a skater who travels a distance of 210 m in a time of 10 s?
3. How far can a person run in 10 min at a speed of 260 m/min?

Average speed

New vocabulary: average speed

The speed found for the biker was an **average speed.** He or she may have biked faster at the beginning or near the end or in the middle. But overall, the speed was 25 m/s.

When you travel a long distance in an automobile, you probably change your speed often. You slow down in towns and going up hills or around curves. You speed up going downhill or on the open road.

Dividing total distance traveled by the total time on the road gives average speed. Suppose you travel a total distance of 800 km in 16 h. Your average speed equals

$$\frac{800 \text{ km}}{16 \text{ h}} = 50 \text{ km/h}$$

Research Topic

Find out the world records for runners in races of 100 m, 200 m, 400 m, 800 m, 1500 m, 5000 m, and 10 000 m. Calculate the average speed for the recordholder of each race.

Figure 4-5. *During a race, the speed of a swimmer usually changes. Is the winner the swimmer with the highest average speed?* Yes

But some of the time you may have traveled at 90 km/h. And some of the time you may have been stopped at a gas station or restaurant.

Quick Review

1. Does an average speed indicate how fast something travels at every moment during a trip? Explain.
2. During a trip, is it possible ever to travel faster than the average speed for the trip?

Constant speed

New vocabulary: constant speed, slope

An object that does not change its speed is moving at **constant speed.** How does an automobile driver know when the car is traveling at constant speed?

Suppose you wanted to jog around a marked track at constant speed for half an hour. How could you check that your speed was constant? Constant speed means equal distances are covered in equal times. You could use a stopwatch to measure how long it takes to jog each lap of the track. It would be even better to measure how long it takes to travel very short distances of equal length. If all the times are the same, your speed must be constant.

Suppose you jogged each lap in 2 min. How long would it take to jog 14 laps? You could calculate the answer. But another way to find out is to make a distance-time graph. On a distance-time graph, distance is marked off on the vertical axis. Study Figure 4-6. It shows distance marked in units of

By reading the speedometer and noting whether the needle remains on the same speed reading.

Main Idea

When something moves at constant speed, what is true for distances it covers in equal times?

Figure 4-6. *Each point represents the number of laps covered (see vertical axis) after the total time shown on the horizontal axis.*

4.1b Recognizing Constant Speed

Science processes: Measuring, collecting data, making a graph

Materials 30 minutes Entire class

- toy tractor (battery-powered)
- meter stick or tape measure
- masking tape
- stopwatch or watch that indicates seconds

Purpose

To recognize motion at constant speed.

Procedure

1. Find a flat, smooth surface at least 2 m long. A long table or an uncarpeted floor can be used. Use a meter stick and masking tape to mark off distances at intervals of 20 cm on the surface.
2. Designate one student to be the timer. The timer will start the watch when the tractor is released at the starting line. The timer should call out the time when the tractor passes each of the distance markers.
3. Designate a second student to be the re-corder. The recorder is to write down the time when the tractor passes each of the distance markers.
4. Designate a third student to release the trac-tor at the starting line.

5. Make at least one practice run before any data is recorded. (The speed of the tractor may make it more convenient to use smaller or larger distance intervals.)
6. Prepare a data table like the one shown. Record the distances of the masking tape from the starting line.
7. Release the tractor, and record the time when it passes each marker.
8. Draw axes for a distance-time graph of your data. Mark distances in centimeters on the vertical axis and time in seconds on the horizontal axis.
9. Plot your data. If the plotted points seem to line up along a straight line or nearly so, draw a straight line through the points. A straight line indicates that the tractor was traveling with constant speed.

Question

Was the speed of the tractor constant?

Conclusion

How can you use data from distance and time measurements to determine whether an object was moving at constant speed?

Step 2

Distance	Time

Figure 4-7. *A distance-time graph for a jogger who covers each lap in 2 min. How long does it take to cover 14 laps?*

28 min

laps. Time is marked off along the horizontal axis. It is marked in units of minutes.

In Figure 4-6, there is a point at zero time and zero distance. At zero time no distance had been covered. The point at the time of 2 min and the distance of one lap shows that it took 2 min to cover the first lap. There is another point for 2 min later. At that time another lap had been covered. The total distance after a total time of 4 min was 2 laps. After another 2 min (total time 6 min), another lap had been covered (total distance 3 laps). Similarly, after a total time of 8 min, a total distance of 4 laps had been covered.

A straight line can be drawn through all five points in Figure 4-6. In Figure 4-7, the straight line has been drawn. Look at where the straight line crosses the distance line for 14 laps. What time line meets the distance line at this point? The answer tells you how long it took to jog 14 laps.

Suppose you are jogging with a friend. Your friend can't keep up with you. He finds that it takes 2.5 min to complete each lap. Nevertheless, he is able to keep going for 12 laps. Each lap takes the same amount of time. After 5 min he has run two laps. After 10 min he has run four laps. After 15 min he has run six laps. He completes the 12 laps in 30 min. A distance-time graph describing your friend's jogging is shown in Figure 4-8. The first graph is included for comparison.

The line describing the motion of your friend is not as steep as the first line. He covered less distance in the same time. His speed was slower. You can compare speeds on a distance-time graph. The greater speed has a steeper line. The line representing the slower speed will have a less steep line. Suppose you time a member of your school track team. She is

Critical Thinking

In Figure 4-6, how much time is represented by the space between the vertical blue lines? How many laps are represented by the space between the horizontal blue lines?

2 min; 2 laps

The time line for 28 min intersects the distance line for 14 laps at the straight line drawn through the points.

Figure 4-8. *You know which jogger was faster. How do you recognize the faster jogger from the graphs?*
The steeper line describes the motion of the faster jogger.

able to cover each lap in 1.5 min. Her speed is greater than yours. A line describing her motion would be steeper than the other two lines.

The steepness of a graph line is called the **slope.** A steeper line has a greater slope. Thus, the greater the slope is on a distance-time graph, the greater the speed.

Quick Review answers:
1. The speed of an object may vary from moment to moment from its average speed. The speed of an object traveling at constant speed does not vary from moment to moment.
2. The less steep line represents the slower constant speed.

Quick Review

1. How is average speed different from constant speed?
2. On a distance-time graph, how can you tell which of two lines represents a slower constant speed?

Acceleration

New vocabulary: acceleration

A baseball rolls down a steep hill. What happens to its speed? An automobile driver places his or her foot on the brake pedal. What happens to the speed of the automobile? The gun sounds for the start of a race. What happens to the speed of the runners? In all these examples, the speed of something changes. The ball rolls faster and faster. The automobile slows down. The runners start moving and quickly reach top speed.

You most likely have felt the effects of changing speed. You lurch forward if you are on a bus that comes to a sudden stop. You get pressed back against your seat on an airplane that is taking off down the runway. The faster the speed changes, the more you feel it. If a bus gently slows down, you don't notice the change.

An object that is changing speed is **accelerating** (ak-SEL′-

er-rayt'-ing). In common speech, an accelerating object is speeding up, but in science, objects slowing down are also said to be accelerating.

An object does not have to be changing its speed to be accelerating. Moving objects that change direction are also accelerating. **Acceleration** (ak-sel'-er-RAY'-shun) is the changing of the speed and/or direction of motion of an object. You feel the effects of acceleration in an automobile that is making a sharp turn. During the turn, you lurch to the side.

Recall that velocity is the speed together with the direction of motion. If either the speed *or* the direction of motion is changing, the velocity is changing. Thus, acceleration can be described as the changing of the velocity of an object.

The acceleration of an object describes how fast the velocity is changing. It equals the change in velocity divided by the time it takes for the velocity to change by that much.

$$\text{acceleration} = \frac{\text{change in velocity}}{\text{time}}$$

For change in speed with no change in direction, the acceleration equals the change in speed divided by the time. The units of acceleration are the units of speed (meters per second) divided by the units of time (seconds):

$$\frac{\text{speed units}}{\text{time units}} = \frac{\left(\frac{\text{meters}}{\text{second}}\right)}{\text{seconds}} = \frac{\text{meters}}{(\text{second})^2}$$

Figure 4-9. *How do each of these three parts cause an automobile to accelerate?*

The brake and the gas pedal cause an automobile to change speed. The steering wheel causes it to change direction.

The thrills come from the acceleration. Acceleration causes you to fly forward in your seat, press against the back of the seat, and lurch to one side or the other of the seat.

Figure 4-10. *Do the thrills in riding a roller coaster come from the speed or the acceleration? Explain.*

Acceleration units are read "meters per second squared" and the symbol for them is m/s².

Sample Problem

A biker starts to move and goes from a speed of 0 m/s to 25 m/s in a total time of 10 s. What is the acceleration?

Solution

Divide the change in speed by the total time.

$$\text{acceleration} = \frac{\text{change in speed}}{\text{time}}$$

$$= \frac{25 \text{ m/s} - 0 \text{ m/s}}{10 \text{ s}}$$

$$= 2.5 \text{ m/s}^2$$

Practice Problem

A biker goes from a speed of 8 m/s to 20 m/s in a total time of 6 s. What is the acceleration? *Answer: 2 m/s²*

Solution to Practice Problem:

$$\text{acceleration} = \frac{\text{change in speed}}{\text{time}}$$

$$= \frac{20 \text{ m/s} - 8 \text{ m/s}}{6 \text{ s}}$$

$$= \frac{12 \text{ m/s}}{6 \text{ s}} = 2 \text{ m/s}^2$$

Suppose you are riding in an automobile. You fasten your seat belt, and the driver starts the car. You can see both the odometer (distance gauge) and the second hand of your watch. The odometer is set at zero when you start. Every 30 seconds you record how far the car has gone. At the end of 240 s, or 4 min, you have the data shown in Table 4-1.

Figure 4-11 shows a distance-time graph based on the data in Table 4-1. If you had actually been riding in the automobile, you would have recognized a change in speed. On a

Table 4-1. *Time and distance data for a car ride.*

Travel time (in s)	Total distance traveled (in km)
0	0.0
30	0.1
60	0.3
90	0.6
120	1.0
150	1.5
180	2.0
210	2.5
240	3.0

See also Activity Record Sheet 4-1C (Lab Manual page 47). Teaching Hints, Answers to Questions, and Conclusion appear on page T85 in the front of this book.

Activity

4.1c Detecting Changes in Speed and Direction

Science processes: Observing, inferring

Materials   20 minutes   Groups of 2 to 4
- **vial with cap or small test tube with stopper**
- **water**
- **small cart or roller skate**
- **masking tape**

Purpose

To determine how changes in speed and direction can be detected.

Procedure

1. Fill a vial with water. Leave only a small space for an air bubble.
2. Cap the vial and turn it on its side. The small air bubble should be visible, floating at the top of the water.
3. Tape the vial in this position to the side or top of a small cart or roller skate. Make sure that the bubble is in the middle of the upper side of the vial when the cart is not moving.
4. Make a data table like the one shown.
5. Give the cart a push. Record the direction the bubble moves.
6. When the cart is moving, quickly bring the cart to a stop. Record the direction the bubble moves.
7. Pull the cart at constant speed. Record what the bubble does.

8. While the cart is moving at constant speed, change its direction by giving it a twist. Record what the bubble does.

Questions

1. What was happening to the cart when the bubble moved forward?
2. What was happening to the cart when the bubble moved backward?
3. What did the bubble do when the direction the cart was moving changed?
4. Under what conditions did the bubble remain in the center?

Conclusion

Under what conditions did the bubble change its position?

Step 3

Motion of cart	Motion of bubble
Pushed forward	
Brought to stop	
Constant speed	
Changes direction	

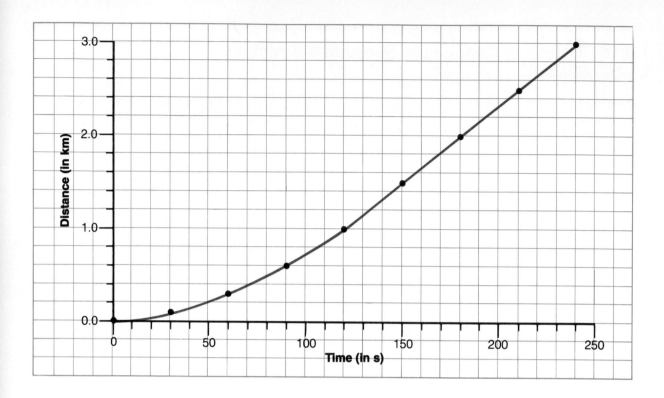

Figure 4-11. *When is the speed of the automobile changing? When is the speed of the automobile constant?*

The speed is changing during the first 120 s, where the graph line is curved. The speed is constant during the next 120 s, where the graph line is straight.

The car was traveling at constant speed from 120 s to 240 s. During this time period, it was traveling equal distances in equal times, that is, 0.5 km every 30 s.

Quick Review answers:
1. Yes, it is changing speed.
2. If the object is changing direction, even if it is moving at constant speed, it is accelerating.
3. A curved line represents motion that is not at constant speed.

distance-time graph also you can recognize a change in speed. Recall that constant speed is recognized on a distance-time graph by a straight line. When the line is not straight, the speed is not constant—it is changing.

Constant speed results in equal distances traveled in equal times. When the speed is changing, the distances traveled in equal times are not equal. According to Table 4-1, the car traveled 0.1 km during the first 30 s but 0.2 km during the next 30 s. It was speeding up. In Figure 4-11 the graph line is curved during the first 60 s. It becomes steeper.

Lay a ruler or the edge of a sheet of paper against the graph line. Find the portion of the line that is straight. When was the car traveling at constant speed? To check your answer, use Table 4-1 to find out when the car was traveling equal distances in equal times.

Quick Review

1. When an object is slowing down, is it accelerating? Explain.
2. How is it possible for an object to be moving at constant speed and yet be accelerating?
3. On a distance-time graph, what kind of line represents motion that is not at constant speed?

4.1 Section Review

Answers to Understanding the Concepts and Solutions to Problems to Solve appear on page T85 in the front of this book. Blackline master test for this section: Section Testsheet 4-1 (TRB page 209)

Vocabulary

4 acceleration
1 average speed
5 constant speed
2 reference object
7 slope
3 speed
6 velocity

Vocabulary Review

Match each term above with the numbered phrase that best describes it.

1. Total distance traveled divided by total travel time
2. Considered nonmoving in relation to a moving object
3. How fast something moves
4. The changing of the speed or direction of a moving object
5. Describes motion of an object that always travels equal distances in equal times
6. How fast something moves, together with the direction of motion
7. Steepness of a graph line

Review Questions

Multiple Choice: Choose the answer that best completes each of the following sentences.

8. The speed of a flight attendant walking down the aisle of a moving plane is NOT the same in relation to a seated passenger as in relation to ? .
   a. another seated passenger
   b. a person on the ground
   c. the cockpit of the plane
   d. the wings of the plane

9. An object is NOT accelerating in the scientific sense when it ? .
   a. speeds up
   b. slows down
   c. moves around a curve at constant speed
   d. moves in a straight line at constant speed

10. A runner travels 300 m in 150 s. The average speed of the runner is ? .
    a. 0.5 m/s
    b. 2 m/s
    c. 2 km/h
    d. 45 000 m/s

Understanding the Concepts

11. The graph shows distance-time lines for three cyclists during a race. Which one was going the fastest? Explain how you know.

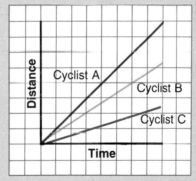

12. When an object moves at constant velocity, what two things are constant?
13. What is the shape of the path of a moving object that has no change in its direction of motion?
14. Suppose an object moves in a circle at constant speed.
    a. Is its direction of motion changing?
    b. Is it accelerating? Explain.

Problems to Solve

15. A cyclist covers a distance of 180 km in 4.0 hours. What is her average speed? 45 km/h
16. A runner travels at an average speed of 12 km/h for 2 hours. How far does he travel? 24 km
17. A cyclist averages 30 km/h on a cross-country trip. She plans to ride 10 hours a day.
    a. How far can she expect to go in one day? a. 300 km
    b. How many days will it take her to travel 4500 km?
       b. 15 days

For ideas for classroom demonstration and discussion, see Getting Started on page T86 in the front of this book.

4.2 Forces and Motion

Supplemental materials: Teaching Diagram 4-2 (TRB page 00), Reading Checksheet 4-2 (TRB page 90), Skillsheet 4-2 (TRB page 136), Investigation 4-2 (Lab Manual pages 55–56)

Section Preview

- **Forces**
- **Newton's first law of motion**
- **Newton's second law of motion**
- **Newton's third law of motion**

- **Momentum**
- **Curved motion**
- **The law of gravitation**
- **Weight and mass**
- **Motion under gravity**
- **Curved motion under gravity**

Bracketed numbers are Section Review numbers correlated to that objective.

Learning Objectives

1. To identify the forces acting on an object both when the forces are balanced and when the forces are unbalanced. [4, 6, 7, 9, 13]
2. To describe the effects of friction on a moving object. [3, 12, 16]
3. To relate the acceleration of an object to the force applied and to the mass of the object being accelerated. [1, 8, 12, 15, 18, 23]
4. To recognize that forces always come in pairs that are described as action and reaction forces. [10, 11, 14, 17]
5. To apply the law of gravitation to the motion of objects near the surface of the earth. [2, 5, 19, 20, 21, 22, 24]

Figure 4-12. *When the horse rises on its hind legs, it pushes the rider backward. Forces cause changes in motion.*

You have observed and described moving objects. You might be wondering, What causes objects to start moving? What must be done to stop moving objects? How do you change the motion of an object? These questions will be explored in this section.

Forces

New vocabulary: force, balanced force

Suppose a book is resting on your desk. You can move it by lifting it. You can push it away from you. You can pull it toward you. The lift, push, or pull is called a **force.**

You use forces to make an object start moving. You also use forces to stop moving objects. You pull on the brake controls of a bicycle. You catch a baseball. Sometimes you use forces to change the direction of the motion of an object. When you hit a tennis ball or a baseball, it reverses direction. You change the direction of your bicycle with a force on the handlebars. Finally, forces can change the shape of objects. You can crumple a sheet of paper or an aluminum can with a force.

Forces can cause changes in the motion of objects. They can cause changes in the shape of objects. Sometimes, however, you can exert a force on an object and no change in motion or shape occurs. A force that produces no change must be balanced by another force. Forces that oppose each other with equal strength are **balanced forces.**

A force has both a strength and a direction. When two forces are balanced, they are equal in strength and opposite in direction. For example, one might be an upward force and the other a downward force.

Suppose a book drops to the floor from the edge of your desk. A force must have caused the motion. You are well acquainted with this force. The force is gravity. Objects are pulled toward the center of the earth by gravity. In other words, gravity pulls objects downward.

Suppose the book is back on top of the desk. The book is again at rest. Is the force of gravity still acting on the book? Yes, the force of gravity is always present, pulling the book downward. Then why doesn't the book move?

There must be another force that balances the force of gravity. The desk top is pushing upward on the book. Since no motion results, the upward force must be exactly as strong as the downward force. The upward push of the desk and the downward pull of gravity are balanced forces.

Figure 4-13 shows how the balanced forces on the book can be shown as arrows. The equal strength is represented by arrows of the same length. The direction of each force is represented by the direction of the arrows.

You may be seated as you read this sentence. Gravity is also pulling you downward. Since you are not moving downward, another force must be pushing you upward. Become aware of the chair seat pushing upward on you. This force must balance the force of gravity. As a result, you do not move.

Quick Review

1. Does a force on an object always cause a change in the motion or shape of the object? Explain.
2. When a force is represented by an arrow, what do the length and the direction of the arrow represent?

Figure 4-13. *Why doesn't the book move?*
The forces on the book are balanced. The force of gravity pulling the book downward and the force of the desk pushing upward on the book are equal.

Quick Review answers:
1. No, the force does not cause a change when it is balanced by another force.
2. The length of the arrow represents the strength of the force. The direction of the arrow represents the direction of the force.

Newton's first law of motion
New vocabulary: Newton's first law of motion, inertia, friction, static friction

If something is not moving, you know the forces on it are balanced. But what about an object that is already moving? What about an object that starts to move? What about an object that stops moving?

Greek philosophers who lived about 2300 years ago studied motion. They thought matter should normally be at rest. They believed all objects in motion tended to stop moving. According to their thinking, an unbalanced force had to be present just to keep an object moving.

A ball thrown upward soon falls back down to earth and stops moving. A cart rolling on a level surface also soon stops. The early Greek philosophers believed that objects stopped because no force was present to keep them moving.

In the seventeenth century, Isaac Newton (1642–1727) suggested a different explanation: as long as the forces on an object are balanced, the object does not change its motion. He stated that an object at rest remains at rest, and an object in motion continues moving in a straight line at constant speed, unless acted upon by an unbalanced force. This has been found to be universally true in nature and is known as **Newton's first law of motion.**

In other words, an unbalanced force is needed to bring a moving object to rest, put an object at rest in motion, or change the direction or the speed of a moving object. An object tends to resist *changes* in its motion. The tendency for an

Main Idea

What is inertia?

Figure 4-14. *How did the early Greek philosophers explain why a rolling cart soon stops? How did Newton explain it?*

Early Greek philosophers thought a rolling cart soon stops because no force is present to keep it moving. Newton said a force known as friction causes a rolling cart to stop.

object to remain at rest, or to keep moving in a straight line at constant speed, is called the **inertia** (ih-NER′-shuh) of the object.

According to Newton, a ball thrown upward comes back down because the force of gravity is acting on the ball. A rolling cart stops because of a force known as **friction.** If there were no forces on the ball and cart, they would keep moving in one direction forever.

One kind of friction acts on moving objects. It is caused by contact between the moving object and another substance. Friction always tends to slow down the moving object. For example, the wheels of a cart are in contact with the ground. Friction between the wheels and the ground makes the cart slow down.

A boat moving through the water is slowed by friction. Water is in contact with the lower part of the boat. Air is in contact with the upper part of the boat. The contacts of the boat with both the air and the water cause friction. The friction slows the boat.

Another kind of friction keeps objects from moving when they are pushed gently. Suppose you wish to move a heavy trunk across the floor. You would have to push hard to get it moving. Friction between the trunk and the floor balances your push up to a certain point. This kind of friction is called **static** (STAT′-ik) **friction.** The word *static* means *at rest.* Static

Figure 4-15. *According to Newton's first law, an unbalanced force of any size can put an object in motion. Yet, this couch is not moving. Explain why it isn't.*

Static friction between the couch and the rug is greater than the push on the couch.

Research Topic

Read about sliding friction. How does it differ from static friction? Does sliding friction depend on the speed of the moving object? What about the friction between a liquid or gas and an object moving through it?

Figure 4-16. *How do seat belts protect people against the effects of Newton's first law of motion?*

Seat belts keep people from continuing to move when a car stops suddenly. They keep people from continuing to move in a straight line when a car changes direction, for example, when it goes around a curve.

Quick Review answers:
1. The Greeks thought that an unbalanced force acting on an object keeps it in motion.
2. Newton said that an object continues to move as long as *no* unbalanced force acts on it.
3. The force of static friction between the bookcase and the floor balances your push.

Main Idea

How do Newton's first and second laws of motion differ?

friction tends to keep an object at rest. To move the trunk, you have to exert a force great enough to overcome the force of static friction.

Even if there is no static friction, some force is required to start an object moving. However, the force can be any size, even very small. Once an object is moving, if there is no friction nor any other force, the object keeps moving at the same speed in a straight line.

You have experienced the effect of Newton's first law of motion. When you are in an automobile, the force to start you moving is supplied by the engine. Once you are moving at constant speed, you keep moving. Even when the brakes are applied, you tend to keep moving forward. What keeps you from hitting the dashboard or windshield? If the braking is gentle, the friction of the car seat is enough to slow you down with the car. If the braking is sharp, only a fastened seat belt can slow you down in time.

What happens to you when the automobile turns a corner? You tend to continue moving in a straight line. A force is needed to keep you from hitting the door when the car changes direction. Again, a seat belt will keep you in place, so you will not slide across the seat.

Quick Review

1. According to early Greek philosophers, what keeps an object in motion?
2. According to Isaac Newton, what keeps an object in motion?
3. What force balances your push when you try to push a heavy bookcase?

Newton's second law of motion
New vocabulary: Newton's second law of motion, newton

Newton's first law of motion predicts what will happen to an object when no unbalanced force acts on it. His second law of motion predicts what will happen to an object when an unbalanced force does act on it.

Suppose two movers start out in an empty moving van. They drive on an expressway to reach the house whose goods they are to load. As they enter the expressway, they speed up quickly until they are at the speed limit. When they reach their exit, the van responds well to the brakes and slows quickly. The driver has no trouble steering the van around the curve of the exit ramp.

At the house, the movers load up the van. Now the van is full of furniture and appliances. The movers drive back onto the expressway. They notice it is much harder to speed up, even with the pedal pressed to the floor. It takes a longer time than before to reach the speed limit. The driver realizes that he will have to start braking for the exit earlier than before. As he steers the van around the exit curve, he has to pull harder on the steering wheel than before. The loaded van seems to be more resistant to any changes in its motion than the empty van.

The same engine speeds up the van whether it is empty or full. The same brakes slow it down. So the forces that change the speed are about the same. But with the same forces, the speed changes less quickly when the van is full than when it is empty.

Newton realized that when the force is the same size, some objects change speed more quickly than others. He said that the mass of the object made the difference. A full van has more mass than an empty van. The more mass an object has, the less quickly it changes speed under the same force.

Recall that changing speed and changing direction are signs of acceleration. An unbalanced force causes changes in speed or direction of motion; in other words, an unbalanced force causes acceleration. As the example of the moving van

■ **Safety Note**
The driver of a vehicle must be aware that when the vehicle is full, it has more inertia. A full vehicle does not respond to braking or go around curves as easily as when it is empty.

Main Idea

How did Newton explain why different objects change speed at different rates under the same size force?

Figure 4-17. *What should the driver of a fully loaded camper remember from Newton's second law?*

The camper changes speed or direction less quickly when it is fully loaded than when it is empty. The driver must brake earlier than usual and should slow down before taking a curve to make it easier to change direction.

If a taxi driver drops off four passengers and their luggage at a hotel, will the empty taxi respond to the brakes more easily or less easily than before?

More easily

illustrates, the more mass an object has, the less acceleration it has under the same force.

Newton also realized that objects of different mass can change speed equally quickly if the forces are adjusted. The object with more mass needs a greater force to change speed at the same rate. Automobiles with more mass are usually made with more powerful engines. Then they can get up to speed as quickly as smaller automobiles. Of course, they use more gasoline doing so.

When an object is changing direction, the mass makes a difference as well. More force is required to move the full van around the exit ramp curve at the same speed. If the driver had not been able to supply more force, what would have happened? The van would have changed direction less quickly. It would have moved on a wider curve and gone off the road. Automobiles with more mass are usually made with power steering. Power steering helps drivers steer around curves.

In other words, in order to produce a given acceleration, the greater the mass is, the greater the force must be. **Newton's second law of motion** summarizes how force is related to mass and acceleration. It states that when an unbalanced force F acts on an object, the acceleration a caused by the force times the mass m of the object equals the force.

$$\text{force} = \text{mass} \times \text{acceleration}$$
$$F = ma$$

Main Idea

What is Newton's second law of motion?

The SI unit of force is named after Isaac Newton. It is called the **newton** (symbol N). One newton is the amount of force required to speed up a 1-kg mass by 1 m/s every second when the force is applied in the direction of motion. (If a 1-N force is applied opposite to the direction of motion of a 1-kg object, it will slow it down by 1 m/s every second.) A 2-N force will speed up (or slow down) the same 1-kg mass by 2 m/s every second. Doubling the force doubles the acceleration. But a 2-N force will speed up (or slow down) a 2-kg mass by only 1 m/s every second. Doubling the mass cuts the acceleration in half.

The change in motion produced by a force depends on both the size and direction of the force. Pushing a bicycle in the direction it is moving will speed it up. Pushing a bicycle in a direction opposite to its direction of motion will slow it down. And pushing it from the side will make it change direction.

Sample Problem 1

An object of mass 5 kg is pushed by a force of 10 N. It starts from rest. What is its acceleration?

Solution

From Newton's second law,

$$\text{force} = \text{mass} \times \text{acceleration}$$

$$\text{acceleration} = \frac{\text{force}}{\text{mass}}$$

$$= \frac{10 \text{ N}}{5 \text{ kg}} = 2 \text{ N/kg}$$

Since 1 N is the amount of force that will accelerate a 1-kg mass by 1 m/s², then

$$1 \text{ N} = 1 \text{ kg} \times 1 \text{ m/s}^2$$

so $1 \text{ m/s}^2 = \dfrac{1 \text{ N}}{1 \text{ kg}} = 1 \text{ N/kg.}$

Thus, the units m/s² are equivalent to the units N/kg, so the acceleration of the object is 2 m/s².

Sample Problem 2

What is the speed of the object in Sample Problem 1 after 3 seconds?

Solution

The speed is increasing by 2 m/s every second. Initially, the speed is 0 m/s. After 1 s, the speed is 2 m/s; after 2 s, it is 2 m/s + 2 m/s, or 4 m/s; after 3 s, it is 4 m/s + 2 m/s, or 6 m/s.

Practice Problem

What acceleration would a 2-N force give to an object of mass 2 kg? *Answer:* 1 m/s²

Quick Review

1. How is the mass of an object related to how quickly the object can change speed or direction when a force acts on it?
2. How is the amount of force on an object related to how quickly the object can change speed or direction?
3. A force of 10 N is applied to a book of mass 2 kg. It moves across the table at constant velocity.
   a. What is the acceleration of the book?

Solution to Practice Problem:

$$\text{acceleration} = \frac{\text{force}}{\text{mass}}$$

$$= \frac{2 \text{ N}}{2 \text{ kg}}$$

$$= 1 \text{ N/kg} = 1 \text{ m/s}^2$$

Quick Review answers:

1. The more mass an object has, the less quickly it can change speed or direction when a force acts on it. It is also true that the less mass the object has, the more quickly it can change speed or direction if the same force acts on it.
2. The greater the force on an object, the more quickly the object can change speed or direction. The smaller the force on the object, the less quickly the object can change speed or direction.
3. a. Since the book moves at constant velocity, the acceleration is zero.

b. There is no unbalanced force on the book.
c. A 10-N friction force balances the force applied to the book.

b. Is there an unbalanced force on the book? If so, what is its strength?
c. What force balances the 10-N force applied to the book?

Newton's third law of motion

New vocabulary: Newton's third law of motion

Another property of forces was described by Newton. It is called **Newton's third law of motion.** Newton realized that if one object pulls on another, the second object also pulls back on the first object. If one object pushes on another, the second pushes back on the first object. In other words, for every action by a force there is a reaction by another force. Forces always come in pairs.

Try pressing your finger against your desk. The desk pushes back against your finger. The harder you press, the harder the desk presses back. The force that the desk exerts on your finger is always the same size as the force your finger exerts on the desk. Another way to state the third law of motion is that for every force, there is an equal and opposite force. The two equal and opposite forces act on different objects. The force of your finger acts on the desk. The force exerted by the desk acts on your finger.

Suppose you jump from a boat to the dock. As you jump, you push against the boat. The boat pushes back against you. The two pushes make a pair of equal and opposite forces. Your push on the boat can be thought of as the action force. It makes the boat move away from the dock. The push of the boat on you can be thought of as the reaction force. It makes you move to the dock. The two motions are the result of the two forces acting on the different objects.

When you walk or run, you make use of reaction forces. With your feet, you push backward against the ground. The ground then pushes forward on you.

A rotating water sprinkler is another example of action and reaction. Water is forced from the sprinkler. This is the action. The reaction is the movement of the sprinkler arms away from the water. You feel the same kind of reaction when you hold a water hose and turn the water on quickly. You may have seen firefighters struggling to control a fire hose. The hose is forced backward when the water leaves it. This reaction makes the hose hard to handle.

Consider the pull of gravity on you. The earth pulls downward on you with a force. According to Newton's third law,

What property of forces is described in Newton's third law of motion?

Push of foot against ground ⟷ Push of ground against foot

Movement of sprinkler arm

Movement of water

Movement of water

Movement of sprinkler arm

you pull upward on the earth with the same size force. But if you jump off a diving board, you fall to the earth. Why doesn't the earth rise toward you? The answer lies in the difference between your mass and the mass of the earth. The mass of the earth is so great that your pull on the earth produces an extremely small acceleration. The force acting on you is no greater than the force you exert on the earth. But the force acting on you acts on a much smaller mass. Therefore, your acceleration toward the earth is much greater. It is so much greater that the acceleration of the earth toward you can be ignored.

Figure 4-18. *How do runners and water sprinklers make use of Newton's third law of motion?*

The ground pushes forward on the feet of runners as their feet push backward against the ground. The arms of water sprinklers spin away from the water as the water spurts from the arms.

Pull of earth on diver

Pull of diver on earth

Figure 4-19. *Why doesn't the diver's pull on the earth make the earth move upward?*

The earth's mass is so great that the acceleration due to the diver's pull on the earth is too small to be detected.

4.2a Action and Reaction

Science processes: Predicting, measuring, inferring

Materials   20 minutes   Student demonstration

- **2 skateboards**
- **3-m rope with knot in center**
- **masking tape**
- **meter stick or tape measure**

Purpose

To show that for an action force, there is an equal and opposite reaction force.

Procedure

1. Have two students of equal or approximately equal mass stand on skateboards. The skateboards should be pointing straight at one another. Designate one student as Student A and the other as Student B.

2. Give the students on skateboards a rope with a knot in the center. Have them move apart so that the rope is fully extended. Have a third person stand halfway between the two (beside the knot) to mark the middle.

3. Predict the point at which the two skateboards will meet when Student B pulls on the rope.

4. Use masking tape to mark the starting points of Students A and B.

5. Have Student B pull on the rope. Measure and record how far each student moves.

6. Return the skateboards to the starting points used in Step 4. Predict the point at which the two skateboards will meet when Student A pulls on the rope.

7. Have Student A pull on the rope. Measure and record how far each student moves.

8. Repeat Steps 1 through 7 with two students with very different masses. (Ideally, one student should weigh twice as much as the other.)

Questions

1. Was the direction of motion of Student A opposite to the direction of motion of Student B in all trials?

2. How did the distance moved by Student A compare to the distance moved by Student B:
   a. when Students A and B had similar masses?
   b. when Students A and B had different masses?

3. If you had only seen their starting and ending positions, could you have told which student did the pulling? Explain.

4. Are your answers to questions 1, 2, and 3 what you would expect if the forces on Students A and B are opposite in direction and equal in magnitude?

Conclusion

How did the size and direction of the reaction force compare to the size and direction of the action force?

Step 5

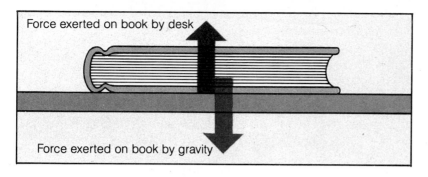

Force exerted on book by desk

Force exerted on book by gravity

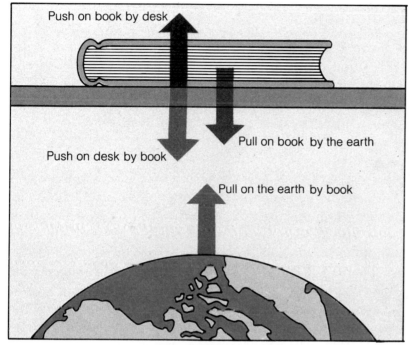

Push on book by desk

Push on desk by book

Pull on book by the earth

Pull on the earth by book

Figure 4-20. *Which pairs of forces are balanced forces? Which pairs are action and reaction forces?*

The upper drawing shows balanced forces. Both forces act on the same object—the book.

The lower drawing shows two pairs of action and reaction forces. The book and the desk push on each other. The book and the earth pull on each other.

Action and reaction forces always act on *different* objects. They should not be confused with two balanced forces that act on the *same* object. For example, a book lying on a desk is acted on by the force of gravity. This force pulls downward. The desk exerts an equal but upward force on the book. The pull by the earth and push by the desk are equal and opposite forces. These are balanced forces. They both act on the same object—the book.

Where, then, are the action and reaction forces? The force of gravity pulls the book downward. The reaction to the earth's pull is the upward pull of the book *on the earth.* These forces are equal and opposite. And they act on different objects.

Another action force is the downward push of the book on the desk. The reaction force is the upward push of the desk

Main Idea

Can a pair of action and reaction forces act on the same object?

on the book. These two forces are equal and opposite. Again, they act on different objects.

Quick Review

1. If you push against a swinging door, what is the equal and opposite reaction force?
2. Explain the difference between a pair of balanced forces and a pair of action and reaction forces.

Momentum

New vocabulary: momentum, conservation of momentum

A moving object has a property called **momentum** (mō-MEN'-tum), which is related to both its mass and its speed. The greater the mass or the speed, the greater the momentum. The amount of momentum of a moving object is equal to the mass of the object multiplied by its speed.

$$\text{momentum} = \text{mass} \times \text{speed}$$

If the speed of the object changes, so does the momentum.

In a collision, momentum is transferred from one object to another. Suppose you roll a bowling ball directly toward a second bowling ball. When they collide, the first one will stop, and the second one will move off at the same speed that the first one had. The total amount of momentum remains the same. This idea is called **conservation of momentum.**

There is conservation of momentum whenever objects interact through forces. Momentum depends on the direction of motion as well as on the mass and speed. If the objects are moving in different directions, the directions must be taken into account.

Consider the simple case of an adult and a child on roller skates. Suppose they face each other and push each other away. Each will move backwards, so they will move in opposite directions. Before the push, neither one had momentum. According to conservation of momentum, the momentum of the child must be equal in size and opposite in direction to the momentum of the adult. If the child has less mass than the adult, the child will have a greater speed.

Conservation of momentum is related to Newton's third law of motion. However, there is an advantage in looking at an interaction from a momentum point of view. You don't have to know the strength of the forces or how long they acted. It is much easier to measure masses, speeds, and directions of motion.

Main Idea

Under what conditions is there conservation of momentum?

Quick Review

1. How is the momentum of an object related to the mass and speed of the object?
2. What is meant by conservation of momentum?

Curved Motion

New vocabulary: centripetal force

The only motion with no change in direction is motion in a straight line. Thus, if an object is moving in a curve, it is changing direction all the time. Change of direction is a sign of acceleration. Therefore, a force must be acting on the object to make it keep changing direction (Newton's second law).

The force that makes any object move in a curve is always directed toward the center of the curve. Such a force is called a **centripetal** (sen-TRIH'-pet-ul) **force**. The word *centripetal* means "center-seeking."

You experience centripetal force every time you round a sharp curve in a car. Your body has inertia—a tendency to keep going in the direction in which it had been moving. The seat belt pushes you *toward the center of the curve* to keep you moving with the car as it rounds the curve.

Figure 4-21. *When the adult and child push each other away, the child moves faster than the adult. Why?*

The mass times the speed is the same for the child as for the adult, so smaller mass results in greater speed.

Quick Review answers:

1. The momentum equals the mass times the speed.
2. Conservation of momentum is the idea that the total amount of momentum remains the same during an interaction.

Figure 4-22. *When an object moves in a curve, a centripetal force acts on it. Is the centripetal force toward or away from the center of the curve?*

Toward the center of the circle.

Figure 4-23. *Which object has the greatest weight?*

You may feel as though there is also a force pushing you outward, away from the center of the curve. However, there is no outward force on you. Your body keeps moving in a straight line (Newton's first law), even though the car is turning, until you are pushing against the seat belt. Then the seat belt pushes back on you (Newton's third law); this push is inward, toward the center of the curve.

Quick Review

1. When you go around a curve in a car, in what direction does the seat belt push you?
2. Explain the feeling that you are being pushed outward by a force when you go around a curve.

The law of gravitation
New vocabulary: weight

All objects on or near the earth are pulled toward the earth by gravity. Gravity pulls harder on some objects than others. You can see this by hanging different objects from a spring. The pull of gravity makes some objects stretch the spring more than others. The pull of gravity on an object has a special name. It is called the **weight** of the object. Weight, like any other force, is measured in newtons. The heavier an object feels, the harder the earth is pulling on it. In other words, the greater is its weight.

During Newton's time, it was known that gravity makes objects fall toward the earth. But Newton was the first to realize that the earth pulls on the moon as well as on nearby objects. Newton proposed that the moon moves around the earth because the earth is pulling on it. He also proposed that the sun has its own pull of gravity. The sun pulls on the earth, moon, and all the planets. The sun's gravity, he said, is what causes the planets to move in curved paths around the sun. Otherwise, according to Newton's first law, the planets would move in straight lines at constant speed. They would leave the sun and never come near it again.

Newton summarized his conclusion in his law of gravitation. He said that there is a pull of gravity between every two objects in the universe. The size of the pull depends on the mass of each object. The greater the masses are, the greater the pull. The pull is extremely small unless one of the masses is very great. The pull of gravity between two buildings is too small to be measured. But the pull of gravity between one building and the earth can be measured.

Newton predicted that objects on the moon would have weight because the moon would pull on them. But because the mass of the moon is less than that of the earth, the weight of the objects would be less. Sure enough, the astronauts who visited the moon were much lighter there. They weighed only one sixth as much as they did on earth. They found they could jump much higher than on earth.

Newton studied measurements that had been made on the paths of the moon and other planets. He figured out how much force was needed to keep these bodies moving in their curved paths instead of straight lines. He found that the pull of gravity between two objects is weaker the farther apart

Main Idea

What did Newton predict about the weight of objects on the moon?

Additional information:
The force of gravity decreases as the *square* of the distance increases. Although the earth has 81 times the mass of the moon, the distance between its surface and its center is 3.7 times greater than for the moon. The ratio of a person's earth weight to moon weight is $81/(3.7)^2$, or about 6 to 1.

Our Science Heritage

Isaac Newton

Isaac Newton (1642–1727) made many important contributions to both mathematics and science. After receiving his degree from Cambridge University, England, he spent the next 18 months at home, working by himself. In those 18 months, he made discoveries about light and color, calculus, gravity, and motion. He returned to Cambridge and joined the faculty.

Newton did not publish his discoveries for a long time. As a result, he did not clearly establish that he was the first person to make them. He carried on quarrels with others who arrived at the same results independently of him as to who should have the credit.

Robert Hooke (1635–1703), for example, believed he should share in the recognition that Newton received for stating the law of gravitation. He had come to some of the same conclusions by himself before Newton published his ideas. Newton, however, had a more complete description and had shown that his theory agreed with observations of the planets' motions.

Newton was so upset by his quarrels with Hooke that he did not publish his book about light until after Hooke had died. This work showed that he was as good in the laboratory as he was at theoretical explanations.

While Newton was unwilling to share the credit for things he had done by himself, he realized his dependence on the work of others. In a letter, he repeated a saying of the time, "If I have seen further than other men, it is by standing on the shoulders of giants."

Figure 4-24. *On Jupiter, you would weigh two and a half times what you weigh on earth. Would your mass be the same as on earth?* Yes.

they are. The pull of gravity depends on the distance between the centers of the objects as well as on their masses. Doubling the distance makes the pull only one fourth as strong.

Even on the earth, the weight of an object is slightly less on a mountaintop than at sea level. When space vehicles move away from the earth, they lose weight the farther out they go. When the astronauts were on the moon, the moon's pull on them was much stronger than the earth's pull. Yet the earth has more mass than the moon. Can you explain how the moon had a stronger pull on them?

Quick Review

1. How are the masses of two objects related to the size of the pull of gravity between them?
2. How is the distance between the centers of two objects related to the size of the pull of gravity between them?

Weight and mass

In everyday speech, the word *weight* is commonly used instead of *mass*. Many people think they mean the same thing. It is true that on earth if one object has more mass than another, it also weighs more. The object with more mass feels heavier. That is, the earth is pulling harder on it—it has more weight.

But mass and weight are not the same thing. The mass of an object is a property of the object. An object has the same mass on earth as on the moon or in outer space. It does not matter whether another object is pulling on it because of gravity.

Weight, on the other hand, is a force. The SI unit of force is the newton, so weight is measured in newtons in SI. Weight depends on the mass of the object as well as on what is pulling on the object. On earth, everything is being pulled by the same object—the earth. And everything on the surface of the earth is about the same distance from the center of the earth. So differences in weight depend only on differences in mass.

But weight is not a property of an object. The weight depends on where the object is. For example, an object of mass 1 kg has a weight of about 10 N on earth. On the moon, that same object would still have a mass of 1 kg. But its weight would be less than 2 N. And on Jupiter, the planet with the greatest mass, the same object would weigh 26 N.

Figure 4-25. *Why is "newton-burger" a good name for this hamburger?*

An object of mass 1 kg has a weight of 10 N (see text on facing page). An object with one tenth the weight (1 N) has one tenth the mass (0.1 kg). This is about the mass of a "quarter-pound" hamburger. Thus, this hamburger has a weight of about a newton, so it can be thought of as a "newtonburger."

Quick Review

Explain why weight is not considered to be a property of an object.

Quick Review answer:
The properties of an object cannot change with the location of the object. Because the weight of an object depends on where the object is, weight is not a property.

Motion under gravity

New vocabulary: escape speed

Every object on earth is pulled downward by gravity. When an object moves, the pull of gravity usually affects its motion.

Galileo (1564–1642) studied the motion of objects falling toward the earth. He did not have instruments that could measure the speeds of objects falling straight down. The travel times were too short for him to measure. So he thought of a way to slow the motion. He had balls of different mass roll down ramps. On a ramp, part of the force of gravity is balanced by the upward push of the ramp. Only the remaining part of the force accelerates the balls. Since the balls move more slowly, it is easier to measure travel times.

Galileo did many experiments with balls on ramps. He concluded that objects of different mass accelerate under the earth's pull of gravity at the same rate. You may be puzzled by this conclusion. After all, if you drop a feather and a coin at the same time, the coin will reach the ground first. But when objects fall downward through the air, gravity is not the only force acting. The air produces a friction force that pushes upward against falling objects. The friction force is greater on a feather than on a coin. As a result, the coin accelerates more than the feather. To show that gravity accelerates all objects equally, you must drop them where there is no air. A glass tube with most of the air removed from it can be used. A similar demonstration was performed on the moon by

Data Search

The pull of gravity at the surface of other planets in the solar system can be compared to that on the earth. On which planets besides Jupiter would you weigh more than you do on earth? Search pages 658–661.

Saturn, Neptune, and Uranus

4.2b Motion Down a Ramp

Science processes: Predicting, observing, inferring

Materials   20 to 30 minutes   Groups of 2 to 4

- 2 long, metal or wood, grooved ramps of equal length, with a metal stop at one end
- ruler
- steel ball and aluminum ball of same diameter but different mass
- 2 books or blocks of wood

Purpose

To determine whether the mass of a ball affects the length of time it takes to roll down a ramp.

Procedure

1. Set up two ramps side by side. Raise one end of each of the ramps slightly. Support the raised end with a book or block of wood. The angle of the ramps must be the same— about 5° from the horizontal.
2. Examine a steel ball and an aluminum ball of the same size. Identify the one with more mass.
3. Predict which ball will take less time to roll down one of the ramps. Record your prediction.
4. Make a data table like the one shown.

5. Place one ball at the top of each ramp. Hold the balls with a ruler.
6. Release the balls at the same time by quickly raising the ruler. Listen for the sound of the metal balls striking the stop. Record your results.
7. Make at least two more trials. Record your results.
8. Reverse the balls used on each of the ramps. Make at least three more trials. Record your results.

Questions

1. Which ball has more mass?
2. Does one ball consistently reach the end of the ramp before the other one?
3. What sources of error might make the results of these tests uncertain?

Conclusion

How does the mass of a ball affect the length of time it takes to roll down a ramp?

Setup	Trial	Which hits first?
Steel ball on ramp A and aluminum ball on ramp B	1	
	2	
	3	
Aluminum ball on ramp A and steel ball on ramp B	1	
	2	
	3	

the astronauts. A hammer and feather were dropped at the same time. The moon's gravity was the only force acting, as the moon has no air. Both objects hit the surface of the moon at the same instant.

On the moon, the hammer and feather accelerated together. But they did not accelerate as much as they would have on earth (in a tube with no air). Acceleration due to gravity does not depend on the mass of the falling object. But it does depend on two other factors. One is the mass of the large object pulling on the falling object. The moon's mass is much less than the earth's mass. The second factor is the distance from the falling object to the center of the pulling object. The moon is smaller than the earth, so its center is closer to its surface. The effect of the smaller distance partly cancels out the effect of the smaller mass. Still, the acceleration due to gravity on the moon is only about one sixth what it is on earth. To our eyes, objects on the moon would accelerate so slowly they would seem to float down to the surface.

Suppose a baseball is thrown straight upward. As it leaves the thrower's hand, it has a certain speed. As soon as the ball is released, gravity starts slowing it down. The ball moves upward more and more slowly. The speed of the ball is eventually reduced to zero. The ball has stopped moving upward. The ball then starts to fall back down. It accelerates toward the earth. The ball speeds up until it is moving as fast as it was when leaving the hand.

Figure 4-26. *Do objects of different mass accelerate at the same rate?*

When two objects fall in air, the air produces a friction force that pushes upward on the falling objects. The greater the friction force on an object is, the more slowly the object accelerates.

However, when there is no air, as on the moon, all objects accelerate at the same rate.

Main Idea

On what two factors does the acceleration due to gravity depend?

Critical Thinking

When a baseball is thrown upward and falls down, at what point(s) in its path is its acceleration zero?

The acceleration of the baseball due to gravity is never zero the whole time the ball is in the air. You know that the ball is always accelerating because its speed is continually changing.

If the ball had been moving faster at the beginning, it could have risen higher before falling back down. The faster it starts out, the higher it can go. If the ball can start upward with enough speed, it can keep moving upward from the earth forever. At a speed of about 40 000 km/h, an object can escape from the earth's gravity. This speed is the **escape speed** for the earth's gravity.

If an object on the earth is allowed to fall, it will accelerate at about 10 m/s^2. This acceleration due to gravity is denoted by the letter g.

$$g = 10 \text{ m/s}^2 \text{ (approximately)}$$

The force on a falling object, by Newton's second law, is

$$\text{force} = \text{mass} \times \text{acceleration}$$
$$= mg$$

Now, the force on a falling object is the weight of the object—the pull due to gravity. Therefore,

$$\text{force} = \text{weight} = mg$$

Recall that the units m/s^2 are equivalent to the units N/kg. Thus, g can be written in either units.

$$g = 10 \text{ m/s}^2 = 10 \text{ N/kg}$$

Sample Problem

What is the weight in newtons of a person of mass 60 kg?

Solution

To find the weight, multiply the mass by g.

$$\text{weight} = mg$$
$$= 60 \text{ kg} \times 10 \, \frac{\text{N}}{\text{kg}}$$
$$= 600 \text{ N}$$

Practice Problem

What is the weight in newtons of a child of mass 13 kg? *Answer:* 130 N

Solution to Practice Problem:

weight = mg

$$= 13 \text{ kg} \times 10 \, \frac{\text{N}}{\text{kg}}$$

$$= 130 \text{ N}$$

Quick Review answers:
1. A ramp slowed the motion of falling objects enough for Galileo to be able to measure their travel time.
2. The two forces on falling objects are the earth's pull of gravity and the friction force produced by the air.

Quick Review

1. How did the use of a ramp help Galileo study falling objects?
2. What two forces act on objects that fall to the ground?

3. Under what condition could something leave the earth's surface and keep moving forever?

Curved motion under gravity

Suppose an object is thrown horizontally. What path will it follow? The earth's gravity pulls the object toward the earth. The object will be accelerated toward the ground. However, it will continue to move horizontally. Its path will curve.

Does horizontal motion affect the time for a thrown object to hit the ground? Suppose three balls are released at the same time from the same height above ground. The first is simply dropped. The second is thrown horizontally at 10 m/s. The third is thrown horizontally at 20 m/s. If friction of the air does not slow down the balls, all three should hit the

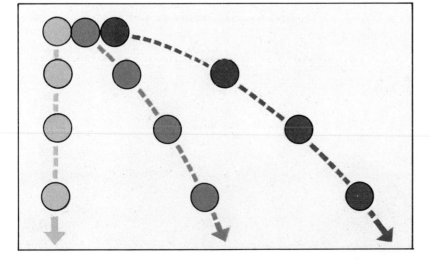

3. If the object is moving at least 40 000 km/h when it is near the earth's surface, it can escape from the earth's gravity. However, it will still be affected by the sun's gravity. It will move forever, but in a closed path around the sun, like a planet or comet.

Figure 4-27. *(Top) A ball thrown horizontally moves downward while continuing to move horizontally. (Bottom) Which ball will reach the ground first?*
All balls should reach the ground at the same time. This is because horizontal motion does not affect vertical acceleration.

Have the students place a ruler under each set of positions for the three balls. As the balls fall, their vertical positions remain the same for all three.

Teaching suggestion:
Point out to the students that Figures 4-27 and 4-28 show several positions of a ball as it moves. The positions are shown at equal time intervals.

Ask: How can you tell when the ball is moving fastest? (The positions are farthest apart.)

4.2c Falling Coins

Science processes: Observing, inferring, controlling variables

Materials   BASIC   15 minutes   Groups of 2 to 4

- **3 coins (same kind)**
- **metric ruler**

Purpose

To determine whether objects with different horizontal speeds fall at different rates.

Procedure

1. Arrange three coins along the edge of a desk or table. The edge of each coin should be at the edge of the table.
2. Place a ruler behind the coins as shown. Move the coins so that they are at the 5-cm, 15-cm, and 25-cm marks of the ruler.
3. Hold one end of the ruler firmly against the table. Swing the other end of the ruler away from the coins. Rapidly reverse the motion, letting the ruler strike the coins.
4. After the coins land on the floor, note whether they are the same horizontal distance from the table edge. If they are not, note which one is farthest away from the table edge.
5. Repeat the trial. This time, listen carefully to the coins striking the floor, and note whether they strike it simultaneously.

Questions

1. Did all coins travel the same horizontal distance?
2. Did all of the coins have the same horizontal speed? Explain how you could tell.
3. Did all of the coins reach the floor at the same time? Explain how you could tell.
4. Did all of the coins have the same downward acceleration? Explain how you could tell.

Conclusion

What can you conclude about the relation between horizontal speed and acceleration downward due to gravity?

Step 2

Step 3

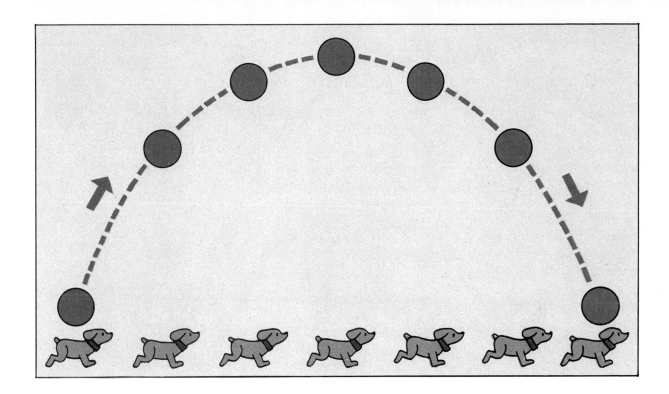

ground at the same time. The horizontal motion does not affect the vertical acceleration. The balls accelerate toward the ground under the pull of gravity in the same way. They travel the same vertical distance in the same time.

Suppose you throw a ball upward at an angle. What will its motion be after you release it? The easiest way to think about the motion is to separate it into two parts. There is a horizontal part that does not change. The ball moves horizontally at constant speed. At the same time, there is a vertical part of the motion. The ball starts out moving upward. Gravity slows down the upward motion. The ball goes to a certain height and then falls. Gravity speeds it up as it falls. It hits the ground some distance away from you.

The path of motion is an arch-shaped curve known as a parabola. The ball slows down on the upward portion and speeds up on the downward portion. But it moves the same horizontal distance each second. A dog racing under the ball would have to travel at constant speed to keep the ball directly overhead.

Figure 4-28. *Even though the speed of a thrown ball changes, it moves the same horizontal distance in equal lengths of time.*

Main Idea

What shape is the path of a ball that is thrown upward at an angle?

Quick Review

What effect does horizontal motion have on the time it takes an object to fall to the ground?

Quick Review answer:
Horizontal motion has no effect on the time it takes an object to fall to the ground.

4.2 Section Review

Answers to Understanding the Concepts and Solutions to Problems to Solve appear on page T87 in the front of this book. Blackline master test for this section: Section Testsheet 4-2 (TRB page 210)

Vocabulary

4 balanced force
9 centripetal force
11 conservation of momentum
5 escape speed
6 force
3 friction
8 inertia
10 momentum
1 newton
13 Newton's first law of motion
12 Newton's second law of motion
14 Newton's third law of motion
7 static friction
2 weight

Vocabulary Review

Match each term above with the numbered phrase that best describes it.

1. Unit of force
2. Depends on both the mass and the location of an object
3. Always acts to slow down motion
4. Causes no change in speed or direction
5. Enables object to keep moving away from the earth
6. Causes greater change in motion of objects of less mass
7. Prevents object from moving when weak force is acting on it
8. Tendency for motion not to change
9. Acts toward center of a curve
10. Depends on both the mass and the speed
11. Idea that momentum does not change
12. Statement that force is proportional to acceleration
13. Statement that motion does not change unless unbalanced force acts
14. Statement that forces act in pairs

Review Questions

Multiple Choice: Choose the answer that best completes each of the following sentences.

15. A change in the motion of an object is evidence that _?_.
    a. the forces on the object are balanced
    b. an unbalanced force is acting on the object
    c. no forces are acting on the object
    d. Newton's law about equal and opposite forces is correct
16. A force that exists because of the motion of matter through or against other matter is _?_.
    a. weight
    b. gravity
    c. mass
    d. friction
17. The pairs of forces referred to in Newton's third law are equal in strength and opposite in direction and _?_.
    a. act on different objects
    b. are balanced forces
    c. produce no motion
    d. act independently of one another
18. The mass of an object is _?_.
    a. greater at sea level than on a mountaintop
    b. greater on Jupiter than on earth
    c. smaller the farther the object is from the earth
    d. the same everywhere
19. Weight and mass _?_.
    a. are the same only on earth
    b. are never the same
    c. are both properties of an object
    d. both depend on where an object is
20. When an object is falling to the ground, _?_.
    a. it has no mass
    b. it has no weight
    c. no forces are acting on it
    d. its weight causes it to accelerate

Understanding the Concepts

21. The sun has a much greater mass than the earth does. Explain how the earth can have a stronger pull of gravity on you than the sun does.
22. Explain the observation that a hammer and a feather fall at the same rate on the moon but at different rates on earth.

Problems to Solve

23. What acceleration would a 3-N force give to an object of mass 6 kg? 0.5 m/s^2
24. What is the weight in newtons of a 6-kg object? 60 N

For ideas for classroom demonstration and discussion, see Getting Started on page T88 in the front of this book.

4.3 Energy

Supplemental materials: Teaching Diagrams 4-3A, 4-3B (TRB pages 22, 23), Reading Checksheet 4-3 (TRB page 91), Skillsheet 4-3 (TRB page 137), Investigation 4-3 (Lab Manual pages 59–60)

Section Preview

- **Kinetic energy**
- **Potential energy**
- **Energy conversion**
- **Friction and mechanical energy**
- **Einstein's theory of relativity**

Bracketed numbers are Section Review numbers correlated to that objective.

Learning Objectives

1. To relate the kinetic energy of an object to its mass and speed. [3, 4, 11, 13]
2. To relate the potential energy of an object to the position of the object. [2, 5, 8, 9, 13]
3. To describe changes in the kinetic energy and potential energy of an object as it changes position. [1, 5, 10, 12, 14]
4. To associate increases in the temperature of moving objects with the presence of friction. [1, 15]

Figure 4-29. *When the red ball hits the stationary yellow ball, energy of motion is transferred to both the yellow and black balls.*

One way to analyze motion is to study the forces acting and use Newton's laws to examine the consequences of those forces. This section introduces another viewpoint which can be used to analyze motion without talking about the forces.

Kinetic energy

New vocabulary: energy, kinetic energy

Forces can set objects in motion. Objects in motion can cause changes. For example, suppose you throw a baseball. The force you exert on the ball causes the ball to move. The moving ball can break a window, dent a car, or cause other things to move. In other words, it has the ability to cause change. The ability of an object to cause change is referred to as its **energy.** The energy of an object in motion is called **kinetic** (kih-NET'-ik) **energy.** The word *kinetic* comes from the Greek word for *moving*.

The more force you use on a baseball before it leaves your hand, the faster it moves. The faster the ball moves, the

Main Idea

What is energy?

4.3a Kinetic Energy

Science processes: Collecting data, inferring, controlling variables

Materials   20 to 30 minutes   Groups of 2 to 4

- 2 identical grooved ramps or grooved rulers
- book
- 2 steel balls with different masses

- 2 identical, small cardboard boxes (approximately 5 cm on a side) with one end open
- meter stick or ruler

Purpose

To determine whether the kinetic energy of a moving object depends on its mass.

Procedure

1. Place two ramps side by side, about 15 cm apart.
2. Raise them at one end by placing a book under them. Make sure the ramps are both raised at the same angle.
3. Place a box at the lower end of each ramp so that the open end of each box can catch a ball as it leaves the ramp.
4. Make a data table like the one shown.
5. Place a ruler or meter stick across the ramps near their upper ends. Then place a ball on each ramp, just above the ruler.
6. Quickly lift the ruler to release the two balls at the same time. The balls should have the same speed when they strike the boxes.

7. Measure and record the distance each box moved.
8. Return the boxes to their original positions at the base of the ramps. Repeat Steps 5, 6, and 7 at least two more times.
9. Total the distances the lighter ball moved the box it hit. Divide your answer by the number of trials to get the average distance the box was moved. Repeat these calculations for the other box.

Questions

1. What happened to the kinetic energy of the balls?
2. What was the average distance the lighter ball moved its box?
3. What was the average distance the heavier ball moved its box?
4. Did the two balls have the same kinetic energy? Explain how you can tell.
5. Did both balls have the same speed when they hit the boxes? Explain how you can tell.

Conclusion

Does the kinetic energy of a moving object depend on its mass?

Step 5

	Distance Box Moved When Hit	
	By lighter ball	By heavier ball
Trial 1		
Trial 2		
Trial 3		
Total		
Average Distance		

Before collision

Collision

After collision

greater the kinetic energy of the baseball. The greater the speed of a moving object is, the greater the kinetic energy.

Suppose a golf ball and baseball are traveling at the same speed. If both hit the same thing, the golf ball will do less damage. The kinetic energy of the golf ball is less than the kinetic energy of the baseball. The greater the mass of a moving object is, the greater the kinetic energy.

The kinetic energy of a moving object is equal to one half the mass times the square of the speed.

$$\text{kinetic energy} = \tfrac{1}{2} (\text{mass}) \times (\text{speed})^2$$

In symbols,

$$\text{K.E.} = \tfrac{1}{2}mv^2.$$

The kinetic energy of a moving object can be transferred to another object. Suppose a ball is rolling on a table. The ball strikes a similar ball head-on. The second ball is set into motion, while the first ball stops. The kinetic energy of the first ball has been transferred to the second ball.

All moving objects have kinetic energy. Objects that are not moving have no kinetic energy. If the speed of something changes, its kinetic energy changes. For example, suppose you start riding your bicycle at the top of a hill. While the bike is not moving, your kinetic energy is zero. You jump on the bike and start down the hill. Your speed increases rapidly. At the bottom of the hill, you may be traveling at 50 km/h. Your kinetic energy has increased.

Quick Review

1. What is the relation between the speed of a moving object and its kinetic energy?
2. What is the relation between the mass of a moving object and its kinetic energy?

Figure 4-30. *Can kinetic energy be transferred from one object to another object?*

Yes. In the illustration, the blue ball is transferring its energy to the red ball.

Quick Review answers:
1. As the speed of a moving object increases, its kinetic energy increases. As its speed decreases, its kinetic energy decreases.
2. The greater the mass of a moving object is, the greater its kinetic energy is. The less the mass of a moving object is, the less its kinetic energy is.

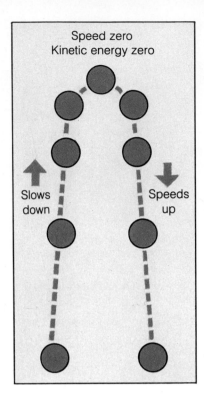

Speed zero
Kinetic energy zero

Slows
down

Speeds
up

Figure 4-31. *When is the ball losing kinetic energy? When is it gaining kinetic energy?*

The ball is losing kinetic energy as it moves upward. It is gaining kinetic energy as it moves downward.

Remind the students that the illustration shows a single ball in different positions at equal time intervals. The positions are closest together where the ball moves most slowly.

Main Idea

Why can potential energy be thought of as stored energy?

Potential energy

New vocabulary: potential energy, gravitational potential energy

Suppose you toss a baseball straight up. The ball soon stops going up and falls back toward the ground. You catch it at the same height as you release it.

While the ball is moving upward, the earth's pull of gravity is making it slow down. If there were no pull of gravity, it could keep going at constant speed. Because of gravity, the ball can go only so high and then come down. When the ball reaches the highest point, it is no longer moving upward. Its speed is zero. It has no kinetic energy. In moving upward, the ball uses up its kinetic energy. Its original kinetic energy has allowed it to move farther from the earth. As the ball starts back downward, the pull of gravity makes it speed up. Its kinetic energy increases. Just before you catch it, it is going about as fast as it was when you first threw it. So its kinetic energy is about the same now as it was then.

When the ball is at its highest point, it has no kinetic energy. Yet, it can still cause damage to something below by falling on it. It still has the ability to cause change. That is, it still has energy. But now the energy is due to its position above the ground, not its motion. The ability of an object to cause change due to its position is called **potential** (pu-TEN′-shul) **energy.**

If a coin is pushed over the edge of a table, it will fall to the ground. As it falls, it has kinetic energy. Where does the kinetic energy come from? When the coin was on the table, it had potential energy because it was above the ground. It had the ability to fall to a lower position. As the coin fell, the potential energy changed into kinetic energy.

Hold a rubber band loosely between your hands. If you let go of one end, you feel nothing. But now stretch the rubber band. If you again let go of one end, your other hand will be stung by the snap. Where did the rubber band get the energy to sting you? When you stretched the rubber band, you changed the position of its ends. You gave the rubber band potential energy. Then it was able to sting your hand.

You can think of potential energy as stored energy. It is energy that can be used to do something. It is stored up, ready to make something move or cause some other change. It exists even when nothing is happening.

You give something potential energy whenever you push it farther apart from something that is pulling on it. The earth's pull of gravity pulls everything downward. If you lift something, you are pushing it farther from the earth. Similarly, when you stretch a rubber band, you push its ends farther apart. But the rubber band is pulling the ends together. So stretching the rubber band gives it potential energy. On the other hand, sliding a book across a table does not change its potential energy. Even though its position has changed, the book is no closer or farther from the earth.

Suppose you were putting a book into a bookcase. Another book falls out and hits your foot. Which would hurt more—a paperback or a large dictionary? The dictionary would; it has more mass. Even though it is just as high on the shelf as a paperback, it has a greater ability to hurt your foot. It has more potential energy because of its greater mass.

Do you think it would make a difference whether the book was on the top shelf or the bottom shelf? A book falling from the top shelf has a greater ability to hurt your foot. It has more potential energy because it is farther above the ground.

In general, the potential energy increases when an object is pushed farther away from the object pulling on it. The higher an object is above the earth, the greater its potential energy. And the potential energy, like the kinetic energy, is greater for objects of greater mass.

The potential energy an object has because of its position above the ground is called *gravitational potential energy*. The gravitational potential energy of an object is equal to the gravitational force on the object times its height above the ground.

gravitational potential energy = gravitational force × height

Quick Review answers:
1. To give something potential energy, push it away from whatever is pulling on it.
2. No, there is no change in potential energy unless the object is moved closer to or farther from whatever is pulling on it.

Figure 4-33. *Where does a pendulum have the most potential energy? Kinetic energy?*
The pendulum has the most potential energy at each end of its swing. It has the most kinetic energy at the bottom of its swing.

As the pendulum moves downward, potential energy is converted into kinetic energy. As the pendulum swings upward, kinetic energy is converted into potential energy.

Recall from the last section that the gravitational force on an object equals its weight, which is equal to its mass times g, the acceleration due to gravity. Thus,

gravitational potential energy = mass $\times$ g $\times$ height

In symbols,

$$P.E. = mgh.$$

Quick Review

1. How can you give something potential energy?
2. Does a change in position always cause a change in potential energy? Explain.

Energy conversion

New vocabulary: energy conversion

As a ball falls, its potential energy decreases. The closer it gets to the ground, the less potential energy it has. At the same time, it is speeding up. Its kinetic energy is increasing. Potential energy is being converted, or changed, into kinetic energy.

When a ball is thrown upward, its potential energy increases. Its speed and its kinetic energy decrease. Kinetic energy is being converted into potential energy.

The change of energy from one form to another is called **energy conversion** (kun-VER′-zhun). Any change from kinetic to potential or potential to kinetic is energy conversion. When anything falls, energy is converted from potential to kinetic. For example, at the top of a waterfall, water usually moves slowly. It has little kinetic energy. As it goes over the fall, potential energy is converted to kinetic energy. At the bottom of the fall, the water has more kinetic energy. It is moving much faster.

When a pendulum swings back and forth, energy is continually being converted. At the end of each swing, the pendulum reverses direction. Like a ball thrown up in the air, it stops for an instant and then moves the other way. At the end of a swing, the pendulum has no kinetic energy. But it has potential energy because it is higher up than at the bottom of the swing. What energy conversion takes place as the pendulum moves downward? What energy conversion takes place as it keeps moving and swings upward?

When you stretch a rubber band or spring and then let go, energy conversion takes place. The potential energy of the rubber band or spring is converted into kinetic energy. An

4.3b Energy of a Pendulum

Science processes: Observing, predicting, inferring

Materials

- string, about 1 m
- lead ball with hole
- 2 or 3 books
- masking tape
- small wood block
- metric ruler or meter stick

Purpose

To determine when a pendulum has the most kinetic energy and when it has the most potential energy.

Procedure

1. Make a pendulum by tying one end of a piece of string to a lead ball with a hole in it.

Step 4

BASIC   20 to 30 minutes   Groups of 4 or teacher demonstration

2. Hang the pendulum over the edge of a desk or table so that it just clears a book placed on the floor.
3. Tape the upper end of the string to the side of the desk so that the pendulum can swing freely. Swing the pendulum to be sure that it does not touch the book.
4. Place a block on the book under the pendulum. The pendulum should hit the block at the bottom of its first swing.
5. Keeping the string taut, release the pendulum from a point 30 cm above the floor. observe what happens when it hits the block.
6. Predict in what part of the swing the pendulum has the most kinetic energy.
7. To test your prediction, move the book and block closer to the release point of the pendulum. If necessary, raise the block by adding another book to the first. Release the pendulum and observe what happens to the block. Use the same release point you used in Step 5.

Questions

1. What happens to the block of wood when it is hit by the pendulum?
2. What kind of energy does the pendulum give to the block?
3. Where in the swing does the pendulum move the block the farthest?
4. During what part of the swing does the pendulum have the least potential energy? Explain how you know.
5. During what part of the swing is the pendulum highest above the ground?

Conclusion

1. Where is the kinetic energy of the pendulum greatest? Explain how you know.
2. Where is the potential energy of the pendulum greatest? Explain how you know.

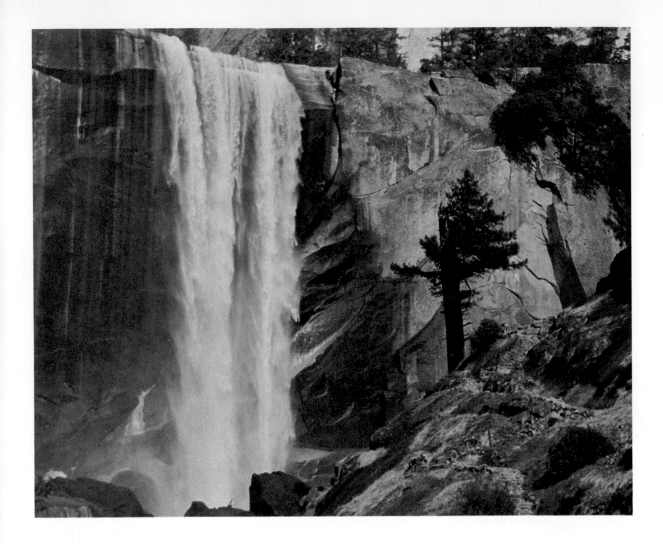

Figure 4-34. *Identify the energy conversion that takes place in a waterfall.*

Potential energy is being converted into kinetic energy as the water falls from the top to the bottom of the waterfall.

Quick Review answers:
1. Answers will vary. When a ball moves upward, its kinetic energy is converted into potential energy.
2. Answers will vary. While an apple is falling from a tree to the ground, potential energy is being converted into kinetic energy.

archer has to stretch the bow to put the arrow in it. When the archer lets go, the potential energy of the bow is converted into kinetic energy for the arrow.

Quick Review
1. Give an example of a conversion from kinetic energy to potential energy.
2. Give an example of a conversion from potential energy to kinetic energy.

Friction and mechanical energy
New vocabulary: mechanical energy

Kinetic energy and potential energy are the two forms of what is called *mechanical energy.* Mechanical energy is energy due to motion or position. Sometimes it seems that mechanical energy is disappearing. For example, in each swing of a pendulum, it goes almost as high up as on the previous swing. It has almost the same amount of potential energy after every swing. But if you watch it long enough, the swings get shorter. Finally, the pendulum comes to a stop. It has lost both its kinetic and its potential energy.

If you stop peddling on a bicycle, you'll coast to a stop. Your kinetic energy becomes zero. But you have no more potential energy than before.

Can mechanical energy disappear? Or is it just converted to another form that is neither kinetic energy nor potential energy?

It is friction that brings most moving objects to a stop. When friction is reduced, the motion continues longer. Objects continue moving longer on smooth surfaces than on rough ones. Lubricants such as oil and grease cut down on friction. But friction cannot be totally eliminated in the real world on earth. And so nothing on earth keeps moving forever without an energy boost from the outside.

What, then, is the relation between friction and mechanical energy? One clue is that where there is friction, there are changes in temperature.

Place the palms of your hands on your face. Notice how warm or cold they feel. Then rub your palms together and place them on your face again. Can you feel any change in temperature?

Friction can be used to melt pieces of ice. When two pieces of ice are rubbed together, friction increases the temperature of the ice. The ice melts. This method works even when the surrounding air is colder than 0°C.

You may have seen a fire started from friction. A stick is turned rapidly in a small opening in another piece of wood. Friction raises the temperature of the wood to the kindling point. A spark is caught on some wood shavings. The wood shavings burst into flame.

The chemicals in the end of a match are ignited by friction. The friction of the match head with another surface causes an increase in the temperature. The increase in temperature causes the chemicals to ignite.

Temperature increases are found wherever friction is present. In fact, the presence of friction is often identified by increases in temperature. Large temperature increases may be a clue to locating unwanted frictional forces.

Large amounts of mechanical energy appear to be used up whenever large temperature increases occur. Is there a

What happens to a swinging pendulum that is left alone?

Your palms should feel warmer.

Figure 4-35. *Friction between the stick and the large piece of wood can make the wood hot enough to start a fire.*

relationship between the mechanical energy used up and the temperature increases? This question will be explored in the next chapter.

Quick Review

1. What is mechanical energy?
2. When there is friction, what happens to the kinetic and potential energy of a moving object?
3. When there is friction between objects that are rubbed together, what happens to their temperature?

Einstein's theory of relativity

New vocabulary: special theory of relativity

All the ideas about motion, mass, and energy covered in this chapter have been verified over and over again for objects moving at "everyday" speeds. However, for extremely high speeds—those about 100 000 times the speed of a jet airplane—they must be modified.

Albert Einstein (1879–1955), a German-born physicist, proposed several revolutionary ideas in 1905 as part of his **special theory of relativity.** First, there is *no* way to tell whether something is at rest or is moving at constant velocity. You can say that you are moving relative to some reference object. You can equally well say that the reference object is moving relative to you. There is no way to tell which one is *really* moving. Motion is completely relative.

Second, the speed of light always has the same value regardless of the motion of the light source or the motion of the persons making the measurement.

Einstein drew interesting conclusions from these ideas. He said that there is a limit on how fast an object can travel relative to *any* reference object. No object can travel faster than the speed of light. He also said that the mass of an object seems to increase as its speed gets close to the speed of light. For example, when electrons are accelerated to very high speeds, they appear to gain mass.

In his famous equation, Einstein stated that the energy E of anything was equal to its mass m times the square of the speed c of light:

$$E = mc^2$$

Einstein thought of mass and energy as equivalent. When something gains energy, it gains mass, and vice versa. It is important to keep in mind that for everyday objects with every-

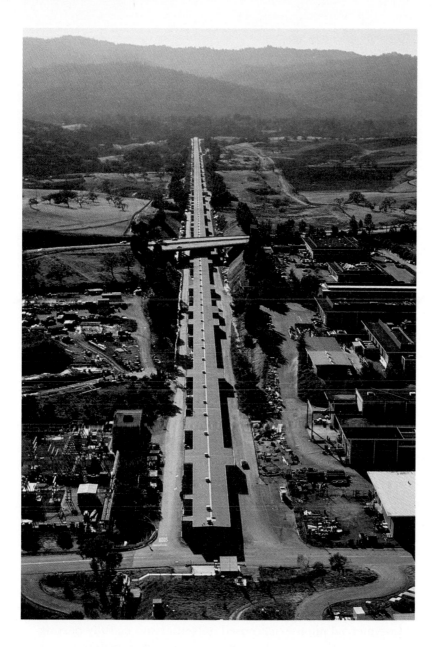

Figure 4-36. *When electrons are accelerated to almost the speed of light in this two-mile-long linear accelerator at Stanford University, their mass seems to increase greatly.*

day energy changes, the change in mass is totally undetectable. Theoretically, a football has more mass when it is moving through the air than when it is caught, but the change is far too tiny to be measured.

Quick Review

1. State the two basic ideas in Einstein's special theory of relativity.
2. What appears to happen to the mass of electrons as the electrons are accelerated to speeds close to the speed of light?

Quick Review answers:
1. (a) There is no way to tell whether something is at rest or is moving at constant velocity. (b) The speed of light always has the same value.
2. The mass appears to increase.

Physicist

Physics is the basic science that deals with the interaction of matter and energy. Physicists may do research, apply basic knowledge to current problems, or teach. Nearly half of all physicists are employed by colleges and universities, where they usually do a combination of research and teaching. Government and industry employ many others.

Creativity and problem-solving ability are good characteristics for a physicist. Physicists may specialize in subfields of physics such as optics, nuclear, atmospheric, or solid state physics. They may also apply physics to other sciences to work in biophysics, astrophysics, geophysics, or physical chemistry.

High school courses in mathematics, physics, and chemistry prepare students for an undergraduate physics major. Graduate training in physics is desirable for most positions. One third of all physicists have Ph.D. degrees.

For further information, write to: American Institute of Physics, 335 East 45th Street, New York, NY 10017

This physicist is using a laser in her research. The bright green light is the laser beam.

Airplane Pilot

Pilots may fly planes that carry passengers or cargo. They may do crop dusting, aerial photography, or perform other flying services. Many serve as members of one of the armed forces.

A career as a pilot demands good judgment, the ability to make quick decisions, and calmness under pressure. The pilot on a commercial airliner carries a heavy responsibility for the lives of the passengers and crew.

Commercial pilots are licensed only after successfully passing both a physical exam and a written exam, and after demonstrating their flying ability. Flight training is taught in both military and civilian schools. A background of high school science and mathematics is valuable. Pilots must know how to read maps and flight instruments, how to interpret weather reports, and how to calculate distances accurately.

For further information, write to: Airline Pilots Association, 1625 Massachusetts Ave. NW, Washington, DC 20036

The pilot of a high-altitude plane must wear a protective flight suit.

4.3 Section Review

Answers to Understanding the Concepts appear on page T89 in the front of this book. Blackline master test for this section: Section Testsheet 4-3 (TRB page 211)

Vocabulary

4 energy
1 energy conversion
5 gravitational potential energy
3 kinetic energy
7 mechanical energy
2 potential energy
6 special theory of relativity

Vocabulary Review

Match each term above with the numbered phrase that best describes it.

1. Occurs when a pencil falls off a desk
2. Increases whenever an object moves farther from another object pulling on it
3. Increases whenever an object speeds up
4. The ability to cause change
5. Increases when an object is moved higher above the ground
6. States that no object can move faster than the speed of light
7. Energy due to either motion or position

Review Questions

Multiple Choice: Choose the answer that best completes each of the following sentences.

8. Energy that exists even when nothing is happening is _?_.
   a. kinetic energy
   b. energy of motion
   c. energy conversion
   d. potential energy

9. The potential energy of an object is a result of _?_.
   a. its motion
   b. the pull of another object
   c. friction
   d. changes in its temperature

10. Kinetic energy is converted to potential energy when _?_.
    a. a ball is thrown upward
    b. a pendulum stops moving after a while
    c. a rock hits the ground and stops
    d. a skater coasts to a stop

11. If a bicycle and a car are moving at the same speed, the bicycle has _?_.
    a. more kinetic energy than the car
    b. less kinetic energy than the car
    c. the same amount of kinetic energy as the car
    d. no kinetic energy

12. At the top of a swing, a pendulum has _?_.
    a. all kinetic energy and no potential energy
    b. neither kinetic nor potential energy
    c. all potential energy and no kinetic energy
    d. the most potential and the most kinetic energy

Understanding the Concepts

13. Can an object have both kinetic and potential energy at the same time? Explain.

14. As the earth goes around the sun, it is closest to the sun in January and farthest from the sun in July.

    a. The earth has potential energy because of the sun's pull of gravity on it. When is the earth's potential energy greatest?
    b. If the total amount of energy does not change, when is the earth's kinetic energy greatest?
    c. When does the earth move the fastest?

15. When a car is driven, its tires get hot, even on a cold day. Explain how the tires get hot.

4 Chapter Review

Answers appear on page T90 in the front of this book. Blackline master test for this chapter: Chapter Testsheets 4A and 4B (TRB pages 247–248)

Science Vocabulary

acceleration	friction	Newton's third law of motion
average speed	gravitational potential energy	potential energy
balanced force	inertia	reference object
centripetal force	kinetic energy	slope
conservation of momentum	mechanical energy	special theory of relativity
constant speed	momentum	speed
energy	newton	static friction
energy conversion	Newton's first law of motion	velocity
escape speed	Newton's second law of motion	weight
force		

Review of Concepts

Motion is the movement or changing of position of an object with respect to a reference object.
- The description of motion may change with a change in the reference object.

Speed is how fast an object changes its position with respect to a reference object.
- Speed is described in units of distance divided by units of time.
- Average speed is the total distance traveled divided by the total time taken to travel that distance.
- An object traveling at constant speed always travels equal distances in equal times.
- On a distance-time graph, a slanting straight line indicates constant speed.

Acceleration is a change in the speed or in the direction of motion of an object.
- On a distance-time graph, a curving line indicates changing speed and thus acceleration.

A **force** is a push or pull.
- Balanced forces act on the same object without producing any changes in its motion.
- An unbalanced force acting on an object produces a change in the speed or direction of the object.
- Friction forces prevent or slow down the movement of objects.
- The greater the unbalanced force on an object is, the greater the acceleration of the object.
- The greater the mass of an object is, the smaller the acceleration of the object.
- When a force acts on an object, the object exerts a reaction force of equal strength but opposite in direction.
- When an object moves in a curve, the force causing it to change its direction acts toward the center of the curve.

Momentum is the product of mass and speed, and depends on the direction of motion.
- When objects interact through forces, the total momentum of the objects does not change.

The **force of gravity** acts between any two objects.
- Weight is the pull of gravity on an object.
- The force of gravity increases as the masses of the objects increase.
- The force of gravity decreases as the distance between the objects increases.
- The acceleration of a falling object does not depend on the mass of the object.

Energy is the ability to cause change.
- Kinetic energy is the energy of an object due to its motion.
- The kinetic energy of an object depends on both its mass and its speed.
- The kinetic energy of an object can be transferred to other objects.
- Potential energy is stored energy due to the position of an object that is acted on by a force.
- Energy can be converted from one form to another.

Critical Thinking

1. If you were describing the path of a space probe traveling from the earth to Mars, what would you use as a reference object? Explain your choice.

2. What information would you need to determine whether a rolling ball is moving at constant speed?

3. Suppose you took an express elevator to the top of a tall building. During what parts of the ride would you be accelerating? What would you feel as you accelerated?

4. If the force on an object is doubled, how does its acceleration change?

5. What force can slow down objects but can never speed them up?

6. Explain how the weight of an object can be different on the moon and on the earth.

7. Describe the path of a ball that is thrown horizontally off a high cliff.

8. A raindrop falls at constant speed for most of its trip from a cloud to the ground. Explain why the force of gravity does not cause it to move faster and faster.

9. Many small cars are without power brakes and power steering. Why do large cars need to have both power brakes and power steering?

10. Suppose a ball were thrown by an astronaut on the surface of the moon.
    a. What two conditions on the moon would affect the motion of the ball?
    b. What effect would each of these conditions have on the distance the ball would travel before reaching the moon's surface?

11. How does the kinetic energy of an object change as the object slows down?

Individual Research

12. A standard 33⅓ rpm record makes 33⅓ turns in one minute. A 45 rpm record makes 45 turns in one minute. Determine how fast a spot on the edge of each type of record moves when it is on the turntable. What must you measure before you can determine the speeds?

13. Use a reference book or text to find out the speed required for a satellite to escape the pull of the earth's gravitational force. What would be the escape speed on the moon? On Jupiter?

14. Place about 500 grams of lead shot in one end of a meter-long cardboard mailing tube. Stopper both ends. Read the room temperature from a thermometer. Invert the tube so that the lead shot falls to the other end. Repeat the inverting about one hundred times. Pour the lead shot into a plastic foam cup. Place the bulb of the thermometer in the lead shot. The lead shot was originally at room temperature. What happened to its temperature? Explain the change.

Bibliography

Berger, Melvin. *Space Shots, Shuttles and Satellites.* New York: Putnam, 1983
  Short history of space flight with an informative section on space shuttles and a final section on civilian and military uses of satellites.

Gardner, Robert, and David Webster. *Moving Right Along; A Book of Science Experiments and Puzzlers About Motion.* Garden City, NY: Doubleday, 1978
  Gives various speed records. Suggests experiments for measuring speed. Presents puzzles about motion.

Ipsen, D. C. *Isaac Newton: Reluctant Genius.* Hillside, NJ: Enslow, 1985
  Well-written biography covering Newton's personal life and scientific career.

Vogt, Gregory. *A Twenty-Fifth Anniversary Album of NASA.* New York: Watts, 1983
  Photos and text chronicling the successes and failures of the U.S. space program.

Chapter 5
Work and Heat

A steam locomotive converts heat energy to energy of motion. The heat from the burning of coal makes steam in a boiler which drives pistons that turn the wheels.

Science background information:
The branch of physics concerned with the movement of heat and the resulting energy changes is known as thermodynamics. The principles of thermodynamics are expressed in three laws. These are important laws in physics as they relate the properties of bulk matter to its behavior in physical and chemical processes, without making any assumptions about atomic or molecular structure. Thermodynamic reasoning can be used to tell whether or not chemical reactions and physical processes are theoretically possible without any consideration of the mechanism involved.

The first law of thermodynamics states that the energy of the universe is constant. This is another way of stating the principle of conservation of energy, that energy cannot be created or destroyed but only change its form. The second law of thermodynamics states that the entropy of the universe is increasing. Entropy is a measure of the degree of randomness, and this law emphasizes that there is a natural tendency toward increasing disorder, and energy must be expended for order to be maintained. In terms of heat, the second law of thermodynamics states that heat will naturally flow from a hotter body to a colder one. A colder body has less random molecular motion and thus is more ordered. The ultimate example of this is expressed in the third law of thermodynamics which states that for a perfect crystal of any pure element or compound, a state of perfect order, or zero entropy, exists at absolute zero temperature. These thermodynamic

Projectsheet 5 (TRB page 177) and Research Lab 5 (Lab Manual pages 77–78) may be used at any point in this chapter.

For detailed information about teaching this chapter, see Chapter 5 Planning Guide on pages T92–T93 in the front of this book.

Chapter Preview

5.1 Work and Machines

- **Defining work**
- **Inclined planes and mechanical advantage**
- **Efficiency of machines**
- **Wedges and screws**
- **Classes of levers**
- **Other simple machines**
- **Power and watts**
- **Measuring work and energy**

Scientists use the term *work* in a special way that relates it to forces and motion. Work can be made easier to do by changing the force required or changing the distance something must move. Things often become warmer when work is done on them.

laws help us to understand the behavior of matter in all of its states, from the perfectly rigid lattice at absolute zero (defined as O K or −273°C) through solidity, plasticity, liquidity, gasousness, atomic ionization, and finally nuclear fission.

Work can be understood as a form of energy in the context of the laws of thermodynamics. Other forms of energy, such as chemical, kinetic, electric, and thermal can be used to perform work. However because of the second law of thermodynamics, in any conversion of energy to work, some energy will be "lost" by producing random molecular motion or heat. Thus, no source of energy can be utilized 100 percent efficiently to perform work. Theoretically, a system can reach a point when all matter is completely disordered and at a uniform temperature, so there is no energy available for doing work. This is a situation of maximum entropy. Many scientists believe that the universe will eventually reach this state.

5.2 Heat and Internal Energy

- **Temperature changes and heat**
- **Specific heat**
- **Phase changes and heat**
- **Explaining heat**
- **Heat transfer**
- **Cooling systems**
- **Insulation**

Heat moves from warmer to cooler substances. When something takes in heat, either it rises in temperature or it changes phase. Heat can be transferred in different ways.

5.3 The Kinetic Theory of Matter

- **Motion in matter**
- **An improved model for gases**
- **An improved model for solids**
- **An improved model for liquids**
- **A model for temperature changes**
- **A model for heat transfer**
- **A model for phase changes**
- **A model for evaporation**
- **A model for specific heat**

The particle model of matter can be expanded by the idea that the particles are in constant motion. This improved model of matter can be used to explain the behavior of solids, liquids, and gases.

For ideas for classroom demonstration and discussion, see Getting Started on page T94 in the front of this book.

5.1 Work and Machines

Supplemental materials: Teaching Diagrams 5-1A, 5-1B, 5-1C (TRB pages 24, 25, 26), Reading Checksheet 5-1 (TRB page 92), Skillsheet 5-1 (TRB page 138), Investigation 5-1 (Lab Manual pages 67–68)

Section Preview

- **Defining work**
- **Inclined planes and mechanical advantage**
- **Efficiency of machines**
- **Wedges and screws**
- **Classes of levers**
- **Other simple machines**
- **Power and watts**
- **Measuring work and energy**

Bracketed numbers are Section Review questions correlated to that objective.

Learning Objectives

1. To define work in terms of a force moving through a distance. [22, 27]
2. To explain how several simple machines assist in doing work. [3, 4, 5, 6, 7, 18, 24, 25]
3. To measure the mechanical advantage and efficiency of different machines. [8, 9, 10, 13, 26, 27, 28, 29]
4. To differentiate between work and power. [2, 12]
5. To relate work to energy. [1]

Figure 5-1. *The design of a screw makes it possible for a person to push a screw into solid wood without using much force. A screw is considered a simple machine because it makes it easier to do work.*

Screws are discussed on page 205.

How much work have you done today? That should be a simple question. But how do you describe the amount of work you have done? By how tired you are? By the number of hours you have spent doing something? By what you have accomplished? You may have used all of these descriptions at one time or another.

What is work? This question may be just as difficult to answer. The same activity may be work one day and fun the next. Work is used to describe many different things. Its meaning changes from one person to another.

Defining work

New vocabulary: work, joule

Scientists use the term **work** in a special way. They relate work to forces and motion. Work is done on an object when two conditions are met. First, the object must move. Second, a force must be acting on the object partly or entirely in the

Main Idea

What conditions are necessary for doing work?

direction of motion. When you lift a rock off the ground, you are doing work. If you slide the rock along the ground, you are also doing work. If you push on the rock and it does not move, you have not done any work. You may feel exhausted from the effort of pushing on the rock, but because the rock does not move as a result of your effort, you have not done any work on the rock.

Pushing a lawn mower is work. You exert a force and the lawn mower moves. When you push a lawn mower, you push downward at a slant, along the handle. Even though your push moves the lawn mower forward, part of the push is toward the ground and does not make the lawn mower move. Only the part of the push that is in the forward direction does any work.

Suppose you are having trouble mowing some thick grass. You lower the handle so that now more of the push you exert is in the forward direction. Without pushing any harder, you can cut the grass more easily. The force in the direction of motion of the lawn mower has increased. The greater the force in the direction of motion, the more work is done.

Mowing a large lawn is more work than mowing a small lawn. The farther you push the lawn mower, the more work is done.

The amount of work done depends on two things. One thing is the amount of force or effort in the direction of motion. The other is the distance moved while the force is acting. The amount of work equals the product of these quantities:

$$\text{work} = \text{force} \times \text{distance}$$
$$W = Fd$$

Figure 5-2. *Only part of the push on a lawn mower moves the lawn mower forward.*

Part of push that is toward ground

Push on lawn mower

Forward part of push

What are two names for the unit for work?

How much energy is given off when 4.5 metric tons of TNT is exploded? Use the Mercalli scale to describe an earthquake of equal energy. Search pages 658–661.

When 4.5 t of TNT is exploded, 2.1×10^{10} joules of energy are given off. An earthquake of equal energy is easily detected. Buildings tremble and hanging objects swing.

Force is measured in newtons, and distance is measured in meters. The unit for work is sometimes called the newton meter. But this unit also has its own name, the **joule** (JOOL). One joule (symbol J) equals the work done by a force of 1 N that moves an object a distance of 1 m. Larger units of work are the kilojoule (1 kJ = 1000 J) and the megajoule (1 mJ = 1 000 000 J).

The joule is named after James Joule, a nineteenth century English physicist. You will learn more about Joule's discoveries in the discussion of work and energy which follows in Section 2 of this chapter.

Two practice problems follow below.

Sample Problem 1
A force of 10 N that moves an object 15 m does 150 J of work. How much work is done by a force of 20 N that moves an object 5 m?

Solution
To find the amount of work done, multiply the force by the distance:

$$\text{work} = \text{force} \times \text{distance}$$
$$= 20\text{ N} \times 5\text{ m}$$
$$= 100\text{ J}$$

Sample Problem 2
If you know that 132 J of work has been done in lifting a heavy box along a distance of 3 m, what was the force needed to lift the box?

Solution
To solve for force, divide work by distance:

$$\text{force} = \frac{\text{work}}{\text{distance}}$$

$$= \frac{132\text{ J}}{3\text{ m}}$$

$$= 44\text{ N}$$

Practice Problem
Two boys together push a sofa 2.5 m. Their combined force in pushing is 120 N. How much work have they done? *Answer:* 300 J Solution: work = force × distance = 120 N × 2.5 m = 300 J

Quick Review

1. How much work do you do if you push with a force of 100 N on a desk that does not move?
2. How much work do you do if you push with a force of 30 N on a box while sliding it 0.6 m?
3. A crane lifts a carton weighing 500 N to a height of 30 m. How much work was done? Give the answer in kJ.
4. Convert 250 kJ to joules and write it as a power of 10.

Inclined planes and mechanical advantage

New vocabulary: machine, inclined plane, mechanical advantage

Suppose you are helping to lift a couch into the back of a truck. You place a long board at a slant from the ground to the back of the truck. You slide the couch up the board. The board allows you to apply less force in lifting the couch. In exchange, you have to move the couch a greater distance.

Anything that changes the size or direction of forces used in doing work is a **machine.** The board is a machine because it allows you to apply less force than is needed to do the work.

Figure 5-3. *Explain why it is easier for a short person than for a tall person to mow the same grass with the same lawn mower.*

A short person holds the handle of the lawn mower closer to the ground than a tall person does. More of the push the short person exerts on the handle is in the direction the lawn mower is moving and less of the push is toward the ground.

Quick Review answers:
1. You do not work. The desk must move before you do work on it.
2. You do 18 J of work
   work = force × distance
       = 30 N × 0.6 m
       = 18 J
3. The work done was 15 kJ.
   work = force × distance
       = 500 N × 30 m
       = 15 000 J
       = 15 kJ
4. 1 kJ = 1000 J
   250 kJ × 1000 J/kJ =
   250 000 J = 2.5×10^5 J

Figure 5-4. *Why is a ramp considered to be a machine?*

A ramp is considered to be a machine because it changes the size and the direction of the force one uses to do work.

What is the mechanical advantage of a machine?

Slanting boards and other ramps are called **inclined planes.** A plane is a flat surface. The term *inclined* means *slanting*.

Most machines reduce the amount of force you have to apply. The applied force is usually less than the force used to move the object directly. The **mechanical advantage** of the machine describes how these two forces compare.

A machine with a mechanical advantage, or *M.A.*, of 1 does not change the force you have to apply. A machine with an *M.A.* of 2 can double your force, so you have to apply only half the force needed. A machine with an *M.A.* of 3 can triple your force. You have to apply only one third the force needed. In general,

$$\text{mechanical advantage} = \frac{\text{force needed to do work directly}}{\text{force applied to machine}}$$

This equation can be applied to an inclined plane. The force needed to do the work directly is the force needed to lift the object. It equals the weight of the object. The force applied to the machine is the force used to move the object along the inclined plane. In the absence of friction the *M.A.* can also be determined based on the distance the object moves.

In Figure 5-5 a force F is required to push an object of weight w up an inclined plane of height h and length L. The work done in moving the object directly is:

$$\text{work} = \text{force} \times \text{distance}$$
$$= wh$$

The work done in moving the object up the inclined plane is:

$$\text{work} = \text{force} \times \text{distance}$$
$$= FL$$

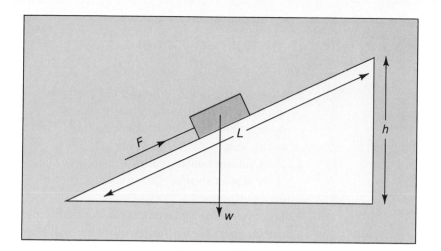

Figure 5-5. *The mechanical advantage of an inclined plane is related to the length (L) and height (h) of the inclined plane. The force (F) required to push an object up the inclined plane is equal to the weight (W) of the object being pushed.*

In the absence of friction the work done in moving the object directly and the work done in moving the object up the inclined plane are equal, so:

$$FL = wh$$

The mechanical advantage of the inclined plane is:

$$M.A. = \frac{w}{F} = \frac{L}{h}$$

So for a frictionless inclined plane:

$$\text{mechanical advantage} = \frac{\text{length of inclined plane}}{\text{height of inclined plane}}$$

Sample Problem

A piano must be moved along a ramp of 10 m up steps that are 2 m high at the top. What is the *M.A.* of the ramp?

Solution

$$\text{mechanical advantage} = \frac{\text{length of inclined plane}}{\text{height of inclined plane}}$$

$$= \frac{10 \text{ m}}{2 \text{ m}}$$

$$= 5$$

Practice Problem

Which has the greater mechanical advantage, a ramp that is 7 m long and 2.8 m high, or a ramp that is 2.8 m long and 7 m high? *Answer:* the first ramp

Solution:
first ramp:

$$M.A. = \frac{7 \text{ m}}{2.8 \text{ m}}$$

$$= 2.5$$

second ramp:

$$M.A. = \frac{2.8 \text{ m}}{7 \text{ m}}$$

$$= .4$$

Activity

See also Activity Record Sheet 5-1A (Lab Manual page 63). Answers to Questions and Conclusion appear on page T95 in the front of this book.

5.1a   Measuring Work with and without an Inclined Plane

Science processes: Observing, measuring, interpreting data

BASIC   30 minutes   Groups of 4 or teacher demonstration

Materials

- wood block with screw eye hook
- spring balance calibrated in N
- meter stick
- table more than 1 m in length
- roller skate or skateboard
- board about 2 m in length
- chair

Purpose

To measure work with and without an inclined plane.

Procedure

1. Attach a wood block to a spring balance.
2. Place the block on a smooth table. Pull horizontally on the spring balance to make the block move at a constant speed. Record the force reading on a data table like the one shown.
3. Move the block a distance of 1 m. Calculate the work you did.
4. Attach the spring balance to a roller skate or skateboard. Record the force needed to lift the skate by the spring balance.

5. Measure the height of a chair seat above the floor. Calculate the amount of work done when the skate is lifted from the floor to the seat.
6. Place a long board against the edge of the chair seat as shown. The board is now an inclined plane.
7. Use the spring balance to pull the skate up the inclined plane. Start with the rear skate wheels just touching the floor. Stop when the rear wheels reach the top of the chair seat. Be sure to pull the balance parallel to the board, not at an angle.
8. Record the amount of force used to move the skate at a constant speed.
9. Measure the total distance you moved the skate.
10. Calculate the amount of work done on the skate when it is pulled up the inclined plane.

Questions

1. What force balanced the force you applied as you pulled the block across the table?
2. How much work did you do when you slid the block a distance of 1 m? How much work would you do if you moved it 2 m?
3. How much work would you do if you held the block stationary 1 m above the floor for 1 minute?
4. Was more work done when lifting the skate to the chair seat or when pulling it up the inclined plane? In which case was a greater force used? In which case was a greater distance traveled?
5. How does the amount of work change when an inclined plane is used?

Conclusion

What is the advantage of using an inclined plane?

Step 6

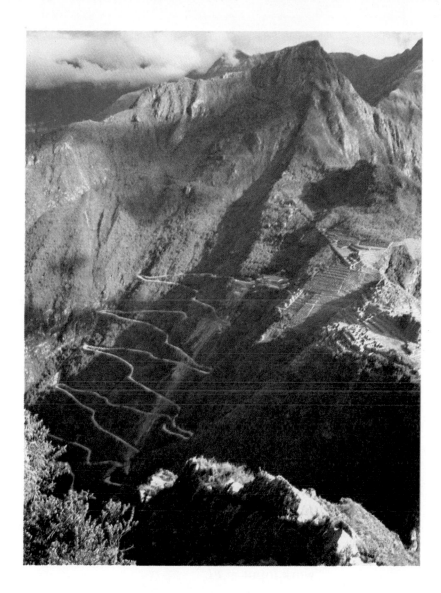

Roads that take you to the top of a hill are examples of inclined planes. Mountain roads often have zigzags, or switchbacks, that make the climb more gradual. But a road with switchbacks is longer than one that goes straight up the side of the mountain.

Quick Review

1. What effect does an inclined plane have on the amount of force you must apply to do work?
2. What effect does an inclined plane have on the distance you have to move something to do work?
3. Which has the greater mechanical advantage, a ramp that is 10 m long and 2 m high or a ramp that is 5 m long and 2 m high?

Quick Review answers:
1. The amount of force you must apply to do work is less when you use an inclined plane.
2. The distance you have to move something to do work is greater when you use an inclined plane.
3. mechanical advantage =

$$\frac{\text{length of inclined plane}}{\text{height of inclined plane}}$$

$$\frac{10}{2} = 5 \qquad \frac{5}{2} = 2.5$$

The first ramp has a greater M.A.

Research Topic

Find out what a "perpetual motion" machine is. Describe how one or two of these machines are supposed to work. Explain why they cannot really work.

Efficiency of machines

New vocabulary: work input, work output, efficiency

A machine makes it easier to do work. You might think that a machine does more work than you put into it. In fact, the reverse is always the case. The work put into a machine or **work input** is always greater than the work done by the machine or **work output.** Whenever you apply less force to a machine than what is needed to do the work, you must move something farther. Force times distance is even greater for you than for the machine.

Some of the work input is always used to overcome friction. The rest does the task required. In an efficient machine, almost all of the work input is changed to useful work. Very little is used to overcome friction. The machine's **efficiency** is the work output divided by the work input. Efficiency is usually described in percentages.

$$\text{efficiency} = \frac{\text{work output}}{\text{work input}} \times 100\%$$

Since the work output is always less than the work input, the efficiency is less than 100%.

For a real inclined plane the applied force F will have to overcome the friction between the object and the surface of the plane. As F increases the $M.A.$ decreases.

In Figure 5-7 a force of 200 N is needed to pull a trunk up an inclined plane of 4 m. The work input is the force needed to move the trunk times the distance the trunk is moved along the plane.

$$\begin{aligned}
\text{work input} &= FL \\
&= 200 \text{ N} \times 4 \text{ m} \\
&= 800 \text{ J}
\end{aligned}$$

The trunk weighs 300 N and is being lifted to a height of 2 m. The work output is equal to the weight of the trunk times the distance it is lifted.

$$\begin{aligned}
\text{work output} &= wh \\
&= 300 \text{ N} \times 2 \text{ m} \\
&= 600 \text{ J}
\end{aligned}$$

Because of friction the work needed to move the trunk up the ramp is greater than the work needed to simply lift the trunk to a height of 2 m. The efficiency of this machine can then be calculated as:

Figure 5-7. *An inclined plane is used to do work more efficiently. In this example F = force, w = weight, l = length, and h = height.*

$$\text{efficiency} = \frac{\text{work output}}{\text{work input}} \times 100\%$$

$$= \frac{600 \, \cancel{J}}{800 \, \cancel{J}} \times 100\%$$

$$= .75 \times 100\%$$

$$= 75\% \text{ efficiency}$$

The efficiency of the machine may be increased by making the surface of the inclined plane smoother so that there is less friction and thus less force is required to move an object up the plane. Lubricants such as oil and grease are used in many machines to help reduce friction, resulting in higher efficiency.

Quick Review

1. Which is greater—the work put into a machine or the work done by the machine?
2. Explain why a machine makes it easier to do work.
3. Why are lubricants used in machines? How do they affect efficiency?

Quick Review answers:
1. The work done by the machine.
2. A machine allows you to apply less force to the machine than is needed to do the work.
3. Lubricants help reduce friction; they result in greater efficiency.

Wedges and screws

New vocabulary: wedge

The blade of an ax, a knife blade, a razor blade, and a door stop are all similar. They all taper from a thick end to a very thin end. They are all examples of a **wedge,** a form of inclined plane. A force is applied to the thick end of a wedge. The thin end of the wedge is driven into something which is to be cut. The sides of the wedge push apart the object being cut. They exert a much greater force than the force applied to the thick end. To make the cut, they have to move the object apart only a short distance. The applied force pushes the wedge forward a much greater distance.

A screw is another form of inclined plane. When a screw is turned, it moves forward. At the same time, it presses against the material around it. Many turns are needed to move the screw a short distance. But the screw produces a far greater force than the force needed to turn it.

Figure 5-8. *How is a wedge like an inclined plane?*
Both a wedge and an inclined plane allow you to apply less force in doing work. You move the force, however, through a greater distance.

Quick Review answers:
1. The wedge.
2. Inclined plane.

Quick Review

1. A knife blade and a doorstop are both examples of a form of inclined plane. What is the term for this?
2. What kind of machine is represented by a screw?

Figure 5-9. *The parts of a lever are shown here. Note how the resistance and effort forces are balanced.*

Classes of levers

New vocabulary: fulcrum, lever, effort force, resistance force, resistance arm, effort arm, first-class lever, second-class lever, third-class lever

A crowbar, a wheelbarrow, and a rake are all machines. They all have a straight part that moves when a force is applied and they all have one point that does not move. On a crowbar, the point is at the center of the curved end. On a wheelbarrow, it is at the center of the wheel. On a rake, it is beside the upper hand of the person holding it. The point that does not move is called the **fulcrum** (FUL′-krum). Machines that do work by moving around a fulcrum are known as **levers** (LEE′-verz).

There are two forces involved in using a lever. The **effort force** is the force applied in moving the lever. The **resistance force** is the weight of an object being lifted or is due to friction that must be overcome, as in removing a tightly fitting lid.

The length of the lever between the fulcrum and the resistance force is the **resistance arm.** The length of the lever from the fulcrum to where the effort force is applied is the **effort arm.** The mechanical advantage of a lever can be stated as:

$$\text{M.A.} = \frac{\text{length of effort arm}}{\text{length of resistance arm}}$$

The work done as one end of a lever is moved is equal to the work done against the resistance force at some other point on the lever.

The three levers in Figure 5-10 are of three different types. A crowbar used to loosen a hubcap is a first-class lever. The effort force is applied at the handle by a person's hand. The

Figure 5-10. *On these three examples of levers, what do the circles mark?* The fulcrum of each lever.

sharp end applies a force to pry up the edge of the hubcap where it fits onto the wheel rim. On a first-class lever, the fulcrum is always between the two forces. A first-class lever changes the direction of a force. When you move one end in a certain direction, the other end moves in the opposite direction.

A wheelbarrow is an example of a **second-class lever.** The force is applied at the handles. Somewhere between the wheel and the handle is the load being lifted. When you lift the handles, you apply less force than the weight of the load. In return, you have to move the handles a greater distance than the load is raised. Does the wheelbarrow change the direction of the force? Where is the fulcrum on a wheelbarrow?

Main Idea

Where is the fulcrum on a second-class lever?

The wheelbarrow does not change the direction of the force when you lift the handles. The load moves in the same direction as the handles. The fulcrum on the wheelbarrow is at the center of the wheel.

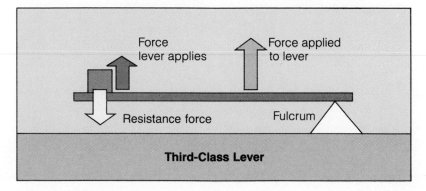

Figure 5-11. *The three classes of levers. Which class changes the direction of the force?*
A first-class lever changes the direction of a force.

Activity

5.1b Three Classes of Levers

Science processes: Observing, interpreting data, experimenting, inferring, making an operational definition

40 minutes   Groups of 4 or teacher demonstration

Materials

- 1-kg standard mass
- spring balance calibrated in N
- wire or strong cord
- metric ruler
- wooden dowel, 1 m long and about 2 cm in diameter
- chair with straight back

Purpose

To compare three kinds of levers.

Procedure

SAFETY NOTE: *Stand so that the 1-kg mass cannot hit you if it falls or slides unexpectedly.*

1. Use a spring balance to measure the weight in newtons of the 1-kg standard mass. Record the weight.
2. Mark the 1-m-long dowel in three places: 20 cm from each end, and in the center.
3. FIRST-CLASS LEVER Put the dowel on top of a chair back so that the dowel rests on the 20-cm mark closest to the mass.
4. Hang the 1-kg mass 5 cm from one end of the dowel. Hang the spring balance 5 cm from the opposite end.
5. Balance the dowel by pulling down on the balance. Record on a data table the force needed to slowly lift the mass.
6. Repeat Step 5 with the fulcrum at the center of the dowel and again with the fulcrum at the third mark.
7. SECOND-CLASS LEVER Remove the mass and spring balance from the dowel.
8. Support the end of the dowel about 10 cm in from the edge of the chair seat. Use books to keep it from rolling or sliding. The dowel must be free to pivot.
9. Attach the spring balance to the dowel.
10. Record the force used to lift the dowel when the mass is on each of the three marks.
11. THIRD-CLASS LEVER Attach the mass 5 cm from the end of the dowel opposite the chair. Record the force needed to slowly pivot the dowel about the end resting on the chair when the balance is at each of the three marks.

Questions

1. FIRST-CLASS LEVER How did the force needed to raise the mass compare to the weight of the mass as the fulcrum was moved toward the spring balance (effort)?
2. SECOND-CLASS LEVER How did the force needed to raise the mass compare to the weight of the mass as the mass (resistance) moved toward the spring balance (effort)?
3. THIRD-CLASS LEVER How did the force needed to raise the mass compare to the weight of the mass as the spring balance (effort) was moved toward the mass (resistance)?

Conclusion

Redraw each of these levers so that they have *more* mechanical advantage. Move only the part marked (*).

Step 6 (first part)   Step 10   Step 11

On a second-class lever, the fulcrum is always at one end. The effort force is applied to the lever at the other end. The lever applies a force against a resistance force between the two ends. This force is always greater than the force applied to the lever. That is, the mechanical advantage is greater than 1.

A rake is an example of a **third-class lever.** When you rake leaves, the fulcrum is beside the wrist of your upper hand. You move the rake by pushing or pulling with your lower hand. The rake applies a force to the leaves at its bottom end where the "teeth" of the rake scrape along the ground.

On a third-class lever, the fulcrum is always at one end. The lever applies a force to something at the other end. The effort force is applied to the lever between the two ends. This force is always greater than the force the lever applies. The mechanical advantage is less than 1. The reason for using a third-class lever is to increase the distance moved, not the force. The tooth end of a rake moves much farther than the hand pulling the rake. You can reach more leaves than you could with bare hands.

Quick Review

1. Where is the fulcrum on each of the three classes of levers?
2. In which type of lever is the mechanical advantage less than 1?
3. Why are third-class levers used?

Other simple machines
New vocabulary: simple machine, compound machine, wheel and axle, pulley, block and tackle

Inclined planes, including wedges and screws, and all classes of levers are examples of what scientists call **simple machines.** When a machine is made up of two or more simple machines it is called a **compound machine.** An example of a compound machine is the wheelbarrow. The handles of a wheelbarrow are levers used to lift while the wheel reduces the force needed to move the load forward.

A steering wheel on an automobile is an example of another simple machine: the **wheel and axle.** It is really a form of the lever. The steering wheel and its shaft, which is the axle, turn together. As the wheel and axle turn together, a point on the wheel moves farther than a point on the axle. In return, the force exerted by the axle is greater than the force applied to the wheel. The wheel and axle allow you to use less

Main Idea

Where is the fulcrum on a first-class lever?

Main Idea

Where is the fulcrum on a third-class lever?

Additional information:
Another example of a third-class lever is a cane fishing pole. The fulcrum is at one end of the fishing pole; the fish is at the other end. The hands pulling on the fishing pole apply a force to it between the two ends. The fishing pole applies a force to the fish, pulling it from the water. The hands apply more force than the weight of the fish, but the fish moves a greater distance than the hands.

Quick Review answers:
1. First-class lever: Fulcrum is between applied force and force lever applies.
   Second-class lever: Fulcrum is at end. Force is applied at other end.
   Third-class lever: Fulcrum is at one end. Lever applies force at other end.
2. In a third-class lever.
3. They are used to increase the distance moved.

Critical Thinking

When you write, you are using the pen or pencil as a machine. What type of machine is this? Can you place it into a class of that type of machine? How would you increase the mechanical advantage of this machine?

The pen or pencil is used as a lever, a simple machine. It is a third-class lever because you apply a force between the two ends. The M.A. could be increased by using a longer pencil and gripping it closer to the end away from the paper.

Steering wheel

Axle
(Steering column)

Force is
transferred to
steering arm

Wheel

force to do work. The larger the wheel, compared to the axle, the greater is the mechanical advantage.

$$\text{M.A.} = \frac{\text{radius of wheel}}{\text{radius of axle}}$$

A **pulley** is a wheel with a groove in its rim. It is turned by a rope or chain that lies against the groove. A pulley, too, is a simple machine that is a type of lever. It changes the direction of a force and can reduce the force needed.

In Figure 5-13 three types of pulleys are shown. The simplest pulley, pictured in Figure 5-13a, allows a load to be lifted the same distance as it is pulled at the other end of the rope. Two or more pulleys in a system can allow a load to be lifted with less force than is needed in a single pulley. In the pulley system shown in Figure 5-13b, two ropes support the load. This cuts the force applied to lift the load in half. At the same time, the force must be applied to twice the length of the

Figure 5-13. *Three types of pulleys.*

Figure 5-14. *A combination of pulleys can be used to lift a very heavy object.*

rope, and twice the distance that the load is actually lifted. In a pulley system, as you add more ropes that support the load, you increase the mechanical advantage and less force is needed to lift the load.

A combination of pulleys can be used to provide a large mechanical advantage. Such a combination is called a **block and tackle.** A block and tackle can produce a great enough force to lift an automobile engine or a piano. A block and tackle is also used to tighten wires and cables.

Quick Review

1. On a wheel and axle, how does the force applied to the wheel compare to the force exerted by the axle?
2. What two things can a pulley do to a force?
3. What is the mechanical advantage of a steering wheel with a radius of 50 mm that turns an axle having a radius of 2mm?

Power and watts

New vocabulary: power, watt

Often, people are interested in how fast work is done, or **power.** Power is the rate at which the work is done. It is equal to the work done divided by the time required to do the work.

$$\text{power} = \frac{\text{work}}{\text{time}}$$

Main Idea

What is a block and tackle?

Quick Review answers:
1. The force applied to the wheel is less than the force exerted by the axle.
2. A pulley can change the direction of a force, and it can reduce the force needed.
3. M.A. = $\dfrac{\text{radius of wheel}}{\text{radius of axle}}$

   $= \dfrac{50 \text{ mm}}{2 \text{ m}}$

   $= 25$

Research Topic

Electric motors and gasoline engines are often rated in units of horsepower. Find out the origin of the horsepower unit and how it is related to the watt, the SI unit of power

5.1c   Using Pulleys

Science processes: Observing, experimenting, interpreting data, making an operational definition

40 minutes   Groups of 2 to 4 or teacher demonstration

Materials

- 1 pulley with attachment points at one end
- 1 pulley with attachment points at both ends
- support (ring stand, clamp, bar)
- cord about 1 m long
- spring balance calibrated in N
- 500-g standard mass
- metric ruler

Purpose

To determine the mechanical advantage of different pulleys.

Procedure

1. Use a spring balance to find the weight in newtons of a 500-g mass. Record its weight.
2. Hang the pulley with two attachment points from the support.
3. Attach one end of the cord to the mass. Run the other end of the cord over the pulley wheel. Attach this end to the spring balance.
4. Lift the mass by pulling down on the spring balance. Record on a data table the force needed to slowly lift the mass.
5. Now attach one end of the cord directly to the support. Hang the mass from the pulley with one attachment point.
6. Extend the other end of the cord under the pulley wheel. Tie the balance to the free end of the cord.
7. Pull straight up on the spring balance to lift the mass. The pulley should move along the cord as you lift.
8. Record the force needed to slowly lift the mass.
9. Move the spring balance a distance of 20 cm. Measure and record how far the mass is lifted.
10. Remove the end of the cord attached to the support. Tie this end to the bottom attachment point of the pulley used in steps 2 through 4.
11. Run the other end of the cord over the pulley's wheel. Attach this loose end of the cord to the spring balance. Repeat Steps 4 and 9.

Questions

1. What is the mechanical advantage of the attached pulley used in Steps 2 through 4?
2. In what way did the attached pulley make it easier for you to lift the mass?
3. What is the *M.A.* of the moving pulley used in steps 5 through 9?
4. Divide the distance the spring balance moved in step 9 by the distance the mass moved. Is your answer the same as the pulley's *M.A.*?
5. What is the *M.A.* of the two-pulley machine used in Steps 10 and 11?
6. Divide the distance the spring balance moved in Step 11 by the distance the mass moved. Is your answer the same as the pulley's *M.A.*?
7. How does the *M.A.* of a pulley system compare to the number of lines supporting the load?

Conclusion

Describe three ways to determine the mechanical advantage of a pulley system.

Weight of 500-g mass _____

Force/distance measurements	Pulley with 1 attachment point	Pulley with 2 attachment points
Force needed to lift mass		
Distance mass is lifted when moving spring scale 20 cm		

When the work is in joules and the time in seconds, the power is in joules per second (symbol J/s). Another name for a joule per second is the **watt** (symbol W). The watt is named after James Watt, an eighteenth-century Scottish engineer. Watt became known for inventing a steam engine that could do work faster and more efficiently than previous engines. One watt equals 1 J/s. One hundred joules of work done per second is equal to 100 watts of power.

Figure 5-15. *Which person has the greater power in moving up a hill?*

The cyclist. The bicycle is a machine that allows the weight of the cyclist to move uphill at a faster rate than is possible on foot.

Sample Problem

A girl runs up a flight of stairs in 2.5 minutes. If the work she has done is equal to 300 joules, how much power did she use to climb the stairs?

Solution

$$\text{power} = \frac{\text{work}}{\text{time}}$$

$$= \frac{300 \text{ J}}{2.5 \text{ min}} \times \frac{1 \text{ min}}{60 \text{ s}}$$

$$= \frac{300 \text{ J}}{150 \text{ s}}$$

$$= 2 \text{ W}$$

Practice Problem

If it takes 840 joules of work for a man to row a boat for 7 minutes, how much power did he use? *Answer: 2 W*

Solution:

$$\text{power} = \frac{\text{work}}{\text{time}}$$

$$= \frac{840 \text{ J}}{7 \text{ min}} \times \frac{1 \text{ min}}{60 \text{ s}}$$

$$= \frac{840 \text{ J}}{420 \text{ s}}$$

$$= 2 \text{ W}$$

Quick Review

1. What is the relation among the following units: joules, watts, and seconds?
2. How many watts of power is represented by a sprinter weighing 80 N who runs a kilometer in 4.3 minutes?

Quick Review answers:

1. The power in watts equals the work in joules divided by the time in seconds. (One watt equals one joule per second.)
2. work $= \text{force} \times \text{distance}$

$$= 80 \text{ N} \times 1 \text{ km} \times \frac{1000 \text{ m}}{1 \text{ km}}$$

$$= 80\ 000 \text{ J}$$

$$\text{power} = \frac{\text{work}}{\text{time}}$$

$$= \frac{80\ 000 \text{ J}}{4.3 \text{ min}} \times \frac{1 \text{ min}}{60 \text{ s}}$$

$$= \frac{80\ 000 \text{ J}}{258 \text{ s}}$$

$$= 310 \text{ W}$$

Measuring work and energy

When you toss a ball, you do work on the ball. While it is in your hand, you push on it and move it in the direction of your push. After you let go, the ball keeps moving. It has kinetic energy. You also do work in stretching a rubber band. A stretched rubber band has potential, or stored, energy. By

Figure 5-16. *Suppose you lift a box that weighs 90 N from the floor to a surface 0.9 m high. By how much do you increase the potential energy of the box?*
The increase in potential energy equals the amount of work done.
90 N × 0.9 m = 81 J

Teaching suggestion:
Ask the class these questions:
What units would you use to measure work? (joules) To measure energy? (joules)
What is the rate of doing work called? (power) What is the rate of using energy called? (power) In what units is power measured? (watts)

Critical Thinking

Why is it impossible to get more work out of a machine than you put in?
Energy cannot be created. The energy of work must be produced from another source of energy. Since no machine is 100% efficient due to friction, you must always put in more work than you get out.

Quick Review answers:
1. Scientists view work as a form of energy.
2. 60 J
3. Power

doing work on a ball and a rubber band, you increase their energy. Scientists look at work itself as a form of energy. When you do work on an object, you transfer energy from yourself to the object. The energy involved in doing work is also known as mechanical energy.

The units for measuring work and energy are the same. If you do one joule of work on an object, you give it one joule of energy. Suppose you lift an object of weight 20 N a distance of 2 m. You do 40 J of work and increase its potential energy by 40 J.

The rate of using energy is called *power,* just as is the rate of doing work. Electric bulbs and appliances are rated by their power use. A 100-W light bulb uses 100 J of energy each second that it is operating. A hair dryer that is rated at 1200 W uses 1200 J of energy every second.

Sometimes work is done on an object but the object does not seem to gain energy. Suppose you put a screw into a piece of wood. You do work to spread apart the fibers of wood and force the screw in. When you are done, neither the screw nor the wood moves. Neither seems to have the ability to cause change. But both the screw and the wood would be warmer. Often, things get warmer when work is done on them. The next section will explore how temperature and energy are related.

Quick Review

1. How do scientists view the relation between work and energy?
2. An electric lamp uses a bulb marked 60 W. How much energy is changed into heat and light each second?
3. What term applies to both the rate of doing work and the rate of using energy?

5.1 Section Review

Answers to Understanding the Concepts and solutions to Problems to Solve appear on page T95 in the front of this book. Blackline master test for this section: Section Testsheet 5-1 (TRB page 212)

Vocabulary

6 block and tackle
14 compound machine
8 efficiency
16 effort arm
17 effort force
10 fulcrum
7 inclined plane
1 joule
5 lever
11 machine
13 mechanical advantage
12 power
22 pulley
19 resistance arm
15 resistance force
18 simple machine
2 watt
3 wedge
4 wheel and axle
9 work
21 work input
20 work output

Vocabulary Review

Match each term above with the numbered phrase that best describes it.

1. SI unit of work and energy
2. SI unit of power
3. Type of machine a knife blade is
4. Type of machine a steering wheel is
5. Type of machine a broom is
6. Used to lift a car's engine
7. Used to raise a heavy load into a truck
8. Close to 100% when there is little friction
9. Transfer of energy when an object moves in the direction of a force
10. Point on lever that does not rotate
11. Anything that changes the size or direction of a force
12. Indicates how fast work is done
13. Indicates how much a force has been multiplied by a machine
14. Machine made up of two or more simple machines
15. The force that must be overcome by the lever
16. Length of the lever from the fulcrum to where there effort force is applied
17. Force that is applied in moving a lever
18. Type of machine that includes inclined planes and wedges
19. Length of the lever between the fulcrum and resistance force
20. The work done by a machine
21. The work put into a machine
22. Simple machine used to lift loads

Review Questions

Multiple Choice: Choose the answer that best completes each of the following sentences.

23. The amount of work done on an object is equal to the ? .
    a. force applied to the object
    b. distance the object moves in the direction of the force
    c. product of the force and the distance the object moves in the direction of the force
    d. product of the force and the time the force acts on the object

24. The advantage of an inclined plane is that the same amount of work can be done ? .
    a. more quickly
    b. more efficiently
    c. without friction
    d. using less force

Understanding the Concepts

25. Describe the difference between a second-class lever and a third-class lever. Give an example of each.
26. Give an example of a machine with a mechanical advantage greater than 1. Describe how this machine makes it easier to do work.
27. What is meant by the efficiency of a machine? Why is the efficiency always less than 100%?

Problems to Solve

28. A box weighing 600 N is to be lifted a vertical distance of 2 m by pushing it up a ramp 5 m long. What force is needed to move the box the length of the ramp? What is the mechanical advantage of this simple machine?
29. A lever with an M.A. of 3 has a resistance arm measuring 2.5 m. What is the length of the effort arm?

5.1 Work and Machines   215

For ideas for classroom demonstration and discussion, see Getting Started on page T96 in the front of this book.

5.2 Heat and Internal Energy

Supplemental materials: Teaching Diagram 5-2 (TRB page 27), Reading Checksheet 5-2 (TRB page 93), Skillsheet 5-2 (TRB page 139), Investigation 5-2 (Lab Manual pages 71–72)

Section Preview

- **Temperature changes and Heat**
- **Specific heat**
- **Phase changes and heat**
- **Explaining heat**
- **Heat transfer**
- **Cooling systems**
- **Insulation**

Bracketed numbers are Section Review questions correlated to that objective.

Learning Objectives

1. To explain heat as energy that is transferred because of a difference in temperature. [16]
2. To recognize that the amount of heat gained or lost by a substance depends on the kind of substance, the amount of the substance, and the change in temperature of the substance. [9, 10, 22, 23]
3. To differentiate among temperature, heat, and internal energy. [3, 12]
4. To describe the different methods by which heat is transferred and how heat is prevented from being transferred. [4, 5, 6, 18, 19, 20, 21]
5. To explain how the principles of heat transfer are used in cooling systems and in insulating. [7, 13, 18, 19, 20, 21]

Figure 5-17. *The temperature inside a volcano is high enough to melt rock, which can be released as molten lava and hot ash when the volcano erupts.*

Main Idea

What is temperature a measure of?

You dip your finger in water to test how hot or cold the water is. You open a window or door to decide if it is hot or cold outside. Parents feel a child's forehead with their hand to see if the child seems to have a fever.

Temperature is a measure of how hot or cold something is. Your skin is not always an accurate judge of temperature. To prove this to yourself, put a bowl of cold tap water next to an ice cube. Place one finger on the ice cube for a few seconds. Then dip that finger and another finger in the water at the same time. The water will feel much warmer to the finger that was on the ice. Thermometers are not fooled. They measure temperatures much more accurately than your skin can.

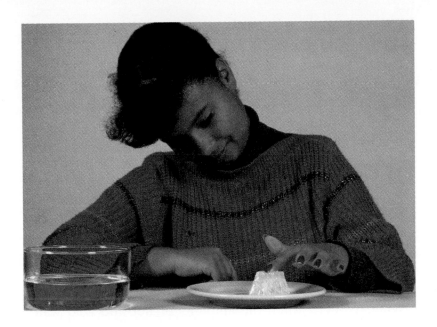

In everyday metric units, temperatures are measured in degrees Celsius. Your body temperature is about 37°C. People try to keep the temperature of rooms at about 20°C.

Temperature changes and heat

New vocabulary: temperature

When something is warmer than its surroundings, it tends to cool down. For instance, a bathtub of hot water cools to room temperature. Colder things tend to warm up. A cold drink left on the kitchen counter will warm to room temperature.

Something that cools down is said to lose heat. Does something that warms up lose cold? Suppose milk is warmed "to take the chill out of it." Is "chill" something real that leaves the milk? Or does milk take in heat from the stove? People have been thinking about the meaning of heat for a long time. At first heat was thought to be a fluid. Today, we still say that heat "flows" from a warmer to a colder substance. But ideas about what heat is have changed a lot. Cold is thought to be just a lack of heat. So milk that is warmed on the stove takes in heat, instead of losing cold.

What is heat? For a start, you can think of heat as what a substance loses when it cools down. Heat tends to move from a hotter substance to a colder substance. The colder substance takes in heat lost by the hotter substance. As a result, the colder substance warms up. When the two substances are at the same temperature, no further movement of heat is observed.

Main Idea

Why is something cold?

Figure 5-19. *How much will the lake be warmed by the warm cans of fruit juice?*
The heat lost when the cans of fruit juice cool will warm the lake so little that you cannot measure the increase in its temperature. This is because the cans of fruit juice are so much smaller than the lake.

Quick Review answers:
1. Chill is not something that can move. When something is warmed, heat moves into it.
2. The amounts of hot and cold water mixed also determine the final temperature of the mixture.
3. No, the temperature of the mixture will be between 20°C and 30°C.
4. The final temperature will be nearer to that of the larger quantity.

Hot and cold water are often mixed. You know that the temperature of the mixture will be somewhere in between. If a bathtub of water is too hot, you add cold water. The more cold water you add, the cooler the tub of water gets. The temperature of the mixture depends on how much hot water and how much cold water are mixed. Of course, it also depends on the temperatures of the hot and cold water. You can cool the tub with less water if you use very cold water.

Suppose equal amounts of hot and cold water are mixed. The hot water gives up heat to the cold water until they are both at the same temperature. You would expect the temperature of the mixture to be halfway between the temperatures of the cold and hot water. The hot water should cool down and the cold water warm up by the same number of degrees.

What happens when the amounts of hot and cold water are not equal? Think of the bathtub of hot water. Suppose you add a cup of ice-cold water to the hot water. The hot water will cool only a little. The temperature of the mixture is closer to the temperature of the larger amount of water.

Suppose you are picnicking by a lake. The canned drinks are warm. You put the warm cans in the cold lake water. Which would you expect to change more in temperature—the drinks or the lake? The drinks

Quick Review
1. Explain why it is incorrect to think that when something is warmed, the chill leaves it.
2. When hot water and cold water are mixed, what besides the original temperatures determines the final temperature of the mixture?
3. Will a mixture of equal quantities of water at 20°C and at 30°C be at 50°C? If not, what will the final temperature be?
4. Two cups of water at 40°C are mixed with one cup of water at 70°C. Will the final temperature be nearer to that of the larger quantity or the smaller?

Specific heat
New vocabulary: specific heat, heating system
In general, the temperature change of a substance that gains or loses heat depends on the amount of the substance. The amounts of different types of substances are best described by mass. Suppose a certain amount of heat is gained or lost

by a substance. The greater the mass of the substance, the less its temperature changes. The smaller the mass of the substance, the more its temperature changes.

If you put a solid metal block on a hot plate, it would soon be too hot to touch. But if you put the same mass of water on a hot plate, it would take much longer to get that hot. Water requires more heat than metal does to warm up by the same amount. Different kinds of substances require different amounts of heat to make the same temperature change.

The amount of heat gained or lost by a substance is determined by three factors:

1. the kind of substance;
2. the amount of the substance;
3. the temperature change that takes place.

The amount of heat gained or lost by a substance is measured in joules. The amount of heat needed to raise the temperature of 1 kg of water by 1°C is equal to 4180 joules. Compared to other substances, water absorbs a large amount of heat when it warms up by 1°C. Only 450 J of heat is needed to raise the temperature of 1 kg of iron by 1°C. And only 140 J of heat will raise the temperature of 1 kg of mercury by 1°C. The amount of heat absorbed or given up per kilogram of a substance and per degree Celsius of temperature change is different for each substance. This property is the **specific heat** of the substance.

How would you calculate the amount of heat needed to raise the temperature of 50 kg of water from 20°C to 50°C?

Main Idea

What three factors determine the amount of heat gained or lost by a substance?

Additional information:
Heat is commonly measured in calories. A calorie is the amount of heat needed to raise the temperature of 1 g of water by 1°C. The unit commonly used to measure the energy in food is also called the calorie but it equals 1000 of the calories defined here. The food calorie is something spelled with a capital C. It is also called the kilocalorie. One kilocalorie is equal to 4180 J.

Main Idea

How do you determine the specific heat of a substance?

Figure 5-20. *The spaghetti can be eaten almost immediately without burning your tongue. It doesn't give up as much heat as an equal mass of boiling water.*

Ask: Which has a lower specific heat—spaghetti or water? (spaghetti) How do you know? (Spaghetti gives off much less heat in your mouth than an equal mass of water at the same temperature.)

5.2a Predicting Temperature Changes

Science processes: Observing, experimenting, interpreting data, predicting, measuring

Materials BASIC 20 minutes Groups of 2 to 4

- 3 plastic foam cups
- thermometer
- 2 100-mL graduated cylinders
- cold water
- hot water
- stirring rod

Purpose

To predict the final temperature when hot and cold water are mixed.

Procedure

1. Place 30 mL of cold water in a plastic foam cup.
2. Place 30 mL of hot water in a second plastic foam cup.
3. Measure and record the temperature of the water in each cup on a data table like the one shown.
4. Predict what the temperature of a mixture of the hot and cold water would be. Record your prediction. Explain why you made your prediction.
5. Pour the hot and cold water together into a third cup and stir well.
6. Measure and record the temperature of the mixture. Compare your results to your prediction.

7. Repeat Steps 1 through 6 with 30 mL of cold water and 60 mL of hot water.
8. Repeat Steps 1 through 6. This time use 60 mL of cold water and 30 mL of hot water.

Questions

1. In which trial did your predicted temperature come closest to the final temperature?
2. How did the temperature of the mixture compare to the starting temperatures when equal volumes of hot and cold water were mixed?
3. When different volumes of hot and cold water were mixed, was the temperature of the mixture closer to that of the larger or smaller sample?

Conclusion

How can the temperature be predicted when hot and cold water are mixed?

Going Further

Repeat steps 1 through 6, using 90 mL of cold water and 30 mL of hot water. How did the temperature of the mixture depend on the volumes of water that were mixed?

Cold Water		Hot Water		Mixture		
					Temperature	
Volume	Temperature	Volume	Temperature	Volume	Predicted	Measured
30 mL		30 mL				
30 mL		60 mL				
60 mL		30 mL				

The specific heat of water is 4180 J per kg per °C. To raise the temperature of 50 kg of water by 1°C would require 4180 J/kg · °C times 50 kg times 1°C, or 209 000 J. To raise the temperature of 50 kg of water by 30°C would require 50 kg times 4180 J times 30°C, or 6 270 000 J. In general, the equation for increasing the heat of a substance is:

$$\text{heat absorbed} = \text{specific heat} \times \text{mass} \times \text{increase in temperature}$$

When a substance is cooled down, the equation would be:

$$\text{heat given out} = \text{specific heat} \times \text{mass} \times \text{decrease in temperature}$$

Data Search

The specific heat capacity of water is 1.00. The specific heat of which element, lithium or helium, is closer to that of water? Search pages 658–661.

Lithium.

Sample Problem

Gold has a specific heat of 129 J per kg per °C. How much heat would be given out when 50 kg of gold cools from 50°C to 20°C?

Solution

$$\text{heat given out} = \text{specific heat} \times \text{mass} \times \text{change in temperature}$$

$$= 129 \frac{J}{kg \cdot °C} \times 50 \text{ kg} \times (50°C - 20°C)$$

$$= 129 \frac{J}{\cancel{kg} \cdot \cancel{°C}} \times 50 \cancel{kg} \times 30\cancel{°C}$$

$$= 193\ 500 \text{ J}$$

Practice Problem

How much heat would be required to raise the temperature of 20 kg of iron from 30°C to 100°C? (Specific heat of iron is 450 J.) Express your answer in kJ. *Answer:* 630 kJ

Solution:
heat needed
= specific heat × mass × change in temperature

$$- 450 \frac{J}{kg \cdot °C} \times 20 \text{ kg} \times (100°C - 30°C)$$

$$= \frac{450 \text{ J}}{\cancel{kg} \cdot \cancel{°C}} \times 20 \cancel{kg} \times 70\cancel{°C}$$

$$= 630\ 000 \text{ J}$$

$$= 630 \text{ kJ}$$

Many uses of water depend on water's high specific heat. Most automobile engines use water for cooling. A lot of excess heat from the engine can be absorbed by the water. Yet, the increase in the temperature of the water will be small. Electric generating plants often use water to absorb some of the excess heat. Many of these electric plants are located near large lakes or rivers. These large bodies of water can absorb a lot of heat with only a small temperature increase.

Research Topic

Discover how waste heat can be removed in industrial processes. Look up articles that describe cogeneration technology and waste heat recovery systems.

A method for bringing heat into a space is a **heating system.** Some heating systems in homes use hot water heat. Pipes carry the hot water through the house. Heat is given up to the room as the hot water cools down. The water delivers a lot of heat to the room. The water is recirculated through a furnace. Here the water again gains heat from the burning fuel.

Quick Review answers:

1. The iron will become hotter than the water, since it takes less heat to raise the temperature of iron 1°C.
2. Water has a relatively high specific heat.
3. Heat absorbed

$$= 4180 \ \frac{J}{kg \cdot {}^\circ C} \times 200 \ kg$$

$$\times \ (100{}^\circ C - 50{}^\circ C)$$

$$= \frac{4180 \ J}{kg \cdot {}^\circ C} \times 200 \ kg \times 50{}^\circ C$$

$$= 4180 \ J \times 200 \times 50$$

$$= 41800 \ kJ$$

4. Heat given out =

$$450 \ \frac{J}{kg \cdot {}^\circ C} \times 20 \ kg \times 30{}^\circ C$$

$$= \frac{450 \ J}{kg \cdot {}^\circ C} \times 20 \ kg \times 30{}^\circ C$$

$$= 450 \ J \times 20 \times 30$$

$$= 270 \ kJ$$

Quick Review

1. If the same amount of heat is added to equal masses of water and iron, which will become hotter?
2. What substance has a relatively high specific heat?
3. How much heat is required to raise the temperature of 200 kg of water from 50°C to 100°C?
4. How much heat is given off when 20 kg of iron cools by 30°C?

Phase changes and heat

New vocabulary: heat of fusion, heat of vaporization

Temperature changes are not the only kind of changes that result from the gain or loss of heat. When heat is added to ice at 0°C, the ice melts. The liquid water that is produced remains at 0°C until all the ice is melted. All pure substances act the same way during melting. When heat is added, the only change is that the solid changes phase to a liquid. There is no temperature increase until all the solid has melted.

Similarly, when heat is added to water at its boiling temperature (normally 100°C), the water boils. The water vapor that is produced remains at the boiling temperature until all the liquid has boiled away. All pure substances act the same way during boiling. As heat is added, the only change is that the liquid becomes a gas. There is no temperature increase until all the liquid has boiled off.

Each kilogram of a pure solid substance requires a certain amount of heat to melt completely. This amount is called the **heat of fusion** (FYOO′-zhun). The heat of fusion of water is about 334 kJ/kg. That is, ice at 0°C must take in 334 kJ of heat for each kilogram of liquid water at 0°C that freezes. Each pure substance has its own heat of fusion.

You add ice when you want to cool your drink. Why not use just cold water? The ice absorbs 334 J from the drink for each gram of ice that melts. Just a few grams of ice can absorb a lot of heat. The cooling effect of the ice is much

Main Idea

What is meant by the heat of fusion of a substance?

greater than just cold water—even water at 0°C. Water at 0°C absorbs only 84 J for each gram of water that warms up to 20°C. And after the water has absorbed this heat, it is warm itself.

Each gram of a pure liquid substance requires a certain amount of heat to become a gas. This amount of heat is called the **heat of vaporization** (vay-per-uh-ZAY'-shun). The heat of vaporization of water at 100°C is 2260 kJ/kg. That is, each kilogram of boiling water that changes to steam must take in 2260 kJ of heat.

During evaporation, a liquid below the boiling temperature changes to a gas. The gas formed when water evaporates is water vapor. The heat of vaporization for the formation of water vapor is about the same as for steam.

An equal amount of heat is released when a gram of water vapor condenses, or becomes liquid. When water vapor in the air condenses, a cloud is formed. The condensation releases much heat to the air. This extra heating from condensation is a major cause of some severe thunderstorms and even tornadoes.

Figure 5-21. *During which changes of phase is heat released? During which changes of phase is heat taken in?*
Heat is released when a liquid changes to a solid and when a gas changes to a liquid. Heat is taken in when a solid changes to a liquid and when a liquid changes to a gas.

Critical Thinking

Why should steam at 100°C burn you more severely than 1 g of boiling water?

One gram of steam would give off 2260 J of heat when it condenses to water on your skin. This water would then give off additional heat in cooling from 100° C to skin temperature. This second amount of heat is all that would be given off by the boiling water on your skin.

Main Idea

What was named *caloric*?

The energy that warms the tire comes from the work done to pump the tire.

Figure 5-22. *When you pump up a tire, it gets warmer than the surrounding air. Where does the energy come from that warms the tire?*

Quick Review

1. Under what circumstances is there no temperature change in water even though it is absorbing heat?
2. Which requires more heat—to melt 1 kg of ice at 0°C or to boil off 1 kg of water at 100°C?
3. What change of phase takes place when a cloud forms? Where is heat given off?

Explaining heat

New vocabulary: internal energy, law of conservation of energy

Early scientists had a hard time explaining what heat was. Heat was not visible. Yet, it could cause changes in both phase and temperature.

One early model of heat was used for nearly a hundred years. Heat was pictured as an invisible fluid. The fluid was named *caloric* (kuh-LOR'-ik). According to the model, caloric could be transferred from one substance to another. A hot substance warmed a cold substance by giving it some of its own caloric. It was known that iron gave off heat when it was hammered. The model explained this by saying that caloric was being pressed out of the iron. It was believed that caloric could not be created or destroyed. Although it could leave or enter a substance, the total amount remained the same.

Benjamin Thompson (1753–1814) was an American who spent most of his life in Europe and became known as Count Rumford. Rumford became famous for his measurements of heat. He was supervising the making of brass cannon barrels. Holes were bored in solid brass to make hollow barrels. The metal chips that were left over were very hot. The barrel itself also was hot. According to the caloric model, caloric was being pressed out of the barrel. Apparently, as long as the process continued, caloric was released. There seemed no end to the supply of caloric, even though less and less metal remained in the barrel. Rumford became convinced that heat was not a fluid.

Over 40 years after Rumford's experiments, James Joule (1818–1889) carefully measured temperature changes caused by doing work. He showed that a certain amount of work always produces the same temperature change as adding a certain amount of heat. As more work is done, the temperature rises more. He measured temperature changes in different substances: water, mercury, oil, and iron. Because of his experiments, the unit of energy, the joule, is named for him.

Work can have the same effect as heat. A certain amount of mechanical energy in the form of work raises the temperature of a substance the same as a certain amount of heat. Joule's repeated measurements always led to the same result. Scientists soon became convinced that heat, like work, is a form of energy. The SI unit for heat, as well as work, is the joule.

The modern definition of heat is that heat is the form of energy transferred because of a temperature difference. Heat always moves from the warmer substance to the cooler substance.

A substance may give off heat or take in heat. However, it does not contain heat. The energy is called heat only when it is moving from one substance to another. The energy has another name when it is inside a substance—**internal energy.**

Internal energy does not produce visible motion. Nor does it reflect a change in position of the substance. But a rise in temperature is a sign of increased internal energy. A change in phase from solid to liquid or from liquid to gas is also a sign of increased internal energy.

A substance can lose internal energy either by giving off heat or by doing work. In electric power plants, steam engines do work that drives the generator. First, water is boiled and changes to steam. As the steam expands, it pushes some blades and makes them rotate. In doing this work, the steam loses some internal energy. As a result, it cools.

Joule's work led scientists to a very important conclusion: _Energy cannot be created or destroyed._ Instead, it can only change from one form to another. This is known as the **law of conservation of energy.**

Quick Review

1. What is the modern definition of heat?
2. What is the difference between heat and internal energy?
3. How can a substance lose internal energy?
4. What is the law of conservation of energy?

Heat transfer
New vocabulary: conduction, conductor, insulator, convection, convection current, radiant energy, radiation, infrared

Heat moves from matter at a higher temperature to matter at a lower temperature. Think about all the movements of heat when you light a wood fire. First, you put a burning match against some kindling wood. Heat moves from the flame to the kindling. The kindling reaches a high enough temperature to ignite. Heat is transferred to bigger pieces of match against some kindling wood. Heat moves from the flame to the kindling. The kindling reaches a high enough temperature to ignite. Heat is transferred to bigger pieces of wood and these pieces also start to burn. The heat reaches you as you stand close to the fire.

Heat moves in three basic ways. First, heat can move through a material without the material itself moving. This type of heat movement is called **conduction** (kun-DUK'-shun). For example, if a metal spoon is placed in a hot drink, the handle becomes warm. Heat travels easily through metals by conduction and warms the metal as it travels. Metals are good **conductors** of heat. Glass, wood, and air are not as good conductors of heat as are metals. Substances that are poor conductors of heat are called **insulators** (IN'-suh-lay-terz). Would you call plastic foam a conductor or an insulator?

Heat can also move through a material by actual movement of the material. This type of heat movement is called **convection** (kun-VEK'-shun). Heat usually moves through liquids and gases by convection. For example, water at the bottom of a pot takes in heat from the burner on a stove. This water expands as it warms. The water at the bottom is then less dense than the cooler water above it. That is, each cubic centimeter of warm water at the bottom is lighter than each cubic centimeter of cooler water above. As a result, the cooler water moves downward. The warmer water is forced upward. The cooler water is now closer to the burner. It too takes in heat, expands, and is forced upward. The movements of the material itself, due to temperature differences, are called **convection currents.** Breezes are caused by convection currents in the atmosphere. Air is heated near the surface of the earth. As the heated air expands, it is forced upward as the surrounding colder air sinks.

The third way heat moves is as pure energy that moves through empty space. Heat from the sun reaches the earth by traveling through empty space. Energy that moves through space, and is not carried by matter, is known as **radiant** (RAY'-dee-unt) **energy,** or **radiation** (ray-dee-AY'-shun). Light, X-rays, and microwaves, as well as heat, move through space as radiation. Although radiation is not carried by matter, it can travel through some kinds of matter. Heat from a fireplace or an electric heater travels through air as radiation.

Heat radiation is called **infrared** (in-fruh-RED'). Quartz heaters give off infrared. If you stand or sit in the path of the radiation, you can feel the heat. But if you move out of the

Additional information:
Although heat moving by conduction may remain within one substance, it is considered heat because it is moving from a warmer part of the substance to a colder part.

Teaching suggestion:
Plastic foam is an insulator of heat.
  Ask: What makes you think plastic foam is an insulator? (It is used in cups to keep drinks warm or cold.)

Main Idea

What is convection?

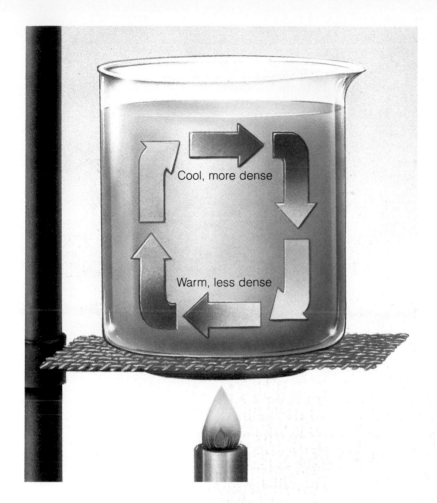

Cool, more dense

Warm, less dense

path, you may feel cold. Air does not absorb infrared as well as human skin does. The room air remains cold.

Infrared is invisible to the human eye, but special film and instruments can detect it. Infrared film can pick up differences between fields of healthy crops and fields with insect damage. Instruments can detect places where heat is escaping from buildings by measuring infrared "hot spots."

Quick Review

1. How does conduction differ from convection?
2. How can heat travel through empty space?

Cooling systems

New vocabulary: cooling system, coolant

The principles you have studied about heat transfer can be used to create **cooling systems** in which heat is removed from a space. In order to cool anything, whether a house, soft drinks, or yourself, it is necessary that heat be removed from it.

■ **Safety Note**
Space heaters used to heat a room should be placed where they will not be easily knocked over and create a fire hazard.

Quick Review answers:
1. In conduction, energy is transferred within the material, but the material does not move. In convection, the material itself moves, carrying its energy with it. Another answer is that conduction takes place best in solids, but convection takes place best in liquids and gases.
2. Only as radiation can heat travel through empty space.

Main Idea

What does a cooling system do?

Activity

See also Activity Record Sheet 5-2B (Lab Manual page 70). Answers to Questions and Conclusion appear on page T97 in the front of this book.

5.2b Transfer of Heat

Science processes: Observing, experimenting, measuring, interpreting data, making operational definitions

Materials

- hot plate
- water
- 250-mL heat-resistant beaker
- aluminum foil
- thermometer
- metal spoon
- glass stirring rod

Purpose

To determine how heat moves from one place to another.

Procedure

SAFETY NOTE: *Hot water, boiling water, and hot plates can cause severe burns if not handled with care.*

1. Plug in a hot plate. Turn the setting to high.
2. Hold your hand about 10 cm to the side and slightly above the hot plate. Do you feel the heat?
3. Turn the hot plate setting to low.
4. Fill the beaker a little more than half full with water. *Carefully* place the beaker on the hot plate.

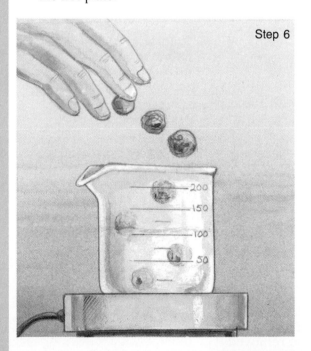

Step 6

20 minutes   Groups of 4 or teacher demonstration

5. Roll very tiny pieces of aluminum foil into small, tightly packed balls.
6. Drop the foil balls into the water. Observe what happens to them as the water warms up.
7. Leave the water on the hot plate for about 5 minutes. Then, hold a thermometer so that the bulb is just below the surface of the water. Read and record the temperature of the water near the top. Record your data on a table like the one shown.
8. Next, hold the thermometer so that the bulb is near the bottom of the beaker. Read and record the temperature of the water near the bottom.
9. Hold a metal spoon in one hand. Hold a glass rod in the other hand. Place the end of each in the heated water. Observe which transfers heat to your hand first—the glass or the metal.
10. Turn off the hot plate. Allow it to cool before returning it to its storage location.

Questions

1. What process transferred heat to your hand when it was held beside the hot plate?
2. Which was hotter, the water near the top of the beaker, or the water near the bottom?
3. What does the movement of the pieces of foil suggest to you about the movement of water within the beaker?
4. How is the water near the top warmed? What is this process called?
5. Did the glass or metal transfer heat to your hand first? Which is the better heat conductor?

Conclusion

Name three different ways that heat can be transferred and give an example of each.

228   *Chapter 5* **Work and Heat**

This can be done in several ways. One of the simplest ways is to cause the heat to radiate. As a hot object radiates heat into the air, the surrounding air becomes warmer and the object becomes cooler. You can speed up this process by continuously bringing fresh, unwarmed air into contact with the object by means of a fan. This increases the rate of radiation of heat from the object and it cools off faster. In cooling a room by using a fan, the warm air inside the room is pushed out of the room through a door or window and cool air from outside is circulated inside the room.

As we have seen, air does not absorb heat well. However, during phase changes, such as evaporation, a great deal of heat is absorbed. When a liquid evaporates, it absorbs heat, increasing the internal energy of the liquid until some of the particles of the liquid have enough kinetic energy to escape the liquid and form a gas. As they escape the liquid, these particles remove heat from their surroundings. As a result, the surroundings cool down. Evaporation of water cools the human body, as well as nuclear reactors.

Evaporation is the principle that is used to operate refrigerators, freezers, and air conditioners. These devices take advantage of the heat transfer that takes place as a result of the evaporation and condensation of a **coolant**, generally freon. In a typical refrigeration system, the coolant is freon. Liquid freon is pumped into the cooling unit, next to the food compartment. In the cooling unit, freon turns into a gas, withdrawing heat from the inside of the compartment. Gaseous freon, now carrying with it the heat in the form of internal energy, is then pumped outside the refrigerator to coils located on the back. There it gives up its heat to the surrounding air. Because the gaseous freon has given up this heat, it no longer has sufficient internal energy to remain a gas, and condenses back into a liquid.

As the freon is pumped through the refrigerator by a motor, it repeats the cycle of evaporation and condensation over and over again. Each time, the freon withdraws heat from the inside of the refrigerator and releases heat on the outside. One gram of freon can absorb approximately 167 joules of heat when it evaporates. Air conditioners operate on the same principle, transferring heat from one part of the unit to another.

Quick Review

1. How does a fan cool things off?
2. How does a refrigerator remove heat from the inside?

Figure 5-24. *A refrigerator operates on a cycle of evaporation and condensation to remove heat from inside.*

■ **Safety Note**
Use care in defrosting a refrigerator so that the tubes carrying freon are not punctured.

Quick Review answers:
1. A fan causes heat to radiate away from an object and moves the heat through a room and out of a door or window.
2. As freon changes from a liquid to a gas, it absorbs heat from the inside of the refrigerator and then carries that heat to the outside where it is released as the gaseous freon condenses back to a liquid.

Figure 5-25. *Jackets filled with down or polyester fiberfill are lightweight and yet warm. How do they keep body heat from escaping?*
Down or polyester fiberfill conducts little heat away from the body. The air between the down or fiberfill stays in place so it does not carry heat away from the body by convection.

Insulation

Heat is transferred through the walls, windows, and roofs of buildings. When it is very cold outside, large amounts of heat are wasted if a building is poorly insulated. The heat is conducted by the materials in the walls, windows, and roofs to the outside. From the outside it radiates into the air. There are several ways to cut down on heat loss. Attics and walls can be lined with insulating materials. Storm windows can be placed over existing windows. Cracks around doors can be sealed.

When it is very hot outside, heat moves readily through the walls, windows, and roof to the inside of buildings. Again, insulating materials reduce the amount of heat transferred. Roof overhangs, awnings, and shade trees cut down on heat from direct sunlight. Then the need for air conditioning is reduced and valuable energy is conserved.

Insulating materials have long fibers that trap air between them. Heat transfer is prevented in two ways. First, since air is a poor conductor, the material does not conduct heat well. Second, the fibers hold the air in place. Heat cannot be transferred by convection currents through the air.

Quick Review

What are the qualities of a good heat insulator?

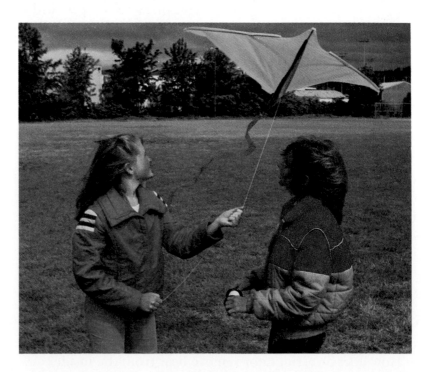

5.2 Section Review

Vocabulary

5 conduction
1 conductor
4 convection
6 convection current
15 coolant
13 cooling system
9 heat of fusion
10 heat of vaporization
7 heating system
2 insulator
12 internal energy
14 law of conservation of energy
8 radiant energy
16 radiation
11 specific heat
3 temperature

Vocabulary Review

Match each term above with the numbered phrase that best describes it.

1. Material through which heat easily moves
2. Material through which heat does not easily move
3. Measure of how hot or cold something is
4. Transfer of heat involving movement of a liquid or gas
5. Transfer of heat through a material but with no movement of the material
6. Movement within liquid or gas caused by temperature differences
7. System for heating a space
8. Energy that travels through empty space

9. Energy required per kilogram of solid for the solid to melt
10. Energy required per kilogram of liquid for the liquid to evaporate or boil
11. Energy required per kilogram and per degree for a substance to warm up
12. Energy inside matter
13. System for removing heat
14. Energy cannot be created or destroyed
15. Substance that removes heat by absorbing it
16. Term meaning radiant energy

Review Questions

Multiple Choice: Choose the answer that best completes each of the following sentences.

17. Heat tends to move from a ? .
    a. conductor to an insulator
    b. liquid to a solid
    c. substance with greater mass to one with less mass
    d. warmer to a cooler substance

18. The greater the specific heat of a substance, the ? .
    a. faster it will cool down
    b. more slowly it will warm up
    c. higher its temperature will be
    d. faster it will melt

Understanding the Concepts

19. Explain how the evaporation of the liquid within the pipes of a refrigerator keep the food in the refrigerator cold.
20. In a hot-air heating system, air heated by a furnace enters a room through a hot-air vent. Will the room be heated better if the vent is closer to the ceiling or to the floor? Explain.

21. People place food in picnic coolers to keep the food cold on a warm day. Does a cooler really cool the food? If not, how does it work?
22. Double-paned windows have two panes of glass with an air space between them. Explain what makes them better than single-paned windows at keeping heat from passing through.

Problems to Solve

23. How much heat is absorbed by an aluminum pan with a mass of 15 kg that is heated from 28°C to 150°C? (Aluminum has a specific heat of 920 J/kg · °C.) Express your answer in kJ.
24. How much heat is given out when 80 g of water condenses from vapor to liquid water?

For ideas for classroom demonstration and discussion, see Getting Started on page T98 in the front of this book.

5.3 The Kinetic Theory of Matter

Supplemental materials: Teaching Diagrams 5-3A, 5-3B, 5-3C (TRB pages 28, 29, 30), Reading Checksheet 5-3 (TRB page 94), Skillsheet 5-3 (TRB page 140), Investigation 5-3 (Lab Manual pages 75–76)

Section Preview

- **Motion in matter**
- **An improved model for gases**
- **An improved model for solids**
- **An improved model for liquids**

- **A model for temperature changes**
- **A model for heat transfer**
- **A model for phase changes**
- **A model for evaporation**
- **A model for specific heat**

Bracketed numbers are Section Review questions correlated to that objective.

Learning Objectives

1. To apply the kinetic theory of matter to the behavior of gases, solids, and liquids. [1,2,4,6,7,8,10,11,12]
2. To relate the internal energy of a substance to the potential and kinetic energy of its particles. [9,13]
3. To use the kinetic theory of matter to explain phase changes, heat transfer, and specific heat. [3,9,14,15,16]

Figure 5-26. *Smoke from stacks spreads out in a cloud as it rises. This is consistent with the theory that smoke is made of small particles that are free to spread out in a gas, the air.*

According to the particle model of matter, all matter is made of tiny particles. The particles are separated from each other by space. In a gas, the amount of space between particles is relatively large. In liquids and solids, the amount of space between particles is much smaller.

You have learned that when matter takes in heat, its internal energy increases. When matter gives off heat, its internal energy decreases. How do changes in internal energy affect the particles of matter? In this section, you will learn about a model for matter that takes into account changes in internal energy.

Motion in matter

New vocabulary: diffusion, random, kinetic theory of matter

Odors quickly spread throughout a room. If a bottle of perfume is opened, the odor is soon noticed all over the room. Onions frying on the stove can be smelled beyond the kitchen.

For odors to spread, particles carrying the odor must move through the surrounding air.

Food coloring spreads through water even if the water is not stirred. When crystals of copper sulfate dissolve in water, they form a blue-green solution. The blue-green color spreads through the water, even with no stirring. For the color to spread, particles carrying the color must move through the surrounding water.

The natural movement within gases and liquids that spreads out odors and colors is called **diffusion** (dih-FYOO'-zhun). Diffusion occurs even when there are no temperature differences that would cause convection currents. It occurs in gases and liquids that appear to be perfectly still.

Diffusion can be explained by thinking of the particles in gases and liquids as constantly moving. The motion is **random,** or without pattern. At any time there are as many particles moving in one direction as in the opposite direction. All the individual motions balance each other. There is no visible motion within the gas or liquid. But because the particles themselves move, odors and colors spread out.

Diffusion takes place faster in gases than in liquids. To understand why, think of moving through a crowd of people to catch up with a friend. It is easier to move through a thin crowd than through a tightly packed crowd. There is much more space between particles in a gas than in a liquid. A gas is like a very thin crowd, while a liquid is like a tightly packed crowd.

Increasing the temperature increases the speed of diffusion. A drop of food coloring diffuses through warm water faster than through cold water. Substances also dissolve faster in warm water than in cold water. A cube of sugar will disappear faster in warm water.

The increased speed of dissolving and diffusion can be explained. You would make your way through a crowd in less

Figure 5-27. *From left to right, the photos above show copper sulfate crystals just after they have been placed in water; after 4 h; after a day; and after 2 days. How can the spreading of the color be explained?*
As copper sulfate crystals dissolve in water, they separate into smaller particles (in this case, copper ions and sulfate ions). These particles slowly spread throughout the water. They spread because they are moving and because moving water molecules collide with them and knock them about.

Main Idea

In what direction do particles move in a gas or liquid?

Research Topic

Find out what John Dalton thought about the question of whether the particles of matter are in motion.

Figure 5-28. *Will the sugar dissolve faster in the hot tea or in the iced tea?* Sugar will dissolve faster in hot tea than in iced tea. See text discussion of the effect of temperature on diffusion.

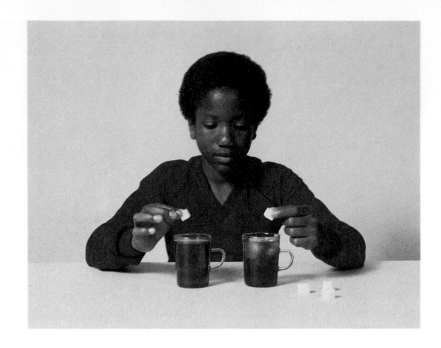

Main Idea

What are the main ideas of the kinetic theory of matter?

time if you were moving faster. Similarly, the particles are moving faster at the higher temperature.

Something that is moving has kinetic energy, or energy of motion. The faster it moves, the more kinetic energy it has. When a substance becomes warmer, its particles move faster. The kinetic energy of the particles increases. The temperature of a substance measures how warm the substance is. Temperature, then, is related to the kinetic energy of the individual particles of a substance. An increase in temperature means an increase in the kinetic energy of the average particle.

These ideas are part of the **kinetic theory of matter.** This theory can be summarized as follows.

1. All matter is made up of particles which are in constant motion.
2. As a substance becomes warmer, its particles move with greater energy. As a substance cools, its particles move with less energy.

Adding motion to the particles of matter leads to an improved model of matter. More observations can be explained. Better predictions of the behavior of matter can be made.

Quick Review

When a substance cools down, what happens to the speed of its particles?

See also Activity Record Sheet 5-3A (Lab Manual page 73). Safety Note, Teacher Note, Answers to Questions and Conclusion appear on page T99 in the front of this book.

Activity

5.3a Diffusion at Different Temperatures

Science processes: Observing, experimenting, interpreting data

Materials   BASIC   15 minutes   Groups of 4

- 2 250-mL beakers or similar containers
- potassium permanganate ($KMnO_4$) or food coloring
- hot water
- cold water
- tweezers
- watch or clock with second hand

Purpose

To determine if the speed of diffusion differs for solids dissolved in liquids at different temperatures.

Procedure

1. Fill one beaker with hot water. Fill the second beaker with an equal amount of cold water.
2. Using a tweezers, add two or three of the potassium permanganate crystals to each of the beakers. Two or three drops of food coloring may be used in place of the potassium permanganate. Do NOT stir.

SAFETY NOTE: *Do not touch the potassium permanganate crystals or solution. It may be irritating to your eyes and skin. If you should get any in your eyes, flush the area with a generous amount of water. Wash any affected skin areas with soap and water.*

3. Notice how fast the color diffuses in the two samples of water. Make a table like the one shown and record your observations.

Questions

1. Does the color diffuse faster in hot water or in cold water?
2. What is the difference in the amount of diffusion in the beakers after 1 minute? After 5 minutes? After 15 minutes?

Conclusion

How is the speed of the diffusion of a solid in a liquid affected by the temperature of the liquid?

Step 2

Potassium permanganate or food coloring	Amount of Diffusion	
	in hot water	in cold water
After 1 minute		
After 2 minutes		
After 3 minutes		

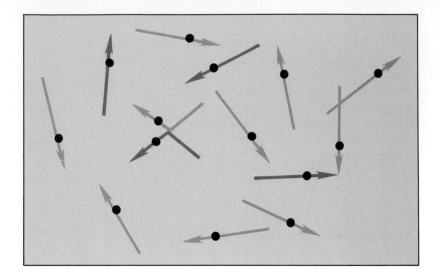

Main Idea

What is the internal energy of a gas?

An improved model for gases
New vocabulary: vibrate

Common gases, such as oxygen, carbon dioxide, and clean air, are made of molecules. Each molecule is made of from one to several atoms. The atoms within a molecule remain close together. The molecules, on the other hand, are relatively far apart from each other. But they are so tiny that a cubic centimeter of air contains more than a million times a million times a million of them! That is $10^6 \times 10^6 \times 10^6 = 10^{18}$ molecules. Despite the large number of molecules, a gas is 99.9% empty space. The molecules themselves take up only about one-thousandth of the space.

The molecules of a gas are in constant, random motion. At room temperature they move at about 500 m/s, on the average. Yet they rarely move very far before they collide with each other or with their container. After a collision, a molecule goes off in a different direction. One molecule may give up some of its kinetic energy to another molecule in a collision. The first molecule will then move more slowly, while the second will move faster. The total amount of kinetic energy stays the same. Because of collisions, both the speed and the direction of a molecule keep changing. But the average kinetic energy of all the molecules does not change.

Within a molecule, the atoms can **vibrate,** or move back and forth. They can also rotate around each other. Thus, a molecule can have additional energy due to the vibration and rotation of its atoms.

The internal energy of a gas is the sum of the energies of all the molecules. This sum includes the total kinetic energy of the moving molecules. It also includes the energy from the vibration and rotation of the atoms within each molecule.

Figure 5-30. *A molecule can move as a whole (left). In addition, its atoms can vibrate (center) or rotate around each other (right).*

If two gases are at the same temperature, their molecules have the same average kinetic energy. But if there are more molecules in one gas, that gas will have more internal energy altogether. You could warm the air in a balloon by holding it near a light bulb. Then the average kinetic energy of the air in the balloon would be greater than that of the room air. But the room air would have so many more molecules that it would still have more internal energy. The internal energy depends both on the temperature and the amount of gas.

Quick Review

1. What three types of motion can a molecule in a gas have?
2. What does the internal energy of a gas refer to?

An improved model for solids

New vocabulary: absolute zero, kelvin

Some solids are made of molecules, but many are not. Ice is made of water molecules, and dry ice is made of carbon dioxide molecules. But metals are made of separate atoms. And salts, including sodium chloride, are made of ions, or atoms with extra or missing electrons. In a discussion of solids, then, the word *particle* can mean molecule, atom, or ion.

The particles in a solid are not free to move throughout the solid. They are held together by forces that keep them close to each other. However, even in a solid, the particles are in constant motion. They each vibrate back and forth around a "home" position. They move as if they were attached to little springs.

The vibrating particles in a solid have both kinetic and potential energy. To understand this, think of a bouncing ball. Whenever the ball is moving toward the ground, it is losing

Quick Review answers:
1. A molecule can move as a whole. Within a molecule, atoms can vibrate; they can also rotate around each other.
2. The internal energy of a gas is the sum of the energies of all the molecules, including total kinetic energy and energy from vibration and rotation of the atoms.

Main Idea

What kind of energy do particles in a solid have?

potential energy. At the same time, it is gaining kinetic energy. On the other hand, when it bounces away from the ground, it is gaining potential energy. And it is losing kinetic energy. The total energy of the ball remains almost unchanged. (The ball loses some energy each time it touches the ground, and it stops moving after a while.)

A bouncing ball has potential energy because the earth is pulling on it with the force of gravity. A particle in a solid has potential energy because its neighbors exert forces on it. As the particle vibrates, potential energy is changed to kinetic and back to potential. But the total energy stays the same. For a solid, the internal energy is the sum of all the energies of its

Our Science Heritage

The Contributions of Boyle and Black to the Theory of Heat

Robert Boyle

Joseph Black

Many persons contributed to the development of the present theory of heat. Robert Boyle (1627–1691) became one of England's first experimental scientists. He is known for Boyle's Law, which describes how the volume of a gas changes when the pressure on it changes. Boyle suggested that when a gas is heated, the particles of the gas move faster. Boyle published his hypothesis more than 150 years before the experiments of Count Rumford and James Joule led scientists to accept this view relating heat to motion.

A century after Boyle's work, the Scottish scientist Joseph Black (1728–1799) was demonstrating that equal amounts of heat produced different temperature changes in different substances. He found that when ice was heated, it melted but did not change temperature. When the same water froze, an equal amount of heat was given off. Black, like other scientists of his day, believed that heat was a fluid. However, this hypothesis could not be used to explain his experiments very easily. They were later well explained by the kinetic theory.

The contributions of Joseph Black have been preserved primarily through the notes of his students, since Black published very little. He founded one of the first chemical societies to be formed.

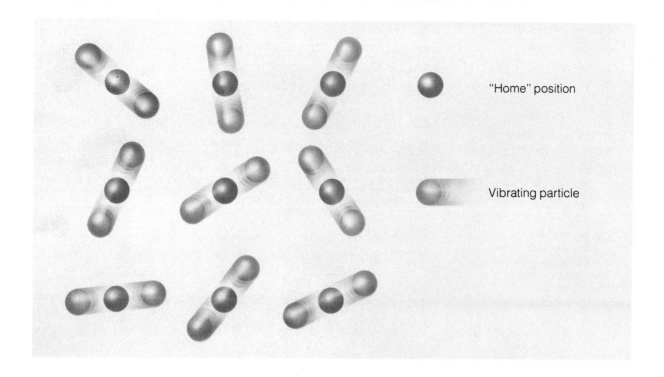

"Home" position

Vibrating particle

particles. That is, the internal energy includes both the kinetic and the potential energies of the particles.

The kinetic energy of a single vibrating particle keeps changing. But the sum for all the particles does not change. The temperature of a solid depends on the average kinetic energy of the particles. This average does not change as long as no heat enters or leaves and no work is done. When two substances are at the same temperature, the particles have the same average kinetic energy. The potential energy does not contribute to the temperature.

When a solid warms up, its particles receive more energy. They move in bigger vibrations. That is, they move farther from the "home" position on each swing. They are like a ball that can make higher bounces when it has more energy. The average kinetic energy of the particles of the solid is greater. The particles are moving faster, on the average.

If the solid happens to be made of molecules, the atoms within the molecules are moving. As in a gas, the atoms can vibrate or rotate inside each molecule. A solid object that appears to be at rest is full of motion!

There is only one situation when the molecules or atoms of a substance are not moving at all. This is at the temperature of **absolute zero.** At absolute zero, the particles of a substance have no kinetic energy. Absolute zero is the lowest unit on the

Figure 5-31. *Particle motions in a solid. How are the motions of particles different in a solid and in a gas?*
In a solid, each particle vibrates around one position. It does not move throughout the solid. In a gas, the particles move throughout the container that the gas occupies.

Critical Thinking

Which would generally be the best conductors of heat, gases, liquids, or solids? Can you think of exceptions?
Because of the closeness of the particles to each other and because of the particles' relatively fixed positions, heat is transferred most easily from one particle to another in solids. An exception would be the solid form of water, ice.

Kelvin temperature scale. The Kelvin temperature scale is named for the British physicist Lord Kelvin (1824–1907). On this scale the units of temperature are named *kelvins* and are the same size as degrees Celsius. Zero Kelvin, absolute zero, is equal to $-273°C$. The freezing point of pure water, $0°C$, is equivalent to a Kelvin temperature of 273 K. Since temperature is a measure of the average kinetic energy of the particles of a substance and since at absolute zero the particles have no kinetic energy, there is no need for negative numbers on the Kelvin scale.

Main Idea

Why are there no numbers below 0 in the Kelvin temperature scale?

Quick Review answers:
1. When two substances are at the same temperature, the values of the average kinetic energy of their particles are equal.
2. At absolute zero (0°K).

Quick Review

1. When two substances are at the same temperature, how do the values of the average kinetic energy of their particles compare?
2. When do the molecules of a substance have no kinetic energy at all?

An improved model for liquids

A liquid can be thought of as a cross between a solid and a gas. As in a solid, the particles in a liquid remain close to each other. As in a gas, the particles can also move past each other.

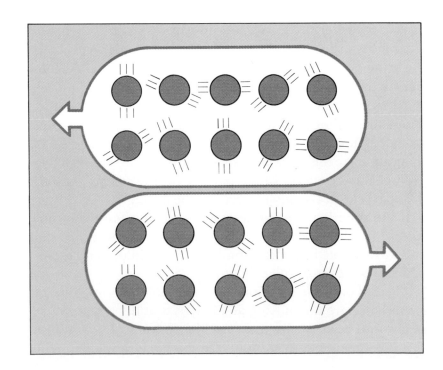

Figure 5-32. *How are the motions of particles in a liquid different from the motions of particles in a solid? In a gas?*
Particles in a liquid move past each other, particles in a solid do not. Particles in a liquid cannot move very far from the other particles in the liquid; particles in a gas spread out and fill the container holding the gas.

The particles in a liquid are in constant motion. Some of the particles may group together for a time. Within the group, the particles vibrate as in a solid. But the whole group of particles moves. After a short time, the group breaks apart. The individual particles separate from the group. They may combine with other particles to form new groups.

On the average, the particles have enough energy to keep from being held in a fixed position. Yet, they do not have enough to free themselves from the forces between particles. They are always close to other particles.

In a liquid, as in a gas and solid, temperature is related to the average kinetic energy of the particles. The potential energy does not contribute to the temperature. At higher temperatures, the particles move faster. The vibrations are bigger. In addition, the particles move faster past each other.

Quick Review

What kind of motion is similar for particles in liquids and in solids?

Research Topic

Fluid mechanics is the study of the properties and behavior of fluids. Aerodynamics is the branch of fluid mechanics dealing with gases. Read about Daniel Bernoulli and his work on the forces that are exerted by fluids in motion. Find out how Bernoulli's principle explains how an airplane flies.

Quick Review answer:
Particles in liquids may group together for a while. Within a group, the particles vibrate just as they do in solids.

A model for temperature changes

The usefulness of a model in science is its ability to explain observations and predict new ones. The model of matter based on the kinetic theory explains many observations of the behavior of matter.

For example, suppose work is done on a substance or heat is added to it. What does the kinetic theory predict will happen to the substance? The internal energy increases when the work is done or the heat is added. In a gas, the internal energy is mainly due to the kinetic energy of the moving molecules. The theory predicts that the molecules will move faster, on the average. The average kinetic energy of the molecules will increase. And the temperature of the gas will increase.

On the other hand, suppose the gas does work on something else or gives off heat. It loses internal energy this way. The theory predicts that the molecules will slow down and have less kinetic energy. The temperature will fall.

In a solid and liquid, the internal energy consists of both kinetic and potential energy. The potential energy comes from the forces between the particles. When the internal energy increases, both the kinetic and potential energies increase. This is true except during melting or boiling, which

Research Topic

Air that rises cools about 1°C for every 100 m that it rises. Find out how the lowering of the temperature can be explained with the kinetic theory.

will be discussed later. When the average kinetic energy of the particles increases, the temperature rises. The increase in potential energy has no effect on the temperature. What happens to the temperature when the internal energy decreases?

When the internal energy decreases, the temperature decreases, too.

Quick Review

If work is done on a solid, what happens to the kinetic energy of its particles?

Quick Review answer:
If work is done on a solid, the kinetic energy of its particles increases.

A model for heat transfer

Suppose one end of a metal bar is placed in a flame. Heat is absorbed by the metal bar at that end. The temperature of the end of the bar increases. The kinetic theory can explain how heat is conducted through the bar. The particles at the hot end have more kinetic energy on the average than other particles in the bar. Particles at the hot end of the bar collide with nearby particles in the bar. In the collisions, particles with more energy lose some energy to particles with less energy. As a result, the nearby part of the bar becomes warmer. The process continues along the bar. Finally, particles all over the bar have the same average kinetic energy. The entire bar is hot.

Suppose a hot cup of tea is sitting on the kitchen counter. How does the kinetic theory explain how heat is conducted away from the tea? Particles in the warmer tea have more kinetic energy on the average than particles in the cooler air.

■ **Safety Note**
Always cover your hands when handling a metal object that has been heated.

Heat will move through the rod from the hotter end toward the cooler end.

Figure 5-33. *In which direction will heat move through this rod?*

Particles of tea and air collide with each other at the top surface of the tea. The tea particles give up some kinetic energy to the air particles. Collisions continue between the particles of tea and air. Finally, the tea and air particles have the same average kinetic energy. The tea and air then have the same temperature.

You may be wondering how the hot tea lower down in the cup cools down. When the tea near the top cools a little, its particles move in smaller vibrations. The particles take up less space than the particles of the warmer tea below. The cooler tea is now more dense and sinks below the warmer tea. Now the warmer tea is near the surface and its particles collide with the air particles. Thus, the kinetic theory can explain convection as well as conduction.

Quick Review

When particles of something warm collide with particles of something cool, what happens to their kinetic energies?

A model for phase changes

Boiling can be understood by thinking about the launching of spacecraft. How are spacecraft able to overcome the pull of the earth's gravity? During launching, the spacecraft's rockets give off tremendous amounts of burning gases at high speeds. The gases, in an equal and opposite reaction, push forward on the spacecraft. The forces are exerted by the gases for some distance. They do work on the spacecraft. The work done on the spacecraft is changed to kinetic energy. The spacecraft is able to move upward at high speed.

As the spacecraft moves away from the earth, some of its kinetic energy is changed into potential energy. The spacecraft gains potential energy because of its separation from the earth. But it has so much kinetic energy that it always has some left. It keeps moving away from the earth.

Particles in a liquid can be thought of as tiny spacecraft. Adding heat to a liquid increases the energy of the particles. The temperature of the liquid increases until the boiling temperature is reached. Any additional heat gives the particles energy to overcome the forces between particles. The particles break away from each other and form bubbles of gas all through the liquid. The bubbles float to the top and break through the surface. The gas escapes from the liquid.

Additional information:
Tea and air are each made of a mixture of different kinds of particles. The phrase *tea particles* or *air particles* refers to the particles of the substance regardless of what kind they are.

Quick Review answer:
The particles in the warm substance lose kinetic energy as the particles in the cool substance gain kinetic energy.

A launched spacecraft has enough energy to keep moving away from the earth, even after some of its kinetic energy has been converted to potential energy. The particles in a boiling liquid have enough energy to break away from each other and escape from the liquid. Like the spacecraft, they have more potential energy when they are free.

Figure 5-34. *How is a launched spacecraft like the particles in a boiling liquid?*

Main Idea

What kind of energy is released during condensation and freezing?

The average kinetic energy of the particles of gas is the same as in the liquid. The gas and liquid have the same temperature until all the liquid has boiled away.

The particles of gas have more potential energy than they did in the liquid. They are like spacecraft that have more potential energy after they have left the earth. The extra potential energy came from the heat added to the liquid after it reached the boiling temperature.

Particles in a solid are held together by forces between them. They vibrate but they are not free to move past each other. When heat is added to a solid at its melting temperature, no change in temperature occurs. The average kinetic energy of the particles does not change. All of the heat is changed into potential energy. The particles receive enough energy to overcome the forces holding them in place. In the liquid formed from the melted solid, the particles are free to move past each other.

At the end of the melting, the particles have the same average kinetic energy as they did in the solid. The liquid is at the same temperature as the solid was when melting began. But the particles have more potential energy.

The reverse of boiling is condensation. The reverse of melting is freezing. No temperature change takes place during these phase changes either. The average kinetic energy of the particles does not change. But heat is given off. During condensation and freezing, the particles lose potential energy. This potential energy is released as heat.

Quick Review

1. When a solid melts, what happens to the kinetic and potential energies of its particles?
2. When a liquid freezes, what happens to the kinetic and potential energies of its particles?

A model for evaporation

A puddle of water dries up. Freshly washed dishes dry in a dish rack. Liquids evaporate even at temperatures way below their boiling temperature. How can the kinetic theory explain evaporation?

The temperature of a liquid is related to the average kinetic energy of the particles. But not all particles in the liquid have the same kinetic energy. During collisions, individual

See also Activity Record Sheet 5-3B (Lab Manual page 74). Answers to Questions and Conclusion appear on page T99 in the front of this book.

Activity

5.3b Melting Materials

Science processes: Observing, measuring, inferring, interpreting data, communicating

30 minutes   Groups of 4 or teacher demonstration

Materials

- **sharpened pencil**
- **2 thermometers**
- **clear tape**
- **water**
- **hot plate**
- **2 250-mL beakers**
- **2 wire screens**
- **2 cardboard circles (9 cm in diameter)**
- **crushed ice**
- **glass stirring rod**
- **watch or clock with a second hand**

Purpose

To show the temperature changes that occur during the melting of ice.

Procedure

1. Use a sharpened pencil to poke a hole in the center of the cardboard disk. Gently ease the bulb of a thermometer through the hole. Slide the bulb down so that when the cardboard rests on the rim of the beaker, the bulb is suspended inside the beaker. Tape the thermometer in this position. Do this for both beakers.

    SAFETY NOTE: *Be sure the hole in the cardboard disk is large enough so the thermometer can be pushed through without breaking. If a thermometer is broken, avoid touching the mercury; notify your teacher.*

2. Fill the first 250-mL beaker half full of water. Add enough crushed ice to fill the beaker. Stir the ice and water. Measure the water temperature and record it on a table.

3. When the water temperature reaches 0°C, remove any remaining ice and transfer it to the second beaker. Add enough additional ice to the second beaker to make the volume in the two beakers about equal.

4. Put a cardboard disk with a thermometer set in it over each of the beakers. Make sure the bulbs of the thermometers are set in the middle of the water and in the middle of the ice. Place both beakers on a wire screen on the cold coils of the same hot plate. Set the hot plate control to low heat. Record the temperature of both beakers.

5. After one minute, record the temperature of each beaker. Take a temperature reading every minute until the ice melts completely. Record all the data on the table.

6. As the ice in the second beaker melts, periodically remove the cardboard for a few seconds and stir the ice and water mixture.

7. Make a temperature-time graph and plot the data you collected for both beakers on the same axes. Use different colored pencils to connect the set of points for each beaker.

Questions

1. How did the temperatures of the two beakers compare at the start?
2. Was the same amount of heat added to each of the beakers? Explain your answer.
3. How did the temperatures of the two beakers compare at the end of 5 minutes?
4. How many minutes did it take to completely melt the ice?

Conclusion

How does the temperature change in an ice-water mixture as heat is added?

Step 4

Figure 5-35. *Cologne contains alcohol. What makes alcohol at room temperature feel so cool on the skin?* As alcohol evaporates, the remaining alcohol cools. Heat moves from your skin into the alcohol, resulting in your skin feeling cooler.

particles gain and lose energy. A few particles may gain very large amounts of energy. Some of them will have enough energy to overcome the forces between the particles. When they reach the surface of the liquid, they escape.

What effect does the escape of the high-energy particles have on the rest of the liquid? To understand, think about the following. Suppose your teacher announced that all the "A" students would be excused from taking the next test. What would happen to the class average on the next test? Without the high scores of the "A" students, the class average would go down.

In the same way, the average kinetic energy of the remaining particles in the liquid is less. The temperature of the liquid is reduced. The liquid becomes cooler than its surroundings. As a result, heat moves into the liquid from its surroundings. Because of this, evaporation has a cooling effect. When drops of water or alcohol evaporate from your skin, your skin feels much cooler. Heat moves from your skin into the evaporating water or alcohol.

Your body maintains its constant temperature in warm weather using this cooling method. Perspiration is evaporated from the surface of the skin. The body cools as a result.

Quick Review

1. What particles of a liquid are the most likely to escape?
2. When some particles escape from a liquid, what happens to the average kinetic energy of the remaining ones?

A model for specific heat

It takes different amounts of heat to raise the temperature of equal masses of different substances by the same number

Figure 5-36. *The tub of golf balls has the same mass as the tub of table tennis balls. Which tub must contain more balls? Explain how you know.* Since a golf ball has more mass than a table tennis ball, there must be more table tennis balls. Otherwise, the tubs could not have the same total mass.

Point out to students that the tub of golf balls is like a gram of lead atoms. The tub of table tennis balls is like a gram of copper atoms.

of degrees. Water requires the most heat. Copper requires much less heat. And lead requires even less than copper. How can the kinetic theory explain these differences?

The mass of a copper atom is only a third of that of a lead atom. As a result, in a gram of copper there are three times as many atoms as in a gram of lead. For the same temperature increase, the average kinetic energy of the atoms must rise by the same amount. But with three times as many copper atoms, three times as much total energy is required. Just as the kinetic theory predicts, the specific heat for copper is three times the specific heat for lead.

A water molecule has even less mass than a copper atom. A gram of water has more than three times as many water molecules as a gram of copper has copper atoms. Furthermore, some of the energy absorbed by water increases the motions of the atoms of oxygen and hydrogen within the molecules. These motions within the molecules do not increase the motion of the total molecule. They have no effect on the kinetic energy of the water molecules. Thus, the energy absorbed in this way does not affect the temperature. As predicted, water absorbs much more heat than an equal mass of copper during the same temperature change.

Quick Review

1. What is the relation between the number of particles in a gram of a substance and the specific heat of that substance?
2. Why does a substance made of molecules absorb more heat for a given change in temperature than a substance made of single atoms?

Data Search

What is the atomic mass of lead? of copper? What is the specific heat capacity of lead? of copper? Search pages 658–661.

The atomic mass of lead is 207.2, and that of copper is 63.546. The specific heat capacity of lead is 0.038, and that of copper is 0.092.

Main Idea

In what way does water absorb energy that has no effect on the temperature of the water?

Quick Review answers:
1. The more particles there are in a gram of a substance, the higher is its specific heat.
2. Some of the energy absorbed by the substance gets used up by motion within the molecule and causes no temperature change.

Careers

Refrigeration and Heating Mechanic

Most refrigeration and heating mechanics work for companies that sell and service cooling and heating equipment. In some cases individuals may operate their own repair and installation service. Mechanics in this field receive their training either by working with experienced mechanics or by attending a trade school offering this specialty. A high school education is preferred for either apprenticeship training or for admittance to the trade school. Science and math courses in high school offer valuable background for such training.

The work can challenge the mechanic's ability to solve problems. Long, irregular hours may be required. Demands are seasonal and, of course, vary with location.

Increasing awareness of the need for conserving valuable energy resources has led to expanded opportunities in this career field. New technological developments and greater use of solar energy promise continued growth in the years ahead.

For further information, write to: Air-Conditioning and Refrigeration Institute, 1815 N. Fort Myer Drive, Arlington, Virginia 22209.

A refrigeration and heating mechanic may be called into a home to repair a heater.

Mechanical Engineer

Mechanical engineers are employed by industries that manufacture metals, machinery, transportation equipment, electrical equipment, or numerous other products. They may specialize in areas such as automobiles, instrumentation, or heating and cooling.

The work of the mechanical engineer emphasizes detail and precision. Special demands require creativity and problem-solving ability. The mechanical engineer often works as part of a team and it is important that he or she be able to work with other members of the team.

Preparation requirements for the mechanical engineer include a bachelor's degree in engineering, in one of the physical sciences, or in mathematics. A strong high school background in science and mathematics can be a great help in ensuring success in a college science or engineering program. Continued study at the graduate level in the field of preparation is increasingly important for advancement.

For further information, write to: The American Society of Mechanical Engineers, 345 E. 47th Street, New York, New York 10017.

Some mechanical engineers specialize in the design of heating systems. This engineer is inspecting solar panels installed on a roof.

5.3 Section Review

Answers to Understanding the Concepts appear on page T99 in the front of this book. Blackline master test for this section: Section Testsheet 5-3 (TRB page 214)

Vocabulary

6 absolute zero
2 diffusion
5 kelvin
3 kinetic theory of matter
4 random
1 vibrate

Vocabulary Review

Match each term above with the numbered phrase that best describes it.

1. Describes what atoms in a piece of metal do
2. Causes smell of burnt toast to spread out
3. Explains how a liquid below its boiling temperature can change into a gas
4. Describes direction of motion of gas molecules
5. Unit of temperature equal to a Celsius degree
6. Temperature at which atoms of a substance do not move

Review Questions

Multiple Choice: Choose the answer that best completes each of the following sentences.

7. The temperature of a substance is most closely related to the _?_.
   a. volume of the substance
   b. mass of the substance
   c. internal energy of the substance
   d. average kinetic energy of the particles

8. The particles in a liquid _?_.
   a. vibrate as well as move past each other
   b. all move with the same speed
   c. all have the same kinetic energy
   d. exert no forces on each other

9. During melting, the effect of adding heat is to increase the _?_.
   a. kinetic energy of the particles
   b. potential energy of the particles
   c. size of the particles
   d. forces between the particles

10. The reverse of boiling is _?_.
    a. freezing
    b. melting
    c. evaporation
    d. condensation

11. Your body cools during warm weather by means of _?_ of moisture through your skin.
    a. condensation
    b. evaporation
    c. absorption
    d. cooling

Understanding the Concepts

12. Explain what makes gases diffuse faster than liquids do.
13. What effect does an increase in temperature have on the motion of the particles of a substance?
14. Compare the motion of particles in a solid with the motion of particles in a liquid.
15. When a substance absorbs heat, is all the energy converted into kinetic energy of the particles? Explain your answer.

16. Use the kinetic theory to explain how heat moves from a heated pot to the soup inside.
17. Use the kinetic theory to explain why a puddle dries up more quickly in the sun than in the shade.
18. Helium and neon are both gases with only one atom in each molecule. The mass of a neon atom is five times that of a helium atom. Predict how the specific heats of the two gases should compare.

5 Chapter Review

Vocabulary

absolute zero
block and tackle
compound machine
conduction
conductor
convection
convection current
coolant
cooling system
diffusion
efficiency
effort arm
effort force
fulcrum
heat of fusion

heat of vaporization
heating system
inclined plane
insulator
internal energy
joule
kelvin
kinetic theory of matter
law of conservation of energy
lever
machine
mechanical advantage
power
pulley
radiant energy

radiation
random
resistance arm
resistance force
simple machine
specific heat
temperature
vibrate
wedge
wheel and axle
work
work input
work output

Review of Concepts

Work is energy that is transferred to an object when the object moves in the direction of a force acting on the object.

- The amount of work done is equal to the amount of force in the direction of motion multiplied by the distance moved.
- No work is done when the object does not move.

A **machine** is something that changes the size and/or direction of a force used to do work.

- Examples of machines include the inclined plane, wedge, screw, lever, wheel and axle, and pulley.
- The mechanical advantage of a machine equals the force needed to do the work directly divided by the force applied to the machine.
- The efficiency of a machine equals the work done by the machine divided by the work put into the machine, expressed as a percentage.
- The efficiency of any machine is always less than 100% because some of the work is used to overcome friction.

Power is a measure of how fast work is being done or how fast energy is being used.

Heat is energy that is transferred as a result of differences in temperature.

- Temperature is a measure of how hot or cold a substance is.
- Heat moves from a warmer to a cooler substance.
- Substances usually become warmer when they take in heat and cooler when they give it off.
- When a substance is changing phase, it gains or loses heat but remains at a constant temperature.
- The amount of heat gained or lost by a substance depends on the amount of substance, the type of substance, and the temperature change.
- Heat is transferred by conduction, convection, and radiation.
- Insulators are substances that are poor conductors of heat.

The **internal energy** of a substance is the energy inside it.

- A substance may gain internal energy either by taking in heat or by having work done on it.
- When a substance gains internal energy, either its temperature increases or it changes phase.

Forms of energy are different kinds of energy, such as kinetic energy, potential energy, work, heat, and internal energy.

- Energy can be changed from one form to another.
- Energy cannot be created or destroyed.

The **kinetic theory of matter** is a model that pictures matter as made of particles that are in constant, random motion.

- The temperature of a substance is related to the average kinetic energy of the particles.
- When a substance becomes hotter, its particles move faster, on the average.
- Models for solids, liquids, and gases picture the particles as having potential energy because of the forces between them.
- Changes in phase are explained by changes in the potential energy of the particles.
- The internal energy of a substance equals the sum of all the energies of the particles.

Critical Thinking

1. To open a swinging door, you usually push on the part of the door farthest from the hinges. Use your knowledge of levers to explain why it would be harder to open the door if you pushed on the center of the door.

2. A hot, dry climate is generally more comfortable than a hot, humid climate. Use your understanding of evaporation to explain why.

3. Suggest an explanation for the good insulation properties of plastic foam. (*Hint:* What causes plastic foam to be so light for its size?)

Individual Research

1. Compare the dissolving times of a fixed amount of granulated sugar in water at different temperatures. Use water samples of equal volume. On a graph, plot the dissolving time vs. the water temperature. How does the dissolving time change with temperature?

2. Measure the heat of fusion of water as follows. Measure the temperature of a known volume of warm water (50°C to 60°C) that half fills its container. Add ice to the warm water and wait until the temperature is just lowered to 0°C. Remove any remaining ice and remeasure the volume of the water. How many grams of ice melted? (*Hint:* Assume each milliliter of water added to the original sample to be from one gram of ice that melted.) How many joules of heat were lost by the original sample of warm water? How many joules were used to melt each gram of ice? Experiment with keeping an ice cube in surroundings that are at room temperature. What kinds of and combinations of materials keep the ice the longest?

Bibliography

Adler, Irving. *Hot and Cold.* New York: John Day, 1975.
   Explains the nature of heat and cold; examines theories of heat and its behavior; describes how very high and very low temperatures can be produced.

Asimov, Isaac, and Karen A. Frenkel. *Robots: Machines in Man's Image.* New York: Harmony, 1985.
   This book traces the history of the development of robots, from descriptions in ancient Greek mythology to modern robots used in industry and research.

Cobb, Vicki. *More Science Experiments You Can Eat.* New York: Lippincott/Harper & Row, 1979.
   Applies some basic principles of science to food. Includes the processes of heating, cooling, freezing, and thawing.

Evans, Peter with Isaac Asimov. *Technology.* New York: Facts on File, 1985.
   How technology has advanced and the new technologies of the future are described and illustrated.

Jollands, David (ed.). *Machines, Power and Transportation.* New York: Arco, 1984.
   This book explains how modern technology works in the machines we use every day.

Kingston, Jeremy. *How Bridges Are Made.* New York: Facts on File, 1985.
   The great bridges of the world are described in terms of the principles used in their design.

National Geographic Society. *How Things Work.* Washington, D.C.: National Geographic Society, 1983.
   This illustrated volume explains how everyday objects, such as bicycles, clocks, calculators, and smoke detectors work.

Prevenson, Alice and Martin. *Leonardo da Vinci: The Artist, Inventor, Scientist.* New York: Viking, 1984.
   This book includes three-dimensional "stand-up" and turntable diagrams that help describe some of Leonardo's inventions and machines.

This highway sign may soon be replaced by higher speed limit signs as a result of the debate in the United States Congress.

The 55 Mile per Hour Speed Limit

In the early 1970s the United States experienced a severe gasoline shortage, due to a decrease in the supply from the Middle East. As a result, there were long lines and gas rationing, prompting the federal government to look for ways to conserve fuel. Research showed that the automobile engine reaches its peak energy efficiency at 35 mph and then steadily declines. To help reduce the speed on highways, Congress passed a law setting the national maximum speed limit at 55 mph. There continues to be a great debate as to whether the lower speed limit accomplishes its goals without sacrificing others.

Does the 55 mph maximum speed limit have benefits that make it a law worth keeping?

PROS

- There is a gasoline savings of 20 percent driving at 55 mph rather than at 70 mph. Saving one gallon of gasoline per week per car would save 5.6 billion gallons per year, or approximately 8 percent of the total yearly amount of gasoline consumed by cars.
- There is reduced wear and tear on the automobile's engine.
- Air pollution is reduced because less fuel is consumed.
- Some believe that the most important savings is not fuel but lives, approximately 2000–4000 per year. Reduced speeds mean less impact in collisions and less serious accident injuries.

CONS

- Reduced speeds increase travel time. This is particularly a problem for the trucking industry which competes with faster planes and trains for transporting goods. They must either lose money, increase their prices, or jeopardize the safety of their drivers and others by cutting back on rest breaks to save time.
- The gasoline shortage is over at the moment and prices are down.
- Driving at higher speeds cleans the engine by burning off built-up carbon deposits.
- Most of our interstate highways and car engines were designed for higher speeds.
- To enforce the 55 mph speed limit, the country needs a larger police force which is expensive.

Congress is now debating the issue of maintaining the 55 mph speed limit. If you were a legislator, how would you vote?

Aerospace Planes of the Future

"Ladies and Gentlemen, this is your Captain speaking. We are now cruising at 27 353 km per hour at an altitude of 48.27 km. We will be starting our descent into Los Angeles momentarily. Total flight time from Washington, D.C. will be 42 minutes."

Science fiction? No, scientists are now designing an "aerospace plane" that will be capable of taking off and landing at regular airports, reaching top speeds of Mach 25 (25 times the speed of sound at that altitude) or 27 353 km per hour, and flying at altitudes of 30 to 105 km (19 to 66 miles above the earth). By contrast, our fastest military plane only reaches Mach 3 (3529 km per hour), the Concorde reaches Mach 2.2 (2252.6 km per hour), and the 747 jet reaches Mach 0.8.

The United States version of this new plane is nicknamed the "New Orient Express" because it will be able to fly from New York to Japan in only two hours, thereby increasing the potential for Asian trade. (The old "Orient Express" was a train that ran from Europe to the Far East, stimulating trade).

The "New Orient Express" relies on a two-engine design to attain its high speeds. At speeds below Mach 6, the plane uses an air-turboramjet (ATR) which uses a gas generator at first to compress the air before mixing it with the fuel for efficient combustion. Then, at speeds from Mach 2 to Mach 6, the speed of the flowing air itself is enough to compress it and the gas generator is used as a supercharger. At Mach 6, this compression causes the air to reach temperatures over 1093°C, hot enough to damage the turbines. Thus, to reach speeds higher than Mach 6, the plane uses another engine design, the scramjet (supersonic combustion ramjet). This engine replaces the compressor-turbine system with one which allows the air to flow through at supersonic speeds, reducing the overheating effect. The fuel is then injected directly into this stream of air and ignited by it. The fuel is a mixture of liquid hydrogen, carried on board, and oxygen taken in from the atmosphere. As the liquid hydrogen vaporizes before injection, it cools the engine. Then this vaporized hydrogen ignites in a millisecond with the air streaming through the engine, providing the thrust needed to reach Mach 25.

With the aid of the new supercomputers, questions about design and materials can be answered without sacrificing a lot of time, or building prototypes as in the past. The target date for operational aerospace planes is mid 1990s. We've certainly come a long way from that day in 1947 when Chuck Yeager broke the sound barrier at a speed of Mach 1 in the X-1 rocket-powered craft that is the ancestor of today's "New Orient Express."

One of several designs proposed for the aerospace plane is this sleek Air Force concept.

3 *Chemical Changes in Matter*

Chapter 6
Chemical Reactions

Chapter 7
Using Energy from Chemical Reactions

Learning Objectives

■ Process

1. To relate a principle, the law of conservation of mass, to specific chemical reactions
2. To identify differences in speed and concentration of chemical reactions and note their relationships
3. To relate defined quantities of particles to the amount of energy released in some chemical reactions
4. To classify groups of carbon compounds according to their bond types
5. To use a food energy pyramid to illustrate relationships in a natural community

■ Content

1. To distinguish between exothermic and endothermic reactions
2. To compare several types of chemical reactions
3. To describe classes of organic compounds that are required to maintain life for living beings
4. To compare the amount of energy obtained from a fuel with the quantity of fuel required
5. To describe and compare the processes of cell respiration, fermentation, and photosynthesis

A fireworks display is actually a spectacular demonstration of a chemical reaction that produces heat, light, and smoke.

Chapter 6
Chemical Reactions

The energy that is released in some chemical reactions can be controlled to do useful work. Controlled chemical reactions are essential for many industries. The photograph at right shows a step in the production of one important industrial chemical: sulfur. Hot, liquified sulfur will turn into a yellow solid as it cools.

Science background information:
Chemical reactions occur as chemical bonds are broken and formed. Chemical reactions are accompanied by heat changes. These heat changes reflect changes in the overall energy of reactants and products.

Exothermic reactions proceed with the release of heat. Endothermic reactions require the input of heat. Whether heat will be given off or absorbed during a chemical reaction depends on two main factors. First, it depends on the difference in heat content, or *enthalpy,* between reactants and products. Second, heat changes in a reaction are affected by *entropy,* a measure of the disorder of the reactants and products. Enthalpy can increase or decrease in a reaction. Entropy can increase or decrease in a reaction. So these two factors can work together or against one another in determining the energy changes in a reaction.

Chemical reactions are said to go to completion if one or more of the reactants is completely used up. Not all reactions will go to completion. The likelihood that the reaction will go to completion may be increased by changing the temperature or pressure of the system or by removing the product as it is formed. Products can be removed either by precipitating them out of solution or if they are given off as a gas. The reason that reactions will or

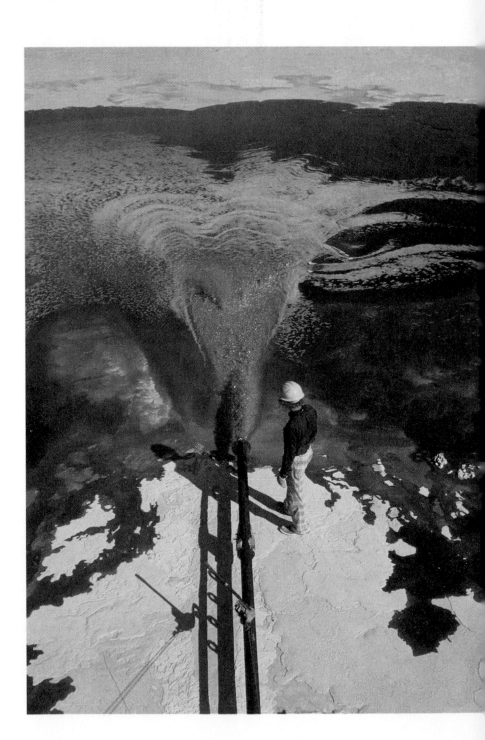

For detailed information about teaching this chapter, see Chapter 6 Planning Guide on pages T102–T103 in the front of this book.

Projectsheet 6 (TRB page 178) and Research Lab 6 (Lab Manual pages 87–88) may be used at any point in this chapter.

Chapter Preview

6.1 Comparing Chemical Reactions

- **Exothermic and endothermic reactions**
- **Chemical bonds and reactions**
- **Complete and incomplete reactions**
- **Types of chemical reactions**
- **Conservation of mass in a chemical reaction**
- **Comparing particles of reactants**
- **Energy changes in chemical reactions**
- **Some everyday chemical reactions**

There are several kinds of chemical reactions that produce chemical changes in substances. These chemical reactions are accompanied by changes in energy. In chemical reactions, the reactants and products interact in fixed ratios.

6.2 Controlling Chemical Reactions

- **Speed of reactions**
- **Effect of reactants**
- **Effect of temperature**
- **Effect of concentration**
- **Activation energy and catalysts**
- **Chemical reactions in industry**

Many chemical reactions give off energy, but these reactions must be controlled to be useful. Chemical properties, temperature, concentration, and catalysts affect the course of reactions.

will not go to completion has to do with the subject of chemical reaction equilibrium which is beyond the scope of this book.

In studying reactions it is important to compare the numbers of reactants and products. Comparing numbers of reactants and products is most easily done by introducing the concept of the mole. The mole is a collective noun that specifies a set number of particles. Specifically, one mole is composed of Avagadro's number of particles, 6.02×10^{23} particles. The mass of a mole of any element is equal to the atomic mass of that element in grams.

Moles and reactions fit together in the following way. Moles relate to a set number of particles. Elements and compounds are composed of atoms with specific masses. Therefore, it is possible to determine the number of atoms, or moles, of substances involved in chemical reactions by determining the masses of the reactants and products.

Several factors affect the rate of a chemical reaction including temperature, the surface area and concentration of reactants, and the presence of catalysts. Chemical reactions frequently will not proceed unless the reactants reach a certain level of energy, known as the activation energy. The activation energy is the amount of energy needed to get a reaction going. Raising the temperature of the reactants is often all that is necessary to give them the energy needed for the reaction to proceed.

Catalysts affect the rate of a chemical reaction by lowering the activation energy of the reaction. This means that the reaction can often take place at lower temperatures than ordinarily. Catalysts, in the form of protein molecules, are essential for the chemical reactions that take place in living organisms.

For ideas for classroom demonstration and discussion, see Getting Started on page T104 in the front of this book.

6.1 Comparing Chemical Reactions

Supplemental materials: Teaching Diagrams 6-1A, 6-1B (TRB pages 31, 32), Reading Checksheet 6-1 (TRB page 95), Skillsheet 6-1 (TRB page 141), Investigation 6-1 (Lab Manual pages 81–82)

Section Preview

- **Exothermic and endothermic reactions**
- **Chemical bonds and reactions**
- **Complete and incomplete reactions**
- **Types of chemical reactions**
- **Conservation of mass in a chemical reaction**
- **Comparing particles of reactants**
- **Energy changes in chemical reactions**
- **Some everyday chemical reactions**

Bracketed numbers are Section Review questions correlated to that objective.

Learning Objectives

1. To distinguish between exothermic and endothermic reactions. [1, 2, 4, 10]
2. To compare complete and incomplete chemical reactions. [3]
3. To describe four types of chemical reactions. [5, 6, 7, 9, 12, 13, 14, 15, 18]
4. To relate the law of the conservation of mass to chemical reactions. [21]
5. To relate defined quantities of particles to the amount of energy released in some chemical reactions. [8, 16, 22]

Figure 6-1. *Copper wire in water and silver nitrate solution. Copper from the wire replaces silver in solution. Silver from the solution makes a deposit on the wire.*

Teaching suggestion:
Remind students that changes in properties of substances are *clues* to chemical changes. Physical changes are ones that can usually be reversed by changing conditions. For example, ice melts when it is heated, and then the water freezes when it is cooled below its freezing point. Chemical changes are usually not reversed by changing the conditions of the environment.

You already have learned to recognize chemical changes. Chemical changes are changes in matter that produce new substances. The new substances have different properties from the original substances. So changes in the properties of matter are important clues that chemical changes may have taken place.

The burning of paper is a chemical change. The gases that are produced and the ash that remains have much different properties from those of paper. What is more, you are unable to restore the original properties of the paper by mixing the ash and gases together. The burning of paper is easily recognized as a chemical change by the changes that occur in properties.

Heat and light are also produced when paper burns. You feel the heat and see the flame. Both heat and light are forms of energy. Energy is released as the paper burns. Sometimes chemical reactions can be recognized by the energy changes that occur. Chemical reactions are accompanied by energy changes and can also be classified by these energy changes.

Exothermic and endothermic reactions

New vocabulary: exothermic reaction, endothermic reaction

Many chemical reactions release energy. Some reactions give off a lot of energy, other reactions release a little energy. Wood gives off a lot of heat as it burns. A compost heap, containing grass clippings, vegetable scraps, and soil, warms up moderately from the energy released as the plant materials break down. Wet concrete warms up noticeably in the chemical reaction that makes it harden. Many other chemical changes release energy. Any chemical change that releases energy is called an **exothermic** reaction.

In some chemical reactions, energy must be added continuously or the reactions stop. The separation of water into hydrogen and oxygen gases is an example. The reaction continues just as long as energy is supplied by an electric current. The cooking of foods is another example. Vegetables boiling in water will cook as long as they get heat energy from the hot water. If they are removed and placed under running cold water, they stop cooking immediately. Any chemical change that absorbs energy is called an **endothermic** reaction.

Figure 6-2. *Burning paper produces heat, light, ash, and gases. It is a chemical change because you cannot get the paper back by mixing the products together.*

Research Topic

Read about the life of Pierre E. M. Berthelot, a French chemist. Find out what contributions he made to the study of the heat of reactions.

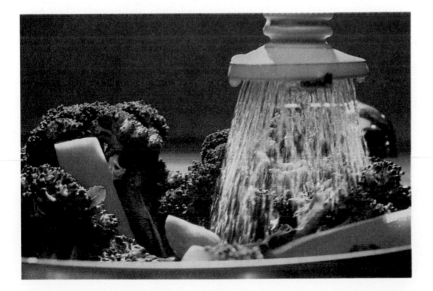

Figure 6-3. *Vegetables cook as long as heat is applied. Adding cold water stops the process. Is cooking an exothermic or endothermic process?*

Endothermic.

■ Safety Note

Confine your chemistry experiments to supervised laboratories. A few household chemicals, in wrong combinations, can be very hazardous.

Some reactions require energy to get started, but release energy as they proceed. For instance, energy must be added from a burning match to start a candle burning. Once started, though, the candle releases much more energy than it absorbed to get started. Any reaction that gives off more energy that it absorbs is still called an exothermic reaction.

Quick Review

1. Compare endothermic and exothermic reactions.
2. Give an example of a reaction that stops when energy is no longer supplied.
3. Give an example of a reaction that needs some energy to get started but releases much more energy than it absorbs.

Chemical bonds and reactions

New vocabulary: bond dissociation energy

As you learned in Chapter 3, chemical reactions require the forming and/or breaking of chemical bonds. These chemical bonds can result from the attraction of two oppositely charged ions or the sharing of electrons between atoms. The first kind of bond is called an ionic bond, the second kind of bond is called a covalent bond. Other types of chemical bonds have also been identified. All types of chemical bonds hold particles together.

Each kind of chemical bond has a specific amount of energy associated with it, the **bond dissociation energy.** Bonds with a high bond dissociation energy require more energy to break them apart than bonds with a low bond energy. For example, more energy is required to break a hydrogen-oxygen bond than to break a hydrogen-carbon bond. See the accompanying Table 6-1. How does the energy needed to break a hydrogen-nitrogen bond compare with the energy needed to break a hydrogen-oxygen bond? A hydrogen-carbon bond? A hydrogen-fluorine bond?

Figure 6-4 shows the breaking and formation of bonds when methane burns. The chemical equation is

$$CH_4 + 2O_2 \rightarrow CO_2 + 2H_2O$$

The first diagram shows that energy is needed to break the bonds within the methane and oxygen molecules. The second diagram shows all the bonds broken. The atoms can now

More energy is required to break a hydrogen-oxygen bond than to break a hydrogen-nitrogen bond. A little more energy is required to break a hydrogen-nitrogen bond than a hydrogen-carbon bond. More energy is required to break a hydrogen-fluorine bond than a hydrogen-nitrogen bond.

Bond dissociation energy	
Bond	kJ/mole
H—H	436
C—C	607
N≡N	945
O=O	498
H—O	427
C≡O	1077
H—N	339
H—F	570
C—H	338
C≡N	770
F—F	158

Table 6-1. *Bond dissociation energy is a measure of how strong different bonds are.*

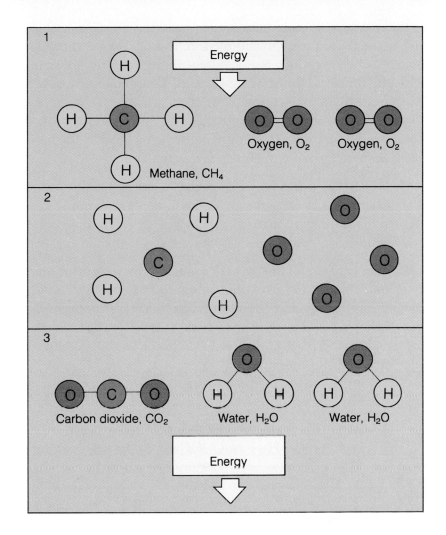

Figure 6-4. *Chemical reactions involve bond breaking and bond forming. Here, methane reacts with oxygen to form carbon dioxide and water. During the in-between step, the atoms in methane must separate and the atoms of oxygen must split apart. Then they can form new combinations.*

Science background information: Knowing just the energy of the bonds of the reactants and products of a chemical reaction is not sufficient information to predict whether a given chemical reaction will occur or not. Other factors, such as entropy, have to be considered.

rearrange themselves and form different molecules. The third diagram shows that new bonds have formed and energy has been released. Overall, energy was released, and the reaction was exothermic.

Quick Review

Which are easier to break apart, bonds with high or low bond dissociation energy?

Quick Review answer:
Bonds with low bond dissociation energy are easier to break apart.

Complete and incomplete reactions

New vocabulary: precipitate

Recall that the original substances in chemical reactions are called reactants. The new substances are called products. When one or more of the reactants are used up, the reaction is described as *complete*. When some amounts of each of the reactants remain, the reaction is described as *incomplete*.

Main Idea

What is a reaction called that uses up one or more of the reactants entirely?

Figure 6-5. *Precipitates, such as barium carbonate, form when reactions go to completion.*

Teaching suggestion:
The subject of complete and incomplete reactions is just an introduction to the theory of chemical equilibrium. You may want to mention this to advanced students.

Quick Review answer:
A chemical reaction may go to completion if one of the products is either a precipitate or a gas. Water is also a correct answer.

New vocabulary: synthesis reaction, decomposition reaction, single replacement reaction, double replacement reaction

Research Topic

Learning about the chemistry of reactions has often been a risky business. Read about Sir Humphry Davy and some of the difficulties he encountered in studying chemistry.

When a product is either a gas or a solid, it is a sign or clue that a reaction may go to completion. In these cases, the gaseous or solid product is essentially removed from contact with any other products being formed. That makes the reaction go in the direction of making more products. The reactants will form additional products until one or more of the reactants is used up. An example in which a solid is formed from the reaction of two liquids is this reaction.

$$BaCl_2 \; + \; K_2CO_3 \; \rightarrow \; 2KCl \; + \; BaCO_3$$

barium	potassium	potassium	barium
chloride	carbonate	chloride	carbonate
solution	solution	solution	solid

Barium carbonate, $BaCO_3$, is a solid. It is formed from the reaction between the two liquid solutions. An insoluble solid formed in this way in a chemical reaction is called a **precipitate.** Barium carbonate is the precipitate formed in this chemical reaction. It does not dissolve in the solution, but settles to the bottom of the container.

An example in which a gas is formed from a reaction is the formation of carbon dioxide when baking soda and vinegar react.

$$NaHCO_3 \; + \; CH_3COOH \rightarrow NaCOOCH_3 \; + \; H_2O \; + \; CO_2$$

baking	vinegar	sodium	water	carbon
soda	(acetic	acetate		dioxide
	acid			gas
	+ water)			

The carbon dioxide gas escapes from the area where the other products are formed unless the gas is confined.

The formation of some other products, such as water, can also be a clue that a reaction will go to completion.

Quick Review

What are two signs that a chemical reaction may go to completion?

Types of chemical reactions

Chemical reactions are sometimes classified as synthesis, decomposition, single replacement, or double replacement reactions. Recognizing the type of reaction can be helpful in predicting the products of the reaction.

Any chemical reaction in which a single compound is formed from the combination of two or more elements or

6.1a Precipitation from Solutions

Science Processes: Experimenting, observing, making inferences

Materials   BASIC   20 minutes   Groups of 3 or 4

- 2 test tubes
- test tube rack
- masking tape
- marking pen
- watch
- cobalt chloride solution
- sodium hydroxide solution
- dropper
- potassium carbonate solution
- 25-mL graduated cylinder
- 50-mL beaker
- safety goggles

Purpose

To compare the precipitation of an element in different solutions.

Procedure

SAFETY NOTE: *Wear safety goggles during this activity. Set two test tubes in a rack. With masking tape, label them "NaOH" and "K₂CO₃".*

SAFETY NOTE: *Sodium hydroxide solution can burn your eyes or skin. If any gets in your eyes, wash it out immediately with lots of water. If any gets on your skin or clothing, wash it off immediately with water. Tell your teacher at once of any accident. Pour 10 mL of sodium hydroxide solution from the supply container into a graduated cylinder. Then pour this into the test tube labelled "NaOH".*

1. Rinse out the graduated cylinder three times with water and dry it.
2. Repeat Step 2 using the potassium carbonate solution and pouring it into the test tube labelled "K₂CO₃".
3. Pour 3 to 5 mL of cobalt chloride solution into a small beaker.
4. With a dropper, drop three to five drops of cobalt chloride solution into each of the test tubes. Record what happens in each tube.
5. Wait five minutes. Record what you see in the test tubes.
6. Carefully swirl each of the test tubes for about 15 seconds.
7. Wait five minutes and record what you see in the test tubes.

8. Dispose of the contents of the test tubes according to the instructions of your teacher.

Questions

1. What evidence for chemical changes did you see when you first added cobalt chloride to the test tubes?
2. Did you see evidence of further chemical changes after you swirled the test tubes?
3. What is a precipitate?
4. From your observations, can you infer that the substances in the test tubes were precipitates?

Conclusion

Is the precipitation of a new substance from a solution evidence of a chemical change?

Step 4

Figure 6-6 *Magnesium metal combines with oxygen to give magnesium oxide. What kind of reaction is this?* Synthesis, also exothermic.

Critical Thinking

If an equation is written for a synthesis reaction between two elements, is the product of the reaction always a compound? Explain your answer.

The product has to be a compound, because a synthesis reaction means the combination of substances into a product. A combination of two elements yields a compound.

Figure 6-7. *When electric current is supplied, water will break down into hydrogen and oxygen gases. Notice the different volumes.*

compounds is a **synthesis reaction.** Many elements combine directly with each other or with another compound to form a single product. For example, many metals combine directly with oxygen to form a compound. Magnesium does this.

$$2Mg \quad + \quad O_2 \quad \rightarrow \quad 2MgO$$
magnesium   oxygen   magnesium oxide

Some non-metals also combine directly with oxygen. Nitrogen forms several different compounds with oxygen.

$$N_2 \quad + \quad O_2 \quad \rightarrow \quad 2NO$$
$$N_2 \quad + \quad 2O_2 \quad \rightarrow \quad 2NO_2$$
$$2N_2 \quad + \quad 5O_2 \quad \rightarrow \quad 2N_2O_5$$
nitrogen   oxygen   oxides of nitrogen

Metals and non-metals also combine with non-metals other than oxygen.

$$H_2 \quad + \quad Cl_2 \quad \rightarrow \quad 2HCl$$
hydrogen   chlorine   hydrogen chloride

$$2Ag \quad + \quad S \quad \rightarrow \quad Ag_2S$$
silver   sulfur   silver sulfide

Compounds also combine with other compounds. For example, sulfur trioxide forms sulfuric acid when it reacts with water.

$$SO_3 \quad + \quad H_2O \quad \rightarrow \quad H_2SO_4$$
sulfur trioxide   water   sulfuric acid

When a compound is broken down into two or more elements or compounds a **decomposition reaction** has taken place. Compounds are decomposed by adding a form of energy such as electricity, light, or heat to the compound. For example, water is broken down into hydrogen and oxygen by adding electrical energy to the water.

$$2H_2O \quad \rightarrow \quad 2H_2 \quad + \quad O_2$$
water   hydrogen gas   oxygen gas

Hydrogen peroxide decomposes into water and oxygen in the presence of light.

$$2H_2O_2 \quad \rightarrow \quad 2H_2O \quad + \quad O_2$$
hydrogen peroxide   water   oxygen

Some compounds break down when heated. For example, potassium chlorate forms potassium chloride and oxygen when heated.

$$2KClO_3 \quad \rightarrow \quad 2KCl \quad + \quad 3O_2$$

potassium chlorate　　potassium chloride　oxygen

The replacement of an element in one compound with another element is characteristic of a group of reactions classified as **single replacement reactions.** Aluminum will replace copper from various copper compounds as in the following reaction with copper chloride.

$$2Al \quad + \quad 3CuCl_2 \rightarrow \quad 2AlCl_3 \quad + \quad 3Cu$$

aluminum　　copper　　aluminum　copper
　　　　　　chloride　　chloride

Figure 6-8. *Aluminum metal reacts with copper in copper sulfate solution. Where does the copper go?*

It collects on the surface of the aluminum.

Another group of single replacement reactions includes the reactions of metals with acids. The metal replaces the hydrogen of the acid. The reaction of zinc with a water solution of hydrochloric acid is an example.

$$Zn \quad + \quad 2HCl \quad \rightarrow \quad ZnCl_2 \quad + \quad H_2$$

zinc　hydrochloric　　zinc　　hydrogen
　　　　acid　　　　chloride　　gas

Two compounds may react by an exchange that is called **double replacement.** The reaction between iron chloride and sodium carbonate is an example.

$$FeCl_2 \quad + \quad Na_2CO_3 \rightarrow \quad 2NaCl \quad + \quad FeCO_3$$

iron　　　sodium　　sodium　　iron
chloride　carbonate　chloride　carbonate
solution　solution　solution　solid

The iron and the sodium replace each other. In this example, the reaction takes place because a precipitate, iron carbonate, is formed.

Acid-base reactions, studied in Chapter 3, make up another group of double replacement reactions.

$$HCl \quad + \quad NaOH \quad \rightarrow \quad NaCl \quad + \quad H_2O$$

hydrochloric　sodium　　sodium　　water
　acid　　　hydroxide　chloride

In this example, the reaction proceeds because water is formed as a product. The hydrogen ion and sodium ions replace each other. Calcium carbonate reacts with hydrochloric acid to form carbonic acid and calcium chloride.

Figure 6-9. *Dark gray precipitate of ferrous carbonate is one product of a double replacement reaction.*

$$CaCO_3 + 2HCl \rightarrow CaCl_2 + H_2CO_3$$
$$\text{and the } H_2CO_3 \rightarrow H_2O + CO_2$$

In this example the carbonic acid breaks up into water and the gas carbon dioxide. Both of these products are a sign that the reaction will be complete.

Quick Review

Name the types of the following reactions:
a. $2Na + 2H_2O \rightarrow 2NaOH + H_2$
b. $C + 2H_2 \rightarrow CH_4$
c. $HCl + KOH \rightarrow KCl + H_2O$
d. $2NaCl \rightarrow 2Na + Cl_2$

Conservation of mass in a chemical reaction

Chemical equations summarize chemical reactions. Earlier you learned that balancing equations is based on accounting. The same number of atoms of each element must be in the products as were present in the reactants. Balanced chemical equations are very useful. Since the number of atoms of each element in the products is equal to the number in the reactants, the total amount of matter is unchanged. <u>Therefore, by knowing the total mass of the reactants consumed in a reaction, you can predict the total mass of the products generated.</u>

Suppose you separated water into hydrogen and oxygen using an electric current. The balanced equation for this reaction is this.

$$2H_2O \rightarrow 2H_2 + O_2$$

Suppose 36 grams of water are separated and 4 grams of hydrogen collected. How many grams of oxygen must have been produced?

$$\frac{\text{Total mass of}}{\text{reactants consumed}} = \frac{\text{Total mass of}}{\text{products generated}}$$
$$36 \text{ g of } H_2O = 4 \text{ g of } H_2 + ? \text{ g of } O_2$$

Since the total mass of the reactants was 36 grams, the total mass of the products has to be the same—36 grams. Only 4 grams of hydrogen were formed, so the remaining 32 grams had to be oxygen.

In another reaction, sodium reacts with chlorine to form sodium chloride (table salt). The balanced equation for the reaction is the following.

$$2Na + Cl_2 \rightarrow 2NaCl$$

When 96 grams of sodium are combined with chlorine gas, 232 grams of salt are formed. What mass of chlorine must have combined with sodium?   136 g of Cl_2

Total mass of reactants = Total mass of products
96 g of Na + ? g of Cl_2 = 232 g of NaCl

The total mass stays the same during the reaction. Another way of summarizing this relationship is to say that mass is conserved in a chemical reaction. This statement is called the *law of the conservation of mass.*

Dramatic support for the law of the conservation of mass during a reaction can be seen in Figure 6-10. A sealed flask neither gains nor loses mass while a candle is burning inside it.

Figure 6-10. *Sealed flask on a balance shows that mass is conserved during a chemical reaction. There is no change in total mass while candle burns or after it goes out.*

Critical Thinking

If one of the products of a reaction is a gas that escapes during a reaction, is the law of the conservation of mass violated? Give reasons for your answer.

No, because the mass of the gas has to be considered in determining the total mass of the products of the reaction. The law of the conservation of mass is not violated.

Quick Review

According to the law of the conservation of mass, in a chemical reaction the mass of the products is equal to what?

Quick Review answer:
The mass of the product is equal to the mass of the reactants.

Comparing particles of reactants

New vocabulary: mole

A balanced chemical equation shows the relative numbers of atoms and molecules involved in the reaction as reactants and products. In the synthesis of ammonia, $N_2 + 3H_2 \rightarrow 2NH_3$, one molecule of nitrogen and three molecules of hydrogen react to form two molecules of ammonia. The same ratio of nitrogen to hydrogen molecules occurs no matter how many total molecules are reacting.

N_2	$+$	$3H_2$	$\rightarrow$	$2NH_3$
1 molecule		3 molecules		2 molecules
10 molecules		30 molecules		20 molecules
1000 molecules		3000 molecules		2000 molecules
10 000 molecules		30 000 molecules		? molecules

A very, very large number of molecules are in the usual amounts of substances reacted in the laboratory. A much larger unit for comparing masses in chemical reactions is very useful. That unit is the mole. The **mole** is the number of particles needed to give a mass of 12.000 g of the carbon-12 isotope. The atomic masses of all of the elements are based on the carbon-12 isotope. As a result, you can think of the mole as the number of particles in the atomic mass of any element measured in grams. Refer to Chapter 3.

Compounds are made of elements. So the mole is also the number of particles in the molecular or formula mass of a compound. The actual number of particles that a mole represents is 6.02×10^{23}. This is known as *Avogadro's number.*

Main Idea

What does the term *mole* mean in chemistry?

Research Topic

What did Amedeo Avogadro contribute to the understanding of chemistry?

Figure 6-11. *One mole of each substance is shown here: sulfur (yellow), copper sulfate (blue), and chromium oxide (green). Do the moles of these substances have the same mass?*
No, they are all different.

The important point is that the mole is always the same number of particles. So in a chemical equation we can compare the numbers of moles of reactants and products. In the synthesis of ammonia, one mole of nitrogen reacts with three moles of hydrogen to give two moles of ammonia.

$$N_2 \quad + \quad 3H_2 \quad \rightarrow \quad 2NH_3$$
one mole   three moles   two moles

Sample Problem

Identify the number of moles of reactants and products in given chemical reactions.

a. $2H_2S + 3O_2 \rightarrow 2SO_2 + 2H_2O$
b. $4Al + 3O_2 \rightarrow 2Al_2O_3$
c. $2C_2H_2 + 5O_2 \rightarrow 4CO_2 + 2H_2O$

Solution

a. 2 moles H_2S, 3 moles O_2; 2 moles SO_2, 2 moles H_2O
b. 4 moles Al, 3 moles O_2; 2 moles Al_2O_3
c. 2 moles C_2H_2, 5 moles O_2; 4 moles CO_2, 2 moles H_2O

Practice Problem

Identify the moles of reactants and products in these reactions.

a. $2Zn + O_2 \rightarrow 2ZnO$
b. $2P_2O_5 + 6H_2O \rightarrow 4H_3PO_4$

Answer:

a. 2 moles Zn, 1 mole O_2; 2 moles ZnO
b. 2 moles P_2O_5, 6 moles H_2O; 4 moles H_3PO_4

Critical Thinking

In terms of the total number of *atoms* involved, explain why a mole of hydrogen *atoms* is equal to one-half mole of hydrogen *molecules*

Although hydrogen *atoms* do not exist separately under normal conditions, if they did, a mole of hydrogen *atoms* would equal 6×10^{23} particles. Since hydrogen atoms normally exist as diatomic molecules, H_2, a half-mole of hydrogen molecules would contain 3×10^{23} particles of H_2, or 6×10^{23} atoms of hydrogen.

From the law of the conservation of mass, we know that the mass of the reactants consumed is equal to the mass of the products generated. In this reaction, the mass of one mole of nitrogen plus the mass of three moles of hydrogen is equal to the mass of two moles of ammonia. From the periodic table, the average atomic mass of nitrogen is approximately 14 and the average atomic mass of hydrogen is approximately 1. We can use this to compute what the masses of the reactants and products should be in this reaction.

Data Search

The approximate atomic masses of nitrogen and hydrogen are used in the computation at the bottom of this page. Find more accurate figures for the atomic masses of these two elements. Search pages 658–661.

Atomic masses: nitrogen, 14.007; hydrogen, 1.008.

Mass of one mole of nitrogen molecules $1 \times 2 \times 14$ g $= 28$ g

Mass of three moles of hydrogen molecules $3 \times 2 \times 1$ g $= \underline{6 \text{ g}}$

34 g

Activity

See also Activity Record Sheet 6-1B (Lab Manual page 80). Answers to Questions and Conclusion appear on page T105 in the front of this book.

6.1b   Counting by Weighing

Science Processes: Observing, measuring, estimating, inferring

Materials   30 minutes   Groups of 2 to 4

- unpopped kernels of popcorn
- balance
- bean seeds

Purpose

To "count" the number of particles in a sample by weighing.

Procedure

1. Count out 25 kernels of unpopped popcorn. Find the mass of the kernels using the balance.
2. Determine the mass of 250 kernels using the average mass of each kernel.
3. Weigh out an amount of popcorn kernels equal to your estimated mass for 250 kernels. Count the number of kernels in that amount of mass.
4. Calculate the mass needed to give 2500 kernels.
5. Repeat Steps 1 through 4, using the bean seeds.

Questions

1. If 250 kernels is the number of kernels in a "bowl" of popcorn, how many "bowls" of popcorn are in 1000 g of popcorn? . . . in a 10 000-g sample? (Use the value you determined for g/bowl.)
2. If 250 beans is the number of beans in a "bowl" of beans, how many "bowls" of beans are in 1000 g of beans? . . . in a 10 000-g sample? (Use your value for g/bowl.)
3. When you weigh out a "bowl" of popcorn kernels and a "bowl" of beans, how do the masses compare?
4. When you weigh out a "bowl" of popcorn and a "bowl" of beans, how do the number of kernels and number of beans compare?
5. How does the concept of "bowls" of popcorn compare to the chemical concept of moles of a substance?

Conclusion

How is it possible that numbers of objects can be counted by weighing?

Step 1

	Corn	Beans
Mass of 25 particles (a)		
Calculated mass for 250 particles (b)		
Actual number of particles in calculated mass (b)		
Calculated mass for 2500 particles (c)		

If the products of this reaction were measured in a laboratory, the results of a complete reaction between 28 g of nitrogen and 6 g of hydrogen would give 34 g of ammonia.

Quick Review

1. In the synthesis of ammonia from nitrogen and hydrogen, what is the ratio of the molecules of the two reactants?
2. What is the ratio of the number of moles of the two reactants in the synthesis of ammonia?
3. Compare the number of particles in one mole of nitrogen molecules to three moles of hydrogen molecules.

Energy changes in chemical reactions

The amount of energy associated with a chemical reaction is sometimes included in the equation. For example, in the combustion of carbon, energy is released.

$$(1)\ C + (1)\ O_2 \rightarrow (1)\ CO_2 + 393\ kJ$$

This means that when one mole of carbon is burned, 393 kJ of heat energy are released. When the energy amount is included in the equation as a product, the reaction is exothermic. One mole of carbon has the mass of 12 g. For every 12 g of carbon, 393 kJ of heat are released. How much heat would be released by burning 24 g of carbon? How much would be released by burning 1200 g of carbon? The ratio of energy released to the mass of carbon burned in oxygen will always be 393 kJ:mole.

$$\frac{393\ kJ}{12\ g} = \frac{\text{heat released}}{\text{grams of carbon burned}}$$

In the electrolysis of water, energy must be added to keep the reaction going. That is why, in the equation for the electrolysis of water, the energy term appears on the side of the reactants.

$$568\ kJ + 2H_2O \rightarrow 2H_2 + O_2$$

To separate two moles of water, 568 kJ of energy must be added. One mole of water has a mass of 18 g. For every 18 g of water separated, 284 kJ of energy is used. How much en-

786 kJ; 39 300 kJ

Figure 6-12. *Carbon, in the form of charcoal, combines with oxygen in a reaction that releases heat.*

Figure 6-13. *This graph of the energy released for each mole of carbon burned shows what?*

That the energy released is directly proportional to the amount of carbon burned.

568 kJ, because 36 g of water is two moles; 28 400 kJ

Quick Review answers:
1. 99 kJ
2. 396 kJ

ergy would be needed to separate 36 g of water? To separate 1800 g of water? The ratio of energy used to amount of water separated will always be 284 kJ:mole.

$$\frac{284 \text{ kJ}}{18 \text{ g}} = \frac{\text{energy used}}{\text{grams of water separated}}$$

Quick Review

1. What is the energy released when 64 g, or 1 mole, of sulfur dioxide combines with oxygen to form sulfur trioxide? The balanced equation is

$$2SO_2 + O_2 \rightarrow 2SO_3 + 198 \text{ kJ}.$$

2. How much heat is released when 256 g of sulfur dioxide forms sulfur trioxide?

■ Safety Note
Confine your chemistry experiments to supervised laboratories. A few household chemicals, in wrong combinations, can be very hazardous.

Science background information:
Tartaric acid and cream of tartar can be obtained from the juice of grapes and acid fruits and from a crust, called *argol,* that forms on wine casks.

Some everyday chemical reactions

You rely on chemical reactions every day. Some are complex but others are easily recognized and described. In most cases you use the products of chemical reactions and processes including energy. Understanding the reactions you rely on has practical and even aesthetic applications. Recognizing the chemistry around you enables you to appreciate much more of your surroundings and activities.

Open a door of your kitchen cupboard. Do you see any baking powder? Baking powder is a chemical used in cooking. It contains both baking soda, $NaHCO_3$, and a weak acid such as tartaric acid, $H_2C_4H_4O_6$, or cream of tartar, $KHC_4H_4O_6$. In the presence of water the weak acid reacts with the baking

Figure 6-14. *Baked and unbaked bread are different in color, shape, and composition. Chemical reactions that occur during baking release carbon dioxide which causes bread to rise. Other reactions cause a change in color and composition.*

soda to produce carbon dioxide. The bubbles of carbon dioxide gas cause the dough in bread or cake to rise.

$$HCO_3^- + H^+ \rightarrow 2H_2O + CO_2$$

Is there a package of baking soda, $NaHCO_3$, in your refrigerator or in a closet? Baking soda is used to remove odors from refrigerators or stains from carpets. Many of the unwanted odors are acid and baking soda reacts to neutralize the odors. Carbon dioxide is a product of the reaction.

Vinegar is a weak acid. It is often used as a cleaning agent. It removes stains that are chemically basic. For example, aluminum surfaces form a thin coating of aluminum oxide. The aluminum oxide, a base, reacts with the vinegar, an acid.

$$Al_2O_3 + 6CH_3COOH \rightarrow 2Al(CH_3COO)_3 + 3H_2O$$

Odors, too, that are basic can be neutralized by vinegar.

Check under the sink, in the laundry room, or in the garage. Soaps, detergents, and other cleaning agents are widely used chemicals. Soap has been made and used for hundreds of years. A strong base, either sodium or potassium hydroxide, reacts with animal fat to produce soap and another product, glycerol.

$$Fat + NaOH \text{ (or KOH)} \rightarrow glycerol + soap$$

The two ends of a soap molecule have different characteristics. One end is similar to water and is attracted to water. The other end is similar to the structure of oil and grease molecules. This end is attracted to the oil and grease. Dirt is held to the skin and clothing usually by oil and grease. The

Main Idea

What substance can be used to remove odors from refrigerators and stains from rugs?

Science background information: Prior to the 18th century soap was made primarily from tallow and wood ashes. In the late 1700s Nicolas Leblanc developed a process to make sodium hydroxide and sodium carbonate from sodium chloride. Combined with the discoveries by Michel Chevreul about the nature of fats, soap became widely available through industrial production in the 1800s.

oil and grease are broken up by the action of the soap and the dirt is washed away with the water.

Soap soon loses its cleaning power in acid solution or in water containing minerals. The positive metal ions combine with the soap molecules. The one end of the soap molecule is then no longer attracted to water molecules. Sodium carbonate, $Na_2CO_3 \cdot 10H_2O$, or washing soda, acts as a water softener by combining with the metal ions in the water and keeping the water basic.

$$\underset{\text{calcium ions}}{Ca^{2+}} + \underset{\text{carbonate ions}}{CO_3^{2-}} \rightarrow \underset{\substack{\text{calcium carbonate} \\ \text{(insoluble)}}}{CaCO_3}$$

Our Science Heritage

Alfred Nobel

Alfred Nobel (1833–1896) is now most well known for the world-famous prizes he established in the fields of peace, chemistry, physics, medicine, and literature. In his own time, he was known as the inventor of dynamite and other explosives.

The son of a Swedish inventor and manufacturer of explosives, Nobel saw how explosives could help people blast roads through mountains, dig canals, and excavate for building construction. He himself started a factory that made the highly dangerous explosive nitroglycerine. Tragically, his younger brother and four other workers were killed when the factory blew up. He decided to find a way to control explosives so that they could be used more safely.

Nobel experimented until he found a way to package nitroglycerine fairly safely in sticks he called dynamite. He also invented blasting gelatin and a smokeless powder that was used by the military. His inventions made him wealthy, but people saw him as responsible for large-scale death and destruction in warfare. To show his concern for humanity, he left all his money toward the establishment of prizes for advancements toward peace as well as toward science. Today, the Nobel Prize is probably the most prestigious award a person can receive.

The Nobel Institute, a research institute in Sweden, is named after Alfred Nobel. Element 102, which was first isolated at the Nobel Institute, was named nobelium.

Winners of the Nobel Prize receive a gold medal like this as well as a large cash award.

Figure 6-15. *Soaps and detergents have different chemical formulas. These soaps are made of fatty acids and sodium. The detergent differs from the soaps in one important way. Can you tell what it is?*

It has sulfur and four oxygen atoms where the soaps have carbon and two oxygen atoms. This is the most important difference. The differences in the carbon chains at left are not as important.

Synthetic detergents have replaced soap for many uses. Their molecules are similar in structure to those of soap. However, detergents are not affected by acids and hard water—water containing calcium and magnesium—to the same extent as soap. Detergents keep their cleaning power even in hard water.

Examine the labels on different boxes of detergents on the store shelves. What are the names of the chemicals in the product? Do some have functions other than cleaning? Many of the chemical names and formulas you find will have more meaning after a study of Chapter 7.

Look for chemicals where the garden supplies are kept. You may find some plant fertilizers. Check the labels. <u>Most fertilizers provide the three elements—nitrogen, phosphorus, and potassium.</u> Nitrogen can be supplied through one or more of several compounds including ammonium sulfate, $(NH_4)_2SO_4$, and sodium or potassium nitrate, $NaNO_3$ or KNO_3. Phosphate is often furnished in the form of the compound calcium phosphate, $Ca_3(PO_4)_2$. Potassium chloride, KCl, and potassium nitrate, KNO_3, supply the third element, potassium. The three numbers on a fertilizer bag indicate

Main Idea

What are the three main elements that most fertilizers supply?

Figure 6-16. *Fertilizer package label shows the ratio of effective ingredients: nitrogen, phosphorus, and potassium.*

Figure 6-17. *Productivity of wheat field depends on getting enough fertilizer to the plants while they are growing. Without fertilizer, what would happen to the harvest?*

There would be much less wheat to gather.

the percentages of these three elements. A label of 20-10-5 tells the user that the fertilizer is 20% nitrogen, 10% phosphorus, and 5% potassium. Check the label on a fertilizer bag or on the bottle container. Are there other compounds or elements present, also?

Many other chemicals and chemical reactions are found around the home or in other places that we might frequently visit. Drugs and medicines are chemical substances. They frequently are organic chemicals (containing carbon) and are more easily studied after Chapter 7.

While you may not think of clothing as a chemical, the synthetic fibers, such as nylon and orlon, are chemical substances. These, along with plastics, will be more understandable after studying some of the topics in Chapter 7. There is an almost endless list of chemicals and chemical reactions that you come in contact with every day. Look for new examples. Your awareness of chemical reactions can increase your interest in and understanding of both your natural and man-made surroundings.

Quick Review

1. Give three examples of chemicals found in or around the home.
2. What household substance would you use to neutralize an acid spill?

6.1 Section Review

Answers to Understanding the Concepts and solutions to Problems to Solve appear on page T105 in the front of this book. Blackline master test for this section: Section Testsheet 6-1 (TRB page 215)

Vocabulary

2 bond dissociation energy

7 decomposition reaction

9 double replacement reaction

4 endothermic reaction

1 exothermic reaction

8 mole

3 precipitate

6 single replacement reaction

5 synthesis reaction

Vocabulary Review

Match each term above with the numbered phrase that best describes it

1. Chemical reaction that releases energy

2. Specific energy associated with a chemical bond

3. Solid formed in the reaction of two liquid solutions

4. Chemical reaction that absorbs energy

5. Reaction in which a single compound is formed from the combination of two or more elements or compounds

6. Reaction in which one element in a compound is replaced by another element

7. Reaction in which a compound is broken down into two or more elements or compounds

8. Number of atoms in 12.00 g of carbon-12

9. Reaction in which an element of one compound is exchanged with an element of another compound

Review Questions

10. A reaction that requires a certain amount of energy to start, but which releases much more energy as it proceeds is categorized as _?_.
    a. an endothermic reaction
    b. an exothermic reaction
    c. a synthesis reaction
    d. a decomposition reaction

11. Soap is formed in a reaction between _?_.
    a. a salt and an acid
    b. an acid and a base
    c. a salt and a base
    d. a fat and a strong base

12. An example of a single replacement reaction is _?_.
    a. $2Ag + S \rightarrow Ag_2S$
    b. $Zn + 2HCl \rightarrow ZnCL_2 + H_2$
    c. $FeCL_2 + Na_2CO_3 \rightarrow 2NaCl + Fe_2CO_3$
    d. $2H_2O_2 \rightarrow 2H_2O + O_2$

13. An example of a double replacement reaction is _?_.
    a. $2Ag + S \rightarrow Ag_2S$
    b. $Zn + 2HCl \rightarrow ZnCl_2 + H_2$
    c. $FeCl_2 + Na_2CO_3 \rightarrow 2NaCl + Fe_2CO_3$
    d. $2H_2O_2 \rightarrow 2H_2O + O_2$

14. An example of a composition reaction is _?_.
    a. $2Ag + S \rightarrow Ag_2S$
    b. $Zn + 2HCl \rightarrow ZnCl_2 + H_2$
    c. $FeCl_2 + Na_2CO_3 \rightarrow$ Fe_2CO_3
    d. $2H_2O_2 \rightarrow 2H_2O + O_2$

15. An example of a decomposition reaction is _?_.
    a. $2Ag + S \rightarrow Ag_2S$
    b. $Zn + 2HCl \rightarrow ZnCl_2 + H_2$
    c. $FeCl_2 + Na_2CO_3 \rightarrow 2NaCl + Fe_2CO_3$
    d. $2H_2O_2 \rightarrow 2H_2O + O_2$

16. The number of iron atoms in one mole of iron atoms is _?_.
    a. 6.02×10^{23}
    b. 602
    c. 6.02×10^3
    d. 1.2×10^{24}

17. Vinegar is useful in cleaning because it _?_
    a. is a weak base
    b. removes stains that are basic
    c. removes stains that are acidic
    d. is a strong acid

Understanding the Concepts

18. Explain the difference between a synthesis reaction and a decomposition reaction? Give an example of each reaction type.

19. What is hard water? How does it affect the cleaning properties of soap?

20. Describe how baking soda is used in the baking of bread.

Problems to Solve

21. Consider the reaction between aluminum and oxygen to produce aluminum oxide:

    $$4Al + 3O_2 \rightarrow 2Al_2O_3$$

    How many grams of aluminum oxide are produced when 4 moles of aluminum react completely with 3 moles of oxygen? (Note that the average atomic mass of aluminum is 27 g and that the average atomic mass of oxygen is 16 g.)

22. Consider the electrolysis of water to give hydrogen gas and oxygen gas:

    $$568 \text{ kJ} + 2H_2O \rightarrow 2H_2 + O_2$$

    How much energy is absorbed in the electrolysis of 72 g of H_2O?

For ideas for classroom demonstration and discussion, see Getting Started on page T105 in the front of this book.

6.2 Controlling Chemical Reactions

Supplemental materials: Teaching Diagram 6-2 (TRB page 33), Reading Checksheet 6-2 (TRB page 96), Skillsheet 6-2 (TRB page 142), Investigation 6-2 (Lab Manual pages 85–86)

Section Preview

- **Speed of reactions**
- **Effect of reactants**
- **Effect of temperature**
- **Effect of concentration**
- **Activation energy and catalysts**
- **Chemical reactions in industry**

Bracketed numbers are Section Review questions correlated to that objective.

Learning Objectives

1. To compare two methods for describing the speed of chemical reactions. [5]
2. To describe the effect of temperature changes on chemical reactions. [9, 22, 25]
3. To identify differences in concentration and relate them to their effect on the speed of reactions. [1, 10, 24]
4. To define catalysts and relate their effect on activation energy to reaction speed. [2, 6, 11, 12, 20, 23]
5. To describe two important industrial chemical processes. [4, 7, 14, 15, 16, 17, 18, 19]

Figure 6-18. *The rate of the reaction between the fuel and oxygen is regulated by vents of the door of this wood stove.*

Science background information: The burning of fuels for heat and the use of gasoline in automobile engines are just two examples of controlled chemical reactions. Other important kinds of reactions include the synthesis of industrial chemicals, the processes of photography, the production of textiles, and the refining of metals.

Chemical reactions are widely used for our benefit, but most of them need to be controlled to be useful. For instance, a mixture of gasoline vapor and air explodes when it is ignited. Uncontrolled, the explosive burning of gasoline is dangerous. Yet, the same reaction, under control in the engine of an automobile, provides energy for transporting people.

It is necessary to control useful, but potentially dangerous, reactions and to prevent unwanted reactions. To accomplish this, we need to have some knowledge of reaction rates and the factors that control the rates of chemical reactions.

Speed of reactions

New vocabulary: reaction speed

The speed of a reaction can be described similarly to the way that the speed of an object in motion is described. Recall your study of motion. The speed of an object in motion is the ratio of the distance traveled over the time needed to travel that distance. The **reaction speed**, or reaction rate, is the ratio of the measure of how far the reaction goes over the time required for the reaction. Measuring how far a reaction goes is done in different ways. You can determine how far a reaction has gone by measuring how much of the reactant is used up. You can also determine how far a reaction has gone by measuring how much product is produced.

Main Idea

What is the speed of a reaction?

$$\text{Reaction speed} = \frac{\text{How far reaction goes}}{\text{Time for reaction}}$$

The speed of a chemical reaction can be described quantitatively, that is, with numbers. You do this by measuring the change in the amount of products or reactants over a period of time. However, often it is enough to give a qualitative description, such as fast, very fast, slow, or very slow, to a reaction. A qualitative description is really an estimate.

Suppose that a gas, such as carbon dioxide, is produced by a reaction. You could estimate the speed of the reaction by counting the number of bubbles of gas that appeared in 10 minutes. If a lot of bubbles appeared, you could say that the reaction was fast. If only a few bubbles appeared, you could say that the reaction was slow. As another example, you could describe the speed of the rusting of iron by estimating the amount of iron that disappears over a period of time. Overall, the longer a reaction takes, the slower is its speed. The shorter the time needed, the faster is the reaction.

You probably have influenced the speed of some chemical reactions already. You may have built a fire in a wood stove or out-of-doors. You probably used small pieces of wood at first.

Data Search

Compare the densities of the gaseous elements hydrogen, nitrogen, and oxygen with the density of a solid, calcium. Search pages 658–661.

Calcium has a density of 1.6 gm/cm³. These three gaseous elements have densities which are at least 1000 times less.

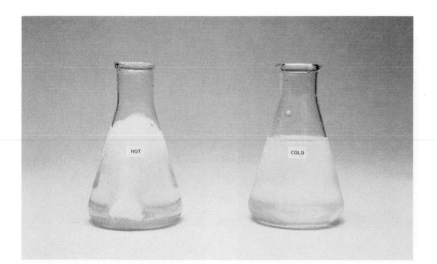

Figure 6-19. *Temperature has an effect on the reaction rate. Here, an antacid tablet bubbles more vigorously in hot water than cold.*

Research Topic

Find out how much wood is cut down each year in the world and what percentage of this is used for fuel.

You may have added air by blowing on the fire to speed up the burning. Once it had started, you probably added more wood. To slow down the burning, you could have reduced the air supply by adjusting a damper.

You may have added meat tenderizer to steak before cooking. It speeds up the breakdown of the long protein molecules in the meat. As a result, you don't have to cook the meat as long. Changing the cooking temperature of food is another way to change the speed of a reaction.

Exposed steel on an automobile will rust very quickly in moist air. You paint the surface to keep the steel from having contact with the air and moisture. Keeping the exposed surface dry slows down the rusting.

These are just a few ways of changing reaction speeds. In the following pages we will discuss four common ways to change the reaction speeds of chemical reactions.

Quick Review

1. How is the speed of a reaction determined?
2. How is the time for a reaction related to the speed of a reaction?

Quick Review answers:
1. By measuring the amount of product formed, or by measuring the amount of reactants used up.
2. The longer a reaction takes, the slower it is. The less time a reaction takes, the faster it is.

Effect of reactants

Different substances react at different speeds, or rates, depending on their chemical properties. For example, various elements combine with oxygen. Some, such as magnesium, combine with oxygen very rapidly. Other elements, such as copper, combine very slowly with oxygen. The two metals, magnesium and copper, react with oxygen at very different

Figure 6-20. *Elements react differently depending on their own chemical properties. Calcium reacts vigorously with water, but copper does not react noticeably.*

Science background information: Calcium is a more active metal than copper and will replace hydrogen from water. Students will study more about the activity of metals in Chapter 12.

rates. The rate of a chemical reaction depends first on the chemical properties of the reactants. Other factors influence the rate of a reaction as well.

For solid reactants, the amount of exposed surface area influences the rate of a reaction. A solid that is finely divided may react explosively, while the same substance in large particles may not react at all. Coal is an example. Finely divided coal, scattered throughout a volume of air in the form of coal dust, may explode when a spark occurs. A large piece of coal, exposed to the same volume of air, remains unreacted indefinitely. With the greater exposed surface area, there is more opportunity for the reactants to come in contact. The more opportunities for contact, the faster is the reaction. In fact, doubling the surface area doubles the reaction rate.

Quick Review

What effect does dividing a substance into finer particles have on the speed of the chemical reaction?

Effect of temperature

You are probably most familiar with the effect of temperature on the speed of a reaction. If you want to cook foods faster, you increase the cooking temperature. If you want to cook slower, you lower the temperature. In the same way, increasing the temperature of the reactants also increases the rate of a chemical reaction. Decreasing the temperature decreases the rate of a chemical reaction.

To understand how temperature affects the rate of a reaction, picture the particles of two gases such as hydrogen and oxygen. Suppose that they are at room temperature, 25°C. All the particles of the two gases are moving. Some are moving faster than others, even at the same temperature. Individually, the particles of these two gases will have quite a range of kinetic energies at any fixed temperature. However, the *average kinetic energy* of all of the particles of a gas depends only on the temperature, not on the nature of the particles. Therefore, at any fixed temperature, the particles of two gases will have the *same* average kinetic energy.

What happens when the temperature of the gases is increased? As you might expect, the particles, on the average, move faster. They have a greater average kinetic energy at the higher temperature. The gas particles collide more often. More importantly, when the particles do collide, they hit each

Main Idea

What is the first thing on which the rate of a chemical reaction depends?

Quick Review answer:
Dividing a substance into finer particles increases the speed of a chemical reaction.

Figure 6-21. *Two photographs show the same balloon in hot and cold water. The higher temperature causes the gas in the balloon to expand.*

other harder. More energy is involved in the collisions. As a result of harder collisions, there is a greater chance that the collisions will result in a reaction. Thus, the gases hydrogen and oxygen will react faster at a higher temperature and more slowly at a lower temperature.

An increase of 10°C in temperature produces roughly a doubling of the speed of the reaction. This approximation is useful in estimating the effect of increasing or decreasing the temperature for many reactions at ordinary temperatures.

Quick Review

1. What effect does increasing the temperature have on a chemical reaction?
2. What effect does increasing the temperature of hydrogen have on the average kinetic energy of its molecules?

Effect of concentration

New vocabulary: concentration

Your experience tells you that adding more fuel or air to a fire increases the rate of burning. This happens because you are increasing the contact of the fuel with the air, or the air with the fuel, or both. In the same way, to speed up a reaction you should add more of the reactants.

In a chemical reaction, when you increase the amount of one or more reactants, you usually increase the amount of reactants in a given space. When the amount of a substance is increased in a given space, the concentration of the substance has increased. **Concentration** is usually expressed as the ratio of the amount of a solute to the amount of solvent it is in.

The concentration of a substance can be expressed in various units. For example, adding one sugar lump to a cup of tea gives a certain concentration: one lump of sugar/250 mL of tea. If you add two sugar lumps to a second cup of tea, you have doubled the concentration: two lumps of sugar/250 mL. By adding another 250 mL of tea to the first cup, the concentration of sugar in the tea is reduced to one-half of the original concentration: one lump of sugar/500 mL of tea.

Increasing the concentration of the reactants increases the rate of the reaction. Decreasing the concentration of reactants decreases the rate of the reaction. The speed of a reaction can be controlled by changing the concentrations of reactants. Reaction rates usually double when the concentration of one of the reactants is doubled. If the concentration of both reactants is doubled, the reaction rate may quadruple.

Main Idea

What is the definition of concentration?

Figure 6-22. *The color differences of the solutions are directly related to the concentration of copper sulfate in each. Which one has the most copper sulfate?* The darkest solution.

Are these results consistent with the model of particles of reactants colliding with each other in order to react? A greater number of particles of reactants in the same space should mean more collisions. Fewer particles of reactants in the same space should mean fewer collisions. Changing the concentration of reactants has the predicted effect on the speed of reactions. You can rely on the kinetic-molecular model of matter.

Quick Review

1. How is concentration defined?
2. How does doubling the concentration of one reactant affect the rate of a chemical reaction?

Activation energy and catalysts

New vocabulary: activation energy, catalyst, inhibitor

Most reactions will not start when the reactants are simply brought together. They must be heated before a chemical change can take place. Heating supplies the push to start the reaction. The burning of wood is a familiar example. You know that wood does not start to burn by itself. It must first be brought to a high enough temperature. It takes energy to bring the wood to this temperature. Once the wood begins to burn, however, it gives off much more energy than was used in getting it started.

An analogy is useful to illustrate how the energy to start a reaction relates to the energy given off by the reaction. Imagine having to climb a small hill before descending to a plain that is some distance lower than your starting place. The energy needed to climb the hill represents the energy to start

Figure 6-23. *Reaction rates depend on the concentration of reactants. Into which test tube was more antacid dropped?* The one with the larger balloon.

Quick Review answers:
1. Concentration is the ratio of the amount of a substance to the volume it occupies.
2. Doubling the concentration of one reactant generally doubles the rate, or speed of a reaction.

Figure 6-24. *Effort is needed to get over the hill from the valley to the plain. Similarly, activation energy is needed to get a chemical reaction started.*

Energy needed to raise temperature of wood = activation energy

Energy of wood at normal temperature = energy of reactants

Energy released when wood burns = energy of products →

6.2a Comparing Speeds of a Reaction

Science Processes: Observing, inferring

Materials BASIC 15 minutes Groups of 2 to 4
- **hydrogen peroxide (3%)**
- **steel wool**
- **sand**
- **beakers, 50 mL (3)**

Purpose

To observe the effect of steel wool and sand on the decomposition of hydrogen peroxide.

Procedures

1. Place equal amounts (20–25 mL) of 3% hydrogen peroxide in each of three beakers. Observe for 2–3 minutes and note any changes.
2. Add a small piece of clean steel wool to one of the beakers containing the hydrogen peroxide.
3. Add a small portion of sand to the third beaker containing hydrogen peroxide.
4. Compare the rate of formation of bubbles in each of the three containers for another few minutes.

Questions

1. Describe the rate of the reaction before adding steel wool.
2. Describe the rate of the reaction after adding steel wool to one of the containers.
3. What changes do you see in the steel wool?
4. Describe the rate of reaction before adding the sand to the third beaker.
5. Describe the rate of reaction after adding sand to the third beaker.
6. How might the steel wool function as a catalyst for the decomposition of hydrogen peroxide?
7. Does sand act as a catalyst for the decomposition of hydrogen peroxide?

Conclusion

Describe the role of a catalyst in a chemical reaction. What happens to the catalyst after the reaction?

Steps 2 and 3

Steel wool

Sand

the reaction. The energy needed to get a chemical reaction started is known as the **activation energy.** The difference between the starting level and the level of the plain represents the energy given off by the reaction.

Some reactions do start without the addition of energy from the outside. Unprotected iron rusts easily when it is wet or when it is exposed to humid air. Rusting is the combining of oxygen from the air with iron to form the reddish compound iron oxide.

$$4Fe + 3O_2 \rightarrow 2Fe_2O_3$$

The hardening of cement is another reaction that needs no energy push to start it.

A **catalyst** speeds up a reaction without being changed itself by the reaction. This is an important characteristic of all catalysts. It speeds up the reaction by providing another, usually easier, way for the reaction to take place. The catalyst does this by lowering the energy of activation needed to get the reaction going. As a result of adding a catalyst, more particles now have enough energy to react, at any particular temperature. While a catalyst plays a definite role in the reaction, after the reaction it is restored to its original condition.

Catalytic converters on automobiles and in wood-burning stoves are quite common. Catalytic converters make it possible for unburned gases to react with oxygen, and thereby make the combustion process more complete. More complete combustion reduces the amount of pollutants that an

Main Idea

What happens to a catalyst during a reaction?

Additional information:
A catalyst may take part in a chemical reaction. The important point is that at the end of the reaction, the catalyst is back to the same condition it was at the start of the reaction.

Figure 6-25. *A catalyst causes a reaction to go faster by lowering the activation energy needed to get the reaction started. Does it affect the energy released overall from start to finish?*

No, the energy difference between the reactants and products is not changed by a catalyst.

Energy needed without catalyst

Energy needed with catalyst

Energy released overall from start to finish

automobile releases into the atmosphere. More complete combustion also makes a wood-burning stove more efficient for heating.

Most of the chemical reactions that take place in living things depend on catalysts. The catalysts in living things are enzymes. Each enzyme functions as a catalyst for a very specific chemical reaction. It is estimated that as many as 30 000 different enzymes are involved in chemical reactions in the human body.

Catalysts always increase the speed of a reaction. However, some substances block or prevent the course of a reaction and, in so doing, slow up the reaction. These substances are called **inhibitors.** Many drugs are believed to have their specific effect on the body by damaging or changing an enzyme. The normal reaction that is catalyzed by the enzyme then would not happen. The drug acts as an inhibitor.

Quick Review

1. What effect does a catalyst have on the speed of a chemical reaction?
2. What effect does a catalyst have on the activation energy of a chemical reaction?

Chemical reactions in industry

New vocabulary: ore, refining

Many kinds of chemical reactions are used in industry. Here we will discuss two important ones.

Refining of metals. Many of our most useful metals are found in nature combined with other elements in compounds called **ores.** Ores are the sources of our metals. Oxygen and sulfur are two elements that are combined with many of the metals. Compounds consisting of a metal and oxygen are called *oxides.* Ores include the iron oxides, Fe_2O_3 and Fe_3O_4, copper oxide, Cu_2O, aluminum oxide, Al_2O_3, manganese dioxide, MnO_2, and tin oxide, SnO_2. Other ores include metals combined with sulfur or with carbonate. Examples include lead sulfide, PbS, lead carbonate, $PbCO_3$, zinc sulfide, ZnS, zinc carbonate, $ZnCO_3$, mercury sulfide, HgS, copper sulfide, Cu_2S, and copper carbonate, $CuCO_3$.

Most metals need to be removed from their ores to be useful to us. The process of removing metals from their ores and from other impurities is known as **refining.** The most common technique for refining metals is by reacting the ores with carbon or carbon monoxide. The oxide ores are reacted

Figure 6-26. *Iron ore is converted to metallic iron in a blast furnace by a reaction with carbon or carbon monoxide from coke.*

directly with the carbon or carbon monoxide. An example of a reaction of this type is the reaction between iron oxide and carbon monoxide. The reaction produces metallic iron.

$$Fe_2O_3 + 3CO \rightarrow 3CO_2 + 2Fe$$

In the industrial process, iron ore is changed to a form of impure iron, pig iron. This takes place in a blast furnace. Iron ore, limestone, and coke are fed in at the top of the furnace. A blast of hot air is forced upward from the bottom of the furnace. The hot air reacts with coke to produce carbon monoxide. The carbon monoxide reacts with iron ore which is changed into molten pig iron. Because of impurities such as phosphorus and sulfur, pig iron is not very useful. Pig iron is very brittle and not very strong. Most pig iron is converted to different forms of steel.

During the steelmaking process, the carbon content of iron is lowered and phosphorus and sulfur are removed. Desired elements, such as chromium, are added to the steel. Then the steel is given a special heat treatment to give it special properties that the steelmaker wants it to have. The result is that many kinds of steel are available for different construction and fabricating needs.

Sulfide or carbonate ores require additional processing steps before the ore can be reacted with carbon or carbon dioxide. Sulfide ores are heated first in air to combine the sulfur with oxygen. The resulting oxide is then reacted with carbon monoxide or carbon.

$$2PbS + 3O_2 \rightarrow 2PbO + 2SO_2$$
$$2PbO + C \rightarrow 2Pb + CO_2$$

Carbonate ores are first heated to convert them to oxides.

$$ZnCO_3 \rightarrow ZnO + CO_2$$

The oxide is then reacted with carbon or carbon monoxide to convert it to a pure metal, as seen in the earlier examples.

Preparation of sulfuric acid. Sulfuric acid is the most widely used of all acids. It is used in many industrial processes, such as the ones shown in Figure 6-27. Sulfuric acid, H_2SO_4, is prepared commercially from sulfur dioxide, which is available from many different sources. After cleaning, the sulfur dioxide is first changed to sulfur trioxide by the *contact process.*

$$2SO_2 + O_2 \rightarrow 2SO_3 + heat$$

Science background information:
Carbon from the coke also reacts in the heat of the blast furnace with iron ore to produce metallic iron and carbon monoxide or carbon dioxide.

Research Topic

The process of refining metals has been known for a long time. Find out what you can about the first processes to refine silver and how that compares to silver refining today.

Science background information:
Zinc sulfide is one of the most important zinc ores. It is converted to zinc oxide before further processing. The reaction that converts zinc sulfide to the oxide is self-sustaining. It gives off heat, once the reaction has started and no further heating is needed.

■ **Safety Note**
Sulfuric acid is a dangerous chemical that can cause severe burns. Use it only for experiments that are supervised by a teacher.

6.2b   Temperature and Reaction Speed

Science Processes: Experimenting, observing, inferring

Materies   10 minutes   Groups of 2 or 3

Materials   10 minutes   Groups of 2 or 3

- 4 Alka-Seltzer tablets
- 2 250-mL graduated flasks
- 2 one-hole rubber stoppers
- stopwatch
- 2 wide-mouth balloons
- hot water
- cold water

Purpose

To observe the speed of chemical changes in hot and cold water.

Procedure

1. Fit a balloon over the top of a one-hole rubber stopper.
2. Test the stopper to see that it will fit tightly into the top of a 250-mL flask with the balloon attached.
3. Repeat steps 1 and 2 with the second balloon, stopper, and flask.
4. Fill one flask with 150 mL of hot water.
5. Squeeze the air out of the balloon while it is attached to the stopper. Hold the deflated balloon and stopper close to the top of the flask.

6. Drop two Alka-Seltzer tablets into the flask and quickly put the stopper with the deflated balloon into the top of the flask.
7. With the stopwatch, time how long it takes for the balloon to fill up completely.
8. Repeat steps 4 through 7 using the second balloon, stopper, flask, and 150 mL of cold water. Time the reaction.

Questions

1. What observations indicated that a chemical change was taking place?
2. What effect, if any, did the water temperature have on how fast the chemical change took place?
3. Does the temperature of the water affect the rate of a chemical reaction?
4. What are some of the variables in this experiment? Identify which ones remain constant, which one is being manipulated, and which one is responding to changes.

Conclusion

How does temperature affect the rate of a chemical reaction?

Rubber stopper
Balloon
2 Alka-Seltzer tablets

Step 5

Step 7

Figure 6-27. *Sulfuric acid is used to make many different substances and in many industrial processes.*

In the contact process, the oxides of either platinum or vanadium are used as catalysts for the reaction. The two gases, sulfur dioxide and oxygen, stick to the surface of the catalyst. There they react to form the gas sulfur trioxide. Sulfur trioxide is not held as strongly to the surface of the catalyst and escapes. This makes room for more sulfur dioxide and oxygen to react.

Sulfur trioxide is absorbed by moderately concentrated sulfuric acid. Pure water or steam cannot be used directly to combine with the sulfur trioxide. Each sulfur trioxide molecule is first combined with a molecule of sulfuric acid.

$$H_2SO_4 + SO_3 \rightarrow H_2SO_4{\cdot}SO_3$$

Water is then added, in just the right amount, to change the product to concentrated sulfuric acid.

$$H_2SO_4 \cdot SO_3 + H_2O \rightarrow 2H_2SO_4$$

The reaction of water with sulfuric acid is a very exothermic reaction. Only small amounts of acid can be added to water at a time. Never add water to this acid. The sulfuric acid molecules have such a strong attraction to water molecules that spattering occurs. Sulfuric acid causes severe burns when it touches the skin. Be very careful when you are working with sulfuric acid.

Quick Review

1. What is the name of compounds we use as sources for metals?
2. Why do many metals need to be refined?

Additional information: About 85 percent of the sulfur produced is converted to sulfuric acid. Most of this sulfuric acid is used to produce fertilizer. In recent years, the production of sulfur in the United States has exceeded 5×10^6 tons.

Research Topic

Other strong acids include nitric and hydrochloric acids. Find how they are made and compare each process to the process for making sulfuric acid.

Quick Review answers:
1. Ores.
2. Metals need to be refined because they often naturally occur in compounds with other elements and because impurities are often present in the ores.

Biochemist

A biochemist works in the branch of chemistry that deals with reactions within living things. About half of all biochemists work in colleges and universities. Their duties are primarily research oriented. However, some teaching and/or administrative responsibilities may be included in their assignment. Others work in private companies or in government agencies and private research institutes.

The occupation of biochemist can be very demanding. Problem-solving ability is a part of the everyday requirements. Precision work with laboratory instruments is often expected. The design and analysis of biochemical laboratory investigations require highly trained and creative individuals.

A person with a bachelor's degree in chemistry or biochemistry is usually employed as a research assistant or as a technician. A graduate degree is normally a requirement for a position as a biochemist. The graduate degree should be specifically in biochemistry, although the background coursework will include considerable chemistry. High school courses in the sciences and in mathematics provide a good start in preparing for this career.

For more information write to American Society of Biological Chemists, 9650 Rockville Pike, Bethesda, Maryland 20014.

Biochemists investigate the chemistry of living things, often using complex laboratory tools.

Chef

A chef is responsible for the preparation of food in the kitchen of a restaurant or institution. In a large kitchen, the chef supervises the work of cooks who may each be in charge of one type of food preparation. A hotel or restaurant chain may have an executive chef who plans menus, hires kitchen chefs, and supervises all the kitchens in the hotel or restaurant chain. At the other end of the scale are small restaurants where one or two chefs, often the owners, do everything themselves.

Chefs must be willing to work nights, weekends, and holidays. They should enjoy both food and working closely with other people. The occupation offers the opportunity to be creative and to receive personal recognition from an appreciative public.

Training can be received in culinary schools, in some community colleges, and on the job. A part-time or summer job in a restaurant can give a high school student a chance to observe firsthand what a chef's work is like.

For more information write to the National Institute for the Foodservice Industry, 20 North Wacker Drive, Suite 2620, Chicago, Illinois 60606.

Chefs prepare food, supervise kitchen helpers, and create new recipes as well.

6.2 Section Review

Answers to Understanding the Concepts and solutions to Problems to Solve appear on page T106 in the front of this book. Blackline master test for this section: Section Testsheet 6-2 (TRB page 216)

Vocabulary

6 activation energy
2 catalyst
1 concentration
3 inhibitor
7 ore
5 reaction speed
4 refining

Vocabulary Review

Match each term above with the numbered phrase that best describes it.

1. A ratio between the amount of a substance and the volume the substance is contained in
2. Substance that speeds up a chemical reaction by lowering the activation energy
3. Substance that hinders the progress of a reaction
4. The process of separating metals from their ores and removing impurities
5. Ratio between how far a reaction has gone and the time it has taken
6. The energy required to get a reaction started
7. Form in which useful metals are often found in nature

Review Questions

8. An increase in the exposed surface area of the reactants generally ?.
   a. increases the rate of reaction
   b. decreases the rate of reaction
   c. does not affect the rate of reaction
   d. lowers the activation energy of the reaction

9. In general, when the temperature of a sample of matter increases, ?.
   a. its particles move faster
   b. the frequency of collision increases
   c. its average kinetic energy increases
   d. collisions are more forceful
   e. all of the above

10. Increasing the concentration of the reactants generally ?.
    a. has no effect on the rate of reaction
    b. increases the rate of reaction
    c. decreases the rate of reaction
    d. stops the reaction

11. Addition of a catalyst will ?.
    a. have no effect on the rate of reaction
    b. increase the rate of reaction
    c. decrease the rate of reaction
    d. stop the reaction

12. Catalysts in the body are called ?.
    a. inhibitors
    b. fats
    c. carbohydrates
    d. enzymes

13. Substances that slow a chemical reaction by blocking its course are called ?.
    a. enzymes
    b. inhibitors
    c. catalysts
    d. oxides

14. Compounds consisting of a metal and oxygen are called ?.
    a. sulfides
    b. carbonates
    c. oxides
    d. chlorides

15. In the steelmaking process, ?.
    a. the carbon content of iron is lowered
    b. phosphorus is removed from the iron
    c. desired elements are added
    d. all of the above

Understanding the Concepts

16. Describe the steps involved in the production of sulfuric acid.
17. Explain why water should never be added to acid, particularly to sulfuric acid.
18. Discuss what is meant by an ore and list some examples of iron, copper, and lead ores.
19. Describe the process of steelmaking from the iron ore stage to the final product stage.
20. How are meat tenderizers and chemical reaction rates related?
21. Explain why it is that finely-divided coal, scattered through a volume of air, will explode with a spark, but a large piece of coal, under similar conditions, will remain unreacted indefinitely.
22. What is the usual effect of a temperature change on reaction rate? Include the concept of kinetic energy in your explanation.
23. Explain how the addition of a catalyst increases the speed of a reaction.
24. Explain the effect of concentration on reaction rate.

Problems to Solve

25. If the temperature at which a reaction is run is increased by 20°C, how is the rate of reaction likely to be affected?

6 Chapter Review

Answers appear on page T107 in the front of this book. Blackline master test for this chapter: Chapter Testsheets 6A and 6B (TRB pages 251–252)

Vocabulary

activation energy

bond dissociation energy

catalyst

concentration

decomposition reaction

double replacement reaction

endothermic reaction

exothermic reaction

inhibitor

mole

ore

precipitate

reaction speed

refining

single replacement reaction

synthesis reaction

Review of Concepts

A **chemical change** is a change in matter that produces one or more new substances.

- Chemical reactions can be classified according to whether they give off more energy than they absorb or whether they must absorb energy continuously for the reaction to keep going.
- Different chemical bonds require different amounts of energy to break them apart.
- Chemical reactions are considered complete if one or more of the reactants is used up in the reaction. They are incomplete if some of each of the reactants remains.
- The formation of a solid or a gas in a reaction is a clue that the reaction will continue until at least one of the reactants is used up.
- Chemical reactions can be classified according to whether the product is a single compound; the reactant is a single compound; one element replaces another in a compound; or two elements switch places.
- Mass is conserved in a chemical reaction.

- A quantity called the mole is used to compare numbers of atoms involved in chemical reactions. The mole represents a fixed number of particles.
- A balanced chemical equation can be used to predict the masses of the products and the amount of energy released or required, given the masses of the reactants.
- Chemical changes are involved in everyday processes in our lives such as baking and cleaning. Vital elements are supplied to plants by fertilizers.

The **reaction speed** of a chemical reaction is a measure of how fast the reactants are used up or how fast the products are formed.

- Different combinations of reactants have different reaction speeds.
- For solid reactants, the amount of exposed surface affects the reaction speed.
- Increasing the temperature of the reactants increases the reaction speed.
- Concentration is a measure of how much of a substance is present in a solution.
- Increasing the concentration of the reactants increases the reaction speed.

- Activation energy is the energy required to get a chemical reaction going.
- A catalyst speeds up a reaction without being changed itself by the reaction.
- An inhibitor slows up a reaction.

An **ore** is a compound that contains a metal in combination with other elements.

- Metals can be removed from their ores by refining.

Critical Thinking

1. Under what condition can a reaction that requires energy to get started be considered exothermic?
2. Would a reaction that starts with the breaking of bonds be likely to require energy to get started? Explain.
3. Which type of reaction is more likely to be endothermic—a synthesis reaction or a decomposition reaction? Explain.
4. Carbon-12 has a larger atomic mass than helium-4. Are there more particles in a mole of carbon-12 atoms than in a mole of helium-4 atoms? Explain.

5. Give an example of a reaction for which it is desirable to decrease the reaction speed and another for which it is desirable to increase the reaction speed.

6. Explain why fire is a hazard in a coal mine, even though large pieces of coal do not react spontaneously with air.

7. If the reaction speed doubles for a temperature increase of 10°C, how is the speed affected by a 20°C increase?

8. How is a reaction rate likely to be affected if you reduce the concentration of one reactant to half its original value?

9. How does the activation energy needed to burn wood compare with that needed to harden cement?

10. Preparing a pure metal from an ore usually involves the removal of other elements. Review the reactions given for the preparation of lead, iron, and zinc and describe these reactions in terms of the four main types of chemical reactions.

Individual Research

1. The hardening of cement releases energy during the chemical reactions that take place. Use a chemistry text to find out the nature of the changes that occur. How might you measure the amount of heat released?

2. One type of animal tissue contains a catalyst that speeds up the decomposition of hydrogen peroxide. To find out which type it is, place 10 mL of 3% hydrogen peroxide in each of four test tubes. Add a piece of animal fat to one tube, the same amount of red meat to the second tube, a piece of bone to the third tube, and use the fourth tube as a control.

3. Interview some car salespeople about catalytic converters. Find out whether people who want to buy a car are interested in whether the car has a catalytic converter. Do the salespeople present catalytic converters in a positive or negative light?

4. Industrial safety is a matter of concern to many people. If possible, visit a local factory and talk to the person in charge of safety about what is being done to promote safe working conditions in the factory.

5. Rusting is an example of a chemical reaction that takes place slowly. Read about the process of rusting and try to devise a way to measure how much rusting occurs on a piece of ungalvanized iron over a period of weeks.

6. Many food products are labelled according to their contents. With the help of a chemistry book or dictionary for names, try to determine whether the ingredients in several packaged foods are proteins, carbohydrates, or fats. List them for each food using these categories. Usually the ingredients that are present in the largest amounts are listed first.

Bibliography

Cobb, Vicki. *Chemically Active! Experiments You Can Do at Home.* New York: Lippincott, 1985
Experiments from the simple to the somewhat sophisticated, using readily available materials, followed by an explanation of chemical theory.

Hess, Fred C. *Chemistry Made Simple.* New York: Doubleday, 1984 (revised edition)
Covers chemistry in simple language; includes chapter summaries.

Neubauer, Alfred. *Chemistry Today: The Portrait of a Science.* New York: Arco, 1983
Readable, illustrated text that highlights modern research.

Wilbraham, et al. *Addison-Wesley Chemistry.* Menlo Park, CA: Addison-Wesley, 1987
Chapter 7, "Chemical Reactions," is a good reference for students who want more indepth coverage of this subject.

Chapter 7
Using Energy from Chemical Reactions

Energy stored in chemical bonds can be made to do useful work. The controlled burning of fuel in the engines of this jet airplane enable it to carry passengers and cargo at a speed of 800 km/hr. In this chapter, you will learn about the chemistry of compounds that are fuels, how fuels can be used for heating and work, and how special fuels supply energy to living organisms.

Science background information:
Complex organic molecules are formed primarily because of the chemical properties of carbon. Carbon is unique in that it has a nucleus with a relatively small positive charge, $+6$, and four unpaired electrons in its outer shell. Because of this, each carbon atom can form four stable single bonds with other atoms. These atoms are located at the corners of a tetrahedron with the carbon nucleus at the center.

Its ability to form bonds with other carbon atoms makes it possible for carbon to form more complex types of molecules than any other element. Linear chains, branched chains, and cyclic molecules may be formed. Because there is free rotation around a C-C single bond, these molecules can assume many different three dimensional shapes or conformations. The highly complex structures of living organisms are possible because of this. The ability of carbon to form double and triple bonds increases the seemingly limitless variety of organic compounds. The organic compounds of living things are formed mainly from six elements: carbon, hydrogen, oxygen, nitrogen, phosphorus, and sulfur.

The synthesis of these complex, highly organized molecules requires a great deal of energy. This energy can be released when these molecules are

For detailed information about teaching this chapter, see Chapter 7 Planning Guide on pages T108–T109 in the front of this book.

Projectsheet 7 (TRB page 179) and Research Lab 7 (Lab Manual pages 101–102) may be used at any point in this chapter.

Chapter Preview

7.1 Carbon Chemistry

- **Organic compounds**
- **Simple carbon compounds**
- **Saturated hydrocarbons**
- **Unsaturated hydrocarbons**
- **Reactivity of hydrocarbons**
- **Carbon compounds with rings**
- **Derivatives of the hydrocarbons**
- **Carbohydrates, fats, and proteins**

Organic compounds contain carbon atoms. There are many kinds of organic compounds because carbon atoms can form covalent bonds with many different kinds of atoms. We will look at some of the kinds of organic compounds. Organic compounds are also the essential chemicals found in living beings.

7.2 Using Fuels for Heat and Work

- **Fuels for heating**
- **Fuels for work**
- **Controlling the rate of burning**
- **Burning fuels to do work**
- **The products of burning fuels**

Fuels that we use for heating and work include natural gas, coal, and petroleum products. Different amounts of energy can be obtained from various fuels. To be useful for heating and for work, the burning of fuels has to be controlled.

7.3 Energy and Living Things

- **The body's energy needs**
- **Supplying cells with energy**
- **Energy from cell respiration**
- **Energy from fermentation**
- **Body heat**
- **Energy stored through photosynthesis**
- **The food energy pyramid**

Your body gets the energy it needs from the food you eat. Living cells get their energy from food through the processes of respiration and fermentation. All living things can trace their energy back to the same source—the sun.

broken down to simpler ones. The burning of carbon compounds as fuel in the presence of oxygen releases energy in the form of heat and produces CO_2 and H_2O. This heat can be used to perform work as it flows from a hotter body to a cooler one. This is the familiar thermodynamic principle used in engines and turbines.

Biological systems such as the human body use the burning of carbon compounds to get energy to perform work. There are basically three types of work done by living organisms: chemical work, osmotic or concentration work, and mechanical work. Although heat is the simplest form in which energy may be transferred or used in a machine, it is not a useful form of energy for performing biological work. This is because heat can only perform work if there is a temperature differential across which it can pass. All parts of a living organism are at the same temperature so there is no such differential.

This problem has been solved in biological systems by the strategy of coupling one chemical reaction to another and transferring energy in that way. The reaction of the oxidation of glucose is coupled to the synthesis of adenosine triphosphate (ATP) from adenosine diphosphate (ADP) and inorganic phosphate (P_i). ATP serves as the link between energy-producing and energy-requiring reactions in the cell. Whenever a reaction requiring energy takes place in the cell, it is coupled to the reaction ATP $\rightarrow$ ADP + P_i.

Another way to transfer energy is by the transfer of electrons (oxidation-reduction). The cell can also use energy from glucose to make a molecule known as NADPH from nicotinamide adenine dinucleotide phosphate, or $NADP^+$. NADPH is a carrier of electrons that can be used to supply energy in cellular oxidation-reduction reactions.

For ideas for classroom demonstration and discussion, see Getting Started on page T110 in the front of this book.

7.1 Carbon Chemistry

Supplemental materials: Teaching Diagram 7-1 (TRB page 34), Reading Checksheet 7-1 (TRB page 97), Skillsheet 7-1 (TRB page 143), Investigation 7-1 (Lab Manual pages 91–92)

Section Preview

- **Organic compounds**
- **Simple organic compounds**
- **Saturated hydrocarbons**
- **Unsaturated hydrocarbons**
- **Reactivity of hydrocarbons**
- **Carbon compounds with rings**
- **Derivatives of the hydrocarbons**
- **Carbohydrates, fats, and proteins**

Bracketed numbers are Section Review questions correlated to that objective.

Learning Objectives

1. To understand why carbon can form so many compounds. [1, 3, 7, 11, 12, 17, 27]
2. To recognize several important groups of carbon compounds. [2, 5, 6, 8, 9, 10, 11, 16, 19, 20, 26, 28, 29, 31, 32]
3. To recognize different kinds of carbon bonds. [6, 8, 9, 10, 20]
4. To relate some chemical properties to different kinds of carbon bonds. [21]
5. To identify classes of organic compounds that are essential for living beings. [13, 14, 15, 22, 23, 24, 30]

Figure 7-1. *Many common materials are made of carbon and its compounds: synthetic-fiber cloth and rope, wood, graphite, and plastics.*

The chemistry of carbon is a vast, varied, and interesting subject. The compounds of carbon are more numerous than the compounds of all the other elements. Carbon chemistry is involved in such subjects as biochemistry, plastics, synthetic fabrics, petroleum, food preparation, agriculture, and medicine. In this section we will take a brief look at some of the variety of carbon compounds and the important roles they play in our lives.

Organic compounds

New vocabulary: organic compounds

Compounds that contain carbon are known as **organic compounds.** They are called organic compounds because they were originally found in living things. Carbon is found in

Main Idea

What is the term for compounds that contain carbon?

hundreds of thousands of compounds. So organic chemistry, while limited to the study of the compounds of carbon, is still a very large field of scientific study. You may wonder why carbon has this unique ability to form so many compounds. A look at the structure of the carbon atom helps to provide an answer.

Carbon shares electrons with other atoms to make covalent bonds. Carbon has four valence electrons to share with other atoms, so potentially it can form bonds with four other atoms. Carbon atoms can form chemical bonds both with carbon atoms and with other kinds of atoms. A clue that you can expect carbon to form a wide variety of compounds is the variation in the forms of carbon.

Carbon atoms bond together to form diamonds. Diamonds are the hardest substance known. Carbon atoms also combine to form graphite. Graphite is the so-called "lead" in your pencil. In a pencil, graphite is firm enough to hold a definite shape, yet soft enough to rub off on a piece of paper. Carbon also forms soot. Soot is soft and crumbly. Diamonds, graphite, and soot are forms of carbon. The differences in the properties of the three substances must be due to the differences in the ways that carbon atoms are bonded. In diamonds, carbon atoms are bonded rigidly to one another in every direction. In graphite, carbon atoms are bonded together in sheets which can slide past each other. In soot, carbon atoms are only bonded occasionally and randomly.

The ability of carbon atoms to bond to other carbon atoms leads to a wide variation in the kinds and structure of organic, or carbon, compounds.

Quick Review

1. What are organic compounds?
2. What accounts for the differences in properties of graphite and diamond?

Simple carbon compounds

New vocabulary: hydrocarbons, tetrahedron, polyatomic ion

Carbon atoms can bond with hydrogen atoms. Compounds that contain only hydrogen and carbon atoms are called **hydrocarbons.** Hydrocarbons, such as oil and natural gas, are two major sources of energy for heating and work. In addition, some hydrocarbons are the raw materials for plastics, synthetics, and drugs. You can see why the hydrocarbons are an important group of compounds.

Figure 7-2. *Diamonds are made of carbon atoms. Heat and pressure cause the atoms to bond tightly to one another.*

Quick Review answers:
1. Organic compounds are those that contain carbon.
2. Different arrangements of the carbon atoms within the two substances.

Main Idea

What elements are found in hydrocarbons?

The simplest hydrocarbon is the compound methane. The methane molecule has a single carbon atom with four hydrogen atoms bonded to it. The formula of methane is CH_4. Remember that the straight lines connecting the atoms in Figure 7-3 represent pairs of electrons. The carbon atom shares a pair of electrons with each of the four hydrogen atoms. The four hydrogen atoms remain as far away from each other as possible around the central carbon atom. The resulting shape of the methane molecule is a pyramid with hydrogen atoms at the four corners and a carbon atom in the center. It is called a **tetrahedron.** The tetrahedral shape is a characteristic feature of many carbon compounds. The figure will be helpful in explaining the shapes and arrangements of atoms in other carbon compounds.

Carbon atoms can form bonds also with oxygen atoms. Carbon dioxide CO_2 is a familiar compound. It is a product of the complete burning of organic compounds. Each oxygen atom shares two pairs of electrons with a carbon atom. Each of the lines in the formula represent a pair of shared electrons.

$$O=C=O$$

Sometimes the burning of an organic compound is incomplete because not enough oxygen is available. One product of incomplete burning is carbon monoxide. Three pairs of electrons are shared between the carbon atom and the oxygen atom. The dots represent the remaining unpaired electrons.

$$:C\equiv O$$

Carbon monoxide is a dangerous substance. The molecule bonds more strongly to the hemoglobin in the blood than does oxygen. A person breathing air that contains even a small percentage (one part in 500) of carbon monoxide may die of suffocation.

Carbon atoms also bond to oxygen atoms in carbonate compounds. The carbonate ion is a polyatomic ion. A **polyatomic ion** is an ion that is composed of two or more atoms, but which chemically acts as a single atom. Just the same as an ordinary ion, a polyatomic ion has a net charge. Carbonate ion has an overall charge of -2. The carbonate ion combines with many positive ions to form compounds such as calcium carbonate, $CaCO_3$, magnesium carbonate, $MgCO_3$, and sodium hydrogen carbonate, commonly known as sodium bicarbonate, $NaHCO_3$.

Figure 7-4. *Stalactites and stalagmites are formed of calcium carbonate in limestone caves. Impurities give them colors.*

Quick Review answers:
1. A tetrahedron.
2. Carbon dioxide is linear; methane is tetrahedral.
3. Carbon dioxide.

Quick Review

1. What is the shape of the methane molecule?
2. How does the shape of the carbon dioxide molecule compare with methane?
3. Name a product of the complete combustion of carbon in oxygen.

Saturated hydrocarbons
New vocabulary: saturated hydrocarbons, alkane series, isomers

There are many different kinds of hydrocarbons. One class of hydrocarbons has carbon atoms that are linked together only with single covalent bonds. These are called **saturated hydrocarbons.** The simplest saturated hydrocarbon is methane.

Saturated hydrocarbons that are more complex than methane can be made by adding other carbon atoms to methane. Suppose another carbon atom is attached to the central carbon atom of methane by replacing one of the hydrogen atoms. The second carbon atom and the first carbon atom each can still share a pair of electrons with three hydrogen atoms. The formula for this compound is C_2H_6. Its name is ethane.

Main Idea

What are saturated hydrocarbons?

Data Search

Compare the melting temperature of carbon with metals such as iron and aluminum and nonmetals such as sulfur and phosphorus. Search pages 658–661.

Melting temperatures: carbon (3550°C), iron (1535°C), aluminum (660°C), sulfur (113°C), phosphorus (44°C).

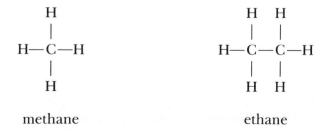

methane   ethane

7.1a Making Hydrocarbon Models

Science processes: Making models, inferring, recording data

Materials BASIC 20 minutes Groups of 2 to 4

- **6 gumdrops of one color**
- **12 gumdrops of a different color**
- **18 round toothpicks**

Purpose

To make three-dimensional models of simple hydrocarbons.

Procedure

1. Find structural diagrams for ethane, ethene, and ethyne molecules in the textbook.
2. Make a model of each molecule, using one color of gumdrop for the carbon atoms and the other color for the hydrogen atoms.
3. Join the atoms in a molecule with toothpicks, following the diagram. Use a different toothpick for each line in the diagram.
4. Use your models to complete a chart like the one shown below and answer the questions.

Questions

1. How do you know these molecules are hydrocarbons?
2. How do the number of carbon atoms compare in the models? the number of hydrogen atoms?
3. What do the toothpicks in the models represent?
4. What kind of bond do the carbon atoms form in ethane? in ethene? in ethyne?
5. What is the relationship between the kind of carbon-carbon bond and the number of hydrogen atoms in the compound?
6. Which model(s) represent saturated hydrocarbons? Which represent unsaturated hydrocarbons?

Conclusion

How do your models help to explain why there can be so many different kinds of hydrocarbon molecules?

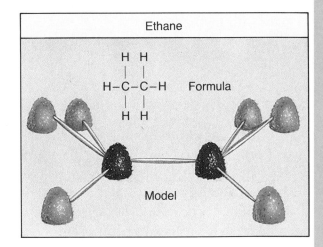

Name of compound	Number of carbon atoms	Number of hydrogen atoms	Kind of C—C bond	Formula
Ethane	2	6	single covalent bond	C_2H_6
Ethene	2	4	double covalent bond	C_2H_4
Ethyne	2	2	triple covalent bond	C_2H_2

Suppose a third carbon atom is added. How many hydrogen atoms could share a pair of electrons with a carbon atom?

$$-\overset{|}{\underset{|}{C}}-\overset{|}{\underset{|}{C}}-\overset{|}{\underset{|}{C}}-$$

From the diagram of the carbon skeleton of this molecule, you can see places for eight hydrogen atoms to bond with carbon atoms. The formula for this hydrocarbon is C_3H_8. Its name is propane.

Compare the formulas for these three hydrocarbons:

$$CH_4, \quad C_2H_6, \quad C_3H_8.$$

What would you predict for the next compounds in this series? Sketch out the structural formula to verify your prediction:

$$C_4H?, \quad C_5H?$$

These compounds are a part of the alkane series. The **alkane series** is made up of saturated hydrocarbons which only have single covalent bonds between the carbon atoms. The names of the compounds in this series all have the *-ane* ending. You may have noticed a pattern. In the alkanes, the number of hydrogen atoms is always two more than twice the number of carbon atoms in the chain ($C_n H_{2n+2}$).

If you tried to sketch the structural formula for the hydrocarbon with four carbon atoms, you encountered a choice of arrangements. The carbon atoms could have been joined in two ways.

H H H H
| | | |
H—C—C—C—C—H   or
| | | |
H H H H
butane

H
|
H—C—H
H | H
| | |
H—C————C————C—H
| | |
H H H
methyl propane

The two hydrocarbons have the same molecular formula, C_4H_{10}, but different structural formulas and different names. Compounds with the same molecular formulas but with different structures are called **isomers.** Isomers have different chemical and physical properties.

Figure 7-5. *Ball and stick model of butane show how carbon and hydrogen atoms can fit together in space. How many carbon atoms are there in butane?*
Four

Additional information:
Butane molecules are not rigid. They can rotate freely around each of the carbon-carbon bonds so that many different shapes are possible for one molecule. This variety of shapes produced by rotation is not the same as the different structures called isomers in the text.

Critical Thinking

If one of the hydrogens in an alkane is replaced by another element, is the resulting compound still an alkane?
No. It would be called a substituted alkane.

Additional information:
Methyl propane is also known as isobutane. The first name is the proper one.

Main Idea

What are isomers?

Some common alkanes	
Name	Formula
Methane	CH_4
Ethane	C_2H_6
Propane	C_3H_8
Butane	C_4H_{10}
Pentane	C_5H_{12}
Hexane	C_6H_{14}
Heptane	C_7H_{16}
Octane	C_8H_{18}
Nonane	C_9H_{20}
Decane	$C_{10}H_{22}$

Table 7-1. *Names and formulas for some common alkanes.*

Additional information:
The formulas that show the carbon chains without any hydrogen atoms attached are called skeletal formulas.

Teaching suggestion:
Remind students that each carbon atom must have four bonds in the completed structural formula. Note that the diagrams here are structural formulas.

Figure 7-6. *Ball and stick model shows hexane molecule, C_6H_{10}.*

Drawing the structural formulas for carbon compounds is not difficult. The necessary steps are explained in the sample problem that follows. Use the procedure to draw the three isomers of C_5H_{12} if you have not already tried to do that.

Sample Problem
Draw two formulas for a saturated hydrocarbon with six carbon atoms.

Solution
1. Draw the six carbon atoms in a row with single straight lines between the atoms to indicate single covalent bonds.

C—C—C—C—C—C

2. Draw H's, for hydrogen atoms, around each carbon atom so that each carbon atom is attached to four other atoms. Two of these atoms may be carbons.

$$
\begin{array}{cccccc}
H & H & H & H & H & H \\
| & | & | & | & | & | \\
H-C-&C-&C-&C-&C-&C-H \\
| & | & | & | & | & | \\
H & H & H & H & H & H
\end{array}
$$

3. Count the number of hydrogen atoms. You should get 14, two more than two times the number of carbon atoms.
4. Repeat the process, only this time start with six carbon atoms forming a branched chain.

$$
\begin{array}{c}
C-C-C-C-C \\
| \\
C
\end{array}
$$

5. Draw H's around the carbon atoms so that each carbon atom is attached to four other atoms. Three of the atoms may be carbons.

$$
\begin{array}{ccccc}
H & H & H & H & H \\
| & | & | & | & | \\
H-C-&C-&C-&C-&C-H \\
| & | & | & | & | \\
H & H & | & H & H \\
& & H-C-H & & \\
& & | & & \\
& & H & &
\end{array}
$$

6. Count the hydrogen atoms. Again, you should get 14.

Practice Problem

Draw two more saturated hydrocarbons with six carbon atoms.

Answer:

Figure 7-7. *Ball and stick model shows 3-methyl-pentane, an isomer of hexane.*

These few examples indicate some of the variation that are possible for hydrocarbons. As the carbon atoms in the chain are increased, more isomers are possible. With eight carbon atoms in the chain there are eighteen possible isomers. Could you sketch the structures of all eighteen?

Quick Review

1. What is a saturated hydrocarbon?
2. What is an isomer?

Unsaturated hydrocarbons

New vocabulary: unsaturated hydrocarbons, alkene series, alkyne series

By sharing more than one pair of electrons, carbon atoms can form double or triple bonds with each other. This adds to the variety of possible carbon compounds. Hydrocarbons that have one or more double or triple bonds <u>are called</u> **unsaturated hydrocarbons.** Below are two examples of unsaturated hydrocarbons. In these formulas two parallel lines represent two pairs of shared electrons, a double bond. Three lines represent three pairs of electrons, a triple bond.

Additional information:

One other possible structure is

ethene (ethylene)   ethyne (acetylene)

Quick Review answers:

1. It is a hydrocarbon in which the carbon atoms are linked to one another only by single bonds.
2. Isomers are molecules that have the same molecular formula but different structures.

Main Idea

What is an unsaturated hydrocarbon?

Critical Thinking

Do you think that all the isomers that are possible actually exist?

Answers will vary. You should make the point of asking how it could be proved that a particular isomer does not exist.

120°

Figure 7-8. *Model of ethane mole-cule shows two springs, which repre-sent a carbon-carbon double bond, holding the carbon atoms together. The four hydrogen atoms are in the same plane. Can the carbon atoms spin freely around the imaginary line from one carbon atom to another? Why or why not?*
No, the double bond holds them rigidly in place.

Alkenes and alkynes	
Name	Formula
Ethene	C_2H_4
Propene	C_3H_6
Butene	C_4H_8
Pentene	C_5H_{10}
Ethyne	C_2H_2
Propyne	C_3H_4
Butyne	C_4H_6
Pentyne	C_5H_8

Table 7-2. *Names and formulas of some alkenes and alkynes.*

Teaching suggestion:
Have students compare the numbers of hydrogen atoms in the different hy-drocarbons listed in Table 7-2. Point out that the number of hydrogen atoms increases in a regular way from one compound in a series to the next.

Quick Review answers:
1. The presence of carbon-carbon double bonds.
2. The presence of carbon-carbon triple bonds.

The formula for the simplest double-bonded hydrocarbon is C_2H_4. The name of the compound is ethene. Its older name, ethylene is still commonly used. By adding carbon atoms to ethene, it is possible to make more complex double-bonded compounds. The next largest hydrocarbon with a double bond is propene.

$$H \quad H$$
$$\diagdown \quad \diagup$$
$$H \qquad\qquad C$$
$$\diagdown \qquad \diagup \quad \diagdown$$
$$C = C \qquad H$$
$$\diagup \qquad \diagdown$$
$$H \qquad\qquad H$$

propene

There is a series of unsaturated hydrocarbons with at least one double bond between two carbon atoms. It is named the **alkene series.** The names of the compounds in this series have the *-ene* ending. The prefix indicates the number of car-bon atoms in the longest chain. What would be the structural formula for butene?

The formula for the simplest triple-bonded hydrocarbon is C_2H_2. The name of the compound is ethyne. The older name, acetylene, is still commonly used. By adding carbon atoms to ethyne, more hydrocarbons with triple bonds can be made. The most simple three-carbon compound with a triple bond is propyne.

$$H$$
$$|$$
$$H - C \equiv C - C - H$$
$$|$$
$$H$$

propyne

There is a series of hydrocarbons with at least one triple bond between two carbon atoms. This series of unsaturated hydrocarbons is called the alkyne series. The names of the compounds in this series all have the *-yne* ending. The prefix again indicates the number of carbon atoms in the longest chain. Could you write a structural formula for butyne?

Quick Review
1. What identifies hydrocarbons in the alkene series?
2. What identifies the hydrocarbons in the alkyne series?

nCH_2=CH_2 ethene

↓ Oxygen, heat,   or $+CH_2CH_2+_n$
   pressure   Polyethylene

CH_2—CH_2—CH_2—CH_2
        Polyethylene

Figure 7-9. *Plastics are made of long chains of repeating units called polymers. Plastics have different properties, depending on the kinds of compounds from which they are made.*

Reactivity of hydrocarbons

The carbon atoms in hydrocarbons are less reactive when they form four single covalent bonds with their neighbors. This is true of the saturated hydrocarbons. They are not especially reactive compounds. When carbon atoms form double or triple bonds between themselves, they are more reactive. The location of the double or triple bond is the place where other atoms are likely to react with the hydrocarbon.

The difference in the reactivity of methane, ethene, and ethyne is dramatic. Methane burns, but it is very slow to react. Energy must be added to methane to start it burning. It is a valuable fuel because natural gas is mostly methane.

Ethene (ethylene) is much more reactive than methane. It, too, burns and can be used as a fuel. Ethene reacts with many other substances including itself. Ethene (ethylene) molecules can be made to form long chains, called polymers. A familiar plastic, polyethylene, is the result. Polyethylene is very unreactive. Because it is so unreactive, it is very valuable to use for containers. Polyethylene bags are a familiar sight to almost everyone.

Ethyne or acetylene is very much more reactive than either methane or ethene. Sometimes a shock may be all that is needed to set off an acetylene explosion. A mixture of oxygen and acetylene gases is used in the oxyacetylene torch. This torch produces one of the hottest temperatures that can be produced from ordinary fuels.

Quick Review

Compare how single, double, and triple-bonded carbon compounds react.

Quick Review answer:
Carbon-carbon triple bonds are more reactive than carbon-carbon double bonds, which are in turn more reactive than carbon-carbon single bonds.

Figure 7-10. *Oxyacetylene torch produces flame that is hot enough to burn through steel from a chemical reaction between oxygen and acetylene.*

| Cyclobutane (bp $-13°C$) | $H_2C—CH_2$ $H_2C—CH_2$ | | | | |
| Cyclopentane (bp 49.5°C) | | Cyclohexane (bp 81.4°C) | | Cycloheptane (bp 118°C) | |

Figure 7-11. *Some carbon compounds form closed rings. These are cyclic hydrocarbons. What are the molecular formulas for these compounds?* C_4H_8, C_5H_{10}, C_6H_{12}, C_7H_{14}

Main Idea

What are cyclic hydrocarbons?

Additional information:
Benzene can be used to synthesize compounds such as phenol, aniline, toluene, and xylene. It is also added to fuels for cars and trucks in some countries.

Research Topic

Look up the biography of the German chemist August Kekulé and learn what he contributed to the understanding of the structure of benzene.

Carbon compounds with rings

New vocabulary: cyclic hydrocarbons

Some carbon compounds consist of closed chains of carbon atoms, or rings. Because their carbon atoms form a ring, these compounds are known as **cyclic hydrocarbons.** For example, propane can form a structure represented by this formula. The name of this compound is cyclopropane.

cyclopropane

In addition, double or triple bonds could be a part of the ring structure. One of the most important of the cyclic hydrocarbons with double bonds is benzene. The formula for benzene is C_6H_6. Its structure can be represented by the following diagram.

benzene

Benzene appears to have three single and three double covalent bonds. However, the carbon-carbon bonds of the benzene ring are unusual. Their character is more like a mixture of single and double covalent bonds. For that reason, a better way of showing the structural formula for the benzene ring is shown below. The circle in the center of the hexagon stands for the intermediate character of benzene's bonds. Carbon atoms would be located at the corners of the hexagon. Hydrogen atoms are not shown.

There is a series of hydrocarbons based on compounds with the benzene ring structure. It is called the *benzene series*. Derived from this, there are even compounds with multiple benzene rings.

Quick Review

1. What is the name for hydrocarbons whose chains form closed rings?
2. How is the bonding between carbon atoms in the benzene ring unique?

Derivatives of the hydrocarbons

New vocabulary: functional groups

Many compounds can be formed from the hydrocarbons by replacing one or more of the hydrogens with other atoms or groups of atoms. The exchange can take place in a variety of ways. The atoms or groups of atoms that are added are called **functional groups.**

One important functional group is the -OH group. Compounds that have added this functional group are called alcohols. Recall the simplest hydrocarbon? Methane, CH_4, becomes methanol when one of its hydrogens is replaced by the -OH functional group.

methanol
(methyl alcohol)

Critical Thinking

Is benzene a saturated or unsaturated hydrocarbon?
Unsaturated

Quick Review answers:
1. Cyclic hydrocarbons.
2. Carbon atoms in benzene are joined in a closed, ring structure. The individual carbon-carbon bonds in benzene have a hybrid character that is intermediate between that of single bonds and that of double bonds.

Main Idea

What is a functional group?

Figure 7-12. *Different compounds can be made of hydrocarbons by adding functional groups such as these. What is the alkane to which these different functional groups have been added?*
Butane, C_4H_{10}

Functional Groups		
—OH	Alcohols	
—COOH	Acids	
$-\overset{\overset{O}{\|\|}}{C}-O-$	Esters	$CH_3-CH_2-CH_2-CH_2OH$ butanol
		$CH_3-CH_2-CH_2-COOH$ butanoic acid
—O—	Ethers	$CH_3-\overset{\overset{O}{\|\|}}{C}-O-CH_2-CH_3$ ethyl acetate
$-\overset{\overset{O}{\diagup\!\diagup}}{\underset{H}{C}}$	Aldehydes	$CH_3-CH_2-O-CH_2-CH_3$ ethyl ether
		$CH_3-CH_2-CH_2-\overset{\overset{O}{\|\|}}{C}-H$ butanol
		$CH_3-CH_2-\overset{\overset{O}{\|\|}}{C}-CH_3$ butanone
$-\overset{\overset{O}{\|\|}}{C}-$	Ketones	
—NH₂	Amines	$CH_3-CH_3-CH_2-CH_2-NH_2$ n-butyl amine
—Cl	Halogens	$CH_3-CH_2-CH_2-CH_2-Cl$ 1-chloro-butane

Research Topic

Find out how alcohol is prepared by fermentation.

Ethane, C_2H_6, becomes ethanol when one of the hydrogens is replaced by the -OH functional group.

$$
\begin{array}{ccc}
H & H & \\
| & | & \\
H-C-C-OH & & \\
| & | & \\
H & H &
\end{array}
$$

ethanol (ethyl alcohol)

Teaching suggestion:
Point out that aldehydes always have at least one hydrogen attached to the carbonyl group (C=O), while in ketones the carbonyl is always attached to two carbon atoms.
  Note that aldehydes are responsible for many familiar odors including those of almond (benzaldehyde), cinnamon (3-phenyl-2-propenal), and vanilla (2-hydroxy-3-methoxybenzaldehyde).

You may be interested in finding out more about some of the alcohol compounds. There are many kinds of alcohols. They have many uses in addition to being used as fuels.

Many of the other functional groups may be familiar to you as well. Organic acids all contain one or more of the -COOH group. Ethanoic (acetic) acid has the formula CH_3COOH and the structure

$$
\begin{array}{ccc}
H & & O \\
| & & \diagup\!\diagup \\
H-C-C & & \\
| & & \diagdown \\
H & & OH
\end{array}
$$

Quick Review

1. What group of hydrocarbon derivatives contain the -OH group?
2. What functional group characterizes the organic acids?

Quick Review answers:
1. Alcohols
2. -COOH

Carbohydrates, fats, and proteins

New vocabulary: carbohydrates, glucose, fats, proteins

Some organic compounds are especially important to living beings. These include carbohydrates, fats, and proteins.

Carbohydrates include sugar, starch, and cellulose. **Carbohydrates** are composed of carbon, hydrogen, and oxygen atoms. Characteristically they have twice as many hydrogen atoms as oxygen atoms. For example, **glucose** (GLOO'-kōs) has the formula $C_6H_{12}O_6$. Fructose, another sugar, also has the formula $C_6H_{12}O_6$. Both of these sugars have the same number of carbon atoms. They are isomers and differ from each other in one important way. Fructose forms a ring of five atoms while glucose forms a ring of six atoms.

Sucrose, table sugar, $C_{12}H_{22}O_{11}$, is a combination of glucose and fructose. The two simple sugars combine chemically with the splitting off of water molecules. These sugars and others are important sources of energy for the vital processes of living beings.

Starch is a long chain of simple sugar molecules hooked together. The chain may include several thousands of the simple sugar molecules. Starch can be digested by humans and by most animals.

Cellulose also consists of a long chain of simple sugar molecules linked together. The long chains twist to form a rope-like bundle. Because of the way that the sugar molecules are linked together, cellulose cannot be digested by humans and by carnivorous animals. Herbivorous animals and termites are able to digest cellulose with the help of microorganisms in their digestive tracts.

Main Idea

Of what are carbohydrates composed?

Additional information:
Note that the word carbohydrate (or "hydrate of carbon") was coined in the early days of carbohydrate chemistry when many of these compounds had been found to have the general formula $C_n(H_2O)_n$.

Critical Thinking

Would human beings be better off if they had microorganisms in their intestines for the purpose of digesting cellulose? Why do you suppose human beings do not harbor such organisms?
Point out that ruminants have an elaborate bacteria-filled digestive structure anterior to the small intestine. The location of this structure permits breakdown of cellulose before the food mass has moved to the small intestine where most absorption takes place. Humans lack such a structure.

Science background information:
Both starch and cellulose are composed of molecules of glucose. However, the links between the glucose molecules are different in starch and cellulose.

Figure 7-13. *Plate of spaghetti with sauce contains mostly carbohydrates, but some proteins and fats. What are the major carbohydrates shown?*
Starches

7.1b Comparing Solvents

Science processes: Experimenting, observing, inferring

Materials 25 minutes Groups of 3 or 4

- three 400-mL beakers
- six round coffee filters
- scissors
- black felt tip markers
- water
- rubbing alcohol
- vinegar
- red cabbage leaf (or other colored leaf or flowers)

Purpose

To compare the effect of organic solvents and water on the solubility of different pigments.

Procedure

1. With scissors, make two parallel cuts about 1 cm apart to the center of a filter paper. Fold the cut strip so that it is perpendicular to the filter. Make three of these for each pigment to be tested.
2. On one piece of cut filter paper make a horizontal mark with the felt tip marker about 2 cm from the outermost end of the folded strip.
3. Add enough water to a beaker so that the tip of the folded strip of the filter paper just touches the water when the circular piece of filter paper is sitting on top of the beaker.
4. Set the paper on top of the beaker containing water.
5. Repeat step 2 using the same marker on the second and third strips of filter paper. Following the procedure of steps 3 and 4, set the second strip in a beaker containing alcohol and the third strip in a beaker containing vinegar. Make sure that the strips just touch the liquid.
6. Repeat steps 2 through 5 using a piece of red cabbage to make the horizontal mark on the strip of filter paper. Use water, alcohol, and vinegar as the solvents.
7. After approximately 10 minutes, remove the filter paper from the beakers. Be sure that you can identify the liquid that each piece of

paper was in and which kind of mark was made.
8. Let the filter papers dry for a few minutes and compare the results.

Questions

1. Which of the liquids separated the colors in the felt tip pen best?
2. Which of the liquids separated the colors in the cabbage (or other leaf) best?
3. Did any of the liquids produce similar results?

Conclusion

Is there a difference in the dissolving effects of organic liquids, such as alcohol and vinegar, and water?

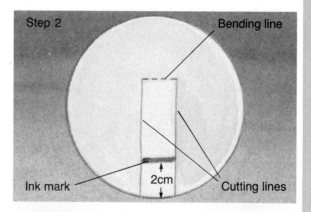
Step 2 — Bending line, Ink mark, 2cm, Cutting lines

Step 4

Fats include butter, vegetable oils, and lard. Chemically, fats are composed of carbon, hydrogen and oxygen atoms. Structurally, fats are combinations of glycerol and fatty acids. See Figure 7-14. In fats, three fatty acids are linked to a glycerol molecule. Fatty acids are hydrocarbons with an organic acid attached to one end. If each carbon atom in the fatty acid is linked to four other atoms, the molecule is said to be saturated. On the other hand, an unsaturated fatty acid contains some double-bonded carbon atoms. A polyunsaturated fatty acid contains several double bonds. You may have heard discussions about possible relationships between eating saturated fats and some health problems. Nevertheless, fats serve as a reservoir of energy for the human body along with some other functions.

Proteins include animal and plant proteins. Proteins are very large, complex molecules consisting of thousands of atoms of carbon, nitrogen, hydrogen, and oxygen. All proteins are made from twenty basic building blocks called amino acids. Amino acids contain both the amine group, $-NH_2$, and the acid group, $-COOH$. The simplest amino acid is glycine.

glycine

Proteins serve many functions. They serve roles of storage, of structure, of transport, of regulation, and as catalysts of biochemical reactions in living beings.

Vitamins are also organic substances. They play a role in some chemical reactions that take place in the body. Vitamins are essential for the health of human beings. The lack of specific vitamins in our diet results in our getting deficiency diseases. Most vitamins have complicated chemical structures. Vitamins are generally identified by capital letters instead of by their chemical name. Do you know the chemical name of Vitamin C?

Quick Review

1. How do starch and cellulose differ from the simple sugars?
2. What functional groups identify an amino acid?

Figure 7-14. *Soaps can be produced by treating fats with sodium hydroxide. Glycerol is also a product of the reaction.*

Teaching suggestion:
Point out that lipids (the class of biological molecules that includes fats, waxes and oils) tend to be soluble in organic solvents such as ether and chloroform. This characteristic sets lipids apart from carbohydrates, proteins, and nucleic acids, the other great classes of biological molecules.

Critical Thinking

What element is present in protein, but absent from fats and carbohydrates?
Nitrogen

Ascorbic acid

Quick Review answers:
1. Both starch and cellulose are long chains of simple sugars.
2. An amine group and an organic acid group.

7.1 Section Review

Vocabulary

5   alkane series

9   alkene series

10   alkyne series

13   carbohydrates

11   cyclic hydrocarbons

14   fats

12   functional groups

16   glucose

2   hydrocarbons

7   isomers

1   organic compounds

4   polyatomic ion

15   proteins

6   saturated hydrocarbons

3   tetrahedron

8   unsaturated hydrocarbons

Vocabulary Review

Match each term above with the numbered phrase that best describes it.

1. Compounds that contain carbon

2. Compounds that contain only hydrogen and carbon atoms

3. Pyramid shape

4. Ion composed of two or more atoms

5. Hydrocarbon series which has only single carbon-carbon bonds

6. Hydrocarbons which have no double or triple carbon-carbon bonds

7. Compound with the same molecular formula, but with different molecular structures

8. Hydrocarbons that have one or more double or triple bonds

9. Series characterized by double bonds between carbon atoms

10. Series characterized by triple bonds between carbon atoms

11. Hydrocarbons that are joined into a ring structure

12. Atom or group of atoms that replaces a hydrogen in a hydrocarbon molecule

13. Sugar, starch, and cellulose are examples

14. Compounds that combine glycerol and fatty acids

15. Compounds that are made from amino acid building blocks

16. A kind of sugar

Review Questions

17. In the methane molecule (CH_4), the atoms are joined in the shape of a ? .
    a. triangle
    b. tetrahedron
    c. line
    d. ring

18. Carbonate is an example of a(n) ? .
    a. unsaturated hydrocarbon
    b. saturated hydrocarbon
    c. carbohydrate
    d. polyatomic ion

19. Methane is a(n) ? .
    a. unsaturated hydrocarbon
    b. saturated hydrocarbon
    c. alkene
    d. carbohydrate

20. Unsaturated hydrocarbons have ? .
    a. no double or triple bonds
    b. no single bonds
    c. some double bonds but no triple bonds
    d. double and/or triple bonds

21. The carbon-carbon bond that tends to be the most reactive is the ? .
    a. single bond
    b. double bond
    c. triple bond

22. Sugar and starch are ? .
    a. carbohydrates
    b. proteins
    c. fats
    d. vitamins

23. Amino acids are the building blocks of ? .
    a. carbohydrates
    b. proteins
    c. fats
    d. vitamins

24. Fats are formed from ? .
    a. glycerol and three fatty acids
    b. fatty acids alone
    c. amino acids
    d. protein

Understanding the Concepts

25. Explain why carbon monoxide is a dangerous substance.

26. Give three examples of hydrocarbons used as fuels.

27. Describe what is meant by an isomer and provide an example.

28. Name four series of hydrocarbons and indicate what distinguishes one series from another.

29. What is a functional group? Give two examples.

30. Describe the characteristics of carbohydrates.

Problems to Solve

31. Draw two formulas for a saturated hydrocarbon with four carbons.

32. Give the general formula for any molecule in the alkane series. Calculate the number of hydrogens that would be present in the alkane having seven carbon atoms (heptane).

For ideas for classroom demonstration and discussion, see Getting Started on page T112 in the front of this book.

7.2 Using Fuels for Heat and Work

Supplemental materials: Teaching Diagram 7-2 (TRB page 35), Reading Checksheet 7-2 (TRB page 98), Skillsheet 7-2 (TRB page 144), Investigation 7-2 (Lab Manual pages 95–96)

Section Preview

- **Fuels for heating**
- **Fuels for work**
- **Controlling the rate of burning**
- **Burning fuels to do work**
- **The products of burning fuels**

Bracketed numbers are Section Review questions correlated to that objective.

Learning Objectives

1. To relate the amount of energy obtained from burning a fuel to the quantity of the fuel. [5, 18]
2. To compare the amount of energy obtained from burning natural gas, coal, and gasoline. [9]
3. To recognize the factors that control the rate of burning. [0, 7, 10, 11, 10, 14, 17]
4. To contrast internal and external combustion engines. [1, 2, 4, 12, 15]

Figure 7-15. *Heat is released by the burning of fuels. This hot air balloon inflates and rises because of the heat from burning propane gas.*

Most of the energy used today comes from the burning of fossil fuels—natural gas, coal, and oil. **Fuels** are any substances that are burned to supply energy. Natural gas, coal, and oil are labeled *fossil fuels* because they are the remains of ancient living plants and animals. The combined processes of decay, pressure, and heat, taking place over hundreds of millions of years produced these fuels. The same processes are going on at the present time. But the long time required for the fuels to be formed means that coal, oil, and natural gas are essentially nonrenewable. Once they are used, no new fossil fuels will replace them.

> **Main Idea**
>
> What are fossil fuels?
>
> **Teaching suggestion:**
> Ask students to think of a renewable fuel resource. The wood from trees is a familiar example.

Fuels for heating

New vocabulary: fuel

Natural gas is a clean and convenient **fuel** that does not need refining. It can be safely used with reasonable precautions. Natural gas is mostly methane, CH_4, although small amounts of ethane, C_2H_6, and propane, C_3H_8, may be present. All of

Figure 7-16. *Natural gas is stored in pressurized tanks after it is taken from gas wells. How is natural gas moved from these tanks to the places where it is used?*
Through a system of pipelines.

these hydrocarbons burn in air to form carbon dioxide and water. The burning of methane is summarized by the following equation.

$$CH_4 + O_2 = CO_2 + 2H_2O + 890 \text{ kJ}$$

Remember that this balanced equation for the burning of methane is written in terms of moles of reactants and products. For each mole of methane burned, 890 kilojoules of heat are released. Sixteen grams is the mass of one mole of methane. When burned, sixteen grams of methane release enough heat to raise the temperature of 21.3 kg of water by 10°C. At ordinary temperatures and pressures, the 16 grams of natural gas would have a volume of about 25 liters. What mass of water would be warmed 10°C by a liter of natural gas?   0.85 kg

Sample Problem

To determine how much energy, measured in joules, is required to raise the temperature of 100 g of water by 10°C.

Solution

The definition of a joule is that 4.184 joules of energy are needed to raise the temperature of one gram of pure water 1°C.

1. To raise one gram of water 10°C,

$$\frac{4.184 \text{ joules}}{\text{gram-degree C}} \times 10°C = 41.84 \text{ gram-degree C}$$

are needed.

2. To raise 100 g of water 1°C,

$$100 \text{ g} \times \frac{4.184 \text{ joules}}{\text{gram-degree C}} = 418.4 \text{ joules/degree C}$$

are needed.

3. To raise 100 g of water 10°C,

$$100 \text{ g} \times \frac{4.184 \text{ joules}}{\text{gram-degree C}} \times 10°C = 4184 \text{ joules}$$

are needed.

Practice Problem

How much energy is required to raise 250 g of water 20°C?
Answer: 20 920 joules

Additional information:
4.18 joules = 1 calorie

■ **Safety Note**
Methane can form explosive mixtures with air. These mixtures can be ignited by a spark. Never strike a match if you suspect there has been a gas leak.

Science background information:
Processes to change coal into combustible gases are being developed. These processes will permit most of the impurities in coal to be removed before burning. In one process, the coal is converted to a fine powder, mixed with hydrogen and a catalyst, and then subjected to high pressure. The product is methane gas, the major component of natural gas.

Coal, too, can be used as a fuel without refining. Coal is mostly composed of carbon, but it contains other hydrocarbons, hydrocarbon derivatives, and impurities as well. Most types of coal give off about 351 kilojoules of heat per mole of carbon burned.

$$C + O_2 = CO_2 + 351 \text{ kJ}$$

The mass of a mole of carbon is 12 grams. Sixteen grams of carbon, the same mass as a mole of methane, would be 16 g ÷ 12 g/mole = 1.3 moles of carbon. The heat given off by burning 1.3 moles of carbon would be 1.3 moles × 351 kilojoules/mole = 456 kilojoules. Burning 16 grams of carbon, in the form of coal, would release enough heat to raise the temperature of 10.9 kg of water by 10°C. So, the heat released by the burning of coal is only half the heat that is released by burning the same mass of natural gas.

Impurities in coal produce other products when coal is burned. One of the most harmful impurities is sulfur. It is converted into sulfur dioxide, SO_2, when coal is burned. It eventually turns into sulfuric acid in the air and falls as acid rain. Acid rain can damage plants and poison lakes. Much effort and expense are involved in removing sulfur dioxide from the waste gases of burning coal before they are released into the environment.

Figure 7-17. *Coal is loaded on barges for shipment. It is a thrifty way to move a bulky fuel.*

Quick Review

1. What is the main fuel component of natural gas? . . . of coal?

2. What is one problem with burning coal for fuel?

Fuels for work

New vocabulary: fractional distillation

Unlike natural gas and coal, crude oil cannot be used as a fuel without being refined. Crude oil is a mixture of hydrocarbons. These hydrocarbons are separated into several useful mixtures, such as gasoline and heating oil, by fractional distillation. *Distilling* is the process used to purify a liquid from a mixture of liquids. **Fractional distillation** separates crude oil into useful mixtures called "fractions."

In fractional distillation, the hydrocarbons with the lowest boiling temperatures are vaporized first. Hydrocarbons with the next to lowest boiling temperatures vaporize next. Then, step by step, groups of heavier hydrocarbons, with higher boiling temperatures vaporize one group at a time. The hydrocarbons with the highest boiling points vaporize last. After vaporizing, the different fractions of the crude oil are collected by condensing them separately. The condensation

Main Idea

What happens in the process of fractional distillation?

Teaching suggestion:
Point out that the boiling points of hydrocarbons tend to increase with increasing molecular weight.

Activity

7.2a   Methane from Coal

Science processes: Experimenting, observing, inferring

20 minutes, plus   Groups of 3 to 4   2 to 3 days

Materials

- **100 g of soft coal**
- **plastic or glass funnel**
- **large glass jar**
- **test tube**
- **matches**

Purpose

To show that coal contains natural gas or methane.

Procedure

1. Break the sample of coal into small pieces.
2. Add the powdered coal to the funnel while holding your finger over the narrow end of the funnel.
3. Turn the large jar upside down and place the funnel into the jar. Hold the wide end of the funnel against the inside of the bottom of the jar. Hold the funnel in that position while turning the jar upright.
4. Hold the funnel in place in the jar while adding water to the jar. Add water to the jar until the water level is 2 to 3 cm above the small end of the funnel.
5. Fill the test tube with water and place your finger over the open end of the tube to hold the water in. Turn the test tube upside down and place the open end, still covered with your finger, under the water level in the jar. Release your finger and place the test tube over the open end of the funnel.
6. Set the jar aside where it won't be disturbed. Note the water level in the test tube—it should be near the top.
7. Set up a control using the same apparatus but without the coal under the funnel.
8. Check the water level in the test tubes in 2 to 3 days.
9. Remove the test tube from the jar containing the coal and keep the test tube upside down. Place a burning match near the open end of

the test tube as you turn the test tube right side up.

Questions

1. What change has taken place in the level of water in the test tube?
2. What evidence is there that the gas came from the coal?
3. How does the density of the gas that you collected compare to the weight of air? Hint: consider equal volumes of gas and air.

Conclusion

Does coal contain a flammable gas that could be used for fuel?

Step 5

of the different fractions takes place in different locations in the fractionating tower.

The demand for the different fractions of the crude oil may not be the same as the relative amounts of each of these fractions in the crude oil. Chemists have been able to change some of the heavier hydrocarbons into lighter ones by a process called cracking. More of the lighter hydrocarbons, such as those in gasoline, then become available. It is also possible to link up some of the lighter hydrocarbons to form the heavier hydrocarbons present in gasoline.

The lighter hydrocarbons, such as propane and butane, can be liquefied and sold as bottled gas. Homes that are not linked to a natural gas pipeline can use these fuels in tanks as a source of energy for cooking and heating. Bottled gas is widely used for camping vehicles and for backyard gas grills as well.

Gasoline is a mixture of as many as twenty-five hydrocarbons. Octane, C_8H_{18}, is used as the hydrocarbon which represents the gasoline mixture. The equation for the burning of gasoline is shown below.

$$C_8H_{18} + 12\tfrac{1}{2}\, O_2 = 8CO_2 + 9H_2O + 6270 \text{ kJ}$$

The energy released from the burning of one mole of gasoline is approximately 6270 kJ. One liter of gasoline contains about 6.7 moles of octane. The energy available from one liter of gasoline is 6.7 moles × 6270 kJ/mole = 42 019 kJ.

It is possible to compare the amount of energy available from gasoline, natural gas, and coal. The mass of one mole of gasoline, C_8H_{18}, is approximately 114g. Sixteen grams of

Figure 7-18. *Oil refinery separates crude oil into different useful fractions by a process of distilling. Can you name three products of a refinery?* Gasoline, diesel fuel, kerosene, oil, asphalt are some possible answers.

Critical Thinking

How do you suppose propane is liquefied? What is the purpose of liquefying this gas?
Propane is readily liquefied under pressure. In liquid form, the fuel can be transported easily.

Table 7-3. *Energy released by burning various fuels.*

Energy Released by Different Fuels		
Name of fuel	Energy released per mole	Energy released per 16 g of fuel	Amount of water raised 10°/16 g
Natural gas (CH_4)	890 kJ	890 kJ	21.8 kg
Coal (C)	351 kJ	456 kJ	10.9 kg
Gasoline (C_8H_{18})	6270 kJ	878 kJ	21.0 kg

Data Search

Compare the energy derived from petroleum to the total use of energy in 1960, 1978, and 1983. Search pages 658–661.

Petroleum consumption and total energy consumption in trillions of joules: 1960 (21 006; 46 483); 1978 (40 034; 82 220); 1983 (31 715; 74 434).

Quick Review answers:
1. It must be refined.
2. 890 kJ (natural gas);
   456 kJ (coal);
   6270 kJ (gasoline)

Main Idea

How does the amount of fuel used affect the amount of heat given off?

octane would be equal to 16 g ÷ 114 g/mole = .14 moles. The energy released by 16 g of gasoline would be .14 moles × 6270 kJ/mole = 878 kJ. The energy released would be enough to raise the temperature of 21 kg of water by 10°C.

For comparison, 16 g of methane releases 890 kJ of energy when it is burned, 16 g of coal releases 456 kJ, and 16 g of gasoline releases 878 kJ. Based on equal masses, methane releases the most energy during combustion, gasoline almost as much, and coal the least. Based on their masses, methane and gasoline are the best fuels.

Burning gasoline in today's automobiles produces large amounts of energy. Several other products of burning gasoline are released into the atmosphere. These include some unburned hydrocarbons, carbon particles, nitrogen oxides, sulfur oxides, and, for cars that still use leaded gasoline, some lead compounds. Carbon dioxide and water vapor are also released as products. Catalytic converters, built into the exhaust system, help remove some of these products from exhaust gases.

Quick Review

1. What is done to crude oil to make it a useful fuel?
2. Compare the heat released by the burning of one mole of natural gas, coal and gasoline.

Controlling the rate of burning

New vocabulary: complete burning, incomplete burning

Using fuels for heat requires that the rate of burning be controlled. It cannot be too rapid or too slow. What are the conditions that affect the rate of burning?

You know that when a wood fire seems to be dying down, you can make it hotter by adding more logs. In a barbecue, you add more charcoal. Increasing the amount of fuel increases the amount of heat released. On a gas stove, you can change the amount of gas released by turning the burner control. Decreasing the amount of fuel decreases the heat.

In burning, a fuel combines with oxygen. Thus, the rate of burning can be controlled by increasing or decreasing the oxygen supply. In a fireplace, the damper in the chimney controls the amount of air that passes through the chimney. Covered barbecues have adjustable vent openings. Since oxygen is part of the air, changing the air supply changes the oxygen supply.

There is a problem with controlling burning by limiting the oxygen supply. When a hydrocarbon fuel burns in the presence of plenty of oxygen, the products are carbon dioxide and water vapor. This reaction is known as **complete burning.** However, when there is not enough oxygen, carbon monoxide and soot are formed, in addition to carbon dioxide and water vapor. This reaction is known as **incomplete burning.**

The less oxygen there is, the more carbon monoxide and soot are formed. Carbon monoxide is a colorless, odorless gas. It can cause death if it is allowed to build up. For this reason, a fireplace should never be used with the damper closed. Soot, which is powdered carbon, can coat chimney flues and later catch on fire.

There is a third way to control the amount of heat given off. In a gas furnace or water heater, the gas supply is closed off when heat is not needed. It is opened when heat is needed. Burning is stopped and started as needed. The length of time of burning controls the amount of heat.

Solid and liquid fuels can be made to burn faster in yet another way. When they are broken up into small pieces or small drops, more of their surface is exposed to oxygen in the air. Twigs catch on fire more easily than heavy logs. Wood shavings and sawdust burn much more rapidly than twigs. Very little heat is needed to start a sawdust particle burning. As it burns, it releases enough heat for the particles around it to burn. Some materials that are not considered fuels can burn rapidly in powdered form. Dust from flour in a mill can set off an explosion if set on fire by a spark. These things happen because increasing the surface area of reactants increases the rate of chemical reactions.

Quick Review

1. Explain the difference between complete burning and incomplete burning.
2. List four ways of controlling the amount of heat given off by a fuel.

Burning fuels to do work
New vocabulary: internal combustion engine, external combustion engine, turbine

Heat released in burning can be used not only to warm things but to do work. For example, most automobile engines run on the energy from burning gasoline vapor. The burning takes place in the cylinders of the engine.

Figure 7-19. *If the coals in a barbecue are giving off too much heat, how can they be cooled easily?*
One can cool coals giving off too much heat by reducing the size of the vent openings so less air gets to the coals.

Additional information:
Different-sized pieces of the same material have the same kindling temperature (the temperature to which they must be warmed before they will burn). For example, a pine shaving has the same kindling temperature as a pine log. The shaving burns more readily than the log because one can warm a small piece of pine to its kindling temperature more quickly than a large one.

Quick Review answers:
1. Complete burning of a hydrocarbon fuel takes place when there is enough oxygen present; carbon dioxide and water vapor are the only products. When there is less oxygen present, incomplete burning takes place. It produces soot and carbon monoxide, as well as carbon dioxide and water vapor.
2. To control the heat given off by a fuel, one can vary the amount of fuel, the amount of oxygen, the length of time burning takes place, and the size of the pieces or drops of fuel.

Research Topic

Find out the advantages and disadvantages of diesel fuel over gasoline fuel for an automobile or truck.

Figure 7-21 shows what happens inside one cylinder. A mixture of air and gasoline vapor enters the cylinder. The mixture is compressed into a small space by the piston. Then it is ignited by an electric spark from the spark plug. Burning occurs so rapidly that an explosion results. The gases produced from the burning gasoline vapors expand because of the heat released. The expanding gases move the piston down in the cylinder. Finally, the burned gases are pushed out of the cylinder.

Modern automobiles have four or six cylinders. The explosion in each cylinder occurs at a different time. The explosions do the work of moving the automobile.

Our Science Heritage

James Watt and His Steam Engine

James Watt (1736–1819) was a Scottish engineer who began his career as a maker of compasses, scales, and other mathematical instruments. In 1763, he was given a model of a standard steam engine to repair. He was amazed at how much steam this Newcomen Engine wasted. In the Newcomen Engine, steam filled a cylinder and forced the piston out. Then the cylinder was cooled so that the steam would condense. This created a vacuum and the piston fell back into the cylinder under atmospheric pressure. Heating and cooling the cylinder required a great deal of fuel, but provided little power output.

As a friend of Joseph Black, Watt understood Black's theories about latent heat. Latent heat is used to change the state—solid, liquid or gas—of a substance. The Newcomen Engine lost a tremendous amount of latent heat. Watt believed that if the steam were simply allowed to enter a connecting chilled chamber, the same vacuum could be created and the piston would fall back into the cylinder. Separate chambers, one heated and one chilled, could be maintained more efficiently than the Newcomen's one chamber. In 1769, Watt obtained a patent for his "New Method of Lessening the Consumption of Steam and Fuel in a Fire Engine." By 1776, the first of Watt's steam engines were installed in factories.

James Watt's steam engines opened the doors to the Industrial Revolution by making possible the mechanization of such industries as cotton mills, grain mills, and iron furnaces.

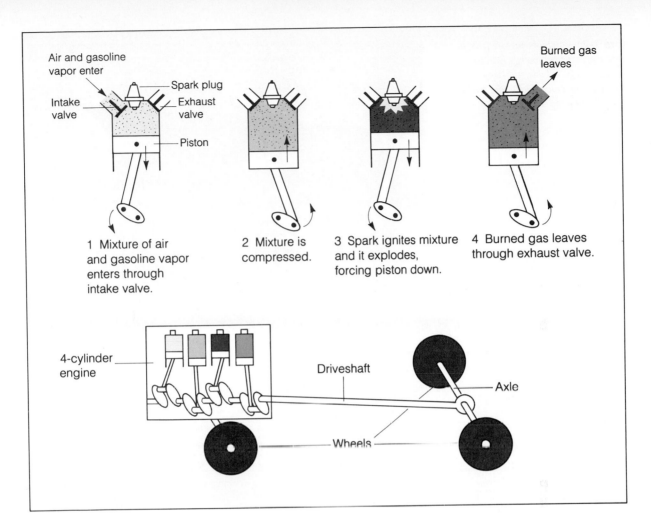

1 Mixture of air and gasoline vapor enters through intake valve.

2 Mixture is compressed.

3 Spark ignites mixture and it explodes, forcing piston down.

4 Burned gas leaves through exhaust valve.

In an automobile engine, the burning, or combustion, takes place inside the engine. For this reason, the engine is called an **internal combustion engine.** Some internal combustion engines use other fuels instead of gasoline. Alcohol, as well as a mixture of alcohol and gasoline known as gasohol, may be used. The diesel engines of buses, trucks, and some automobiles use diesel oil.

Diesel engines have cylinders, but they operate differently from those of gasoline engines. First, air with no fuel mixed with it enters the cylinder. The air is compressed much more than the air and gasoline mixture in a gasoline engine. In the same way that bicycle tires become hot when pumped up, the compressed air becomes hot. It is so hot that when fuel is sprayed into the cylinder, the fuel explodes at once. No spark plug is needed.

A steam engine does work as a result of the burning of fuel outside the engine itself. It is an example of an **external combustion engine.** The fuel is burned to boil water. The water

Figure 7-20. *The four steps in the burning of gasoline vapor in one cylinder of a gasoline engine. The engine does work only in the third step. Explain why an engine runs more smoothly if it has more than one cylinder.*

A cylinder does work only one quarter of the time, during the third of the four steps. When an engine has more than one cylinder, the explosion in each cylinder occurs at a different time. Work is done more frequently toward moving the automobile. As a result, the engine runs more smoothly.

Main Idea

A steam engine is an example of what kind of engine?

Figure 7-21. *A steam turbine can be used to convert heat energy into mechanical energy. The steam from a boiler turns the moveable blades which turn a shaft or rod.*

changes to steam (water vapor at 100°C or higher). Normally, a vapor takes up much more space than the liquid phase. However, the steam is confined to a small space, and pressure builds up. The steam is then allowed to move through an opening and expand.

In one widely used type of steam engine, there are several sets of fanlike blades. The blades are attached to a shaft that can rotate. The expanding steam enters the chamber containing the blades. It pushes against the blades and causes them and the shaft to rotate. This type of engine is known as a steam **turbine** (TER´-bin). Steam turbines are used to generate most of our electrical energy.

Quick Review

1. What is an internal combustion engine?
2. List three ways in which a diesel engine differs from a gasoline engine.
3. Describe how a steam turbine works.

Quick Review answers:

1. An internal combustion engine is an engine in which the burning of the fuel takes place inside the engine.
2. (1) In a diesel engine, air enters the cylinder instead of a mixture of air and fuel as in a gasoline engine. (2) The air is compressed much more in the diesel engine than the mixture is in the gasoline engine. (3) The hot air causes fuel sprayed into the cylinder of the diesel engine to explode. A spark from a spark plug causes the mixture to explode in the gasoline engine.
3. Inside a chamber, there is a set of blades attached to a shaft. Steam enters the chamber, expands, and pushes against the blades, causing them and the shaft to rotate.

See also Activity Record Sheet 7-2B (Lab Manual page 94). Safety Note, Preparation Notes, Answers to Questions, and Conclusion appear on page T113 in the front of this book.

Activity

7.2b Making a Steam Turbine

Science processes: Making a model, observing, inferring

BASIC   20 minutes   Groups of 4 or teacher demonstration

Materials

- 2 aluminum foil pie pans
- ballpoint pen cap
- modeling clay, small lump
- scissors
- tape
- water
- hot plate
- large paper clip
- flowerpot (empty)
- teakettle with narrow spout

Purpose

To show how a steam turbine works.

Procedure

1. Cut off the sides of an aluminum foil pan to make a flat circle. Make a hole about ½ cm in the center of the pan with the scissors.
2. Using the illustration below as a model, measure eight evenly-spaced sections. Make eight cuts from the edge toward the center, stopping 2 cm short of the hole.
3. Bend down each section from the point of the cut near the center to a location on the outside edge that is 2 cm above the cutting line. See the illustration at upper right.
4. Remove the clip from the cap of the ballpoint pen. Push the cap through the hole in the pan and tape it in place. See the third illustration.

5. Put a small lump of clay in the center of the second aluminum pan. Straighten out the large paper clip and stand it in the clay. Place the "turbine" over the paper clip as shown in the third illustration.
6. Now set up the steaming teakettle and the turbine as shown in the third illustration. SAFETY NOTE: *Keep the spout of the teakettle pointed away from you. Steam can scald you.*

Questions

1. Describe what happens to the steam turbine when the steam is directed at the blades.
2. What direction do the blades move in relation to the direction of the steam?

Conclusion

How does a steam turbine work?

Step 3 — Ball point pen cap, Cut edge, Bending line, Tape

Step 2 — 2 cm, Cut, Bend, Bend, Cut, Cut, 2 cm, 2 cm, Bend, Bend, Cut, 2 cm

Step 5

The products of burning fuels

When a fuel burns, it combines with oxygen in a chemical reaction. Not only is heat released, but substances are formed. Most fuels contain hydrocarbons. The complete burning of a hydrocarbon produces water and carbon dioxide. For example, the burning of methane, CH_4, is summarized in the following chemical equation.

$$CH_4 + 2O_2 \rightarrow CO_2 + 2H_2O$$

Gasoline is a mixture of hydrocarbons. The complete burning of one of them, C_8H_{18}, is summarized in the following chemical equation.

$$2C_8H_{18} + 25O_2 \rightarrow 16CO_2 + 18H_2O$$

Both water vapor and carbon dioxide are normally present in the air. Burning large amounts of hydrocarbons increases the amount of water vapor and carbon dioxide in the air.

Hydrocarbon fuels normally have impurities such as sulfur. Sulfur reacts with oxygen to form a colorless gas, sulfur dioxide (SO_2). The equation for the reaction is this.

$$S + O_2 \rightarrow SO_2$$

Sulfur dioxide irritates the lungs and is especially harmful to people with lung disease. In addition, it combines further with oxygen in the air to form sulfur trioxide, SO_3.

$$2SO_2 + O_2 \rightarrow 2SO_3$$

Sulfur trioxide combines with water vapor to form sulfuric acid, H_2SO_4.

$$SO_3 + H_2O \rightarrow H_2SO_4$$

Research Topic

Petroleum products are one of our main sources of fuels. Find out who was responsible for making these substances so useful.

Science background information:
In the United States, the following are major sources of air pollution. Eighty percent of the sulfur dioxide and 50 percent of the nitrogen oxides in the air are produced by electric power plants, industrial boilers, and residential furnaces that use fossil fuels. Eighty percent of the carbon monoxide and 40 percent of the nitrogen oxides result from the burning of gasoline and diesel fuel by cars and trucks.

Figure 7-22. *How does the burning of fuel contribute to pollution problems?*
Sulfur dioxide, nitrogen oxides, acids, and hydrocarbon-based smog are products of the burning of impure hydrocarbon fuels. For details, see text on these two pages.

When sulfuric acid forms in the air, it washes down during the next rain. Sulfuric acid is a very corrosive substance, damaging both living and nonliving things. For instance, the acid in rain kills off the fish in lakes and attacks limestone buildings. One way to prevent the problems caused by sulfur compounds is to use fuels with a low sulfur content.

The high temperatures in automobile engines allow nitrogen from the air to react with oxygen from the air. Many different compounds of nitrogen and oxygen, known as oxides of nitrogen, are formed. They contribute to the brownish smog that often pollutes the air over cities. Also, some of the oxides react with water vapor to form acids that increase the acid rain problem.

All fuels burn incompletely to some degree. The incomplete burning of hydrocarbons results in the production of carbon and carbon monoxide. It also puts some unchanged hydrocarbons into the air. The energy from sunlight causes the unchanged hydrocarbons to react with the oxides of nitrogen and with oxygen to form smog. Antismog devices on automobiles trap hydrocarbons before they can enter the air. In cars with catalytic converters, the hydrocarbons and carbon monoxide react with oxygen and form carbon dioxide and water. In effect, the converters make gasoline burn more completely.

When hydrogen gas burns in air, only water vapor is formed.

$$2H_2 + O_2 \rightarrow 2H_2O$$

No dangerous pollutants are produced. Thus, hydrogen can be thought of as a clean fuel. It is being suggested by many as a substitute for both gasoline and methane. To produce the same amount of heat, however, larger volumes of hydrogen than of gasoline must be burned. Difficulties in the storing and transporting of hydrogen may also be encountered.

Which fuels are best? You can see that each fuel has advantages and disadvantages. Many factors must be considered. These include cost, the amount of the fuel available, and the ease of storing and obtaining it. They also include the ease of burning the fuel and the products produced by the burning.

Quick Review

1. List some harmful effects caused by sulfur in fuels.
2. Describe how antismog devices and catalytic converters help reduce the formation of smog.

Main Idea

What causes the formation of the brownish smog made of oxides of nitrogen?

Additional information:
The lowest cost way to manufacture hydrogen at the present time is known as steam-reforming. Natural gas is reacted with steam at high temperatures in the presence of a catalyst. The products include hydrogen and oxides of carbon.

Quick Review answers:
1. The burning of fuels containing sulfur produces sulfur dioxide, which irritates people's lungs. In the air, some sulfur dioxide is converted to sulfuric acid, which forms acid rain. Acid rain kills fish in lakes and attacks limestone buildings.
2. In sunlight, unchanged hydrocarbons react with oxides of nitrogen and with oxygen to form smog. Antismog devices on automobiles trap the unchanged hydrocarbons before they enter the air. In a catalytic converter, the unchanged hydrocarbons and carbon monoxide react with oxygen to form carbon dioxide and water.

7.2 Section Review

Answers to Understanding the Concepts and Solutions to Problems to Solve appear on page T113 in the front of this book. Blackline master test for this section: Section Testsheet 7-2 (TRB page 218)

Vocabulary

6 complete burning
2 external combustion engine
3 fractional distillation
5 fuel
7 incomplete burning
1 internal combustion engine
4 turbine

Vocabulary Review

Match each term above with the numbered phrase that best describes it.

1. Does work when fuel is burned inside it
2. Does work when fuel is burned outside it
3. Process to separate crude oil into useful components
4. Has blades that turn when hot water vapor expands
5. When burned, releases great amount of energy
6. Occurs when there is enough oxygen available
7. Results in the production of carbon monoxide

Review Questions

Multiple Choice: choose the answer that best completes each of the following sentences

8. A steam turbine is an example of a(n) ? .
   a. internal combustion engine
   b. external combustion engine
   c. pollution control device
   d. fuel-producing system
9. Natural gas consists primarily of ? .
   a. hydrogen
   b. propane
   c. butane
   d. methane

10. Burning is a chemical change in which a substance combines with ? .
    a. carbon
    b. carbon monoxide
    c. carbon dioxide
    d. oxygen
11. The rate of burning can be reduced by ? .
    a. breaking the fuel into smaller pieces or drops
    b. decreasing the air supply
    c. using a catalyst
    d. raising the temperature of the fuel
12. Both a gasoline engine and a diesel engine ? .
    a. use energy from burning fuel for heating
    b. use energy from burning fuel to do work
    c. rely on spark plugs
    d. are external combustion engines
13. ? is added to the air as a result of incomplete burning.
    a. Carbon monoxide
    b. Carbon dioxide
    c. Sulfur dioxide
    d. Water vapor

Understanding the Concepts

14. In some fireplaces, the hot air from the fire seems to escape up the chimney opening. Why is it dangerous to solve this problem by keeping the chimney opening closed?
15. The engine walls of a diesel engine are much thicker than those of a gasoline engine. Explain why thicker walls are needed.
16. Explain how rain becomes acid and what can be done about this problem.

17. When solid and liquid fuels are broken into smaller particles or drops, they are easier to burn. Explain why this is so.

Practice Problem

18. When chemical bonds between atoms are formed, energy is stored in the bond until a reaction takes place to release it. An example of a reaction that releases energy is burning in air, or combustion. The following molecules are commonly burned for various purposes:

methane   propane

$H - C \equiv C - H$

acetylene

Which of the above compounds do you predict will release the most energy when it is burned? the least?

The table below lists the amount of energy contained in some different types of bonds:

Bond type	Energy stored
C – H	406 kJ/mole
C – C	349 kJ/mole
C ≡ C	840 kJ/mole
C = C	613 kJ/mole

Using the information in the table, calculate the total amount of energy contained in one mole of each of the fuels listed above. Was your prediction in the first part correct?

For ideas for classroom demonstration and discussion, see Getting Started on page T114 in the front of this book.

7.3 Energy and Living Things

Supplemental materials: Teaching Diagram 7-3 (TRB page 36), Reading Checksheet 7-3 (TRB page 99), Skillsheet 7-3 (TRB page 145), Investigation 7-3 (Lab Manual pages 99–100)

Section Preview

- **The body's energy needs**
- **Supplying cells with energy**
- **Energy from cell respiration**
- **Energy from fermentation**
- **Body heat**
- **Energy stored through photosynthesis**
- **The food energy pyramid**

Bracketed numbers are Section Review questions correlated to that objective.

Learning Objectives

1. To explain how cell respiration releases energy to carry on the body functions and growth. [1, 2, 3, 8, 9, 12, 13, 19, 20]
2. To explain how the fermentation process supplies the body with energy and how fermentation differs from respiration. [10, 14, 20]
3. To describe the process of photosynthesis and its importance. [4, 5, 7, 14, 16]
4. To use a pyramid to illustrate the energy relationships in a natural community of plants and animals. [15, 21]

Figure 7-23. *A hummingbird hovers in front of a flower. What is the source of the energy that this bird uses to fly?* The nectar of the flower.

Sit with your feet flat on the floor. Without moving, try to push your feet forward. Become aware of the tightening of your upper thigh muscle in each leg. Now, without moving, try to push your feet backward. What muscle in your thigh tightens now? Your lower thigh muscle

Muscles are made up of many fibers, which are like the threads in a heavy string. The muscle fibers can shorten, or **contract.** Bones move when the muscles attached to them contract.

Usually a bone has two muscles attached to it. The muscles are attached in opposition to one another. The muscles and bones together act as a system of opposing levers. Only one muscle contracts at one time. When the second muscle contracts and the first relaxes, the bone is pulled back into its original position. Muscles attached to bones allow organisms to move about.

Main Idea

What is the term for the shortening of muscle fibers?

Additional information:
Muscle fibers contract without any change in their volumes.

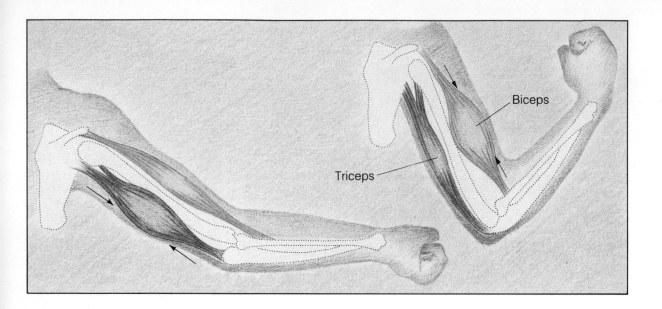

Figure 7-24. *Which muscle contracts when you bend your elbow? Which muscle contracts when you straighten your elbow?*
The biceps muscle in the front of your upper arm contracts when you bend your elbow. The triceps muscle in the back of your upper arm contracts when you straighten your elbow.

Critical Thinking

Heat is given off in the process of work. Would you expect the heat output of your body to change during the day?
Yes, your body would give off more heat when you are active than when you are at rest.

Quick Review answers:
1. A muscle contracts and pulls the bone in one direction. A second muscle contracts while the first one relaxes to pull the bone back into its original position.
2. While you are asleep, your heart pumps blood and you breathe. Food also moves through your digestive system. These activities involve the contraction and relaxation of muscles.

The body's energy needs
New vocabulary: contract, biochemistry

When muscles contract, they exert a force. This force may cause movement. Some muscles in your body do not cause a part of your body to move. Instead, they move blood or food through your body. Or they push air in and out of your body. Even when you are sound asleep, your heart is pumping blood and the muscle under your lungs is making you breathe.

Whenever a force makes anything move, work is done. Your body is always doing work. In order to do this work, it needs energy.

Every cell of your body needs energy to be able to do its job. Within cells, many different chemical reactions take place. New compounds are formed. They are used in growing new cells, helping the body digest its food, carrying messages from the brain to the muscles, and so on.

The study of the chemistry of your body, and of all living things, is known by a special name: **biochemistry.** The word *biochemistry* really means biological chemistry. For the rest of this section, we will be studying different areas of biochemistry.

Quick Review

1. What advantage is there to the fact that each bone is usually attached to two muscles?
2. Give two examples of muscle activity that takes place while you are asleep.

Supplying cells with energy

New vocabulary: simple sugar

You get energy from the food you eat. Of course, food is not only a fuel for the body. Some parts of food are used for growth and repair. Some are used in making body chemicals that control the activities of the cells. If the body has more fuel than it needs, some of the food is stored as body fat.

The fuel part of food consists of sugars, starches, fats, and even protein under certain conditions. Sugars are found naturally in fruit, milk, honey, and many vegetables. In addition, desserts, candy, soft drinks, and many cereals are prepared by adding sugar. Starches are found in grain products—bread, cereal, spaghetti, rice, and anything made with flour. Certain vegetables, such as peas, beans, corn, and potatoes, are high in starch.

Fats are found naturally in nuts, seeds, meat, eggs, and dairy products. Prepared foods that are high in fat include mayonnaise, margarine, chocolate, and potato chips. Proteins are found in grains, dried beans, eggs, meat, fish, and dairy products.

Main Idea

What in foods can be used as fuel?

Figure 7-25. *Which of these foods contain sugar? You may be surprised to learn that they all do!*
Any of the following names on a list of ingredients is a name for some form of sugar:
sucrose
glucose
dextrose
fructose
maltose
lactose
corn syrup

Teaching suggestion:
Ask interested students to see how many dry cereals they can find on the shelf of a grocery store that do not contain sugar. (Three are shredded wheat, puffed wheat, and puffed rice.)

Research Topic

Find out how much glucose is normally present in the cells of people.

Quick Review answers:
1. The most common kind of fuel used by cells is glucose.
2. One's digestive system breaks the food one eats into small pieces. The tiny pieces pass into the blood, which carries them to the cells of the body.

After you eat food, your body's digestive system breaks it down into small bits. The small bits enter the blood stream and are carried to all the cells of the body. Sugars and starches are broken down into molecules of glucose. Glucose is sometimes called a **simple sugar.** Fats and proteins are broken down into other kinds of molecules. Glucose is the most common kind of fuel used by cells.

When you read the word *fuel*, you probably imagine something burning. But burning requires a high starting temperature, high enough to destroy cells. Also, in burning, most of the energy is released rapidly as heat. Cells cannot use heat to do the work they do. Thus, cells cannot get energy directly from glucose and other food fuels. Instead, they get it in a form they can use.

Quick Review

1. What substance is the most common kind of fuel used by cells?
2. How does food fuel reach all the cells of the body?

Energy from cell respiration
New vocabulary: ATP, phosphate group, ADP, cell respiration

In an automobile, some of the energy released in the combustion of gasoline is stored in the battery. Later on, the energy can be used to start the engine or to turn on the headlights. Similarly, some of the energy from food is stored by making a compound known as **ATP** for short. Later on, the energy can be used to move muscles, grow new cells, and so on.

The *T* in the name ATP comes from the prefix *tri-*, meaning *three*. Think of a tricycle, which has three wheels, or a triangle, which has three sides. An ATP molecule has three groups of atoms called **phosphate groups.** The *P* stands for *phosphate*.

ATP is an extremely important compound because it can react with water within the cell. In this reaction, energy is released. One of the products of the reaction is a compound called **ADP.** The *D* comes from the prefix *di-*, meaning *two*. Think of carbon dioxide, which has two oxygen atoms. As you may have guessed, ADP has only two phosphate groups. In the reaction, ATP loses a phosphate group and becomes ADP.

$$ATP + water \rightarrow ADP + phosphate + energy$$

See also Activity Record Sheet 7-3A (Lab Manual page 97). Advance Preparation, Answers to Questions, and Conclusion appear on page T115 in the front of this book.

Activity

7.3a   Energy from Burning Nuts

Science processes: Using numbers, measuring, inferring, making models

BASIC   30 minutes   Groups of 4 or teacher demonstration

Materials

- nail
- hammer
- water
- thermometer
- needle
- cork
- matches
- hot pad
- small can with one end removed
- 100-mL heat-resistant beaker

- balance with standard masses
- 10 shelled walnut halves
- 10 shelled cashew nuts
- 10 shelled almonds
- aluminum foil pie pan
- lump of modeling clay

Purpose

To determine which kind of nut—a walnut, a cashew, or an almond—gives off the most energy per gram when it is burned.

Procedure

1. Measure the masses of each of the following in grams: 10 walnut halves, 10 almonds, and 10 cashew halves. Then determine the average mass of each kind of nut. Record the data on a table like the one shown.
2. Fill the beaker with 100 mL of water. Place the thermometer in the water.

3. With a nail and hammer, punch 10 holes all over the side of a small can.
4. Place a lump of modeling clay in the center of a foil pan. Stick the thick end of the needle into the cork.
5. Carefully spear a walnut half on the other end of the needle, and press the cork firmly into the clay as shown in the diagram.
6. Read the thermometer that has been sitting in the water and record the temperature on the chart.
7. Set the walnut on fire with a match. Put the can with the holes in it over the nut, cork and clay. Put the beaker with the water and thermometer on top of the can as shown in the diagram.

   SAFETY NOTE: *Take care when lighting the nut with a match. Use a hot pad when handling the hot can.*
8. When the nut is completely burned, measure and record the temperature of the water. Calculate the temperature change and divide the change by the average nut mass.
9. Repeat this procedure with a cashew half and an almond.

Step 7

Questions

1. When burned, which kind of nut releases the most energy? How do you know?
2. Which kind of nut releases the most energy per gram? Explain your answer.
3. Would 100 grams of walnuts, cashews, or almonds have the most food energy? Which one would have the least?

Conclusion

What can you conclude about the differences in the amount of energy per gram given off by a walnut, a cashew, and an almond?

Figure 7-26. *The full name of ATP is adenosine triphosphate. Each ATP molecule is made of four groups of atoms. Which elements are found in the adenosine group but not in the phosphate groups?*
Carbon and nitrogen are found in the adenosine group but not in the phosphate groups.

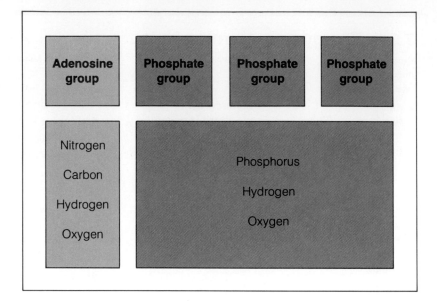

Main Idea

What is cell respiration?

Additional information:
Two ATP molecules react with each glucose molecule converting the glucose to glucose-1,6-diphosphate which then enters the process of cell respiration.

Whenever a cell needs energy, it gets it from the reaction of ATP with water. There are always molecules of ATP in the cell. As they react and release energy, a supply of ADP molecules and phosphate groups builds up.

How does the ATP used by the cell get replaced? This is where glucose is important. Glucose is used to start a whole series of reactions within the cell. At the end, energy has been stored through the forming of ATP from ADP and phosphate. The whole process is called **cell respiration** (SEL res′-per-RAY′-shun). Cell respiration requires oxygen as well as glucose. Carbon dioxide and water, as well as energy, are produced.

glucose + oxygen → carbon dioxide + water + energy

Note that ATP is not formed directly from glucose. Rather, some of the energy released in cell respiration is used in forming ATP from ADP and phosphate.

ADP + phosphate + energy → ATP + water

Cell respiration needs an "uphill energy push" to get started. For each molecule of glucose, two molecules of ATP react and give up energy. The energy starts the cell respiration process.

During cell respiration, energy is released in several steps. Much of this energy is used to allow ADP to react with phosphate and form more ATP. Altogether, for each molecule of glucose, 38 molecules of ATP are formed! The net result,

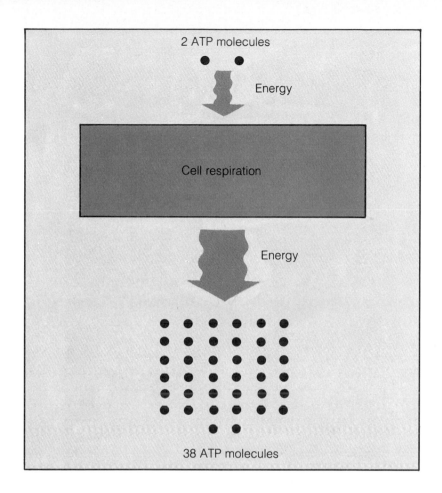

2 ATP molecules

Energy

Cell respiration

Energy

38 ATP molecules

counting the two that were "spent" to start the process, is that 36 molecules of ATP are formed in cell respiration. The energy from the glucose is now in a usable form.

Quick Review

1. What is the difference between ATP and ADP?
2. Why is the reaction of ATP with water so important to living organisms?
3. What is produced as a result of cell respiration?

Quick Review answers:
1. ATP contains three phosphate groups, while ADP has only two.
2. The reaction of ATP with water is so important to living organisms because cells get the energy they need from the reaction.
3. As a result of cell respiration, ATP is formed.

Energy from fermentation

New vocabulary: fermentation

Most organisms, from green plants to one-celled amebas to large elephants, carry on cell respiration. In that process, energy is released when glucose breaks down in the presence of oxygen. Carbon dioxide and water are produced.

Some kinds of bacteria and yeast cells break down glucose and release energy without using oxygen. But the glucose is not broken down into carbon dioxide and water. Instead, in

Research Topic

Read about cheese and other foods that are produced through the fermentation of milk. Write a report.

Activity

See also Activity Record Sheet 7-3B (Lab Manual page 98). Advance Preparation, Teacher Notes, Answers to Questions, and Conclusion appear on page T115 in the front of this book.

7.3b Heat Release in Fermentation

Science processes: Observing, measuring, inferring, controlling variables, experimenting

Materials

- masking tape
- water
- 3 fermentation tubes
- 10% molasses solution
- dry yeast
- thermometer
- potassium hydroxide (KOH)

Purpose

To find what variables affect the amount of heat released during fermentation.

Procedure

1. Use masking tape to label the three fermentation tubes "A," "B," and "C."
2. Fill tubes A and B with 10% molasses solution. Fill tube C with water. The closed end of the tubes will be almost full. The bulk side of the tubes will be about one-third full.
3. Add 15 grains of dry yeast to tube A. Add 10 grains of dry yeast to tubes B and C. Cover the opening with your thumb and shake each tube thoroughly.
4. Test the temperature of each tube and record the data on the chart in the Activity Record Sheet. Place the three tubes in a dark place at room temperature.
5. After 24 hours, note the temperature of each tube. Note the amount of gas in each tube. Record the data on the chart.
6. Observe what happens when the teacher places a small amount of potassium hydroxide in tube A.
   SAFETY NOTE: *Do not touch the potassium hydroxide or the solution in tube A. If you should get it on your skin or clothing, or in your eyes, flush the affected area with large amounts of water.*
7. With the water running, pour the contents of tube A directly into the drain. Be careful not to spill any on yourself. Then clean and wash all the fermentation tubes.

2 days   Groups of 4 or teacher demonstration

Questions

1. In which tube is the greatest amount of heat given off? The least amount?
2. Which tube has the greatest amount of gas in the closed end? The least amount of gas?
3. In which tube did the most fermentation take place?
4. Did the presence of molasses affect the amount of heat given off? How do you know?
5. Did the amount of yeast affect the amount of heat given off? Explain your answer.
6. Which of the tubes had the highest temperature change?
7. What is the relationship between the amount of gas and the amount of heat given off?
8. Potassium hydroxide absorbs carbon dioxide. Does the gas in tube A appear to be carbon dioxide? Explain your answer.

Conclusion

What variables affect the amount of heat released during fermentation? How was a control used to determine this?

Step 2

the absence of oxygen, bacteria cells break down glucose into an acid. Yeast cells, in similar conditions, break down glucose into alcohol and carbon dioxide.

The breakdown of glucose without using oxygen is called **fermentation** (fer'-men-TAY'-shun). The energy released during fermentation is used to form ATP. But not as much ATP is formed in fermentation as in cell respiration.

It takes the energy from two molecules of ATP to start the fermentation of one glucose molecule. Only four molecules of ATP are formed in fermentation. So the net result of fermentation is the formation of two molecules of ATP. Compare this to cell respiration, which nets 36 molecules of ATP. Does fermentation or cell respiration provide more usable energy from glucose? In which process would you expect more energy to be given off as unusable heat?

What happens to your breathing rate when you do a strenuous activity? You breathe faster. Also, your heart beats faster. Because of this, more glucose and oxygen are carried by your blood to your cells. When a muscle is used, it quickly runs out of its store of ATP. More ATP can be produced through cell respiration. Cell respiration occurs at a higher rate during the activity because more glucose and oxygen are available.

Muscle cells are able to supplement cell respiration with fermentation. Even more ATP can be produced, because fermentation does not require oxygen. However, fermentation produces an acid that builds up in the muscle cells. It is the acid that makes your muscles feel tired.

Quick Review

Compare the net amounts of ATP formed as a result of fermentation and of cell respiration.

Body heat

Your body is always warm. Except in very hot weather, your body is warmer than the air around it. Heat radiates away from your body to the cooler surroundings. In addition, air carries away body heat through convection currents.

Where does the body get the energy to replace the heat that is lost? Much of this energy comes directly from cell respiration. Only about 40% of the energy from cell respiration is used to make ATP. The other 60% is given off as heat. Cell respiration occurs 24 hours a day, so your body never cools down.

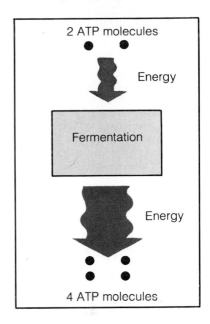

Figure 7-28. *What is the net number of ATP molecules formed during fermentation?*
2 for each molecule of glucose used

Cell respiration provides more usable energy from one molecule of glucose. One would expect more energy to be given off as unusable heat in the fermentation process.

Quick Review answer:
For each molecule of glucose used, fermentation nets 2 molecules of ATP and cell respiration nets 36.

Main Idea

What percent of the energy from cell respiration is used to make ATP?

Figure 7-29. *What causes the body temperature to rise during a sport activity? What causes the muscles to feel tired?*

Because cell respiration takes place at a higher rate during muscular activity, more heat is produced. This causes the body temperature to rise.

Fermentation in muscle cells also takes place during strenuous activity. Fermentation in muscle cells produces an acid that builds up in the muscle cells and causes the muscles to feel tired.

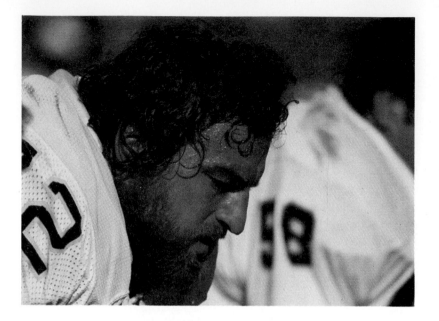

When there is muscular activity, cell respiration takes place at a higher rate. Thus, more heat is produced. Furthermore, fermentation in muscle cells produces heat. Only about 7% of the energy from fermentation is used to make ATP. The other 93% is given off as heat.

Quick Review

What process produces the heat that keeps your body warm?

Energy stored through photosynthesis

New vocabulary: photosynthesis, chlorophyll

As glucose and other food fuel is broken down inside the cell, energy is released. It must take energy to make food. How is food made, and where does the energy come from?

All organisms get energy from the breakdown of food. But only green plants and certain green one-celled organisms can make food. Food-making organisms can trap part of the energy in sunlight. They use the energy to change carbon dioxide and water into sugar and oxygen. This food-making process is called **photosynthesis** (fō′-tō-SIN′-thuh-sis), which means *made with light*.

Food-making organisms are green because they contain a green material called **chlorophyll** (KLOR′-uh-fil). Without chlorophyll, plants could not carry on photosynthesis. Chlorophyll is able to absorb energy from sunlight.

Some of the solar energy trapped by chlorophyll is used to split water into hydrogen and oxygen. This is the crucial first

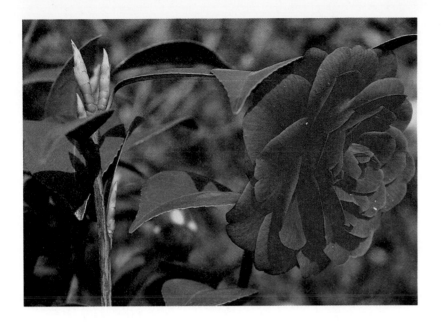

Figure 7-30. *Where in a plant does photosynthesis go on—in the stems, leaves, or flowers? Explain how you know.*
Photosynthesis takes place in the leaves and in green stems, but not in flowers or in woody stems. It takes place in the parts of a plant that contain the green material chlorophyll.

step of photosynthesis. The hydrogen joins with carbon dioxide in the plant cells to form glucose. The oxygen is given off as a waste material. The word equation for this process is the following one.

water + carbon dioxide + energy → glucose + oxygen

Compare photosynthesis with cell respiration. Is it correct to think of them as the reverse of each other? Explain.

Yes, photosynthesis and cell respiration can be thought of as the reverse of each other. The chemical equation for photosynthesis given here is just the reverse of the chemical equation for cell respiration shown on page 332.

Photosynthesis is the most large-scale chemical reaction on earth. More materials are used and produced in photosynthesis than in any other earth process. It is a process which requires the input of energy from the sun. The energy is used to make food. Later, when the food is broken down, the energy is released and can be used to do work. Thus, you can think of photosynthesis as a process in which solar energy is stored in food.

Quick Review

1. What is produced as a result of photosynthesis?
2. What is the importance of the green color common to food-making organisms?

Quick Review answers:
1. Glucose and oxygen are produced during photosynthesis.
2. The green color indicates the presence of chlorophyll. Chlorophyll absorbs energy from sunlight, which is used in the food-making process.

The food energy pyramid

In general, plants are able to trap only one to two percent of the available solar energy. Most of the solar energy is used in the heating of the air, ground, and water and in evaporation.

Figure 7-31. *What happens to the energy stored in an uneaten apple peel?*

Most of the energy is released as heat when organisms of decay break down the apple peel.

Figure 7-32. *About one percent of the solar energy reaching a forest is stored in the trees in the food they make.*

Of the solar energy trapped by plants, about half is used to make food for their own cell respiration. The other half is available to the animals that feed on the plants.

Some animals, such as deer, cattle, and grasshoppers, eat only plants. These animals, in turn, are eaten by animals that eat meat. Ultimately, other animals may eat these meat eaters. Humans and a few kinds of animals are able to eat both plants and meat.

The plant eaters do not eat 100 percent of each plant. The uneaten part is left to decay. Thus, not all the energy stored as food in plants is passed on to plant eaters.

The plant eaters are food for the meat eaters. Again, only part of the energy stored in the food eaten by the plant eaters is passed on. Most of the energy is used in keeping the plant eaters alive. And the meat eaters eat far less than 100 percent of the plant eaters. The uneaten parts of the plant eaters are left to decay.

The energy relationships in a natural community of plants and animals can be shown in a diagram that looks like a pyramid. Look at Figure 7-33. The bottom of the pyramid represents the energy stored in food by all the plants (and other

Energy locked up in bodies
of animal eaters that eat
other animal eaters

Energy locked up in
bodies of animal eaters
that eat plant eaters

Energy locked up in
bodies of plant eaters

Energy in food
made by food makers

food-making organisms) of the community. The next step represents the energy stored by the plant eaters. The next step represents the energy stored by the meat eaters that eat the plant eaters. The top step (the thin line) represents the energy stored by the meat eaters that eat the meat eaters that eat the plant eaters.

On the average, each step represents about 10 percent of the step below. Less than one tenth of one percent of the energy stored in the plants ends up at the top of the energy pyramid. What happens to all the energy that is not passed on? It is converted to heat as a result of cell respiration, body activity, and decay of waste material. Eventually, this energy will radiate away from the earth into empty space. This represents an enormous loss of energy, but it is replaced by more energy that travels to earth from the sun.

Smile! Blink your eye! Wiggle your thumb! Each of these movements used a little energy. What steps did this energy pass through on its way to you from the sun?

Figure 7-33. *An energy pyramid for a natural community. The amount of solar energy available to the food makers is not shown. On the same scale, you would need a bar as long as an Olympic-size swimming pool.* The plants and animals depicted in this drawing are not all in the same natural community. They are shown simply as examples of each type of organism.

Here is one possible set of steps. Grass used energy from the sun to make food. A steer ate the grass to obtain its food. You ate a hamburger made from the steer. Respiration in your cells released energy from the digested hamburger. The energy was stored in ATP molecules. ATP molecules reacted with water to release energy, which you used to make a movement.

Quick Review

1. What does a food energy pyramid show?
2. What happens to the energy locked in different organisms as you move upward from the base of the pyramid?

Quick Review answer:
1. A food energy pyramid shows the amount of energy passed from plants to plant eaters to animal eaters in a natural community.
2. The total diminishes rapidly.

Careers

Nutritionist

Nutritionists apply the principles of nutrition, or how diet affects health, in their daily work. Through their studies of food science and human nutrition they develop a practical knowledge of biochemistry and how nutrients are obtained and used by the body. From this research, they can make recommendations about the dietary needs of people.

Nutritionists may counsel individuals or institutions such as hospitals and nursing homes. They advise doctors, administrators, and patients in meal planning and preparation as well as nutrition practice to prevent disease and maintain health.

The basic educational requirement is a bachelor's degree with a major in foods and nutrition offered by departments of home economics and food and nutrition sciences. High school courses to prepare for this career include biology, chemistry, health, mathematics, and home economics.

For further information, write to: The American Dietetic Association, 430 North Michigan Avenue, Chicago, Illinois 60611.

Hospital dietician offers advice to patient about dietary supplements.

Welder

Welders are highly skilled workers who have a practical understanding of properties of metals and alloys. The process of welding is used to join metal parts to form a permanent bond. Welders work on ships, automobiles, spacecraft, and nuclear reactors, to name a few of the many products requiring welded parts. A maintenance welder repairs tools, equipment, and machines.

Good eyesight, eye-hand coordination, physical condition, and manual dexterity are important attributes for a welder. A common welding process uses heat in the form of an electric arc between the welding electrode and the metal to melt the metal and form a bond. A skilled welder knows the melting points of steel, aluminum, and other metals. Safety gear such as goggles and helmets are worn while welding to protect the welder from burns and eye injuries.

A skilled welder has usually spent several years of on-the-job training. Entry level welding skills are taught in vocational-technical institutions and many community colleges. High school training in welding as well as courses in physics, chemistry, mechanical drawing, and blueprint reading are helpful in preparing for this career.

For further information, write to: The American Welding Society, 550 N.W. LeJeune Avenue, Miami, Florida 33126.

Welders know how to use torches to join metals in permanent bonds.

7.3 Section Review

Answers to Understanding the Concepts appear on page T115 in the front of this book. Blackline master test for this section: Section Testsheet 7-3 (TRB page 219)

Vocabulary

1 ADP
3 ATP
2 biochemistry
9 cell respiration
4 chlorophyll
6 contract
10 fermentation
8 phosphate group
7 photosynthesis
5 simple sugar

Vocabulary Review

Match each term above with the numbered phrase that best describes it.

1. Has two phosphate groups
2. The study of the chemical reactions of living things
3. Takes part in reaction that releases energy in amount that cell can easily use
4. Green material that can trap energy from the sun
5. Glucose is one example of this
6. To become shorter
7. Uses water, carbon dioxide, and solar energy to make glucose
8. Is given off by ATP in a reaction which releases energy
9. Uses oxygen and releases energy which is used to make ATP
10. In absence of oxygen, releases energy which is used to make ATP

Review Questions

Multiple Choice: Choose the answer that best completes each of the following sentences.

11. Your body does work ? .
    a. only when you are moving
    b. only after you have just eaten
    c. only when you are asleep
    d. all the time
12. The compound ATP ? .
    a. is made directly by sunlight and chlorophyll
    b. is used up in the process of respiration
    c. is a way for cells to store energy
    d. contains three glucose molecules
13. During the process of cell respiration, most of the energy released is ? .
    a. used directly by muscles
    b. given off as heat
    c. used to make ATP
    d. trapped by chlorophyll
14. One thing fermentation and photosynthesis have in common is that neither process ? .
    a. requires oxygen
    b. releases oxygen
    c. requires an input of energy
    d. releases energy
15. Food-making organisms include ? .
    a. green one-celled organisms
    b. plant eaters
    c. meat eaters
    d. meat eaters that eat meat eaters

16. Oxygen is given off as a waste material in ? .
    a. cell respiration
    b. the reaction of ATP and water
    c. fermentation
    d. photosynthesis
17. Biochemistry is concerned with ? .
    a. the study of fats
    b. the study of sugars
    c. the study of chemical reactions inside living cells
    d. all of these
18. In an energy pyramid ? .
    a. there is more energy stored in the organisms on the top than on the bottom
    b. you can see that there is no energy stored by meat-eating organisms
    c. all levels of organisms store the same amount of energy
    d. less energy is locked in the bodies of organisms at each higher level

Understanding the Concepts

19. Describe the advantages of cell respiration over burning of glucose.
20. How are cell respiration and fermentation similar? Different?
21. Trace the path of the energy in a dinner of spaghetti (made from wheat flour) and meatballs (made from beef) in tomato sauce, from the sun to your muscles.

7 Chapter Review

Answers appear on pages T116–T117 in the front of this book. Blackline master test for this chapter: Chapter Testsheets 7A and 7B (TRB pages 253–254)

Vocabulary

ADP	cyclic hydrocarbon	isomer
alkane series	external combustion engine	organic compound
alkene series	fat	phosphate group
alkyne series	fermentation	photosynthesis
ATP	fractional distillation	polyatomic ion
biochemistry	fuel	protein
carbohydrate	functional group	saturated hydrocarbon
cell respiration	glucose	simple sugar
chlorophyll	hydrocarbon	tetrahedron
complete burning	incomplete burning	turbine
contract	internal combustion engine	unsaturated hydrocarbon

Review of Concepts

An **organic compound** is a compound that contains carbon.

- Carbon atoms can form chemical bonds with carbon atoms as well as with other kinds of atoms.
- Many different compounds can be formed from only the elements hydrogen and carbon.
- Hydrocarbons can be classified according to the types of bonds that connect the carbon atoms to each other within the compound.
- Carbon can form compounds with single, double, or triple carbon-carbon bonds.
- Carbon can form compounds with closed ring structures.
- Two compounds may have the same molecular formula but different structures.
- Carbon compounds have different chemical reaction rates that depend on their structures.
- Many compounds can be formed from hydrocarbons by replacing one or more hydrogen atoms with other atoms or groups of atoms.

- Organic compounds that are especially important to living things include those that are classified as carbohydrates, fats, proteins, or vitamins.

A **fuel** is a substance that burns easily and is burned to supply energy.

- The most widely used fuels are hydrocarbons.
- Most of the energy released when a fuel burns is in the form of heat.
- The amount of heat released can be controlled by changing the amount of fuel, the amount of oxygen, the length of time that burning takes place, or the surface area of solid and liquid fuels.
- The heat released by burning can be used to do work in an engine.
- The burning of fuels adds substances to the atmosphere, some of which are responsible for pollution problems.

Biochemistry is the study of the chemical reactions of living organisms.

- All living organisms require a supply of energy.
- Energy is supplied by chemical reactions in the cells.

Cell respiration is a process inside a cell in which glucose combines with oxygen to form carbon dioxide and water, and energy is released.

- The energy released in cell respiration is not used directly by the cell; some is used to form ATP from ADP, and some is given off as heat.
- When a cell needs energy, it gets it from the reaction of ATP and water.

Fermentation is a process inside a cell in which glucose is broken down in the absence of oxygen.

- Smaller amounts of ATP are formed in fermentation than in cell respiration.
- More energy is given off as heat in fermentation than in cell respiration.

Photosynthesis is a process in which the energy in sunlight is used to change carbon dioxide and water into glucose and oxygen.

- Food-making organisms include plants and other green organisms that contain chlorophyll, the green substance that can absorb energy from sunlight.
- Animals that eat food-making organisms gain the energy stored in the food.
- Plant eaters are eaten by other animals, which may be eaten in turn by still other animals.
- A food energy pyramid shows that when animals eat their food, they eat less than the total food available; thus, less energy is available in food to those that eat them in turn.

Critical Thinking

1. Silicon, like carbon, has four valence electrons. What can you infer about the variety of compounds that silicon can form?

2. A kerosene heater is a portable heater that burns kerosene to provide heat. What precautions should a person take to avoid carbon monoxide poisoning when a kerosene heater is used in the home?

3. Methane (CH_4) and butane (C_4H_{10}) are two simple hydrocarbons.
   a. Which fuel has more chemical bonds in a molecule?
   b. Which of the two hydrocarbons would need more energy added to start burning?

4. Study the structural formulas for ethane, ethene, and ethyne that appear in Section 7.1 of the text.
   a. How are they alike? What does the *eth-* part of the names seem to imply?
   b. How are they different? What do the *-ane, -ene,* and *-yne* parts of the names mean?
   c. Look at the structural formula for methane. Could there exist compounds called *methene* and *methyne*? Explain.

Individual Research

1. Make a list of everything you can see in your room at home. Put a check beside the name of each item that you are sure contains carbon. Put a question mark beside the name of each item that you think *may* contain carbon.

2. Look in an organic chemistry book for the structural formula of some complicated compound. Write a short paragraph explaining what information that formula conveys to someone familiar with chemistry.

3. Two elements in carbon's family on the periodic table, silicon and germanium, are very important in the manufacture of transistors. Find out how their properties make them useful.

4. Find out what pollution properties have been most serious in your community. What is being done to improve the situation?

Bibliography

Bershad, Carol, and Deborah Bernick. *Bodyworks; the Kids' Guide to Food and Physical Fitness.* New York: Random House, 1981
A humorous approach to the subject of how the body stores and uses energy. Teaches about nutrition through games, riddles, and activities.

Limburg, Peter R. *Engines.* New York: Franklin Watts, 1970
Very readable book about internal combustion, diesel, steam, turbine, and jet engines. Has excellent line drawings.

Millard, Reed, and the Editors of Science Book Associates. *Clean Air—Clean Water for Tomorrow's World.* New York: Messner/Simon and Schuster, 1977
Well organized, fast-moving account of what has happened, what is now being done, and what can be done about air and water pollution.

Rice, Karen. *Does Candy Grow on Trees?* New York: Walker, 1984
Discusses candy ingredients found in plants (sugar, corn syrup, chocolate, vanilla, peppermint, gum arabic, etc.) and the role that chemicals play in producing flavors in plants.

Issues in Physical Science

Very large quantities of coal must be mined to fuel power plants. Forty-four million kilograms (enough to fill a freight train 1.6 km long) of coal are needed to fuel a 1000-megawatt power plant to service 100 000 people for 24 hours.

Use of Coal as Fuel

Coal is our nation's most abundant fossil fuel, making up 89 percent of our total fossil fuel reserves. In addition to being burned directly to provide energy or to generate electricity, coal can be used to artificially synthesize natural gas and fuel oil, two fuels with much lower reserves in the United States. Unfortunately, both mining and burning of coal are not without some environmental and economic consequences.

Are these consequences outweighed by the benefits of using coal as our nation's primary fuel?

PROS

- There is an abundant supply of coal. It is predicted that our reserves will last another 200–300 years, even if we use coal to synthesize gas and oil.
- Coal is easy to obtain through strip mines or underground mines.
- There is not the same potential for long-term adverse medical effects for those living near a coal-fueled power plant as for those near a nuclear power plant.
- Congress has established a clean-coal program to research methods to burn coal more efficiently and cleanly.
- Scrubbers can be added to exhaust stacks which clean the smoke of the particulate matter and most of the sulfur.
- Laws exist which govern the location of strip mines and which require mining companies to reclaim the land after mining.
- Coal can be transported through pipelines as a slurry made by combining coal with water.

CONS

- Sulfur is released when coal is burned and sulfur is known to contribute to acid rain.
- Deaths among miners can occur due to black lung disease or the hazards of mine fires and collapses.
- Miners' strikes could cause supplies to be halted or prices to be increased dramatically.
- Strip mining causes lasting damage to the landscape of an area.
- Ten percent of the coal remains as slag after burning, presenting a disposal problem.
- Pollution control devices such as scrubbers are expensive.
- The slurry method of transporting coal would use up much needed water for agriculture.

Increasing our use of coal would decrease our dependence on both foreign oil and nuclear power. Do the benefits outweigh the consequences? What is your opinion?

Solutions to Acid Rain

The scene is a beautiful mountain lake in the Adirondacks of New York. The water is crystal clear, inviting. Yet there is a quietness here that is almost eery. When you look through the water to the pebbled bottom of the lake, there is no movement, no flash of silver fins. The lake is dead, a victim of acid rain.

The effects of acid rain on a lake or stream are gradual and cumulative. Pure rainwater has a pH of 5.6. Moderately acid rain has a pH of 4.6, more than 10 times as acidic as "pure" rain. As the water becomes more acid, all forms of animal and plant life begin to change, sicken, and eventually die.

But acid rain does not just fall on the lake. It falls on the soil surrounding the lake, too. It leaches out metals in the soil, which are deposited in the lake in runoff. These metals speed up the death spiral of the living things in the water.

Acid rain begins with industrial pollution. Daily we deposit into the atmosphere thousands of tons of sulfur dioxide (SO_2) from fossil-fueled power plants, oil refineries, copper smelters, and other industries, and nitrogen oxides (NO_x) from automobile exhaust. Aloft for periods of up to five days, these pollutants combine with water in the atmosphere to form sulfuric acid (H_2SO_4) and nitric acid (HNO_3). These acids are often carried hundreds of miles on the wind and then fall to earth as acid rain, snow, or dry precipitation.

The phenomenon of acid rain has been known for at least the past 45 years. But the problem has increased dramatically in the last ten years. In the northeastern United States, eastern Canada, Germany, Sweden, and many other places, acid rain is poisoning lakes and streams and killing forests. Acid rain also causes heavy metals to leach out of soil or water pipes, raising the amounts of lead, copper, aluminum, and other metals in drinking water to unhealthy levels. Buildings and monuments that have stood for hundreds or even thousands of years are showing signs of increasing corrosion.

Scientists are searching for and beginning to find solutions to the problem of acid rain. Adding lime to lakes and streams can help to reverse an acid pH and bring temporary improvements. International agreements between countries, such as the one between the United States and Canada, are addressing the source of the original pollutants, particularly SO_2. Washing coal before it is burned, using scrubbers to remove SO_2 from plant emissions before they are released into the atmosphere, and coal gasification are some measures that are under consideration.

A new, and as yet experimental, technology uses bacteria that are photochemical, that is, they rely on a chemical, in this case SO_2, for the energy they need to survive and grow. The bacteria can "eat" the SO_2 at the source.

In the next few years, we can hope to see these and other new technologies applied so that, one day, acidic streams and lakes may once again hum with life.

An environmental scientist skims off the deposits left by acid precipitation in a lake in Sweden. Adding lime will help to reverse the acidic condition.

4 Waves, Sound, and Light

Learning Objectives

■ **Process**

1. To identify the frequency, wavelength, and amplitude of both compressional and transverse waves
2. To relate wavelength to frequency and wave speed
3. To use a specific model, the wave model of sound, to explain the Doppler effect
4. To identify the different ways in which light reacts with matter
5. To identify the types of radiation that are a part of the electromagnetic spectrum

■ **Content**

1. To describe reflection, refraction, diffraction, and interference of waves
2. To analyze the effect of different materials on the speed of sound
3. To explain the wave model of sound
4. To describe the formation of light images
5. To compare the particle and wave models of light

A lighthouse beacon helps sailors find their way along a foggy coast. Foghorns on the boats are a way of using sound to pinpoint locations.

347

Chapter 8
Waves and Sound

*A saxophone is a source of sound.
When the player blows into the mouth-
piece, a reed vibrates and causes the
column of air within the brass body to
vibrate. The sound waves produced by
the vibrating air column travel outward from the bell-shaped end.*

Science background information:
Sound and light both travel as waves.
A wave is a repeating pattern that
moves without the net movement of
matter along with it.

In a sound wave, the pattern is made
up of compressions and rarefactions of
the matter through which the sound
wave travels. (Sound cannot travel
through a vacuum, or empty space.)

A light wave is more complicated
conceptually. Its pattern is made up of
electric and magnetic fields. The important thing is that light *can* travel
through a vacuum as well as through
some kinds of matter (such as air,
water, and glass).

Sound travels as a *compressional*
wave; the matter it travels through is
moved back and forth parallel to the
direction the wave is traveling in. A
water wave travels partly as a *transverse* wave and partly as a compressional wave. In a transverse wave, the
motion is perpendicular to the direction
the wave is traveling in. (As students
will learn in Chapter 9, light travels
as a transverse wave.)

Waves carry energy from one place
to another even though they do not
carry matter along with them. Sound
and light are forms of energy carried
by sound and light waves, respectively.

Chapter 8 develops the basic concepts of waves and then treats sound
in particular. Chapter 9 follows with a
study of light.

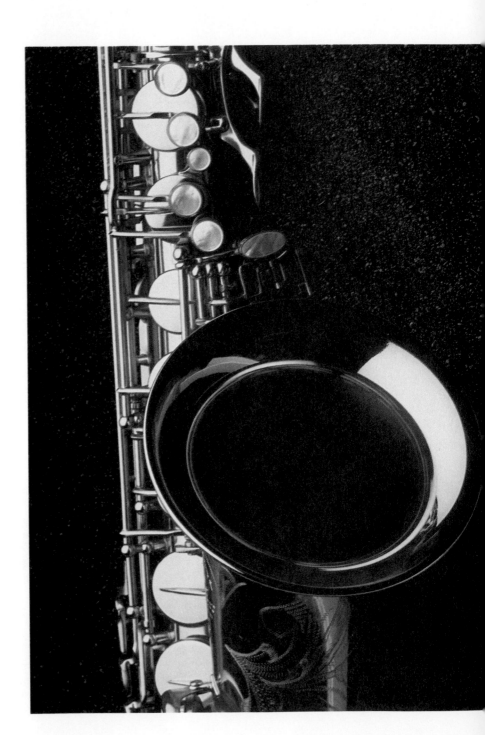

For detailed information about teaching this chapter, see Chapter 8 Planning Guide on pages T118–T119 in the front of this book.

Projectsheet 8 (TRB page 180) and Research Lab 8 (Lab Manual pages 119–120) may be used at any point in this chapter.

Chapter Preview

8.1 Waves

- **Compressions in springs and air**
- **Compressional waves**
- **Transverse waves**
- **Parts of a wave**
- **Frequency, wave speed, and wavelength**
- **Reflection and refraction**
- **Diffraction and interference**

A wave is a repeating pattern that moves without the net movement of matter along with it. Waves can move through materials as diverse as springs, air, and the surface of water.

8.2 Properties of Sound

- **Sound production**
- **Sound carriers**
- **The speed of sound**
- **Pitch**
- **Loudness and noise level**
- **Amplifying sound**
- **Controlling noise and sound**
- **Quality**

Sound can travel through different substances. Properties such as loudness and pitch can be used to distinguish sounds. The properties of a sound can be changed by making changes in the object that produces the sound.

8.3 The Wave Model of Sound

- **Sound as wave energy**
- **Frequency and pitch**
- **Music**
- **Loudness and amplitude**
- **The Doppler effect**

A good model for sound must be able to explain how the properties of a sound can be changed. It must also explain how sound behaves as it travels through matter. The wave model of sound can explain these things.

For ideas for classroom demonstration and discussion, see Getting Started on page T118 in the front of this book.

8.1 Waves

Supplemental materials: Teaching Diagrams 8-1A, 8-1B, and 8-1C (TRB pages 37–39), Reading Checksheet 8-1 (TRB page 100), Skillsheet 8-1 (TRB page 146), Investigation 8-1 (Lab Manual pages 107–108)

Section Preview

- **Compressions in springs and air**
- **Compressional waves**
- **Transverse waves**
- **Parts of a wave**
- **Frequency, wave speed, and wavelength**
- **Reflection and refraction**
- **Diffraction and interference**

Bracketed numbers are Section Review numbers correlated to that objective.

Learning Objectives

1. To distinguish between compressional and transverse waves. [4, 5, 7, 18, 21]
2. To identify the frequency, wavelength, and amplitude of both compressional and transverse waves. [1, 3, 6, 12, 19, 23]
3. To relate the wavelength to the frequency and the wave speed. [22, 24]
4. To recognize reflection, refraction, diffraction, and interference of waves. [8, 9, 10, 11, 17, 20]

Figure 8-1. *When circular ripples on the surface of a pond spread out from the center, they carry energy outward but there is no net movement of water.*

In this section you will learn about a type of motion which is different from the motion of objects from one place to another. A knowledge of this type of motion is helpful in understanding sound and light.

Compressions in springs and air

New vocabulary: compression, rarefaction

When the coils at one end of a long, loose wire spring are compressed, or squeezed together, they spread apart again. At the same time, the coils next to them move together. Then these coils spread apart and the next ones move together. The **compression,** or "squeeze," travels along the spring to the other end. Although the compression travels, the coils do not. Each coil simply moves away from and back to its original position.

Suppose there were two compressions, one shortly after the other. Then both would travel along the spring. Look at

Main Idea

How does a compression travel along a spring?

Figure 8-2. From top to bottom, it shows how the spring would look as the compressions were traveling to the right. In the illustration, the first compression is always to the right of the second one. The second compression reaches any given coil after the first compression has left it and traveled forward toward the right.

Sound is produced by the vibration (rapid back-and-forth motion) of some matter. As matter vibrates, it pushes again and again on the surrounding air. Each time, it must push the nearby particles of air closer together.

When you push against a filled balloon, you can compress it somewhat. As soon as you let go, however, the balloon fills out again. In the same way, the air compressed by a sound vibration spreads apart again.

Figure 8-2. *This spring has been given two squeezes, one after the other. Each drawing shows the spring at a later time, looking from top to bottom.*

Teaching suggestion:
Ask your class to examine Figure 8-2. Use these questions: Do the positions of the ends of the spring change? (No) Do the coils move while a compression is traveling by? (Yes) If so, do they move far? (No) Do they move back to their original positions? (Yes) Where in the spring are the coils farthest apart? (Between the two compressions)

8.1a Travel Through Matter

Science Processes: Observing, predicting

Materials BASIC 20 minutes Entire class

- **4 marbles**
- **book**
- **pencil**
- **long, loose wire or plastic spring (such as a Slinky)**
- **small piece of yarn**

Purpose

To observe something traveling through matter without making the matter travel.

Procedure

PART 1

1. Place four marbles next to each other in the groove along the front cover of a book. The marbles must touch each other.
2. With the bottom edge of the book toward you, press your fingers against the tops of the three closest marbles. Do not touch the fourth marble.
3. Hold the end of a pencil in your hand. Swing the pencil so that it strikes the front of the first marble. The first three marbles cannot move because you are holding them.
4. Record what happens to the fourth marble when you hit the first marble.

PART 2

5. Place a long, loose wire spring on an uncarpeted floor or long table. Stretch it just enough so that all the coils of wire are separated.
6. Tie a piece of yarn to one of the center coils.
7. Squeeze together the coils near one end and quickly let go. Observe what happens to the coil with the yarn and to the other coils of wire.
8. Predict what would happen if you squeezed the coils twice. Test your prediction.

Questions

1. What happened to the fourth marble when you hit the first marble?
2. What happened to the coil of wire with the yarn on it?
3. How did the coils move as the compression traveled through them?
4. Did the whole spring travel with the compression?
5. What happened when you squeezed the coils at one end twice?

Conclusion

What traveled through the coils of the spring and through the marbles?

Step 3

Can a compression travel through air? Suppose the window is open and there are curtains hanging in front of it. If you quickly open the door to the room, the curtains will swing toward the outside. Opening the door compresses the air near the door. The compression travels through the air and pushes the curtains out.

Now suppose the door is quickly closed. The curtains will swing into the room. Closing the door pushes some air out of the room. The air remaining near the door is thinner, or less dense. There is said to be a **rarefaction** (rayr-uh-FAK′-shun) near the door. Since the curtains get sucked into the room, the rarefaction must travel toward the window.

Figure 8-3. *What causes the curtains to move when the door is opened and closed?*

The door compresses the air near it when it is opened. This compression travels through the air to the window. It pushes on the curtains with more force than the air outdoors does. The curtains move out the open window.

When it is closed, the door pushes some air out of the room, forming a rarefaction that travels through the air to the window. Its push against the curtains is less than that of the air outdoors. The curtains swing in.

Quick Review

1. How is the movement of one coil on a spring different from the movement of a compression on the spring?
2. What evidence is there that compressions and rarefactions travel through air?

Quick Review answers:
1. One coil on a spring moves a short distance and then returns to its original position. In contrast, a compression travels the length of the spring.
2. The movement of curtains in front of an open window when a door is opened or closed is evidence that compressions and rarefactions travel through air.

Compressional waves

New vocabulary: compressional wave, frequency, hertz

When a musical instrument is played, something in it vibrates, or moves back and forth rapidly. It acts like a door being opened and closed over and over again. Many compressions, one after the other, travel through the surrounding air. Traveling in between each two compressions is a rarefaction. In other words, air acts like a spring. Of course, on a spring compressions travel in one direction—along the spring. In air, compressions travel outward in all directions.

Figure 8-4. *The compressions created by playing a trumpet move outward in all directions.*

Additional information:
If compressions are not constrained as they are by a megaphone, they travel through air in all directions from a vibrating object. As they travel, they tend to become spherical in shape. Between each two compressions is a rarefaction. It, too, tends to become spherical in shape.

Main Idea

What is a compressional wave?

Main Idea

What is meant by the frequency of a wave?

When 15 compressions are arriving each second, the frequency is 15 Hz.

The compressions and rarefactions sent out through the air by a musical instrument form what is called a **compressional wave.** The compressional wave disturbs the air as it passes through. It makes the air particles move back and forth. They move together and spread apart, over and over again. But they do not travel with the wave.

A compressional wave causes many compressions to pass through one place. The number of compressions arriving per second is called the **frequency** (FREE'-kwen-see) of the wave. The faster the source vibrates, the higher is the frequency of the wave it sends out. The SI unit for frequency is the **hertz** (HERTS), whose symbol is Hz. A frequency of one hertz means that one compression is arriving each second. What frequency means that 15 compressions are arriving each second?

Figure 8-5. *The compressions are closer together in the wave on the right than in the wave on the left. More compressions will reach the person in one second from the wave on the right. Which wave has the higher frequency?*
The wave on the right, in which the compressions are closer together, has the higher frequency.

8.1b A Model for a Compressional Wave

Science Processes: Making models, inferring, predicting

Materials   20 minutes   Groups of 2

- scissors
- index card
- metric ruler
- clear tape
- drawing on this page

Purpose

To make a model of a compressional wave.

Procedure

1. Cut an index card in half. Mark a length 6 cm long along the center of one cut edge.
2. Draw a rectangle 1 cm wide along this length. Cut out the rectangle and discard it.
3. Slide the cut end of the card over the cut edge of the other half to form a slit 6 cm long but only 1 mm wide. Tape the two pieces in this position.
4. Place the slit horizontally at the top edge of the drawing of wavy lines. Through the slit you should see short lines which are closest together near the center of the slit. These lines which are closest together represent a compression.
5. Slowly slide the card and slit down the drawing. Count the number of additional compressions to reach the center of the slit. Record the direction the compressions moved.
6. Predict what will happen to the compressions if you slide the card from bottom to top.
7. Test your prediction.
8. Watch how the short colored line moves as you slide the card. Describe the motion of the colored line.
9. Mark a spot on the card somewhere between the end and the center of the slit. Count how many compressions arrive at this spot as you slide the card from one end of the drawing to the other.
10. Assume that it took one second to move the card, and calculate the frequency of the compressional wave.

Questions

1. What happened to the compressions when you slid the card from top to bottom?
2. What happened to the compressions when you slid the card from bottom to top?
3. What do you think the short colored line represents?
4. What was the frequency of your compressional wave if you took one second to move the card?

Conclusion

In what ways did what you observed through the slit resemble a compressional wave?

Even though matter does not move with a wave, energy does. When a wave reaches a place, the particles there receive enough energy to move back and forth. As the wave passes on, the particles give up their energy to the next group of particles. Thus, energy travels along with the compressions.

Quick Review

1. What effect does a compressional wave have on the matter it travels through?
2. What does it mean for a compressional wave to have a frequency of 120 Hz?

Transverse waves

New vocabulary: transverse wave, ripple tank

There are two basic kinds of waves. In a compressional wave, particles move back and forth along the direction of the wave motion. The other kind of wave is called a **transverse** (trans-VERS') **wave.** In a transverse wave, particles move perpendicular, or crosswise, to the direction of the wave motion. Look at Figure 8-6. It shows the wave that results when the end of a long, loose wire spring is shaken from side to side.

Figure 8-6. *The motion of a transverse wave on a spring. From top to bottom, the wave is shown as it moves to the right.*

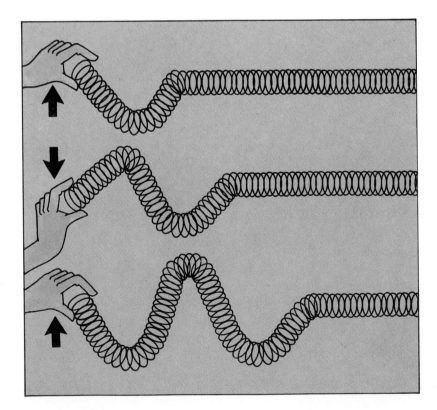

(The illustration shows what you would see if the spring were on the floor and you were above it, looking down on it.) As the wave passes down the spring, the coils move from side to side. They do not move with the wave.

Water waves that move across the surface of water show how transverse waves behave. If you toss a pebble into water, a ripple moves outward from the pebble. The ripple is circular. As it moves, the circle gets larger and larger. The direction of motion of the ripple is outward from the center of the circle, along the water surface.

You can make one circle after another if you dip your finger in water at the same spot repeatedly. A leaf floating in the water will bob up and down as the ripples pass. But the leaf will not move outward with the ripples. As in a compressional wave, matter does not move along with a transverse wave.

Water waves can be studied in a device called a **ripple tank.** The tank is usually a rectangular or circular transparent container on legs. A strong light source is above the tank and a white screen or paper is below it. Images of water ripples in the tank are visible on the screen or paper. The images form because the water acts like lenses when its surface is curved by the ripples.

Additional information:
Although water waves are the traditional example used in teaching about transverse waves, they are actually part transverse and part compressional. The individual particles of water move in ellipses rather than straight up and down.

Teaching suggestion:
If you have access to a ripple tank, by all means set it up so that the students may observe the wave behavior described in the next five pages of the text.

Figure 8-7. *A ripple tank. An electric motor can make a metal ball or strip dip up and down at regular intervals. An image of the water wave can be seen on the screen under the tank.*

8.1c Water Waves

Science Processes: Observing, inferring, predicting

Materials   20 minutes   Groups of 4

- clear pan (20 cm to 30 cm across and at least 3 cm deep)
- water
- white paper
- pencil
- small bits of paper

Purpose

To observe the behavior of water waves on the surface of water.

Procedure

1. Place a sheet of white paper under a clear pan in bright light.
2. Pour water into the pan to a depth of 1 to 2 cm. Dip the eraser end of a pencil in the water once. Observe the ripple that moves along the surface of the water. You can see the image of the ripple on the paper under the pan. The image is produced because light is refracted as it passes through the ripple. Record the shape of the ripple.
3. Dip the pencil again. Record what happens to the ripple when it reaches the side of the pan.
4. Predict how you would make a series of evenly spaced ripples. Test your prediction. If your method does not work, keep changing it until you create a series of evenly spaced ripples.
5. Sprinkle the surface of the water with small bits of paper. Dip the pencil into the water. Observe what happens to the paper. Record your observation.

Questions

1. What shape ripple was produced by dipping the pencil once?
2. Did the single ripple change shape when it hit the side of the pan?
3. How did the direction of motion of the single ripple change after it hit the side of the pan?
4. How can a series of evenly spaced ripples be created?
5. How did the bits of paper move after a ripple reached them?
6. Did the ripple carry the paper to the edge of the pan, or did the ripple move right past the paper?

Conclusion

Does the water move along with a water wave, or does a water wave move through the water?

Step 2

When a metal or wood strip is dipped in the water, a straight ripple moves away from it. An electric motor may be attached to the strip. Then the strip will dip up and down at regular intervals. A wave made of a series of straight ripples will move away from the strip. Like a compressional wave, a transverse wave is started by something that vibrates.

Quick Review

1. How is a transverse wave different from a compressional wave?
2. In what ways is a transverse wave similar to a compressional wave?
3. What happens to a ripple that is created when a pebble is tossed into water?
4. How can straight ripples, rather than circular ones, be made in a ripple tank?

Parts of a wave

New vocabulary: crest, trough, wavelength, amplitude

A water wave causes the surface of water to move up and down. Look at Figure 8-8. The places where the water surface is highest are called the **crests.** The places where the water surface is lowest are called the **troughs** (TROFS). In a ripple tank, the crests appear bright, while the troughs appear dark.

Figure 8-8. *The parts of a transverse water wave. A wavelength is the distance between two neighboring crests or troughs.*

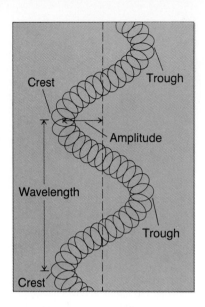

Figure 8-9. *The parts of a transverse wave on a spring.*

How do you determine the wavelength of a compressional wave?

When a water wave is produced by a ball or strip that dips up and down at regular intervals, the crests of the wave are evenly spaced. The distance between two neighboring crests in the wave is called the **wavelength.** The troughs are the same distance apart as the crests are: one wavelength.

The height of a crest above the normal water surface is called the **amplitude** (AMP'-lih-tewd) of the wave. The troughs are usually the same distance below the normal water surface. As the wave travels along the surface, the particles of water move a maximum distance of one amplitude from their normal positions.

All transverse waves, not just water waves, have crests and troughs. For example, on a spring, the farthest positions of the coils on either side of the spring are the crests and troughs. (You are free to choose which side to label "crests" and which side to label "troughs.") The distance between two neighboring crests is the wavelength. The distance of a crest from the normal position of the spring is the amplitude.

A compressional wave also has a wavelength and an amplitude. The wavelength of a compressional wave is the distance between two neighboring compressions. It is also the distance between two neighboring rarefactions. The amplitude of a compressional wave is the maximum distance a particle moves from its normal position as the wave passes by. (The amplitude of a compressional wave is not obvious from a single diagram, as it is for a transverse wave.) Two waves can have the same wavelength but different amplitude. Thus, only the wavelength is shown in Figure 8-10.

Figure 8-10. *The parts of a compressional wave.*

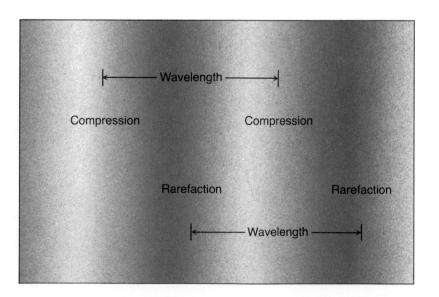

Quick Review

1. Distinguish between the wavelength and the amplitude of a water wave.
2. Is it possible for two waves to have the same wavelength but different amplitude?

Frequency, wave speed, and wavelength

New vocabulary: wave speed

Just as a compressional wave has a frequency—the number of compressions passing through one place per second—so does a transverse wave. The frequency of a transverse wave is the number of crests passing through one place per second.

In a ripple tank, it is easy to determine the frequency of a water wave. Suppose that 18 crests pass a point on the screen in a time of 10 s. The frequency is 18 crests divided by 10 s, or 1.8 crests per second. The SI unit for the number of events per second is the hertz (Hz). The frequency of the water wave is 1.8 Hz.

The frequency of a wave is the same as the frequency of whatever produced the wave by vibrating. For example, a water wave in which 18 crests pass by in 10 s can be produced by a metal strip that dips into the water 18 times in 10 s.

The **wave speed** is the speed at which the crests or compressions travel. Like the speed of an object, the wave speed is measured in units of distance divided by time, such as meters per second.

The wavelength of a wave is related to the frequency. The more crests that pass a point per second, the closer together they must be. Thus, the higher the frequency is, the shorter the wavelength must be. The waves with lower frequencies have longer wavelengths.

The wavelength of a wave is also related to the wave speed. Compressional waves travel faster through warm air than through cold air. For waves of the same frequency, a compression traveling through warm air can travel farther during the time it takes for the neighboring compression to arrive. Thus, the wavelength is longer in warm air. In general, when the frequency is the same, the wavelength is greater when the wave speed is greater.

The relation among wavelength, frequency, and wave speed can be summed up in the following equation.

$$\text{wavelength} = \frac{\text{wave speed}}{\text{frequency}}$$

Critical Thinking

If neither the source nor the material through which the wave travels is moving, the frequency of a wave is the same as that of the source. Does this mean that the frequency does NOT depend on the wave speed through the material?

That is correct: The frequency does not depend on the wave speed. The wavelength changes if the wave speed changes, but the frequency does not.

Main Idea

What is the relation between wavelength and wave speed?

Data Search

A bat has a hearing range from 1000 Hz to 120 000 Hz. Name four musical instruments that a bat cannot hear. Search pages 658–661.

A bass tuba, French horn, guitar, and trumpet

Solutions to Practice Problems:

1. wavelength $= \dfrac{\text{wave speed}}{\text{frequency}}$

    $= \dfrac{344 \text{ m/s}}{440 \text{ Hz}}$

    $= 0.782 \text{ m}$

2. wave speed $=$ wavelength $\times$ frequency

    $= 3.2 \text{ cm} \times 9 \text{ Hz}$

    $= 29 \text{ cm/s}$

Quick Review answers:

1. The frequency of the wave is the same as that of the vibrating wave source.

2. frequency $= \dfrac{21 \text{ crests}}{5 \text{ s}}$

    $= 4.2 \text{ Hz}$

Sample Problem

A water wave has a frequency of 10 Hz and a wavelength of 2.5 cm. What is the wave speed?

Solution

To find the wave speed, write the equation for wavelength, frequency, and wave speed in a form with wave speed alone on one side of the equation.

$$\text{wave speed} = \text{wavelength} \times \text{frequency}$$

Put in the known values of wavelength and frequency, and calculate the wave speed.

$$\text{wave speed} = 2.5 \text{ cm} \times 10 \text{ Hz}$$
$$= 25 \text{ cm·Hz} = 25 \text{ cm/s}$$

Note that the unit cm·Hz is the same as cm/s, since the hertz is a unit that means "per second."

Practice Problems

1. A compressional wave travels through air at 20°C at a speed of 344 m/s. What is the wavelength of a wave of frequency 440 Hz? *Answer:* 0.782 m
2. A wave of wavelength 3.2 cm is produced by something vibrating at a frequency of 9 Hz. What is the wave speed? *Answer:* 29 cm/s

Quick Review

1. What determines the frequency of a wave?
2. Give the frequency, in hertz, for a wave in which 21 crests pass a point in 5 s.

Reflection and refraction

New vocabulary: reflection, refraction

A water wave made in a ripple tank by a straight strip has crests and troughs that look like straight lines. A straight wave moves perpendicular to the straight lines of its crests and troughs.

Figure 8-11 shows what happens to a straight wave when it strikes a straight barrier. The strip that makes the wave is to the right of the barrier. The wave moves toward the barrier from right to left. When it strikes the barrier, it is reflected, or bounced back, at an angle. It moves away from the barrier toward the bottom of the photo and diagram.

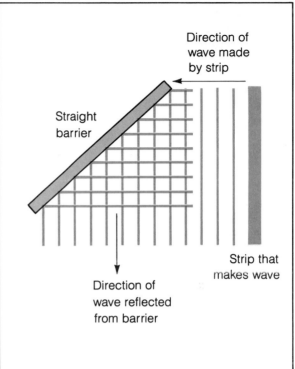

Compare the direction of the wave before and after it strikes the barrier. The change in direction caused by bouncing off a barrier is called **reflection.**

A glass plate can be placed over part of the bottom of a ripple tank (see Figure 8-12). In the shallow water over the glass plate, the wave slows down. Each crest does not travel as far by the time the next crest arrives at a point. As a result, the crests are closer together. If the crest is at an angle to the edge of the plate, it bends at the plate. The direction of the wave changes.

Figure 8-11. *A straight water wave moves toward a barrier from the right. The reflected wave moves away from the barrier and crosses the first wave.*

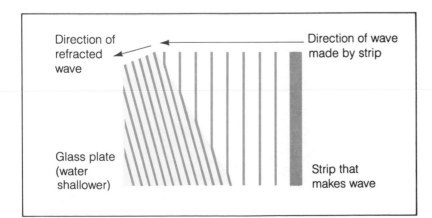

Figure 8-12. *When a straight wave passes over a glass plate in the tank, it slows down. What happens to its direction of motion?*
The direction of motion changes.

The change in direction caused by crossing some kind of boundary is called **refraction** (ree-FRAK'-shun). The change in direction is due to a difference in wave speed on either side of the boundary.

The bending of water waves can be noticed along a beach. The water close to the beach is shallower than the water farther out. The waves moving toward the shoreline at an angle are changed in direction. This causes the wave to bend as in a ripple tank.

Quick Review answers:
1. Reflection of water waves can be demonstrated by allowing a wave to strike a barrier.
2. Refraction of water waves can be demonstrated by directing a wave toward a place where the water is more shallow.

Quick Review

1. How can reflection of water waves be demonstrated in a ripple tank?
2. How can refraction of water waves be demonstrated in a ripple tank?

Research Topic

A *standing wave* is created by a particular kind of interference. It occurs when a wave is reflected back onto itself so that there are places (*nodes*) where complete cancellation always occurs. Find out under what conditions standing waves are created, and how the lengths of organ pipes meet these conditions.

Diffraction and interference

New vocabulary: diffraction, reinforce, interference

An interesting wave pattern is produced as follows. A piece of wood with a small notch in the top reaching below the water line is placed in the ripple tank. When a wave with straight crests reaches the wood, most of the wave is reflected. However, a wave with circular crests spreads out beyond the notch. See Figure 8-13. The notch acts like a small ball dipping into the water at regular intervals. A notch can act like a source of a circular wave.

Any spreading out of a wave after it passes through an opening in a barrier is called **diffraction** (dih-FRAK'-shun).

Figure 8-13. *A straight wave is moving toward a barrier with a small notch in it. A circular wave spreads out from the notch. The part of the wave that goes through the notch looks just like a wave made by dipping a small ball into the water.*

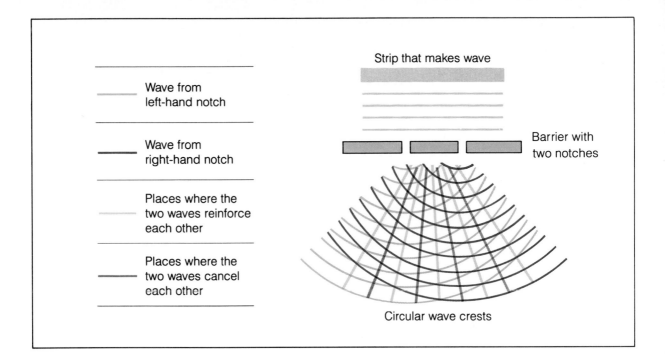

Wave from left-hand notch

Wave from right-hand notch

Places where the two waves reinforce each other

Places where the two waves cancel each other

Strip that makes wave

Barrier with two notches

Circular wave crests

Another example of diffraction is the bending of a wave around an obstacle or around the edge of a barrier. Because of diffraction, waves can appear in places where objects would be blocked off.

When two notches are in a similar piece of wood, a circular wave spreads out from each notch. See Figure 8-14. The crests and troughs from each notch pass right through each other. Where two crests reach the same point, the water is twice as high. Where two troughs reach the same point, the water is twice as low. In both these cases, the two waves are said to **reinforce** (ree-in-FORS′) each other at these points. And where a crest and a trough reach the same point, the water is at its normal level. The crest and trough cancel each other.

The reinforcement or cancellation of two waves as they pass through each other is called **interference.** Despite the name, interference has no effect on the waves themselves. Each wave continues to move with the same frequency, wavelength, amplitude, and speed.

Figure 8-14. *The two notches create two circular waves that pass through each other. The blue lines show places where two crests or troughs reinforce each other. In between are gray lines, which show areas where a crest and a trough cancel each other.*

Main Idea

What effect does interference have on waves?

Quick Review answers:
1. Allow a water wave to pass through a small opening in a barrier (or around an obstacle or the edge of a barrier).
2. Two circular waves interfere with (cancel or reinforce) each other where they meet.

Quick Review

1. How can diffraction of water waves be demonstrated in a ripple tank?
2. What happens to two circular waves that meet?

8.1 Section Review

Answers to Understanding the Concepts and solutions to Problems to Solve appear on page T121 in the front of this book. Blackline master test for this section: Section Testsheet 8-1 (TRB page 220)

Vocabulary

6 amplitude
4 compression
5 compressional wave
14 crest
8 diffraction
3 frequency
1 hertz
11 interference
2 rarefaction
9 reflection
10 refraction
17 reinforce
16 ripple tank
7 transverse wave
15 trough
12 wavelength
13 wave speed

Vocabulary Review

Match each term above with the numbered phrase that best describes it.

1. SI unit of frequency
2. A thinning out
3. The number of crests or compressions passing a point per second
4. Formed when something like a spring is squeezed
5. A traveling disturbance that makes matter compress and spread apart
6. Maximum distance something moves from its original position as it moves back and forth
7. Type of wave in which vibrations are crosswise to the direction of motion

8. Spreading of a wave after it passes through an opening in a barrier
9. Change in direction of a wave caused by bouncing off a barrier
10. Change in direction of a wave caused by a change in wave speed
11. Cancellation and reinforcement of two waves that are passing through each other
12. Distance between two neighboring crests or compressions
13. How fast the crests or compressions of a wave travel
14. High point in a water wave
15. Low point in a water wave
16. Device for studying water waves
17. What crests (or troughs) from two waves do when they meet at the same point at the same time.

Review Questions

Multiple Choice: Choose the answer that best completes each of the following sentences.

18. When a compressional wave travels through matter, the particles of matter _?_.
    a. do not move at all
    b. move back and forth but are not carried along with the wave
    c. move back and forth and are carried along with the wave
    d. spread farther and farther apart like an expanding balloon

19. The greater the number of compressions that arrive per second, the greater is the _?_ of the wave.
    a. amplitude
    b. wavelength
    c. frequency
    d. wave speed

20. When water waves in a ripple tank strike a barrier, they are _?_.
    a. reflected
    b. refracted
    c. diffracted
    d. absorbed

Understanding the Concepts

21. Cite two similarities and one difference between compressional and transverse waves.
22. How can the wavelength of a wave in a ripple tank be changed?

Problems to Solve

23. If the strip on a ripple tank makes 32 vibrations in 5 seconds, what is the approximate frequency of the wave it produces?   6 Hz
24. If a wave of frequency 100 Hz travels through air at 350 m/s, what is its wavelength?   3.5 m

For ideas for classroom demonstration and discussion, see Getting Started on page T122 in the front of this book.

8.2 Properties of Sound

Supplemental materials: Teaching Diagrams 8-2A and 8-2B (TRB pages 40–41), Reading Checksheet 8-2 (TRB page 101), Skillsheet 8-2 (TRB page 147), Investigation 8-2 (Lab Manual pages 111–112)

Section Preview

- **Sound production**
- **Sound carriers**
- **The speed of sound**
- **Pitch**
- **Loudness and noise level**
- **Amplifying sound**
- **Controlling noise and sound**
- **Quality**

Bracketed numbers are Section Review numbers correlated to that objective.

Learning Objectives

1. To recognize that sound is a form of energy produced by vibrations. [2, 6]
2. To compare the effect of different materials on the speed of sound. [9, 10]
3. To relate the pitch of sound to the length and thickness of the vibrating object. [5, 11]
4. To identify the conditions that affect the loudness of sound. [3, 7, 8, 12, 14, 15, 17, 18]
5. To recognize ways to control sound. [4, 13, 15, 17, 18]
6. To describe the sources of differences in the quality of sounds. [1, 14]

Figure 8-15. *A breeze causes the pieces of this metal wind chime to hit each other and vibrate, producing tinkling sounds.*

How does something make sounds? What is needed for sounds to travel? How can different sounds be described? These questions are explored in this section.

Sound production

New vocabulary: vocal cord

Cut a rubber band and stretch it between your hands. Then pluck it with a free finger. You will see it vibrate, or move back and forth. At the same time, you will hear a humming sound.

Whistle a note. While you are whistling, place a finger on the center of either your upper or lower lip. Can you still whistle? Do you think your lips vibrate when you whistle? Explain the reason for your answer. Answers are on next page.

Figure 8-16. *When a rubber band is plucked, the vibration can be seen and a humming sound can be heard.*

The vibrations stop when you stop humming. You should not feel vibrations when you breathe in and out.

You cannot whistle after you place a finger on one of your lips. You would think your lips do vibrate when you whistle. You may reason that your lips were vibrating because the sound stopped when you touched one of them. You could support this by showing that the vibrating rubber band stops vibrating and humming as you touch it.

Quick Review answer:
Sound is caused by vibrations, but it does not follow that all vibrating objects produce sound. An object can vibrate too slowly or too rapidly for people to hear a sound.

Main Idea

What characteristics do all sound insulators have in common?

Place one hand around the front of your throat. Rest your fingers lightly against the skin. Hum a low note and feel the vibrations within your throat. What happens to the vibrations when you stop humming? Do you feel vibrations when you breathe in and out?

The vibrations in your throat are produced by your **vocal cords.** When you use your voice, your vocal cords vibrate. Sometimes when people have bad colds, they lose their voice. This happens because the vocal cords have become swollen and can no longer vibrate. When the swelling goes away, the voice comes back.

A guitar is played by plucking the strings. When a guitar string is plucked, it vibrates. When the wind blows through a tree, the leaves vibrate and make a rustling sound. All sounds are caused by vibrations.

Quick Review

What is the relation between sound and vibrations?

Sound carriers
New vocabulary: sound insulator

When you talk to someone, the sound travels through the air from your throat to the other person. Sound from a jet airplane can travel through the air to you from far away.

Can sound travel through anything besides air? Put your ear against your desk and tap the opposite side of the desk. You can hear the sound clearly through the desk top. Even when swimming underwater, you can hear sounds. Sounds travel through gases, solids, and liquids.

Some solids are not good carriers of sound. Sounds tend to be muffled in rooms with thick carpets and heavy drapes. Special tiles are often placed on ceilings to reduce the noise level. Materials which carry sound poorly are called **sound insulators.** All sound insulators have something in common. They are made of materials which trap air.

Some kinds of matter carry sound better than others. But all matter carries sound. Is matter needed for sound? Or can sound travel through empty space, just as sunlight does?

Look at Figure 8-17. It shows a setup that can be used to answer this question. An electric doorbell is placed inside a piece of glass known as a bell jar. When the doorbell is connected to a battery on the outside of the jar, it starts to ring. Then a vacuum pump is connected to the jar. As the air is removed from the jar and a vacuum is created, the sound of

8.2a Sounds in Solids

Science Processes: Observing, inferring

Materials   10 to 15 minutes   Groups of 2
- watch that ticks
- wooden dowel, about 80 cm long
- metal rod, about 80 cm long
- 1-m-long string
- stainless steel spoon

Purpose

To compare sound transmission in air to that in wood, metal, and string.

Procedure

PART 1

1. Hold a ticking watch as far from your body as you can. Record whether or not you hear ticking.
2. Press one end of a wooden dowel against the metal back of the watch. Press the other end against the little flap that is beside your ear. Record whether you hear ticking and/or other sounds from the watch.
3. Repeat Step 2 using the metal rod instead of the wooden dowel.

PART 2

4. Tie the handle of a stainless steel teaspoon to the center of a string about a meter long.
5. Hold the string near each end and knock the spoon against a table to make it ring.
6. After listening to the ringing spoon for about five seconds, press the string against your ears. Record the changes in the sound you observed when you pressed the string against your ears.
7. Repeat Step 5. This time, press the string against your ears as soon as you can no longer hear the ringing of the spoon through the air. Record whether or not you could again hear the ringing of the spoon.

Questions

1. Could you hear the watch ticking when you held it at arm's length?

2. Could you hear the watch ticking when you held it against the wooden dowel? Did you hear any other noises through the dowel?
3. Could you hear the watch ticking when you held it against the metal rod? Did you hear any other noises through the rod?
4. Based on what you heard, which is the best carrier of sound—air, metal, or wood? Which one is second best?
5. How did the sound of the spoon change when the string was held against your ears?
6. When the ringing of the spoon was too quiet to be heard through the air, could it be heard through the string?
7. Is string a better carrier of sound than air is?

Conclusion

What kind of material is probably the best carrier of sound—a solid or air?

Step 2

Step 5

the bell gets fainter and fainter. When air is allowed to enter the jar again, the sound of the bell gets louder.

This experiment shows that matter must be present for sound to travel from one place to another. Sound does not travel through empty space.

Quick Review

1. Through what else besides air can sound travel?
2. Can sound travel through empty space?

The speed of sound

It may seem that sound gets from one place to another in no time at all. When you talk to someone, you don't have to wait for your voice to reach the person. But an echo is proof that it does take some time for sound to get someplace. When you hear an echo, sound has traveled to a distant wall or hillside, then bounced back to you. You hear the echo after the original sound. The time difference equals the length of time it took the sound to reach the wall and come back to you.

Do sounds travel in all kinds of matter at the same rate? One can hear the sound of footsteps through the ground before they can be heard through the air. The sound of a motorboat can be heard underwater earlier than through air. Sound does not travel at the same speed in all kinds of matter.

In general, sound travels faster in solids than in liquids, and faster in liquids than in gases. As Table 8-1 shows, sound depends on temperature as well as on the kind of matter.

Material	Speed of sound, in m/s
Air at 0°C	331
Air at 20°C	344
Air at 100°C	390
Water at 25°C	1498
Wood (oak)	3850
Steel	5200

Table 8-1. *The speed of sound in different kinds of materials.*

The warmer the matter, the faster it carries sound. Suppose a morning class and an afternoon class measured the speed of sound in air. Which class would likely measure a higher speed?

Data Search

How much faster does sound travel through glass than through water? Search pages 658–661.

3672 m/s

Our Science Heritage

Breaking the Sound Barrier

The first flight faster than the speed of sound was in October 1947. A Bell X-1 aircraft made a diving flight from a B-29 aircraft that had carried it to a high altitude. The X-1 reached a speed of more than 300 m/s, greater than the speed of sound in the high-altitude air.

Flying aircraft at supersonic speeds—greater than that of sound—created problems beyond just how to go faster. A supersonic aircraft produces a shock wave similar to the wake a motorboat makes in water. A cone-shaped high-pressure region spreads out from the nose of the aircraft. Aircraft had to be redesigned to withstand the forces produced by the shock wave. The swept-back wings on a supersonic air-craft are the mark that it is designed to break the sound barrier.

When a shock wave reaches the ground, it produces a sonic boom that is like loud thunder. In addition, the shock wave can cause damage to buildings. Supersonic passenger transports such as the Concorde are restricted to certain flight paths to avoid shock wave problems.

The speeds of aircraft are often described by Mach numbers. An aircraft that cruises at Mach 2.7 travels at 2.7 times the speed of sound. Mach numbers are named in honor of the work done by Austrian physicist Ernst Mach (1838–1916), who studied the flow of air over objects moving at high speed.

The Bell X-1 aircraft that was the first aircraft to fly faster than sound.

Quick Review

1. If you make a sound that echoes off a wall 75 m away, how far did the sound travel before you heard the echo?
2. Would sound travel through air faster in the winter or the summer? Explain.

Pitch

New vocabulary: pitch

When you sing a high note and then a low note, you are changing **pitch.** Pitch refers to how high or low a sound is. When two sounds seem equally high, they have the same pitch.

How can the pitch of a sound be changed? One way is to change the length of the vibrating object. On a guitar or violin the pitch of one string can be changed by pressing down on the string at a different place. This changes the length of the part that can vibrate. When the length of the vibrating string is shortened, the pitch rises.

Some of the strings on a guitar are thicker than others. When a thick string vibrates, it produces a lower sound than a thinner string of the same length would.

The tightness of a string also affects the pitch. A stringed instrument is tuned by tightening or loosening the strings. The tighter the string, the higher will be the sounds it makes. The looser the string, the lower the sounds will be.

Figure 8-18. *Which hand is controlling the pitch of the sounds?*

The left hand is controlling the pitch of the sounds by controlling the length of the strings.

See also Activity Record Sheet 8-2B (Lab Manual page 110). Teaching Hints, Answers to Questions, and Conclusion appear on page T122 in the front of this book.

Activity

8.2b Pitch and Length

Science Processes: Observing, inferring

BASIC 15 minutes   Teacher demonstration or groups of 2

Materials

- plastic ruler
- rubber band

Purpose

To compare the length of a vibrating object with the pitch of the sound it makes.

Procedure

1. Press a ruler tightly against a desk or table top. Allow most of the ruler to stick out beyond the edge.
2. With the other hand, *gently* pull down and release the free end. Listen to the sound made by the vibrating ruler.
3. Slide a little more of the ruler onto the desk or table. Press the ruler near the edge of the desk. Make it vibrate and listen to the sound.
4. Continue to shorten the portion of the ruler that can vibrate. Listen to what happens to the pitch.
5. Predict what will happen to the pitch if you move the ruler back in the other direction. Test your prediction.
6. Stretch a rubber band over the ruler lengthwise.
   SAFETY NOTE: *Stretched rubber bands can be dangerous. Be sure that the ruler and rubber band are aimed at the floor, away from other students.*
7. Put your thumb under the rubber band at the 8-cm mark.
8. Pluck the long side of the stretched rubber band halfway between your thumb and the end. Listen to the sound it makes.
9. Move your thumb a few centimeters toward that end to shorten that side of the stretched rubber band. Pluck the stretched rubber band again. How is the pitch different from before?
10. Repeat several times, making the length of the vibrating side shorter each time. Note how the pitch changes as the length decreases.

Questions

1. Does the pitch rise, fall, or stay the same as the length of the vibrating part of the ruler decreases?
2. Does the pitch rise, fall, or stay the same as the length of the vibrating part of the ruler increases?
3. Does the pitch rise, fall, or stay the same as the length of the vibrating part of the stretched rubber band decreases?

Conclusion

How does the length of the vibrating part of a ruler or rubber band affect the pitch of the sound it makes?

Step 2

Step 8

Quick Review

1. What effect does tightening the strings on a piano have?
2. Which produces a lower pitch—a thick string or a thin one?

Loudness and noise level

New vocabulary: intensity, noise level, decibel

If you lightly tap your desk, you will produce a softer sound than if you bang your fist. The amount of energy used to make the sound is one factor that affects the loudness. The more energy that is used to make the sound, the louder is the sound.

A ringing telephone sounds louder when you are beside it than when you are in another room. Distance from the source of the sound is the second factor that affects loudness. The greater the distance you are from the source, the quieter is the sound.

The amount of sound energy received per second is called the **intensity** (in-TEN′-sit-ee) of a sound. Intensity, which is measured by instruments, is similar to loudness but not exactly the same. The human ear is more sensitive to certain pitches than others. One sound may seem louder than another of the same intensity if they differ in pitch.

Noise level compares the intensity of a sound with that of the quietest sound the ear can hear. Noise level is measured in units called **decibels** (DES′-uh-belz). A sound of 0 decibel is the quietest sound that can be detected by the human ear. A sound of 120 decibels is the loudest the ear can hear without pain. However, a sound above only 90 decibels can cause a hearing loss, depending on how long the sound is heard.

Main Idea

What is meant by intensity of sound?

Research Topic

Read about Alexander Graham Bell, after whom the decibel is named. Prepare a report on his life and work.

Table 8-2. *Noise levels of various sounds.*

■ **Safety Note**
Exposure to very loud noise over time can cause permanent damage to the ear, sometimes causing the eardrum to become punctured.

Sound	Noise level, in decibels
Jet airplane, 30 m away	140
Rock music, live	120
Riveting	95
Busy traffic	70
Conversation	65
Quiet automobile	50
Quiet radio in home	40
Whisper	20
Rustle of leaves	10

Figure 8-19. *How do megaphones help cheerleaders communicate with the crowd?*
Megaphones prevent the sound from spreading out, and allow the cheerleader to direct it to certain places. The sound is amplified in those places because it is less spread out, or more concentrated.

Quick Review

1. According to Table 8-2, which would sound louder—a whisper or the rustling of leaves?
2. What two factors affect the intensity of a sound?
3. What sounds in Table 8-2 could cause permanent damage to the ear?

Amplifying sound

New vocabulary: amplify

At a sports event, cheerleaders will often yell through megaphones in order to make their voices heard. Megaphones seem to make sounds louder. That is, they **amplify** (AMP′-lif-fī) the sound.

Sounds coming through a megaphone are best heard directly in line with the megaphone. Therefore, if several cheerleaders are leading the cheer, they will point their megaphones in different directions. That way, the people spread out in the crowd can hear.

Megaphone-shaped objects are used in receiving as well as sending sound. The fleshy part of the ear itself is something like a megaphone. It gathers sound and directs it inside the skull. Many years ago, a person with a hearing loss would hold to the ear a hollow ram's horn. The horn was called an ear trumpet. Sounds entering the ear were amplified by the horn. Nowadays, sound is usually amplified by changing it into an

Quick Review answers:

1. A whisper would sound louder. Its noise level is 20 decibels while that of rustling leaves is 10 decibels.
2. The intensity of a sound depends on (1) the amount of energy used to make the sound and (2) the distance from the sound source.
3. Sounds that have noise levels over 90 decibels are a jet airplane 30 m away, live rock music, and riveting.

Main Idea

What is meant by amplifying sound?

Critical Thinking

One component of a stereo system is known as an amplifier. What is its role?

It increases the electrical signal before it is converted to sound, so as to make the sound louder.

8.2c Noisy Backgrounds

Science Processes: Measuring, using numbers, reading a table, estimating

Materials   30 to 40 minutes   Groups of 2

- **ticking portable clock (or portable tape recorder, or portable radio)**
- **metric tape measure or meter stick**

Purpose

To compare how different background noises affect your ability to detect a particular sound.

Procedure

1. With a partner, take a ticking alarm clock and a metric measuring tape or meter stick to a quiet place. One person should hold the clock.
2. Move far enough apart so that the clock cannot be heard by the other person.
3. Measure how close together you must be for the clock to be heard. Repeat.
4. Trade places and make two more trials.

5. Repeat Steps 2 through 4 for two noisy backgrounds. You might try a sidewalk or yard near traffic, the cafeteria during lunchtime, or a bandroom during practice.
6. Divide your longest distance (for the quietest place) by your shortest distance (for the noisiest place).

Questions

1. How many times farther away were you when you heard the clock against a quiet background rather than against the noisiest background?
2. What happens when you try to talk to someone against a noisy background?
3. What other unpleasant effects have you experienced due to noise in the background?

Conclusion

How does noise in the background affect your ability to hear a particular sound?

Trial	Place	Maximum distance at which clock can be heard (in m)

electrical signal before changing it back to sound. Greater amplification can be achieved by using electrical signals.

Quick Review

What effect does a megaphone have on sound?

Controlling noise and sound

What is music to one person may be noise to another. Noise is any sound that is unwanted. The noise level in our society increases each year. Highway and air traffic, powered household machines, industrial noise, and amplified music are a few of the causes.

Too much sound can be harmful. Sound causes the ear to work. Loud sounds overwork the ear. As the noise level increases, people are more likely to suffer hearing loss.

Moderately loud sounds over a long period of time may also cause ear damage. Many people suffer hearing loss without being aware of it. Yet they do not hear as well as people who live in quiet regions.

Sounds with decibel ratings between 60 and 100 can be annoying. Such sounds include a garbage disposal, food blender, subway train, and freeway traffic. Sounds above 100 decibels that last a few minutes can cause temporary or permanent loss of hearing. A snowmobile, power mower, and rock band make sounds over 100 decibels.

There are many things that can be done to cut down on noise. At the same time, people can be helped to hear sounds they want to hear.

One way to cut down on noise is to pass laws that set limits on the loudness of sounds. For example, there are laws that set limits on noise by new motors. The motors are made quieter by surrounding them by materials that absorb sound. In many communities near airports, there are laws about how close to the ground planes may fly and about hours of takeoff and landing. People who must work near loud noises are required to wear ear protectors. Heavy trucks may not be allowed on residential streets.

Unwanted sound can be reduced by different sound absorbing materials. You may not have thought of bushes and trees as sound absorbers. But they are effective in sheltering a community from highway noise. Does your school have carpeting or rough-textured ceiling tiles? They absorb sound. So does insulation between the walls of rooms.

Only the person with the earphones hears the broadcast; the sound does not travel beyond the earphones.

Figure 8-20. *How do earphones help reduce noise pollution?*

Figure 8-21. *What design features in this concert hall help to control the sound the audience hears?*

The disks hanging from the ceiling reflect sound down to the audience. The niches in the upper wall reflect sound to various parts of the audience. The slits in the wall behind where the orchestra sits absorb sound, preventing echos among the musicians.

Research Topic

Read about the sound problems encountered when modern concert halls first open. Write a report about what steps have been taken to improve the sound in a hall after it has opened. One hall which had to be totally changed was Avery Fisher Hall (formerly Philharmonic Hall) in New York City.

1. Hearing sounds over a long period of time can cause ear damage if the sounds are moderately loud.

You can help control the amount of noise others must hear. When you listen to a recording or broadcast, keep the sound volume as low as you can hear comfortably. Before making loud noises, think of people nearby who may be disturbed by the noise.

Auditoriums can be designed so that speech or music can be easily heard from every seat. The word *auditorium* comes from the Latin words meaning *hear* and *place for.* Reflecting panels behind and above the stage can prevent the sound from being lost backstage. They bounce the sound back out to the audience.

On the other hand, sound should go out from the stage or loudspeakers to the audience without too much echo. Echo makes speech hard to understand. For music, some echo is desirable as it makes the music sound smoother and richer. But too much echo covers up the music. Echo can be controlled through the use of carpeting, drapery, and other materials that absorb sound.

Quick Review

1. What, besides the loudness of a sound, can make sound cause ear damage?

2. List three ways noise can be reduced.

3. What sound problems have to be solved in designing an auditorium?

Quality

New vocabulary: quality

Sounds which have the same loudness and pitch may sound quite different. A tune played on a piano does not sound the same as the same tune played on a violin. The sounds of a piano and a violin are said to differ in **quality.**

Some sounds have a metallic quality. Others may be mellow, harsh, or shrill. Objects made from different materials produce sounds of different quality. The shape of the vibrating object also affects the quality of sound.

Quick Review

What is meant by the statement that two instruments produce sounds of different quality?

2. Noise can be reduced by keeping radio volumes down, using good auto mufflers, not shouting, etc.
3. Sound problems that must be solved are: lost sound and too much echo.

Main Idea

How do sounds differ in quality?

Quick Review answer:
Though two instruments are producing sounds of the same loudness and pitch, one can tell the sounds apart. This is because the sounds differ in quality.

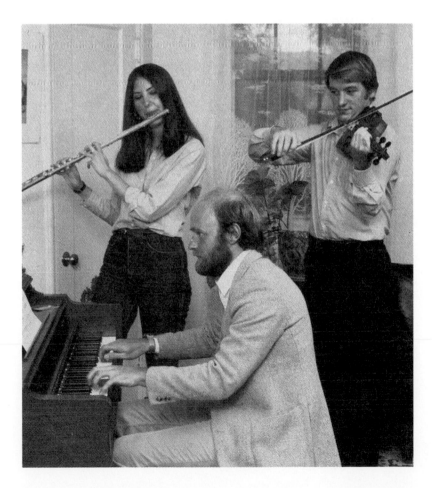

Figure 8-22. *Composers of music for groups of instruments take into account that the quality of a sound depends on the instrument that makes it.*

8.2 Section Review

Answers to Understanding the Concepts appear on page T123 in the front of this book. Blackline master test for this section: Section Testsheet 8-2 (TRB page 221)

Vocabulary

7 amplify
3 decibel
6 intensity
8 noise level
5 pitch
1 quality
4 sound insulator
2 vocal cord

Vocabulary Review

Match each term above with the numbered phrase that best describes it.

1. Is different for sounds made by a trumpet and by a piano
2. Vibrates in the throat
3. Unit for measuring noise level
4. Absorbs sound instead of carrying it
5. How high or low a note sounds
6. Amount of energy being received per second because of a sound
7. Make louder
8. Intensity of sound compared to intensity of quietest sound ear can hear

Review Questions

Multiple Choice: Choose the answer that best completes each of the following sentences.

9. Sound can travel through each of the following EXCEPT FOR ?.
   a. air
   b. empty space
   c. water
   d. wood

10. Of the following, sound travels fastest in ?.
    a. air
    b. empty space
    c. water
    d. wood

11. The pitch of the sound made by a guitar string can be lowered by ?.
    a. shortening the part that can vibrate
    b. tightening the string
    c. replacing the string by a thicker string
    d. plucking the string more vigorously

12. A sound of 65 decibels ?.
    a. can be heard without discomfort or damage
    b. cannot be heard by anyone
    c. can cause permanent damage to the ear
    d. causes intense pain

13. The echo in an auditorium could be cut down by using ?.
    a. sound-absorbing materials
    b. reflecting panels at the back of the stage
    c. a more powerful amplifying system
    d. sound insulation in the walls

14. A note played by a saxophone and a note played by a trumpet will always differ in ?.
    a. pitch
    b. loudness
    c. intensity
    d. quality

Understanding the Concepts

15. Explain why a hand placed on a bell that has just been rung will stop the sound immediately.

16. Suppose there was an enormous explosion on the sun. The sun is 150 million kilometers from the earth. How long would it take for the sound of the explosion to reach the earth?

17. People who work on the ground near jet runways wear big ear muffs filled with a sound insulator. Explain why they wear the earmuffs.

18. Imagine that you have been hired by your school to reduce the amount of noise that can be heard in the classroom. What recommendations would you make?

For ideas for classroom demonstration and discussion, see Getting Started on page T124 in the front of this book.

8.3 The Wave Model of Sound

Supplemental materials: Teaching Diagram 8-3 (TRB page 42), Reading Checksheet 8-3 (TRB page 102), Skillsheet 8-3 (TRB page 148), Investigation 8-3 (Lab Manual pages 115–116)

Section Preview

- **Sound as wave energy**
- **Frequency and pitch**
- **Music**
- **Loudness and amplitude**
- **The Doppler effect**

Bracketed numbers are Section Review numbers correlated to that objective.

Learning Objectives

1. To use the wave model of sound to explain the behavior of sound. [3, 13, 15]
2. To relate the pitch of a sound to the frequency of the compressional sound wave. [1, 5, 8, 11, 14]
3. To relate the loudness of a sound to the amplitude of the compressional sound wave. [9, 10]
4. To use the wave model of sound to explain the Doppler effect. [2, 12]

Figure 8-23. *The wave model of sound can explain why a person waiting at a railroad crossing hears a sudden drop in pitch of the train whistle just as the train passes.*

Sound travels through matter. If there is no matter—only empty space—sound cannot travel. Yet, the matter itself does not travel. Sound can travel through air when there is no breeze. It can travel through a wooden table top while the table remains in place.

What is sound? A model for sound must explain how it can travel through matter.

Sound as wave energy

New vocabulary: wave model of sound

It is reasonable to think that sound is the energy that travels in a compressional wave. After all, sound is produced by vibrating matter, which sends out a compressional wave. And compressional waves carry energy.

The theory that sound is the energy that travels in a compressional wave is known as the **wave model of sound**. It explains many observations. First, it explains how people in different locations can hear the same sound. When your teacher talks, the compressional wave spreads out into the classroom.

Main Idea

What is the theory known as the wave model of sound?

Figure 8-24. *In a "dead spot" direct sound from the stage is cancelled out by sound that first bounces off the walls or ceiling. How can the wave model of sound be used to explain the cancelling of sound?*

A "dead spot" occurs when compressions from direct sound from the stage and rarefactions from bounced sound arrive at the same spot at the same time, and so do rarefactions from direct sound and compressions from bounced sound. Compressions tend to move the particles in the air closer together at the same time rarefactions tend to move them apart. As a result, the particles move little; compressions and rarefactions have cancelled each other out.

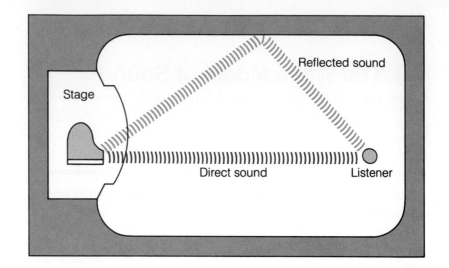

Research Topic

Read about and prepare a report on how high-frequency sound, or ultrasound, is used in the medical field. How does ultrasound compare to X-rays? Has ultrasound been used successfully in the treatment of disease as well as in diagnosis?

Main Idea

Why do metals act as good carriers of sound?

Quick Review answers:
1. The wave model of sound is the theory that sound is the energy traveling in a compressional wave.
2. They cancel each other out. As a result the sound is faint.

Second, it explains why sound stops when air is removed by a vacuum pump. There can be no compressional wave where there is no matter.

Third, the wave model of sound explains "dead spots" in auditoriums. A "dead spot" is a place where sound coming from the stage is much weaker than other places. It is very hard to hear if you are sitting in a "dead spot." Sound from the stage not only goes directly out to the audience but also bounces off the walls and ceilings. In a "dead spot," compressions from direct sound arrive at the same time as rarefactions from bounced sound. And rarefactions from direct sound arrive at the same time as compressions from bounced sound. The compressions and rarefactions cancel each other out. As a result, the sound is faint.

Sound can travel through liquids and solids as well as through gases. Gases are easily compressed but liquids and solids are not. How can compressional waves travel through them?

Although it is harder to compress a liquid or solid than a gas, it is not impossible. Sound does compress a liquid or solid. A compressional wave can travel through the liquids and solids that are carriers of sound. The best carriers are materials that return quickly to their original state after the compression has passed. Metals are excellent sound carriers.

Quick Review

1. What is the wave model of sound?
2. What happens in an auditorium when compressions from direct sound arrive at the same time as rarefactions from bounced sound?

Frequency and pitch

How can the wave model of sound explain pitch? Suppose the end of a ruler is made to vibrate. The pitch of the sound depends on the length of the end free to vibrate. The longer that end, the lower is the pitch.

A ruler vibrates too quickly for you to count the number of back-and-forth movements in a time period. A pendulum, made by hanging a small object from a string, swings more slowly than a ruler vibrates. You can find the frequency of a pendulum by counting how many back-and-forth swings it makes in a minute. The shorter the pendulum, the higher is its frequency. A ruler behaves similarly. The shorter the vibrating part, the higher is the frequency of the vibration.

The shorter the vibrating part of the ruler, the higher is the pitch of the sound it gives off. In other words, the higher the frequency, the higher is the pitch of the sound.

Other sound sources behave the same way. The frequency of the vibration is the same as the frequency of the sound wave it produces. Thus, the higher the pitch of the sound, the higher is the frequency of the sound wave. Conversely, the lower the pitch, the lower is the frequency.

Some sounds seem to have a definite pitch, while others do not. A tuning fork vibrates at a single frequency. The sound it produces has a very pure quality. Most sounds do not have this pure quality. They are a combination of several different frequencies at once. When different musical instruments play the same note, each produces a different combination of frequencies. This is what gives each musical instrument its own quality.

Figure 8-25. *When a tuning fork is struck, it vibrates at a single frequency. Tuning forks are used by piano tuners to set the frequency of the first set of strings they tune.*

Quick Review

1. How is the frequency of vibration of a sound source related to the pitch of the sound it produces?
2. How can the different sound qualities of musical instruments be explained?

Quick Review answers:
1. The higher the frequency of vibration of a sound source, the higher is the pitch of the sound it produces. The lower the frequency of a sound source, the lower is the pitch of the sound it produces.
2. When different musical instruments play the same note, each instrument produces a different combination of frequencies.

Music

New vocabulary: octave, overtone

When you sing *do, re, mi, fa, sol, la, ti, do,* you are singing a musical scale. Each note has a higher pitch than the previous one. The high *do* and the low *do* sound the "same" except that one is higher. The reason they sound the "same" is that the high *do* has a frequency exactly twice that of the low *do*. Whenever one note has double the frequency of another

Main Idea

What is meant when we say two notes are an octave apart?

8.3a Length and Frequency

Science Processes: Collecting data, making a graph, inferring
Materials   BASIC   20 to 30 minutes   Entire class

- ball of string
- scissors
- washer or paper clip for each student
- watch or clock that indicates seconds
- masking tape

Purpose

To determine the relation between length and frequency for a pendulum.

Procedure

1. Take a piece of string between 15 cm and 150 cm long. Each student should have a string of a different length.
2. Tie a washer or paper clip to one end of the string. Tie a knot close to the other end.
3. Hold the knot, and make sure that the washer or paper clip is free to swing. The string and washer or paper clip make up a pendulum.
4. Have someone be the timekeeper and call out the beginning and end of one minute.
5. Each person should silently count the number of complete back-and-forth swings his or her pendulum makes in one minute. The number of complete back-and-forth swings per minute is the frequency of the pendulum.
6. Measure and record the frequency of your pendulum three times. Find the average frequency.
7. Put a piece of masking tape below the knot. Write the average frequency of your pendulum on the masking tape.
8. Have someone draw a horizontal line near the top of the chalkboard. Number along the line by 5s, starting at 0 and ending with 100. Label the line "Frequency in swings per minute."
9. Using masking tape, each person should stick his or her pendulum to the chalkboard so that the knot is on the line at the proper frequency.

Questions

1. Are all the pendulums in order of length? Do you see any that perhaps should be tested again?
2. Do the bottoms of the pendulums lie along a straight line?
3. From the pendulums on the chalkboard, estimate how long a pendulum would have a frequency of one swing per minute.
4. Do the longest pendulums have the lowest or the highest frequencies?

Conclusion

How does the frequency of a pendulum depend upon its length?

Going Further

Test your answer to Question 3 by making a pendulum that should have a frequency of one swing per minute. Does it?

Step 3

Middle C

do re mi fa sol la ti do
C D E F G A B C

Figure 8-26. *Near the center of the piano keyboard is the white key called middle C. Playing the eight white keys starting with middle C produces a musical scale.*

note, the two are said to be an **octave** (OK′-tiv) apart. The word *octave* comes from the Latin for *eight*. There are eight different pitches on the scale within one octave.

Musical instruments are tuned, or adjusted, to play a certain note, called A, at 440 Hz. At the beginning of an orchestra performance, the oboe player sounds an A. The string players tighten or loosen their strings until their A's have the same pitch.

The wind instruments, such as the flute and trombone, all contain columns of air. They are played by blowing at one end to make the air vibrate. The pitch is changed by changing the length of the air columns. The lowest notes are produced by the longest air column.

Every musical instrument has its own quality of sound. The quality is produced by the combination of frequencies heard for each note played. A violin note contains not only the frequency of the pitch heard but double, triple, four

Data Search

What instruments cannot match the pitch of the oboe's A note? Search pages 658–661.

The piccolo and the tuba

Figure 8-27. *These people are playing recorders of different sizes. Which would you expect to play notes of the highest pitch? Of the lowest pitch?* You would expect the shortest recorder to play notes of the highest pitch and the longest recorder to play notes of the lowest pitch.

8.3b Musical Bottles

Science Processes: Hypothesizing, predicting, collecting data

25 to 30 minutes   Groups of 8 or demonstration

Materials

- **8 identical bottles**
- **water**
- **metric ruler**

Purpose

To make eight bottles play a musical scale.

Procedure

1. Put a little water in one of eight identical bottles.
2. Blow across the opening until the bottle hums.
3. Make a hypothesis that explains the source of the hum.
4. Use your hypothesis to predict what will happen if you hold the bottle as you blow across the opening. Test your prediction.
5. Use your hypothesis to predict what will happen to the pitch of the hum if you add water to the bottle. Test your prediction.
6. Adjust the water levels in two bottles until their hums are one octave apart. Adjust the water levels in the other six bottles to fill in the remaining notes of a musical scale.
7. Make a table like the one shown. Record the height of the water and the air column for each bottle. (Your readings should be to the nearest tenth of a centimeter.)

Questions

1. How did increasing the water height affect the pitch of the sound produced?
2. How did decreasing the height of the air column affect the pitch of the sound produced?
3. Which acted more like a vibrating string or rubber band—the water in the bottle or the air column in the bottle?

Conclusion

Was the bottle vibrating or was the column of air inside it vibrating? Explain how you can tell.

Step 2

Note on scale	do	re	mi	fa	sol	la	ti	do
Height of water, in cm								
Height of air column, in cm								

times, and so on that frequency. The higher frequencies are called **overtones**. Each kind of instrument produces a different combination of overtones at different intensities.

Quick Review

1. What is the frequency relationship between two notes one octave apart?
2. What vibrates in a wind instrument?

Loudness and amplitude

New vocabulary: resonance

Suppose you had an extremely long spring. You could send a compressional wave down the spring by moving one end in and out. As the wave moved, it would make the spring coils move back and forth.

The distance each coil moves from its original position is the **amplitude** of the wave. You could change the amplitude by moving the end of the spring more gently or more vigorously. What would you expect more vigorous movements to do to the amplitude?

When you move the end more vigorously, you give the spring more energy with each push. The wave must carry more energy. Thus, the greater the amplitude of the wave, the more energy it carries.

A sound wave is similar to a wave on a spring. Bigger vibrations of the sound source produce a sound wave with a bigger amplitude. A sound wave carries energy away from the source. The bigger the vibrations of the source, the more energy the sound wave carries. Thus, a sound wave with a bigger amplitude carries more energy.

The sound energy that reaches a place per second is the intensity of the sound wave. For the same pitch, louder sounds are produced when the intensity is greater. Thus, the greater the amplitude, the louder the sound. When sound is amplified, or made louder, the amplitude of the wave is increased.

Sound waves move out from the source something like an expanding balloon. However, a sound wave expands without ever breaking. As a balloon gets larger and larger, the rubber wall of the balloon gets thinner and thinner because it must cover a larger area. The "wall" of a sound wave is energy. As the wave gets larger, the energy gets spread out over a larger area.

The farther you are from the source, the "thinner" is the wall of sound energy that reaches you. The particles of air or

Figure 8-28. *The energy carried by a sound wave gets spread over a larger area as the sound wave spreads out like a balloon. What happens to the amplitude of the wave?*

The amplitude becomes smaller.

other matter move with a smaller amplitude the farther they are from the sound source. At great distances from the source, the energy wall is so "thin" that the amplitude of the wave is too small for your ear to hear the sound. You are not even aware that an energy wall is striking your ear.

A megaphone directs the sound in one general direction. It keeps the sound from spreading out very much. As a result, the amplitude does not decrease as rapidly when the sound travels outward. The sound can be heard a greater distance from the source.

Two tuning forks that tend to vibrate at the same frequency can exhibit an interesting behavior. Suppose they are about a meter apart, and you hit only one. The other will start to make an audible sound after a few seconds. (To hear the second one better, stop the vibrations of the first one by placing it against your arm.)

To understand the reason, think of pushing a child on a swing. You can make the child go higher each time by pushing in rhythm with the swinging. Similarly, the sound wave from the first tuning fork pushes the second tuning fork at its own frequency. The second tuning fork vibrates with increasing amplitude. After a few seconds, its vibrations are big enough for it to emit an audible sound. The vibration of something due to a wave that has its own frequency is called **resonance** (REZ'-uh-nuns).

Quick Review

1. What is the relation between the amplitude of a sound wave and the loudness of the sound?
2. How is a sound wave like an expanding balloon?

The Doppler effect

New vocabulary: Doppler shift, Doppler effect

A very interesting effect can be heard when a train blows its whistle at a railroad crossing. To a person at the crossing, the train whistle seems to be at one pitch as the train is approaching. However, as the engine passes the crossing, the pitch seems to drop. The person hears a lower pitch as the train moves away from the crossing.

The wave model of sound can explain this change of pitch. When the whistle blows, it sends out compressions at a certain frequency. When the train moves, each compression is sent out from a different point. Look at Figure 8-29. Ahead of the train, the compressions get crowded together. Behind

Why does resonance occur only when the tuning forks tend to vibrate at the *same* frequency?
If the pushes from the sound wave do not come at the right frequency, some will tend to go against the motion started by earlier pushes and thus cancel their effect.

Quick Review answers:
1. The greater the amplitude of a sound wave, the louder is the sound. The smaller the amplitude of a sound wave, the softer is the sound.
2. Just as the rubber wall of an expanding balloon becomes thinner to cover more space, the energy becomes thinner as it spreads out over a larger area.

Research Topic

Find out how Christian Doppler experimented to measure the Doppler effect. Look up information about A. H. Fizeau and his research in applying Doppler's ideas to light waves as well.

the train, the compressions get spread out. Thus, a person ahead of the train hears a higher frequency sound than for a nonmoving train. A person behind the train hears a lower frequency sound.

What happens if the listener is moving but the sound source is not? Suppose you were on a moving train and a bell was ringing at the crossing. When you were moving toward the crossing, you would meet each compression a little sooner. Thus, you would receive more compressions in one second. The frequency of the bell would seem higher than if you were not moving. After you passed the crossing, you would meet each compression a little later. You would receive fewer compressions in one second. The frequency of the bell would seem lower than if you were not moving.

As you can see, the apparent frequency of the sound depends on whether either the source or the listener is moving. The apparent change in frequency due to motion is called the **Doppler shift.** It is named after the Austrian scientist Christian Doppler (1803–1853). The sudden drop in pitch when the source and the listener pass each other is called the **Doppler effect.**

Quick Review

1. If you were on a moving train, how would the pitch of the bell at a crossing seem to change as you passed by?
2. Does the Doppler shift occur when either the source or the listener is moving?

Figure 8-29. *As the train passes, the person on the bicycle hears a sudden drop in pitch of the train whistle. How can this be explained?*
When a train is moving, its whistle sends out each compression at a different point. As the train travels beyond the person on the bicycle, the compressions are farther apart. Fewer of them reach the person each second. The frequency of the sound waves decreases. The person hears a drop in the pitch of the train whistle.

Main Idea

What is meant by the Doppler shift?

Quick Review answers:
1. The bell's pitch would seem to drop.
2. Yes, movement of either one will create a Doppler shift (unless they are both moving at the same velocity).

An acoustical engineer might have to decide whether construction noise is within allowed limits.

Acoustical Engineer

Acoustical engineers help to control sound. Some work on the development of techniques and sound-absorbing materials to reduce sound pollution. Others try to find new ways to conduct sounds over long distances. Architectural and design firms hire acoustical engineers to help in the design of buildings and rooms to make them quiet. They also work with architects in designing auditoriums and halls to make them suitable for hearing music or speech.

Acoustical engineers must know a lot about sound. They must be familiar with how various materials affect sound. They also must know how to measure and record different properties of sound. Acoustical engineers usually have a college degree and on-the-job training. High school students interested in becoming acoustical engineers should take courses in mathematics and physics to prepare for engineering courses at the university level.

For further information, write to: National Organization to Insure a Sound-Controlled Environment, 1620 Eye Street N.W., Suite 300, Washington, DC 20006; or The American Institute of Architects, 1735 New York Avenue N.W., Washington, DC 20006.

A sound mixer uses sophisticated equipment to blend sound tracks recorded separately.

Sound Mixer

In a recording studio, different types of sound are recorded on separate tapes, or tracks. Sound mixers direct the installation of microphones and amplifiers to pick up the sound for the different tracks. During the recording session, they operate a console to regulate the volume level and quality of sound. In preparing the final recording, sound mixers put together the different tracks to produce a mixture they think sounds best.

Sound mixers may also work in the motion picture or videotape industry or in radio and television broadcasting. When there is music, dialogue, and sound effects, they try to achieve a good balance among all three.

Sound mixers must have a good ear for music and other sounds. They must be able to operate electronic equipment. They must have some knowledge of the technical aspects of sound. A sound mixer may receive on-the-job training by working as an apprentice for several years.

For further information write to: National Association of Broadcasters, 1771 N Street N.W., Washington, DC 20036.

8.3 Section Review

Answers to Understanding the Concepts appear on page T125 in the front of this book. Blackline master test for this section: Section Testsheet 8-3 (TRB page 222)

Vocabulary

2 Doppler effect
4 Doppler shift
1 octave
5 overtone
6 resonance
3 wave model of sound

Vocabulary Review

Match each term above with the numbered phrase that best describes it.

1. Relation between two pitches, one with double the frequency of the other
2. Drop in pitch when sound source and observer pass each other
3. Theory that sound is the energy that travels in a compressional wave
4. Apparent change in frequency due to motion of source or observer
5. A higher frequency produced when an instrument plays a pitch
6. Vibration due to a wave at the same frequency as that of the object

Review Questions

Multiple Choice: Choose the answer that best completes each of the following sentences.

7. Compressions and rarefactions can move through ? .
   a. empty space
   b. gases but not liquids and solids
   c. gases and liquids but not solids
   d. gases, liquids, and solids
8. When the frequency of a sound wave changes, a person would hear a change in ? .
   a. pitch
   b. loudness
   c. quality
   d. length of time for echo to return
9. When the amplitude of a sound wave changes, a person would hear a change in ? .
   a. pitch
   b. loudness
   c. quality
   d. length of time for echo to return
10. As a sound wave spreads out from its source, there is a decrease in ? .
    a. amplitude
    b. frequency
    c. speed
    d. the total amount of energy it carries
11. The overtones that are produced when an instrument plays a pitch ? .
    a. form a musical scale
    b. give the instrument its quality
    c. are eliminated when the instrument is tuned
    d. are caused by changing the length of the vibrating air column

12. The Doppler effect is ? .
    a. a sudden increase in pitch when a moving sound source passes a listener
    b. a sudden increase in pitch when a moving listener passes a sound source
    c. a sudden drop in pitch when a moving sound source passes a listener
    d. a continuous drop in pitch when a moving sound source approaches a listener

Understanding the Concepts

13. Suppose a long metal pipe is banged at one end. Would you expect the sound to be heard farther away through the pipe or through the air? Explain.
14. What are the frequencies of the notes one octave below and one octave above the A used in tuning up an orchestra?
15. Suppose a fine crystal glass suddenly shattered while a home stereo system was being played. Use your knowledge of resonance to explain how this could happen.

8 Chapter Review

Vocabulary

amplify	intensity	reinforce
amplitude	interference	resonance
compression	noise level	ripple tank
compressional wave	octave	sound insulator
crest	overtone	transverse wave
decibel	pitch	trough
diffraction	quality	vocal cord
Doppler effect	rarefaction	wavelength
Doppler shift	reflection	wave model of sound
frequency	refraction	wave speed
hertz		

Review of Concepts

A **wave** carries energy from one place to another without transfer of matter.

- In a compressional wave, particles vibrate back and forth in the direction of the wave motion as a series of compressions and rarefactions travel from one place to another.
- In a transverse wave, particles vibrate perpendicular to the direction of the wave motion as a series of crests and troughs travel from one place to another.
- The wavelength of a wave is the distance between neighboring crests or compressions.
- The frequency of a wave is the number of crests or compressions that arrive at a place per second.
- The amplitude of a wave is the distance the particles move from their normal positions as the wave passes.
- The frequency of a wave is determined by the vibration frequency of whatever is producing it.

- The wavelength of a wave depends on both the frequency and the wave speed.
- A wave can be reflected, refracted, or diffracted.
- When two waves reach the same point, they reinforce or cancel each other at that point without change in their own frequency, wavelength, amplitude, or speed.

Sound is energy that is produced and transferred by vibrating matter.

- All sounds are caused by vibrations.
- Sound can travel through solids, liquids, and gases.
- Some materials transmit sound better than others do.
- Sound cannot travel where matter is absent.
- The speed of sound depends on the temperature and on the kind of matter carrying the sound.
- Pitch refers to how high or low a sound is.

- Loudness depends on the amount of energy used to make the sound, distance from the source, and pitch.
- Noise can be controlled by restricting the use of its sources and by using materials that absorb sound.
- Lecture halls and concert halls can be designed so that listeners can hear sounds the way they are most acceptable.
- Quality of sound refers to the difference in sounds from two sources even when the loudness and pitch are the same.

The **wave model of sound** is the theory that sound is energy that travels in a compressional wave.

- Amplitude is related to loudness.
- Frequency is related to pitch.
- Combinations of frequencies are related to quality.
- The frequency of a sound wave appears to change when either the source or the listener is moving.

Critical Thinking

1. Vibrations caused by earthquakes travel through the solid earth as waves that are similar to sound waves. How might differences in the composition of the earth's interior affect these waves?

2. Describe what happens to the particles in a material when a sound wave moves through the material.

3. The energy in a sound wave is like an expanding soap bubble as it spreads out in all directions. What property of a sound wave changes in the same way as the thickness of the surface of the soap bubble?

4. Do you think that singers produce overtones when they sing? Explain your reasoning.

5. How might noises from a busy highway be reduced within a nearby office building?

6. Compare the frequency of sound waves reaching your ear when the source moves away from you and when the source is stationary.

Individual Research

7. Examine a musical instrument. Determine what it is in the instrument that vibrates to produce the sound. Find out what the player of the instrument must do to change the pitch of the sound.

8. Compare several samples of acoustical tile that are sold in a building materials center. What properties do the samples have that would prevent the transfer of sound energy?

9. Add water to a plastic foam cup until it is about three-fourths filled. Slide the cup slowly across the surface of a desk or table. Observe the movement of the surface of the water. What is the evidence that the cup is vibrating?

10. Find out what regulations related to noise are enforced in your city. Interview a number of community residents to find out if additional steps are needed to reduce noise pollution.

Bibliography

Kavaler, Lucy. *The Dangers of Noise.* New York: Crowell/Harper & Row, 1978
How we hear, the effects of noise on people and wildlife, and what people can do to control noise.

Lutrell, Guy L. *The Instruments of Music.* New York: Lodestar, 1978
How different instruments make their sounds, their roles in an orchestra, and information about their origins.

Pierce, John R. *The Science of Musical Sound.* New York: Scientific American Books, 1983
Beautifully illustrated, clear and concise information on pitch, resonance, scales, beats, hearing, loudness, architectural acoustics, and quality of sound.

Tannenbaum, Beulah, and Myra Stillman. *Understanding Sound.* New York: McGraw-Hill, 1973
A clear and interesting outline of the physics of sound, production of animal sounds, hearing in mammals, and uses of sound waves. Suggestions for demonstrations and experiments.

Chapter 9
Light

Three colors of light are visible at the ends of these fiber optic bundles. Each of the different colors of light came from a separate source. Light can travel in thin fibers made of glass or plastic. The fibers do not need to be perfectly straight. They can bend and go around corners. You will discover more about the interesting properties of light and why it can do these things in this chapter.

Science background information:
Light and color, as we perceive them, are a manifestation of the visible part of the electromagnetic spectrum. The electromagnetic spectrum refers to the entire range of forms of radiant energy known as electromagnetic radiation. These forms include—in order of increasing wavelength—gamma rays, X-rays, ultravioletlight, visible light, infrared rays, microwaves, and radio waves. The different forms are characterized by particular ranges of wavelengths and frequencies, which are described in this chapter.

Electromagnetic radiation consists of transverse waves made up of mutually perpendicular electric and magnetic fields. The most important forms of electromagnetic radiation can be considered to be visible light and infrared radiation (heat). Life, as we know it, would be impossible without these forms of radiant energy supplied by the sun.

All forms of electromagnetic radiation are produced by subatomic changes. When electrons within an atom decelerate, vibrate, or change energy levels, energy is emitted from the atom in the form of electromagnetic radiation. Vibrating electrons in the metal of a transmitting aerial produce long wavelength, low frequency radio waves. High frequency, short wavelength X-rays are

For detailed information about teaching this chapter, see Chapter 9 Planning Guide on pages T128–T129 in the front of this book.

Projectsheet 9 (TRB page 181) and Research Lab 9 (Lab Manual pages 133–134) may be used at any point in this chapter.

Chapter Preview

9.1 Properties of Light

- **Transmission in matter**
- **Reflection in mirrors**
- **Refraction and lenses**
- **Refraction in the human eye**
- **The speed of light and the index of refraction**
- **Total internal reflection**
- **Brightness and distance**
- **The electromagnetic spectrum**

Light can pass through, bounce off, and be absorbed by matter. Images of objects are formed when the direction of light is changed by its interaction with matter. Light travels extremely fast. The brightness of light from a source depends on the distance to that source.

9.2 Color

- **White light and colored light**
- **The color spectrum**
- **Seeing color**
- **Paints and inks**
- **Why the sky is blue**

The color of an object that does not give off its own light depends on two factors. One is the nature of the object itself and the other is the type of light that strikes it. Sunlight is a combination of light of different colors.

9.3 Models for Light

- **Light as energy**
- **The wave model**
- **The particle model**

A model of light as energy carried by a wave can explain many observations. However, it cannot explain why a beam of light striking a metal can cause electrons to be released. This can be explained if light is thought of as a stream of particles. Scientists now realize that light has properties of both waves and particles.

produced by the rapid deceleration of fast-moving electrons.

The way that electromagnetic radiation interacts with matter depends upon the effect this energy has on the electrons in the receiving substance. Electromagnetic radiation is said to be absorbed when the energy received causes a random movement of the electrons and nuclei of a substance. This increases the internal energy of the substance and warms it.

Electromagnetic radiation is said to be reflected or transmitted when the energy does not induce random movement, thus becoming internal energy, but instead is re-emitted. This occurs in transparent materials, such as glass, and on highly reflective surfaces, such as metals. In both cases, the energy is only momentarily absorbed. The electrons in these substances are temporarily excited. As they return to their normal state, the absorbed energy is re-emitted as electromagnetic radiation.

The energy may or may not be re-emitted, depending on whether or not the frequency of the incoming electromagnetic waves and the natural vibration frequency of the electrons in the receiving substance are closely matched. If the frequencies are similar, a phenomenon known as resonance facilitates the absorption of the energy. For example, glass, which is transparent to visible light, does not transmit ultraviolet light. Therefore, glass absorbs ultraviolet light.

This process of selective absorption of some frequencies and not others is also responsible for the phenomenon of color. Any visible object absorbs some frequencies of light and reflects others. The reflected frequencies are what we perceive as the color of the object.

For ideas for classroom demonstration and discussion, see Getting Started on page T130 in the front of this book.

9.1 Properties of Light

Supplemental materials: Teaching Diagrams 9-1A, 9-1B, 9-1C (TRB pages 43, 44, 45), Reading Checksheet 9-1 (TRB page 103), Skillsheet 9-1 (TRB page 149), Investigation 9-1 (Lab Manual pages 123–124)

Section Preview

- **Transmission in matter**
- **Reflection and mirrors**
- **Refraction and lenses**
- **Refraction in the human eye**
- **The speed of light and the index of refraction**
- **Total internal reflection**
- **Brightness and distance**
- **The electromagnetic spectrum**

Bracketed numbers are Section Review questions correlated to that objective.

Learning Objectives

1. To identify the different ways in which light interacts with matter. [9, 20, 23]
2. To describe how images are formed by mirrored surfaces. [2, 3, 6, 7, 17, 24, 28]
3. To describe how images are formed by lenses, including the lens of the human eye. [4, 8, 12, 14, 21, 31]
4. To recognize that the bending of light (refraction) is the result of the changing of the speed of light in different substances. [11, 19, 25, 29, 32]
5. To relate the brightness of a light source to its distance from an observer. [26]
6. To identify the types of radiation that are a part of the electromagnetic spectrum. [1, 30]

Figure 9-1. *Fish-eye lens on camera attached to wing of hang-glider gives a wide-angle photograph. The shapes of objects are distorted because of the properties of the lens.*

Research Topic

Among the objects visible in the night sky are the moon, stars, planets, and galaxies. Find out which of these are sources of light and which can be seen only because of reflected light.

Some things are sources of light. They give off light by themselves. Sources of light include the sun, light bulbs, and flames. There are two major types of light sources. One type, which includes flames and ordinary light bulbs, gives off light as the result of its high temperature. The second type, which includes fluorescent tubes, gives off light at cooler temperatures.

Most objects do not produce light and cannot be seen unless light is thrown upon them by a source. A chair in a dark room, for instance, cannot be seen. But if a lamp is turned on, light from the lamp allows the chair to be seen.

Transmission in matter

New vocabulary: transparent, opaque, translucent

There are three ways light can interact with matter. One is for the light to pass right through the matter. Light easily passes through air, for example. It can pass through glass and water as well. Matter is said to *transmit* (trans-MIT′) light that passes through the matter. Matter that transmits most of the light that strikes it is said to be **transparent** (trans-PA′-rent). If you can see through something, it is transparent.

Second, light can bounce off, or reflect from, matter. We can see things that are not sources of light because of reflected light. Light from a source bounces off such objects and travels to our eyes. Dark-colored objects do not reflect as much light as do light-colored objects. Snow, for example, reflects enough light to give skiers a sunburn.

Third, light can be absorbed by matter. Dark-colored objects absorb more light than light-colored objects do. Solar collectors for buildings usually have black coverings so that they will collect the most sunlight.

No kind of matter transmits 100 percent of the light that strikes it. Even air absorbs some light. Nor does any matter reflect 100 percent or absorb 100 percent of the light. Matter that reflects and absorbs but does not transmit is said to be **opaque** (ō-PAYK′). Most solids are opaque. If a book, for example, is held in front of a flashlight, the light cannot be seen. A book is opaque.

If the book is replaced by a piece of waxed paper, on the other hand, some of the light can be seen. Yet, details of the flashlight cannot be seen. Waxed paper is neither transparent nor opaque. It is **translucent** (trans-LOO′-sent). It transmits some light but also reflects and absorbs a good deal of light. Other examples of translucent matter include frosted glass, sheets of paper, and thin fabrics.

Quick Review

1. List three ways light can interact with matter.
2. How do dark-colored objects differ from light-colored objects in their interactions with light?

Reflection and mirrors

Rough, light-colored surfaces such as sand and paper reflect much light. Smooth, shiny surfaces also reflect much light but in a different way. When you look at a shiny surface, you can see a likeness, or **image,** of objects facing the surface.

Figure 9-2. *The etched glass shown here has both transparent and translucent areas.*

Data Search

Some solar radiation is reflected from the earth's surface. What percentage is reflected from freshly fallen snow? Search pages 658–661.

80% to 90%

Critical Thinking

Explain the difference between transparent matter and translucent matter.

Transparent matter transmits most of the light that strikes it. Translucent matter transmits some light, but also absorbs and reflects a considerable amount of incident light.

Quick Review answers:

1. Light can pass through matter, be reflected by matter, or be absorbed by matter.
2. Dark-colored objects absorb more light and reflect less light than light-colored objects do.

New vocabulary: image, ray, incident ray, reflected ray, angle of incidence, normal, angle of reflection, virtual image, real image

Silver, aluminum, and other metals have smooth, shiny surfaces. Mirrors are made by coating a piece of glass with silver or aluminum. Light that strikes the glass is transmitted through the glass but is reflected by the metal coating.

If you hit a tennis ball toward a wall at an angle, the ball will not come straight back to you. It will bounce off the wall and move away from you. It acts very much like light that strikes a mirror.

A narrow beam of light is used in studying the path of light that strikes a mirror. Black paper with a narrow slit can be put over the front end of a flashlight. A narrow beam of light comes through this slit. Look at Figure 9-3. The beam is aimed toward the mirror at the point where it touches the line on the paper. The beam lights up the paper along its path. Look at the angle between the line and the path of the beam after it is reflected from the mirror. How does this angle compare to the angle between the line and the original path of the beam?

In drawings the path of a very narrow beam of light is shown as a line called a **ray.** Light rays are drawn with arrows that show in which direction the light is moving. The path of light moving towards something is called an **incident** (IN′-sid-ent) **ray.** The path of light after it has been reflected from a surface is called a **reflected ray.**

Main Idea

What is the difference between an incident ray and a reflected ray?

Figure 9-3. *A narrow beam of light is reflected from a mirror, exhibiting the law of reflection.*

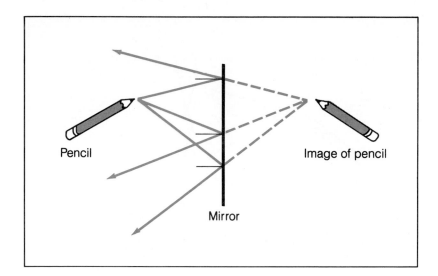

Figure 9-4. *Reflection of light from a pencil tip by a flat mirror. The reflected rays all appear to come from the same point behind the mirror. The mirror image of the pencil tip is at this point.*

The angle between an incident light ray and a line drawn perpendicular to the reflecting surface is called the **angle of incidence.** This angle is labeled "i" in Figure 9-3. The perpendicular line is called a **normal.** The angle between a reflected light ray and the normal to the reflecting surface is called the **angle of reflection.** This angle is labeled "r" in Figure 9-3. When a light ray is reflected, the angle of reflection is equal to the angle of incidence. This is the law of reflection.

angle of reflection = angle of incidence

Figure 9-4 shows light rays that start at the end of a pencil. The pencil is to the left of a mirror. The mirror is shown as a heavy black line, as if you were looking down on its upper edge. Three incident rays, which hit the mirror at different angles, are shown. For each incident ray, there is a reflected ray. The dotted lines extend the reflected rays backwards, to the right of the mirror. Notice that the dotted lines all meet at one point. The reflected rays *seem* to start from this point, in back of the mirror. This point is where the image of the end of the pencil is located.

The image formed by a flat mirror always seems to be behind the mirror. However, light from the object does not really travel behind the mirror. The image from a flat mirror is called a **virtual** (VERCH′-uh-wul) **image.** A virtual image cannot be projected on a screen because light from the object does not really meet there. It only appears to.

Suppose the mirror is replaced by a white concrete wall. The surface of the wall is rough, not smooth. It reflects light

Main Idea

What is the law of reflection?

Figure 9-5. *Reflection of light from a pencil tip by a concrete wall. The reflected rays do not appear to come from a single point behind the wall. No image is formed.*

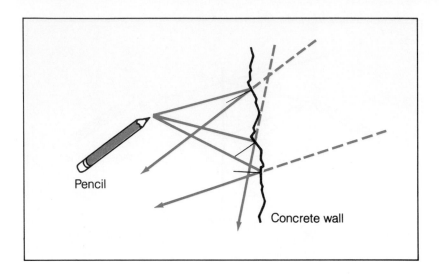

like many mirrors, all at different angles. Look at Figure 9-5. The reflected light does not all seem to come from the same point beyond the wall. No image is formed.

Curved, as well as flat, smooth surfaces reflect images. You have seen images reflected from chrome bumpers, shiny metal pans, and the surface of sunglasses.

Surfaces that curve outward in the center, like the back side of a spoon, are said to be *convex*. Convex mirrors are used in stores. They help clerks watch a large area of the store at once. A convex mirror reflects beams of light in a way that causes them to spread out. See Figure 9-6. The image is a virtual image that is smaller than the original object.

Surfaces that curve inward in the center, like the bowl of a spoon, are called *concave*. Concave mirrors are used as shaving or makeup mirrors. When you hold one close to your face, you see an enlarged image. See Figure 9-7. A curi-

Critical Thinking

What are some practical ways in which convex and concave mirrors are used?

Convex mirrors are used in stores to observe a large area at one time. Concave mirrors are used as shaving or makeup mirrors to enlarge areas seen close up.

Main Idea

How does a convex surface differ from a concave surface?

Figure 9-6. *A convex mirror, like the ones used in stores, produces smaller images that appear to be behind the mirror.*

400   *Chapter 9*   **Light**

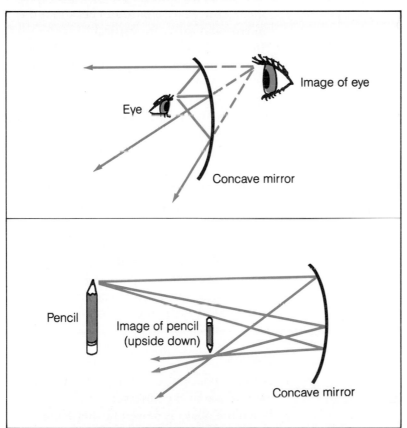

ous thing happens if you back away from a concave mirror. When you are more than a certain distance away (depending on the mirror), your image is upside down. The upside-down image can be focused on a small card. It is a **real image;** that is, it is formed by light rays that actually meet in front of the mirror.

Main Idea

What is meant by a real image?

9.1a Mirror Images

Science processes: Observing, inferring, formulating hypotheses

Materials BASIC 20 minutes Groups of 2 or 3

- sheet of lined paper
- lined index card
- scissors
- small, plane mirror
- modeling clay

Purpose

To determine how the image distance is related to the object distance for a plane mirror.

Procedure

1. Darken the center line on a sheet of lined paper. Number the other lines downward and upward to show how far each line is from the darkened center line.
2. Trim an index card along the top and bottom lines. Cut the wider trimming in half crosswise. Fold each piece in half to form two V's. Save the V's for Step 5.
3. If the card has an even number of ruled spaces, cut it in half lengthwise along the center line. If not, first trim off one space and then cut the card in half.

Step 5

4. At one end of each piece of index card, cut two 1-cm-long slits along the lines next to each edge.
5. Fit the V's you made in Step 2 into the slits of each card so that the cards stand upright.
6. Place a piece of modeling clay at the center of the darkened line on the paper. Stand the mirror upright in the clay so that the reflecting surface is on the line.
7. Place one card behind and the other card in front of the mirror, with the lines toward the mirror. Have a partner check that the mirror and cards are vertical.
8. Bend down and look straight into the mirror as your partner aligns the rear card along a numbered line. You should see the top of this card over the mirror.
9. Move the front card until its image in the mirror is the same width as the top of the rear card. The lines on the image of the front card should line up with the lines on the rear card.
10. Record the positions of the front and rear cards in terms of the numbered lines. Repeat the measurement for two other positions of the rear card.
11. Back away from the mirror. Check to see if the image and the rear card remain the same size as each other as you move.

Questions

1. Does the position of an image depend on the position of the observer?
2. When the object is moved farther from the mirror, what happens to the position of the image?

Conclusion

How is the position of an image related to the position of the object whose image it is?

Quick Review

1. Where does the image formed by a plane mirror seem to be?
2. Suppose a ray of light strikes a plane mirror at an incident angle of 20° and is reflected. What will the angle of reflection be? Through what angle is the light ray turned in this reflection?
3. Suppose the angle between an incident light ray and the plane mirror it strikes is 50°. What is the angle of incidence? What will the angle of reflection be? Through what angle is the light ray turned in this reflection?
4. How can an image form in front of a mirror?

Refraction and lenses

New vocabulary: refraction, convex lens, focal length, concave lens

You have probably noticed that a straw or spoon in a glass of water seems to be broken in two at the water line. Another strange effect of water on light can be seen if you place a coin in the bottom of an empty opaque cup. Slowly back away until the coin is just cut off from view by the top of the cup. Have someone carefully add water to the cup without disturbing the coin. As the water level in the cup rises, the coin will reappear even though it has not moved!

Light travels in a straight line as long as it is moving through one substance (or empty space). When it passes from one substance to another—as from water to air—it changes direction.

The light that reaches your eye from the coin follows a different path when water is in the cup. The path bends where the light leaves the water.

Figure 9-8. *A coin that is blocked from view by the top of an empty cup can be seen when water is added to the cup. How is this possible?*

Reflection is the bouncing of light off a surface. Refraction is the bending of light as the light moves from one substance into another.

Main Idea

What is meant by the focal length of a lens?

Its path bends. The bending of light as it moves from one substance to another is called **refraction** (ree-FRAK′-shun).

The amount of refraction depends on the two substances. Light is refracted more when it passes from air to glass than when it passes from air to water. The path of the light does not depend on the direction in which the light travels. It is the same whether the light is moving *from* air or *into* air. For example, suppose a gull in the air and a fish in the water are watching each other. The gull sees the fish with light that moves from water to air. The fish sees the gull with light that moves along the same path in the reverse direction.

Curved, transparent objects known as *lenses* (LENZ′-uz) form images through refraction of light. Magnifying glasses, cameras, and binoculars all contain lenses. Lenses are usually made of glass or plastic.

A lens that is thicker in the middle than at the edge is called a **convex lens.** A convex lens makes parallel rays of light come together at one point. The distance between this point and the center of the lens is called the **focal** (FŌ-kul) **length** of the lens.

Figure 9-9. *The focal length of a convex lens (top) and a concave lens (bottom).*

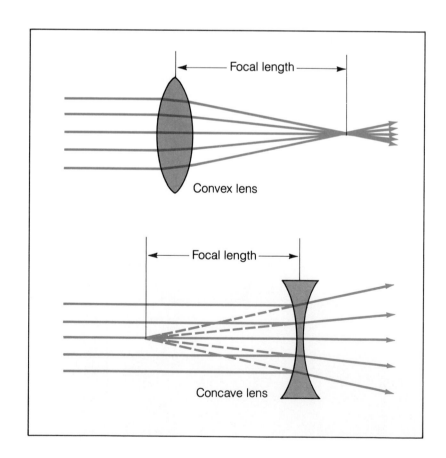

Focal length

Convex lens

Focal length

Concave lens

Slide projectors contain convex lenses. The lens produces an image of the slide on a screen. The image can be seen without looking through the lens. The image is real, not virtual.

A convex lens can be used as a magnifying glass. When it is held *close* to an object, an enlarged image is seen. The image is on the same side of the lens as the object and is a virtual image. In order to see a virtual image, you must look through the lens.

A lens that is thinner in the middle than at the edge is called a **concave lens.** A concave lens makes parallel rays of light spread out as if they were coming from a single point. The distance between this point and the center of the lens is the focal length of the lens. Whether the object is close to or far from a concave lens, the image is always virtual. It is also closer to the lens and smaller than the object. The position and size of the image formed by a convex lens can be precisely determined on the basis of two equations. The first equation is:

$$\frac{1}{d_o} + \frac{1}{d_i} = \frac{1}{f}$$

d_o is the distance between the object and the center of the lens, f is the focal length of the lens, and d_i is the distance between the image and the center of the lens.

Additional information:
An image that can be focused on a screen is a real image.

Main Idea

What is a concave lens?

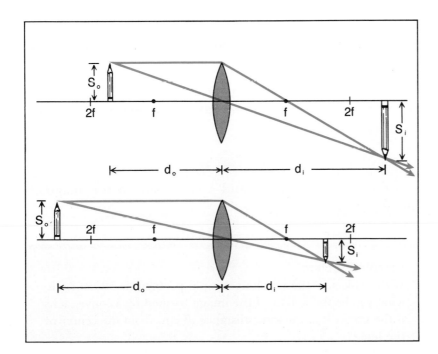

Figure 9-10. *These ray diagrams show how the nature of an image formed by a convex lens depends on the distance between the object and the lens. In the top diagram, the object is at a distance between f and 2f from the lens. The image is real, inverted, and larger than the object. In the bottom diagram, the object is at a distance greater than 2f from the lens. The image formed is real, inverted, and smaller than the object. In both diagrams, s_o stands for the size of the object and s_i for the size of the image.*

Sample Problem

Suppose the focal length of a convex lens is 5 cm. If an object is placed at a distance 8 cm from the center of the lens, at what distance from the center of the lens will the image of the object be brought to a focus?

Solution

$$\frac{1}{d_o} + \frac{1}{d_i} = \frac{1}{f}$$

$$d_o = 8 \text{ cm} \quad f = 5 \text{ cm} \quad d_i = ?$$

$$\frac{1}{8 \text{ cm}} + \frac{1}{d_i} = \frac{1}{5 \text{ cm}}$$

$$\frac{5}{40 \text{ cm}} + \frac{1}{d_i} = \frac{8}{40 \text{ cm}}$$

$$\frac{1}{d_i} = \frac{8}{40 \text{ cm}} - \frac{5}{40 \text{ cm}}$$

$$\frac{1}{d_i} = \frac{3}{40 \text{ cm}}$$

$$d_i = \frac{40 \text{ cm}}{3} = 13\frac{1}{3} \text{ cm}$$

Practice Problem

Suppose the focal length of a convex lens is 8 cm and an object is placed at a distance 10 cm from the center of the lens. At what distance from the center of the lens will the image of the object be brought to a focus? *Answer:* 40 cm

Once the position of the image has been established, the size of the image can be determined by using the following equation:

$$\frac{d_o}{d_i} = \frac{s_o}{s_i}$$

s_o is the size of the object and s_i is the size of the image of the object.

Sample Problem

If the object in the previous sample problem is 50 cm high, what will be the height of the image formed by a convex lens if the object is at the same distance (8 cm) from the center of the lens?

Solution

$$\frac{d_o}{d_i} = \frac{s_o}{s_i}$$

$$d_o = 8 \text{ cm} \quad d_i = \frac{40 \text{ cm}}{3} \quad s_o = 50 \text{ cm} \quad s_i = \,?$$

$$\frac{8 \text{ cm}}{40 \text{ cm}/3} = \frac{50 \text{ cm}}{s_i}$$

$$\frac{24 \ \cancel{\text{cm}}}{40 \ \cancel{\text{cm}}} = \frac{50 \text{ cm}}{s_i}$$

$$\frac{24}{40 \times 50 \text{ cm}} = \frac{1}{s_i}$$

$$\frac{1}{s_i} = \frac{24}{2000 \text{ cm}}$$

$$s_i = \frac{2000 \text{ cm}}{24} = 83\frac{1}{3} \text{ cm}$$

Practice Problem

If an object 10-cm high is placed 15 cm from the center of a convex lens and the image of the object is located 30 cm from the center of the lens, what will be the height of the image of the object? *Answer:* 20 cm

---

The following general statements can be made about the images formed by convex lenses: (1) If the object is farther than $2f$ away from the lens then the image formed is smaller than the object, is inverted, and is brought to a focus at a distance between f and $2f$. (2) If the object is between f and $2f$ then the image is larger than the object, inverted, and brought to a focus at a distance beyond f. (3) If the object is within the distance f then the image is rightside up and bigger than the object. In this case, the image is virtual, not real. Note that these general statements are consistent with the equations just presented and with the ray diagrams provided in Figure 9-10.

Research Topic

Read about telescopes and write a report about them. Include a description of the difference between refracting and reflecting telescopes. Explain why the largest telescopes are reflecting telescopes.

Quick Review

1. What type of lens can form a real image of an object?
2. Does the amount of refraction change when light moves from glass to air, rather than from air to glass?
3. What happens to parallel rays of light that pass through a convex lens?

Quick Review answers:
1. A convex lens forms a real image if the object is not too close to the lens.
2. No. The amount of refraction is the same.
3. They are focused at a point.

See also Activity Record Sheet 9-1B (Lab Manual page 122) Answers to Questions and Conclusions appear on page T131 in the front of this book.

9.1b Bending of Light

Science processes: Observing, inferring

Materials 15 minutes Groups of 4
- transparent rectangular container at least 4 cm deep
- water
- cardboard at least 10 cm longer and wider than container
- 4 pins
- ruler
- protractor

Purpose

To measure the way light bends as it moves from one substance to another.

Procedure

1. Place water in a transparent rectangular container to a depth of at least 3 cm.
2. Mark the outline of the container on the cardboard.
3. Place a pin in the cardboard behind the container. The pin should be as close to the container as possible.
4. Place a second pin 4 to 5 cm behind the first. The two pins should form a line that forms an angle of less than 45° with the side of the container.
5. Lean over so that you are viewing the pins through the water in the container. Place a third pin close to the front of the container. This pin should appear to line up with the pins behind the container.
6. Place a fourth pin 4 to 5 cm in front of the third pin so that it lines up with the other pins. Readjust the position of any of the pins so that they all appear to be in line when you look along the pins through the water in the container.
7. Carefully remove the container of water, leaving the pins in their positions.
8. Use a ruler to draw a line connecting the positions of the two pins that were behind the container. Repeat this procedure for the two pins that were in front of the container.

9. Draw a third line connecting the two lines already drawn. These three lines represent the path the light followed to your eye.
10. With a protractor, measure the angle between the side of the container and the line connecting the two pins that were behind the container.
11. Repeat Step 10 for the line connecting the two pins that were in front of the container.

Questions

1. Did the light bend toward or away from the side of the container as it entered the water?
2. Did the light bend toward or away from the side of the container as it left the water?
3. Were the angles measured in Steps 10 and 11 equal?
4. How did the direction of the light entering the water compare to the direction of the light leaving?

Conclusion

Did the light bend the same way as it went from water to air as when it went from air to water? Explain.

Step 4

Refraction in the human eye

Light that enters the human eye is refracted so that real images form on the *retina* (RET'-ih-nuh) at the back of the eye. The retina contains nerve cells sensitive to light. Messages about the images are carried to the brain by a nerve attached to the retina.

The front of the eye is covered by tough, transparent tissue called the *cornea* (KOR'-nee-uh). Light is refracted as it passes through the cornea. In a person with perfect eyesight, the cornea forms images of distant objects on the retina.

The colored part of the eye is called the *iris* (Ī'-ris). In the center of the iris is an opening, called the *pupil*, which appears black. The pupil can change size, and this affects how much light can enter the eye. Would you expect a person's pupils to be larger in bright sunlight or in a dim room?

Just behind the pupil is a sac of jelly known as the *lens.* Muscles attached to the lens can cause it to thicken when a person is looking at nearby objects. Refraction of light by the thickened lens allows images of nearby objects to form on the retina. The thickening changes the focal length of the cornea and lens combination.

Main Idea

What is the cornea, and what is its function?

The pupils would be larger in a dim room than in bright sunlight.

Figure 9-11. *Light passes through the cornea, pupil, and lens before reaching the retina. What role does each of these four parts of the eye play in allowing a person to see?*

These four parts of the eye play the following roles:
- Cornea: refracts light to focus it on the retina
- Pupil: changes size to control amount of light entering eye
- Lens: thickens to focus nearby objects on the retina
- Retina: contains nerve cells sensitive to light, sends messages about images to the brain

Figure 9-12. *If the eyeball is too long, images form in front of the retina (nearsightedness). If the eyeball is too short, images form behind the retina (farsightedness). What shape lens can correct each problem?* Nearsightedness is corrected by a concave lens. Farsightedness is corrected by a convex lens.

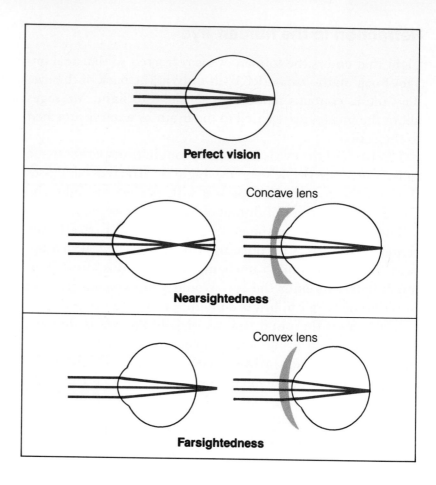

Perfect vision

Concave lens

Nearsightedness

Convex lens

Farsightedness

Persons who are *nearsighted* have eyeballs that are too long. See Figure 9.12. Images of distant objects form in front of the retina. Persons who are *farsighted* have eyeballs that are too short. Images of distant objects form behind the retina. Eyeglasses or contact lenses can correct a person's vision so that the images form right on the retina.

Quick Review

1. What two parts of the eye refract light and form images on the retina?
2. What happens to the lens of the eye when a person is looking at nearby objects?

The speed of light and the index of refraction
New vocabulary: index of refraction

How fast does light travel? Light seems to take no time at all to get from one point to another. It is now known that it does take some time for light to travel. Light travels so fast, however, that it is difficult to measure the time unless the distance is very great.

Light travels fastest in empty space. Its speed in empty space is about 300 000 000 m/s ($= 3 \times 10^8$ m/s). It moves very slightly slower in gases, such as air. In liquids and transparent solids, the change in speed is more marked. Even so, the speed is always very great.

Light travels so fast that its speed is difficult to comprehend. A beam of light could travel more than seven times the distance around the equator in one second. It takes only a little over a second for light to travel from the moon to the earth. Light from the sun reaches the earth in just over eight minutes.

The speed of sound in air is about 300 m/s. The speed of light is about one million times the speed of sound. Can you explain why you see lightning before you hear the thunder that accompanies it?

When light passes from air into water or glass, it slows down. At the same time, it changes direction. The reason for the change in direction can be explained by the following analogy. Suppose there is a piece of carpet in the center of a linoleum floor. You wheel a stroller on its two rear wheels across the linoleum toward the carpet. There is more friction when you reach the carpet, and the wheels slow down. If you cross the carpet at an angle, one wheel rolls onto the carpet before the other. The wheel on the carpet moves more slowly than the one on the floor. The stroller turns because the wheel remaining on the floor moves in a curve around the wheel on the carpet. For a light beam that crosses from air into water at an angle, air is like the linoleum floor. Water is like the carpet. The light beam is turned just as the stroller wheels are. Light is slowed down more by some substances than by others. Consequently, the degree to which light is bent (or refracted) varies for different substances. Glass slows light down more than water does, for instance, and therefore

Main Idea

Where does light travel fastest?

Critical Thinking

What can cause light to slow down?

Light has different speeds in different kinds of matter. It may be slowed down as it enters a different substance, as for example, when it passes from air into glass.

Table 9-1. *The speed of light in different substances.*

Substance	Speed of light, in millions of m/s	Percent of speed in empty space
Empty space	300	100%
Air	300	99 + %
Water	223	74%
Glass	200	67%
Diamond	124	41%

light entering glass is bent through a larger angle than is light entering water. A diamond slows light down much more than either glass or water, and light entering a dia-

Our Science Heritage

Measuring the Speed of Light

Michelson's eight-sided mirror rotated as light traveled 70 km round trip.

Measuring the speed of a moving object is normally quite easy. The distance traveled by the object during some time interval is determined. Measuring the speed of light, however, presents problems. Light travels so fast that early observers thought it took no time at all for light to get from one place to another.

The first evidence that light had a travel time was found by Olaus Roemer (1633–1710). Roemer was a Danish astronomer who was observing the four large moons of Jupiter. A moon would disappear from view, or be eclipsed, when it moved behind Jupiter. Several days later, as it traveled around the planet, the moon would be eclipsed again. Roemer discovered that the time between eclipses of the same moon was greater during the months when the earth was moving away from Jupiter. He concluded that light from Jupiter's moons was taking longer to reach the earth because the light had farther to travel. He said that it took 22 min for light to

cross the earth's orbit around the sun. (We now know it takes only 16 min.) Another scientist divided his own value for the distance by Roemer's time value. He concluded that light traveled at 200 000 km/s.

In the 1920s, Albert A. Michelson (1852–1931), an American physicist, made a very accurate measurement of the speed of light. He used a rotating eight-sided mirror. One side of the mirror reflected a beam of light to a flat mirror 35 km away. The reflected beam returned to a different side of the eight-sided mirror and was reflected to the observer. The mirror was rotated at a speed so that it would make one-eighth of a revolution while the light traveled the 70-km distance. The rate of revolution of the mirror could be determined. The small interval of time needed for light to travel the 70-km distance could be found from the rate of revolution. Dividing 70 km by this time interval gave the speed of light as just under 300 000 km/s.

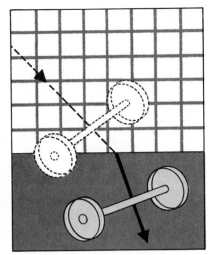

mond is bent through a larger angle than light entering glass or water.

The degree to which a substance slows light down and, therefore, the degree to which that substance bends incident light rays is indicated by a ratio called the **index of refraction.** The index of refraction compares the speed of light in a vacuum with the speed of light in the particular substance.

$$\text{index of refraction} = \frac{\text{speed of light in vacuum}}{\text{speed of light in substance}}$$

The greater the index of refraction of a substance, the greater the degree to which light is slowed down as it moves through the substance and larger is the angle that the light is bent through.

Figure 9-13. *The stroller wheel that reaches the carpet first is slowed down and causes the stroller to turn. How is this like the refraction of light passing from air into water?* The light is slowed down as it strikes the water and, as a result, is bent.

Table 9-2. *Indexes of refraction for different substances.*

Substance	Index of Refraction	Substance	Index of Refraction
Air	1.00	Benzene	1.50
Ice	1.31	Glass, crown	1.52
Water	1.33	Glass, flint	1.63
Ethyl alcohol	1.36	Carbon disulfide	1.63
Quartz	1.46	Zircon	1.92
Glycerin	1.47	Diamond	2.42

Sample Problem

What is the speed of light in heat-resistant glass which has an index of refraction equal to 1.61?

$$\text{index of refraction} = \frac{\text{speed of light in a vacuum}}{\text{speed of light in substance}}$$

index of refraction = 1.61
speed of light in a vacuum = 3×10^8 m/s
speed of light in substance = ?

$$1.61 = \frac{3 \times 10^8 \text{ m/s}}{\text{speed of light in substance}}$$

$$\frac{1.61}{3 \times 10^8 \text{ m/s}} = \frac{1}{\text{speed of light in substance}}$$

$$\frac{3 \times 10^8 \text{ m/s}}{1.61} = \text{speed of light in substance}$$

$$= 1.86 \times 10^8 \text{ m/s}$$

Practice Problem

Calculate the index of refraction for a diamond if the speed of light in this substance is 1.24×10^8 m/s. *Answer:* 2.42

Quick Review answers:
1. The speed of light is about a million times the speed of sound.
2. Parts of the light wave are slowed down before other parts just as in the stroller wheel analogy.

Quick Review

1. How does the speed of light compare with the speed of sound in air?
2. Explain why a light beam is refracted as it passes from air to water.

Total internal reflection

New vocabulary: critical angle, total internal reflection

Light is not always refracted at a boundary between two transparent substances. Sometimes it does not pass through the boundary at all. Consider a waterproof flashlight immersed in a bathtub filled with water. If the flashlight is aimed above a certain angle to the normal to the water-air surface, the light no longer emerges from the water. This special angle is called the **critical angle** for the water-air boundary surface. Light rays meeting the boundary surface at angles above the critical angle exhibit the phenomenon of **total internal reflection**. These light rays are not refracted at the surface, but rather are reflected back at an angle equal to the angle of incidence. See Figure 9-14.

Figure 9-14. *Light shining into fish tank from above reflects from three mirrors in the bottom of the tank. Light, reflecting from two mirrors, bends as it emerges from the water. One beam of light does not emerge from the water. It undergoes total internal reflection at the water-air boundary.*

There are different critical angles for different boundary surfaces. The critical angle for the water-air boundary is approximately 43°, for instance, while the critical angle for the glass-air boundary is 48.5°. The critical angle for the diamond-air boundary is 24.6°, the smallest critical angle for any known substance-air boundary. The small critical angle of a diamond is responsible, in part, for its brilliance. Any light that enters a facet of a cut diamond is likely to be totally internally reflected a number of times before it is refracted out at another facet.

The phenomenon of total internal reflection is made use of in the technology known as *fiber optics*. In this technology, total internal reflection is used to direct light rays through thin glass tubes (See Figure 9-14). Fiber optics has many applications. It has proven useful in communications because light can carry information more efficiently than can electricity and because the glass tubes that carry the light are less expensive and less bulky than the copper wire used for carrying electric current. In medicine, fiber optics technology is used to bring light to areas that were previously difficult or impossible to see without significant surgical exposure. The technique of arthroscopic knee surgery was made possible by the advent of fiber optics technology, for instance.

Main Idea

What phenomenon does fiber optics make use of?

Quick Review

1. What happens to light rays meeting a boundary surface at an angle greater than the critical angle?
2. What modern technology makes use of total internal reflection?

Quick Review answers:
1. They are totally internally reflected.
2. Fiber optics

At a greater distance the light spreads over a greater area and is spread more thinly.

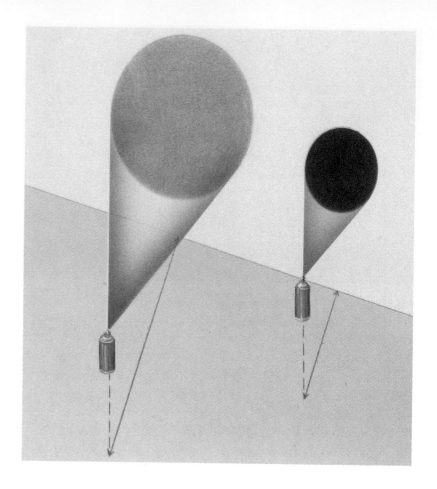

Brightness and distance

New vocabulary: laser, coherent

Imagine that you are in a room lit only by a candle. You find a note on the floor. In order to read the note, you hold it close to the candle. Otherwise, there would not be enough light on the note. The brightness of the light depends on how far you are from the candle.

Light, like sound, spreads out equally in all directions. As it does, the same amount of light spreads over a much greater area. Light acts like paint that is sprayed on a wall. The farther the sprayer is from the wall, the more spread out and thin the coating of paint will be. The farther a surface is from a light source, the dimmer the light is that reaches that surface.

A light meter can be used to measure the change in brightness of light at different distances from the source. Moving twice as far from the source decreases the brightness to, not half, but only one fourth the first brightness. Moving ten times as far away decreases the brightness to only one hun-

Main Idea

How is light like sound?

dredth. Light from a source becomes very much dimmer as you move away from the source.

This spreading phenomenon is typical of light from sources that produce light of many different wavelengths and send it in all directions. Not all light is produced from such sources and not all light exhibits this spreading. Light produced by a **laser,** for instance, can travel great distances with very little spreading. This has to do with the fact that light from a laser is generally of one wavelength, travels in one direction, and is **coherent.** By coherent is meant that the crests of the waves of light all match up with one another and move in the same direction. Lasers produce light of high intensity and laser light can travel over great distances without significant reduction in intensity because of the small amount of spreading.

Because of its special characteristics, laser light has many useful applications. Lasers are used in surveying because laser light can travel in straight lines over great distances with little spreading. Lasers are used in eye surgery because they permit a very intense beam of light to be directed with extreme precision. Lasers are also commonly used in supermarkets to read product codes and record the prices of items at the checkout counter. In compact disc players, laser light is used to read the information encoded on the disc. Note that the word laser is an acronym for **l**ight **a**mplified by the **s**timulated **e**mission of **r**adiation.

Quick Review

1. Suppose you measure the brightness of a light source when you are 50 cm from the source. How far from the source would you expect to find the light only one-fourth as bright?
2. Name three characteristics of the light produced by a laser.

The electromagnetic spectrum

New vocabulary: electromagnetic spectrum

As noted before, the speed of light in a vacuum is 3×10^8 m/s. This speed was already well-known in the 1860s when the great British physicist, James Clerk Maxwell, arrived at a stunning conclusion on the basis of complicated mathematical calculations. Maxwell determined that an electromagnetic wave could be propagated in a vacuum with no gain or loss of energy only if it travelled at a very special speed—3×10^8 m/s— the same speed that had already been determined for light.

Additional information:
In other words, the brightness of light is inversely proportional to the square of the distance from the source. It is said to obey an "inverse square law."

Main Idea

How is laser light characterized?

Quick Review answers:
1. At twice the distance—at 100 cm— from the light source.
2. It is of one wavelength; it travels in one direction; it is coherent.

Frequency in hertz

| 10^{24} | 10^{23} | 10^{22} | 10^{21} | 10^{20} | 10^{19} | 10^{18} | 10^{17} | 10^{16} | 10^{15} | 10^{14} | 10^{13} | 10^{12} | 10^{11} | 10^{10} | 10^{9} | 10^{8} | 10^{7} | 10^{6} | 10^{5} | 10^{4} |

Gamma radiation   X-rays   Ultraviolet light   Light   Infrared radiation   Microwaves   Radio waves

Figure 9-16. *The electromagnetic spectrum. Each mark on the frequency scale represents a frequency ten times higher than the mark to its right. The small numbers after the 10s tell how many zeros are in the number. For example, 10^8 is 1 followed by eight zeros (100 million).*

Main Idea

What are the characteristics of electromagnetic radiation?

Data Search

When and to whom was a Nobel prize in physics awarded for using radiotelescopes to probe outer space? Search pages 658–661.

Martin Ryle of England won the Nobel prize in 1974.

Maxwell's result suggested that light itself might be an electromagnetic wave. It further suggested that there might be an infinite variety of invisible electromagnetic waves all travelling at 3×10^8 m/s, but varying in their frequency and wavelengths according to the equation for wave speed.

wave speed = wavelength × frequency or wave speed = λf

Studies spurred by Maxwell's results have revealed the existence of previously undreamt of waves. With instruments sensitive to different frequencies, scientists have been able to detect many kinds of energy similar to light. All of this energy moves as transverse waves. It all moves at the same speed as light. It can all move through empty space. The general name for energy with these properties is *electromagnetic* (ih-lek'-trō-mag-NET'-ik) *radiation*. The name comes from the fact that this radiation has electric and magnetic properties.

The **electromagnetic spectrum** is made up of the whole range of electromagnetic radiation from the highest to lowest frequency. Visible light is just one small part of the vast spectrum of electromagnetic waves all travelling at 3×10^8 m/s in a vacuum. Different names are applied to radiation in different frequency ranges.

At the high-frequency end is *gamma radiation*. It was originally discovered in the radiation that comes to the earth from outer space (cosmic radiation). It is used in the treatment of cancer, as it destroys cancer cells more easily than normal cells.

X-rays are just lower than gamma radiation in frequency. X-ray pictures of the teeth and bones are used by dentists and doctors to identify problems.

Microwaves have a lower frequency than infrared. Microwave ovens send microwaves into food. The food absorbs the energy of the microwaves and cooks. Since metal reflects microwaves, metal cooking pans cannot be used. Paper and china dishes transmit microwaves without absorbing the energy. The dishes remain much cooler than the food.

Figure 9-17. *This radio telescope collects low-frequency electromagnetic waves. The waves are focused at the point where the three straight supports meet. The supports hold a feed antenna at that point. The feed antenna can send out radio waves as well as receive them.*

This telescope has been used during space missions and for studying the moon and the upper atmosphere.

The lowest frequency electromagnetic waves are *radio waves.* These are the waves that carry broadcast signals to radios and televisions. Each station broadcasts at its own frequency. When you tune into an FM station at 88.5 megahertz (MHz), your radio is picking up 88.5 million crests per second from the station. AM stations broadcast in the kilohertz (kHz) range. Which broadcast at higher frequencies—AM or FM stations?

Ultraviolet light consists of electromagnetic waves having frequencies just higher than those of visible violet light. Ultraviolet light is invisible to humans, but is visible to bees. Ultraviolet light can expose camera film just as ordinary light does.

Infrared radiation consists of electromagnetic waves having frequencies just lower than those of visible red light. Humans detect infrared radiation not with their eyes, but with their skin, as heat.

Research Topic

Find out the origin of the word *radar.* How are radar waves used? What frequency range do radar waves have?

Main Idea

How does the frequency of ultraviolet light compare to that of visible violet light?

Quick Review

1. Name the three types of electromagnetic radiation that have higher frequencies than visible light.
2. Name the three types of electromagnetic radiation that have lower frequencies than visible light.

Quick Review answers:
1. Ultraviolet light, gamma radiation, and X-rays have higher frequencies than visible light.
2. Infrared radiation, microwaves, and radio waves have lower frequencies than visible light.

Photographer

Photographers find work in many locations. Some work in commercial studios, while others work for newspapers and magazines or for government agencies. Many photographers work freelance, selling their pictures to magazines and other customers. Some colleges and universities employ photographers as teachers. About one-third of all photographers are self-employed.

Artistic and creative skills, along with the ability to meet the public, are requirements for the work of a photographer. Good color vision and manual dexterity are also necessary assets for a person working in this field.

The possibilities for preparing to become a photographer are extremely varied. Some aspiring photographers may work as assistants in on-the-job training for two to three years. Others attend art schools and colleges that offer special programs. Specialized training is needed where photography is to be used in a field such as science or medicine. High school chemistry and physics courses provide good background for the specialized training and for understanding the photographic process.

For further information, write to: Professional Photographers of America, Inc., 1090 Executive Way, Des Plaines, Illinois 60018.

Photographers rely on lenses and light meters in photographing subjects.

Optometrist

Optometrists perform eye examinations. They can prescribe glasses, contact lenses, or other treatment that does not involve drugs or surgery. Many optometrists have their own practice. Some work in partnership with one or more other members of the profession. Others may work in hospitals. Some have a practice for particular groups, such as the elderly.

Many demands are placed on an optometrist. He or she must be able to work with detail and with precision. Problem-solving ability is necessary for success. The capacity to deal effectively with individual patients is required. Maintaining a private practice requires additional business skills.

Preparation for a career as an optometrist is accomplished by completing an accredited four-year program in a college of optometry. A state board examination must be passed before a person may practice optometry. Specialized work in the field usually requires an advanced degree. High school biology and physics courses are good preparation for a career in optometry.

For further information, write to: American Optometric Association, Education and Manpower Division, 243 North Lindbergh Boulevard, St. Louis, Missouri 63141.

The condition of a person's eye can be studied by looking through an instrument like the one shown.

9.1 Section Review

Answers to Understanding the Concepts and solutions to Problems to Solve appear on page T131 in the front of this book. Blackline master test for this section: Section Testsheet 9-1 (TRB page 223)

Vocabulary

2 angle of incidence
3 angle of reflection
5 coherent
8 concave lens
12 convex lens
18 critical angle
1 electromagnetic spectrum
4 focal length
7 image
10 incident ray
11 index of refraction
15 laser
17 law of reflection
6 normal
9 opaque
13 ray
14 real image
16 reflected ray
19 refraction
22 total internal reflection
20 translucent
23 transparent
21 virtual image

Vocabulary Review

Match each term above with the numbered phrase that best describes it.

1. Range of different frequency waves traveling at 3×10^8 m/s in a vacuum
2. Angle between incident ray and normal to reflecting surface
3. Angle between reflected ray and normal to reflecting surface
4. Distance between focal point and center of lens
5. A characteristic of laser light
6. Line drawn perpendicular to a surface
7. A likeness, such as a reflection in a mirror
8. Lens that is thicker in the middle than at the ends
9. Transmits no incident light
10. Representation of path of light striking a surface
11. Indicates degree to which light will be bent when traveling from one substance to another
12. Lens that is thicker at ends than in the middle
13. Line representing path of beam of light
14. Image that can be projected on a screen
15. Form of light that can travel great distances without spreading
16. Representation of path of light "bounced" off a surface
17. Angle of reflection equals angle of incidence
18. Light is totally internally reflected above this angle
19. The bending of light
20. Transmits some incident light
21. Image that cannot be projected on a screen
22. Phenomenon in which light is unable to escape from a transparent substance
23. Transmits a large portion of any incident light

Review Questions

Multiple Choice: Choose the answer that best completes each of the following sentences.

24. When an object is in front of a plane mirror, _?_.
    a. a virtual image is formed in front of the mirror
    b. a virtual image is formed behind the mirror
    c. a real image is formed in front of the mirror
    d. a real image is formed behind the mirror

25. Moving a light source halfway in toward a wall causes the brightness of the light shining on the wall to be _?_.
    a. decreased to half
    b. decreased to one fourth
    c. increased by two
    d. increased by four

26. Fiber optics technology is made possible by the phenomenon of _?_.
    a. diffraction
    b. total internal reflection
    c. refraction
    d. magnification

Understanding the Concepts

27. If you look into a store window on a sunny day, you will see your reflection. How can glass act like a mirror if it is transparent to light?

28. What happens to a stroller when it rolls from a carpet to a linoleum floor at an angle? What behavior of light is like the behavior of the stroller?

29. Explain why metal pans are not used in microwave cooking. What types of pans are used and why do they not get hot?

Problems to Solve

30. Suppose the focal length of a convex lens is 6 cm. If an object is placed 10 cm from the center of the lens, at what distance from the center of the lens will the image of the object be brought to a focus? If the object is 4 cm high, what will the height of the image be?

31. What would the index of refraction be for a substance in which light traveled at a speed of 1.5×10^8 m/s?

For ideas for classroom demonstration and discussion, see Getting Started on page T132 in the front of this book.

9.2 Color

Supplemental materials: Teaching Diagram 9-2 (TRB page 46), Reading Checksheet 9-2 (TRB page 104), Skillsheet 9-2 (TRB page 150), Investigation 9-2 (Lab Manual pages 127–128)

Section Preview

- **White light and colored light**
- **The color spectrum**
- **Color vision**
- **Paints and inks**
- **Why the sky is blue**

Bracketed numbers are Section Review questions correlated to that objective.

Learning Objectives

1. To recognize that an object's color, in most cases, is due to the light reflected by the object. [10, 12, 13, 15]
2. To understand how white light is dispersed into a color spectrum. [5, 6, 7, 9, 11]
3. To explain how the eye "sees" colored objects. [2, 8, 15]
4. To describe how the blue appearances of the sky and water are produced. [14, 17]

Figure 9-18. *Most kinds of matter have color. The color of any substance depends on the light it absorbs and the light it reflects. What do you think that the different bands of color in this desert mean?*
Different substances in the soils.

Data Search

What percentage of solar radiation that strikes a field of green crops is reflected? Search pages 658–661.

5% to 25%

One of the first things you notice when you look at something is its color. You choose clothing for its color as well as its style and fit. You refer to things by their colors—the green book, the blue car, the yellow house on the corner.

White light and colored light

New vocabulary: white light, filter

Most objects reflect light, rather than giving off their own light. The light reflected from an object makes the object appear to have a color. The color depends not only on the object but on the light that strikes the object. Objects look different in bright sunlight and inside stores. They look different under fluorescent lighting and under incandescent lighting (the kind provided by common light bulbs).

In a photo taken under red light, the lightest objects are those that reflect the most red light. When the same objects are photographed under green light, the lightest objects are those that reflect the most green light. The objects that reflect the most red are not the same as the ones that reflect the most green. An object that normally looks red reflects more red light than green light.

Colored light makes objects appear to be either black or the same color as the light. Sunlight, on the other hand, allows all the different colors to be seen. Sunlight is an example of **white light.** Under white light, the different colors are reflected from objects. A red object reflects red light, while a green object reflects green light.

Colored cellophane acts like a filter for colors. Red cellophane, for example, transmits red light but filters out other colors. What would green cellophane do to red light? How would a red strawberry look if you put green cellophane in front of your eye?

Quick Review

1. What color light does a blue object reflect?
2. What color does a green object appear under red light?

Figure 9-19. *These photos were taken with (left) no filter; (center) a green filter; (right) a red filter. How do the tomatoes appear in the three photos?*

With no filter they are bright red. With the green filter, they are dark red. (Some red light gets through the filter.) With the red filter, they are bright red but so are the carrots, squash, bowl, and background.

Green cellophane would filter out red light.

A red strawberry would appear nearly black when looked at through green cellophane.

Quick Review answers:

1. A blue object reflects blue light.
2. Under red light a green object appears nearly black, since there is little green light for it to reflect.

The color spectrum

New vocabulary: disperse, color spectrum, prism

Objects appear colored when they reflect colored light. Since they look colored under white light, white light must contain colors. It is possible to split, or **disperse,** white light into a group of colors called the **color spectrum** (SPEK′-trum). The spectrum is a band of colors starting with red and including orange, yellow, green, blue, and violet.

An easy way to disperse white light into a spectrum is to pass the light through a **prism** (PRIZ′-um). Commonly, prisms are made of solid glass or plastic and have triangular ends. Light is refracted when it enters one side and again when it comes out another side. The colors in white light do not refract equally. Red light bends the least, while violet light bends the most. The colors leave the prism at slightly

Main Idea

What is a prism, and what does it do to white light? Which color in white light is bent the most in passing through a prism?

Main Idea

What is a rainbow?

different angles. They can be seen if a white surface is placed in their path.

A rainbow is a color spectrum that is caused by refraction of sunlight by water drops in the air. For you to see a rainbow, the sun must be behind you, and the air ahead of you must be moist. Each point on the rainbow you see is caused by the interaction of sunlight with a different drop of water. Sometimes only a short length of rainbow is visible. In these cases, there are not any water drops in the right positions to create the missing portions.

You do not have to wait until it rains in order to see a rainbow. On a sunny day, you can make a rainbow with the spray from a garden hose. Direct the spray into the air, away from the sun, and look for the rainbow. Try this in the early morning or late afternoon, when the sun is low in the sky.

If white light can be split into colors, can colored light be mixed to make white light? Look at Figure 9-21. Three projectors are throwing light on the same area of a screen. One has a red filter, so it projects red light. The other two project green and blue light by means of green and blue filters. The projectors can be moved closer or farther to adjust the brightness of each beam on the screen. Projector positions can be found that will produce a spot of white where the red, green, and blue beams come together.

Figure 9-21. *Beams of red light, green light, and blue light can produce white light where they come together.*

Quick Review

1. Name two ways in which light can be split into a band of colors

2. How can beams of blue, red, and green light be used to make white light?

Seeing color

New vocabulary: cone, colorblind, rod

Light that enters the human eye is absorbed by the retina, at the back of the eye. The cells in the retina which are sensitive to color are the **cones.** The cones are closest together near the center of the retina. Thus, the center is most sensitive to color.

There are materials in the cones sensitive to red, green, or blue light. Each one contains only one kind of this material. Thus, some cones absorb red light, some absorb green light, and some absorb blue light.

When a mixture of light of different colors enters our eyes, we see the mixture as a single color. For example, a mixture of red light and blue light looks purple. In contrast, we can hear two distinct notes played on a piano at the same time. If our sight were like our hearing, we would see the red and blue, not the purple. We would not need to use a prism in order to see the colors in white light.

Quick Review answers:
1. Light can be split into a band of colors by using a prism and with tiny drops of water (as in a rainbow).
2. Blue, red, and green light can be combined to form white light by overlapping the three colored lights on a screen.

Research Topic

During the late nineteenth century, a style of painting known as impressionism developed among artists in France. Find out how the impressionist painters used color differently from other artists.

Most colors that we see around us are really mixtures. The cones in the retina respond to the red, green, and blue in the mixture. The brain interprets the cones' response as a single color.

About 8 percent of males and 1.5 percent of females have trouble telling red from green. They are said to be **colorblind.** Their condition seems to be due to a lack of either red-absorbing or green-absorbing material in the cones. A few people lack the blue-absorbing material and have a different kind of colorblindness.

The retina also contains **rods,** cells which are very sensitive to low levels of light but not to color. In dim light, you use your rods to see. You can see light and dark but you cannot see color. Almost all the objects in the night sky appear colorless to the eye, even through telescopes, because the eye receives so little light from them. Yet, when they are photographed through telescopes and exposed to color film for a long time, beautiful colors can be seen.

The cones are more sensitive than the rods to detail. That is why you see most clearly out of the center of your eyes. But the rods are very quick to detect motion. You can notice something moving out of the side of your eye even if you cannot tell what it is or what color it is.

Although humans can see color, most mammals cannot. The only other mammals whose eyes can distinguish color are the apes, monkeys, and other primates.

Bees, butterflies, fish, reptiles, and birds can see color. Bees do not see the same range of colors that humans do. They cannot see red. However, they can see *ultraviolet* (UL′-truh-vī-uh-let), which is light beyond violet. The ultraviolet in the sun's radiation is what burns our skin. Bees can see ultraviolet as it is reflected from patterns in some flowers.

Why do bees visit red roses if they cannot see red? Most red flowers reflect blue light as well as red. The bees see the blue. There are a few red flowers that do not reflect blue or even ultraviolet. These flowers would look black to a bee, just like a dark shadow. The bees do not visit these flowers, but hummingbirds, which do see red, visit them.

The color patterns of butterflies, fish, reptiles, and birds enable them to find their own kind. Some animals have colors that make them blend with their background. Such colors protect them from their enemies. The viceroy butterfly is protected by the fact that it looks like the monarch butterfly.

Research Topic

When you enter a dark movie theater, you probably have trouble seeing the seats at first. After a while, your eyes adjust to the darkness and you can see much better. Find out what happens inside your eyes that allows them to adjust to darkness.

Main Idea

What is ultraviolet, and what effect does it have on humans?

Figure 9-22. *The color of flowers enables bees to find flowers.*

The monarch tastes unpleasant to birds, but the viceroy does not. Birds learn to avoid anything with that color pattern.

Quick Review

1. What are cone cells, but not rod cells, sensitive to?
2. How does a bee's ability to see color differ from a human's?
3. Name two ways body color can be helpful to an animal.

Paints and inks

Because of the way the human eye sees color, color pictures can be printed in books with only four colors of ink. All the pictures in this book are printed in tiny dots of these four ink colors. One ink color is a purple-pink known as magenta. Magenta ink absorbs green light but reflects other colors. One ink color is a yellow that absorbs blue light but reflects other colors. One ink color is a blue-green known as cyan. Cyan ink absorbs red light but reflects other colors. The fourth ink color is black, which absorbs all colors.

When the ink colors overlap, more than one color is absorbed. The light that is reflected combines to look different from either ink color. For example, the overlap of magenta and cyan absorbs both green and red. The result looks blue-purple. Figure 9-23 shows how magenta, cyan, and yellow look when they overlap. All three together produce a brownish black. Black ink is used when a purer black is desired.

Cyan and yellow ink produce green; yellow and magenta ink produce red-orange.

Figure 9-23. *The dots of colored ink in printed pictures look like these under magnification. What combination of the four ink colors produces green? Red-orange?*

9.2a Using Colored Light and Combining Colors

Science processes: Measuring, inferring

Materials   BASIC 30 minutes   Group of 4 or teacher demonstration

- **3 flashlights or slide projectors**
- **construction paper of all the following colors: white, black, red, green, blue**
- **cellophane or filters of the following colors: red, green, blue**
- **transparent tape**
- **white screen or wall**

Purposes

PART 1 To see how colored light affects the color of colored objects.

PART 2 To see what colors are produced when different colors of light are combined.

Procedure

PART 1

1. In large lettering, write the name of the color of each piece of construction paper on the paper itself. Overlap the red, green, and blue pieces of paper.
2. Place the white and black pieces on either side of the colored papers as they are in the photograph.

Step 2

3. Tape red cellophane over the front of a flashlight. Carry out the rest of this activity in a darkened room.
4. For each color of paper, record the color the paper appears to be under red light. Record whether each piece of colored paper looks more like the white or the black paper.
5. Replace the red cellophane with green cellophane. Repeat Step 4 using the green cellophane.
6. Repeat Step 4 using blue cellophane.

PART 2

7. Cover the front of each of three flashlights, or the lens of each of three projectors with cellophane or a filter of a different color. Tape the cellophane or filters in place.
8. Direct the three colored beams of light to the same spot on a white wall or screen. Observe the color of the spot where all three beams overlap. If the spot seems reddish, move the red light source farther back. If the spot seems greenish or bluish, move the light source of that color back.

Questions

1. Does white paper reflect all colors? What about black?
2. Which of the three colors did each piece of colored paper reflect and which did each absorb?
3. Can red, green, and blue light combine to form white light?
4. What color does the screen appear where the blue and green beams overlap? Where the blue and red beams overlap? Where the green and red beams overlap?

Conclusion

Explain how an object illuminated with white light can be a color other than white.

Paints work just a little differently from inks. You may have been taught that you could make all colors from red, yellow, and blue paint. In truth, you can make most, but not all, colors from these three.

Your impression of the color of a surface is affected by more than the colors of light the surface reflects. It is strongly affected by the surrounding background, as well. Look at the purple squares in Figure 9-24. Does one look darker than the other? Which one?

Quick Review

1. What four colors of ink are used in printing colored pictures in books?
2. What affects your impression of the color of a surface besides the colors of light reflected by the surface?

Why the sky is blue

New vocabulary: scatter

On a clear day, the sky is blue. Why does it have a color, when sunlight contains all colors? The atmosphere contains molecules of air and water, as well as tiny dust particles. The molecules and dust particles **scatter** light, or redirect it in all directions. As sunlight passes through the atmosphere, more blue and violet light is scattered than other colors. Thus, much of the blue and violet light reaches our eyes from all directions in the atmosphere. This produces a blue sky. The sun looks yellow, but we are really seeing a mixture of green, yellow, orange, and red light coming from the sun.

Clouds are made of small drops of water. These drops are much bigger than air and water molecules. The drops scatter all colors of sunlight equally. As a result, clouds appear white.

When the sun is very low in the sky, at sunrise or sunset, it looks orange or red. Sunlight must travel through a thicker layer of atmosphere to reach us at these times. The green and yellow light is scattered out, as well as the blue and violet. Only the orange and red light remains.

The sky at sunrise or sunset looks spectacular when there are clouds near (but not in front of) the sun. The orange and red light from the sun is reflected off the clouds. The clouds appear bright orange, pink, and red.

Water, like air, is colorless in small amounts. Deep lakes, however, are a brilliant blue. Water absorbs most colors of sunlight to some extent. The deeper the water, the more sunlight is absorbed. Blue is the last color to be absorbed. In

Figure 9-24. *What differences do you see in the two purple squares? Does the background affect how you see color?*

The purple square on the red background appears darker than the one on the blue background. The background does affect the way you see color.

Encourage students to paint or paste up other examples that illustrate the effect of background on the appearance of a color.

Main Idea

What causes sunlight to be scattered?

Quick Review answers:
1. Magenta, cyan, yellow, and black inks are used in printing colored pictures in books.
2. The background.

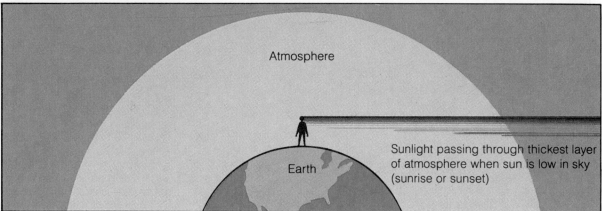

Atmosphere

Earth

Sunlight passing through thickest layer of atmosphere when sun is low in sky (sunrise or sunset)

Figure 9-25. *What makes the sun and clouds look orange and red when the sun is very low in the sky?* The green, yellow, blue, and violet light is scattered out by the atmosphere, leaving only orange and red light.

Quick Review answers:
1. Orange and red light are best able to pass through the atmosphere.
2. Sunlight must travel through a thicker layer of atmosphere at these times. Light other than orange and red is largely scattered out.
3. Drops of water. These drops are larger than the molecules in air and act to scatter all wavelengths equally.
4. The deeper the water, the more light is absorbed. Because blue light is the last color to be absorbed, it tends to remain unabsorbed at greater depths than the other colors.
5. The water can take on the color of the microorganisms or mud.

a deep lake, the blue light that is not absorbed is scattered by the water molecules. Some is scattered upward and can be seen by someone looking at the lake.

When the water is full of microscopic living things or mud, light cannot pass deeply. Water that has these things may take on their color, which is often green or brown.

Quick Review

1. What colors of sunlight are best able to pass through the atmosphere without being scattered?
2. Why does the sky appear orange or red at sunset and sunrise?
3. What are clouds made of? Explain how this is related to the fact that clouds generally appear white.
4. Why are deep lakes commonly observed to be a brilliant blue in color?
5. What effect can the presence of microscopic organisms or mud have on the color of water that is observed?

See also Activity Record Sheet 9-2B (Lab Manual page 126) Answers to Questions and Conclusion appear on page T133 in the front of this book.

Activity

9.2b Benham's Disks

Science processes: Measuring, inferring

Materials 30 to 40 minutes Groups of 2 or 3
- white tagboard, about 15 cm by 15 cm
- small bowl or compass
- scissors
- designs from this page
- ruler
- broad-tip black felt-tip pen
- pencil
- transparent tape
- cap of pen

Purpose

To construct Benham's Disks and observe colors in the spinning black and white disks.

Procedure

1. Use a compass or bowl to make a circle with a diameter between 10 and 13 cm on a piece of white tagboard. Cut out the circle to form a white tagboard disk.
2. Copy the designs shown here on to opposite sides of the tagboard disk. Use a ruler to make the straight lines. Lightly pencil in the blue lines, which are construction lines.
3. Use a black felt-tip pen to fill in the black portions of each design.
4. Poke a sharpened pencil through the center of the disk. Push the disk halfway up on the pencil. Tape the disk to the pencil.

5. Put the point of the pencil inside the cap of a pen.
6. Hold the cap in one hand and gently keep twirling the eraser end of the pencil.
7. Look for colors on both sides of the twirling disk. You may have to adjust the twirling speed before you are able to see colors.
8. Reverse the direction of the twirling and again look for colors. Record any differences in the colors observed for the two directions of spin.

Questions

1. When you watched Design A spin clockwise, what colors did you see on the inner and outer circles? What happened to these colors when the disk was spun in the opposite direction?
2. When you watched Design B spin clockwise, what colors did you see? (List the colors in order moving from the edge to the center.) What happened to these colors when the disk was spun in the opposite direction?

Conclusion

What do you think that Benham's Disks tell us about human perception of color?

Design A

Design B

9.2 Section Review

Answers to Understanding the Concepts appear on page T133 in the front of this book. Blackline master test for this section: Section Testsheet 9-2 (TRB page 224)

Vocabulary

8 colorblind
5 color spectrum
2 cone
6 disperse
3 filter
9 prism
4 rod
1 scatter
7 white light

Vocabulary Review

Match each term above with the numbered phrase that best describes it.

1. Redirect in all directions
2. Color-sensitive cell in retina
3. Device for selective absorption of light
4. Cell in retina that is sensitive to low levels of light
5. Band of colors into which white light can be dispersed
6. To split apart
7. Light containing all colors
8. Unable to see all colors
9. Transparent object designed to disperse white light into colors

Review Questions

10. Objects that produce no light but appear red must ? .
    a. absorb red light
    b. absorb all colors of light equally
    c. reflect or transmit red light
    d. reflect or transmit green and blue light

11. White light is dispersed into color when it enters a prism because ? .
    a. the colors in white light are refracted to different degrees
    b. the colors in white light are reflected in different directions
    c. some colors in white light are scattered more easily than others
    d. the colors in white light speed up by different amounts when they move from air into glass

12. Under blue light, a piece of red paper will appear ? .
    a. red
    b. blue
    c. white
    d. black

13. Besides black, the colors of ink used in printing color pictures are ? .
    a. red, yellow, and blue
    b. red, green, and blue
    c. magenta, yellow, and cyan
    d. magenta, green, and cyan

14. The sky appears blue because the atmosphere ? .
    a. transmits only blue light
    b. absorbs blue and violet light
    c. scatters blue and violet light
    d. scatters all colors of light except blue and violet

Understanding the Concepts

15. In some supermarkets, the lighting over the produce counter is green, and the lighting over the meat counter is red. What effect does this type of lighting have on the appearance of the produce and meat?

16. Clear glass transmits all the colors in sunlight that humans see, but it filters out ultraviolet light. Can you get sunburned through a closed glass window? Explain your answer.

17. To astronauts above the earth's atmosphere, the sky appears black, even when the sun is visible. Explain why this is so.

For ideas for classroom demonstration and discussion, see Getting Started on page T134 in the front of this book.

9.3 Models for Light

Supplemental materials: Teaching Diagram 9-3 (TRB page 47), Reading Checksheet 9-3 (TRB page 105), Skillsheet 9-3 (TRB page 151), Investigation 9-3 (Lab Manual pages 131–132)

Section Preview

- **Light as energy**
- **The wave model**
- **The particle model**

Bracketed numbers are Section Review questions correlated to that objective.

Learning Objectives

1. To recognize that light is a form of energy and travels from place to place. [9]
2. To compare the particle and wave models of light and the properties of light that support each model. [4, 5, 6, 7, 8, 9, 11]
3. To gain an appreciation of the dual, wave-particle nature of light. [12, 13]

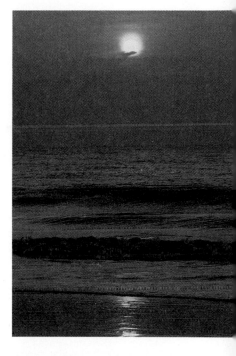

Figure 9-26. *Like light from the sun, ocean waves carry energy long distances from one place to another. Light itself has properties of moving waves. Can you see waves of light with unaided eyes?*
No. You can see the effects caused by the wave properties of light with various devices.

What is light? Is there a model that can explain the behavior of light? The behavior of light can be summarized as follows.

☐ Light travels in straight lines until it comes to a surface.

☐ When light strikes a smooth surface, it is reflected at an equal angle.

☐ When light crosses the boundary between one transparent material and another at an angle, it is refracted; that is, it changes direction.

☐ Sunlight and other white light can be dispersed into several colors.

☐ The colors in sunlight are refracted by different amounts, with red refracted the least and violet the most.

☐ Light can travel through empty space.

Light as energy

In some ways, light is similar to heat. Heat and light are released together in some chemical reactions, including burning. When an electric light bulb is turned on, the wires inside give off both heat and light.

Figure 9-27. *When an electric heating element is turned on, it gives off both heat and light.*

Main Idea

What evidence would support the wave model of light?

Heat is a form of energy. Is there evidence that light, too, is a form of energy? Energy causes changes in things. There are changes that happen only when light is present. Plants need light in order to make food from carbon dioxide and water. They cannot make food in darkness. Light causes a change in photographic film, so that an image is recorded. Sunlight triggers reactions that change some of the products in auto exhausts into poisons.

Light, then, like heat, must be a form of energy. Like heat, it can travel from one place to another.

There are two basic ways energy can travel. Energy can be carried by moving objects. A baseball carries energy from the batter toward the fielder. Energy can also be carried by a wave. When sound moves through air, the air molecules move back and forth but do not move with the wave.

Light, unlike sound, can travel through empty space. Light from the stars—including the closest star, the sun—travels through empty space to the earth. Is the energy of light carried by moving particles? Or is there some kind of wave that can travel through empty space? A model for light must answer these questions.

Quick Review

1. In what two ways can energy travel?
2. Name one difference between the travel of light and the travel of sound?

The wave model

New vocabulary: monochromatic light, polarizing filter, polarized light

As noted in Chapter 8, two of the characteristic properties of water waves are that they can be reflected and refracted. Examples have already been given to demonstrate that light behaves as a wave in that it can be reflected and refracted. Other characteristics of waves, also noted in Chapter 8, are that they can be diffracted (spread out) by passage through small openings and that interference patterns can then be observed. (See Figure 8-14.) If it could be shown that light can also be diffracted and that it exhibits interference patterns, such evidence would be strong support for the wave model of light. In 1800, this evidence was provided by the English scientist, Thomas Young (1773–1829).

In his landmark experiment, Young allowed light of one color (**monochromatic light**) to pass through two pinholes

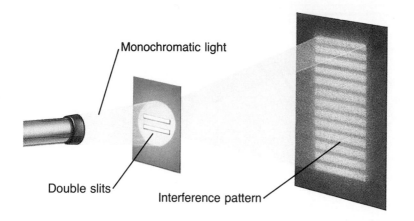

Monochromatic light

Double slits

Interference pattern

Figure 9-28. *When monochromatic light is passed through two closely spaced slits, a striped interference pattern is produced. Note that slits are used here rather than the pinholes used in Young's original experiment. The figure below shows Young's original drawing of the interference effects expected when waves from two pinhole sources, A and B, overlap.*

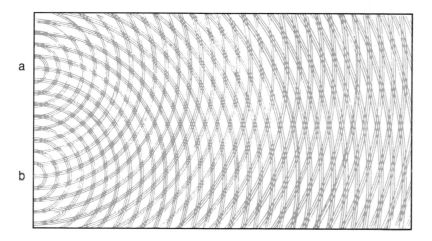

a

b

that were very close together. When the light reached a screen behind the holes, dark lines could be observed within a lighted region (See Figure 9-28.). If either one of the two pinholes was covered, the dark lines disappeared from the lighted region.

Young explained his results by saying that light behaved as a wave. Just as a wave, light was diffracted by passing through the pinholes. And, just as a wave, the diffracted light from each pinhole interfered with the light from the other pinhole. According to Young, the dark lines on the screen represented areas where the waves of light from one pinhole and the waves of light from the other pinhole completely cancelled each other out.

Additional evidence of light behaving as a wave can be observed on city streets after a rain. Have you ever noticed colors glistening from the top of a puddle of water? The colors are produced when there is some oil (or gasoline) on the ground. Oil and gasoline float on water and form a thin layer

Data Search

Who won a Nobel Prize for discovering the layer of the atmosphere that reflects radio short waves? Search pages 658–661.

Sir Edward Appleton (1947)

Figure 9-29. *All or part of a color spectrum can be seen when a thin layer of oil or gasoline floats on water. The colors are caused by the interference of two slightly different reflected light waves—one from the top of the oil and one from the top of the water.*

at the top of the water. The colors are additional evidence that light acts like a wave. They can be explained as follows.

When light strikes the oil surface, some is reflected from the top of the oil layer. Some passes through the oil and is then reflected from the water surface. The oil layer is very thin. The light reflected from the water travels only slightly farther than the light reflected from the oil. Light reflected from the water surface interferes with light reflected from the oil surface. At some places, colors are cancelled out. At other places, colors are reinforced. These are the colors you see when you look at the puddle.

The colors are not all cancelled out at the same place. Some are cancelled where others are reinforced. This observation can be explained by assuming that each color of light in white light has a different wavelength. Red light has the longest wavelength, violet the shortest. Cancellation and reinforcement depend on the wavelength of the wave. They occur at different places for the different colors in white light.

The hypothesis that each color in white light has a different wavelength can explain how a prism makes the colors visible. Recall how water waves are refracted when they slow down. Water waves slow down when they pass into a region where the water is shallower. A tiny change in water depth slows the water only slightly. The direction of the wave changes only slightly. The greater the change in depth, the more the water slows down and the more the wave is refracted.

When light passes from air into glass or water, it slows down. The colors with the shortest wavelengths (violet and blue) happen to be slowed the most. Because they are slowed the most, they are refracted the most. Each color of light is refracted differently and comes out of a prism in a slightly different direction.

Research Topic

Find out what a diffraction grating is. How does it separate white light into a color spectrum?

Main Idea

Why are the colors of light separated by passage through a prism?

See also Activity Record Sheet 9-3A (Lab Manual page 129) answers to Questions and Conclusion appear on page T135 in the front of this book.

Activity

9.3a Diffraction

Science processes: Observing, inferring, formulating hypotheses

Materials   BASIC   20 minutes   Groups of 3

- **diffraction grating, 1 cm²**
- **cardboard tube**
- **masking tape**
- **knife**
- **aluminum foil**
- **source of incandescent light (light bulb)**
- **source of fluorescent light**

Purpose

To observe the diffraction of light through a diffraction grating. To compare the diffraction spectrum produced by an ordinary light bulb with that produced by a fluorescent light.

Procedure

1. Obtain a piece of cardboard tubing similar to the one shown below.
2. Cut two pieces of aluminum foil large enough to cover the ends of the tube.
3. Cut a slit in one piece of foil, using a knife. The slit should resemble the one shown in the figure.
4. In the other piece of foil, cut an opening for the diffraction grating. (The diffraction grating should be 1 cm².)
5. Mount the diffraction grating in the piece of foil.
6. Place the two pieces of foil on the ends of the tube and position the pieces so that the lines in the grating are parallel to the slit.

7. Tape the pieces of foil to the tube.
8. Looking through the diffraction grating end of the tube, observe the light from a lamp. Record your observations.
9. In the same manner, observe light from a fluorescent light source. Record your observations.
10. Remove the diffraction grating from the foil and remount it so that its lines are perpendicular to the slit. Observe both light from the regular bulb and from the fluorescent light source through the repositioned grating. Record your observations.

Questions

1. How does the spectrum of light from a normal light bulb compare with that from a fluorescent light source?
2. What happens when the diffraction grating is repositioned so that its lines are perpendicular to the grating? Explain your observations.

Conclusion

The light from a fluorescent source appears the same as that from a normal light bulb, but the spectra are different. What do the differences in the spectra tell you about the difference between light from a normal light bulb and light from a fluorescent source?

Aluminum foil

Diffraction grating

Slit

Cardboard tube

Masking tape

Figure 9-30. *The picture at the right was shot with a polarizing filter. What effect did the filter have on the reflections?*
The filter practically eliminated the reflections.

The action of **polarizing filters,** such as those used in sunglasses to reduce glare, provides additional evidence of the wave nature of light.

The effect of a polarizing filter on light can be explained in terms of a wave model of light. In this model, light moves as a transverse wave. That is, the vibrations are perpendicular, or crosswise, to the direction of wave motion.

A polarizing filter acts like a picket fence. Think of a long, loose wire spring with its center between two of the pickets in such a fence. You could send a transverse wave all the way down the spring only if you shook the spring up and down. Then the crests and troughs could move through the space in the fence. Suppose you shook the spring from side to side. When the crests and troughs reached the fence, the pickets would not let them pass through. This effect is illustrated in Figure 9-31.

Light seems to move as a transverse wave with vibrations in all directions perpendicular to the direction of motion. A polarizing filter allows vibrations in only one direction. When light goes through the filter, only the vibrations in that direction can pass through. When the light has passed through, it is said to be *polarized.* All its vibrations are in the same direction.

What happens when **polarized light** strikes another polarizing filter? It can go right through if the second filter is aligned in the same direction. If it is crosswise to the original direction, the light will be stopped.

A single polarizing filter has an effect on light reflected from a shiny surface. Reflection partially polarizes light. It makes most of the vibrations parallel to the surface. When

Main Idea

What is polarized light?

Figure 9-31. *A vertical wave can pass through the space between the pickets, but a horizontal wave is stopped.*

the polarizing filter is aligned so that parallel vibrations cannot pass through, the reflected light is stopped. In this way, reflected glare is cut down.

Sound moves as a compressional wave. Its vibrations are back and forth in the direction of wave motion. A compressional wave, such as sound, cannot be polarized.

Quick Review

1. How could the dark lines that appeared in Young's experiment be explained?
2. What happens when polarized light strikes a polarized filter?
3. What evidence supports the model that light is a transverse wave and not a compressional wave?

Quick Review answers:

1. Light waves from the two sources cancelled each other where the crests of one wave met the troughs of the second wave.
2. It will go right through if the filter is aligned in the same direction as that in which the light is polarized; otherwise, it will be stopped.
3. Light can be polarized, and only transverse waves can be polarized.

Activity

See also Activity Record Sheet 9-3B (Lab Manual page 130) Teaching hints and answers to Questions and Conclusion appear on page T135 in the front of this book.

9.3b Polarizing Filters

Science processes: Observing, inferring

Materials   15 minutes   Groups of 3 or 4

- **2 polarizing filters or 2 pairs of polarizing sun glasses**
- **book or magazine with shiny cover**

Purpose

To observe the effect polarizing filters have on light.

Procedure

1. Look at a light source through a single polarizing filter. The light source can be a candle, light fixture, or flashlight.
   SAFETY NOTE: *Do not look at the sun. Looking at the sun, even through a polarizing filter, can cause permanent eye damage.*
2. Rotate the filter. Observe any changes in the brightness of the light source.
3. Place a second polarizing filter in front of the first. Look through both filters as you rotate one of them.
4. Find the position which lets the least light through the filters. Then find the position which lets the most light through the filters.
5. Place a book or magazine with a shiny cover on the desk or table in front of you. Move

your head until the cover appears very shiny. Now look at the cover through a single polarizing filter.

6. Slowly rotate the filter. Find the position for which the shine disappears. Find the position for which the cover appears shiniest.

Questions

1. Was the light from your light source polarized? How do you know?
2. Was the light reflected from the shiny cover polarized? How do you know?
3. Polarizing sunglasses are helpful in cutting the glare from the surface of roads and water. Does it matter whether the filter material is placed in the frames in a particular direction? Explain.

Conclusion

Describe two ways that light can be polarized.

Going further

Line up two polarizing filters so that no light is transmitted through them. Borrow a third polarizing filter from another lab group. Place this third filter between the two other filters. Is there any change in the amount of light transmitted?

Step 4

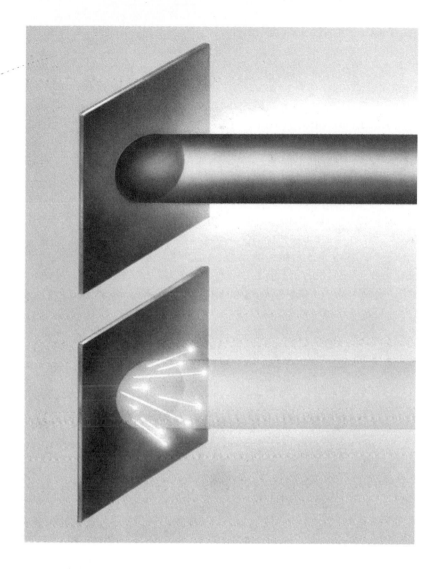

The particle model

New vocabulary: photoelectric effect, photon

The wave model of light can be used to explain much of the behavior of light. But one difficulty remains. It cannot explain what happens when light shines on a metal and electrons are released.

The energy of light causes electrons to be released from the surface of metals. You would expect that if the light were bright enough, it would provide enough energy to release the electrons. In reality, the release of electrons depends on the color of the light. Light at the red end of the color spectrum does not seem to have enough energy to release electrons at all.

The release of electrons due to light is called the **photoelectric effect.** Albert Einstein (1879–1955), the great

Main Idea

What is the photoelectric effect?

German-born American physicist, proposed an explanation for the photoelectric effect in 1905. He said that light acted like a group of energy particles, which are now called **photons** (FŌ′-tonz). The energy of a photon is related to the frequency of the light in the wave model. A photon of violet light has more energy than a photon of red light. The higher the frequency of the light in the wave model, the more energy each photon has in the particle model. The brighter the light, the more photons it has.

Einstein suggested that no electrons could be released from a metal unless the photons each had enough energy to release an electron. The photons at the red end do not have enough energy. Although Einstein's idea was very controversial at the time, it came to be accepted. He was awarded the 1921 Nobel Prize for it, not for his even more controversial theory of relativity.

A photon is different from a particle of matter in one important way. A photon always moves at the speed of light. When it is absorbed by matter, it ceases to exist. A particle of matter can be at rest or it can move at a speed less than that of light.

What about the wave properties of light? Is light really made of energy particles and not waves? This question cannot be answered yes or no.

In science, models are developed to explain observations. The models are based on the behavior of familiar things. Models are never exactly like the thing they are supposed to describe.

Light has both wave and particle properties. A wave model describes light as a wave and not particles. A particle model describes light as particles and not a wave. The problem is with the models we can imagine. We cannot think of anything else that acts like both waves and particles.

Light seems to act like a wave when it is traveling. It seems to act like particles when it is being absorbed by or given off by matter. Light should not be thought of as switching back and forth from particle to wave. Rather, it has the properties of both.

Main Idea

What is the relation between the frequency of light and the energy of the photons?

Research Topic

The smallest particles of matter, namely electrons, have observable wave properties themselves. Read about the experiments of Davisson and Germer in 1927. Report on how they discovered the wave properties of electrons.

Critical Thinking

What is a scientific model?
A scientific model is a description of something unfamiliar in terms of something familiar. It is used to explain observations and as a basis for predictions.

Quick Review answers:
1. The wave model of light could not explain why the release of electrons from metals depended on the color of the light rather than on the brightness of the light striking the metal.
2. A photon of blue light has more energy than a photon of orange light.

Quick Review

1. What fact about the photoelectric effect could not be explained in terms of the wave model of light?
2. Which has more energy—a photon of orange light or a photon of blue light?

9.3 Section Review

Answers to Understanding the Concepts appear on page T135 in the front of this book. Blackline master test for this section: Section Testsheet 9-3 (TRB page 225)

Vocabulary

1 monochromatic light
5 photoelectric effect
4 photon
2 polarizing filters
3 polarized light

Vocabulary Review

Match each term above with the numbered phrase that best describes it.

1. Light of one color
2. Used to reduce glare
3. Light vibrating in only one direction
4. Energy particle moving at speed of light
5. Phenomenon explained by particle theory of light

Review Questions

6. Young's experiment showed that light _?_.
   a. could be polarized
   b. could exhibit interference patterns
   c. was made of photons
   d. traveled through empty space
7. The properties of polarized light are evidence for a model of light as _?_.
   a. particles
   b. compressional waves
   c. transverse waves
   d. the highest frequency radiation in the electromagnetic spectrum
8. A light phenomenon that cannot be explained by the wave theory is _?_.
   a. diffraction
   b. the photoelectric effect
   c. refraction
   d. reflection

9. In Young's experiment, what happened when one of the pinholes was covered?
   a. the number of dark regions increased
   b. the dark regions disappeared completely
   c. the area of the dark regions increased
   d. the area of the dark regions decreased, but dark regions remained
10. Which of the following is not evidence that light is a form of energy?
    a. plants require light to produce food from carbon dioxide and water
    b. light produces changes in photographic film
    c. light converts products in auto exhaust to poisons
    d. light is dispersed by a prism
11. The colors in light that are slowed the most when passing through a glass prism are _?_.
    a. violet and blue (shortest wavelengths)
    b. red and orange (longest wavelengths)
    c. green (intermediate wavelength)
    d. none of the above; all colors are slowed equally
12. After light has passed through a polarizing filter, the vibrations of the light are _?_.
    a. in three different directions
    b. all in the same direction
    c. in all directions
    d. unpredictable
13. According to Einstein's explanation of the photoelectric effect, no electrons can be released from a metal surface unless _?_.

   a. the photons striking the surface have enough energy to release the electrons
   b. some minimum number of photons strike the metal surface
   c. the metal is a transition metal
   d. the photons strike the metal surface at a speed greater than the speed of light
14. Which of the following statements is not true of a photon?
    a. it moves at the speed of light
    b. it ceases to exist when absorbed by matter
    c. it has an energy content that increases with the frequency of the associated light
    d. it is no different from a particle of matter
15. Light has the properties _?_.
    a. only of waves
    b. only of particles
    c. of both waves and particles

Understanding the Concepts

16. Name three ways in which light behaves as a water wave behaves.
17. What do radio waves and light have in common? How are they different?
18. The photon model of light applies to all electromagnetic radiation. How would you expect photons of infrared radiation and ultraviolet light to compare in terms of energy content?
19. Describe the photoelectric effect and explain the problem it posed to scientists trying to understand the nature of light.
20. Explain why light is said to have both wave and particle properties.

9 Chapter Review

Answers appear on page T136 in the front of this book. Blackline master test for this chapter: Chapter Testsheets 9A and 9B (TRB pages 257–258)

Vocabulary

angle of incidence	focal length	photon
angle of reflection	image	polarizing filters
coherent	incident ray	polarized light
colorblind	index of refraction	ray
color spectrum	infrared radiation	real image
concave lens	laser	reflected ray
cone	law of reflection	refraction
convex lens	monochromatic	translucent
critical angle	normal	transparent
disperse	opaque	total internal reflection
electromagnetic spectrum	photoelectric effect	virtual image
filter		

Review of Concepts

Light is energy that can be detected by the eye.

- Matter may be a source of light. It may also transmit, reflect, or absorb light.
- Light is reflected from a mirror or shiny surface at an angle equal to the angle at which the light strikes the surface.
- The path of light bends as light moves from one substance to another. The degree of bending is different for different substances and is indicated by the index of refraction.
- Light travels at extremely high speed—close to 3×10^8 m/s in empty space.
- Light generally appears dimmer as the observer moves away from the source. An exception is laser light.

Electromagnetic radiation is any kind of energy that behaves as light does and travels at the speed of light, but which may have a frequency higher or lower than visible light.

- Electromagnetic radiation includes gamma radiation, X-rays, ultraviolet light, visible light, infrared radiation, microwaves, and radio waves.

White light is a combination of light of all colors.

- The color of an object depends on both the object itself and on the colors of the light striking the object.
- The ability to distinguish among colors of light is limited to humans and only a few other animals.
- White light can be dispersed into colors because different colors are diffracted to different degrees.

The **wave model of light** describes light as energy that travels as a transverse wave.

- The pattern produced when light passes through a tiny double slit is evidence for light as a wave.
- The polarization of light is evidence for light as a transverse wave.

- The colors of light can be explained by the hypothesis that each color in white light has a different wavelength and, therefore, a different frequency.

The **particle model of light** is the theory that light consists of energy particles called photons.

- The photoelectric effect is evidence for light as particles.
- The colors of light can be explained by the hypothesis that each color corresponds to photons of a different energy.
- Neither the wave model alone, nor the particle model alone, can explain all the known behaviors of light.

Critical Thinking

1. Is it always true that light travels in straight lines? Explain.
2. Explain why it would be incorrect to assume that the brighter a star appears in the sky, the closer it is to the earth.

3. Why might it be wise to examine clothing or other colored goods you plan to buy under different lighting than that present in the store?

4. How might you arrange polarizing filters in headlights and windshields of automobiles to reduce the glare of oncoming traffic? Remember, the driver must still see the light from his or her own headlights on the road ahead.

5. To prevent accidents from happening as you walk along a road at night, it is recommended that you wear something white so that you are visible to approaching vehicles. Why does this work?

6. Explain how nearsightedness and farsightedness are determined by the length of the eyeball.

7. Most mammals, excluding man and other primates, cannot distinguish color. Describe any survival advantages that might be associated with the ability to distinguish color.

8. If you observe a shadow, you will notice that the edges are always "fuzzy." How can this fuzziness be explained?

9. A science class created models of different molecules to hang from the ceiling in the classroom. What color thread should be used to make the models appear to be floating in the air?

Individual Research

10. Set up two cups as shown in Figure 9-8 on page 403. Put a coin in the bottom of each cup. Put water in one cup and an equal volume of mineral oil in the other. In which cup is light bent more when it travels from the liquid into air?

11. Use a prism to disperse a beam of white light into the colors of the spectrum. Experiment with a second prism to see if the colors can be recombined to form white light. Trace the paths of the colors as they separate and recombine.

12. Bring a book or magazine with colored pictures to a place where the light is very dim. Look at the pictures. Are some colors easier to identify in dim light than others?

13. Conduct a survey among your classmates to determine what feelings are conveyed by different colors. Prepare a short questionnaire that will help organize the responses.

14. Obtain a set of cards used to determine whether or not a person is colorblind. Test your classmates to determine the percentage that are colorblind. How does the percentage compare with the figures given in this textbook?

Bibliography

Branley, Franklin M. *The Electromagnetic Spectrum; Key to the Universe.* New York: Crowell/Harper & Row, 1979.
  Discusses light and the other parts of the electromagnetic spectrum. Describes the theories of the nature of this radiation.

Filson, Brent. *Exploring with Lasers.* New York: Messner, 1984.
  Describes how lasers work in understandable language. Discusses uses of lasers in communications, medicine, art, science, industry, and the military. Explains holography.

Jollands, David (ed.). The Science Universe Series (Vol. 3) *Sun, Light and Color.* New York: Arco, 1984.
  A beautifully illustrated volume that presents information on light, color, and vision in a clear and accurate fashion.

Simon, Hilda. *The Magic of Color.* New York: Lothrop/Morrow, 1981.
  Explains how colored inks are used to print illustrations. Gives examples of colorblindness, magic with color, and color illusions.

Simon, Hilda. *Sight and Seeing: A World of Light and Color.* New York: Philomel, 1983.
  Text and drawings compare the sense of sight in a variety of animals ranging from insect to man.

Focal point

Incisions

Blurred image
Focal point

In a person who is myopic, or nearsighted, the eye focuses light rays at a point in front of the retina. To correct this condition by radial keratotomy, several incisions are made in the cornea. Pressure created by the incisions causes the cornea to flatten. This shortens the distance between the corneal surface and the retina and allows light rays to focus directly on the retina. The eye can now form sharp, clear images.

Better Vision Through Radial Keratotomy

If a person's eyeballs are oval-shaped instead of round, then the light rays entering the eye through the cornea and lens will come together in front of the retina instead of on the retina at the back of the eye. This will result in a blurred image. Normally, this condition, called myopia, or nearsightedness, is easily corrected by placing a concave lens in front of the eye, either in eyeglasses or as a contact lens. The concave lens will refocus the light rays onto the retina, giving a sharp image.

In 1978, an American eye doctor introduced a procedure he had learned in Russia that surgically corrects myopia. In this procedure, called radial keratotomy (RAY'-dee-ul kayr-uh-TAH'-tuh-mee), eight to sixteen cuts are made in the cornea which cause it to flatten out, thereby permanently changing the oval-shaped eyeball into a rounded one. As of May, 1985, 60 000 to 100 000 people had undergone this "pinwheel" surgery.

Approximately 11 million Americans have myopia. Is radial keratotomy a practical solution for them to consider?

PROS

- One would no longer need to wear glasses or contact lenses which can be troublesome in some sports or other activities, and which some people feel can affect their appearance.
- Sixty-six percent of the patients seem to have a complete cure at this point.
- Without the cost of replacing glasses and contact lenses, the cost of the surgery would be offset somewhat.

CONS

- It is an expensive procedure. In 1985, the operation cost $1500 per eye.
- Twenty-five to thirty-three percent of the patients have developed problems such as fluctuating vision, infections of the cornea, glare, and the inability to focus on close items (farsightedness). A minority of these patients have also experienced uncorrectable vision loss.
- Corneas can take up to four or five years to heal, leaving them vulnerable to infections, changes in shape, and changes in vision.

Radial keratotomy seems to have short-term success but does it have long-term safety? Is it just a type of cosmetic surgery or is it a medical solution that will someday be routine? Is the risk of blindness too great or do the benefits outweigh the risks? Would *you* undergo this surgery?

TRENDS IN TECHNOLOGY

Holography and Its Applications

Have you looked at a major credit card lately? Have you had your groceries scanned by computer at the checkout counter? If so, then you have experienced just two of the many uses of the new science of holography.

Although holograms (Greek for "whole message") are best known as three-dimensional images that float in space, as seen on credit cards or in the movies, they are actually no more than a series of lines that bend the light passing through them. To create this series of lines, a laser beam is first split into two beams. One beam is then reflected off the three-dimensional image onto a piece of photographic film while the other beam goes directly to the film. These two beams, traveling as identical waves, cross paths as they reach the film and set up an interference pattern. They create a strong line where the waves reinforce each other or no line where they cancel each other out. This pattern of lines is recorded on the film and when a laser is passed through this developed piece of film, the original image is exactly recreated in three dimensions. The hologram can then undergo a process to make it visible in ordinary light for use on credit cards, book covers, or magazines.

Holography was first invented in 1947 by a Hungarian scientist, Dennis Gabor, who wanted to improve the images from an electron microscope. It wasn't until the development of lasers in the 1960s, however, that holography began to develop as a science. Lasers are necessary because ordinary white light consists of all wavelengths and when there are too many wavelengths interfering, the image becomes blurred. Lasers, on the other hand, have only one wavelength and so they give a sharper interference pattern and thus a sharper image.

The art and science of holography is still in its beginning stages, but already holograms are used to prevent the counterfeiting of credit cards, to speed up the checkout line at the grocery store, and to make three-dimensional models of two-dimensional computer-assisted designs for new cars, buildings, and DNA molecules. New holographic systems are making airplane landings safer and increasing productivity on assembly lines. Future uses may include the linking of holography with X-rays to get three-dimensional views of cells and body parts for better diagnoses. Holography is being developed for long term storage of data.

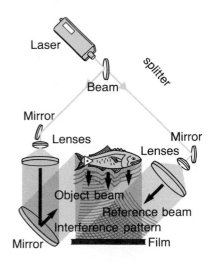

The technology behind making a hologram of a fish is illustrated above. A laser beam is first split into two beams. One beam, the object beam, *is reflected along a series of mirrors and lenses until it reflects off the object of the hologram, the fish. The second beam, the* reference beam, *is not reflected from the object but is directed across the reflected object beam. Where the two beams intersect, an interference pattern is created. This pattern is what is transmitted to the film surface. In this illustration, the colored triangle shows what is happening as a tiny area of the fish is transmitted into part of a hologram. In order to project the completed hologram, light from a laser is passed through the film.*

If this illustration were to try to show how all parts of the fish are transmitted at once into a hologram, the multiple interference patterns would be far too complex to illustrate clearly.

5 Electricity and Electromagnetism

Chapter 10
Electric Charges and Currents

Chapter 11
Electromagnetism

Learning Objectives

■ Process

1. To relate the power rating of an electric appliance to the energy used by the appliance
2. To apply Ohm's Law to electric circuits
3. To infer the need for careful electric safety measures
4. To observe the behavior of magnets and their interaction with magnetic materials
5. To demonstrate the magnetic effect of an electric current
6. To identify sources of electric energy

■ Content

1. To explain the charging of objects by a variety of means
2. To understand the necessary conditions for an electric current to exist
3. To compare the characteristics of series and parallel circuits
4. To interpret the behavior of magnets and their interactions
5. To explain the process used to transfer electric energy over long distances
6. To describe ways in which electric energy is used

Electricity and magnetism are linked together in nature because of the properties of atoms. This electric power substation is a step on the pathway from the machines that produce electricity to its users.

Chapter 10
Electric Charges and Currents

The invisible particles that make up matter have electric charges. We can tell this by some of their effects. Moving electric charges, in the form of electric current, can be harnessed to do work by circuits. At the right you can see the outline of a piece of electronic equipment called an integrated circuit in the middle of a green printed circuit board. Devices such as this are at the heart of computers and other electronic machines that help people to handle information. Electric charges, currents, and circuits are the subject of this chapter.

Projectsheet 10 (TRB page 182) and
Research Lab 10 (Lab Manual pages
147–148) may be used at any point.

For detailed information about teaching this chapter, see Chapter 10 Planning Guide on pages T138–T139 in
the front of this book.

Chapter Preview

10.1 Electric Charges

- **Charging by friction**
- **Electric charges and atoms**
- **Charging by contact**
- **Charging by induction**
- **Lightning**
- **Coulomb's law**

All matter is made of particles that have electric charges. There are two kinds of charge, negative and positive. They may be separated from each other so that an object has more of one kind than the other. Charged objects exert forces on each other.

10.2 Electric Currents

- **Moving charges**
- **Direct and alternating current**
- **Measuring current**
- **Resistance and voltage drop**
- **Electric power**

Moving charges create an electric current. The current flows in a closed path called a circuit. The charges receive energy from a cell or battery in the circuit. They lose energy as they travel through the rest of the circuit.

10.3 Electric Circuits

- **Ohm's law**
- **Series circuits**
- **Parallel circuits**
- **Circuit safety devices**
- **Complex circuits and computers**

The conductors in a circuit may be connected in a row or in separate branches. The current in a circuit depends upon what things are in the circuit and on how they are connected. Safety devices shut off the current when it starts to become too high. Computers and other electronic machines depend on complex circuits.

For ideas for classroom demonstration and discussion, see Getting Started on page T140 in the front of this book.

10.1 Electric Charges

Supplemental materials: Teaching Diagrams 10-1A, 10-1B, 10-1C (TRB pages 48, 49, 50), Reading Checksheet 10-1 (TRB page 106), Skillsheet 10-1 (TRB page 152), Investigation 10-1 (Lab Manual pages 137–138)

Section Preview

- **Charging by friction**
- **Electric charges and atoms**
- **Charging by contact**
- **Charging by induction**
- **Lightning**
- **Coulomb's law**

Bracketed numbers are Section Review questions correlated to that objective.

Learning Objectives

1. To explain the charging of objects by friction.
2. To explain how objects can be charged by contact.
3. To explain how objects are charged by induction.
4. To describe how lightning and thunder occur in clouds.
5. To relate the electric force to kinds of charges, amount of charge, and distance between charges.

Figure 10-1. *Large amounts of electric charge build up on clouds during thunderstorms. Finally, charged particles move off the clouds to the ground, producing flashes of lightning.*

Lightning is discussed on pages 458 to 460 of the text.

Main Idea

What kinds of particles is all matter made of?

All matter is made of particles that have electric charges. The effects of these charges are both familiar and mysterious. For example, a hard rubber comb is run through your hair. Afterward, the comb picks up small pieces of paper. A balloon is rubbed against your sweater. Afterward, the balloon sticks to the wall. A charged balloon can bend a stream of water from the faucet.

Charging by friction

New vocabulary: repel, attract

Some objects can be charged by rubbing. Friction between unlike materials can cause charges to move from one to the other. A balloon and a piece of wool flannel work well. Many other materials can also be used.

The photos in Figure 10-2 show how a balloon interacts with flannel after they are rubbed together. The balloon sticks to the flannel. A second balloon is rubbed with the same flannel. The two balloons now push each other away, or **repel** (ree-PEL′) each other. If you brought the flannel near, but not touching, the two balloons, they would begin to move toward the flannel. The flannel would **attract** the balloons, or pull the balloons toward it.

How can we explain these observations on the basis of charges? We have said that friction between unlike materials causes charges to move from one to the other. Rubbing a balloon with flannel causes charges to move.

What is the effect of these charges on one another? We see that the two balloons repel each other after both are rubbed with flannel. We can deduce that the rubbed balloons have the same kind of charge and that objects with like charges repel. Then, thinking about the balloon and the flannel, we can deduce that they have opposite charges. Objects with opposite charges attract each other.

Quick Review

1. How can charging by friction be explained?
2. How do objects with the same charge affect one another?

Figure 10-2. *When a balloon is rubbed with wool flannel, they stick together. A second balloon is rubbed with the flannel. The balloons push each other away. Explain these observations.*

Friction between objects can leave them oppositely charged. Oppositely charged objects (the balloon and flannel) attract. Objects with like charges (the two balloons) repel.

Quick Review answers:
1. Electric charges that are not moving.
2. It can contain equal numbers of positively and negatively charged particles.

Figure 10-3. *Hair is sometimes attracted toward a comb that has just been run through it. This attraction is due to electric charges.*

The flannel becomes positively charged when negative electrons move it. The balloon becomes negatively charged when it gains electrons.

What is the term for electric charges that are not moving?

Electric charges and atoms

New vocabulary: static charges, static electricity

The effects of electric charges were observed more than 2500 years ago. However, explanations did not develop until about 200 years ago. At first, charge was explained as a fluid. No one knew that matter was made of atoms. It is now known that atoms themselves are made of charged and neutral particles. The charged particles, electrons and protons, are the cause of the effects of electricity that we are familiar with.

Electrons are negatively charged. Protons are positively charged. Matter that has equal numbers of electrons and protons is electrically neutral. Negatively charged matter has more electrons than protons. Positively charged matter has more protons than electrons.

The diagram in Figure 10-4 shows the charges on the balloon and flannel. At first there are equal numbers of protons (+) and electrons (−) on each. Rubbing causes electrons to come off the flannel onto the balloon. After rubbing together, the flannel and the balloon have different static charges. Which object is then positively charged? Which is negatively charged?

Opposite charges attract. An object with a positive charge attracts an object with a negative charge. On the other hand, like charges repel. Two objects with the same charge repel each other.

Electric charges can either be not moving or moving. Electric charges that are not moving are called **static charges.** When we talk about properties of charges that are not moving, we are really talking about **static electricity.** An example of static electricity is a charged comb that will pick up bits of paper after you run it through your hair. After you run the comb through your hair, it is not electrically neutral. It has a

Figure 10-4. *What happens to the positive and negative charges on a balloon and wool flannel after they are rubbed together?*

Some of the negative charges leave the flannel and go to the balloon.

static charge. Later in this chapter we will talk about electric charges that are moving.

Quick Review

1. What are static charges?
2. Explain why matter can be electrically neutral even though it is made up of charged particles.

Quick Review answers:
1. Rubbing causes charges to move from one object to the other.
2. Objects with the same charge repel each other.

Charging by contact

New vocabulary: conductor, insulator

Metals are good **conductors** of electric charge. That is, electrons are able to move through them easily. Other materials, such as glass, wood, hard rubber, and plastic, are good **insulators.** Electrons do not move through them.

Suppose a metal rod is attached to an insulator. A negatively charged object is brought to the metal rod. The object touches the rod. What happens to the charge? Since a negatively charged object has extra electrons, some will move onto the rod. They stay in the rod, because they cannot move through the insulator. The rod is negatively charged.

On the other hand, suppose the object is positively charged. This means it has more protons than electrons. Electrons will move from the rod onto the object. The negative electrons are attracted by the positively charged object. The metal rod now becomes positively charged itself.

Conductors can be charged by contact with a charged object. The charge on the conductor always has the same sign (positive or negative) as the charge on the object.

Dry air is a good insulator. Moist air is a fair conductor of electric charge. In wet weather, it is hard to charge objects

Main Idea

What is the difference between a conductor and an insulator?

Data Search

Which metal listed in the table on electric conductivity is the best electrical conductor? Search pages 658–661. Silver

The metal rod becomes positively charged when the charged rod is positively charged. It becomes negatively charged when the charged rod is negatively charged.

Figure 10-5. *The metal rod on the insulator is being charged by contact with a charged rod. When does the metal rod become positively charged? When does it become negatively charged?*

Activity

See also Activity Record Sheet 10-1A (Lab Manual page 135). Answers to Questions and Conclusion appear on page T141 in the front of this book.

10.1a   Identifying Positively and Negatively Charged Objects

Science Processes: Observing, recording data, making inferences

Materials   BASIC   20 minutes   Groups of 3 or 4

- balloon
- ring stand
- clamp
- piece of thread
- wooden dowel

- wool flannel
- silk
- solid glass rod
- hard rubber comb
- plastic bag

Purpose

To demonstrate how the electric charge on an object can be identified.

Procedure

1. Inflate a balloon.
2. Attach a wooden dowel to a ring stand with a clamp. Hang the balloon from the dowel by a piece of thread.
3. Rub the balloon with wool flannel. The balloon is now negatively charged.
4. Rub a glass rod with a piece of silk. Without touching the balloon, bring the rod toward the balloon. Record what happens.
5. Bring the silk toward the balloon. Record whether the silk attracts or repels the balloon.

6. Rub a hard rubber comb with the flannel. Bring the comb near the balloon; then bring the flannel near the balloon. Record what happens to the balloon each time.
7. Briskly comb clean hair. Test both the hair and the comb. Record what happens.
8. Test other combinations of the materials available. Record what happens.

Questions

1. What is the charge on a balloon that has been rubbed with wool flannel?
2. What is the charge on a material that repels a balloon rubbed with wool flannel?
3. What is the charge on a material that attracts a balloon rubbed with wool flannel?
4. What charge did each of the materials you used have after rubbing?

Conclusion

How can a charged balloon be used to identify the electric charge on an object?

Step 2

Step 4

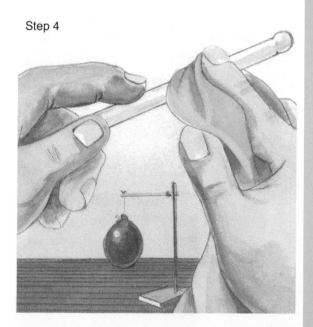

because the moist air conducts the charge away from them and they do not stay charged. In dry weather, objects become charged more easily. You may have felt an electric shock after walking across a rug and touching a metal doorknob. You yourself had become charged by friction between your shoes and the rug and were carrying a static charge. Then you charged the doorknob by contact.

Quick Review

1. How can charging by contact be explained?
2. How is an insulator different from a conductor?

Charging by induction

New vocabulary: induced charges, induction

Bits of paper will stick to a negatively charged rubber comb. They will also stick to a positively charged glass rod. How can the same objects be attracted to both types of charge?

The bits of paper are electrically neutral. They have equal numbers of electrons and protons. The charged rubber comb is brought near the bits of paper. The electrons in the paper are free to move away from the comb, but they remain in the paper. Now the part of the paper closest to the comb is positively charged. The part farthest from the comb is negatively charged. The comb attracts the positively charged part more than it repels the negatively charged part.

The excess negative charge on the one part of the paper and the excess positive charge on another part of the paper are called **induced charges.** Induced charges are ones that result from an object being near another strongly charged object. The charges on the paper will not remain separated. When the comb is taken away, the electrons will spread out through the paper.

A metal object can be charged by a nearby charged object. The metal object must be attached to an insulator. Next, a charged object is brought near. The electrons in the metal move toward the charged object if its charge is positive. They move away from the charged object if its charge is negative. They cannot actually leave the metal. The metal still has equal numbers of protons and electrons, so it is not yet charged. To charge the metal, a conductor is touched to it briefly. Electrons move in the direction that will give the metal an opposite charge from that of the other object. When the conductor is taken away, the metal is charged. The conductor

Critical Thinking

When talking about these charged objects, why are we mostly talking about static electricity?

Once the objects are charged, the charges won't move unless the object touches a conductor or an object with a different charge.

Quick Review answers:
1. Electrons may move from one object to another when the two objects are in contact. They tend to move off a negatively charged object and toward a positively charged object.
2. Insulators do not conduct electricity easily.

This question is answered in the paragraph that follows.

Additional information:
The charges are unequally distributed in the paper only while the charged comb is close by. These charges are called induced charges.

Main Idea

What are induced charges?

Negatively charged rod

Metal rod

Electrons

Positively charged rod

Metal rod

Electrons

Figure 10-6. *The metal is being charged by induction because it is near a charged rod. When does the metal rod become positively charged? When does it become negatively charged?*
The metal rod becomes positively charged when a negatively charged object is close by. It becomes negatively charged when a positively charged object is close by.

Quick Review answers:
Charges become unequally distributed in a metal when a charged object is brought near. If a conductor is touched to the metal, electrons will flow toward the metal if the charged object is positive. They will flow away from the metal if the charged object is negative. Removing the conductor leaves the metal with an excess of charge opposite to that of the charging object.

Main Idea

What is lightning?

which was briefly attached to the metal rod to allow excess electrons to leave or enter the rod is called a **ground** because the conductor is often attached to the earth or ground. It can also be attached to any large object that can freely accept electrons or give up electrons. This process is called *grounding*.

The process of charging an object by grounding it while it is near another charged object is called charging by **induction** (in-DUK′-shun). An object that is charged by induction does not actually touch the charged object.

When an object is charged by induction, its charge is opposite to that of the charging object.

Quick Review

How can charging by induction be explained?

Lightning
New vocabulary: lightning rod

Lightning is a result of charges that become separated in thunder clouds. The top of the cloud becomes positively charged. The bottom of the cloud becomes negatively charged. The negative part of the cloud induces positive charges on the ground under it.

When the charge difference is great enough, the air becomes a conductor. Electrons move toward the positively charged ground. The interaction of the electrons with the air causes the glowing spark we call lightning. The air becomes greatly heated by the lightning and expands rapidly. An exploding noise that we call thunder is heard. Lightning also occurs within a thunder cloud or between one cloud and another.

Activity

10.1b Observing Charges with an Electroscope

Science Processes: Observing, recording data, making inferences

Materials   20 minutes   Groups of 3 or 4

- foil gum wrapper
- scissors
- 15-cm stiff wire with uninsulated ends
- jar with narrow neck
- modeling clay
- plastic bag
- wool flannel

Purpose

To charge an object without touching it.

Procedure

1. Make an electroscope, or charge detector, as follows.
   a. Carefully strip the paper backing off a foil gum wrapper. Cut a lengthwise strip of foil about 1 cm wide. Fold the foil strip in half.
   b. Bend one end of a stiff wire to form a hook.
   c. Poke the hook into the foil just below the fold. Be sure that the two ends of the foil hang straight down, or nearly so, from the hook. Also be sure that the foil is in contact with the uninsulated part of the wire.
   d. Lower the hook and foil into a jar with a narrow neck. Keep the upper end of the wire above the neck.
   e. Seal the neck of the jar by carefully packing pieces of modeling clay around the wire.
2. Lay a plastic bag flat on a desk or table.
3. Rub the bag with wool flannel.
4. Bring the flannel close to the top end of the wire. Do not touch the wire. Record whether the foil ends spread apart or stay close together.
5. Move the flannel away from the wire. Record whether the foil ends spread apart or move closer together.
6. Bring the flannel back again. Record what the foil ends do.

Teacher Note

Activities that involve charging work best on dry days. Dry winter days are best.

7. Repeat Steps 3, 4, 5, and 6 using the plastic bag instead of the flannel. Record what the foil ends do.

Questions

1. What charges do wool flannel and a plastic bag have after they have been rubbed together?
2. Was the induced charge on the foil ends positive or negative when the charged wool flannel was near the top of the electroscope?
3. Was the induced charge on the foil ends positive or negative when the charged plastic bag was near the top of the electroscope?

Conclusion

What is a hypothesis that explains the behavior of the foil in your electroscope?

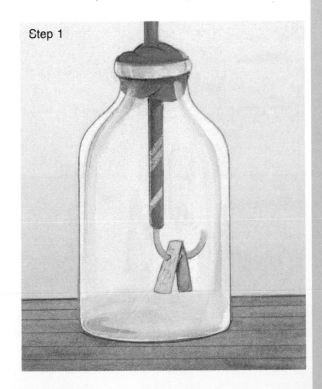

Step 1

Figure 10-7. *When the bottom of a cloud becomes negatively charged, what causes the ground underneath it to become positively charged?* The ground underneath the cloud is charged by induction.

Benjamin Franklin (1706–1790) was an American statesman who enjoyed experimenting with electricity. He discovered that sparks leave a sharply pointed object more readily than a rounded one. He invented the **lightning rod.** The lightning rod is a pointed rod that is attached at the top of a building. It is connected by a cable to the ground.

In a thunderstorm, charge builds up in the ground. The charge can leave from the point of the lightning rod. Even if lightning does strike, it will hit the lightning rod and protect the building.

Lightning tends to strike the highest nearby point. Suppose you are riding in a car out in the country during a thunderstorm. What is the best thing to do? Staying in the car is best. You will be safe inside the car even on an open road. Electric charge moves freely on the outside of a metal surface such as a car. No charge will build up inside the car. That means that lightning is unlikely to injure people in the car.

What should you do if you are caught out in open country during a thunderstorm? Avoid taking shelter under a tall tree. The tree could get hit by lightning and fall on you. Do not stand out in the open either. Immediately get to the lowest place you can find. Get into a ditch or lie flat on the ground until the storm has passed.

Quick Review

What condition in clouds leads to lightning and thunder?

Coulomb's law

The small pieces of plastic foam used in packing cling to skin and clothes easily. The charge on them creates a force far stronger than their own weight. This force allows them to be lifted against the force of gravity.

The force between charged objects is often much greater than the force of gravity between them. We tend to think of the force of gravity as being very large. It is large only when at least one object has a very large mass, such as the earth.

The force due to charges depends on the amount of charge on each object. The more charge on either object, the greater the force is. The force also depends on the distance between the changes. Like the force of gravity, it is stronger the closer together the objects are. The relationship between force, electric charge, and distance is known as Coulomb's law, after the French scientist who investigated it. Coulomb's law can be written as a proportion.

$$\text{force is proportional to } \frac{\text{charge 1} \times \text{charge 2}}{(\text{distance})^2}$$

$$\text{or, } F \propto \frac{Q_1 \times Q_2}{D^2}$$

Notice that if the amount of one charge is doubled, that the force is doubled. However, if the distance between the charges is doubled, the force between them is only one-fourth as strong, because the distance effect is squared.

There is one big difference between the gravitational and electric forces. Gravity always makes objects attract each other. Charged objects attract each other if one charge is negative and the other is positive. They repel each other if both charges are positive or both are negative.

When charged objects attract each other, it takes energy to move them farther apart. They have more potential energy when they are moved apart. On the other hand, when charged objects repel each other, it takes energy to bring them closer. They have more potential energy when they are closer.

Quick Review

1. In what way is the force between charged objects like the force of gravity?
2. In what way is the electric force between charged objects different from the force of gravity?

Figure 10-8. *How does the force of gravity between objects compare to the force between them due to their charge?*

Additional information:
The force due to the charge between objects is far stronger than the force of gravity between them. It can be even greater than the force of gravity between an object and the earth (i.e., the object's weight).

Research Topic

The SI unit of charge is the coulomb (KOO'-lōm), named after the French scientist Charles Augustin de Coulomb (1736–1806). Find out what scientific contribution Coulomb made that led to the honor of having a unit named after him.

Science background information:
The SI unit of charge is the coulomb. To have one coulomb of negative charge, you would need about 6 million million million (6.25×10^{18}) electrons.

Quick Review answers:
1. Both forces are stronger when the objects are closer together.
2. Gravity is always a force of attraction. The force between charged objects can attract or repel.

10.1 Section Review

Answers to Understanding the Concepts appear on page T141 in the front of this book. Blackline master test for this section: Section Testsheet 10-1 (TRB page 226)

Vocabulary

5 attract
2 conductor
8 ground
9 induced charges
4 induction
6 insulator
10 lightning rod
1 repel
3 static charges
7 static electricity

Vocabulary Review

Match each term above with the numbered phrase that best describes it.

1. To push away
2. Material through which charges can move easily
3. Charges that are not moving
4. Process of charging an object by bringing it near a charged object
5. To pull toward
6. Material through which charge cannot move easily
7. Refers to all of the properties of charges which are not moving
8. A conductor that is attached to a very large body which can accept or supply electrons
9. Charges that result when a charged object is brought near another charged object
10. Pointed piece of metal attached to top of a building

Review Questions

Multiple Choice: Choose the answer that best completes each of the following sentences.

11. When two materials are charged by friction between them, ?.
    a. both lose electrons
    b. both gain electrons
    c. one loses electrons to the other
    d. there is no change in the number of electrons each has

12. When two balloons are rubbed by a piece of flannel, you would expect the balloons to ?.
    a. attract each other
    b. repel each other
    c. charge each other
    d. have no effect on each other

13. When an object is charged by contact with a charged object, ?.
    a. both lose electrons
    b. both gain electrons
    c. one loses electrons to the other
    d. there is no change in the number of electrons each has

14. When an insulated object is charged by induction because of a nearby charged object, ?.
    a. both lose electrons
    b. both gain electrons
    c. one loses electrons to the other
    d. there is no change in the number of electrons each has

15. When two charged objects are moved farther apart, the force between them ?.
    a. always increases
    b. increases only if both have the same kind of charge
    c. increases only if both have opposite kinds of charge
    d. always decreases

16. To charge a piece of steel on an insulated post by induction, it is necessary for the piece of steel to ?.
    a. be touched by the charged object
    b. be connected to a grounding wire when the charged object is near
    c. be connected to a grounding wire when the charged object has been removed
    d. be insulated with thick insulation

Understanding the Concepts

17. How do conductors differ from insulators?
18. If you hold a charged balloon near your arm, you will feel a tickle as the hair on your arm reaches toward the balloon. Explain what might cause your hair to do this.
19. How can the potential energy of two charged objects be increased?
20. What is necessary for lightning to occur between a cloud and the earth?

For ideas for classroom demonstration and discussion, see Getting Started on page T142 in the front of this book.

10.2 Electric Currents

Supplemental materials: Teaching Diagram 10-2A, 10-2B (TRB pages 51, 52), Reading Checksheet 10-2 (TRB page 107), Skillsheet 10-2 (TRB page 153), Investigation 10-2 (Lab Manual pages 141–142)

Section Preview

- **Moving charges**
- **Direct and alternating current**
- **Measuring current**
- **Resistance and voltage drop**
- **Electric power**

Bracketed numbers are Section Review questions correlated to that objective.

Learning Objectives

1. To know the necessary conditions for an electric current to exist.
2. To know the differences between direct and alternating current.
3. To describe the measures of current, voltage drop, and resistance.
4. To relate the power rating of an electric appliance to the energy used.

Figure 10-9. *A photographer's strobe light has two parts. The center guide light remains on constantly. The outer ring gives a bright flash when a powerful current flows through it.*

Moving electric charges do work. They are a source of energy. The energy of moving charges is used to light buildings and to transport people. It puts people in touch with each other through telephones, radio, and television. Whenever a storm or heat spell causes a loss of electric service, we are reminded of how much we depend on electricity.

Moving charges New vocabulary: electric current, negative terminal, positive terminal, batteries, voltage, volt, coulomb, circuit, open circuit, closed circuit

The movement of electric charges creates an **electric current.** Moving electric charges cannot be seen. The movement must be inferred from indirect observations. The presence of an electric current is usually indicated by its effects.

Charges move only when energy is supplied to them. One source of energy is a dry cell. Chemical reactions within the cell supply energy to electrons. Electrons inside the cell collect at the **negative terminal** of the cell. In the common flashlight cell, the negative terminal is the flat metal base of the

Main Idea

What causes an electric current?

Research Topic

After whom is the volt named? What did this person accomplish that led to such an honor?

Additional information:
The term *emf* (electromagnetic force) is sometimes used in place of voltage but is avoided in this text because it implied that a force is being talked about.

cell. When the top and bottom of the cell are connected by wires, electrons move through the wires toward the **positive terminal.** The positive terminal in a flashlight cell is the one with the bump on it.

Dry cells are sometimes called **batteries.** A true battery is a series of cells. The cells in a battery may be in a single container. The chemical reactions that make cells work are described in Section 1 of Chapter 10.

Cells and batteries are marked with the **voltage** (VŌL´-tuj) they supply. Voltage is the amount of energy supplied per unit of charge. The SI unit of voltage is the **volt** (symbol V). The SI unit of charge is the **coulomb** (symbol C), the amount of charge equal to the charge of 6.25×10^{18} electrons. A 1.5-V flashlight cell supplies one joule of energy for every four million million million electrons (4×10^{18}) that pass through it. This is about the number of electrons that might pass through the cell each second. This relationship can be written as an equation.

$$\text{voltage} = \frac{\text{energy}}{\text{charge}}$$

A cell will operate for only a limited time. After a while, the chemical reactions inside it stop. A cell will wear out quickly if the top and bottom are directly connected by wires, with no bulb in between. The reason is that electrons can move through a wire more easily than through a bulb. They move more quickly and use up the cell's energy faster when there is no bulb.

Figure 10-10. *Explain why one bulb is lit and the other is not.* Wire is a conductor of electric charge. String is not a conductor.

For charges to move through a cell, there must be an unbroken path of conductors between the top and bottom of the cell. The path is called a **circuit** (SER'-kit). Figure 10-10 shows a cell and a bulb connected by wire and by string. The bulb lights up when wire is used but not when string is used. Wire is a conductor, but string is not.

The circuit must be unbroken, or **closed.** If any of the wires is disconnected, the current stops. An **open circuit** is one in which there is an opening in the path. A switch may be connected into the circuit. The switch makes it easy to open and close the circuit.

Quick Review

1. What role does a dry cell play in a circuit?
2. What conditions must be met for current to exist in a circuit?
3. Why do electrons in a circuit tend to move from the negative to the positive terminal?

Direct and alternating current
New vocabulary: direct current, alternating current

There are two kinds of current. In a **direct current,** the electrons move in one direction. They leave the cell or battery at the negative terminal. They travel through the circuit toward the positive terminal.

Main Idea

How many directions do electrons move in direct current?

Figure 10-11. *Electrons leave the negative terminal of the cell or battery. They travel through the bulb and wires toward the positive terminal.*

Electron movement

Positive terminal

Negative terminal

Figure 10-12. *The electrons in a standard 60-Hz alternating current change direction 120 times each second.*

Any of the conductors in the circuit can be reversed with no effect on the direction of the electrons. For instance, the connections to the bottom and side of the base of a bulb can be switched. Wires can be turned around. The electrons will still move toward the positive terminal.

The same amount of charge passes through each part of the circuit each second. Charge does not build up in any part. The same amount of charge that leaves the negative terminal enters the positive terminal.

Direct current is provided by cells and batteries. Cars use direct current to run their lights and radios. In older cars, a direct-current (dc) generator supplies the direct current.

In the second kind of current, the electrons move back and forth in a regular repeating cycle. This kind of current is called **alternating current** (ac).

Household current in North America is alternating current that reverses direction every 1/120 second. The current makes a complete back-and-forth cycle every 1/60 second. In one second, it makes 60 cycles. It has a frequency of 60 cycles per second, or 60 Hz (hertz). In some parts of the world, the common household current has a frequency of 50 Hz.

An ac circuit must be closed, just like a dc circuit. It may seem as though electric appliances have only one wire to connect to the wall outlet. However, the cord has two wires, side by side. They are separated from each other by the plastic

Research Topic

Find out what voltage and what frequency current are standard for three countries on different continents. What can a traveler do to be able to use an appliance designed for a different voltage or frequency of current?

insulation you see. When the electrons in one wire are moving away from the outlet, the electrons in the other wire are moving toward it. They change direction at the same time. No charge builds up anywhere in the circuit.

Alternating current has some advantages over direct current. Today, most electric energy is generated at large power plants. The energy has to be transported large distances. Alternating current can carry the energy with less energy loss along the way than direct current.

In modern cars, alternating current is produced by the generator. The current is changed to direct current before it passes through the rest of the car's electrical system.

Main Idea

What happens to the current when a circuit is opened?

Quick Review

1. What are the two kinds of current?
2. What happens when a current has a frequency of 60 Hz?

Quick Review answers:
1. The two kinds of current are direct current (dc) and alternating current (ac).
2. When a current has a frequency of 60 Hz, the electrons move through one complete back-and-forth cycle 60 times per second.

Measuring current

New vocabulary: ampere, ammeter

A current is created by moving charges. The amount of the current depends on the amount of electric charge that passes a point in the circuit in a second. The SI unit of current is the **ampere** (AM'-pihr), whose symbol is A. A current of one ampere carries one coulomb of electric charge past a point in a circuit in one second. People commonly refer to the number of "amps" in a circuit. Most of the circuits in a home are designed to carry a current of 15 to 20 amps.

Additional information:
The ampere is the basic electrical unit in SI. Other electric units are derived from the ampere.

Figure 10-13. *The water moves around and around in this garden waterfall system. The pump gives the water enough energy to reach the top. Compare the parts of this system with an electric circuit.*

The pump is like the cell or battery. The path of the water is like the circuit. The water is like the moving charges. The waterfall is like a bulb. (It takes energy from the water as the water splashes on the rocks.)

10.2a Using an Ammeter

Science Processes: Observing, recording data

20 minutes   Groups of 4 or teacher demonstration

Materials

- 2 "D" cells
- flashlight bulb and socket
- dc ammeter of range 0 to 1 A
- switch
- 4 20-cm lengths of bell wire
- masking tape

Purpose

To learn how to use an ammeter.

Procedure

1. Using one of the cells, make a circuit like the one shown. Connect the negative terminal of the ammeter toward the negative terminal (bottom) of the cell. Connect the positive terminal of the ammeter toward the positive terminal (top) of the cell.
2. Record the reading on the ammeter when the switch is open.
3. Close the switch and record the reading on the ammeter.
4. Predict whether the ammeter reading will be different if the bulb and ammeter are switched. Record your prediction.
5. Test your prediction by reconnecting the bulb and ammeter in the switched positions. Connect the positive terminal of the ammeter toward the positive terminal (top) of the cell.
6. Record the reading on the ammeter. Compare the brightness of the bulb to its previous brightness.
7. Predict whether the ammeter reading will be different if another cell is added to the circuit. Record your prediction.
8. Test your prediction by adding another cell to the circuit. Use masking tape to hold the two cells together firmly.
9. Record the reading on the ammeter. Compare the brightness of the bulb to its previous brightness.

Questions

1. What was the current reading when the switch was open?
2. What was the current reading when one cell was used?
3. Did the current reading change when the bulb and ammeter were switched in the circuit?
4. Did the brightness of the bulb change when a second cell was added to the circuit?
5. What was the current reading when two cells were used?
6. From your data, what relation can you see between the voltage supplied to a circuit and the current in a circuit?

Conclusion

How should an ammeter be connected to a light bulb to measure the current through the bulb?

Step 3

Electric current can be compared to the movement of water. Figure 10-13 has a diagram of the path of water that falls over some rocks in a garden. A pump gives the water enough energy to reach the top of the rocks. When the water goes over the rocks, it is carried back to the pump.

The water current could be increased by pumping the water faster. The pump would use more energy. The pump acts like a cell in a circuit. An electric current can be increased by using more cells in the circuit. The electrons would get more energy and would move faster. More electrons would pass a point in the circuit in a second.

Electric current is measured by an **ammeter** (AM′-mee-ter). The ammeter is connected into the circuit. It is important to use only a dc meter in a dc circuit and an ac meter in an ac circuit, unless the meter is designed for both. On a dc meter, the negative terminal of the meter should be connected toward the negative terminal of the cell or battery.

Quick Review

1. What things should be checked on an ammeter that is connected into a dc circuit?
2. Define "ampere."

Resistance and voltage drop
New vocabulary: resistance, ohm, voltage drop, voltmeter

Electrons move through metal wires easily. They give up only a small amount of energy as they move. This energy makes the wires warm. It is easier for electrons to move through thicker wires than thinner wires. To understand why, think of water moving through a pipe. The wider the pipe, the easier it is for the water to flow.

Critical Thinking

Compare what happens as a cell grows weaker with a pump as the pump slows down.

As the pump slows down, the water current diminishes. As the cells weaken, the electric current becomes weaker.

Quick Review answers:
1. Be certain that it is a dc ammeter, that the negative terminal of the ammeter is connected to the negative terminal of the cell, and that the range of the ammeter is correct for the expected current.
2. The standard unit of electric current measures the number of electrons passing a given point in one second.

Figure 10-15. *The resistance of a wire depends on the material of the wire as well as the thickness.*

Data Search

Which kind of wire is a better conductor of electricity, aluminum or copper? What is the IACS percentage for each? Search pages 658–661.

Copper is better with 100% IACS versus aluminum with 65% IACS.

The **resistance** of a conductor is a measure of how hard it is for charge to move through it. The greater the resistance, the harder it is for charge to move through the conductor. The SI unit of resistance is the **ohm** (ŌM). Light bulbs contain a very thin wire called a filament. Electrons move through the filament as they travel between the side and bottom of the base of the bulb. The filament has a high resistance. The electrons lose more energy as they move through the filament than when they move through the base. The filament becomes very hot. It gives off both heat and light.

Consider a simple circuit containing a flashlight cell, a flashlight bulb, and wires connecting them. The cell supplies energy to the electrons. As they move through the circuit, they lose most of that energy in the bulb. They lose an additional, but small, amount of energy in the wires.

The voltage of a cell is the energy it supplies per coulomb of charge passing through it. The **voltage drop** across a conductor is the energy removed per coulomb of charge passing through it. Like voltage, voltage drop is measured in volts. The total voltage drop of all the conductors in a circuit equals the total voltage of the cells in the circuit.

Voltage drop is measured with a **voltmeter.** A voltmeter is connected differently from an ammeter. The voltmeter is connected across the conductor being measured. The current has a choice between passing through the conductor or

Main Idea

How is the voltage drop across a conductor measured?

passing through the voltmeter. Figure 10-16 shows a voltmeter that has been connected across a flashlight bulb.

There are both ac and dc voltmeters. The type of voltmeter must match the type of circuit it will be used in. Like ammeters, voltmeters can measure different ranges. The correct range must be chosen. Finally, in a dc circuit the voltmeter is connected so that its negative terminal is toward the negative terminal of the cell or battery.

The voltage drop across a conductor depends on two things. One is the resistance of the conductor. The higher the resistance is, the harder it is for electrons to move through the conductor. Thus, the electrons give up more energy as they pass through it. The voltage drop is greater.

The voltage drop also depends upon the current. In bulbs and wires, the voltage drop increases when the current increases. A bulb becomes brighter when more current passes through it. The increase in brightness is a sign that the bulb is taking more energy from the electrons that pass through its filament. The voltage drop across the bulb is greater.

Quick Review

1. Suppose two copper wires have the same length but different thicknesses. Which should have the greater resistance?
2. Which would be rated at the lowest number of ohms?

Figure 10-16. *The voltmeter is connected so that it measures the voltage drop across the bulb.*

Activity

10.2b   Using a Voltmeter

Science Processes: Observing, recording data, predicting

BASIC   20 minutes   Groups of 4 or teacher demonstration

Materials

- 2 "D" cells
- flashlight bulb and socket
- dc voltmeter of range 0 to 5 V
- switch
- 5 20-cm lengths of bell wire
- masking tape

Purposes

To learn how to use a voltmeter.

Procedure

1. Using one of the cells, make a circuit like the one shown. Connect the negative terminal of the voltmeter toward the negative terminal (bottom) of the cell. Connect the positive terminal of the voltmeter toward the positive terminal (top) of the cell.
2. Record the reading on the voltmeter when the switch is open.
3. Close the switch and record the reading on the voltmeter. Open the switch.
4. Add another cell to the circuit. Be sure that the top of one cell is in good contact with the bottom of the other cells. Use masking tape to hold them together firmly.
5. Close the switch. Record the reading on the voltmeter. Open the switch.

6. Reconnect the voltmeter so that it is connected across the wire between the switch and the bulb.
7. Close the switch. Record the voltmeter reading. Open the switch.

Questions

1. What was the voltmeter reading when the switch was open?
2. According to the cell label, what is the voltage of the cell?
3. When the switch was closed, how did the voltage drop across the bulb compare with the voltage of the cell?
4. How did the voltmeter reading change when the second cell was added to the circuit?
5. How does the voltage drop across a conductor depend on the total voltage of the cells in the circuit?
6. How did the voltage drop across the wire compare with the voltage drop across the bulb?

Conclusion

How should a voltmeter be connected in order to measure the voltage drop across part of a circuit?

Step 1

Step 7

Electric power

The energy of moving charges is converted to heat, light, and motion in electric appliances. Heat is the desired product in electric stoves, toasters, and clothes dryers. Light is the desired product in light bulbs. Motion is the desired product in blenders, fans, and typewriters.

The total amount of energy an appliance uses is measured in joules. The amount of energy it uses per second is its power.

$$\text{power} = \frac{\text{energy}}{\text{time}} \quad \text{or} \quad P = \frac{E}{t}$$

Power is measured in joules per second, or watts. Electric power is also related to voltage and current.

Main Idea

What is the definition of power?

Our Science Heritage

Thomas Edison

Thomas Edison (1847–1931) is remembered as the greatest of inventors. More than a thousand patents were issued in his name. The phonograph, the electric light bulb, and the motion picture are probably his most famous contributions.

Edison concentrated on making items immediately useful to society. In only one instance is he credited with a scientific discovery. He was the first to use a vacuum tube to permit negative charges to move in only one direction.

The inventor received only a limited formal education. He admitted to having great difficulty with mathematics. His curiosity and hard work helped overcome these limitations. By accident, he came across some of the descriptions of the findings of Michael Faraday. They provided Edison with ideas and background for some of his later inventions.

Edison developed his inventions chiefly by trial and error. He is famous for being an extremely hard worker. He sometimes worked as many as twenty hours a day. He had a large number of people working for him. At times his staff would be working on fifty different inventions.

The interests of Edison encompassed many different fields. As an illustration, at one time he worked on problems related to cement, storage batteries, flamethrowers, periscopes, and the production of rubber from domestic sources. No other inventor has had such an impact on our daily lives.

$$\text{power} = \text{voltage} \times \text{current} \quad \text{or } P = V \times I$$

In this equation, power is defined as volt-amps. However, volt-amps are the same as joules per second, or watts.

Appliances are often marked with the power in watts that they use. They use their rated power only when the standard voltage (110 V or 220 V) is supplied. In North America, clothes dryers and electric stoves are expected to run on 220 V. All other appliances are expected to run on 110 V.

The electric power company charges customers for the amount of energy they use. The amount of energy on the bill is stated in kilowatt-hours. A typical home might use 500 kilowatt-hours of electricity in a month.

One kilowatt is equal to 1000 watts. It is a unit of power. If a kilowatt of power is used for one second, the amount of energy used is 1000 joules. There are 60 seconds in a minute and 60 minutes in an hour. Thus there are 60×60, or 3600, seconds in an hour. A kilowatt of power used for one hour is equal to 3600×1000, or 3 600 000, joules of energy.

$$1 \text{ kilowatt-hour} = 3\ 600\ 000 \text{ joules}$$

Why do you think that electric bills are stated in kilowatt-hours instead of joules?

The amount of energy an appliance uses depends both on the power rating and on how long it is used.

$$\text{energy} = \text{power} \times \text{time} \quad \text{or, } E = P \times t$$

An 1100-W toaster may be used for two minutes each day. A 400-W refrigerator turns on and off all the time. Which uses more energy in a day?

Research Topic

Try to determine the annual electric power use per person in the United States. Compare residential power use with industrial and agricultural power use.

Additional information:
The kilowatt-hour is a more convenient size unit to describe the energy used.

Figure 10-17. *Appliances that heat (or cool) things tend to have higher power ratings than appliances that only move things.*

Sample Problem 1

A dishwasher is rated at 1200 watts. On a 120-volt circuit, how many amps of current does it draw?

Solution

Use the equation for power and solve for current.

power = current × voltage

$$P = V \times I \quad \text{or } I = \frac{P}{V} \quad \left(\text{current} = \frac{\text{power}}{\text{voltage}} \right)$$

$$I = \frac{1200 \text{ watts}}{120 \text{ volts}} = \frac{1200 \text{ volt-amps}}{120 \text{ volts}} = 10 \text{ amps}$$

Sample Problem 2

If the dishwasher is used for one hour a day and the cost of electricity is $0.11 per kilowatt hour, how much does it cost to use it each day?

Solution

Use the equation for energy, power, and time.

energy = power × time   or E = P × t

E = 1200 watts × 1 hour = 1200 watt-hours

Convert to kilowatt-hours.

$$E = \frac{1200 \text{ watt-hours}}{1000 \text{ watts/kilowatt}} = 1.2 \text{ kilowatt-hours}$$

Multiply times the cost.

$$\text{Cost} = 1.2 \text{ kilowatt-hours} \times \frac{\$0.11}{1 \text{ kilowatt-hour}}$$

Cost = $0.132

Practice Problems

1. A washing machine is rated at 540 watts. On a 120-volt circuit, how many amps does it use? *Answer:* 4.5 amps
2. A microwave oven is rated at 700 watts. If electricity costs $0.09 per kilowatt-hour, what does it cost to use the microwave for one hour per week? *Answer:* $0.063

Quick Review

1. How is the amount of energy an appliance uses related to the power rating of the appliance?
2. How many watts are in a kilowatt?

Quick Review answers:
1. The larger the power rating, the greater is the amount of energy used per second of use. The energy use also depends on how long the appliance is used.
2. 1000.

10.2 Section Review

Answers to Understanding the Concepts and Solutions to Problems to Solve appear on page T143 in the front of this book. Blackline master test for this section: Section Testsheet 10-2 (TRB page 227)

Vocabulary

10 alternating current

7 ammeter

3 ampere

9 battery

16 circuit

17 closed circuit

18 coulomb

11 direct current

13 electric current

1 negative terminal

4 ohm

14 open circuit

2 positive terminal

12 resistance

15 volt

5 voltage

6 voltage drop

8 voltmeter

Vocabulary Review

Match each term above with the numbered phrase that best describes it.

1. Part of cell where electrons collect

2. Part of cell towards which electrons move

3. SI unit of current

4. SI unit of resistance

5. Energy supplied per coulomb of charge passing through a cell

6. Energy removed per coulomb of charge passing through a conductor

7. Used to measure current

8. Used to measure voltage drop

9. Contains two or more cells

10. Kind of current commonly used for household appliances

11. Kind of current in which electrons move in one direction

12. Measure of how hard it is for electrons to move through a conductor

13. Movement of electric charges

14. A circuit having an opening in the path

15. The SI unit of voltage

16. An unbroken path along which electrons travel

17. A circuit in which the path is unbroken

18. The SI unit of charge

Review Questions

Multiple Choice: Choose the answer that best completes each of the following sentences.

19. In a dc circuit, the positive terminal of an ammeter must be connected ? .
    a. to a flashlight bulb socket
    b. toward the positive terminal of the cell or battery
    c. toward the negative terminal of the cell or battery
    d. directly to the base of the cell or battery

20. For an electric current to exist in a circuit, the circuit must ? .
    a. be closed
    b. contain a light bulb
    c. contain an ammeter
    d. contain a voltmeter

21. The purpose of a switch in a circuit is to ? .
    a. reverse the direction of the current
    b. increase the voltage of the cell or battery
    c. increase the resistance of the wires in the circuit
    d. make it easy to open and close the circuit

Understanding the Concepts

22. Silver is a better conductor than aluminum. If a silver wire and an aluminum wire have the same length and same diameter, which should have a higher resistance? Explain.

Problems to Solve

23. How much energy, in kilowatt hours, is used by a 100-W light bulb that is on for 24 hours?

24. How many joules will a 1.5-V cell supply in 15 hours if it delivers 1 joule of energy per second?

25. A clothes dryer, rated at 4200 watts, runs for 3 hours per week. In four weeks, how many kilowatt-hours of electricity does it use?

26. If the utility company charges 5¢ per kilowatt-hour for electricity, how much would it cost to use the dryer above for four weeks?

For ideas for classroom demonstration and discussion, see Getting Started on page T144 in the front of this book.

10.3 Electric Circuits

Supplemental materials: Teaching Diagrams 10-3A, 10-3B (TRB pages 53, 54), Reading Checksheet 10-3 (TRB page 108), Skillsheet 10-3 (TRB page 154), Investigation 10-3 (Lab Manual pages 145–146)

Section Preview

- Ohm's law
- Series circuits
- Parallel circuits
- Circuit safety devices
- Complex circuits and computers

Bracketed numbers are Section Review questions correlated to that objective.

Learning Objectives

1. To apply Ohm's law to simple electric circuits.
2. To describe the characteristics of series circuits.
3. To describe the characteristics of parallel circuits.
4. To explain how safety devices for circuits work.
5. To recognize some components of complex circuits and computers.

Any complex circuit is made of simple circuits put together. Learning more about simple circuits is the first step toward understanding complex circuits.

Ohm's law

Georg Simon Ohm (1789–1854) was a high school teacher in Cologne, Germany. He wanted to find out how the current through a wire was related to the voltage of the battery attached to it. He tested wires of different materials.

Ohm discovered that the current depended on the material of the wire. It also depended upon the thickness and length of the wire. He kept the material, thickness, and length the same and changed only the voltage. He found that the voltage divided by the current always had the same value. When the voltage doubled, the current doubled. When the voltage tripled, the current tripled. Ohm called this constant value the resistance of the wire.

$$\frac{\text{voltage}}{\text{current}} = \text{resistance}$$

Figure 10-18. *Driver adjusts trolley poles to make contact with overhead power lines. The lines supply electric current to move the trolleybus.*

Main Idea

What is the constant value called in the ratio between voltage and current?

1 Cell

0.5 A

1.5 V

2 Cells

1.0 A

3.0 V

3 Cells

1.5 A

4.5 V

Figure 10-19. *Putting more cells in a circuit increases the current. When the current increases, the voltage drop across the bulb increases. In this circuit, is the voltage drop divided by the current always the same?*

Yes, for this circuit the voltage drop divided by the current is always 3.0 V/A, or 3.0 ohms.

Research Topic

Find out what semiconductors are. How are they different from conductors? Why are they so important nowadays?

Science background information: At temperatures near absolute zero, some metals and alloys show the property of superconductivity. This means that their resistance to electric current drops to nothing and they can conduct electric current continuously without loss.

This relation came to be known as Ohm's law. In honor of Ohm, the unit of resistance was named the ohm. The symbol for the ohm is Ω.

The relationship can be written as an equation where V is the symbol for voltage, I is the symbol for current, and R is the symbol for resistance.

$$\frac{V}{I} = R$$

Ohm's law can be expressed in other forms. In Ohm's simple circuit, the voltage of the battery equaled the voltage drop across the wire. Even when there are other conductors in a circuit, Ohm's law holds for each conductor.

$$\frac{\text{voltage drop}}{\text{current}} = \text{resistance}$$

That is, the voltage drop across a conductor divided by the current through the conductor equals the resistance of the conductor. For example, if a voltmeter across the conductor reads 6 V and an ammeter reads 3 A, then the resistance is 2 ohms. Another way to express Ohm's law is this.

$$\text{voltage drop} = \text{current} \times \text{resistance}$$

$$\text{or } V = IR$$

For example, if you know that the current is 4A and the resistance is 3Ω, the voltage drop is 12 V.

Ohm thought that the resistance of wire was a property of wire that did not change. We know that when wires heat up, their resistance increases. Ohm's law describes an ideal situation. It works fairly well for metals, but not at very low temperatures or for semiconductors such as silicon.

Figure 10-20. *The three bulbs are connected in series. The same current passes through all three.*

Series circuits

New vocabulary: in series

Suppose you wanted to put more than one flashlight bulb in a circuit. Figure 10-20 shows three bulbs connected so that the same current goes through all three bulbs. The bulbs are said to be connected **in series.**

In a series circuit, there is only one path for the current. The same current flows through all parts of the circuit. Breaking the circuit at any point reduces the current to zero. For instance, if a light bulb burns out in a series circuit, all the lights on that circuit will go out. The current is measured by connecting an ammeter in series with the other conductors in the circuit. See the upper photo in Figure 10-21. Does it make any difference which conductor the ammeter is placed next to?

The voltage drop across one conductor is measured by connecting a voltmeter across the conductor. See the lower photo in Figure 10-21. The total voltage drop in a series cir-

Figure 10-21. *In a series circuit, the current is measured by connecting an ammeter in series with the other conductors (top). The voltage drop across one bulb is measured by connecting a voltmeter across the bulb (bottom).*

Activity

See also Activity Record Sheet 10-3A (Lab Manual page 143). Answers to Questions and Conclusion appear on pages T145 at the front of this book.

10.3a Bulbs in Series

Science Processes: Observing, recording data

BASIC 40 minutes Groups of 4 or teacher demonstration

Materials

- **3 flashlight bulbs and sockets**
- **switch**
- **2 "D" cells**
- **masking tape**
- **7 10-cm pieces of bell wire**
- **dc ammeter of range 0 to 1 A**
- **dc voltmeter of range 0 to 5 V**

Purpose

To study properties of a series circuit.

Procedure

1. Connect three bulbs in sockets in series with a switch, an ammeter, and two "D" cells that are firmly taped together top to bottom. Connect the ammeter between the switch and the two-cell battery.
2. Close the switch. Read and record the current value on the ammeter. Open the switch.
3. Reconnect the ammeter so that it is between two of the bulbs. Close the switch. Read and record the current value. Open the switch.
4. Reconnect the ammeter as it was in Step 1.
5. Connect a voltmeter across one of the bulbs.
6. Close the switch. Read the value of the voltage drop on the voltmeter. Record the value. Open the switch.
7. Repeat Steps 5 and 6 with the voltmeter connected across two bulbs.
8. Predict what will happen to the voltage drop if the voltmeter is connected across all three bulbs. Repeat Steps 5 and 6 with the voltmeter connected across all three bulbs. Open the switch.
9. Remove one bulb from its socket. Remove the voltmeter. Close the switch. Record the ammeter reading. Open the switch.
10. Reconnect the circuit so that there are only two bulbs and sockets in series with the ammeter, switch and battery. Reconnect the voltmeter across one bulb. Close the switch.

Record the current value and voltage drop. Open the switch.

Questions

1. Is the current between the switch and the 2-cell battery the same as the current between two of the bulbs?
2. How does the voltage drop compare across one, two and three bulbs?
3. Do the other bulbs remain lit when one bulb is removed from a series circuit? Explain.
4. How does the current compare in a "two-bulb" circuit and in a "three-bulb" circuit?

Conclusion

Describe the current and voltage in a series circuit.

Step 5

480 *Chapter 10* **Electric Charges and Currents**

cuit is the sum of the voltage drops across each of the conductors. The electrons give up some energy as they move through each conductor.

The total voltage drop is approximately equal to the voltage supplied by the cell or battery. Any difference is due to the resistance of the cell or battery itself. The electrons must use some of their energy in passing through it.

If one of the conductors is removed from the series circuit, the total voltage drop will be the same as before. It still is about equal to the voltage of the cell or battery. However, there will be less resistance in the circuit. According to Ohm's law, the current should be greater. If the conductors are bulbs, they will light more brightly than before. What would happen to the brightness of the bulbs if two more bulbs were added in series to the circuit?

Circuits are represented in diagrams that use symbols for each part of the circuit. A circuit diagram for the series circuit shown in the photo of Figure 10-20 is shown in Figure 10-22. The bulbs are each represented by the symbol for resistance, the jagged line that is shown in Figure 10-22. They provide almost all the resistance in the circuit. The wires are shown by straight or curved lines.

Circuit diagrams can be drawn for circuits that are much more complex than these. For example, circuit diagrams for radios and televisions are much more complicated than Figure 10-22. You will learn more about complex circuits and

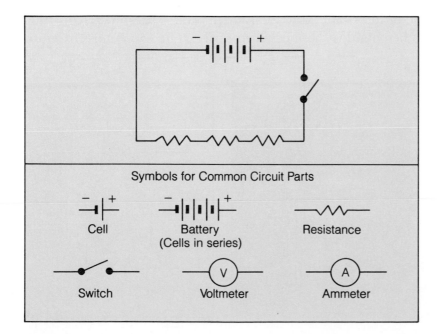

Figure 10-22. *A circuit diagram for the circuit pictured in the photo of Figure 10-20. The symbols for many common circuit parts are shown in the key.*

Symbols for Common Circuit Parts

Cell

Battery
(Cells in series)

Resistance

Switch

Voltmeter

Ammeter

some special devices that are made of complex circuits—computers—at the end of this chapter.

Quick Review

1. In a series circuit, is the current through each conductor the same as the current through the cell or battery?
2. In a series circuit, when there are fewer conductors in series, how does the current change?
3. Draw a circuit diagram that shows an ammeter and two bulbs in series with a battery. Use the symbols shown in Figure 10-22.

Parallel circuits

New vocabulary: in parallel

In a series circuit, the current flows through everything in the circuit. Bulbs in series are either all on or all off. Imagine if your home were wired in a series circuit. Shutting off one lamp would shut off everything at once.

There is a way to connect conductors so that each can operate independently in a circuit. Figure 10-23 shows three bulbs connected **in parallel.** The bulbs are in separate branches of the circuit. The branches are alternate paths for the current. The current divides up among the branches. Some of the current flows through the first branch. Some flows through the second. The rest flows through the third.

A voltmeter is always connected in parallel with the conductor whose voltage drop is being measured. The voltmeter is an alternate path for the current. An ammeter, on the other hand, is connected in series. The same current must

Main Idea

How can conductors be connected to operate independently?

Figure 10-23. *The three bulbs are connected in parallel. The current splits up among the three branches.*

Activity

10.3b   Bulbs in Parallel

Science Processes: Observing, recording data, predicting, making inferences

Materials

- **3 flashlight bulbs and sockets**
- **switch**
- **2 "D" cells**
- **masking tape**
- **10 10-cm pieces of bell wire**
- **dc ammeter of range 0 to 1 A**
- **dc voltmeter of range 0 to 5 V**

Purpose

To study properties of a parallel circuit.

Procedure

1. Connect three flashlight bulbs in sockets in parallel.
2. Connect them in series with a 2-"D"-cell battery, a switch, and an ammeter.
3. Close the switch. Read and record the current value. Notice how bright the bulbs are. Open the switch.
4. Without disconnecting the socket, remove one of the bulbs from its socket. Close the switch. Record the current value. Compare the brightness of the remaining bulbs to their brightness before. Open the switch. Replace the bulb.
5. Reconnect the ammeter so that it is in one branch next to a bulb. (See star in illustration.) Predict how the ammeter reading will compare to the previous reading.
6. Test your prediction by closing the switch. Record the current value and open the switch.
7. Remove a bulb in a different branch from the ammeter. Close the switch and read and record the current value. Open the switch.
8. Connect a voltmeter across one socket. Close the switch, read the meter and record the voltage drop. Open the switch.
9. Reconnect the voltmeter across a different socket. Close the switch, read the meter, and record the voltage drop. Open the switch.

Teacher Note

Use three identical light bulbs in the circuit.

40 minutes   Groups of 4 or teacher demonstration

Questions

1. Did the brightness of the other light bulbs increase, decrease, or remain the same when a bulb was removed from the circuit?
2. How did the current in one branch compare to the current in the main part of the circuit?
3. Does breaking one branch of the circuit affect the amount of current in the other branches?
4. How do the voltage drops across bulbs in different branches compare?
5. How does the voltage drop in a branch compare to the voltage of the battery?

Conclusion

Describe the current and voltage in a parallel circuit.

Step 8

Figure 10-24. *The cells at the top are connected in series. The cells at the bottom are connected in parallel. Which type of connection supplies the greater voltage to the circuit?*
Connecting the cells in series supplies the greater voltage to the circuit

Research Topic

Many homes are equipped with both 110 V and 220 V circuits. Usually these homes have three wires entering them from utility poles. Find out how these two voltages are supplied through three lines.

flow through the ammeter as flows through the part of the circuit whose current is being measured.

When one branch in a parallel circuit is open, current can still go through the other branches. A lamp can be shut off by opening a switch in the branch. The current in the other branches does not change. In homes and other buildings, all lights and appliances are connected in parallel.

The voltage drop across each of the branches is the same. The same amount of energy is used per unit of charge no matter which path the current follows. In a home the voltage drop across each branch is the standard 110 V or 220 V.

Cells, as well as conductors, can be connected in series or parallel. Cells connected in series increase the voltage supplied to the circuit. When "D" cells are connected top to bottom, they are in series. The total voltage is the sum of the voltages of each cell.

Cells connected in parallel have the same voltage as a single cell. However, they last longer than a single cell would. Each supplies energy to only part of the charge moving through the circuit.

Quick Review answers:

1. No, the current through each branch of a parallel circuit is less than the current through the cell or battery.
2. The current in the other branches remains the same.
3. Cells connected in parallel provide the same voltage as a single cell. However, they last longer than a single cell.
4. No, the voltage drop is the same.

Quick Review

1. In a parallel circuit, is the current through each branch the same as the current through the cell or battery?
2. In a parallel circuit, what happens to the current in the other branches when one branch is opened?
3. In what way do cells connected in parallel act like a single cell? In what way do they act differently?
4. In a series circuit, is the voltage drop across each of the branches different?

Circuit safety devices

New vocabulary: short circuit, fuse, circuit breaker, ground-fault interrupter

Wires get hot when they carry current. The greater the current, the hotter the wire becomes. Each wire can safely carry up to a certain amount of current. If it carries more than that amount, it may melt or heat up and start a fire.

A cord designed for alternating current has two groups of wires side by side. The two groups are separated from each other by plastic insulation. If the insulation should crack open, the two groups could touch. Then current would go directly through the opening. It would bypass the appliance at the end of the cord. The resistance in the circuit would be far less than normal. The current would be much greater than normal. The cord could start a fire.

When the part of a circuit with the most resistance is bypassed, a **short circuit** is said to exist. Short circuits are dangerous because of the heating of the wires. Circuits in buildings contain safety devices that immediately open the circuit if the current becomes too great.

A **fuse** (FYOOZ) is a safety device that contains a substance with a low melting temperature. Should the current increase beyond a safe limit, the heat melts the fuse. The circuit is broken. The potential danger is avoided.

Fuses are rated according to the number of amperes of current that the circuit can safely carry. Fuses should be

Main Idea

What is a fuse, and how does it work?

Figure 10-25. *Fuses come with different ratings. It is important to check what maximum number of amperes the fuse will permit in a circuit. The fuse should never have a greater rating than the circuit it is protecting.*

Figure 10-26. *(Left) The fuses for the main circuits in a building are found in the fuse box. (Right) In modern buildings, circuit breakers are used instead of fuses.*

■ **Safety Note**
Do not put anything but the proper size fuse in a fuse box. Otherwise, an overloaded circuit may cause a fire.

Figure 10-27. *The ground-fault interrupter is placed in sockets that are used around water.*

chosen to match the kind of wiring in the circuit. A fuse with too high a rating for the wiring cannot protect the wiring.

In a building, several wall sockets are connected in parallel in one of the main building circuits. The current in the main circuit is the sum of the currents in the parallel branches. If many appliances that draw high currents are used at the same time, the fuse on the main circuit will burn out. Simply replacing the burned-out fuse does not solve the problem. Instead, some of the appliances should be disconnected.

A **circuit breaker** is an alternative to a fuse. It works because a current produces a force on a magnet. When the current becomes too large for safety, the force is great enough to operate a switch. The switch opens the circuit.

One advantage of circuit breakers over fuses is that they do not have to be replaced each time the circuit is opened. The switch can simply be moved back to the "on" position. First, though, the problem that made the circuit open must be found and corrected.

A safety device that may be found in newer circuits is the **ground-fault interrupter.** It is designed for bathrooms, around pools, or in places where there is water. The human body conducts current more easily when it is wet than when it is dry. The interrupter opens the circuit if it senses that some current is passing through a person instead of all going through an appliance. The circuit can be closed again by pressing a reset button.

1. What is the first thing that should be done when a safety device opens a circuit?
2. Why is it important not to use a fuse with a higher amperage rating than is called for in a circuit?

Complex circuits and computers

So far, we have talked about simple electric circuits. Simple circuits are mostly used to supply energy to machines that do work. A simple circuit usually consists of a conductor, a power source, and an energy-using device such as an electric light, motor, or heater.

Complex circuits have more components than simple circuits. Complex circuits usually control the flow of electric current. So, they handle information in the form of electric current rather than supply energy to do mechanical work. Machines with complex circuits include radios, telephones, televisions, radar, and computers. The field of science that studies and develops machines with complex circuits is known as **electronics.**

Like simple circuits, complex circuits have conductors and a power source. They also have other kinds of components. Some of these are described below.

A **resistor** is a device with a specific resistance that is put in a circuit to limit the flow of current or to provide a voltage drop.

A **capacitor** is a device in a circuit that can store electric energy. A capacitor can also be used to block the flow of direct current and to allow the flow of alternating current in a circuit.

A **vacuum tube** is a glass tube, from which the air has been removed, containing two or more metal electrodes. Vacuum tubes can be used for purposes, such as *rectifying*—converting alternating current to direct current—and *amplifying*—increasing the voltage, current, or power of an electric signal. Vacuum tubes were used initially in radios and then in televisions and computers.

A **transistor** is a piece of semiconducting material that is used in a circuit as an amplifier, rectifier, or switch. *Semiconducting materials* are elements, such as silicon and germanium, which conduct electricity more poorly than metals but better than insulators. Semiconductor transistors have other elements, such as boron and phosphorus, added to

New vocabulary: electronics, resistor, capacitor, vacuum tube, transistor, integrated circuit, computer, input, process, output, binary number, program

Data Search

Give the names of three men who were awarded the Nobel prize in physics for the development of solid-state electronic devices. Search pages 658–661.

Philip W. Anderson, John H. Van Vleck, and Sir Nevill F. Mott.

Figure 10-28. *Components of complex circuits include, clockwise from the top, vacuum tubes, transistors, capacitors, and resistors. Transistors have mostly replaced vacuum tubes.*

Figure 10-29. *Tiny silicon chip sitting on a penny contains integrated circuits. Such chips make it possible to build much smaller computers than with vacuum tubes and hand-wired circuits.*

Figure 10-30. *A desk top computer is a marvel of engineering for the miniature. Circuits to make it operate once would have filled a large room.*

change their conducting characteristics. Because they are much smaller, sturdier, and need much less electric power, transistors have replaced vacuum tubes almost completely.

Integrated circuits are complete electric circuits containing thousands of transistors, resistors, capacitors, and conductors on a tiny piece, or "chip," of silicon. Silicon chips are typically 2 to 4 mm square. Integrated circuits need less space and power than circuits of individual transistors.

A **computer** is a complex electronic machine that stores information, does calculations, helps write letters, runs factories, and even figures change on purchases. It is a valuable tool that is used to solve many kinds of problems. A computer cannot think for itself, but must be told what to do by specific instructions.

Computers can be divided into two classes. *Analog computers* handle information by using voltages that vary with the quantities that they represent. Analog computers are widely used in engineering. On the other hand, *digital computers* handle information by patterns of electronic pulses. Digital computers are more popular because they can be used on a wide range of general problems.

Every computer performs three main functions. A computer accepts information, called **input,** in many forms. Electronic devices that are used for input include keyboards, magnetic tapes, and disks. Input devices are usually outside of the computer. They convert information into electric signals which the computer can receive and use.

Once it is received, the information is **processed,** or changed in some way, inside the computer by a set of instructions. Processing is performed by electronic switching devices. These switches form patterns of electronic pulses that the computer recognizes as instructions or data. The patterns can represent numbers, letters of the alphabet, punctuation, and many other symbols.

The results of processing the information, or **output,** is then sent to other electronic machines. These include printers, magnetic tapes or disks, and cathode ray tubes like those found in television.

The central processing unit (CPU) is the so-called "brain" of the computer. It contains the control unit and the arithmetic/logic unit. The control unit directs the flow of instructions, and the arithmetic/logic unit manipulates data. The control unit also manages the flow of data to and from the computer's memory.

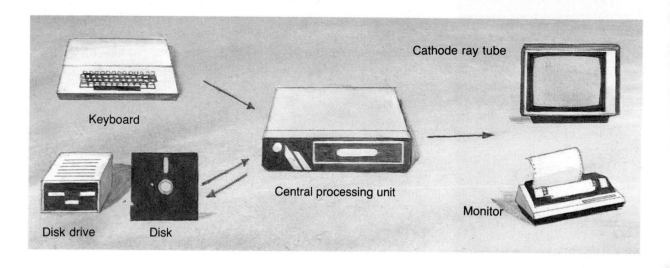

Cathode ray tube

Keyboard

Central processing unit

Monitor

Disk drive

Disk

The central processor and the internal memory of a computer can only work with information sent to them in a special code. All instructions and data must be sent as **binary** (BĪ'-ner-ee) **numbers.** The binary number system has only two symbols: 1 (one) and 0 (zero). The numbers correspond to electronic switches in the on and off positions. A binary number *1* is assigned when a switch is on. A binary number *0* is assigned when a switch is off.

The internal memory of a computer is made up of banks of integrated circuits that hold binary information. The internal memory is used to store computer programs as well as data. Computer **programs** are a series of instructions to the computer telling it what steps to take to solve a particular problem.

It is very difficult and tedious to write a program in the binary numbers of the computer's basic language, called machine language. Programming languages such as BASIC, PASCAL, FORTRAN, COBOL, and many others have been developed to provide an easier way to give the computer instructions. These languages have words and symbols that are more like words of English than binary-coded machine language. However, the computer cannot understand these words directly. These languages have to be translated by special programs that are either built into the computer or loaded into computer memory by some input device.

Quick Review

1. What are three functions that a computer performs?
2. What is a binary number system?
3. What are two main kinds of computers?

Figure 10-31. *Typical computer system contains these components. The keyboard and disk give input to the central processing unit. The central processing unit gives output to the cathode ray tube, printer, and disk.*

Quick Review answers:
1. Input, processing, output.
2. A number system with two symbols: *1* and *0*.
3. Analog and digital.

Decimal numbers	Binary numbers
1	0 0 0 0 0 1
2	0 0 0 0 1 0
3	0 0 0 0 1 1
4	0 0 0 1 0 0
5	0 0 0 1 0 1
6	0 0 0 1 1 0
7	0 0 0 1 1 1
8	0 0 1 0 0 0

Figure 10-32.

Careers

Electrical engineers help to develop electrical and electronic devices that benefit many people.

Electrical Engineer

Electrical engineers specialize in areas such as electric power distribution, communications systems, integrated circuits, or computer design. They find employment in private industry, in public utilities, in government agencies, and in colleges and universities.

Electrical engineers are called upon to be creative, to solve problems, and to work with detail and precision. They often have to work with other people as part of a team. Good communication skills are also important to an electrical engineer.

Entry into the field is usually through completion of a bachelor's degree in electrical engineering. Some people may enter the field with a degree in physics or mathematics. Graduate study is increasingly important. To prepare for an engineering program in college, high school students should take physics and as much mathematics as is offered.

For more information write to: Institute of Electrical and Electronic Engineers/United States Activity Board, 1111 19th St. N.W., Suite 608, Washington, D.C. 20036.

Electricians install, maintain, and repair electrical systems.

Electrician

Electricians install and repair electrical systems that operate heating, lighting, air conditioning, or anything needing electric power. Some electricians are self-employed. Others work for contractors or power companies. Construction work is seasonal, but since the electrician generally works indoors, the electrician usually has year-round employment.

Special skills in dexterity and physical stamina are often needed in doing the work of an electrician. The work can be hazardous, and extra care must always be exercised. Outdoor work under adverse weather conditions may be required. Even short interruptions in electric power can cause hardship to the general public. The power company electrician can be called upon at any time.

The training needed to be an electrician is normally gained through a three- or four-year apprenticeship program. Some training is offered in high school or trade school course work. In some cities, electricians must be licensed before they can work. A high school physics course can provide a good background for the training required to be an electrician.

For more information write to: Independent Electrical Contractors, Inc., 1101 Connecticut Ave. N.W., Suite 700, Washington, D.C. 20036.

10.3 Section Review

Answers to Understanding the Concepts and solutions to Problems to Solve appear on page T145 in the front of this book. Blackline master test for this section: Section Testsheet 10-3 (TRB page 228)

Vocabulary

12 binary number
18 capacitor
5 circuit breaker
8 computer
10 electronics
6 fuse
4 ground-fault interrupter
3 in parallel
15 input
2 in series
11 integrated circuit
17 output
14 process
7 program
16 resistor
1 short circuit
9 transistor
13 vacuum tube

Vocabulary Review

Match each term above with the numbered phrase that best describes it.

1. Created when a conductor with large resistance is bypassed
2. Describes conductors that are in the same current path
3. Describes conductors that provide alternate paths for the current
4. Used in circuits that are in places where there is water
5. Opens a switch when the current is too large
6. Burns out when the current is too large
7. A set of instructions for a computer
8. A calculating machine
9. A switching device made of semiconducting materials
10. The science that deals with complex circuits
11. Thousands of electronic components on a small chip
12. Has values of *1* and *0*
13. Holds electrodes in an airless container
14. To change information in a computer
15. Information that goes into a computer
16. A component of a circuit with a specific resistance
17. Information that has been processed by a computer
18. A device in a circuit that can store an electric charge

Review Questions

Multiple Choice: Choose the answer that best completes each of the following sentences.

19. According to Ohm's law, when the voltage in a circuit is doubled, the current ?
    a. is doubled
    b. is four times as great
    c. is reduced by half
    d. does not change
20. According to Ohm's law, when the resistance is doubled, the current ? .
    a. is doubled
    b. is four times as great
    c. is reduced by half
    d. does not change

Understanding the Concepts

21. Suppose you plug a portable heater into the wall. As soon as you turn it on, all the lights in the room go out. Explain what must have happened.
22. Common flashlights require two "D" cells. The cells are pressed against each other by a spring. Explain what advantage two cells have over a single cell.

Problem to Solve

23. When the switch in the circuit shown below is closed, the voltmeter measures 3.0 V. Assume that the resistance of bulb 2 is 0.3Ω. What is the current flowing through bulb 2?

10 Chapter Review

Answers appear on page T146 in the front of this book. Blackline master test for this chapter: Chapter Testsheets 10A and 10B (TRB pages 259–260)

Vocabulary

alternating current	fuse	positive terminal
ammeter	ground	process
ampere	ground-fault interrupter	program
attract	induced charges	repel
battery	induction	resistance
binary number	in parallel	resistor
capacitor	input	short circuit
circuit	in series	static charges
circuit breaker	integrated circuit	static electricity
closed circuit	insulator	transistor
computer	lightning rod	vacuum tube
conductor	negative terminal	volt
direct current	ohm	voltage
electric current	open circuit	voltage drop
electronics	output	voltmeter

Review of Concepts

Electric charges cause pushes and pulls between objects that do not have equal numbers of positive and negative charges.

- Neutral objects have equal numbers of protons and electrons.
- Objects that gain electrons are negatively charged.
- Objects that lose electrons are positively charged.
- Opposite charges attract; like charges repel.
- Electrons move easily through conductors of electric charge but do not move through insulators.
- Objects can be charged by friction, contact, and induction.
- The force between charged objects depends on the amount of charge on each object and the distance between them.
- Energy is required to separate opposite charges or to bring together like charges.

An **electric current** is created by the movement of electric charges.

- Electric charges move only when energy is supplied.
- A current will flow when there is an unbroken path of conductors connected between the negative and positive terminals of an energy source such as a cell.
- The size of a current is measured as the amount of charge that passes a point per second.
- In a direct current, electrons move in only one direction.
- In an alternating current, electrons move back and forth in a regular cycle.
- Resistance is a measure of how hard it is for charge to move through a conductor.
- The amount of energy removed per unit of charge passing through a conductor is the voltage drop across the conductor.

- The voltage drop across a conductor equals the resistance times the current through it.
- The amount of electric energy used per second by an electric appliance is its power.

An **electric circuit** is a conducting path or set of paths through which current can flow.

- A closed circuit is an unbroken loop, while an open circuit has a break in the path.
- A series circuit provides only one path for all the charges moving through the circuit.
- A parallel circuit provides branches, or alternate paths, so that the moving charges divide up among the branches.
- Fuses, circuit breakers, and ground-fault interrupters open a circuit when the current becomes too high for safety.

A **computer** is an electronic machine that handles data and does calculations using complex circuits.

- Components of complex circuits include capacitors, resistors, vacuum tubes, and transistors.
- Two classes of computers— analog and digital—handle information differently.
- Computers perform three functions with information: input, processing, and output.

Critical Thinking

1. When rubbed with flannel, a balloon becomes negatively charged. Which must have a greater ability to attract electrons?
2. You may have tried to clean a vinyl plastic record by rubbing it with a cloth. Results were probably discouraging. Explain why the record collects lint and dust again almost immediately.
3. Compare how voltmeters and ammeters are connected in a circuit. How would you expect the resistance of a voltmeter to compare with the resistance of an ammeter? Explain your answer.
4. Using your understanding of the effect of increased temperature, explain why the resistance of a wire increases as its temperature increases.
5. Even though electrical forces are much stronger than the force of gravity, why does gravity seem stronger to us?
6. Explain how you would connect a group of dry cells together to get the longest time of energy output from them.

7. Several machines are connected in parallel in a circuit. All have different resistances. If the voltage drop across each one is the same, which one will conduct the most current when it is being used?

Individual Research

8. Charge a filled balloon by rubbing it with flannel. Bring the charged balloon close to a fine stream of water from a faucet. Note what happens to the stream of water. Does the wool flannel have any effect on the stream of water? Find out what causes charged objects to affect the stream of water.
9. Add some pieces of plastic foam used as packing to a plastic container. Find out how the plastic foam pieces behave when rubbed with a piece of wool flannel. Find out what kind of charge is present on the pieces of plastic foam.
10. Examine a monthly electric bill for your home. Record the number of kilowatt-hours used. Determine the average cost of electricity per kilowatt-hour and the cost per joule. Note whether the bill indicates that the cost per kilowatt-hour changes when the usage is over a certain amount.
11. An ammeter can easily be damaged if excess current flows through it. Examine an ammeter. Find out what effect of the moving electric charges causes the needle to move. Find out what characteristics of the ammeter make it so susceptible to being damaged.

12. Find out from a physics text or other source how different amounts of electric current affect the human body.

Bibliography

Asimov, Isaac. *How Did We Find Out About Electricity?* New York: Walker, 1973.
 Historical breakthroughs in our knowledge about electric charges and currents are presented from the time of the ancient Greeks.

Bender, Alfred. *Science Projects with Electrons and Computers.* New York: Arco, 1977
 This book is a collection of experiments involving electric charges, batteries, motors, generators, and even a primitive computer.

Boltz, C. L. *How Electricity Is Made.* New York: Facts on File, 1985
 The author discusses the relation of electricity to the modern theory of the electron and explores natural and man-made sources of electricity.

Cosner, Shaaron. *The Light Bulb: Inventions that Changed our Lives.*
 This is a readable biography of Thomas Alva Edison, who changed our lives with his inventions.

Math, Irvin. *Wires and Watts; Understanding and Using Electricity.* New York: Scribner, 1981
 The author describes imaginative do-it-yourself projects using easily obtained, inexpensive materials.

Chapter 11
Electromagnetism

In this chapter, you will learn about the relationship between magnets and electric currents. In the photo at right is an experimental Japanese train. It is raised about 1 cm above the center rail by a magnetic field. Because friction is reduced, the train can travel at speeds of 300 km/hr.

Science background information:

The property known as magnetism is produced by the movement of electric charges. This is true not only on the macroscopic level, as in motors and solenoids, but also at the subatomic level. Electrons are the most fundamental unit of electric charge. Any motion of an electron, therefore, produces a corresponding magnetic field. Electrons in an atom move around the nucleus. At the same time they also spin about their own axis. It is believed that in commonly magnetic materials, such as iron, cobalt, and nickel, the spinning electrons are responsible for most all the magnetic properties.

A spinning electron acts as a tiny permanent magnet. However, an electron can spin in either a clockwise or counterclockwise direction. This is known in quantum mechanics as having a spin value of $+\frac{1}{2}$ or $-\frac{1}{2}$. Two magnetic fields generated by two electrons with opposite spins exactly cancel each other. When electrons are not paired off in this way and there are several spinning in one direction, the magnetic field is enhanced. In most substances the spin of electrons cancels out and there is no net magnetic effect. In iron, cobalt, and nickel, however, the electronic configuration is such that the spins do not cancel. Iron, for example, has four unpaired electrons in the outermost *d* orbital. Similarly, cobalt has three unpaired electrons and nickel two. Each atom of

For detailed information about teaching this chapter, see Chapter 11 Planning Guide on pages T148–T149 in the front of this book.

Projectsheet 2 (TRB page 174) and Research Lab 2 (Lab Manual pages 29–30) may be used at any point in this chapter.

Chapter Preview

Projectsheet 11 (TRB page 183) and Research Lab 11 (Lab Manual pages 159–160) may be used at any point in this chapter.

11.1 Magnets

- **Magnetic poles and domains**
- **Magnetic fields**
- **Electromagnetism**
- **Electromagnets**
- **Galvanometers**
- **Electromagnetic induction**

There are two kinds of magnetic poles on a magnet. Like poles repel, while unlike poles attract. Electric currents produce magnetic effects, and magnets produce electric effects.

11.2 Electric Energy

- **Generation of electric energy**
- **Electric energy from other sources**
- **Transportation of electric energy**
- **Uses of electric energy**

Electric energy is produced by a conversion from other forms of energy. It is usually transported over large distances. Most often, it is used to make things move or converted to heat or light.

these substances acts as its own tiny magnet due to the spin of its unpaired electrons.

Not all samples of iron, cobalt, and nickel are magnets. This is because the individual magnetized atoms are naturally oriented in random directions because of the internal energy of the metals. A majority of the magnetic atoms must be aligned in one direction to create a magnetic domain of 1 million to 1 billion atoms. These magnetic domains in turn must be primarily oriented in one direction if the sample of metal is to be a magnet. The actual alignment of magnetic domains have been visualized under the microscope by smearing a colloidal of suspension of fine iron oxide powder on the metal to outline the domains. They can be seen and heard to click into alignment when the sample is subjected to a strong magnetic field.

The unit of measure of magnetic field strength is the gauss, named for Karl Friedrich Gauss, 1777–1855, a German astronomer and mathematician. The earth's magnetic field at the latitude of New York City is approximately 0.3 gauss. The strongest permanent magnet has a field of approximately 10 000 gauss. Conventional electromagnets can produce a field up to 60 000 gauss and strengths of several million gauss have been reached by electromagnets operating without cores in a vacuum. Several million gauss provide enough energy to melt steel.

It is important to remember that because magnetism is produced by motion it is relativistic. If a charge is in motion relative to the observer there is a definite magnetic field. However, if the charge and observer are moving along together, the observer will perceive no magnetic field.

For ideas for classroom demonstration and discussion, see Getting Started on page T150 in the front of this book.

11.1 Magnets

Supplemental materials: Teaching Diagrams 11-1A, 11-1B, (TRB pages 55–56), Reading Checksheet 11-1 (TRB page 109), Skillsheet 11-1 (TRB page 155), Investigation 11-1 (Lab Manual pages 153–154)

Section Preview

- **Magnetic poles and domains**
- **Magnetic fields**
- **Electromagnetism**
- **Electromagnets**
- **Galvanometers**
- **Electromagnetic induction**

Bracketed numbers are Section Review questions correlated to that objective.

Learning Objectives

1. To describe the behavior of magnets and their interaction with other magnetic materials. [6, 9, 10, 12, 18, 20]
2. To define a magnetic field and explain the behavior of magnetic materials in a magnetic field. [1, 4, 13, 19]
3. To demonstrate the magnetic effects of an electric current. [2, 5, 8, 15]
4. To illustrate how a changing magnetic field can be used to produce an electric current. [3, 7, 14]

Figure 11-1. *Iron tacks are attracted to the end of a bar magnet. The magnetic forces are strongest at the two ends of the magnet.*

Main Idea

What are the poles of a magnet?

Magnets are fascinating. A small magnet can pick up many paper clips or tacks. People have known about magnets for thousands of years. Yet, a real understanding of them has developed only in the last two centuries.

Magnetic poles and domains

New vocabulary: pole, magnetic domain, permanent magnet

Paper clips and tacks cluster at the ends of a straight, or bar, magnet. These places on a magnet where the magnetic forces are strongest are called the **poles.** The poles of a bar magnet are at either end. The poles of a horseshoe magnet are at the ends of the "legs."

The two poles of a magnet are different. If you bring them close to one of the poles of another magnet, they respond differently. One pole of the first magnet will attract the third pole and stick to it. The other pole of the first magnet will repel the third pole. This is evidence that the two poles are different.

If a bar magnet is allowed to swing freely, one pole will line up toward the north, more or less. This pole is called the north-seeking pole, or simply the *north pole*. The other pole lines up toward the south. It is called the south-seeking pole or *south pole*.

The north poles of different magnets repel each other. So do the south poles of different magnets. The south pole of one magnet and the north pole of another magnet attract each other. It is a rule of magnetism that like poles repel and unlike poles attract. The strength of these forces is greatest when the poles are closest together and weakest when they are farthest apart. In this way, magnetic poles behave just like electric charges.

Magnetic poles are unlike electric charges in one very important way. Positive electric charges can be separated from negative electric charges. They exist as separate entities. The north and south poles of a magnet, however, cannot be separated. Breaking a bar magnet produces two magnets. Each of the magnets has a north and a south pole. Breaking each of these magnets in half produces twice as many complete magnets. Each smaller magnet has a north and a south pole. This process can be continued until the magnets are very, very tiny.

A magnet attracts paper clips even though the clips are not magnets themselves. Here, a magnet acts like a charged balloon that sticks to the wall. A charged balloon can make a wall act as though it is temporarily charged. A magnet can make a paper clip act as though it is temporarily a magnet.

The properties of a magnet can be explained by the following model. A magnet is pictured as a collection of many tiny magnets. These are called **magnetic domains.** In a magnet, the domains are all lined up so that their north poles point in the same direction. The domains are actually clusters of atoms which act together as tiny magnets.

In any material that is unmagnetized, the magnetic domains point in all different directions. In some materials the domains will temporarily line up if they are near a large magnet. These materials are ones that are attracted to magnets. They include iron, cobalt, and nickel. When the large magnet is removed, the magnetic domains return to their original positions.

These materials, iron, cobalt, and nickel can be made into **permanent magnets.** This is done by placing the material near a strong magnet or stroking the material many times with a magnet. This makes the magnetic domains line up.

Figure 11-2. *When a magnet is broken, each piece has both a south and a north pole.*

Science background information: The magnetic properties of various substances ultimately relate to the fact that the individual atoms of these substances have magnetic fields because of their electrons.

Main Idea

What is a magnetic domain?

Additional information: Other materials, because of their atomic structure, do not form magnetic domains, and therefore are not attracted to magnets.

Figure 11-3. *(Left) In nonmagnetic iron, the domains are lined up in all directions. (Right) When iron is made into a magnet, the domains line up with their north poles all pointing in the same direction.*

 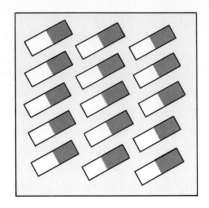

The magnetic properties of a magnet can be destroyed by heating. When the temperature of a substance rises, its particles move faster. The domains move around and get out of order. Banging a magnet can also destroy its magnetic properties. The domains are pushed out of order.

Quick Review

1. What happens when the south poles of two magnets are brought close to each other?
2. How can the attraction between a magnet and an iron nail be explained?
3. What is a magnetic domain?
4. Must every magnet have a north and south pole?

Magnetic fields

New vocabulary: magnetic field, magnetic field line

A magnet does not have to touch something to exert force on it. Magnetic forces, like electric and gravitational forces, act at a distance. Two magnets repel or attract each other without direct contact.

The region around a magnet is where magnetic forces can act and is said to be filled with a **magnetic field.** The field is strongest where an object would feel the strongest force.

At each position around the magnet, the field has a direction as well as a strength. The direction of the field is the direction that a compass needle would point if placed there.

A magnetic field can be represented by curving lines. These lines are called **magnetic field lines.** A tiny compass needle would line up along the magnetic field line at any place in the field. The magnetic field lines around a magnet are a map of the magnetic field. Where the lines are closest together, the magnetic field is strongest. Where the lines are farthest apart, the field is weakest.

Main Idea

What is a magnetic field?

Activity

11.1a Mapping a Magnetic Field

Science Processes: Observing, collecting data, recording data, communicating by a drawing, inferring

Materials   30 minutes   Groups of 2 to 4

- bar magnet
- sheet of unlined paper
- small compass

Purpose

To map the magnetic field around a bar magnet.

Procedure

1. Place a bar magnet near the center of a piece of unlined paper.
2. Outline the position of the magnet with a pencil. Label the north and south poles.
3. Place a small compass near the north pole. Draw a small arrow at the end of the compass needle closest to the magnet. Make sure that your arrow points in the same direction as the north end of the compass needle.
4. Move the compass to many different locations around the north end of the bar magnet. At each location draw an arrow that points in the same direction as the north end of the compass needle.
5. Repeat step 4 for different locations near the south pole and the center of the bar magnet.

Teacher Note
The smaller the compass compared to the bar magnet, the more accurate are the results.

6. Fill in the spaces between the arrows that you already have drawn. Continue until the paper around the magnet is filled with small arrows. The more arrows that you draw, the clearer will be the results.
7. Starting at the north pole, draw a smooth line through a nearby arrow. Continue the line, curving it as necessary, and keeping it parallel to the arrows near it or passing through the arrows, until the line reaches the south pole of the bar magnet.
8. Draw at least five lines on each side of the magnet.

Questions

1. Are the lines, which represent a magnetic field, closer together at the poles or at the center of the magnet?
2. Where is the direction of field, as shown by the lines, parallel to the magnet?
3. Where is the direction of the field, shown by the lines, directly toward or away from the magnet?

Conclusion

Describe the magnetic field around a bar magnet.

Step 2

Step 3

Iron filings may be used to outline a magnetic field. A piece of paper, glass, or plastic is placed over the magnet. Iron filings are sprinkled on the paper. Each of the iron filings acts like a tiny, temporary magnet. The filings line up in the field like little compass needles. The positions of the filings show the direction of the magnetic field lines all around the magnet.

The iron filings are closest together where the magnetic field is the strongest. They are farthest apart where the magnetic field is the weakest. Thus, they show the positions of the magnetic field lines for the magnet.

The needle in a compass is a magnetized needle that is free to turn. It tends to point north because the earth itself has a magnetic field. A compass needle lines up with the magnetic field lines of the earth's own field.

The earth's magnetic field is nearly the same as that produced by a large bar magnet. The earth acts as though there were a bar magnet deep inside, near the earth's center.

Figure 11-4. *Iron filings outlining the magnetic field of a bar magnet (top) and horseshoe magnet (bottom). How can you tell where the poles of the magnets must be?*
Iron filings are concentrated at the poles of the magnets.

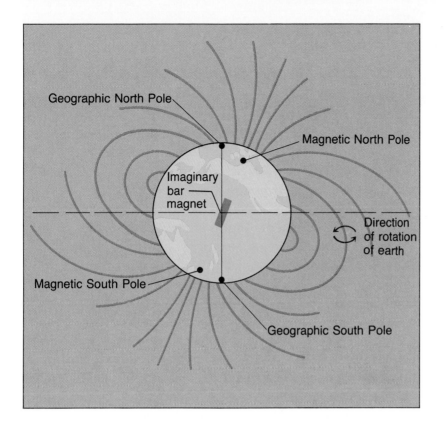

A compass needle does not point to the earth's true geographic north pole. This is because the imaginary bar magnet does not point directly north and south. Instead, it points northward to what is called the earth's magnetic north pole. The earth's magnetic north pole is in northern Canada, just north of the Arctic Circle. Similarly, the earth's magnetic south pole is right near the Antarctic Circle, south of Australia. The earth's magnetic poles slowly move. Studies indicate that there have been major changes in the earth's magnetic field over long time periods.

Pieces of iron can be magnetized with the help of the earth's field. A piece of iron is lined up with the earth's field. The iron is given a sharp blow with a hammer. The magnetic domains inside the iron are shaken by the blow. They realign in the direction of the earth's field. Now the entire piece of iron is a magnet.

Quick Review

1. How do magnetic field lines represent the strength of a magnetic field?
2. Explain why the magnetic north pole is in a different location from the geographic north pole.

Data Search

If you were standing on the Mexico-California border, how many degrees should you adjust your magnetic compass to find geographic north? Search pages 658–661.

15° adjustment is necessary

Additional information: Recent theories propose that the earth's magnetic field is created by slow convection currents in the earth's molten iron and nickel core.

Critical Thinking

If the magnetic field of the earth were to reverse, what would be the effects on navigation, on machinery and on animals such as bees and migrating birds?

Navigators use compasses that depend on the earth's magnetism; some machinery is sensitive to the earth's magnetism; bees and some migrating birds use magnetic material in their bodies to help navigate.

Quick Review answers:
1. The closer together the magnetic field lines, the stronger the magnetic field.
2. The earth's magnetic field is not in alignment with the axis of rotation.

Electromagnetism

New vocabulary: electromagnetism

Main Idea

What is the evidence that a current can produce a magnetic field?

A compass can be used to detect whether a wire is carrying an electric current. The needle of the compass is deflected, or turned, away from north when an electric current is present. This is evidence that there must be a magnetic field around the wire. Yet, there is no magnet to produce the magnetic field. The field must come from the current itself. The process by which an electric current produces a magnetic field is known as **electromagnetism.**

The discovery that a current produces a magnetic field caused great excitement. It was the first experimental evidence of a link between electricity and magnetism. The discovery was made by a Danish physics professor, Hans Christian Oersted (1777–1851). He was giving a classroom demonstration. He had a wire lying above a compass. He noticed that when the circuit was closed, the compass needle moved. It lined up at a right angle to the wire. He reversed the connections, so that the current moved in the opposite direction. The needle reversed its direction. It lined up in the opposite direction from before. This not only demonstrated that the current was producing the magnetic field, but also that the direction of the current directly affected the direction of the magnetic field. The direction of the current and of the magnetic field are linked in a definite pattern.

Figure 11-6. *When there is no current in a wire, a nearby compass needle points toward the north. A current causes the needle to line up at right angles to the wire. What happens to the compass needle when the direction of the current is reversed?*
The compass needle reverses direction when the direction of the current is reversed.

Quick Review

1. How can a compass be used to determine if a wire is carrying a current?
2. What was the first experimental evidence that electricity and magnetism are related?

Electromagnets

New vocabulary: coil, electromagnet

A wire that carries a current has a magnetic field around it. Increasing the current makes the magnetic field stronger. Another way to make the magnetic field stronger is to put many wires side by side. A **coil** of wire—a wire wrapped in a series of loops—is like many wires side by side. The same cur-

Our Science Heritage

Hans Christian Oersted

The Danish scientist Hans Christian Oersted (1777–1851) discovered somewhat by accident that a current exerts a force on a magnet. He was lecturing to students at the time. Because of his background, he was able to realize the importance of his discovery. He repeated and refined the experiment outside of class. Then he demonstrated the effect for other scientists and published his findings.

Prior to the discovery, Oersted believed that electricity and magnetism were connected. Ten years earlier, he had suggested the connection in a paper he wrote. One reason the connection may not have been discovered earlier is that the direction of the force is unusual. The current neither pulls the needle toward

itself nor pushes it directly away. Instead, the current makes the needle align at a right angle to the wire.

Many important scientific discoveries have been made by accident. They might have been overlooked had not a person with the right training noticed the unexpected. Before a discovery is accepted by other scientists, it must be observed many other times.

Oersted made other contributions to science. He was the first to determine the compressibility of water accurately. He experimented with thermocouples. He also improved the tension balance to measure electric forces.

To make the public aware of new findings in science, Oersted founded a society to promote science in Denmark.

Hans Christian Oersted linked electric current with magnetism during a classroom demonstration.
Several characteristics of science are illustrated in the story of Oersted. The possible discovery of principles of science by "accident," the importance of observation and training, and the necessity of submitting the discovery for review by other scientists are some characteristics that can be pointed out.

11.1b   The Magnetic Field of a Current-Carrying Wire

Science Processes: Observing, collecting data, recording data, communicating, inferring

Materials   20 minutes   Groups of 4

- 2 "D" cells
- masking tape
- 30-cm × 30-cm heavy cardboard
- at least 60-cm insulated wire with ends exposed
- 4 small compasses
- 5 thick books

Purpose

To map the magnetic field around a straight current-carrying wire.

Procedure

1. Tape together two "D" cells top to bottom to form a battery.
2. Punch a small hole in the center of a 30-cm by 30-cm piece of cardboard.
3. Push one end of the wire through the hole in the cardboard and tape it to the negative terminal (flat end) of your battery.
4. Place one side of the cardboard in the center of a stack of five books so that most of the cardboard sticks out.
5. Lay the upper end of the wire over the top book. Make sure the wire passes straight up and down through the cardboard.
6. Put four small compasses on the cardboard around the wire. Record the direction each needle points.
7. Close the circuit for a few seconds by touching the free end of the wire to the positive terminal of the battery. Record the direction each compass needle points when the current flows through the wire.
8. Reverse the direction of the current through the wire by reversing the connections to the battery. Again record the direction each compass needle points when current flows through the wire.

Questions

1. Do the compass needles point in the same direction when no current is flowing?
2. What happens to the compass needles when current flows through the wire?
3. What happens to the compass needles when current flows the opposite way?

Conclusion

What is the shape of the magnetic field lines around a straight current-carrying wire?

Step 3

Step 6

rent goes through each loop of the coil. The magnetic field is much stronger than it would be if the wire were straight.

The magnetic field of a coil of wire can be made stronger by inserting an iron bar in the coil. The iron bar with the coil around it is then an **electromagnet** (ih-lek′-trō-MAG′-net). The magnetic domains in the iron line up in the magnetic field. When the current stops, the domains return to their original positions. Electromagnets are useful because they can be turned on and off.

Increasing the number of turns in the coil makes the magnetic field stronger. The fields of all the turns add together to make up the field of the whole coil.

Another way to strengthen the magnetic field of an electromagnet is to increase the current in the coil. This can be done by increasing the voltage supplied to the coil.

Quick Review

1. Why are electromagnets useful?
2. Name two ways to make the magnetic field of an electromagnet stronger.

Galvanometers

New vocabulary: galvanometer

A **galvanometer** (gal-vuh-NOM′-uh-ter) is an instrument that can detect small currents. It has a needle that is deflected by the magnetic field of a coil of wire. Greater currents produce stronger magnetic fields. The stronger the magnetic field is, the more the needle is deflected.

A simple galvanometer can be made with a coil of wire and a compass. Figure 11-7 shows such a galvanometer, made with about 50 turns in the coil. The coil is vertical. A compass fits horizontally inside it.

The ends of the coil can be connected into a circuit. When current flows through the coil, a magnetic field is produced. The direction of the magnetic field inside the coil is at a right angle to the whole coil. The needle is deflected in the direction of the field. When the current reverses direction, the magnetic field is in the opposite direction. The needle is deflected toward the other side. Thus, a galvanometer can measure the direction of a current.

Quick Review

1. What are the parts of a simple galvanometer?
2. What is the primary use of a galvanometer?

Quick Review answers:
1. A compass and a coil of wire connected to a circuit.
2. To measure the direction of a current.

Figure 11-7. *A simple galvanometer can be made with a coil of wire and a compass. When the coil is connected to a circuit, current flows through it. The magnetic field inside the coil makes the compass needle turn.*

Electromagnetic induction

New vocabulary: electromagnetic induction, induce, electric generator

A wire with a current through it has a magnetic field. A coil of wire with a current through it acts like a bar magnet.

If a magnet can be made by using a current, can a current be made by using a magnet? Michael Faraday (1791–1867), an Englishman, was the first person to announce that it could be done. An American physics professor, Joseph Henry (1797–1878), had discovered it on his own. However, he had been too busy teaching to publish his results.

A coil of wire is attached to a galvanometer to make a closed circuit. No cell or battery is included. The coil is then placed around the end of a bar magnet. When the coil is moved along the magnet, a current is created in the wire. The current changes direction when the coil is moved in the opposite direction. How does this occur?

The wire coil contains electrons that can move easily. When the coil is moving, the electrons are acted on by a magnetic force that makes them move through the coil, producing a current. When neither the coil nor magnet is moving, the electrons are not acted on by a magnetic force and do not move within the coil. Hence, no current is produced.

The direction of the current can be changed by moving the coil in the opposite direction. This reverses the direction of the force on the electrons and they move through the coil in the opposite direction.

Another way to change the direction of the current is to change the direction of the magnetic field. This can be done by passing the other end of the bar magnet through the coil of wire.

Figure 11-8. *A current can be detected in a coil when either the coil moves through the field of a magnet (left) or a magnet moves through the coil (right).*

Figure 11-9. *A large electric generator. It uses steam turbines to turn coils within a magnetic field, thereby producing electric current.*

Moving a coil over the end of a bar magnet produces a current. So does moving a bar magnet through a coil. It makes no difference whether it is the coil or the magnet that is moving. The important thing is the motion. When the motion stops, the current stops.

The production of an electric current by using a magnet is known as **electromagnetic induction** (in-DUK′-shun). The current is said to be **induced** (in-DEWST′). The discovery of induction made it possible for every home and business to have electric currents. Currents could be produced without using cells or batteries of any kind which made electricity less expensive and more convenient.

Devices that produce electric current by turning a coil through a magnetic field are called **electric generators** (JEN′-er-rayt-erz). In most communities, the current is supplied by large generators, which may be far away.

At the generating plant, energy to turn the coils of wire is supplied by one of several kinds of sources. Sometimes falling water turns the coils. More often, large steam turbines turn the coils. Water is changed into steam by heat produced from burning fossil fuels such a natural gas or coal. Nuclear

Main Idea

What is the term for the production of an electric current by using a magnet?

Research Topic

Modern electric generators produce alternating current. Find out how an alternating current is produced by a generator.

11.1c   Making an Electromagnet

Science Processes: Observing, collecting data, recording data, communicating, predicting, inferring

Materials   20 minutes   Groups of 2

- 1-m insulated wire with ends exposed
- pen or pencil
- masking tape
- 2 "D" cells
- iron tack or brads
- long iron bolt

Purpose

To make an electromagnet and determine how its strength can be changed.

Procedure

1. Prepare a narrow coil of wire by winding the middle part of a 1m insulated wire around a pencil or pen. Leave about 30 cm free at each end. Remove the pencil or pen.
2. Using masking tape, attach one end of the wire to the negative (flat) end of a "D" cell.
3. Place a pile of tacks or brads near one end of the coil. Briefly touch the free end of the wire to the positive (top) end of the cell. Record what happens to the tacks.
4. Place an iron bolt inside the coil. Hold the end of the coil over the tacks. Touch the free end of the wire to the top of the cell. Record how many tacks are picked up.

5. Increase the number of turns in the coil. Leave only 3 to 5 cm of wire free at each end. Leave the bolt in the coil during the following steps.
6. Briefly close the circuit and record the number of tacks picked up.
7. Tape a second cell to the first, top to bottom.
8. Predict how the second cell will affect the electromagnet. Record your prediction.
9. Briefly close the circuit. Record how many tacks are picked up by the electromagnet.

Questions

1. Was there any evidence that the empty coil of wire had a magnetic field?
2. What happens to an electromagnet when the circuit is broken?
3. How did putting an iron bolt in the coil change the magnetic field?
4. How did increasing the number of turns in the coil change the magnetic field?
5. What happened to the magnetic field when the second "D" cell was added?
6. What advantages does an electromagnet have over a permanent magnet?

Conclusion

What factors change the strength of an electromagnet?

Step 3

Step 4

reactions are used in some generating plants. Sunlight is being tried as the source in a few experimental plants with solar collectors.

Faraday made another important discovery about electric currents. A changing current in one circuit produces a current in another circuit, even though the circuits are not connected.

Look at Figure 11-10. It shows a circuit containing a battery and a coil of wire wound around an iron bar. A second circuit with no battery has a coil that is wound over the first coil. The two coils are separated by insulation. Electrons cannot move from one circuit to the other. The second circuit contains a galvanometer.

When the first circuit is opened or closed, a current is observed in the second circuit. When the first circuit has a steady current, there is no current in the second circuit. Only a *changing* current in the first circuit produces a current in the second circuit.

Closing the circuit creates a magnetic field around the first coil. Since there is no field when the circuit is open, closing the circuit changes the magnetic field. Similarly, opening the circuit changes the magnetic field. The second coil is then in a changing magnetic field. The changing field has the same effect as motion through a field. Even though there is no motion, the change in the field induces a current in the second coil.

Thus, electric currents can be induced three ways. A coil in a closed circuit can be moved within a magnetic field. A magnetic field can be moved in relation to the coil. Or the magnetic field around the coil can be changed.

With a cell or battery, the only way to change the current is to open or close the circuit. However, alternating current is constantly changing. If one coil is connected to a source of alternating current, there will always be a current in the second coil. The second current will be an alternating current, too.

Moving charges produce magnetic fields. Changing magnetic fields produce electric currents. Clearly, electric and magnetic forces are linked.

Quick Review

1. Describe three ways that a current can be induced in a circuit.
2. Explain how an electric generator works.

Iron bar

Galvanometer

Battery

Switch

Figure 11-10. *A current can be induced in the circuit connected to the galvanometer. The current is induced when the circuit connected to the battery is opened or closed. The changing magnetic field of the inner coil induces a current in the outer coil.*

Main Idea

What are the ways to induce an electric current?

Quick Review answers:
1. Move a coil in a magnetic field, move a magnet through a coil of wire, or change the magnetic field around a coil.
2. A coil is moved through a magnetic field, generating a current in the wire.

A computer scientist may do much of her work at a computer keyboard.

Computer Scientist

Employment opportunities for persons trained in the use of computers are available in many varied situations. Firms that have large computer systems hire computer scientists as programmers and systems analysts. These firms include major companies as well as banks and insurance companies. Educational institutions also hire computer scientists.

An increasing number of companies are putting out computer products for personal or business use. These companies need computer scientists to write programs that can be used by people with no computer backgrounds.

Developing programs for computers demands attention to detail and persistence in solving problems. Competition among computer firms and the rapid growth of the field ensure excellent job opportunities to people who are highly capable, skilled, and ambitious.

College training is generally required for someone entering this field. High school mathematics and science courses provide valuable background for the study of computer science. The opportunity to work with computers in school or after school can also be a helpful experience.

For further information, write to: Computer Careers—DOL DPMA, 505 Busse Highway, Chicago, Illinois 60068.

In repairing part of a stereo system, a technician uses test equipment to find the problem.

Radio and Television Technician

Radio and television technicians repair radios, television sets, and other electronic products. Many own their own repair shops. Others work for repair shops or for stores that both sell and repair these products. Technicians usually work in their shops, but sometimes are called to do repairs at the home of their customers.

The ability to use tools and certain test instruments is needed. Technicians must be able to diagnose problems and correct them, often by referring to wiring diagrams and service manuals. They must also be able to work with precision. The changing design of products provides variety and new challenges.

Entry into the field usually requires two or more years of technical training. The training may be obtained in a trade school, a community college, or in vocational courses in high school. Additional on-the-job training is needed after the schooling.

For further information, write to: National Association of Television and Electronic Servicers of America (NATESA), 5930 S. Pulaski Road, Chicago, Illinois 60629.

11.1 Section Review

Answers to Check Your Understanding appear on page T151 in the front of this book. Blackline master test for this section: Section Testsheet 11-1 (TRB page 229).

Vocabulary

3 electric generator
2 electromagnet
7 electromagnetic induction
8 electromagnetism
5 galvanometer
11 induce
9 magnetic domain
1 magnetic field
4 magnetic field line
10 permanent magnet
6 pole

Vocabulary Review

Match each term above with the numbered phrase that best describes it.

1. Fills the region around a magnet
2. Becomes a magnet when a current passes through it
3. Produces electric current by turning a coil through a magnetic field
4. Shows how a compass needle would line up
5. Is used to measure the size and direction of small currents
6. One of the places on a magnet where the magnetic forces are strongest
7. Production of a current by a magnetic field
8. The process by which an electric current produces a magnetic field
9. Cluster of atoms that behaves like a tiny magnet
10. Magnet that cannot be turned on and off
11. To generate a current by passing a magnet through a coil

Review Questions

Multiple Choice: Choose the answer that best completes each of the following sentences.

12. One way that magnetic poles differ from electric charges is that ? .
    a. like poles push each other away
    b. unlike poles attract each other
    c. the force between poles becomes weaker as the poles are moved farther apart
    d. a single pole cannot be removed from a magnet
13. The magnetic field of the earth is ? .
    a. strongest at the equator
    b. much like that of a bar magnet
    c. unchanging according to very sensitive measurements
    d. what makes objects fall to the earth
14. Current will be induced in a circuit containing a coil that is ? .
    a. near a magnet
    b. touching a magnet
    c. around a moving magnet
    d. connected to a galvanometer
15. A current in one circuit can induce a current in a second circuit when ? .
    a. the current in the first circuit is constant
    b. the current in the first circuit is alternating
    c. both circuits are in a constant magnetic field
    d. the field due to the current in the first circuit is at right angles to the earth's magnetic field

16. The direction of flow of a current induced by passing a magnet through a coil of wire can be changed by ? .
    a. using a stronger magnet
    b. reversing the poles of the magnet
    c. using a coil with more loops
    d. using a weaker magnet
17. An electric generator converts ? into electric energy.
    a. chemical energy
    b. heat energy
    c. mechanical energy
    d. all of these

Understanding the Concepts

18. Brass is not attracted to a magnet, but steel is. How could you use a magnet to test whether a brass bed was solid brass or brass-coated steel?
19. If you were on an Arctic expedition and were trying to find the true north pole, could you use a compass? Explain.
20. Alnico is an alloy made of steel, aluminum, nickel, and cobalt. It is hard to magnetize. However, once magnetized, it remains magnetic for a long time. Explain why it would not be a good choice for the core of an electromagnet.

For ideas for classroom demonstration and discussion, see Getting Started on page T151 in the front of this book.

11.2 Electric Energy

Supplemental materials: Teaching Diagram 11-2 (TRB page 57), Reading Check-sheet 11-2 (TRB page 110), Skillsheet 11-2 (TRB page 156), Investigation 11-2 (Lab Manual pages 157–158)

Section Preview

- **Generation of electric energy**
- **Electric energy from other sources**
- **Transportation of electric energy**
- **Uses of electric energy**

Bracketed numbers are Section Review questions correlated to that objective.

Learning Objectives

1. To identify the various sources of electric energy. [3, 7, 8, 9, 10, 12, 15]
2. To describe the procedures used to transfer electric energy over large distances. [4, 5, 6, 16, 18, 19]
3. To identify and describe the ways in which electric energy is put to use. [1, 2, 11, 13, 14, 17]

Figure 11-11. *Lights of a city at dusk show how much we depend on electricity to provide energy for our daily lives. Electricity is one of the most widely used forms of energy.*

The use of energy from electric currents has increased dramatically all over the world during the past few decades. This trend is expected to continue in the years ahead.

Existing electric generating plants are being expanded. New electric generating plants are being built each year. They all require energy from an outside source. This energy is used to produce electric currents. The energy carried by currents can be thought of as electric energy.

Research Topic

One of the first electric power plants was the Pearl Street Station, constructed by Thomas Edison in New York City. Find out how power plants have changed over the years. Why is it no longer feasible for each community to have its own power plant?

Generation of electric energy

New vocabulary: steam turbine, hydroelectric

An electric current can be induced when a coil of wire is moved in the magnetic field of a magnet. Large electric generators operate on this principle. Coils of wire are rotated in a strong magnetic field. The magnetic field is generally supplied by large stationary electromagnets.

The rotating coils are usually on a shaft connected to the blades of **steam turbines.** These machines convert heat energy into the energy of motion. The turbine blades are turned by steam formed from the heating of water (Chapter 7, Section 2). When the turbine blades turn, the coils rotate in the magnetic field. Current is induced. See Figure 11-12 below.

As the steam does work by turning the blades, it cools and becomes a liquid. The liquid water is reheated and the process continues. The steam again does the work of turning the blades of the turbine.

The heat needed to change water to steam can come from different sources. Most generating plants now burn coal, oil, or natural gas. Shortages of these fossil fuels have resulted in a wider use of nuclear reactions.

The heat from the nuclear reactions is used in the same way as heat from the burning of fossil fuels. Safeguards are provided to prevent dangerous radiation from leaving the nuclear reactor. Nuclear reactions are described in detail in Chapter 13, Section 2.

A small but important part of the electric energy we use is generated by falling water. Water moves downhill in rivers. When a dam is built across a river, water is held back at the higher level. This is a way of storing the potential energy of the water. A small amount of water is allowed to leave the higher level. As it falls, it turns turbine blades for an electric generator. The potential energy of the falling water is converted to kinetic energy and then to electric energy.

Figure 11-12. *What are the steps that convert the energy released in burning a fossil fuel into electric energy in a generating plant?* Answers in diagram.

Burning of fossil fuel

Water boiling

Steam turning turbine blades

Coil turning between poles of electromagnet

Electric current produced

Figure 11-13. *Hydroelectric plants are built near large dams. What is the source of energy that is used in turning the generator coils?*
The potential and kinetic energy of the falling water.

Data Search

Of the energy consumed in 1983, what percent came from water-power sources? Search pages 658–661.

$$\frac{4092}{74454} = 0.055 = 5.5\%.$$

Quick Review answers:
1. Falling water, nuclear reactions, and solar energy
2. Some sources, such as falling water, drive electric generators directly. Other sources heat water to steam, which in turn drives electric generators.

A generating plant that gets energy from falling water is referred to as **hydroelectric.** The prefix *hydro-* comes from the Greek word for *water.* Hydroelectric plants can provide an inexpensive source of electric energy. Pollution problems that accompany the use of fossil fuels and nuclear reactions can be avoided. However, dams can create other problems because they affect the wildlife that lives in the rivers.

Large solar generating plants are starting to operate in areas that have lots of sunny weather. Rows of mirrors gather and concentrate the sun's radiation. The radiant energy heats the water for a steam turbine.

Quick Review

1. Besides fossil fuels, what can be used as a source of energy in electric generating plants?
2. How are these energy sources converted into electric energy?

Electric energy from other sources
New vocabulary: thermocouple, solar cell

Using magnetic fields and coils of wire is the most common method of generating electric current. There are other methods that are less common. They are used in some very specific situations. They are interesting because they illustrate some very important principles.

Contact between two different metals that are at different temperatures causes a flow of electrons. The amount of current produced depends on the difference in temperature. A device that produces current by contact of two at different temperatures is a **thermocouple** (THER'-mō-kuh-pul).

A simple thermocouple is shown in Figure 11-14. Copper wire and iron wire are twisted together at the ends. The ends, where the two kinds of wire meet, are called junctions. The copper wire has been cut so that a galvanometer could be connected in the middle. The galvanometer can measure any current in the circuit.

One junction is in ice water, at 0°C. The other junction is being heated by a candle. As the second junction becomes hotter, the current in the circuit increases.

Thermocouples are often used as safety devices in furnaces. Suppose the temperature above the burner becomes too high for safety. The thermocouple either can operate the switch for a blower fan or turn off the fuel supply. Thermocouples are also used to indicate the temperature in an automobile engine. Should the temperature reach a danger level, a warning light is turned on. Thermocouples are used to measure temperatures where use of other devices may be difficult. One such example is in very high-temperature furnaces.

Some crystals, such as quartz, produce a flow of electrons when they are compressed under forces. The compression causes changes in the shape of the crystal. The electrons are moved from their normal positions. When the forces are removed, the electrons return to their normal positions. Varying the forces on the crystal varies the current produced. This is known as the *piezoelectric* (pē-Ā'-zō-i-LEK'-trik) *effect*.

Main Idea

What is a thermocouple?

Science background information: One of the most common laboratory thermocouples is made of platinum and a rhodium-platinum alloy. It can measure temperatures in the range of −50° to 1600°C. Industrial thermocouples are made of less expensive metals.

Figure 11-14. *A simple thermocouple. What would happen to the current if the candle were blown out?* The current would be reduced.

Galvanometer

Copper wire

Iron wire

Candle

Ice water

Figure 11-15. *The energy that runs this pocket calculator comes from the sun.*

Quick Review answers:
1. The contact of two different metal wires at different temperatures causes electrons to move.
2. Pressure on the crystal causes electrons to move in the crystal.
3. Energy from the sun causes electrons to move in the solar cell.

Main Idea

What factor must be considered in transporting energy over long distances?

Sound produces compressions. Crystals have been used in microphones. The compressions in the sound wave change the shape of the crystal. These shape changes are converted into a varying electric current. The current can be carried through conductors. Then it can be converted back to sound at a distant location.

Up until the last decade, crystals were common in phonograph cartridges. As the needle moved through the grooves on a record, it changed the shape of the crystal in the cartridge. The changes in shape produced a varying current. The varying current was converted back into the original sounds at the speaker. Modern phonograph cartridges use electromagnetic induction to change motion into current.

Some materials release electrons when light shines on them. Selenium, silicon, and germanium have this property. Cells made of these materials are called **solar cells.** When sunlight falls on a solar cell, electrons move and create a current. The energy of the current comes from the sunlight.

Orbiting satellites and spacecraft rely to a large extent on this source of energy to operate their controls and to send communications. The amount of electric energy produced in a solar cell is small. However, several solar cells can be connected in series to provide the energy needed.

Solar cells have been used in exposure meters for photographers for many years. New uses for them have been found recently. They are the source of energy in many wristwatches and pocket calculators. The energy of light is used to recharge a battery that operates the watch or calculator.

Quick Review

1. How does a thermocouple produce a current?
2. How does a crystal produce a current?
3. How does a solar cell produce a current?

Transportation of electric energy

New vocabulary: transformer, step-up transformer, step-down transformer

Electric generating plants normally serve large areas. Some of the electric energy must be transported great distances. Electric energy cannot be stored very efficiently. It must be produced as it is needed.

The transmission lines that carry the electric energy must heat up as little as possible. The heating of the lines reduces the amount of electric energy available at the receiving end. Thus, the lines should be made of good conductors, which have the lowest resistance.

Silver and copper are the best conducting materials. Copper is used most often. Because of its high cost, silver is used in only very special cases. Although not as good a conductor, aluminum is sometimes used.

The resistance of a conductor increases with its length. Resistance decreases with the thickness of the wire. Using short, large-diameter wires is not possible. The heat loss must be reduced in other ways.

The amount of electric energy transported per unit of time is the power. The power depends on the voltage as well as on the current in the transmission lines. This relationship can be expressed as:

$$\text{electric power} = \text{current} \times \text{voltage}$$

The unit of electric power is the watt (Chapter 10, Section 2, page 474). The same amount of electric power or wattage can be transported at high voltage and low current, or at high current and low voltage.

A low current is preferable. The amount of energy lost in heating increases rapidly as the current increases. When the current is low, large-diameter wires do not need to be used. Thus, electric power is transported at high voltage and low current.

Voltages of more than 300 000 V are used in some transmission lines. Voltages can be raised and lowered by using **transformers.** A transformer consists of two separate coils of wire that are wound on the same piece of iron. The coils are insulated from each other and are in separate circuits. An alternating current in one circuit induces an alternating current in the other circuit.

Figure 11-16. *Power transmission lines transport electric energy at high voltage to make the energy loss as small as possible.*

Main Idea

What does a transformer consist of?

Figure 11-17. *In this transformer, the second coil has five times as many turns as the first coil. If the voltage drop across the first coil is 100 V, what voltage will be induced in the second coil?*
The voltage in the second coil is 500 V.

100 V   ? V

The voltage drops across the two coils are related in a simple way. They depend on the number of turns in each coil. If one coil has three times as many turns, it will have three times the voltage drop of the other coil. If it has one tenth as many turns, it will have only one tenth the voltage drop. This relationship can be expressed in the equation:

$$\frac{\text{Voltage drop of 1st coil}}{\text{Voltage drop of 2nd coil}} = \frac{\text{Turns in 1st coil}}{\text{Turns in 2nd coil}}$$

A very high voltage can be created by using a much greater number of turns on the second coil. How can a high voltage be lowered? Transformers that increase the voltage are called **step-up transformers.** They are used at generating plants to raise the voltage for transmission. Transformers that lower the voltage are called **step-down transformers.** The voltage is stepped-down in stages.

A high voltage can be lowered by using a smaller number of turns on the second coil.

Science background information: Although large transformers are very efficient—as much as 99% efficient—there is some loss due to heating. To reduce heating losses, large transformers are equipped with cooling systems. Point out to students that the fins on transformers at power substations are for cooling to increase their efficiency.

Sample Problem

A step-down transformer is required to transform 110 V to 12 V. If the first coil has 800 turns, how many are in the second coil?

Solution

Use the equation for voltage drop and number of turns to determine the number of turns in the second coil.

$$\frac{110 \text{ V}}{12 \text{ V}} = \frac{800 \text{ turns}}{?\ turns}$$

To solve, multiply both fractions by (12) and (*? turns*), and cancel V.

$$(110)\,(?\ turns) = (12)(800 \text{ turns})$$

Then divide both sides by (110).

$$?\ turns = \frac{(12)(800 \text{ turns})}{110}$$

Dividing out, this gives $\frac{960 \text{ turns}}{11}$, or approximately 81 turns in the second coil.

Practice Problem

Assuming that the second coil has 800 turns, determine the number of turns needed for the first coil in transforming 220 V to 110 V. *Answer:* 1600 turns

See also Activity Record Sheet 11-2A (Lab Manual page 155). Answers to Questions and Conclusion appear on page T152 in the front of this book.

Activity

11.2a Converting Electric Energy to Energy of Motion

Science Processes: Observing, collecting data, recording data, communicating, identifying variables, inferring

20 minutes   Groups of 4 to 6 or teacher demonstration

Materials

- **4-m lacquered wire (#22-26)**
- **fine sandpaper**
- **masking tape**
- **"D" cell**
- **horseshoe or bar magnet**
- **2 books**
- **ring stand and clamp**
- **15-cm × 3-cm diameter wooden dowel**
- **new pencil**

Purpose

To test the hypothesis that electrical energy can be converted to energy of motion.

Procedure

1. Sand the insulation from the ends of the wire. Make sure that the ends are bare and shiny.
2. Wrap the wire around the 3-cm wooden dowel at least 30 times to make a coil. Leave 40 cm of uncoiled wire at each end.
3. Tape the turns of wire together with masking tape and slide the coil off the dowel.
4. Mount the pencil on the ring stand.
5. Wrap the two straight lengths of the wires around the pencil three to four times so that the coil hangs 20 cm below the pencil. Leave 10 cm of wire free at each end. Tape the wires to the pencil.
6. Label one end of the wire "A" and the other end "B" with small pieces of masking tape.
7. Use two books to prop up the horseshoe magnet with the N pole in the air. (Mount a bar magnet between two books so that the N half of the magnet sticks out.)
8. Adjust the height and position of the coil so that it hangs freely around the magnet, but does not touch the magnet.
9. Hold end "A" of the wire against the flat end, or bottom of the "D" cell and briefly touch end "B" to the top. Record the direction that the coil moves. Reverse the pro-cess by touching the wires to the opposite ends of the "D" cell. Record the direction of movement.
10. Change the magnet so that the S pole is inside the coil. Repeat Step 9.

Questions

1. Did reversing the current through the coil reverse the direction that the coil moved when it was around the same pole?
2. Did reversing the pole change the direction that the coil moved when the direction of the current stayed the same?
3. Under what conditions did the coil move the same direction?

Conclusion

Can a magnet and a coil that is carrying current be used to convert electrical energy to energy of motion? List five examples of devices which use this principle.

Step 9

Clamp

"D" cell

Dowel

Ring stand

Coil of wire

B

A

High-voltage transmission lines enter substations, which serve particular areas. Transformers in the substations lower the voltage to several thousand volts. From the substations, the power is distributed to the places where it will be used. The voltage is lowered again (to 110 V in North America) outside small groups of buildings.

In some communities, underground distribution lines are used. Underground lines improve the appearance of the area, but are more expensive. The lines must be surrounded by heavy insulation. *Insulation* is any non-conducting material, such as plastic or rubber, that coats the outside of electrical lines. Insulation keeps the electricity in the conducting lines. The ground is a reasonably good conductor and would absorb energy from the lines. The heavily insulated lines are known as cables.

Many overhead power lines are not covered with insulation. Air itself is a poor conductor. Where the lines are supported by towers or poles, special devices known as insulators keep the lines from making direct contact.

Power lines and transformers are protected from lightning by lightning arrestors. A lightning discharge near a power

Main Idea

Why are some overhead power lines not covered with insulation?

Figure 11-18. *A severe storm can cause power lines to fall and electric service to be interrupted.*

line causes a sharp increase in the current. The arrestors then become conductors. The large current is carried through connecting cables to the ground. The protection offered by arrestors is not complete. Some lightning discharges do cause damage to the lines and transformers. Electric storms sometimes do interrupt electric service.

Other types of weather can also do damage. Winter ice storms are especially dangerous. Rain or drizzle falling through cooler air near the ground freezes on the power lines. The weight of the ice may snap the lines. Sometimes tree branches give way and fall across power lines. Wind storms may have the same effects by either directly or indirectly bringing down portions of the lines. Removing nearby trees and branches is about the only way to protect the lines from these weather hazards.

■ **Safety Note**
Never touch or get near a power line that has fallen to the ground.

Quick Review

1. What is done to reduce energy loss in power lines?
2. What changes in voltage are made between the time a current is generated and the time the energy is used by the consumer?
3. How do lightning arrestors help to protect power lines from damage by lightning?

Quick Review answers:
1. Electric energy is transported at low current and high voltage in insulated lines.
2. The voltage is stepped up before being transported large distances, then stepped down in several stages before it is used by the consumer.
3. Arrestors become conductors when lightning strikes and carry the excess current into the ground.

Uses of electric energy

New vocabulary: electric motor, incandescent

Electric energy is produced from other forms of energy. In similar ways, electric energy is used to provide energy in other forms. Electric motors provide the energy of motion. Light bulbs provide us with light. Electric energy is frequently used as a source of heat. It is even used to make chemicals react. Electric energy is a convenient form of energy. It is relatively easy to change it to forms which are directly useful.

All of the changes in energy include "loss" of energy. That is, some of the energy changes into a form that cannot be recovered. Some of the energy is also "lost" because of the inconvenience of reusing it. Considerable heat is "lost" in the process of generating the electricity. Methods of using this heat may have to be considered in the future. At present, devices such as cooling towers are built to help dispose of the excess heat.

Additional information: Students may find it interesting to investigate electroplating. Mention examples such as gold-plated jewelry, chromium-plated auto bumpers, etc.

Electric motors are devices that convert electric energy to energy of motion. Heat is also a product of the conversion. The electric motor is an application of familiar principles.

Main Idea

What is an electric motor?

Electromagnets are a part of most electric motors. Two electromagnets interact. Like poles repel and unlike poles attract. The forces of attraction and repulsion provide the means of turning the shaft of an electric motor.

Electric motors have many different uses. They are found in electric razors, blenders, fans, electric trolleys, refrigerators, and vacuum cleaners.

Electric energy is frequently used in heating as well as to create motion. Coils of high-resistance wire are used in toasters, irons, curling irons, ovens, and portable heaters. High-resistance wire warms up rapidly. Electric energy is converted to internal energy. This energy leaves the wire as heat. The wire may give off light, also, if it is hot enough.

Heating devices often use more electric energy than devices with motors. First, they usually have higher power ratings. A portable heater uses about 1500 W. A toaster may use 1100 W. On the other hand, a blender uses about 300 W. An electric toothbrush uses about 1 W. Second, heating devices may be used for longer time periods than devices with motors.

High-resistance wires are also used as a source of light. The common **incandescent** (in-kun-DES'-ent) light bulb uses a very thin filament of high resistance. The filament glows when an electric current moves through it. Even more energy is given off as heat than as light. In fact, *incandescent* means *glowing with intense heat*. A 100-W light bulb gives off 97 J of heat and only 3 J of light each second.

■ **Safety Note**
Never touch a heating element while an appliance is plugged in.

Research Topic

Read about the problems Thomas Edison had in trying to make an incandescent light bulb. Write a report that describes his failures and successes in making a light bulb that would last.

Figure 11-19. *The high-resistance wire in a toaster gives off red light as well as heat when electric current passes through it.*

Sample Problem

Suppose that incandescent light bulbs give off 3 J per second of light for every 100 watts of their rated power. What would you expect the rated power to be of a light bulb that gives off 4.5 J per second of light?

Solution

Set up a ratio between the power and light output of the unknown and known light bulbs.

$$\frac{?\ W}{4.5\ J/s} = \frac{100\ W}{3\ J/s}$$

Multiply both sides by 4.5 J/s and cancel units as shown:

$$?\ W = \frac{(4.5\ \cancel{J/s}) \times (100\ W)}{3\ \cancel{J/s}}$$

Cancel the similar factors and divide out the numbers.

$$?\ W = (1.5) \times (100\ W) = 150\ W$$

Practice Problem

Based on the assumption made in the example above, calculate the rated power of a light bulb that gives off 5.2 J per second of light. *Answer: 173 W*

Incandescent light bulbs use tungsten filaments. Tungsten filaments have a high resistance but do not melt at the high temperatures produced. Ordinary air is also removed from the bulb. The air is replaced by nitrogen and argon gases. These gases do not react with the metal filament. They also help to keep the filament from gradually wearing down and sticking to the inside of the bulb which would darken it. Oxygen, which is part of ordinary air, does react with metals at high temperatures. The presence of oxygen would reduce the life of the light bulb by causing the filament to burn up completely.

Main Idea

Why is tungsten used in incandescent light bulbs?

Quick Review

1. What kind of force makes something move in an electric motor?
2. What is the function of high-resistance wire in a circuit?
3. What prevents the filament of an incandescent light bulb from melting or wearing out quickly?
4. List at least three forms of energy that can be produced from electric energy.

Quick Review answers:
1. Magnetic forces
2. To produce heat and/or light
3. The filament has a high melting temperature and the oxygen in the bulb is replaced with an inert gas.
4. Light, heat, motion.

11.2b Making a Model of an Incandescent Light Bulb

Science Processes: Observing, making a model, recording data, communicating, inferring

Materials

- 3 pieces of copper wire
- 2-hole rubber stopper
- 2-cm strand of iron picture wire
- narrow-neck glass jar or flask that fits rubber stopper

- switch
- 2-"D"-cell battery
- masking tape
- several clear incandescent light bulbs of different wattages

20 minutes   Groups of 6 or teacher demonstration

7. Carefully examine a clear incandescent light bulb. Locate the filament as shown in the illustration at lower right.
8. Compare the filaments of light bulbs with different wattages.

Questions

1. How does the thickness of the picture wire compare to that of the copper wire?
2. When the switch was closed, did the picture wire melt?
3. In the light bulbs you examined, did the bulbs with higher wattages have thicker or thinner filaments?
4. Would you expect low-wattage or high-wattage bulbs to have filaments with a higher resistance?
5. In what important ways did your model light bulb differ from the commercial light bulbs? How are these differences necessary for the success of commercial light bulbs?

Purpose

To make a model of an incandescent light bulb.

Procedure

1. Insert two copper wires through the holes in a 2-hole rubber stopper.
2. Attach a piece of picture wire to the ends of the copper wires by twisting them.
3. Place the stopper in the neck of a glass jar with the picture wire inside the jar.
4. Connect one of the copper wires to a two-cell battery and the other wire to a switch.
5. Connect the switch to the second pole of the battery using the third piece of copper wire. Use masking tape to make tight connections.
6. Close the switch. Record what happens to the picture wire.

Conclusion

Can light be produced by the heating of a wire by a current?

Step 5

Inside of bulb filled with Argon gas

Coiled filament

11.2 Section Review

Answers to Check Your Understanding and solutions to Problems to Solve appear on page T152 in the front of this book. Blackline master test for this section: Section Testsheet 11-2 (TRB page 230).

Vocabulary

2 electric motor
3 hydroelectric
1 incandescent
8 solar cell
9 steam turbine
6 step-down transformer
5 step-up transformer
7 thermocouple
4 transformer

Vocabulary Review

Match each term above with the numbered phrase that best describes it.

1. Glowing with intense heat
2. Converts electric energy to the energy of motion
3. Involving the conversion of the potential energy of falling water to electric energy
4. Provides a way to raise or lower a voltage
5. Used at generating plants
6. Used at substations
7. Produces current because of the contact of two metals at different temperatures
8. Produces current when light strikes it
9. Converts heat energy into the energy of motion.

Review Questions

Multiple Choice: Choose the answer that best completes each of the following sentences.

10. Most electric energy used today is generated by ? .
    a. thermocouples
    b. electromagnetic induction
    c. solar cells
    d. compression of crystals

11. An electric motor and an electric generator ? .
    a. both use electric energy
    b. both convert another kind of energy to electric energy
    c. are both found in many common household appliances
    d. convert energy in opposite ways

12. Most of the energy for generating electric current today is supplied by ? .
    a. the burning of fossil fuels
    b. falling water
    c. nuclear reactions
    d. solar radiation

13. The energy in light is converted directly into electric energy by ? .
    a. quartz
    b. tungsten
    c. germanium
    d. copper

14. A filament in an incandescent light bulb should have ? .
    a. long life and low resistance
    b. long life and high resistance
    c. short life and low resistance
    d. short life and high resistance

15. A step-up transformer is ? .
    a. used to convert electric energy to energy of motion
    b. consists of a series of coils of wires in a stairstep arrangement
    c. has more windings in the first coil than in the second coil
    d. has more windings in the second coil than in the first coil

Understanding the Concepts

16. For each energy source used in an electric generating plant, list one advantage and one disadvantage.

17. Power lines are often linked together so that a community may receive electric power from different plants at different times. Suggest as many reasons as you can for why this is done.

18. List five ways in which you have made use of electric energy recently. For each way, what form was the electric energy converted to?

19. Most of the electricity that enters an incandescent bulb is not converted to light. What happens to that electric energy? What is the effect on the temperature of a room if a lot of incandescent bulbs are used to light it?

Problems to Solve

20. A step-up transformer is used in a T.V. set to transform 110 V to 1200 V. If the first coil has 40 turns, how many turns are needed in the second coil?

21. Electric power is transported from the power station at 300 000 V to substation where it is stepped down to 9000 V. Before use the voltage is stepped down to 110 V. What are the ratios of the number of turns needed in the first and second coils for each of the two transformers?

11 Chapter Review

Vocabulary

electric generator	incandescent	solar cell
electric motor	induce	steam turbine
electromagnet	magnetic domain	step-down transformer
electromagnetic induction	magnetic field	step-up transformer
electromagnetism	magnetic field line	thermocouple
galvanometer	permanent magnet	transformer
hydroelectric	pole	

Review of Concepts

Magnets exert forces on each other and on materials such as iron, cobalt, and nickel.

- The poles of a magnet are the places on the magnet where the magnetic forces are strongest.
- There are two kinds of poles—north poles and south poles; like poles repel and unlike poles attract.
- A magnet can be pictured as a collection of tiny bar magnets all lined up with their north poles in the same direction.

A **magnetic field** is said to exist in a region where magnetic forces can act.

- A magnetic field can be represented by curving lines known as magnetic field lines.
- The earth has a magnetic field similar to that of a large bar magnet deep inside the earth.
- A magnetic field is produced by an electric current as well as by a magnet.
- A temporary magnet known as an electromagnet consists of a coil of wire with an iron bar inside it; it produces a magnetic field only when there is current in the coil.

- The strength of an electromagnet increases as the number of turns in the coil and the current through the coil increase.

Electromagnetic induction is the production of an electric current by a changing magnetic field.

- A current is induced in a circuit that is in a magnetic field that is either moving in relation to the circuit or is changing in strength.
- Electromagnetic induction is the principle by which electric generators work.

Electric energy is the energy carried by electric currents.

- Electric generators convert energy from other sources—fossil fuels, nuclear reactions, falling water, solar energy—into electric energy.
- Electric energy is also obtained from thermocouples, crystals, and solar cells.
- Electric energy is transported most efficiently at high voltage and low current.
- Electric motors convert electric energy into energy of motion.
- High-resistance wires convert electric energy into heat and light.

Critical Thinking

1. The earth's magnetic south pole is located near the edge of Antarctica. Explain why a compass is not very reliable on Antarctica.
2. What is the major advantage of an electromagnet over a permanent magnet? Give an example of a use that demonstrates this advantage.
3. What advantage does alternating current have over direct current to induce a current in a second circuit?
4. Electric energy is sometimes used to pump water to an elevated storage area. Later the water is released, and the falling water is used to generate electric energy. Under what conditions would you expect this might be done?
5. How might some of the extra heat released during the generation of electricity be used?
6. Why is the presence of oxygen in an incandescent light bulb undesirable?
7. Why can't some materials, for example, wood, aluminum, and plastic, be magnetized?

8. A stereo system requires 60 volts to operate. Since the wall plug provides 120 volts, the voltage must be reduced or else the system will be damaged. How is the voltage reduced to protect the system?

9. Bees may travel miles away from their home hive in their search for nectar, yet they always find their way back. It is known that they have a small amount of magnetic material in their abdomens. How are these facts related?

Individual Research

10. Place several kinds of materials between a magnet and some iron nails or tacks. Which ones allow the magnetic force to pass through them?

11. Magnetic declination is the difference between the direction of true north and magnetic north. Find out the magnetic declination for your location by using a compass and a map of your city or locale showing true north.

12. Find out the location of the electric generating plant that is the major supplier of your electricity. What is the source of energy used to generate the electric energy?

13. Examine a bulb used in automobiles as a combination brake and tail light. Look closely, also, at a 3-way bulb used in some table and floor lamps. Find out how many filaments are included in each bulb and how the filaments differ from each other.

14. Look for the wattage rating on several home appliances. Find out which appliances would use the most energy in the same interval of time and which would use the least.

15. Set up the thermocouple described on pages 440 and 441. Find out if another combination of wires, such as aluminum and copper, produces a different amount of current for the same temperature difference.

16. What are some hazards to electrical service in your community?

17. Look at the dial on the electric meter at your home. Record the positions of the pointers. Go back one month later and record the new positions of the pointers. Determine how many kilowatt hours of electricity your household has used in a month's time.

Bibliography

Lachenbruch, David. *Television*. Milwaukee: Raintree, 1985
   This is an excellent history of television and its uses in medicine, manufacturing, and space research.

Renner, Al G. *How to Make and Use Electronic Motors*. New York: Putnam, 1974
   Detailed instructions for constructing three types of battery-powered electromagnetic motors.

Ruchlis, Hy. *The Wonder of Electricity*. New York: Harper & Row, 1965
   How people learned to use electricity and magnetism, and how such applications as fluorescent lights, electromagnets, television, and computers work.

Ryder, John D., and Donald G. Fink. *Engineers & Electrons: A Century of Electrical Progress*. New York: IEEE Press, 1984
   This history of the electrical engineering profession spotlights some important electrical engineers and their contributions.

Sootin, Harry. *Michael Faraday; from Errand Boy to Master Physicist*. New York: Messner/Simon and Schuster, 1954
   A biography of an extraordinary scientist who was largely self-educated.

Vogt, Gregory. *Electricity and Magnetism*. New York: Watts, 1985
   This book is about how people have learned about electricity, how these forces work and gives ideas for experiments you can do with electricity and magnetism.

Weiss, Harvey. *Motors and Engines and How They Work*. New York: Crowell/Harper & Row, 1969
   A clear and simple overview of many types of motors and engines.

Microwave dishes are becoming a common sight as more and more uses are found for this form of electro-magnetic energy.

Everyday Use of Microwaves

Microwaves are a widely used form of electromagnetic energy. They are used not only in ovens but also in the operation of FM radios, CB radios, cellular (mobile) phones, UHF television, radar, communications satellites, long-distance phone service, and many scientific and medical devices. Microwaves are waves of energy that vibrate at very high speeds (2.45 billion cycles per second in a typical microwave oven). In ovens, this energy passes through glass, plastic, or paper and enters the food where it causes molecules of water, sugar, or fat to vibrate. These vibrations cause friction which produces the heat that warms, defrosts, or cooks the food. In communications systems, these high-speed waves can transmit information with virtually no distortion.

The issue is whether or not microwaves are safe to use.

PROS

- Microwaves cook food quickly, saving not only time but also the electricity or gas that would be used by a conventional oven.
- Microwave ovens must have a three-step safety system that greatly reduces the risk of leaking. These ovens must pass rigorous standards before they can be sold.
- Microwaves make the communication of information, both words and images, possible over long distances and with great speed without the need for cables. Communications microwaves are of lower-level frequency than those used in ovens and are beamed high up in the atmosphere.

CONS

- Although microwave ovens have many safety features, some people feel that most mechanical devices do fail eventually and ovens would be no exception. Oven failure could result in the leaking of harmful radiation.
- Microwaves, particularly at the intensity that they are produced in ovens, could damage human tissue as easily as they cook food.
- Some studies have shown that microwaves can cause DNA in test tubes to vibrate and can cause cancer and immune system damage in animals.
- Some scientists are concerned about the cumulative effects of all the microwaves that we are subjected to in everyday life.

Microwaves make our lives easier and more interesting. Are we gaining this at the risk of long-term harmful effects? Do you feel that the use of microwaves needs to be made safer?

Communications Satellites

From high above the surface of the earth, communications satellites receive high-frequency radio signals from stations on the ground and rebroadcast them to other ground stations that may be thousands of km away. A single satellite can handle thousands of telephone conversations, carry multiple networks of television broadcasts, allow powerful computers to talk to each other, conduct worldwide business and banking transactions, and much more, all simultaneously. Although satellites are expensive to build and to launch into orbit, they can fill many communications needs less expensively than systems on the ground. Ground systems require thousands of km of wire cables, numerous towers with antennas and equipment to relay signals, and complicated switching systems to route signals to their proper destinations.

A major advantage of communications satellites is the wide area that they can cover. Because satellites are so high above the earth's surface, each can be in a direct line of sight of over one third of the earth. Only three satellites in proper orbits are required to provide high frequency radio signal coverage to the entire planet. The INTELSAT system of satellites uses this arrangement to provide a worldwide network servicing many countries. Most other communications satellites serve individual countries or groups of countries and have their antennas focused to cover only their own territory. A ground antenna can establish communica-

tions with a satellite simply by pointing directly at it. Because satellites can cover such a wide area the ground antenna can be located anywhere in the area of focus of the satellite antenna, even in remote areas or on mobile stations.

Most communications satellites must remain at fixed points in the sky to allow ground stations to continuously focus on them. There is only one orbit, called the Equatorial Geostationary orbit, that allows this. Satellites in this circular orbit are approximately 36 400 km above the equator and circle the earth in exactly 24 hours. This causes them to remain stationary above a point on the equator as the earth rotates below them. There are many satellites in this one orbit, all moving at the same speed and maintaining a constant distance from each other.

Communications satellites are growing in importance as their potential uses are developed. Important new uses such as air traffic control and aviation are now in development. We will soon have navigation and guidance systems that will allow us to determine our location anywhere on earth to within a few feet or even a few millimeters using receivers in our cars or even small enough to fit in a pocket. Mobile communications and communications to remote areas are two important uses that are not likely to be replaced soon by other technologies. Communications satellites will be relaying signals from their homes in space for a long time to come.

This ultra-miniature satellite navigation receiver is the size of a cassette tape.

6 Electrochemical and Nuclear Energy

Chapter 12
Electrochemical Reactions

Chapter 13
Nuclear Reactions

Learning Objectives

■ Process

1. To use oxidation numbers to study atoms in their oxidized and reduced states
2. To infer that usable energy can come from a variety of electrochemical sources
3. To predict the relative activity of a metal according to its oxidation ability
4. To demonstrate the concept of a half-life
5. To identify the nuclear change accompanying each type of nuclear radiation

■ Content

1. To analyze some everyday chemical processes in terms of oxidation and reduction reactions
2. To compare different kinds of electrochemical cells
3. To apply the concept of oxidation to corrosion problems
4. To compare two models of the nucleus of an atom
5. To explain how energy from nuclear changes can be used as an energy resource

The energy from electrochemical and nuclear reactions is available to be harnessed for work. Here, steam rises from the earth as a geyser. The heat that produced the steam comes from nuclear reactions that occur naturally underground.

Chapter 12
Electrochemical Reactions

The green material on this building is copper carbonate, formed when copper reacts with carbon dioxide and water vapor in the air. During this reaction, the copper is said to be oxidized.

Science background information:
When a metallic element forms a compound with oxygen, the metal atoms generally transfer electrons to the oxygen atoms and become positive ions. The term *oxidation,* originally applied to the combining of an element with oxygen, has come to mean the loss of electrons in *any* reaction, whether or not oxygen is involved.

When a metallic oxide is broken down and the pure metal is extracted, there is a considerable decrease in volume of solid material. The term *reduction,* originally applied to this kind of reaction, has come to mean the *gain* of electrons in *any* reaction.

The loss or gain of electrons may be complete or partial. That is, when ionic bonds are formed (as in NaCl), there is a complete transfer of electrons. When covalent bonds are formed between atoms of different elements (as in H_2O), the electrons are generally closer to one element than the other. In this case, there is a partial transfer of electrons. The terms *oxidation* and *reduction* apply to partial transfers as well as to complete transfers.

Whenever the atoms of one element lose electrons in a reaction, the atoms of another element must gain them. Oxidation and reduction always occur at the same time. The term *redox* is short for oxidation-reduction.

Common flashlight cells are an example of something that uses the energy given off in a chemical reaction to produce an electric current. Inside the cell a redox reaction occurs when the terminals of the cell are connected to

For detailed information about teaching this chapter, see Chapter 12 Planning Guide on pages T154–T155 in the front of this book.

Projectsheet 12 (TRB page 184) and Research Lab 12 (Lab Manual pages 167–168) may be used at any point in this chapter.

Chapter Preview

12.1 Oxidation and Reduction

- **Losing and gaining electrons**
- **Oxidation numbers**
- **Corrosion of metals**
- **Activity of metals**
- **Oxidizing and reducing agents**

Oxidation and reduction are chemical processes involving the loss and gain of electrons from atoms. Oxidation numbers can be assigned to atoms which are oxidized or reduced. Three types of common chemical reactions involve oxidation and reduction. The activity of metals is related to the ease with which they are oxidized or reduced.

an outside circuit. At the inside of the zinc case, zinc atoms lose electrons. The electrons travel through the outside circuit and enter the cell through the positive terminal, which is attached to a graphite rod inside the cell. At the graphite rod, manganese atoms gain electrons.

Electroplating of a metal onto another metal is an example of a redox reaction that occurs when an outside source of electric energy is connected. A similar process is electrolysis, in which a compound is broken down in a redox reaction when an electric current is passed through it. Electrolysis is the basis for the refining of aluminum from bauxite, or aluminum ore.

12.2 Electric Energy and Chemical Reactions

- **Electric energy from chemical changes**
- **Types of electrochemical cells**
- **Using electric energy to produce chemical changes**
- **Electroplating**

Chemical changes can be used to produce electrical current. Electrochemical cells can be made from dry materials or solutions of chemicals. Electric energy can be used to produce desirable chemical changes. Electricity can be used to plate metals on various objects.

533

For ideas for classroom demonstration and discussion, see Getting Started on page T156 in the front of this book.

12.1 Oxidation and Reduction

Supplemental materials: Teaching Diagram 12-1 (TRB page 58), Reading Checksheet 12-1 (TRB page 111), Skillsheet 12-1 (TRB page 157), Investigation 12-1 (Lab Manual pages 163–164)

Section Preview

■ **Losing and gaining electrons**

■ **Oxidation numbers**

■ **Corrosion of metals**

■ **Activity of metals**

■ **Oxidizing and reducing agents**

Bracketed numbers are Section Review questions correlated to that objective.

Learning Objectives

1. To relate oxidation and reduction to the loss and gain of electrons. [2, 4, 17]
2. To use oxidation numbers to keep track of electrons transferred in oxidation-reduction reactions. [9, 12, 19, 20]
3. To relate oxidation and reduction to four types of chemical reactions. [13]
4. To relate oxidation and reduction to the activity of metals. [3, 5, 10]
5. To relate oxidation and reduction to some everyday chemical processes. [1, 6, 7, 8, 11, 14, 15, 16, 18]

Figure 12-1. *Chromium is used as a protective coating over steel to prevent the iron in the steel from rusting.*

Many of the chemical reactions that you are familiar with involve oxidation and reduction. The burning of fuels, corrosion of metals, and photographic processes are oxidation-reduction reactions. The synthesis, decomposition, and single replacement reactions discussed in Chapter 6 also include oxidation and reduction. What happens during oxidation? During reduction? How are these two processes related? How do you use these processes? And how do you protect against unwanted oxidation-reduction reactions? These questions will be explored in this section.

Losing and gaining electrons

New vocabulary: oxidation, reduction, redox reactions

The terms *oxidation* and *reduction* originally referred to the gain and loss of oxygen. A substance that combined with oxygen was oxidized. A substance that lost oxygen was reduced.

The burning of carbon is an example of the original meaning of oxidation. In that reaction, carbon (C) is oxidized to carbon dioxide (CO_2).

$$\text{Oxidation: } C + O_2 \rightarrow CO_2$$

In terms of the original definition, a metal oxide is reduced when it loses oxygen and is changed to the metal. For example, iron oxide (Fe_2O_3) is reduced to iron (Fe).

$$\text{Reduction: } Fe_2O_3 + 3CO \rightarrow 2Fe + 3CO_2$$

Today, chemists use the terms oxidation and reduction to refer to the losing and gaining of electrons in a chemical reaction. **Oxidation** is the losing of electrons. **Reduction** is the gaining of electrons.

Earlier, on page 265, the reaction of aluminum foil and copper sulfate in water solution was pictured in Figure 6-8. When aluminum foil reacts with solutions of copper sulfate or copper chloride, a reddish brown deposit collects on the foil. This deposit is copper metal. The chemists say that the aluminum is oxidized and the copper ions are reduced.

$$Al^0 \rightarrow Al^{3+} + 3e^- \text{ (aluminum loses 3 electrons)}$$
$$Cu^{2+} + 2e^- \rightarrow Cu^0 \text{ (copper ions gain 2 electrons)}$$

Electrons are given up by the aluminum and gained by the copper ions.

Oxidation and reduction occur simultaneously. <u>Neither oxidation nor reduction takes place by itself.</u> Reactions of this type are called oxidation-reduction reactions or, sometimes, **redox reactions.**

In all redox reactions the number of electrons gained equals the number of electrons given up. This happens in the reaction between aluminum and copper chloride. Each neutral aluminum atom forms ions with a +3 charge. Each copper

Main Idea

Name some common chemical reactions that are oxidation–reduction reactions.

Critical Thinking

Why doesn't the copper deposit in Figure 6-8 look like the copper of an old penny?

In an old penny, the copper on the outside has formed chemical compounds which are darker than pure copper.

Main Idea

Can oxidation and reduction reactions occur independently of each other?

Additional information:
A reaction equation such as
$$Al^0 \rightarrow Al^{3+} + 3e^-$$
is known as a half-reaction. A half-reaction can either be an oxidation reaction or a reduction reaction.

Critical Thinking

Why are there no electrons shown in the equation for the total reaction between aluminum metal and copper ions?

There would be six electrons on each side of the reaction equation, so there is no net change in the number of electrons.

Quick Review answers:

1. Chemists define oxidation as the loss of electrons by an element; reduction is the gain of electrons.
2. Electrons move from aluminum to copper.

Figure 12-3. *A chromium atom has an oxidation number of +6 when it is in the compound potassium dichromate (left) and +3 when it is in the compound chromium(III) oxide (right).*

ion has a +2 charge and forms neutral copper atoms. To balance the number of electrons gained and given up in the reaction, two atoms of aluminum must form ions for every three ions of copper that form copper metal.

$$2Al^0 \rightarrow 6e^- + 2Al^{3+} \quad \text{oxidation reaction}$$
$$3Cu^{2+} + 6e^- \rightarrow 3Cu^0 \quad \text{reduction reaction}$$
$$3Cu^{2+} + 2Al^0 \rightarrow 3Cu^0 + 2Al^{3+} \quad \text{total reaction}$$

The chloride ions, from copper chloride, remain in the solution as chloride ions. They are neither oxidized nor reduced.

Quick Review

1. How do chemists today define oxidation and reduction?
2. What is the direction of movement of electrons when aluminum reacts with copper chloride solution?

Oxidation numbers

New vocabulary: oxidation numbers

In the reaction just described, the charges on the aluminum and copper ions were known. It was then easy to see both how the electrons were being transferred and the number of electrons that must be involved. In some reactions, it is not as clear. As a result, chemists have adopted a system that uses **oxidation numbers** to help keep track of the electrons being transferred.

Oxidation numbers are assigned to atoms and ions. The numbers are based on the number of electrons gained, lost, or shared when atoms or ions combine with other atoms or ions. Also there is a set of rules for assigning oxidation numbers. Oxidation numbers help in understanding chemical changes. They also provide a way to balance a chemical equation that represents the changes. A summary of the rules used in assigning oxidation numbers is below:

1. An atom in a molecule that is a single element has an oxidation number of zero.
2. An ion that is a single charged atom has an oxidation number equal to the charge on the ion.
3. Oxygen has an oxidation number of −2 in all of its compounds (except peroxides).
4. Hydrogen has an oxidation number of +1 in all of its compounds (except hydrides).
5. All other oxidation numbers are assigned so that the sum of the oxidation numbers equals the net charge on the molecule or ion. Table 12-1 gives charges of common ions.

Figure 12-4. *In a steel mill, iron oxide reacts with carbon monoxide at very high temperatures, and pure molten iron is produced. How does the oxidation number of iron change in this reaction?*
It is reduced from +3 to 0.

The rules are easy to apply. Suppose we need to identify an oxidation number for the following:

☐ O_2—Oxygen has an oxidation number of 0 (see rule #1)

☐ Fe^{2+}—Iron (II) has an oxidation number of +2 (see rule #2)

☐ Fe_2O_3—Iron has an oxidation number of +3 (see rules #3 and #5)

☐ SO_4^{2-}—Sulfur has an oxidation number of +6 (see rules #3 and #5)

☐ MnO_2—Manganese has an oxidation number of +4 (see rules #3 and #5)

If it is possible to identify the oxidation number of an element in a reactant and in a product, you can then determine whether that element has been oxidized or reduced or remains unchanged. For example, a metallic ore is reacted with carbon monoxide or carbon in the refining of metals.

$$\overset{\text{oxidation}}{\underset{\text{reduction}}{\underset{+3}{Fe_2O_3} + \underset{+2}{3CO} \rightarrow \underset{+4}{3CO_2} + \underset{0}{2Fe}}}$$

Oxidation number

Iron, in the compound iron oxide, has an oxidation number of +3. As a product it has an oxidation number of 0. This decrease in oxidation number corresponds to a gain of electrons. The iron is reduced in the reaction. The carbon in carbon monoxide has an oxidation number of +2, to balance the −2 of oxygen. The carbon in carbon dioxide has an oxidation number of +4, to balance the −4 of two oxygen atoms.

Name of Ion	Symbol and Charge
Ammonium	NH_4^+
Carbonate	CO_3^{2-}
Chlorate	ClO_3^-
Chromate	CRO_4^{2-}
Hydroxide	OH^-
Nitrate	NO_3^-
Nitrite	NO_2^-
Permanganate	MNO_4^-
Phosphate	PO_4^{3-}
Sulfate	SO_4^{2-}

Table 12-1. *Names, symbols, and charges for some common polyatomic ions.*

This increase in oxidation number from $+2$ to $+4$ corresponds to a loss of electrons. The carbon is oxidized in the reaction.

In some ways, it is easier to think of oxidation and reduction as changes of oxidation numbers. Then, oxidation can be defined as a gain in oxidation number. Reduction would correspond to a decrease in oxidation number.

In an earlier section, reactions were described as synthesis, decomposition, single replacement, or double replacement. Let's look at examples of those types of reactions in terms of oxidation and reduction.

An example of a synthesis reaction is the combination of silver and sulfur.

$$\text{Oxidation number} \quad \underset{2Ag}{0} \quad + \underset{S}{0} \quad \rightarrow \quad \underset{Ag_2}{+1} \, \underset{S}{-2}$$

oxidation

reduction

In this reaction, silver changes from an oxidation number of 0 as a reactant to $+1$ as a product. Silver is oxidized in the reaction. Sulfur has an oxidation number of 0 as a reactant and -2 in the compound. Sulfur is reduced in this reaction.

The breakdown of potassium chlorate was used as an example of a decomposition reaction.

$$\text{Oxidation number} \quad \underset{2KClO_3}{+1 \; +5 \; -2} \quad \rightarrow \quad \underset{2KCl}{+1 \; -1} \quad + \underset{3O_2}{0}$$

oxidation

reduction

Main Idea

How can oxidation and reduction be defined in terms of oxidation number?

Critical Thinking

How do you know that silver and sulfur each have an oxidation number of 0 before they combine to form silver sulfide?

According to rule #1, atoms in pure elements have an oxidation number of 0.

Oxygen has an oxidation number of -2 in the compound and an oxidation number of 0 as an element. The oxidation number increases for oxygen. Oxygen is oxidized.

The oxidation number of chlorine in potassium chlorate can be determined by using the rules for assigning oxidation numbers. The chlorate ion has a charge of $1-$. Since $KClO_3$ is neutral, the potassium must have a charge of $1+$ and an oxidation number of $+1$. The sum of the oxidation numbers of chlorine and oxygen in the chlorate ion must equal -1. The three oxygen atoms have a total oxidation number of -6. Thus, the chlorine must have an oxidation number of $+5$. In the product KCl, potassium is still an ion of charge $1+$ and oxidation number of $+1$. Thus, the chlorine has an oxidation number of -1. The oxidation number of chlorine decreases from $+5$ to -1, so chlorine is reduced.

In one of the single replacement reactions, zinc metal reacted with hydrochloric acid.

$$\text{Oxidation number} \quad \overset{0}{} \quad \overset{+1}{} \quad \xrightarrow{\text{oxidation}} \quad \overset{+2}{} \quad \overset{0}{}$$

$$Zn + 2HCl \longrightarrow ZnCl_2 + H_2$$

reduction

Zinc changes in oxidation number from 0 as a reactant to $+2$ in the product $ZnCl_2$. The zinc is oxidized. The hydrogen in hydrochloric acid has an oxidation number of $+1$. The oxidation number of hydrogen as an element is 0. The oxidation number of hydrogen decreases from $+1$ to 0. Hydrogen is reduced.

An example of a double replacement reaction was barium chloride and sodium carbonate.

$$BaCl_2 + Na_2CO_3 \longrightarrow BaCO_3 + 2NaCl$$

Comparing the oxidation numbers of the elements in the reactants and products shows that there was no change in oxidation number for any of the elements.

Reactants		Products	
Ba in $BaCl_2$	$+2$	Ba in $BaCO_3$	$+2$
Cl in $BaCl_2$	-1	Cl in NaCl	-1
Na in Na_2CO_3	$+1$	Na in NaCl	$+1$
C in Na_2CO_3	$+4$	C in $BaCO_3$	$+4$
O in Na_2CO_3	-2	O in $BaCO_3$	-2

Of the four types of reactions, only the double replacement reaction did not involve oxidation and reduction.

Figure 12-6. *In a single replacement reaction, zinc from a strip replaces the hydrogen in hydrochloric acid. The zinc is oxided and the hydrogen is reduced.*

Sample Problem

For a redox reaction, identify the changes in the oxidation numbers of the reactants and products.

a. $Cl_2 + 2NaBr \rightarrow 2NaCl + Br_2$

b. $2KNO_3 \rightarrow 2KNO_2 + O_2$

c. $2Na + 2H_2O \rightarrow 2NaOH + H_2$

Solution

Use the rules for assigning oxidation numbers to atoms in the reactants and products.

a.

$$\underset{0}{Cl_2} + \underset{+1\ -1}{2NaBr} \rightarrow \underset{+1\ -1}{2NaCl} + \underset{0}{Br_2}$$

(oxidation: from Br -1 to 0; reduction: from Cl 0 to -1)

b.

$$\underset{+1\ +5\ -2}{2KNO_3} \rightarrow \underset{+1\ +3\ -2}{2KNO_2} + \underset{0}{O_2}$$

(reduction: N from $+5$ to $+3$; oxidation: O from -2 to 0)

c.

$$\underset{0}{2Na} + \underset{+1\ -2}{2H_2O} \rightarrow \underset{+1\ -2\ +1}{2NaOH} + \underset{0}{H_2}$$

(oxidation: Na from 0 to $+1$; reduction: H from $+1$ to 0)

Practice Problems

a. $3Mg + 2Al(NO_3)_3 \rightarrow 2Al + 3Mg(NO_3)_2$

b. $Pb + H_2SO_4 \rightarrow H_2 + PbSO_4$

c. $H_2 + CuO \rightarrow Cu + H_2O$

Answers:

a.

$$\underset{0}{3Mg} + \underset{+3\ +5\ -2}{2Al(NO_3)_3} \rightarrow \underset{0}{2Al} + \underset{+2\ +5\ -2}{3Mg(NO_3)_2}$$

(oxidation: Mg; reduction: Al)

b.

$$\underset{0}{Pb} + \underset{+1\ +6\ -2}{H_2SO_4} \rightarrow \underset{0}{H_2} + \underset{+2\ +6\ -2}{PbSO_4}$$

(oxidation: Pb; reduction: H)

c.

$$\underset{0}{H_2} + \underset{+2\ -2}{CuO} \rightarrow \underset{0}{Cu} + \underset{+1\ -2}{H_2O}$$

(reduction: Cu; oxidation: H)

1. What is the oxidation number of Mn in K_2MnO_4?
2. In a reaction, the oxidation number of chlorine (Cl) changes from $+7$ to -1. Has the chlorine been oxidized or reduced?

Corrosion of metals

New vocabulary: corrosion

The process in which a metal combines with water, air, or other materials in the atmosphere is called **corrosion.** The rusting of iron is a familiar example of corrosion. You already know what happens when iron rusts. When water is present, iron combines with oxygen from the air. The compound that is formed is iron oxide, commonly called rust. Rust is weak and crumbles. In rust, the element iron has lost its characteristic shininess and strength.

Besides iron, many other metals also corrode. Copper combines with carbon dioxide and water vapor in the air. The compound formed is copper carbonate. Copper carbonate has a pale green color. Untreated aluminum combines with oxygen in the air, forming aluminum oxide. However, aluminum oxide does not crumble away as iron oxide does. A thin layer of aluminum oxide quickly forms on the surface of uncoated aluminum and sticks to it. The thin layer of aluminum oxide protects the aluminum underneath from further corrosion. Chromium behaves in a similar way to aluminum. Both aluminum and chromium are used on automobiles. The oxides formed on the surfaces of these metals protect them against further corrosion.

Main Idea

Why is aluminum more resistant than iron to corrosion in air?

Figure 12-7. *These steel reinforcing rods have become badly rusted. Steel is weakened by rust, which crumbles easily.*

12.1a   Corrosion of Metals

Science Processes: Observing, experimenting, inferring, defining operationally, formulating hypotheses

Materials

- piece of steel wool
- two galvanized nails
- one ungalvanized nail
- one painted, ungalvanized nail
- two pieces, 10 cm by 10 cm, of porous cloth

Purpose

To discover what factors slow down and speed up the process of corrosion.

Procedure

1. Scratch one of the galvanized nails along one side by rubbing it with steel wool.

Step 2

← 10 cm →

←10 cm→

BASIC   20 minutes plus later observation time   Groups of 3 or 4

2. Dampen a cloth and set the four nails and a small piece of steel wool on it so that they are not touching each other.
3. Dampen the second piece of cloth and set it on top of the nails and steel wool so that they are completely covered.
4. Keep the cloth damp during the course of the activity.
5. Lift off the top cloth and inspect the nails and steel wool once a day for the next three days. Record your observations on the chart provided.

Questions

1. Describe the changes that took place on the metal objects.
    a. steel wool
    b. ungalvanized nail
    c. painted ungalvanized nail
    d. galvanized nail
    e. scratched ungalvanized nail
2. How do you know that the changes that took place were chemical changes?
3. What methods of protecting metals from corrosion are suggested by this activity?

Conclusion

What can you conclude about the changes that take place in metals that are exposed to corrosive conditions?

Object	Observation 1	Observation 2	Observation 3
Steel wool			
Ungalvanized nail			
Painted nail			
Galvanized nail			
Scratched nail			

When a metal corrodes, it loses electrons. For example, metallic iron, Fe, loses electrons to form the ion Fe^{3+} during corrosion. The oxidation number increases. The iron is oxidized. The oxygen atoms that combine with iron gain electrons. The oxidation number decreases. The oxygen is oxidized. Because the corrosion of metals involves the transfer of electrons (gain by one substance and loss by another substance), corrosion reactions are oxidation-reduction reactions. The oxidation and reduction occur simultaneously. Neither one can occur without the other.

Zinc is another metal used to protect iron from rusting. Galvanized nails have a layer of zinc covering their surface. Zinc combines with oxygen to form a thin protective coating of zinc oxide. If the surface layer of zinc oxide is scratched, the exposed zinc metal quickly changes to zinc oxide. The iron remains protected from the action of the oxygen in the air.

The rusting of iron can also be prevented by covering iron with paint. The paint keeps the air from making contact with the iron. If the paint is scratched or removed and moisture is present, the exposed iron is likely to rust.

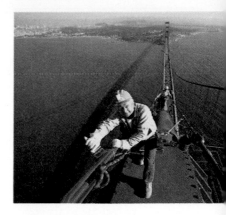

Figure 12-8. *Painting San Francisco's Golden Gate Bridge protects the steel from oxygen and moisture in the air, so that the iron in it will not rust.*

Quick Review

1. What is the type of reaction taking place when a metal corrodes?
2. Aluminum and chromium also corrode but, unlike iron, remain strong. How are they different from iron?

Activity of Metals
New vocabulary: activity, activity series

Some metals corrode easily, while others, such as gold and silver, resist corrosion. When metals corrode, they give up electrons. There must be differences in the ease with which metals give up electrons. Experiments and measurements provide observations that support this hypothesis. Metals can even be arranged in order according to the ease with which they give up electrons. Metals that give up electrons more easily are said to be more active. The metals that give up electrons less easily are less active. The **activity** of a metal refers to its tendency to give up electrons. When two metals are in contact, the atoms of the more active metal give up electrons and the atoms of the less active metal take on electrons. The metals which take on the electrons must be in the form of positive ions.

Critical Thinking

Do you think that the corrosion-resistance of gold contributes to its value? Why or why not?
Yes. Because of this resistance to corrosion, articles made of gold can endure unchanged for long periods with little care. This characteristic certainly contributes to the value of gold.

Main Idea

What is meant by the activity of a metal? What determines whether one metal is more active than another?

Activity series of some metals

Magnesium	Most active
Aluminum	
Zinc	
Chromium	
Iron	
Nickel	
Tin	
Lead	
Hydrogen	
Copper	
Arsenic	
Mercury	
Silver	
Platinum	
Gold	Least active

Table 12-2. *An activity series for some common metals.*

Teaching suggestion:
Ask your students which metal in the table is the most active and which is the least active. Remind them that the most active metal is the one that gives up its electrons most easily.

The activities of metals differ. The metals in Table 12-2 are arranged with the most active metals at the top and the least active metals at the bottom. Elements arranged according to their activities are known as an **activity series.** A metal gives up electrons to the ions of any of the metals below it in the table. Magnesium gives up electrons to any of the ions of the metals below it on the table. Ions of gold take on electrons from any of the other elements in the table. Since oxidation is the giving up of electrons, the most active metals are the ones most easily oxidized. Among the elements in the table, magnesium is most easily oxidized and gold is the least easily oxidized.

The differences in the activities of the metals explain how zinc is used to prevent corrosion. Suppose zinc and iron are in contact with each other and with water. Zinc and iron are different in their activities. Zinc is more active than iron. As a result, zinc furnishes electrons to iron. Any iron atoms that are oxidized and form ions will then take electrons from zinc atoms. Thus, iron is protected from corrosion by the more active metal zinc. From the table you can see that any metal above iron in the activity series would work to prevent the corrosion of iron.

Practical applications of this property are common. Ships made of iron often have bars of magnesium metal attached to the sides of the ship. The magnesium furnishes electrons to the iron that starts to corrode. The iron is protected while the magnesium is used up in the process. Underground cables of copper are protected in a similar way. Any metal

Figure 12-9. *How could the rust on these hulls have been prevented?* By attaching magnesium bars to the hulls to furnish electrons to the iron.

that is more active than copper can be attached to the copper. The attached metal will be eventually oxidized, but the chemical process of reduction has prevented the destruction of the copper.

Differences in activity are also found in different places on the same piece of metal. This helps explain how corrosion takes place. Usually there is a different amount of stress in different locations on a metal surface. Also there is a difference in the tendency for electrons to be given up in those locations. The locations under greatest stress tend to give up electrons more easily. That is where the metal then corrodes. The locations where electrons are held more strongly are less likely to corrode.

Quick Review

1. What is meant by the activity of a metal?
2. What property of a metal is used to protect iron from corrosion?

Oxidizing and reducing agents

New vocabulary: oxidizing agent, reducing agent, ozone

The processes of oxidation and reduction occur at the same time. A substance that gives up electrons is oxidized. The electrons that are given up must be transferred to another substance. The substance that gains the electrons, in a way, causes the oxidation. It is called the **oxidizing agent.** The substance that furnishes the electrons causes the reduction. It is called the **reducing agent.**

To oxidize a substance, you would react it with an oxidizing agent. The strongest oxidizing agents are chemicals that have the greatest attraction for electrons. To reduce a substance, you would react it with a reducing agent. The strongest reducing agents are chemicals that give up their electrons very easily. Some important oxidizing and reducing agents are probably familiar to you.

Household bleach is used as a source of a strong oxidizing agent. The active ingredient in bleach is sodium hypochlorite, $NaOCl$. Sodium hypochlorite releases oxygen as the oxidizing agent that whitens clothes.

Hydrogen peroxide, H_2O_2, is also used as an oxidizing agent. Again, oxygen is released to do the oxidizing.

Ozone, O_3, concentrations are frequently reported as part of a city's air pollution monitoring. Ozone is a strong oxidizing agent and is harmful to vegetation. Much of the smog

Main Idea

How does physical stress affect a metal's tendency to corrode?

Quick Review answers:
1. The tendency to give up or take on electrons.
2. A more active metal is used to protect iron. Whenever an iron atom is oxidized, the more active metal gives up its electrons to reduce the iron atom. The protective metal is oxidized, but the iron is kept from corroding.

Main Idea

What is an oxidizing agent? What is a reducing agent?

Figure 12-10. *The orange pigment in this piece of felt turns white when oxided by sodium hypochlorite in household bleach.*

12.1b   Oxidation and Reduction on the Same Metal

Science Processes: Observing, inferring, experimenting

Materials   20 minutes   Groups of 3 or 4

- prepared agar mixture (contains phenolpthalein and potassium ferricyanide)
- petri dish
- steel nail or screw

Purpose

To identify the location of separate oxidation and reduction reactions in the corrosion of a metal object.

Procedure

SAFETY NOTE: *Hot agar can burn your skin. Be careful how you pour it into the dishes.*

1. Pour the prepared agar mixture into the petri dish to a depth of approximately 0.5 cm. Allow the agar to solidify.
2. Press the nail or screw into the layer of solid agar until it is partially embedded in the agar.

3. Pour another layer of the hot agar mixture into the petri dish until the nail or screw is completely covered.
4. Observe the petri dish until color changes appear at several locations near the nail. Then allow the setup to stand until the end of class so that the changes can be seen more clearly.

Questions

1. In which region does the dissolving of iron appear to be taking place?
2. In which regions does a different color change appear to be taking place in the agar?
3. How do the characteristics of the nail differ in the areas where the colors of the agar are different?

Conclusion

Can oxidation and reduction occur to a single metal object at the same time?

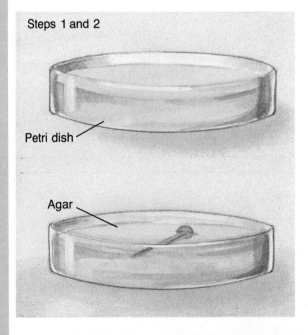

Steps 1 and 2

Petri dish

Agar

Step 3

damage done to trees and plants is the result of high concentrations of ozone. Ozone also is responsible for damage to items made of rubber and to some textile materials as well. All of these damaging effects are the result of ozone's strong oxidizing properties.

Ozone may be formed as a result of lightning discharges. It is also a product of the breakdown of nitrogen dioxide by ultraviolet light. Nitrogen dioxide is the brown gas associated with smog conditions. Atomic oxygen, formed from the breakup of nitrogen dioxide, combines with molecular oxygen to form ozone.

$$O \quad + \quad O_2 \quad \rightarrow \quad O_3$$

atomic oxygen   molecular   ozone
from breakup of   oxygen
nitrogen dioxide

Photographic film is made up of silver bromide crystals embedded in a thin layer of gelatin. The gelatin is supported on a transparent sheet of plastic. Exposure to light sensitizes the silver bromide crystals. The parts of the film that are not

Our Science Heritage

In a Minute: The Miracle of Instant Photography

In 1943, after a question from his young daughter sparked his interest, American inventor Edwin H. Land (1909–) decided to develop a camera and film system that would give "instant" photographs.

The original instant photograph film and camera system was introduced by Land in 1947. The film was developed in a process similar to that used for noninstant black and white film. However, the film pack contained not only the negative film but also the positive paper and a capsule of developing chemicals. The

capsule was broken and squeezed between the layers as the film was advanced through rollers. After a minute, the two sheets were pulled apart and the print was covered with another chemical to prevent further development. The result was an "instant" black and white photograph!

In the 1960s, Land introduced self-developing color film. The technology has improved so that instant photographs today are high quality and truly instant.

Figure 12-11. *The dark areas in a black-and-white negative (left) are where the film received the most exposure to light. The silver in the sensitized silver bromide crystals there was reduced to metallic silver. What happened to the silver bromide crystals in the areas that are now light?* They were dissolved away by the hypo solution.

Data Search

Of the metals listed in Table 12-2, name in order the five that are highest in electric conductivity. Search pages 658–661.

Silver, copper, gold, aluminum, and magnesium

Main Idea

What is an antioxidant?

Quick Review answers:
1. The oxidizing agent is reduced.
2. Bleach is an oxidizing agent. Photographic developer is a reducing agent.

Research Topic

Find out what types of chemicals are used as antioxidants. Do these chemicals have any negative effects? What types of foods are antioxidants used in?

exposed to light are not affected. When a developer is added to the film that has been exposed to light, the sensitized crystals are reduced. The silver ion is reduced to silver.

$$Ag^+ + e^- \rightarrow Ag^0$$

The developer is a reducing agent. The conversion of silver ions to metallic silver takes place where light struck the film. The unsensitized silver bromide crystals are removed by adding a solution of sodium thiosulfate, called *hypo,* to the film. The hypo solution dissolves the unsensitized silver bromide crystals and removes them from the emulsion. The metallic silver remains in the film to form the negative.

The developer has to be a weak reducing agent. Both the sensitized silver bromide crystals and the unsensitized silver bromide can be reduced by a strong reducing agent. When a weak reducing agent is used, the sensitized crystals are reduced faster than the unsensitized ones. So the reaction can be controlled by carefully choosing the developer.

The deterioration of some foods is slowed down by the addition of substances called antioxidants. These substances act as preservatives by reacting with the oxygen in air, which prevents the oxygen from oxidizing the food itself. Oxygen, the oxidizing agent, is then not as abundant. As a result, the foods retain their edible characteristics for a longer period of time. The rate of oxidation is reduced by lowering the concentration of the oxygen available to react with the food.

Quick Review

1. What change takes place in an oxidizing agent during a redox reaction?
2. Give an example of (a) a substance used as an oxidizing agent; (b) a substance used as a reducing agent.

12.1 Section Review

Answers to Understanding the Concepts and Solutions to Problems to Solve appear on page T157 in the front of this book. Blackline master test for this section: Section Testsheet 12-1 (TRB page 231)

Vocabulary

3   activity
5   activity series
1   corrosion
2   oxidation
9   oxidation number
6   oxidizing agent
7   ozone
8   reducing agent
4   reduction

Vocabulary Review

Match each term above with the numbered phrase that best describes it.

1. Combining of a metal with a part of the air
2. Loss of electrons by a substance
3. The tendency of a metal to give up electrons
4. The gain of electrons by a substance
5. A group of substances ranked by the ease with which they give up electrons
6. A substance that causes oxidation to occur
7. An oxidizing agent that's found in polluted air
8. A substance that causes reduction to occur
9. A way of telling whether an atom has gained or lost electrons

Review Questions

Multiple Choice: Choose the answer that best completes each of the following sentences.

10. Electrons move from zinc to copper in one cell, but from copper to silver in another cell. The arrangement of these metals from most active to least active is ? .
    a. zinc-copper-silver
    b. silver-copper-zinc
    c. copper-silver-zinc
    d. copper-zinc-silver

11. Corrosion of iron can be prevented by ? .
    a. painting the iron to keep it away from air
    b. putting the iron under water
    c. blocking the formation of ozone in the atmosphere
    d. attaching a metal to the iron which accepts electrons easily from iron

12. In a chemical reaction, the oxidation number of chlorine changes from 0 to −1. This means that ? .
    a. chlorine has lost electrons
    b. chlorine has been oxidized
    c. chlorine has been dissolved
    d. chlorine has been reduced

13. In a single replacement reaction, oxidation and reduction ? .
    a. never occur
    b. occur only when a precipitate is formed
    c. occur at the same time
    d. occur at different times

14. When photographic film is being developed, ? .
    a. a strong oxidizing agent is used to make the film sensitive to light
    b. silver grains are encased in a thin layer of gelatin
    c. a weak reducing agent acts on silver bromide crystals that have been sensitized by light
    d. a strong reducing agent is used to remove bromide ions from the gelatin layer

Understanding the Concepts

15. Both iron and aluminum corrode in air. Why is the corrosion of iron more of a problem than the corrosion of aluminum?

16. More active metals can serve to protect less active metals from corrosion. Why is this true?

17. In a redox reaction, electrons are transferred between one substance and another. Explain what you think would happen to the reaction if all of the substance that receives the electrons is used up.

18. Household bleach is a strong oxidizing agent. Knowing that bleach can remove some food stains from clothes, explain what bleach does chemically to the food substances in the stains.

19. Oxidation numbers can be used to indicate changes in the electric charge of atoms that take part in chemical reactions. If the oxidation number of an atom does not change, can it still be involved in a chemical reaction? Explain your reasoning.

Problems to Solve

20. Using the rules for assigning oxidation numbers, show the oxidation-number changes for the following reactions:
    a. $2SO_2 + O_2 \rightarrow 2SO_3$
    b. $2H_2 + O_2 \rightarrow 2H_2O$
    c. $Zn + H_2SO_4 \rightarrow ZnSO_4 + H_2$
    d. $HCl + NaOH \rightarrow NaCl + H_2O$

For ideas for classroom demonstration and discussion, see Getting Started on page T157 in the front of this book.

12.2 Electric Energy and Chemical Reactions

Supplemental materials: Teaching Diagrams 12-2A and 12-2B (TRB pages 59–60), Reading Checksheet 12-2 (TRB page 112), Skillsheet 12-2 (TRB page 158), Investigation 12-2 (Lab Manual pages 167–168)

Section Preview

- **Electric energy from chemical changes**
- **Types of electrochemical cells**
- **Using electric energy to produce chemical changes**
- **Electroplating**

Bracketed numbers are Section Review questions correlated to that objective.

Learning Objectives

1. To relate the production of electric energy to chemical changes. [2, 5, 7, 10, 11, 14, 15, 18]
2. To compare different kinds of electrochemical cells. [2, 4, 8, 10, 12, 13, 19, 21]
3. To compare two processes in which electricity is used to produce chemical changes. [1, 3, 6, 9, 16, 17]
4. To relate the processes of electroplating to corrosion. [9, 16, 17, 20]

Figure 12-12. *Aluminum is extracted from aluminum ore in a process in which electric current is run through molten ore.*

Many chemical changes release energy. The energy released is often in the form of heat. The most familiar example is the burning of fuels to release heat energy. Sometimes the heat released is used to generate electric energy. Some chemical changes can be used to produce electric energy without first producing heat. These chemical changes produce electric energy by causing electric charges to move. The moving electric charges have energy and can do work. Some very common chemical charges cause the movement of electric charges. What are some of these chemical reactions? What do these reactions have in common? What are the everyday applications? How is electric energy used to produce chemical changes? These are some of the questions to be explored in this chapter.

Electric energy from chemical changes

New vocabulary: electrochemical cell, electrolyte, wet cell, dry cell

When aluminum is in a solution containing copper ions, electrons move from the aluminum atoms to the copper ions. A conducting wire can provide a path for the electrons outside the solution. The electrons moving through the wire can be detected with a sensitive electric meter. A galvanometer or a milliammeter (which measures thousandths of an ampere) can be used.

For example, a copper strip and an aluminum strip can be placed in a copper sulfate solution. See Figure 12-13. One end of a wire is attached to the aluminum strip. The other end of the wire is attached to a meter. A second wire is attached to the second terminal of the meter and to the copper strip. A complete path is provided for the electrons through the wires. The reading on the meter indicates there is a current.

The aluminum, copper, and copper sulfate solution make an **electrochemical** (ih-lek'-trō-KEM'-ih-kul) **cell.** An electrochemical cell uses chemical changes to produce electric energy. In a chemical change, electrons may be transferred from one substance to another. The electrons that are transferred have energy. They move through conductors. These moving electric charges are a source of electric energy. Because of their energy they can do work or produce light or heat.

The ability of metals to furnish electrons is different for different metals. For example, aluminum, zinc, and iron all

Research Topic

The SI unit of voltage, the volt, was named after Count Alessandro Volta. Find out what important contributions Volta made to the field of electricity. What was Volta's pile?

Main Idea

What energy changes occur in an electrochemical cell?

Figure 12-13. *How does this electrochemical cell produce electric energy?*
Electrons are transferred in the chemical changes. The moving electrons have energy and can do work.

Activity

12.2a   Making a Simple Electrochemical Cell

Science Processes: Experimenting, observing, inferring

20 minutes   Groups of 3 or 4 or teacher demonstration

Materials

- 15-cm square of aluminum foil
- copper penny
- sandpaper
- paper towel
- salt water solution
- galvanometer
- 2 30-cm copper wires

Purpose

To construct a simple electrochemical cell.

Procedure

1. Lay the piece of aluminum foil on a flat surface.
2. Fold the paper towel to form a square slightly smaller than the foil.
3. Dip the folded towel into the salt water solution. Drain off the excess liquid, then lay the towel on top of the foil.
4. Polish one side of the penny with sandpaper. Put it on the towel shiny side up.
5. Connect one end of each wire to the galvanometer. Touch the other ends to the outside of the foil and penny.
6. Record the galvanometer reading.

Questions

1. Why must you use two different metals for the electrodes in an electrochemical cell?
2. Why did you polish the surface of the penny?
3. What is the function of the salt water solution?
4. How can you tell the direction in which the electrons move in the cell?
5. Why do the electrons move from the aluminum to the copper?
6. If the cell were made of aluminum and magnesium, in which direction would the current flow?

Conclusion

How does an electrochemical cell produce an electric current?

Step 3

Step 5

Galvanometer

give up electrons more easily than copper does. They are more active metals than copper. Two metals that have different activities can be used to make an electrochemical cell.

Electrochemical cells are made of two different metals separated in a liquid or moist paste. The liquid or paste has to be a conductor of electricity and is called an **electrolyte** (ih-LEK′-truh-līt). An electrolyte is made up of ions. These ions carry the electric charges through the liquid or paste. When the cell contains a liquid, it is called a **wet cell.** Common flashlight cells are known as **dry cells** because they contain a paste instead of a liquid.

Quick Review

What makes up an electrochemical cell?

Types of electrochemical cells
New vocabulary: electrode, alkaline cell, storage battery, fuel cell

The voltage of a cell depends on the combination of metals used. (Voltage was discussed in Chapter 10, Section 2.) The greater the difference in the activity of the metals in the cell, the greater the voltage. When zinc and copper are used in a particular solution, the voltage is about 1.1 V. Suppose magnesium metal were used in place of zinc. Would you expect the voltage to increase or decrease? The voltage would increase.

The common flashlight cell is a dry cell that uses zinc and carbon. The zinc and carbon act as **electrodes** (ih-LEK′-trōdz). Electrodes are conductors that carry electrons into or out of a cell. The zinc is in the form of a can. The can holds a moist paste with a carbon rod in the center. The paste is a mixture of ammonium chloride, manganese dioxide, and water. The ammonium chloride serves as the electrolyte. The carbon, which is a nonmetal, does not take part in the chemical reaction.

The zinc gives up electrons and enters the paste as zinc ions. The electrons travel through the outside circuit and enter the cell through the carbon rod. The manganese dioxide accepts the electrons, and a substance called manganous oxide is formed. When the cell is fresh, it produces a voltage of 1.5 V. The voltage decreases as the manganese dioxide is used up, until the cell is finally "dead."

An **alkaline** (AL′-kuh-lin) **cell** is a type of dry cell. It provides longer and better service than the common flashlight cell. The electrolyte in an alkaline cell is potassium hydroxide, a strong base. The voltage of this cell is also 1.5 V.

Positive (+) terminal

Carbon rod

Porous paper

Water paste of ammonium chloride and manganese dioxide

Zinc can

Negative (−) terminal (bottom of can)

Figure 12-15. *What are some common uses for cells and batteries like these?*

Cells or batteries are commonly used in calculators, flashlights, radios, clocks, cameras, etc. The large battery in the photo is an automobile storage battery.

Main Idea

What is a storage battery?

Critical Thinking

How would the voltage of an electrochemical cell with aluminum and lead electrodes compare to one with zinc and lead electrodes?

The cell with the aluminum electrode would have a greater voltage because aluminum is above zinc in the activity series.

A mercury cell is a third type of dry cell. As in the common flashlight cell and the alkaline cell, one electrode is made of zinc. However, the other electrode is made of mercuric oxide. As in the alkaline cell, the electrolyte in a mercury cell is potassium hydroxide. The advantage of a mercury cell over the other two kinds is that its voltage remains constant during use. This makes it suitable for devices such as hearing aids and light meters.

Cells can be combined to produce batteries of larger voltage. A battery consists of two or more cells wired together. Two flashlight cells can be used together to make a battery of 3 V. Single flashlight cells are often called batteries by mistake. The manufacturers sometimes print the name "battery" on their labels. Even though it is incorrect, they think that more people are familiar with this term. However, some batteries are correctly labeled. The common 6-V lantern battery contains four separate 1.5-V cells. How many of these cells would you expect to find in a 9-V battery? Six separate 1.5-V cells.

The chemical reactions in all these cells and batteries will sooner or later "use up" the initial substances. Then the cells and batteries can no longer be used. The products cannot be easily changed back into the original substances. The chemical reactions that produce the electric current often are not easily reversed.

Some electrochemical cells are put together so that the reaction can be easily reversed. Batteries made of these cells are called **storage batteries.** You are probably most familiar with the storage battery in an automobile. The automobile storage battery uses lead and lead dioxide plates. These plates are separated by an electrolyte of sulfuric acid and water. Six of these cells connected together in series produce a voltage of 12 V. Most of today's automobile storage batteries are of this size. How many volts are produced by each cell in the automobile storage battery? Each cell produces 2 V.

As the storage battery supplies electric energy, the lead plates give up electrons. The electrons move to the lead dioxide plates through an outer electric circuit. The sulfate from the sulfuric acid combines with lead on the plates. Water is also formed by the reaction. As the reaction continues, the amount of sulfuric acid in the electrolyte decreases. At the same time, the amount of water increases. The battery is discharging.

The battery is recharged by connecting it to a source of electric current moving in the opposite direction (usually

Figure 12-16. *One cell of a storage battery. How is the storage battery recharged?*
The chemical changes that produce the electric current are reversed by an electric current from the generator or alternator in the automobile or by an outside source of electric current.

Lead plate (–)

Lead dioxide plates (+)

Dilute sulfuric acid

from the car's generator). The chemical reactions are reversed. The sulfate is returned to the electrolyte. The lead and lead dioxide plates are restored. The battery can again be used to supply electric current. The battery can be recharged many times. Eventually, other chemical changes and loss of material from the plates make the battery wear out.

The storage battery is a very convenient device in an automobile. Electric current from the battery works the starter. Once the engine is running, electric current is produced by the generator, which recharges the battery. Before the storage battery was used, cars had to be started with cranks. Cranking a car was not an easy task, and the person cranking was sometimes injured from "kick-back" by the engine.

Some alkaline cells are also designed so that they can be recharged. These may be used in some calculators, flash cameras, and electronic games.

Another source of electric current, which has been used in the spacecraft flights, is the **fuel cell.** It differs from other cells in one important way. Some of the materials that react are supplied from outside the cell.

In one type of fuel cell, two electrodes are in an electrolyte of potassium hydroxide. The electrodes are connected by an outside circuit. Hydrogen gas is released at one electrode. The hydrogen combines with hydroxide ions and releases electrons. Hydrogen is oxidized.

$$H_2 + 2OH^- \rightarrow 2H_2O + 2e^-$$

Research Topic

The famous inventor, Thomas Alva Edison, devoted much of his time to the development of a certain type of storage battery. Find out what Edison's storage battery was like and how it worked. How does it differ from storage batteries of today? For what purpose did Edison first use his storage battery?

Main Idea

How does a fuel cell differ from other electrochemical cells?

12.2b   A Wet Cell

Science Processes: Observing, measuring, defining operationally, experimenting, formulating models

Materials   BASIC   30 minutes   Groups of 3 or 4

- 250-mL beaker
- two pieces of bell wire (40 cm long)
- zinc strip (1 cm × 10 cm)
- aluminum strip (1 cm × 10 cm)
- copper strip (1 cm × 10 cm)
- iron strip (1 cm × 10 cm)
- copper sulfate ($CuSO_4$) solution (saturated)
- voltmeter
- flashlight bulb in socket
- large container (to dispose of copper sulfate solution)
- masking tape

Purpose

To find out how the voltage changes when different combinations of metals are used in a wet cell.

Procedure

1. Fill the beaker two-thirds full with the copper sulfate solution.

   SAFETY NOTE: *Copper sulfate solution may be irritating to the skin. If you should spill any of the solution on yourself, wash the affected area with soap and water. If you should get the copper sulfate solution in your eyes, flush the affected area with generous amounts of water.*

2. Tape one section of bell wire to the aluminum strip. Tape a second section of bell wire to the copper strip. Connect the other ends of the wire to the voltmeter as shown in the diagram.

3. Place the two strips of metal in the solution. Note the reading on the voltmeter. If the reading is zero, reverse the connections on the voltmeter and record the reading.

4. Remove the wires from the voltmeter and connect them to the socket of the flashlight bulb. Note if the bulb lights.

5. Remove the strips from the solution. Replace the aluminum strip with a zinc strip. Place the zinc and copper strips in the solution. Reattach the voltmeter and record the new reading. Now test the flashlight bulb as you did in step four, using the zinc and copper strips.

6. Remove the strips from the solution. Replace the zinc strip with an iron strip. Place the iron and copper strips in the solution and record the voltmeter reading. Again test the flashlight bulb. Record whether the bulb lights.

7. Remove the metal strips from the solution. Rinse all the strips with water and dry thoroughly. Pour the copper sulfate solution into the large water-filled container provided by the teacher.

Questions

1. Which combination of metals gave the highest voltage?
2. Which combination of metals gave the lowest voltage?
3. Which of the combinations of metals caused the flashlight bulb to light?

Conclusion

Explain how the voltage of a wet cell changes when different combinations of metals are used.

Strips of Metal	Voltmeter Reading	Flashlight Bulb (check if lit)
aluminum & copper		
zinc & copper		
iron & copper		

Figure 12-17. *A fuel cell. The current it produces can be used to run an electric motor. What substance is produced in this cell?*
Hydrogen and oxygen gases react to form water.

Oxygen gas is released at the other electrode. The oxygen accepts the electrons, which have traveled through the outside circuit. Oxygen is reduced and reacts with water to form more hydroxide ions.

$$O_2 + 2H_2O + 4e^- \rightarrow 4OH^-$$

For every four electrons that travel from one electrode to another, two molecules of hydrogen and one molecule of oxygen are used. The net result is that water is formed, and an electric current is produced.

Quick Review

1. What substance is oxidized in a carbon and zinc cell? What substance is reduced?
2. What happens to the auto storage battery while the engine is running?

Quick Review answers:
1. Zinc is oxidized. Manganese dioxide and possibly other substances in the paste are reduced.
2. The storage battery is recharged, if necessary, while the engine is running.

Using electric energy to produce chemical changes

New vocabulary: spontaneous, electrolysis, cathode, anode

The chemical changes that take place in an electrochemical cell do not need any energy to get started. They are said to be **spontaneous** (spon-TAYN'-ee-us). As a result of the changes, electric energy is released.

Some chemical changes require a continuous input of energy in order to continue. One example of this kind of change is the recharging of a storage battery. Here, electric energy is

Main Idea

What constitutes a spontaneous chemical reaction?

Figure 12-18. *What two dangerous substances are formed when an electric current splits table salt apart?* Sodium metal and chlorine gas.

used to reverse the changes that produce an electric current. Another example is the breakdown of water into hydrogen gas and oxygen gas. This change, which happens when an electric current passes through water, also uses electric energy. It is just the reverse of the reaction inside a fuel cell that uses hydrogen and oxygen gas.

The breakdown of any compound by use of an electric current is called **electrolysis** (ih-lek-TROL'-uh-sis). Compounds other than water can also be separated into elements by electrolysis.

Table salt (sodium chloride) forms a liquid at a very high temperature. The liquid is made up of sodium ions (Na^+) and chloride ions (Cl^-). Two carbon electrodes are placed in the container of liquid sodium chloride. A battery is connected to the two carbon electrodes. Bubbles soon start appearing near one of the electrodes. The electrode connected to the positive end of the battery attracts the chloride ions. The chloride ions give up electrons and form chlorine gas (Cl_2). For every two chloride ions that are oxidized, one chlorine molecule is formed.

$$2Cl^- \rightarrow 2e^- + Cl_2^0$$

The sodium ions (Na^+) are attracted to the electrode connected to the negative post of the battery. Each sodium ion

Main Idea

What is electrolysis?

gains a single electron. The sodium ions are reduced to form sodium metal.

$$Na^+ + e^- \rightarrow Na^0$$

Both sodium and chlorine are dangerous substances with very different properties from those of table salt.

Most metals are found in nature as part of a compound. Electrolysis can be used to separate some pure metals from the substances they are combined with. Aluminum is an example. It is found combined with oxygen in an ore called bauxite.

The modern method by which aluminum is separated from bauxite was developed by Charles Martin Hall. When Hall was a young chemistry student at Oberlin College in 1886, his professor told him there was no inexpensive way of extracting aluminum. Hall decided that he would try to find a way. Some time later he came into class with a handful of small aluminum pellets, which he had obtained from bauxite. Hall's process for obtaining inexpensive aluminum has been used ever since!

In Hall's process, the bauxite (Al_2O_3) is melted and placed in a graphite (carbon) container. The graphite is connected to the negative terminal of an outside source. It serves as the negative electrode, or **cathode** (KATH'-ōd). The aluminum ions (Al^{3+}) in the melted ore are attracted to the cathode. At the cathode, the aluminum ions gain electrons and form aluminum metal. The temperature must be kept very high so that the aluminum can be liquid and run off the bottom of the container.

Figure 12-19. *Charles Martin Hall.*

Additional information:
Chemists define the cathode as the electrode at which reduction (gain of electrons) takes place. In electrolysis, electrons from the negative terminal of the outside source move to the cathode. In Hall's process, these electrons are gained by Al^{3+} ions.

According to the chemist's definition, the cathode *in an electrochemical cell* is the *positive* electrode. For example, in the cell in Figure 12-14 on page 553, manganese dioxide gains electrons at the carbon rod, so the carbon rod is the cathode. Thus, the simplified definition of the cathode as the negative electrode is true only for an electrode connected to an outside source.

Figure 12-20. *Separating aluminum from its ore. Why are large amounts of energy needed?*
Electric energy is needed to maintain the high temperature needed and to separate the aluminum from the ore.

Electric current

Melted aluminum is run off here

Melted aluminum settles here

$$Al^3 + 3e \rightarrow A^{10}$$

Graphite container

$$Al^{3+} + 3e^- \rightarrow Al^0$$

Are the aluminum ions oxidized or reduced? Reduced

Other electrodes are immersed in the melted bauxite. They are connected to the positive terminal of the outside source. They serve as positive electrodes, or **anodes** (AN'-ōdz). The oxygen ions (O^{2-}) are attracted to the anodes. They give up electrons, and oxygen gas is formed.

$$2O^{2-} \rightarrow O_2 + 4e^-$$

Are the oxygen ions oxidized or reduced? Oxidized

Even though Hall's process is relatively inexpensive, it still requires enormous amounts of electric energy. Far less energy is required to recycle old aluminum products. Returning aluminum cans for recycling is an important way of saving energy!

Additional steps are necessary in the refining of some metals from their ores. But the idea is the same. The metal can be separated from its ore using an electric current. The addition of electric energy causes the compound to break down. What energy change must have taken place when the compound was formed? Energy must have been released.

Quick Review

1. Name one important use for electrolysis.
2. What kind of chemical reaction takes place at the anode?
3. What kind of chemical reaction takes place at the cathode?

Electroplating

New vocabulary: electroplating

Metals can also be deposited on a conducting material. This process is called **electroplating** (ih-LEK'-trō-play'-ting). Electroplating is also an application of electrolysis. You probably know of many materials that have been electroplated. The less expensive metals such as iron corrode easily. Covering them with a thin coat of metal that does not corrode makes the metal last much longer.

Gold does not corrode. But gold is a very expensive metal. Gold can be added in a very thin layer to another metal by electroplating. Silver, too, can be plated on another metallic surface. Silver does tarnish. That is, it combines with sulfur in the air to form silver sulfide. But the deposit of silver sulfide can be removed quite easily.

Chromium metal is often plated on steel or iron surfaces. Chromium protects the iron from exposure to the oxygen of

---

Additional information:
Chemists define the anode as the electrode at which oxidation (loss of electrons) takes place. The simplified definition of the anode as the positive electrode is true only for an electrode connected to an outside source.

Critical Thinking

In Hall's process, what happens to the electrons released at the anode when oxygen gas is formed?

The electrons travel toward the positive terminal of the outside source. They enter the source, come out the negative terminal, and travel toward the cathode, where they are gained by the aluminum ions.

Quick Review answers:
1. Separating metals from their ores
2. Oxidation—loss of electrons
3. Reduction—gain of electrons

Research Topic

Find out when electroplating was first used. What were some of the early products that were electroplated? Can metals be plated any other way than by electroplating? What is anodized aluminum?

the air. Chromium also reacts with air to form a thin layer of chromium oxide. The layer of chromium oxide prevents any further reaction of chromium with the oxygen of the air. And it protects the iron from rusting.

A battery supplies electrons to the metal to be electroplated, which is always attached to the negative terminal. It serves as the cathode. The metal is in a salt solution that contains positive ions of the metal that forms the plating. These positive metal ions move toward the extra electrons on the metal to be plated. At the same time, negative ions in the salt solution move toward the anode. The anode is connected to the positive terminal of the battery. It is made of the metal that forms the plating.

The metal ions in the solution combine with the extra electrons on the object to be plated. For example, suppose a piece of iron is to be plated with copper. Copper ions from the solution combine with electrons on the surface of the iron, and form a copper plating.

$$Cu^{2+} + 2e^- \rightarrow Cu^0$$

At the anode, copper atoms give up electrons and enter the solution.

$$Cu^0 \rightarrow 2e^- + Cu^{2+}$$

The speed at which electroplating takes place is determined by the electric current. Each copper atom that is plated on the iron requires two electrons. Increasing the number of electrons that move to the iron increases the number of atoms of copper that form. Thus, increasing the current increases the speed of the electroplating. Increasing the length of time the current flows also increases the amount of copper that is plated.

Nickel, chromium, silver, and gold are frequently used for electroplating. What kinds of products would you expect to be plated with these metals? Brass, an alloy of copper and zinc, is also frequently used. Products such as nails, screws, door knobs, and fireplace screens are often plated with brass.

Figure 12-21. *Which terminal of the battery should be connected to the spoon that is to be plated with copper? Does oxidation or reduction take place at the spoon?*
The negative terminal should be connected to the spoon. Reduction (gain of electrons) takes place at the spoon.

Data Search

If a piece of iron plated with chromium is heated to a very high temperature, which would melt first—the iron or the chromium? Search pages 658–661.
The chromium would melt first, as its melting point is 2672°C, while that of iron is 2750°C.

Silver and gold are used for plating of jewelry, silverware, etc. Nickel is used for plating of tools and chromium for plating of parts of automobiles.

Quick Review

1. What must the battery supply to a metal that is to be electroplated?
2. Name six metals that are frequently used for electroplating.
3. In electroplating, which metal should act as the cathode?

Quick Review answers:
1. An excess of electrons
2. Chromium, nickel, silver, brass, copper, and gold
3. The metal to be covered

Electrolysis engineer

Electrolysis and corrosion-control engineers, like most engineers, are good at locating and solving problems. Specifically, electrolysis and corrosion-control engineers try to prevent stray electric currents in the earth from harming underground structures. Energy-related companies and municipalities frequently employ corrosion-control engineers.

To perform their job well, engineers must be observant, analytical, and knowledgeable. They study soil conditions and causes of corrosion. Voltmeters and ammeters are sensing equipment which help these engineers determine the strength and source of an electrical current. Often electrolysis and corrosion-control engineers are like detectives. They carefully examine a corroded pipe, and then mentally reconstruct the conditions which caused the corrosion. When they understand the cause, the engineers suggest actions which will prevent further damage.

Students interested in this field should take classes in math, chemistry, and physics. Bachelors' degrees are necessary for a career as an electrolysis and corrosion-control engineer. Many engineers continue their education at the graduate level.

For more information, write to: Federation of National Electrolysis Associations, 2311 E. Stadium Boulevard, Suite 214, Ann Arbor, Michigan 48104.

Electrolysis and corrosion-control engineers try to prevent corrosion of pipes and other underground structures by stray electric currents.

Electroplater

About half of all electroplaters work in shops that specialize in metal plating and polishing. Others work in plants that manufacture plumbing fixtures, cooking utensils, household appliances, electronic components, automobiles, and other metal products.

Work as an electroplater can be hazardous. Toxic fumes and acid spills may be part of the workers' environment. Protective masks and clothing may have to be worn. Patience, concern for detail, and attention to job specifications are important qualities of successful electroplaters.

Most electroplaters learn their skills by helping experienced workers in an on-the-job type apprenticeship. Some workers complete a one- to two-year electroplating course in a technical institute or in a vocational school. High school chemistry and physics courses provide students with an understanding of the process of electroplating. Experience in shop courses can provide a good general background for the field.

For more information, write to: American Electroplaters' Society, 12644 Research Parkway, Orlando, Florida 32826.

Electroplating involves the use of strong chemicals as well as electric current.

12.2 Section Review

Vocabulary

8 alkaline cell
1 anode
6 cathode
12 dry cell
2 electrochemical cell
7 electrode
3 electrolysis
5 electrolyte
9 electroplating
13 fuel cell
11 spontaneous
10 storage battery
4 wet cell

Vocabulary Review

Match each term above with the numbered phrase that best describes it.

1. Place where electrons are given up
2. Produces an electric current from a chemical reaction
3. Separating of a compound using electric current
4. An electrochemical cell that contains a liquid
5. A liquid or paste made up of ions
6. Place where electrons are gained
7. Conductors that carry electrons in or out of a cell
8. This type of dry cell contains a strong base
9. Using electricity to cover an object with metal
10. A cluster of electrochemical cells that can undergo a reversible reaction
11. Chemical changes that do not need any energy to get started
12. A cell that contains a paste
13. Some materials that react in this cell are supplied from outside

Review Questions

Multiple Choice: Choose the answer that best completes each of the following sentences.

14. In an electrochemical cell, ? .
    a. chemical change causes an electric current
    b. electric current produces heat
    c. electric current is increased
    d. metals combine to form alloys

15. A chemical change that releases energy as the change takes place is ? .
    a. electrolysis
    b. electroplating
    c. battery recharging
    d. battery discharging

16. In the electroplating of copper onto iron, a reaction that takes place at a cathode is ? .
    a. oxidation of copper ions
    b. reduction of copper ions
    c. oxidation of copper metal
    d. reduction of copper metal

17. Objects to be electroplated should be connected to ? .
    a. the positive terminal of the battery
    b. the negative terminal of the battery
    c. either the positive or negative terminals
    d. both the positive and negative terminals

Understanding the Concepts

18. What three substances are normally needed to make an electrochemical cell?
19. How is a fuel cell different from other types of electrochemical cells?
20. What procedures would you follow to increase the thickness of a copper layer that is being plated on a piece of iron?
21. What is the advantage of a storage battery?

12 Chapter Review

Answers appear on page T159 in the front of this book. Blackline master test for this chapter: Chapter Testsheets 12A and 12B (TRB pages 263–264).

Vocabulary

activity	electrode	oxidizing agent
activity series	electrolysis	ozone
alkaline cell	electrolyte	reducing agent
anode	electroplating	reduction
cathode	fuel cell	spontaneous
corrosion	oxidation	storage battery
dry cell	oxidation number	wet cell
electrochemical cell		

Review of Concepts

Oxidation is the loss of electrons in a chemical change; **reduction** is the gain of electrons in a chemical change.

- Oxidation and reduction always occur simultaneously; neither can take place without the other.
- If the oxidation number of an element has increased, the element has been oxidized; if the oxidation number has decreased, the element has been reduced.

Corrosion is the combining of a metal with water, air, or other materials in the atmosphere.

- When a metal corrodes, it loses electrons.
- Metals differ in their tendency to give up electrons.

The **activity** of a metal refers to its metal tendency to give up electrons. The most active metals are those that are most easily oxidized.

- The activity series ranks metals with respect to tendency to give up electrons. A metal above another metal in the activity series will give up electrons to ions of any of the metals below it in the series.

- Differences in the activities of metals are made use of in protecting some metals against corrosion; an important metal (e.g. iron) that is vulnerable to corrosion is coated with or electrically connected to a more active metal (e.g. zinc or magnesium) that will be corroded preferentially.
- Different activities can exist in different places on the same piece of metal. Locations under the greatest stress tend to give up electrons most easily; these areas will corrode most easily.

Oxidizing agents accept electrons. **Reducing agents** give up electrons.

- The strongest oxidizing agents have the greatest attraction for electrons; the strongest reducing agents give up electrons most easily.
- The development of film involves the use of a weak reducing agent, the developer, to reduce light-sensitized crystals of silver bromide.
- Antioxidants retard the deterioration of some foods by combining preferentially with oxygen.

An **electrochemical cell** uses a chemical change involving oxidation and reduction to produce electric energy.

- Two metals that have different activities can be used to make an electrochemical cell.
- The chemical reactions that take place in electrochemical cells are spontaneous.
- A storage battery can be recharged by using electric energy to run a current through it in the reverse direction.
- In a fuel cell, the materials that react are supplied from outside the cell.
- Electric energy can be used to produce chemical changes such as the separation of metals from their ores and the electroplating of metals.

Critical Thinking

1. Why do you suppose the oxidation number of hydrogen is −1 in hydrides? What is unusual about these compounds? (Examples of hydrides are lithium hydride, LiH, sodium hydride, NaH, and potassium hydride, KH.)

2. Suppose that a reaction occurs in which calcium replaces aluminum in a compound. Write equations for the half reactions to show the changes in oxidation numbers for calcium and aluminum. Then write an equation for the redox reaction between calcium and aluminum.

3. Magnesium metal is commonly attached to the sides of iron ships to prevent corrosion. Could zinc metal be used as effectively for the same purpose? (Consider the relative positions of magnesium, zinc, and iron in the activity series.)

4. A galvanized nail is an iron nail coated with a thin layer of zinc metal. How would the corrosion resistance of the nail be affected if the nail were coated with magnesium rather than zinc? (Consider the relative positions of magnesium, zinc, and iron in the activity series.)

5. Will silver tarnish if placed in a sample of air from which all sulfur compounds have been removed?

6. List at least three characteristics that antioxidants should have if they are to be used in food. Indicate why these characteristics are desirable.

7. How would the performance of a lead storage battery be affected if all its water were to evaporate?

8. Some cells and batteries can be recharged. Describe what takes place during the recharging of a battery. What are the advantages of a rechargeable battery?

9. Suppose you wished to separate a metal from its ore by electrolysis. At which electrode would you expect the metal to be collected? Would the metal ion be reduced or oxidized?

10. In what way would a galvanized nail be more resistant to corrosion than a nail that had simply been painted?

Individual Research

11. Find out if water increases the speed at which iron rusts by setting up a controlled experiment. Decide what variables you need to control and how you will measure the rate of the reaction.

12. Use a hacksaw to cut a standard carbon-zinc flashlight cell in half. Identify the electrodes and the electrolyte.

13. Obtain a strip of zinc, a strip of copper, and a sensitive galvanometer. Place the metal strips through the skin of a lemon, taking care that they do not touch. Connect the strips to the galvanometer and look for evidence of a current. Replace the lemon by a potato. Is there any difference in the amount of current?

Bibliography

Morgan, Alfred. *Adventures in Electrochemistry.* New York: Scribner, 1977
    Describes experiments that can be performed and gives a historical overview of electrochemistry.

Wilbraham et al. *Addison-Wesley Chemistry.* Menlo Park, CA: Addison-Wesley, 1987.
    Chapter 20, "Oxidation-Reduction Reactions," of this high-school chemistry test covers oxidation and reduction in depth. Chapter 21, "Electrochemistry," covers wet and dry cells, storage batteries, fuel cells, electrolysis, and electroplating.

Chapter 13
Nuclear Reactions

Changes in the nuclei of atoms release great amounts of energy. That energy could do useful work if mankind can harness nuclear reactions. Here you see a research device to test how to control the process of nuclear fusion with lasers. In this chapter, you will learn more about two kinds of nuclear changes, how these changes release energy, and some methods to harness that energy.

Science background information:
The nucleus of an atom is made up of protons and neutrons, both of which are known as *nucleons*. The charge of the nucleus, or the number of protons, determines the electron structure of the atom. This, in turn, determines the atom's chemical identity as an element. Since the number of neutrons in the nucleus can vary, atoms of the same element can have different atomic masses. These are known as isotopes of an element.

Each individual combination of protons and neutrons is known as a *nuclide.* Over 1000 different nuclides are known to exist. Of these, only about one-quarter are stable. The others are all unstable and have lifetimes that vary from a fraction of a second to several billion years.

Unstable nuclei tend to become more stable by ejecting material. This spontaneous decay process is known as radioactivity. Radioactivity is characterized by the emission of mass from the nucleus in the form of alpha particles or beta particles (electrons) and energy in the form of gamma rays.

The stability of the nucleus can be understood in terms of the two competing forces at work within it. These forces are the electrostatic force of repulsion between the positively charged protons and a force of attraction known

For detailed information about teaching this chapter, see Chapter 13 Planning Guide on pages T160–T161 in the front of this book.

Projectsheet 13 (TRB page 185) and Research Lab 13 (Lab Manual pages 179–180) may be used at any point in this chapter.

Chapter Preview

13.1 The Nuclear Structure of Atoms

- **Natural radioactivity**
- **Describing radiation**
- **Detecting radiation**
- **Changes in the nucleus**
- **Using radioisotopes**
- **Rate of nuclear decay**
- **Nuclear models**

Radioactivity is the release of particles or energy from the nucleus of an atom. There are three main kinds of atomic radiation. Radiation is invisible, so it must be detected by its effects. When radiation is given off, there are changes in the nucleus of an atom. How fast the nucleus of an atom breaks down depends on the kind of atom involved.

13.2 Energy from Nuclear Changes

- **Mass and energy in nuclear changes**
- **Binding energy**
- **Producing changes in the nucleus**
- **Fission of the nucleus**
- **Nuclear fusion**

In the nucleus, some mass of the particles is converted into energy to hold the particles together. Changes in the structure of the nucleus can result in the release of energy. Atomic nuclei can split—fission—or be joined together—fusion. Energy given off in the processes of fission and fusion can be harnessed for human needs.

as the *strong* force. The strong force acts at close range to hold all nucleons together, regardless of charge. The presence of neutrons and the action of the strong force makes it possible for many positively charged protons to stick together in the tiny nucleus. The more protons in a nucleus, the larger the number of neutrons needed to hold it together. However, for elements with more than 83 protons, even the addition of many neutrons cannot stabilize the nucleus. The force of electrostatic repulsion is too great and these atoms fly apart. In the process they give off an alpha particle that consists of two protons and two neutrons.

In addition, neutrons themselves tend to be unstable when there are not enough protons around. They will decay spontaneously, producing a proton and an electron. This emission of electrons is the source of beta particles.

When unstable nuclei undergo changes, they can also emit high-energy electromagnetic radiation known as gamma rays. By emitting a gamma ray, the nucleus can reach a lower energy state and thus become more stable.

There are three naturally-occuring radioactive series in nature. These are called the uranium, thorium and actinium series. These series start with a parent element, such as U-238, Th-232, and Ac-227. These pass through a series of alpha and beta decays until they finally become stable isotopes of lead. For example, in the uranium series U-238 emits an alpha particle to become Th-234, which then emits a beta particle to become Pa-234. This process continues until the stable isotope Pb-206 is produced. This process also releases energy which is thought to contribute to the heat of the interior of the earth. Each step in this process occurs at its own rate and has its own half-life.

13.1 The Nuclear Structure of Atoms

Supplemental materials: Teaching Diagrams 13-1A, 13-1B (TRB pages 61, 62), Reading Checksheet 13-1 (TRB page 113), Skillsheet 13-1 (TRB page 159), Investigation 13-1 (Lab Manual pages 173–174)

Section Preview

- **Natural radioactivity**
- **Describing radiation**
- **Detecting radiation**
- **Changes in the nucleus**
- **Using radioisotopes**
- **Rate of nuclear decay**
- **Nuclear models**

Bracketed numbers are Section Review questions correlated to that objective.

Learning Objectives

1. To compare the properties of alpha, beta, and gamma radiation. [2, 5, 8, 12, 15, 16, 25]
2. To explain different methods for detecting various kinds of radiation. [4, 6, 7, 13, 19, 26]
3. To identify the nuclear change that accompanies each kind of radiation. [8, 12, 15, 17]
4. To illustrate the concept of half-life used in describing the rate of decay of a radioactive substance. [14, 18, 24]
5. To compare two models of the nucleus of atoms. [21]

Figure 13-1. *Complex machines are used in nuclear research. Seen here is the inside of an electron gun shell. It is part of an experiment on starting nuclear changes with lasers.*

Science background information:
The discovery of X-rays in 1885 by Wilhelm Roentgen directly led to the discovery of radioactivity by Henri Becquerel. Becquerel was studying fluorescent substances to see if they gave off X-rays when he discovered radioactivity.

Main Idea

What does the term radioactivity refer to?

The radiation emitted from the nuclei of atoms has provided some clues about the make-up and structure of the nucleus. Knowing something about the structure of the nucleus has led to the harnessing of nuclear changes as sources of energy. What are the characteristics of nuclear radiation? How is nuclear radiation detected? What are its effects? How are nuclear changes described? What are some proposed models for nuclei? These are some of the questions explored in this section.

Natural radioactivity

New vocabulary: radioactivity

Radioactivity (ray'-dee-ō-ak-TIV'-uh-tee) refers to the release of particles and/or energy from the nucleus of an atom. Some atoms are naturally radioactive. Many other atoms can be made radioactive by causing the atoms to gain or lose particles and become unstable.

Radioactivity was first noticed in 1896. A French scientist, Henri Becquerel, was experimenting with uranium ore. He found that photographic plates left close by but covered up were exposed. Becquerel was puzzled. No visible light could have reached the plates. The mysterious radiation was evidently able to penetrate where visible light could not. With further study he became convinced that atoms of uranium were responsible. Uranium atoms must be giving off invisible radiation that had reached the photographic plates.

Becquerel had discovered that uranium was radioactive. His discovery led to more experiments. Marie and Pierre Curie soon discovered two more radioactive elements, radium and polonium. Now, many radioactive elements are known. In fact, many common elements, such as hydrogen, carbon, and nitrogen, have radioactive isotopes. In addition, a number of radioactive isotopes have been produced artificially for use in scientific research and in medicine.

Quick Review

What strange effect led Becquerel to discover natural radioactivity?

Figure 13-2. *Blurry image was made by piece of radioactive ore placed on a covered photographic film. How could you be certain that the cause of this image was not stray light?*
By putting a piece of radioactive ore on a covered sheet of film in the dark.
Quick Review answer:
Photographic plates left close to uranium ore were exposed even though visible light could not have reached them.

Describing radiation

New vocabulary: alpha radiation, beta radiation, gamma radiation

Scientists began to study the radiation given off by these radioactive elements. It was soon found that more than one kind of radiation seemed to be given off. Each different kind of radiation produced different effects. For instance, each kind of radiation differed in its ability to pass through certain substances. The mystery became more challenging. Not only did the nuclei of atoms give off radiation, but they gave off different kinds of radiation.

Three kinds of radiation were described. One kind behaved as if it had a positive electric charge. It was called **alpha** (AL'-fuh) **radiation.** Further studies identified the characteristics of alpha radiation more closely. Alpha radiation was found to consist of particles. The amount of positive charge and the mass of the particles are equal to those of the second smallest atomic nucleus—the helium nucleus. Alpha radiation has the same properties as helium nuclei.

A second kind of radiation was found to have a negative charge. It became known as **beta** (BAY'-tuh) **radiation.** It, too, consists of particles. The mass and charge of the particles are the same as those of electrons.

Main Idea

What kind of electric charge does alpha radiation have?

Research Topic

Alpha radiation was used to study the nucleus by Ernest Rutherford. Try to find the source of alpha radiation that Rutherford used and write a brief report on it.

The third kind of radiation was found to have no mass and no electric charge. Its properties are similar in some ways to visible light and X-rays. This type of radiation became known as **gamma radiation.** It is now known to be electromagnetic

Our Science Heritage

Marie Curie

Marie Curie in her laboratory

Marie Sklodowska was born in Poland in 1867. As a student in school she had a great interest in science. After graduation from high school she went to work in order to save money for further education. Her older brother and sister were studying in Paris, and after she had saved enough money, she joined them there. She entered the great French university, the Sorbonne. She studied and worked very hard, just barely supporting herself, but graduated at the top of her class in 1894.

After graduation she married a French scientist, Pierre Curie, who had been working with electricity. She became very interested in Becquerel's discovery and decided that she, herself, would investigate radioactivity. In fact, Marie was responsible for naming the process of giving off rays "radioactivity."

She used some of her husband's findings in developing a method to measure radioactivity and to separate radioactive ores into several parts. She found that certain uranium ores seemed to be more radioactive than others. She guessed that there must be radioactive elements other than uranium in these ores.

She and her husband separated many ores, looking for these other elements. They found samples of the element thorium which were radioactive but not as radioactive as they had expected. They decided that there must be something else. Then they discovered a new element, polonium, which was highly radioactive. But they still believed that some ores contained minute quantities of an even more radioactive substance. After separating enormous amounts of ore, they finally had a tiny sample of an even more radioactive element that they called radium.

In 1903, the third Nobel Prize in physics was awarded to Pierre and Marie Curie and to Henri Becquerel. In 1911, she received a second Nobel Prize, this time in chemistry.

Among other things, radium has been used as a treatment for some kinds of cancer. Ironically, Marie Curie died of cancer in 1934. Her death was caused by too much exposure to radiation.

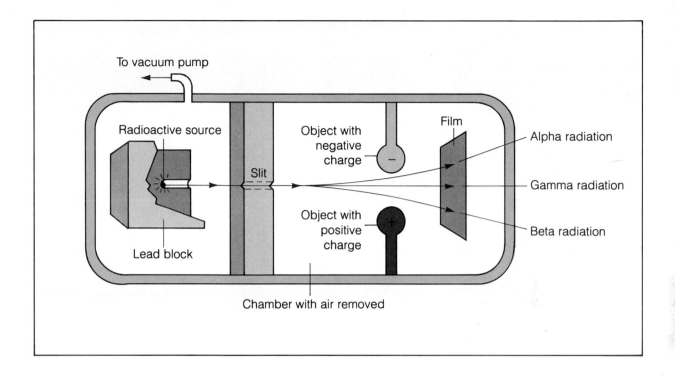

To vacuum pump

Radioactive source

Slit

Object with
negative
charge

Object with
positive
charge

Film

Alpha radiation

Gamma radiation

Beta radiation

Lead block

Chamber with air removed

radiation of a very high frequency. Gamma rays, along with alpha and beta rays, are often released together by the nuclei of radioactive atoms.

Figure 13-3 shows how nuclear radiation becomes divided when it passes between two electrically charged objects—one negative and the other positive. Positively charged alpha particles are attracted toward the object with the negative charge. Negatively charged beta particles are attracted toward the object with the positive charge. Gamma radiation, having no electric charge, is not attracted toward either object; it continues to move straight ahead.

Gamma radiation is the most dangerous form of nuclear radiation. It is even more dangerous than X-rays. Gamma radiation has enough energy to pass through several centimeters of lead. It is very damaging to the skin and body tissue of living organisms. Beta radiation is less damaging than gamma radiation but does penetrate the skin and even thin sheets of metal. Alpha radiation is the least penetrating of the three types. Most alpha particles can be stopped by a thin sheet of paper.

Quick Review

1. Describe the three different kinds of radiation.
2. Which kind of radiation is the most dangerous? Why?

Figure 13-3. *What difference among the three kinds of radiation causes them to separate when passing electrically charged objects?*
Alpha particles have a positive charge. These repel other positively charged objects and are attracted to negatively charged objects. Beta particles have a negative charge. These repel other negatively charged objects and are attracted to positively charged objects. Gamma radiation has no charge and is not affected by charged objects.

Main Idea

Which is the least damaging kind of radiation?

Quick Review answers:
1. ■ Alpha particles have the same charge and mass as a helium nucleus.
   ■ Beta particles have the same charge and mass as an electron.
   ■ Gamma radiation is similar to visible light and X-rays with even greater penetrating power than X-rays.
2. Gamma radiation is most dangerous because of its high energy.

Main Idea

How does an electroscope detect radiation?

Science background information:
The cloud chamber was developed by the British physicist Charles T. R. Wilson in the early 1900s. He had noticed that water vapor condenses on dust particles in clouds and wondered if water vapor would also condense on atomic particles. It does. In the cloud chamber, ionizing radiation, such as alpha and beta particles, makes characteristic tracks which are recorded by photography.

Figure 13-4. *Bubble chamber holds liquid hydrogen near its boiling point. When pressure is dropped by moving the piston, bubbles appear along tracks made by ionized particles. The tracks can be photographed and studied.*

Detecting radiation
New vocabulary: electroscope, cloud chamber, bubble chamber, Geiger tube

Nuclear radiation cannot be seen. But its effects can be made visible. Badges worn by workers in areas of possible radiation contain film. The film is protected from ordinary visible light. But dangerous radiation will expose the film. The worker then knows if he or she has been exposed to any dangerous radiation.

Some chemicals produce a flash of visible light when the invisible radiation strikes them. These flashes of light can be picked up by a photoelectric cell. The amount of current produced can be measured. The current is then a measure of the amount of radiation that is present.

An **electroscope** is a device for detecting electric charge. You had the opportunity to use one in an earlier activity. When the electroscope is charged, the leaves repel and separate from each other. A source of radiation will cause ionization of the air around the electroscope. The ions formed will be attracted to the electroscope and will neutralize the charge on the electroscope. The leaves will fall back together. Workers who could be exposed to radiation at one time carried small electroscopes shaped like pens (called *dosimeters*). These devices were marked to indicate the amount of radiation and could be read at any time.

A **cloud chamber** is also used to detect radiation. An investigation accompanying this text uses a cloud chamber. Alcohol vapor in a small container is cooled with dry ice. Condensation of the alcohol vapor takes place where ions are formed by the radiation. Alpha particles, because of their size and charge, produce a very visible track in the cloud chamber.

Labels within figure:
- Wire with positive charge
- Gas particle
- Ionized gas particle
- Electron released by gas particle
- Window
- Path of single charged particle of radiation
- Geiger tube case with negative charge
- Counter
- Click Click Click
- Battery

A **bubble chamber** uses a dense liquid such as hydrogen to detect the presence of higher energy particles. In this device, the hydrogen is kept at its boiling temperature. A slight reduction of pressure causes bubbles to appear along the path of the particle. You have seen the condensation trails (contrails) along the path of jet aircraft. Although the jet contrails are formed differently, the results resemble the tracks left by particles in cloud and bubble chambers.

Probably the most familiar device for detecting radiation is the **Geiger** (GĪ'-ger) **tube.** Gas particles in the tube are ionized, or changed into ions, by the radiation that strikes them. The more radiation, the more gas particles are ionized. An electric current flows through the tube. The amount of current depends on the amount of ionized gas particles, and is therefore a measure of the amount of radiation. A counter is usually attached to the tube, and the entire device is called a Geiger counter. The counter registers the amount of radiation. It also produces the audible "clicks" that you hear when a radioactive source is nearby.

Quick Review

1. How does a cloud chamber differ from a bubble chamber in the way it shows the radiation it detects?
2. Which means of detecting radiation are used to warn a person of possible overexposure to radiation?
3. What happens inside a Geiger tube when radiation strikes the tube?

Figure 13-5. *The Geiger tube for detecting radiation.*

Science background information:
The bubble chamber was invented in 1953 by American physicist Donald Glaser. It uses superheated liquid hydrogen at a temperature of −253°C. The temperature is kept just above the boiling point by pressure. Whenever a subatomic particle passes through the chamber, it causes a path of bubbles to form. These are recorded by photographs.

Research Topic

Read about how German physicist Hans Wilhelm Geiger invented the radiation-detecting device named after him.

Quick Review answer:
1. A visible track is produced in a cloud chamber by condensing vapor droplets. In a bubble chamber, the evidence is a path of bubbles.
2. Two means are film badges and pen-sized electroscopes.
3. Gas particles in the tube are ionized by the radiation, and the current that flows through the tube increases.

Figure 13-6. *An alpha particle is just the nucleus of a helium atom. How many protons and neutrons does it contain?*
Two protons and two neutrons.

Main Idea

What change in a nucleus is brought about by a change in the number of protons it contains?

Additional information:
The mass number of an element is always a whole number. The atomic mass of an element is usually not a whole number.

7 protons and 6 neutrons

An atom of uranium-238 has 146 neutrons.
The new nucleus will have 90 protons and 144 neutrons. It will be thorium, not uranium.

Changes in the nucleus
New vocabulary: mass number, nucleons, beta particles

Radioactive elements release both particles and energy. The release is accompanied by changes in the nucleus. You are already familiar with two kinds of particles found in the nucleus of an atom. These particles are protons and neutrons.

The number of protons in the nucleus determines the kind of element. For example, any nucleus with 6 protons is carbon. Or, any nucleus with 7 protons is nitrogen. Protons have a positive charge.

Neutrons have no charge, but they add mass to the atom. The number of neutrons in the nucleus determines what isotope is present. The isotope carbon-12 has 6 protons and 6 neutrons. Carbon-13 has 6 protons and 7 neutrons. Both are isotopes of the same element—carbon. The number written after the name of the element is the **mass number** of the isotope. The mass number equals the sum of the numbers of protons and neutrons.

A change in the number of protons changes the element to a different element. A change in the number of neutrons changes the original isotope to a different isotope of the same element. Both of these changes are nuclear changes.

Isotopes of elements with more neutrons than protons in the nucleus are often naturally radioactive. Hydrogen atoms with a mass number of three have two neutrons and one proton. The isotope is called tritium. It is naturally radioactive. Carbon atoms with a mass number of 14 are also radioactive. These atoms have 6 protons and 8 neutrons.

Sometimes isotopes with more protons than neutrons are associated with natural radioactivity. How many protons and neutrons does an atom of this isotope have?

Most of the heavier elements have radioactive isotopes. Uranium-238 is an example. Its atomic number is 92. Each atom has 92 protons. How many neutrons does each atom of uranium-238 have? Uranium-238 breaks down, or decays, by giving off an alpha particle. An alpha particle, like a helium nucleus, has two protons and two neutrons. Therefore, the uranium-238 nucleus changes to another nucleus having two fewer protons and two fewer neutrons. What will be the number of protons in the new nucleus? Will it still be uranium? If not, what element will it be? How many neutrons does it have?

Alpha particles are represented in nuclear reactions by the symbol ^4_2He. He represents the element helium, 2 is the

See also Activity Record Sheet 13-1A (Lab Manual page 171). Preparation Notes, Teacher Notes, Answers to Questions, and Conclusion appear on page T162 in the front of this book.

Activity

13.1a   Detecting Radiation with an Electroscope

Science Processes: Observing, recording data, using numbers

Materials   20 minutes   Teacher demonstration

- **flask electroscope**
- **alpha source (radioactive)**
- **plastic ruler**
- **stopwatch**
- **ring stand**
- **extension clamp**
- **clamp holder**
- **flannel cloth**

Purpose

To show how an electroscope can be used to detect radiation

Procedure

1. Set up the electroscope in an area that is visible to the students.
2. Charge the electroscope by rubbing the plastic ruler with the cloth. Bring the ruler near the electroscope ball, but do not touch it. With your other hand touch the electroscope ball briefly. Remove the ruler. The leaves should be apart.
3. With the stopwatch, immediately begin timing how long it takes for the leaves to collapse. Record the time.
   SAFETY NOTE: *Do not handle the radioactive source except according to the instructions.*
4. Attach the radioactive alpha source to the extension clamp. Attach the extension clamp to the ringstand.

6. Immediately move the ring stand with the alpha source as close as possible to the electroscope without touching it.
7. Time how long it takes the leaves to collapse. Record the time.
8. Move the alpha source away from the electroscope.
9. Repeat Steps 5, 6, and 7 two more times and record the time for each.
10. Take an average of the time for the leaves to collapse when the radiation source is present and compare that to the time when no source was present.

Questions

1. What does an electroscope detect?
2. Why do the leaves of the electroscope collapse after being charged?
3. How long did it take for the leaves to collapse when there was no radiation source and when a radiation source was present?
4. What can you infer about using an electroscope to detect radiation?

Conclusion

Is an electroscope a useful device for detecting radiation?

Step 2

Step 6

What would happen to the atomic mass and the atomic number of an element that decayed by giving off a proton?

The atomic number would decrease by one and the atomic mass would decrease by one amu.

Protactinium-234

Figure 13-7. *Uranium-238 decays to thorium-234 by giving off an alpha particle. Thorium-234 decays, in turn, by giving off a beta particle. What isotope results?*

atomic number of helium (number of protons) and 4 is the mass number (total number of protons and neutrons) of this particular isotope of helium. Protons and neutrons are often referred to as **nucleons,** or nuclear particles. So the mass number also refers to the total number of nucleons.

Radium with a mass number of 226 releases alpha particles when it decays. The equation for the nuclear reaction is

$$^{226}_{88}\text{Ra} \rightarrow {}^{4}_{2}\text{He} + {}^{222}_{86}\text{Rn} + \text{gamma rays.}$$

The number of protons is indicated to the lower left of the element's symbol. The mass number is placed to the upper left of the same symbol.

Radon with a mass number of 222 is also a product of the reaction. Radon decays, releasing potentially dangerous gamma radiation. Notice that in this equation the sum of the mass numbers (total number of nucleons) after the reaction is the same as before the reaction. How does the number of protons after the reaction compare with the number of pro-

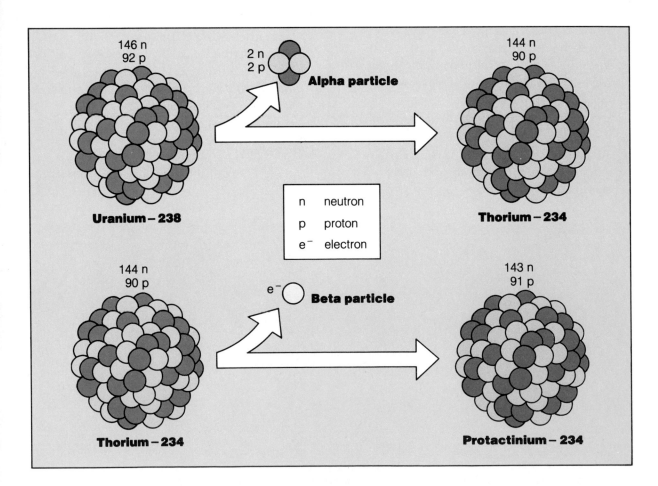

tons before? Since protons are positively charged does the total charge change? Energy is also released in the form of gamma rays.

Nuclei that give off a beta particle change in a different way. When an electron is given off as beta radiation, the number of protons increases by one. The mass of the nucleus stays about the same. Scientists have theorized that a neutron can break into a proton and an electron. Electrons have very little mass compared to a proton or neutron. Thus, the loss of an electron does not have much effect on the total mass of the nucleus.

Beta particles are represented by the symbol $_{-1}^{0}e$. The thorium nucleus changes to the nucleus of the element proactinium accompanied by the release of a beta particle. The reaction is summarized by the equation

$$_{90}^{231}\text{Th} \rightarrow {}_{-1}^{0}e + {}_{91}^{231}\text{Pa} + \text{gamma rays.}$$

The beta particle has the same properties as an electron. It has a mass number of zero and a charge of -1 (same charge size as the proton but opposite in kind). Notice that the number of protons has increased by one while the total number of protons and neutrons remains unchanged.

Quick Review

1. What kinds of isotopes are likely to be radioactive?
2. What does a nucleus become when it loses one or more protons?
3. When a nucleus loses a beta particle, what does it gain?

Using radioisotopes

New vocabulary: radioisotope

Isotopes of some of the common elements can be artificially made. Some are also produced in nuclear reactions used for other purposes. Many of these isotopes are radioactive: they are called **radioisotopes.** Phosphorus-32 is one example. It has the same properties as ordinary phosphorus-31. But it is also radioactive. Plants and animals both use small amounts of phosphorus. The path that the phosphorus takes through a plant or animal can be followed by a detector such as a Geiger counter. Much can be learned about the way the plant or animal uses phosphorus by following the tagged, or radioactive, isotope. Isotopes of other elements can be used in a similar way.

Two protons are lost from the nucleus. The positive charge of the nucleus is reduced by two. That means that each new atom will also have to lose two electrons from its electron energy levels in order to remain electrically neutral.

Quick Review answers:
1. Isotopes that have more neutrons than protons in the nucleus.
2. A nucleus of another element.
3. One proton.

Main Idea

What are some properties of a beta particle?

They are used to destroy cancer cells.

Figure 13-8. *How are radioactive isotopes used in the treatment of disease?*

13.1b   Model of Half-life

Science Processes: Experimenting, observing, recording data, making a chart

Materials

- **250-mL beaker**
- **sand**
- **balance**
- **graph paper**
- **ruler**
- **pencil**

Purpose

To model the half-life of a radioactive isotope.

Procedure

1. Determine the mass of an empty 250-mL beaker using the balance. Record the mass on line 1 of the chart on the Activity Record Sheet.
2. Put 200 mL of sand in the beaker. Determine the mass of the beaker and sand. Record the mass on line 1 of the chart.
3. Pour off 100 mL of sand and determine the mass of the beaker and remaining sand. Record the mass on line 2 of the chart.
4. Repeat step 3 three more times, pouring off half of the sand remaining in the beaker each time. Record the masses on lines 3, 4, and 5 of the chart.
5. Calculate the mass of the sand in the beaker for each trial by subtracting the mass of the empty beaker from the mass of the beaker and sand.
6. On the graph in the Activity Record Sheet, plot the mass of the sand against the number of trials. Draw a smooth curve through the points.

Questions

1. What do the grains of sand in the beaker represent?
2. What does the time interval between trials represent?

Groups of 2 or 3   25 minutes   and time to plot graph

3. Why did you pour off half of the sand left in the beaker each trial?
4. Use your graph to project how many trials would be needed to completely empty the beaker.

Conclusion

What is the half-life of a radioactive isotope?

Number of trials	Mass of empty beaker	Mass of beaker and sand	Mass of sand
1			
2			
3			
4			
5			

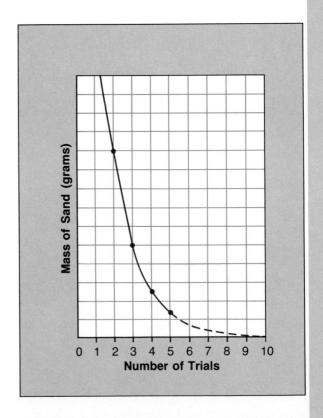

Radioisotope	Use of Isotope
Calcium-45	Observing plant nutrition
Carbon-14	Treating brain tumors, measuring age of ancient objects
Cobalt-60	Treating cancer, irradiating food
Iodine-131	Studying and treating the thyroid gland, finding leaks in water pipes
Iron-59	Examining the blood circulation
Phosphorus-32	Studying plants' use of fertilizer
Sodium-24	Diagnosing circulatory diseases
Strontium-90	Treating small lesions
Sulfur-35	Studying body's use of certain amino acids

Table 13-1. *Uses of some radio-isotopes.*

Some radioisotopes are used in the treatment of disease. Cancer cells can be destroyed by radiation from certain atoms. The radiation must be carefully controlled and directed. Otherwise, healthy cells are destroyed at the same time.

Radioactive isotopes are also used in industry. Leaks in pipes can be detected by tagging some of the material that flows through the pipes with radioactive isotopes. Changes in thickness of a material such as sheet metal can be mea sured by the changes in the amount of radiation that passes through it.

The ability to detect the movement of otherwise invisible atoms makes it possible to understand chemical changes even better. For example, in a certain experiment some green algae were exposed to carbon dioxide containing radioactive carbon. With detectors scientists could then tell how the green algae used the carbon in their food-making process. This is one of the ways in which radioisotopes are used as tracers.

Science background information:
György Hevesy, a chemist, was the first person to use radioactive isotopes to study the metabolism of living things. In 1923 he used radioactive lead to study uptake of nutrients by plants.

Research Topic

Investigate the use of nuclear substances in medicine. What radioisotopes are most used, and for what purposes? What is the rate of success of such treatments?

Quick Review

How does radioactivity cure some kinds of cancer? What caution must be followed?

Quick Review answer:
Cancer cells can be destroyed by radiation from certain atoms. Caution must be exercised to prevent the destroying of healthy cells.

Rate of nuclear decay

New vocabulary: nuclear decay, half-life

Any sample of a radioactive substance, even a very tiny amount, contains many, many atoms. Predicting which nucleus will break down at a certain time is not possible. But a prediction of the percentage of a sample that will break

Figure 13-9. *How long a time will pass before all the carbon-14 in the 10-gram sample is gone?*
The carbon-14 in the sample will never be totally gone.

Science background information:
Half-lives of radioactive elements vary from billionths of a second for radon-214 to 10^{16} year for samarium-149.

Main Idea

What is meant by the half-life of a radioactive isotope?

1.25 grams

On the third day, you could eat ⅛ of a jar. The half-life is one day. You would never completely finish the jar although after several days the amount of peanuts remaining would be essentially nonexistent.

down in any time period is possible. The breakdown of a nucleus is called **nuclear decay.**

The decay rate, or number of nuclei that decay per second, depends only on the type and amount of the sample. Factors such as temperature or pressure do not change the decay rate for an isotope. However, as the sample decays, less of the radioactive isotope remains. This means that the number of nuclei that decay will decrease. The rate of decay decreases as the amount of the remaining radioactive isotope decreases. The rate of decay therefore slows down with time.

The rate of decay of a radioactive isotope can also be described using the term **half-life.** Half-life refers to the time required for half of the nuclei in a sample of a radioactive isotope to decay. For example, the half-life of carbon-14 is about 5930 years. This means that a 10-gram sample of carbon-14 will diminish to a 5-gram sample of carbon-14 in 5930 years. After another 5930 years there will remain only 2.5 grams. How much will remain after another 5930 years?

Suppose you were given a jar of peanuts. You are told that each day you are to eat one-half of the peanuts that remain. The first day you eat half the jar of peanuts. The second day you would be able to eat only half of the peanuts that remain. That would be only one-fourth of a jar. What fraction of a jar would you be able to eat the third day? What is the half-life of the jar of peanuts? The number of peanuts you could eat each day would certainly change. How many days do you think it would take you to finish the jar of peanuts?

The radioactive carbon-14 isotope has been used to determine the age of materials that were once living. Products

Radioisotope	Half-Life	Radioisotope	Half-Life
Bismuth-212	60.5 minutes	Polonium-215	0.0018 second
Carbon-14	5930 years	Polonium-216	0.16 second
Chlorine-36	400 000 years	Radium-226	1620 years
Cobalt-60	5.26 years	Sodium-24	15.0 hours
Iodine-131	8.14 days	Strontium-90	19.9 years
Iron-59	46.3 days	Uranium-235	710 million years
Phosphorus-32	14.3 days	Uranium-238	4.5 billion years

Table 13-2. *Half-lives of some common radioisotopes.*

made from the wood in trees contain carbon. The carbon came from the carbon dioxide the tree absorbed from the atmosphere. A small percentage of the carbon dioxide in the atmosphere is made of carbon-14. While a tree is still alive, it keeps replacing the carbon inside it with carbon from the atmosphere. The percentage of carbon-14 in the tree is the same as in the atmosphere. When the tree dies, the carbon-14 inside it decays but is not replaced. So the percentage of carbon-14 in the wood decreases as the wood gets older. By careful measurement scientists can estimate how long ago the tree was killed or cut down. Some animals eat plant materials containing carbon-14. The age of their remains can be determined in the same way.

Several other isotopes are used to determine the age of rocks. Uranium-238 has a half-life of 4.5 billion years. Rocks formed billions of years ago still contain U-238. The percentage of U-238 that has not decayed gives away the age of the rock being studied. Uranium-235, potassium-40, and rubidium-87 also are used in determining the age of rocks.

Quick Review

1. What is meant when it is said that the half-life of a substance is 2500 years?
2. What isotope is used to determine the age of things that were once living?

Nuclear models

A picture of the nucleus of atoms that has both protons and neutrons in a very, very tiny region of the atom seems well established. Questions remain about the arrangement of these particles in the nucleus. One model suggests that the

Quick Review answers:
1. Half of the remaining substance will decay in a period of 2500 years.
2. Carbon-14

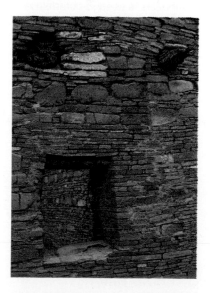

Figure 13-10. *The age of the wood used in old buildings, such as this one in Chaco Canyon, New Mexico, can be determined by measuring the percentage of carbon-14 in it.*

Figure 13-11. *In the liquid drop model of the nucleus, the protons and neutrons move around like atoms in a water drop. In the nuclear shell model, protons and neutrons occupy definite shells.*

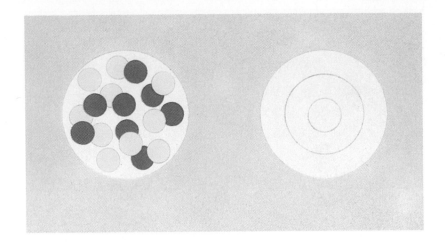

Main Idea

What basis is used to determine the location of nucleons using the nuclear shell model?

Science background information: Japanese physicist Hideki Yukawa predicted in 1935 the existence of a subatomic particle that would be present in the nucleus to transfer forces between protons and neutrons. In 1947, with the discovery of the pi-meson, this prediction was confirmed.

Quick Review answers:
1. Liquid drop and nuclear shell models
2. Some nucleons can escape from the nucleus if they pick up enough energy from the collisions that take place inside the nucleus.

protons and neutrons are closely packed but in continuous motion within the nucleus. It is given the name of *liquid drop model*. The nucleons are thought to behave in much the same way as the atoms in a drop of a liquid. According to this model some nucleons may escape the nucleus if they pick up enough energy from collisions with other nucleons (natural radioactivity). Particles from outside the nucleus may penetrate the nucleus and add enough energy for other particles to be released (artificial radioactivity).

A second picture of the nucleus suggests that the nucleus has a definite structure. The nucleons are arranged within the nucleus in definite shells. <u>Their location in the nucleus is based on their energy.</u> Nucleons leaving the nucleus have different energies because of the location of the particular shell they left. Nucleons change their energy by moving from one shell to another within the nucleus. This is known as the *nuclear shell* model.

In addition, dozens of subatomic particles have been discovered in the nucleus. These particles apparently interact with other particles and depend upon one another for their existence. While much is known about the nucleus and nuclear particles, a complete and consistent model is not yet available.

Many questions remain to be answered about the structure of the nucleus, including the nature of the forces holding the nucleons together.

Quick Review

1. Name two models for the nucleus of atoms.
2. According to the liquid drop model, what is the cause of natural radioactivity?

13.1 Section Review

Answers to Understanding the Concepts appear on page T163 in the front of this book. Blackline master test for this section: Section Testsheet 13-1 (TRB page 233)

Vocabulary

5 alpha particles
8 alpha radiation
2 beta particles
12 beta radiation
7 bubble chamber
13 cloud chamber
4 electroscope
15 gamma radiation
6 Geiger tube
14 half-life
3 mass number
11 nuclear decay
9 nucleons
1 radioactivity
10 radioisotope

Vocabulary Review

Match each term above with the numbered phrase that best describes it.

1. Release of particles and/or energy from the nucleus of an atom
2. Also known as electrons
3. Total number of protons and neutrons
4. Detects radiation by falling metal leaves
5. Helium nuclei
6. Detects radiation by flow of an electric current
7. Detects particles using liquid hydrogen
8. A stream of helium nuclei
9. Components of the nucleus of an atom
10. Unstable atom that breaks down by nuclear decay
11. The breakdown of the core of an atom
12. A stream of electrons
13. Detects radiation by tracks in alcohol vapor

14. The time for 5 of 10 unstable atoms to decay
15. A kind of electromagnetic radiation

Review Questions

Multiple Choice: Choose the answer that best completes each of the following sentences.

16. A type of nuclear radiation that has no charge but is very damaging is ? .
    a. alpha radiation
    b. beta radiation
    c. gamma radiation
    d. delta radiation
17. Beta radiation from the nucleus of an atom changes the nucleus by ? .
    a. increasing the number of protons
    b. increasing the number of neutrons
    c. decreasing the number of protons
    d. decreasing the total number of protons and neutrons
18. If a radioactive material has a half-life of 10 years, the fraction of the material that will remain after 30 years is ? .
    a. one-half
    b. one-third
    c. one-fourth
    d. one-eighth
19. The most practical device for detecting the presence of harmful radiation is a ? .
    a. Geiger tube
    b. moderator
    c. magnet
    d. control rod

20. A radioisotope has which of these characteristics: ? .
    a. can naturally occur
    b. can be made by bombarding atoms with radiation
    c. has an unstable nucleus
    d. all of the above
21. Two models of the nucleus of atom are known as ? .
    a. the energy shell and ionization potential models
    b. the nucleon and ion cloud models
    c. the quasar and nucleon level models
    d. the nuclear shell and liquid drop models

Understanding the Concepts

22. What property of radioactivity was responsible for its discovery?
23. Give two examples of how radioisotopes are used.
24. What two factors determine the rate of decay of a sample of radioactive material?
25. An unknown form of radiation is passed between two electrically charged poles. The radiation is not deflected. Which of the three common forms of radiation that you have studied does it resemble most? Why?
26. Compare a Geiger tube with an electroscope for detecting radiation.

For ideas for classroom demonstration and discussion, see Getting Started on page T163 in the front of this book.

13.2 Energy from Nuclear Changes

Supplemental materials: Teaching Diagram 13-2 (TRB page 63), Reading Check-sheet 13-2 (TRB page 114), Skillsheet 13-2 (TRB page 160), Investigation 13-2 (Lab Manual pages 177–178)

Section Preview

- **Mass and energy in nuclear changes**
- **Binding energy**

- **Producing changes in the nucleus**
- **Fission of the nucleus**
- **Nuclear fusion**

Bracketed numbers are Section Review questions correlated to that objective.

Learning Objectives

1. To relate the energy involved in nuclear reactions to the change in mass of the substances. [3, 11, 18]
2. To relate nuclear changes to changes of elements. [7, 10, 12, 20]
3. To compare the changes taking place in nuclear fission and nuclear fusion. [2, 4, 5, 6, 13, 14, 16, 17, 19]
4. To explain how energy from nuclear changes can be harnessed as an energy resource for people. [1, 5, 6, 8, 13]

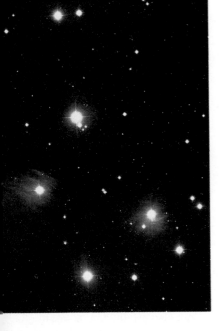

Figure 13-12. *The light from these stars is one form of energy that comes from nuclear reactions. In time, will these stars use up all of their fuel?* Yes, but for most stars it takes billions of years.

Research Topic

Find out what interested the American chemist William D. Harkins about the nucleus of atoms.

You have heard a great deal about nuclear energy. Still, nuclear changes have not been known to scientists for very long. Efforts to better understand nuclear forces continue while the threat of nuclear war and destruction remains. The peaceful uses of nuclear energy increase slowly amidst concern and controversy over the safety of power plants and the disposal of nuclear wastes. Everyone needs to be well informed about nuclear energy. What is the source of nuclear energy? How is nuclear energy released? What problems arise in using nuclear energy? These are questions that will be explored in this section.

Mass and energy in nuclear changes

The helium atom has four nucleons—two protons and two neutrons. The masses of individual protons and neutrons have been measured and are known quite precisely.

$$\text{mass of one proton} = 1.00796 \text{ am}$$
$$\text{mass of one neutron} = 1.00898 \text{ am}$$

The sum of the masses of the four nucleons in helium would then be

mass of two protons   = 2 1.00769 amu   = 2.01538 amu
mass of two neutrons = 2 × 1.00898 amu = 2.01796 amu
mass of two protons and two neutrons   = 4.03334 amu

However, when the mass of the helium nucleus is actually measured, it is found to be 4.00260 amu. The helium mass is actually less, by .03074 amu, than the total mass of the particles that comprise it. Is it possible that mass is not conserved in nuclear reaction? Apparently, some mass has disappeared or been lost by positioning these four nucleons very close together in the tiny space occupied by the nucleus.

It was Einstein who found a solution for this discrepancy. He proposed that the "disappearing mass" is transformed into energy. This energy holds the nucleons together in the small space occupied by the nucleus. The amount of energy gained from even a small loss of mass is very, very large. Einstein's famous equation, $E = mc^2$, relates the amount of energy, E, formed to the amount of mass lost, m. The amount of mass is multiplied by the velocity of light, $c = 3.0 \times 10^8$ m/s, squared—a very, very large number. In order to accommodate the change in thinking, the conservation of mass relationship had to be expanded to the *conservation of mass and energy principle*— the sum of the mass and energy is conserved. It means that mass and energy must both be forms of the same thing. The total amount of mass-energy doesn't change during a nuclear reaction although total amounts of mass may change as well as the total amounts of energy.

Science background information: English physicist Francis W. Aston was able to show, in 1925, that there were slight discrepancies in masses of isotopes from their predicted whole-number values. These discrepancies were the amount of mass that went into binding the particles of the nucleus together. To do this, Aston used a mass spectrograph, a device invented by J. J. Thomson, and improved by Aston.

Additional information: The change of 1 gram of mass into energy will produce 9×10^{10} kilojoules of energy.

Main Idea

What is meant by the conservation of mass and energy?

Figure 13-13. *One situation when the conservation of mass apparently does not hold. The nucleons individually have more mass than the nucleus which they make. What happens to the rest of the mass?*
It is converted to energy.

Figure 13-14. *Binding energy holds the nucleons together in the nucleus like glue. It comes from the conversion of a small amount of mass to energy when the nucleons join.*

Quick Review answers:
1. Mass is converted into energy.
2. In a nuclear reaction, the sum of mass and energy does not change.

Research Topic

Read about how German physicist Hans Wilhelm Geiger invented the radiation-detecting device named after him.

Figure 13-15. *A graph of binding energy per nucleon indicates which elements should be most stable—the ones with the highest binding energy. Iron has the most stable nucleus.*

Quick Review
1. How is the apparent loss of mass in a nuclear change accounted for?
2. What is the conservation of mass-energy principle?

Binding energy

New vocabulary: binding energy

The energy holding the nucleus together is referred to as **binding energy.** The binding energy comes from the mass lost when the nucleus was formed from the particles making it up. The binding energy per nucleon varies for different nuclei. It is the greatest for elements close to iron in the periodic table. The elements with the greatest binding energy per nucleon are most stable. Both the elements with smaller atomic numbers than iron and the elements with larger atomic numbers than iron have smaller binding energies per nucleon and are less stable. See the comparison of binding energies for different elements in Figure 13-15.

When the less stable nuclei change, they tend to form more stable nuclei. It is something like a ball—it always ends up at the bottom of the hill.

For example, large uranium nuclei split to form smaller nuclei that are closer to iron in stability. Hydrogen nuclei join together to form helium, an element that is closer to iron in binding energy per nucleon, and therefore more stable. Both the splitting of large nuclei and the joining together of small nuclei result in the release of energy.

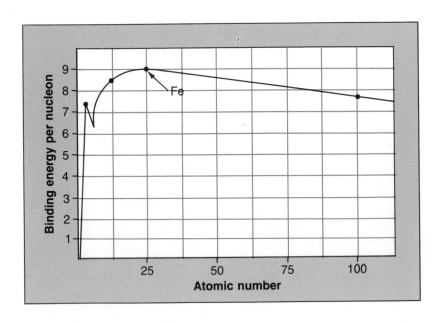

Producing changes in the nucleus
New vocabulary: transmutation

Many of the isotopes of elements are naturally radioactive. Some nuclear changes occur spontaneously. Additional changes in the nucleus were brought about by experimentally bombarding atoms. Scientists first used alpha particles and then neutrons to bombard the nuclei of atoms. In 1919, Ernest Rutherford bombarded nitrogen atoms with alpha particles. A nuclear reaction took place. The overall nuclear reaction is summarized by this equation.

$$_2^4\text{He} + {}_7^{14}\text{N} \rightarrow {}_8^{17}\text{O} + {}_1^1\text{H}$$

One element had been changed into another. Nitrogen atoms became oxygen atoms. This process is called the **transmutation** of elements.

Shortly thereafter, Irene Curie, daughter of Marie and Pierre Curie, and her husband bombarded aluminum with alpha particles. The new element formed was phosphorus. But the artificially produced phosphorus was different from natural phosphorus. The isotope was itself radioactive. The equation summarizing its formation is this.

$$_{13}^{27}\text{Al} + {}_2^4\text{He} \rightarrow {}_{15}^{30}\text{P} + {}_0^1\text{n}$$

Science background information:
Ernest Rutherford demonstrated the process of transmutation and became the first man to change one element into another. The efficiency of the process was poor, but it fulfilled a long-held dream of alchemists.

Main Idea

What happens during the transmutation of elements?

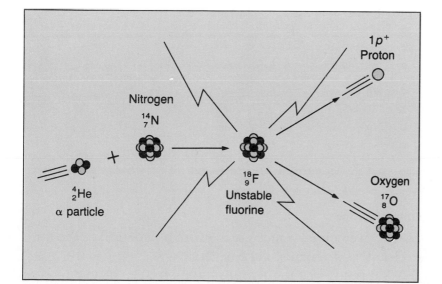

Figure 13-16. *Transmutation is changing one element into another. Here, nitrogen is changed into an unstable isotope of fluorine when it is bombarded by an alpha particle. What are the end products of this nuclear reaction?*
Oxygen and proton.

What additional particle was released? It has zero charge and a mass number equal to the proton.

Other attempts were made to produce nuclear changes with alpha particles. Additional reactions were difficult to accomplish. The protons in the nucleus of an atom repelled the positively charged alpha particles. After the discovery of the neutron by James Chadwick in 1932, scientists began to use neutrons to bombard nuclei. Neutrons are neutral in charge and are not repelled by the nuclei in the same way that alpha particles are. Experiments with neutron bombardment of various elements led to our present understanding and use of nuclear energy.

Research Topic

Read about the life of James Chadwick and learn how he discovered the neutron.

Sample Problem

Balance the following equations for nuclear reactions.

a. $^{9}_{4}Be + ^{4}_{2}He \rightarrow ^{?}_{6}C + ^{1}_{0}n$

b. $^{?}_{92}U + ^{1}_{0}n \rightarrow ^{239}_{92}U$

c. $^{14}_{7}C \rightarrow ^{?}_{8}N + ^{0}_{-1}e$

Solution

Equations for nuclear reactions are similar to chemical equations. The total mass number is unchanged in a nuclear reaction. The mass numbers on each side of the equation should balance, and the charge numbers on each side of the equation should balance.

a. $^{9}_{4}Be + ^{4}_{2}He \rightarrow ^{12}_{6}C + ^{1}_{0}n$

b. $^{238}_{92}U + ^{1}_{0}n \rightarrow ^{239}_{92}U$

c. $^{14}_{7}C \rightarrow ^{14}_{7}n + ^{1}_{-1}e$

Science background information:
Neutrons that are used to bombard nuclei are given off by radioactive elements in nuclear reactors. Also, neutrons are given off when elements with light nuclei, such as beryllium, are bombarded with alpha particles, protons, and other charged particles.

Practice Problems

a. $^{239}_{92}U \rightarrow ^{?}_{93}Np + ^{0}_{-1}e$

b. $^{?}_{89}Ac \rightarrow ^{4}_{2}He + ^{218}_{87}Fr$

c. $^{14}_{7}N + ^{1}_{0}n \rightarrow ^{?}_{6}C + ^{1}_{1}H$

Answers:

a. $^{239}_{92}U \rightarrow ^{239}_{92}Np + ^{1}_{0}n$

b. $^{222}_{89}Ac \rightarrow ^{4}_{2}He + ^{218}_{87}Fr$

c. $^{14}_{7}N + ^{1}_{0}n \rightarrow ^{14}_{6}C + ^{1}_{1}H$

Quick Review answers:
1. Neutrons have no charge so they are not repulsed by the positive protons of atomic nuclei.
2. Transmutation involves the change of the atomic number of an element so that the nucleus either gains or loses protons.

Quick Review

1. Why are neutrons more successful in penetrating the nuclei of atoms than alpha particles?
2. What is involved in the transmutation of an element?

Fission of the nucleus
New vocabulary: nuclear fission, chain reaction, critical mass, control rod, moderator

Energy is released when the nucleus of an atom decays. The amount of energy can be very large. Efforts to tap this source of energy led to scientists finding a way of splitting a nucleus. The nucleus was split by adding neutrons, which were shot at the nuclei of uranium-235 atoms. Some of these nuclei absorbed an extra neutron. The nucleus became unstable. As a result, it broke up into two smaller nuclei. Energy was released. Other neutrons were also released. This process of breaking a nucleus into two or more smaller nuclei is called **nuclear fission** (FISH'-un).

In one such fission process, the nucleus of uranium-235 splits into barium and krypton nuclei. Uranium atoms have 92 protons. The atomic number of barium is 56 and that of krypton is 36. The total number of protons is still 92 (= 56 + 36). The number of protons has not changed. One neutron is added to the uranium-235 nucleus. The mass number of the barium nucleus formed is 144. The mass number of the krypton nucleus formed is 90. The total mass number of barium and krypton is 234. Two additional neutrons are released. The total mass number remains unchanged at 236.

The nuclear change can be summarized in a nuclear equation.

$$^{235}_{92}\text{U} + ^{1}_{0}\text{n} \rightarrow ^{144}_{56}\text{Ba} + ^{90}_{36}\text{Kr} + 2\,^{1}_{0}\text{n}$$

The extra neutrons can be absorbed by other uranium-235 nuclei. If they are absorbed, the same reaction is repeated. More uranium-235 nuclei split. A chain reaction is said to take place. A **chain reaction** is a series of repeated reactions that occur very rapidly. You may have heard of a chain reaction on the road. A number of cars collide in rapid succes-

Main Idea

How did scientists split the atomic nucleus?

Additional information: The first chemical evidence that uranium atoms split into much smaller atoms was provided by Irene Joliot-Curie and Pavle Savitch who found traces of lanthanum in uranium samples that had been exposed to neutron bombardment. The first report on uranium fission was published in 1939 by Lise Meitner.

Total number of particles = 238

Number of protons = ?

Number of neutrons = ?

$^{238}_{92}\text{U}$

Figure 13-17. *How many neutrons and how many protons are found in the nucleus of a uranium-238 atom?* 92 protons and 146 neutrons

Activity

See also Activity Record Sheet 13-2A (Lab Manual page 175) Answers to Questions and Conclusion appear on page T164 in front of this book.

13.2a Model of a Chain Reaction

Science Processes: Observing, using time relations, using numbers, predicting, interpreting data, formulating models

Materials BASIC 10 minutes Groups of 3 or 4

- 15 to 20 dominoes
- watch or clock with second hand

Purpose

To illustrate a chain reaction by using dominoes.

Procedure

1. Set a domino upright on its shortest edge. Stand a second domino upright directly in front of the first. The dominoes should be set apart about one-half of their length. Place the rest of the dominoes along the same line and the same distance apart.
2. Tap the first domino so that it falls onto the second and knocks it over. Note how long it takes for all the dominoes to fall. Record the time in seconds on a data table like the one shown.
3. Using the same number of dominoes as before, arrange them so that each domino will knock over two others. Tap the first domino so that it falls onto the others. Note how long it takes all the dominoes to fall. Record the time on the data table.

Questions

1. How many seconds did it take for all the dominoes to fall when they were lined up singly in the first trial?
2. How many seconds did it take for all the dominoes to fall when they were set up so that each domino struck two others in the second trial?
3. How does the speed of the reaction time in the first trial compare to the speed of the reaction time in the second trial?
4. What would happen to the reaction speed if each domino was set up to knock down three dominoes?

Conclusion

How can dominoes be used to illustrate a chain reaction?

Trial	Seconds required for the dominoes to fall
Trial 1—dominoes set up singly	
Trial 2—dominoes set up in doubles	

Step 1

Step 3

Figure 13-18. *Nuclear reactors are used to control the release of energy by nuclear fission. Deep in the center of this tank control rods slow the speed of nuclear chain reactions.*

sion. One car collides with the one in front of it. The car following does the same, and so on. The series of collisions is sometimes called a chain reaction.

If each car that is hit were to hit two others, the reaction would be even faster. If the road were very crowded, a large number of cars would be involved in a very short time. How can these chain reactions be avoided? One way is to leave space between the cars. Under these conditions the chain reaction may be stopped completely.

Nuclear chain reactions can also be controlled. Suppose only small amounts of uranium-235 are present. The reaction will not become a chain reaction. A certain amount of fuel is needed to sustain a chain reaction. This amount is called the **critical mass.**

The neutrons given off during fission can also be captured. This prevents or slows down the reaction. Rods made of materials such as cadmium or boron are used for this purpose. They are called **control rods.** The amount of energy needed can be obtained by using the control rods.

A nuclear reactor must also include material that slows down the neutrons released. Natural uranium contains 140 times more uranium-238 than uranium-235. Only uranium-235 is likely to split. Both isotopes absorb fast neutrons, but only uranium-235 also absorbs slow neutrons. The neutrons must be slowed down or they will be absorbed by the wrong nuclei. Materials that slow down the neutrons are called **moderators** (MOD'-er-ray-terz). Graphite and water are often used as moderators.

Research Topic

The first controlled nuclear chain reaction was accomplished December 2, 1942, under an old stadium at the University of Chicago. Find out the circumstances that led the scientists Leo Szilard and Enrico Fermi to undertake this project. Why was it a top secret project? What was Albert Einstein's involvement?

Additional information: Graphite and water are often used as moderators because although they will slow down neutrons, they are not very likely to absorb the neutrons and stop the chain reactions.

Data Search

How many joules of energy were supplied to the United States by the combustion of coal in 1960 and 1980? Search pages 658–661.

10 661 × 10^{12} J in 1960 and 16 172 × 10^{12} J in 1980.

The reaction is controlled by using cadmium or boron control rods.

Figure 13-19. *A nuclear reactor is a place where nuclear fission occurs under controlled conditions. How is the reaction controlled?*

A small amount of nuclear fuel releases tremendous amounts of energy. One kilogram of uranium that undergoes fission produces about 100 trillion joules of energy. To produce the same amount of energy would require the burning of about 4 million kg of coal.

Where does the energy released in fission come from? Albert Einstein had theorized that mass and energy are related. That is, the more mass something has, the more energy it has, and vice versa. If m is the mass, E is the energy, and c is the speed of light, energy and mass are related by Einstein's famous equation, $E = mc^2$.

Now, when fission takes place, the total mass of the products seems to be slightly less than the total mass of the reactants. Only about one thousandth of the mass seems to have disappeared. When 1 kg of uranium undergoes fission, 1 g of mass disappears. According to Einstein, the 100 trillion joules of energy released is equivalent to a mass of 1 g. When the uranium releases energy, it also gives up a little mass.

Energy from nuclear fission is used to generate electricity. Heat energy given off by the nuclear reaction changes water into steam. The steam drives a turbine which generates the electricity. The electric generators work the same as in conventional plants. Only the fuel is different.

Safety practices must be followed strictly in the use of nuclear reactors. Excessive heat can lead to meltdown of the reactor. Radioactive substances can escape. Safety considerations have so far restricted the use of fission reactions to produce electric energy.

Another problem with nuclear fission is what to do with the waste materials that are produced. Many will remain dangerously radioactive for centuries to come. Although many scientists have been searching for answers, no one yet has developed a completely safe way of disposing of these wastes. For this reason, many people oppose the use of nuclear fission. Others favor careful use and continued scientific investigation into the waste disposal problem.

Quick Review

1. What occurs during nuclear fission?
2. How do control rods help control nuclear reactions?
3. How does a nuclear reactor slow down the neutrons that are released during fission?
4. What are some of the problems caused by nuclear fission?

Nuclear fusion

New vocabulary: nuclear fusion, plasma

The sun and other stars are sources of even greater amounts of energy. This energy release is the result of the fusion of nuclei. **Nuclear fusion** (FYOO'-zhun) is the joining together of two or more nuclei. Most fusion reactions involve the joining of hydrogen atoms to form helium atoms. Some mass again seems to disappear, as in a fission reaction. But the reaction is the reverse. The heavier elements release energy when they split. The lighter elements release energy when they fuse.

Fusion takes place only at very high temperatures. The temperature has to be several million degrees Celsius. Temperatures that high are found only in the center of stars. They are difficult to produce in a laboratory. At such high temperatures electrons have been removed from the atoms. Under these conditions matter consists of bare nuclei and free electrons. This form of matter—a hot, ionized gas—is sometimes referred to as **plasma** (PLAZ'-muh). In this form of matter the nuclei can be close enough to fuse in the interiors of stars.

The heavy isotopes of hydrogen—deuterium and tritium— can be used as the fuel in a nuclear fusion reaction. Deu-

Research Topic

Find out about the accidents that occurred to the nuclear power plants at Chernobyl in the Soviet Union and Three-Mile Island in Pennsylvania. What was the cause of each accident? What were the damages and casualties?

Quick Review answers:
1. A nucleus breaks into two smaller nuclei. Energy is released.
2. Control rods capture neutrons given off by nuclear reactions in a nuclear reactor. Capturing neutrons slows down the rate of the nuclear reactions.
3. In nuclear reactors, substances called moderators slow down neutrons released during fission.
4. The potential for escape of radioactive substances, the heat produced, and the dangerous waste materials.

Science background information:
English astronomer Sir Arthur Eddington calculated that if $1/10$ of the mass of hydrogen present in the sun was changed into helium, it would provide enough heat to radiate energy for a billion years.

Main Idea

How does plasma differ from other forms of matter?

13.2b   Modeling Nuclear Fusion

Science Processes: Making models, inferring

Materials   15 minutes   Groups of 2 or 3
- **red modeling clay**
- **yellow modeling clay**

Purpose

To construct models of fusion reactions between different types of nuclei.

Procedure

1. Make two red clay balls, approximately 1 cm in diameter.
2. Make three yellow clay balls about the same size.
3. Join one red ball and one yellow ball to form a deuterium nucleus.
4. Join one red ball and two yellow balls to form a tritium nucleus.
5. Join together the two nuclei, removing one yellow ball as they fuse.
6. Make a second model of a fusion reaction using two deuterium nuclei. For each deuterium nucleus, join together one yellow and one red clay ball.
7. Join the two deuterium nuclei together, removing one red ball as they fuse.

Questions

1. What do the red balls represent? the yellow balls?
2. How do deuterium and tritium nuclei differ from the nucleus of an ordinary hydrogen atom?
3. In step 4, what is the main product of the fusion reaction?
4. What is another product of the reaction?
5. Where does this reaction take place?
6. In step 7, what are the products of the fusion reaction?

Conclusion

What is nuclear fusion?

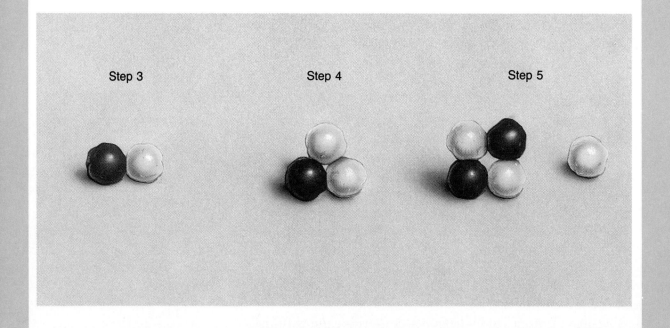

Step 3   Step 4   Step 5

The sun's energy is produced by nuclear fusion—the fusion of hydrogen nuclei into helium nuclei.

terium has one proton and one neutron in its nucleus. Tritium has one proton and two neutrons in its nucleus. The fusion reaction forms helium and releases one neutron.

$$_1^2H + _1^3H \rightarrow _2^4He + _0^1n$$

Once the reaction is started, more heat energy is released than is used to start the reaction. Again, this heat can be used to generate electricity.

Fusion does not produce as many dangerous wastes as fission. Also, it can be controlled more easily. The reaction does take place at very high temperatures. But it can be more easily stopped by removing the fuel for the reaction.

Fusion has another advantage. There is an almost unlimited supply of fuel. Deuterium makes up a part of the hydrogen in sea water, which is very plentiful. Tritium can be prepared from lithium. Lithium also is available in quantities large enough to supply energy needs for a long, long time.

The use of nuclear fusion to supply energy may not be possible for quite some time. Still, its advantages are great enough to encourage researchers in their efforts. It may someday be possible to overcome the problems in putting fusion to a peaceful use.

Quick Review

1. What elements are involved in most fusion reactions?
2. What are three advantages of using nuclear fusion instead of nuclear fission for generating electricity?

Main Idea

What would be a useful product of a fusion reaction?

Teacher suggestion: Have students look up the word *Tokamak* and discuss what it has to do with controlling nuclear fusion.

Quick Review answers:
1. Hydrogen and helium.
2. It does not produce as many dangerous wastes as nuclear fission. The reaction can be easily stopped by removing the fuel. There is almost an unlimited supply of fuel.

Nuclear scientist

Nuclear scientists are usually employed directly by universities or by research establishments supported by private or government funding. Their efforts are aimed at developing a better understanding of the nuclei of atoms. The research tools are large accelerators that direct high energy particles toward target nuclei. Products of the interaction are studied. Models of the nucleus are developed and tested on the basis of these clues.

The ability to analyze problems, to raise questions, and to think abstractly are important characteristics of the nuclear scientist. Most nuclear research is done as a team effort and the ability to cooperate with other scientists and technicians is crucial.

A Ph.D. in physics with a specialty in nuclear studies is the requirement for entry into this field. Research efforts and employment opportunities are limited because of the expense of the equipment needed. High school courses in physics, chemistry, and mathematics are necessary for entry into the needed college courses.

For further information, write to: American Nuclear Society, 555 North Kensington Avenue, LaGrange Park, Illinois 60525.

This nuclear scientist is moving a radioactive sample by remote control.

Radiologic technologist

Radiologic technologists use X-rays, radioisotopes, and sound waves to help diagnose and treat medical patients. With the help of a radiograph (X-ray negative), a doctor can diagnose diseases without exploratory surgery. Radiation therapy is an important part of cancer treatment. Guided by a doctor's prescription, a radiation therapy technologist exposes the diseased area to radiation. The radiation destroys or stops the growth of the cancer.

Although some radiologic technologists work regular business hours, many work evenings or are "on call." Each shift includes a variety of tasks. Technologists check equipment, update medical records, read prescriptions, and position patients and equipment. They must know and comply with safety regulations.

Nearly all radiologic technologists complete some post-secondary education. Programs in radiologic technology are offered at colleges, trade schools, hospitals, and medical centers. Specialties such as magnetic resonance imaging demand additional training. High school classes in biology, chemistry, physics, and math are excellent preparation for a career in radiologic technology.

For more information, write to: American Society of Radiologic Technologists, 15000 Central Avenue SE, Albuquerque, New Mexico 87123.

Radiologic technologies such as ultrasound and fluoroscopy allow doctors to see inside a living body without performing surgery.

13.2 Section Review

Answers to Understanding the Concepts appear on page T164 in the front of this book. Blackline master test for this section: Section Testsheet 13-2 (TRB page 234)

Vocabulary

3 binding energy
5 chain reaction
1 control rod
6 critical mass
8 moderator
2 nuclear fission
4 nuclear fusion
9 plasma
7 transmutation

Vocabulary Review

Match each term above with the numbered phrase that best describes it.

1. Slows or prevents a nuclear reaction
2. Splitting of nucleus into two or more fragments
3. Holds things together in the nucleus
4. Joining smaller nuclei to form a larger nucleus
5. Series of repeated reactions that occur very rapidly
6. The amount of fuel needed to sustain a chain reaction
7. Changing one element into another
8. Material that slows down neutrons
9. Form of matter with bare nuclei and free electrons

Review Questions

Multiple Choice: Choose the answer that best completes each of the following sentences

10. An element with atomic number 92 and mass number 235 gains one neutron, then splits into two fragments, one of which has an atomic number of 50. The atomic number of the second fragment is _?_.
    a. 185   c. 50
    b. 143   **d. 42**

11. The principle of mass-energy conservation states that _?_.
    a. atoms with more mass have less energy
    b. energy and mass are never changed
    c. the sum of the mass and energy in a nuclear reaction does not change
    d. atoms conserve energy by not using up their mass

12. Elements can be changed into other elements by _?_.
    a. chemical reactions
    b. redox reactions
    c. fermentation
    d. transmutation

13. Nuclear fission can be used as a source of energy because _?_.
    a. the breakdown of nuclei results in the release of free electrons
    b. the breakdown of nuclei results in the release of heat
    c. the breakdown of nuclei produces harmonic vibrations in surrounding materials
    d. light energy is one of the main products of fission

14. The sun gives off enormous amounts of light and heat because _?_.
    a. it is very far from the earth
    b. heavy nuclei in the center of the sun undergo rapid fission into smaller nuclei
    c. it is undergoing a spontaneous chemical reaction
    d. light nuclei in the sun undergo fusion to produce heavier nuclei

15. Nuclear decay involves the _?_.
    a. most stable nuclei
    b. chemical reaction of decomposition
    c. breakdown of nuclei
    d. gain of mass and energy

Understanding the Concepts

16. What is the source of energy that is released in a nuclear reaction?
17. What advantages does the use of nuclear fusion have over nuclear fission as a source of energy for the future?
18. Why does the conversion of a small amount of mass produce so much energy in a nuclear reaction?
19. Why is it difficult to produce the right conditions for nuclear fusion in a laboratory?
20. Alchemists sought to turn lead into gold. Is it possible, at least in theory, to do that? Explain your reasoning.

Problems to Solve

21. Indicate the mass numbers and charge numbers for each of the following elements.
    a. $^{238}_{92}U$ d. $^{250}_{98}Cf$
    b. $^{107}_{47}Ag$ e. $^{1}_{0}n$
    c. $^{23}_{11}Na$

22. Balance the mass or charge numbers in the following nuclear reaction equations.
    a. $^{133}_{53}I \rightarrow {}^{0}_{-1}e + {}^{?}_{54}Xe$
    b. $^{222}_{86}Rn \rightarrow {}^{4}_{2}He + {}^{?}_{?}Po$
    c. $^{?}_{1}H + {}^{3}_{1}H \rightarrow {}^{4}_{2}He + {}^{1}_{0}n$
    d. $^{6}_{?}Li + {}^{1}_{0}n \rightarrow {}^{3}_{1}H + {}^{4}_{2}He$

13 Chapter Review

Answers appear on page T165 in the front of this book. Blackline master test for this chapter: Chapter Testsheets 13A and 13B (TRB pages 265–266)

Vocabulary

alpha particle	control rod	nuclear decay
alpha radiation	critical mass	nuclear fission
beta particle	electroscope	nuclear fusion
beta radiation	gamma radiation	nucleons
binding energy	geiger tube	plasma
bubble chamber	half-life	radioactivity
chain reaction	mass number	radioisotope
cloud chamber	moderator	transmutation

Review of Concepts

Radioactivity is the release of particles and/or energy from the nucleus of an atom.

- Three kinds of radiation can be given off by radioactive atoms: alpha radiation, beta radiation, and gamma radiation.
- Gamma radiation is the most penetrating of the three common types of nuclear radiation; gamma radiation can penetrate several centimeters of lead. Beta particles can penetrate skin or thin sheets of metal, and alpha particles can be stopped by a thin sheet of paper.
- In alpha radiation, a particle having the mass and charge of a helium nucleus is released.
- In beta radiation, a particle with the mass number and charge of an electron is released.
- Radioactivity cannot be detected with the senses, but can be detected by a variety of devices, including dosimeters, cloud chambers, bubble chambers, and Geiger counters.
- Atoms in which there are more neutrons than protons are more likely to be radioactive than are atoms that have the same number of protons and neutrons;

atoms in which there are fewer neutrons than protons may also tend to be radioactive.

- The number of nuclei in a sample of a radioactive isotope that may decay per second depends only on the type and amount of the sample.
- The half-life of a radioactive isotope is the time required for half of the nuclei in a sample of that isotope to decay.
- Radioisotopes have many practical uses. They are used as tracers in biological research as anticancer agents, for example.
- There are two models of how nucleons are arranged in the nucleus. In the liquid drop model, nucleons are closely packed in the nucleus and are in constant motion; in the nuclear shell model the nucleons are arranged in discrete shells of different energies within the nucleus.

Mass and energy are different forms of each other.

- The mass of a helium nucleus is slightly less than the sum of the masses of two protons and two neutrons; the missing mass has been converted to energy according to the formula $E = mc^2$.

- The sum of the mass and energy is conserved in a nuclear reaction; this is the conservation of mass and energy principle.
- The binding energy is the energy holding the nucleus together; the binding energy comes from the mass lost when the nucleus is made from its particles.
- The magnitude of the binding energy is greatest for elements close to iron in the periodic table; the elements with the greatest binding energy are the most stable.
- The conversion of one element into another element in a nuclear reaction is called transmutation.
- Alpha particles are of limited usefulness in the production of nuclear changes. This is because the positive charge of these particles causes them to be electrically repelled by the nucleus which is also positively charged; neutrons, which are neutral, do not suffer from this limitation.

Nuclear fission is the breaking up of a nucleus into two or more smaller nuclei.

- Uranium-235 is commonly used for fission.
- A chain reaction is a series of fission reactions that occur when the neutrons released in one fission reaction cause another fission reaction.
- Einstein explained the energy released in a nuclear change by saying it was the equivalent of the mass that is given up in the reaction.
- Fission reactions can be controlled, and the energy can be used to generate electricity.
- Safety considerations and the production of radioactive waste material have restricted the use of nuclear fission for generating electricity.

Nuclear fusion is the joining together of two or more nuclei.
- Fusion most commonly involves the joining of hydrogen nuclei to form helium nuclei.
- Fusion occurs only where the temperatures are very high, such as in stars.
- The heat released by fusion may someday be used to generate electricity.
- The use of nuclear fusion to supply energy has many potential advantages over nuclear fission.

Critical Thinking

1. At what speed do you think gamma radiation travels? Why? What do you think the speeds of beta and alpha radiation are? Why?
2. Beta radiation involves beta particles, and alpha radiation emits alpha particles. Is gamma radiation associated with any type of particle?
3. What type(s) of nuclear radioactivity can be detected using a cloud chamber? Explain how a cloud chamber functions.
4. Why does the loss of an electron not have much effect on the total mass of the nucleus?
5. Do you think that carbon-14 would be as useful for dating purposes if its half-life were 2 weeks, rather than 5930 years? Why or why not?
6. Why do you think that the meticulous cleaning of samples is of great importance to the accuracy of carbon dating?
7. The radioactive dating of once-living materials using carbon-14 is based on an assumption that the percentage of radioactive carbon in the atmosphere remains the same over long periods of time. Suppose that scientists found evidence that the percentage of radioactive carbon in the atmosphere has been increasing. How would this affect the estimates of the ages of materials that have already been dated by carbon-14?
8. Explain why the rate of decay decreases as the amount of radioactive material decreases, but the half-life of the material remains constant regardless of quantity.
9. How is the nuclear shell model similar to the electron shell model?
10. When a nucleus decays by giving off a beta particle, the number of protons in it increases. Explain how it is possible for the nucleus to lose a particle and yet show an increase in the number of protons.
11. Do you think that electrons would be good particles to be used in the transmutation of elements via bombardment? Why or why not?
12. In a nuclear reactor, how is the chain reaction controlled? What kind of dangers exist if the reaction should for some reason get out of control?

Individual Research

13. Look through newspapers and magazines to find stories about any controversies over the use of nuclear fission reactors to generate electricity. What arguments do the proponents use? What arguments do the opponents use?

Bibliography

Fermi, Laura. *The Story of Atomic Energy.* New York: Random House, 1961
A dramatic account of the research on the atomic nucleus and the men and women who took part in it. Written by the wife of Enrico Fermi, who won a Nobel Prize for his work on bombarding uranium with neutrons.

Moché, Dinah. *Radiation: Benefits/Dangers.* New York: Franklin Watts, 1979
A clear discussion of the many uses of nuclear radiation.

Weiss, Anne E. *The Nuclear Question.* New York: Harcourt, 1981
Describes nuclear reactors and the pros and cons of using nuclear energy.

Hazards of Producing Nuclear Power

The United States relies on nuclear power for 16 percent of its energy. In the early 1970s it was predicted that nuclear power would be the primary source of energy by the year 2000. In 1979, however, a major accident occurred at the Three Mile Island plant near Harrisburg, Pennsylvania. People began to re-examine the safety of these plants. Then, in April 1986, a reactor at Chernobyl in the Soviet Union experienced a partial meltdown, a major fire, and an explosion that resulted in a major release of radiation. A number of people were killed and even more will suffer the long-term effects of radiation exposure. The environment too will suffer greatly.

Should nuclear power continue to be pursued as a source of energy?

PROS

- According to some U.S. scientists, accidents such as the one at Chernobyl could not happen in the U.S. because of design differences. The moderator used at the Chernobyl reactor was graphite, which caught fire and burned at 5000°C. All but two U.S. reactors use water as the moderator.
- U.S. nuclear fuel supplies will last up to 1000 years, particularly if used in breeder reactors which produce their own fuel.
- Reactors do not contribute to the pollution of air or water unless a leak occurs.
- There have been no non-worker deaths from reactors in the U.S.
- New research is investigating new and safer fuels and moderators.

CONS

- Human errors cannot be completely prevented, resulting in the possibility of a major accident that could cause deaths, long-term illnesses, and environmental damage. Evacuation plans do not seem adequate for moving large numbers of people quickly out of an area.
- The waste products of producing nuclear power are still highly radioactive and must be disposed of properly. Disposal methods have not yet been found to meet the need. In addition, there is a hazard in transporting nuclear waste to disposal sites.
- Cost overruns in building reactors have increased the cost of producing the power, making nuclear power an expensive alternative to other sources.

Should the U.S. continue to develop nuclear power sources or should we halt the program? Should we allow those plants already in operation to continue?

Three Mile Island, Pennsylvania, site of a nuclear accident in which small amounts of radiation were released into the air and nearby river.

Diagnosing Illness with MRI

Throughout history, physicians have searched for new and better tools to diagnose disease. For centuries, they were limited to what they could observe through their senses. As early as 2000 B.C., Egyptian physicians looked at what the patient excreted, felt the pulse, and examined the body. But they could not see inside the body to correctly diagnose internal problems.

It was not until the dawn of the twentieth century and the development of the X-ray that this limitation disappeared. For the first time, doctors could "see" inside a patient. The X-ray allowed doctors to base their diagnoses on more than experience, intelligent guesswork, and external symptoms and signs. However, X-rays can cause damage to human tissues. So, over the last 20 years or so, a search for safer diagnostic tools has been conducted. The result has been a number of new technologies for looking inside the human body.

One of the newest and most promising of these technologies is called magnetic resonance imaging, or *MRI*. MRI is even better than X-rays at imaging soft tissues and organs and there are no known risks to the patient.

MRI relies on some basic properties of human tissue and magnetic fields to create its extraordinarily accurate pictures. A patient is placed in a device, called a scanner, with a high-powered magnet, about 40 times stronger than the earth's magnetic field. It causes the hydrogen nuclei in cells of the part of the body being scanned to line up with the magnetic field. Low-energy radio waves are then applied, which cause the hydrogen nuclei to give off tiny amounts of energy.

MRI measures the amount of energy given off by the part of the body being scanned. The more energy measured, the more hydrogen present in the tissue. Since each type of human tissue has in its water molecules a different amount of hydrogen, the amount of energy released can be matched to a specific tissue type—fat, muscle, bone, and so on. Computer technology developed in the U.S. space program helps refine the "picture" of the body by assigning a different color to each type of tissue.

The technology of MRI is advancing rapidly. We may be close to the time when physicians can tell, without surgery, the difference between a benign, or non-life-threatening, tumor and one that requires immediate surgery. That is an important step in diagnosis that will benefit both physicians and patients.

A picture of internal tissues and structures produced by an NMR scanner can be used to detect abnormalities such as tumors and nervous disorders such as multiple sclerosis.

7 Future Energy Needs and Resources

Chapter 14
Our Energy Needs

Learning Objectives

■ Process

1. To recognize our dependence on the earth's limited energy resources
2. To identify specific steps in a variety of energy pathways
3. To identify alternative energy resources
4. To infer ways of improving one's own energy-conservation efforts
5. To observe the energy-conservation efforts of others and apply those ideas in everyday life

■ Content

1. To relate the concept of entropy to our current and future energy needs
2. To compare past and present energy-use practices
3. To distinguish between renewable and nonrenewable energy resources
4. To describe methods for conserving energy
5. To explain the need for increasing use of renewable energy resources

Solar One at Barstow, California, is a solar generating station now in operation. Here solar energy is used to turn an electric generator to produce electricity. Development of solar energy sources will become more and more important in order to meet future energy needs.

Chapter 14
Our Energy Needs

The earth receives huge amounts of energy every day from the sun. The energy released when we burn fossil fuels—oil, natural gas, and coal—can be traced back to the sun. Yet, we are told that we will run out of fossil fuels and must find new energy sources. This chapter explores why fossil fuels cannot satisfy our energy needs indefinitely and suggests some viable alternatives to fossil fuels.

Science background information:
In recent times we have seen sharp rises in the cost of fuel, followed by drops in prices as the shortages were alleviated and supplies became plentiful again. As a result, many people think that fuel shortages are a result of manipulations by oil-producing nations and that there is enough fuel for everyone's needs.

This is true only in the short term. The exponential increase in the world population, coupled with the increased demand in nations moving from a rural to an industrial economy, is producing a long-term swelling demand for energy sources that will eventually drain the earth of fossil fuels.

An awareness that the supply of fossil fuels is limited can help students understand why it is important to take energy-conserving measures even when fuel prices drop. The more fossil fuel we can save in the twentieth century, the more there will be available for the twenty-first century.

There are two main ways of ensuring that future generations will have the energy they need. One is by finding alternatives to fossil fuel and developing safe and economical ways to use such energy sources. The other is by reducing our own energy needs by preventing unnecessary energy loss

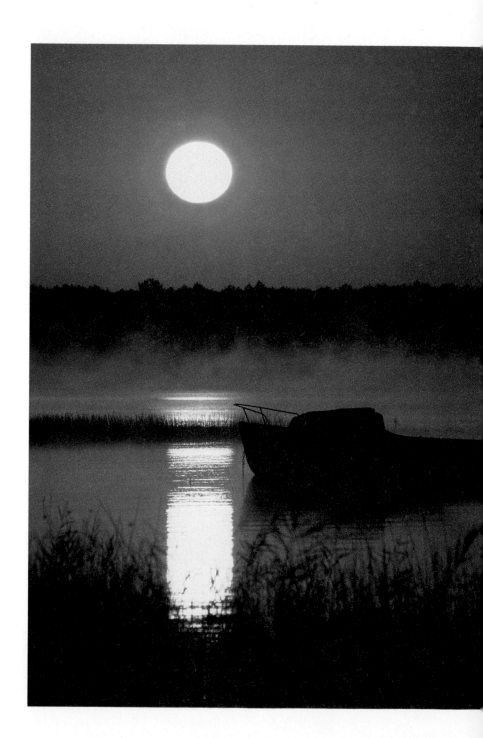

For detailed information about teaching this chapter, see Chapter 14 Planning Guide on pages T166–T167 in the front of this book.

Projectsheet 14 (TRB page 186) and Research Lab 14 (Lab Manual pages 193–194) may be used at any point in this chapter.

Chapter Preview

14.1 Present Energy Resources

- **Our dependence on energy**
- **Energy in the universe**
- **Energy pathways**
- **Fossil fuel pathways**
- **The fossil fuel dilemma**
- **Environmental problems**
- **Nuclear pathways**

Energy comes from the sun to the earth along various pathways. The pathway we use most is one in which energy has been stored for a long period in fossil fuels. The world supply of fossil fuels is being used up at an increasing rate. Sooner or later, we will have to find other energy sources.

and practicing measures that require less energy.

Among the alternatives to fossil fuels are energy from nuclear fission, nuclear fusion, oil shale, tar sands, renewable energy sources (wood, synfuels, biomass, fuel cells), the sun, wind, hydroelectric sources, solar ponds, geothermal sources, and tides. All of these alternatives are discussed in this chapter.

14.2 Alternative Energy Resources

- **Alternative fuel sources**
- **Energy directly from the sun**
- **Energy from sun-powered systems**
- **Energy from other natural sources**

Some people are now using energy from alternative sources. These include fossil fuels from other places; energy that comes directly from the sun; wind; and flowing water. In the future more and more energy is likely to come from these alternative sources.

14.3 Energy Conservation

- **Transportation and energy conservation**
- **Energy conservation in the home**
- **Energy conservation in industry**
- **Future energy usage and conservation**

It is going to take a long time to convert to alternative energy sources. In the meantime, we can conserve the energy we are now using. This will give us the time we need to develop new energy resources. It will also help to cut down on pollution that has been caused by excessive use of fossil fuels.

For ideas for classroom demonstration and discussion, see Getting Started on page T168 in the front of this book.

14.1 Present Energy Resources

Supplemental materials: Teaching Diagram 14-1A, 14-1B, and 14-1C (TRB pages 64–66), Reading Checksheet 14-1 (TRB page 115), Skillsheet 14-1 (TRB page 161), Investigation 14-1 (Lab Manual pages 183–184)

Section Preview

- **Our dependence on energy**
- **Energy in the universe**
- **Energy pathways**
- **Fossil fuel pathways**
- **The fossil fuel dilemma**
- **Environmental problems**
- **Nuclear pathways**

Bracketed numbers are Section Review questions correlated to that objective.

Learning Objectives

1. To recognize that we depend on energy and that energy supplies are limited. [4, 13, 18]
2. To recognize that changes in the form of energy reduce the amount of available energy. [5, 12, 18]
3. To identify the steps in several energy pathways. [11, 17]
4. To describe the rate of growth of energy usage. [10, 13]
5. To relate energy usage to our current and future environmental problems. [2, 14, 15, 16, 19]

Figure 14-1. *Crude oil, like natural gas and coal, is an important energy resource that is found underground.*

The cave dwellers' demand for energy was small. They used only a small amount of energy to cook their food and make their tools. When they first tamed animals, more energy was made available to them. They then began to grow their food on fields plowed by animals. They also used animals to carry heavy objects.

For many years energy usage increased at about the same rate as the population grew. After the invention of the steam engine, the use of energy increased rapidly. Since 1900, the use of energy has increased much faster than the population growth.

Our dependence on energy

How do you use energy? List all of the things you have done since you got up this morning. Which of these activities used energy? Was the source of energy electricity, natural gas, food, or some other fuel? What activities did not use energy?

People seldom think about the many ways in which they use energy. They take it for granted that it will be there when they need it. It was therefore a shock when on November 17, 1965, the lights went out in most of the New England states and all of New York City. The people of many towns and cities found themselves in total darkness. Thousands were stranded in subways and elevators. In some places power was not restored for several days. Fortunately, most of the people survived with only minor inconvenience. But a point was made. Our complex society is dependent upon energy. And the supply of energy can be cut off!

At present, oil is the most commonly used energy resource in the industrialized nations. The demand for oil in most of these countries is much larger than the supply. As a result, they have had to import much of the oil they use from countries in the Middle East.

Several times within the past decade, there have been shortages of gasoline and heating oil. You and your parents may remember waiting in long gasoline lines. These shortages served as another reminder that our energy supply is not unlimited.

When there are fuel shortages, energy prices rise. An increase in the cost of energy has an effect on lifestyle. People buy small cars that get high gas mileage. They insulate their homes. They start to think about using other methods to heat their homes, such as solar heat. Even when fuel prices come down, people should not be fooled into thinking that there will always be plenty of fuel for everyone.

Quick Review

1. What is the most commonly used source of energy in industrialized nations?
2. In what ways have people been reminded in recent times that the energy supply is limited?

Energy in the universe

The energy supply in the universe seems endless. Huge stars and galaxies give off enormous amounts of energy each second. The energy of the universe seems to be concentrated in certain places, such as in hot stars. Other parts of the universe have little energy and are extremely cold and dark. Energy is constantly flowing from places of higher energy concentration to places of lower concentration. For example,

Figure 14-2. *A ringing alarm, a toaster, and bicycling all use energy.* Encourage students to be aware of how dependent we are on the use of energy.

Quick Review answers:
1. Oil is the most commonly used source of energy in industrialized nations.
2. Power shortages, long gasoline lines, and increasing costs for energy remind people that the energy supply is limited.

Model Universe A
Entropy low
Much available energy

Model Universe B
Entropy high
Little available energy

Figure 14-3. *Model universe A has many hot stars surrounded by cold regions. Much available energy is flowing from the hot stars. Entropy is low.*

In model universe B, the stars have all cooled off. They are the same temperature as the surrounding regions. Entropy is high. Why is there no available energy in universe B? In universe B there are no differences in temperature to direct the flow of energy.

Quick Review answers:
1. Energy seems to be flowing away from places of high concentration to regions of lower concentration.
2. As entropy increases, the amount of energy available for use decreases.

energy flows from our sun to all the objects in the solar system and beyond. Or, even when we light a campfire on a cold night, energy flows out and warms all the people sitting around the fire.

We can trace this great flow of energy from the sun along many pathways. We use this energy to grow our food, heat our homes, and run our machines. Our very survival depends on this flow of energy.

Scientists have theorized that the energy of the universe is gradually becoming more evenly distributed. It is gradually flowing away from places of high concentration and spreading throughout the entire universe. They call this evening-off process an increase in **entropy** (EN′-truh-pee).

Entropy is a measure of the distribution of energy in a system. When the energy is evenly distributed, the entropy is at its highest, but the energy is no longer available. There are no hot and cold places for it to flow between. Look at the two model universes in Figure 14-3.

Does this mean that the universe will eventually become "wound down" once all of the energy is evenly distributed? No one is really sure, but such an event would be so far in the future that it is not worthy of our concern. The amount of energy stored in stars such as our sun is enormous. These stars are expected to be giving off energy for billions of years to come.

The fact that energy is constantly flowing to us from the sun *is* important to us. For all practical purposes, we have an unlimited source of energy in the sun. Why, then, are some people worried about an energy crisis? To find out, we need to study some of the pathways of energy from the sun.

Quick Review
1. How does energy seem to be flowing in the universe?
2. Explain what happens to the availability of energy as entropy increases.

Energy pathways
New vocabulary: fossil fuel

Energy can change from one form to another. Yet energy changes are not reversible. That is, energy cannot be completely changed back into its original form. With each conversion the amount of usable energy gets smaller and smaller.

The bouncing ball shown in Figure 14-4 is an example of

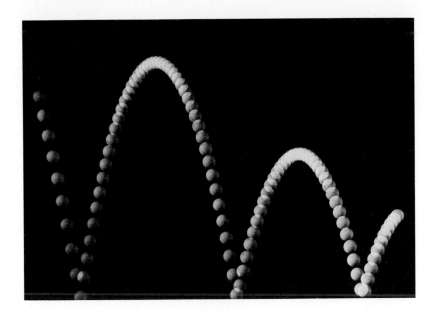

all energy pathways. At the height from which it is dropped, the ball has a certain amount of potential energy. As the ball falls, this energy changes into kinetic energy. When the ball strikes the ground, the energy again changes to potential energy. Since the ball is elastic, it rebounds. On the rebound the energy is again changed to kinetic energy. But the ball does not return to its original bounce-height. Some of the energy is changed, due to friction, into unusable heat energy. Each time the ball bounces, it does not go quite as high as the time before.

Energy keeps coming to us from the sun, but each time it changes form, some is lost. It is not destroyed, but it becomes unusable. However, we are finding ways of making more and more use of the sun's energy.

Heat from the sun causes water to evaporate and rise in the air. It later condenses and comes down as rain or snow. Run-off rainwater turns turbines which generate electricity. The heat energy of the sun is converted into kinetic energy in moving water. The energy in the moving water moves the turbines. The energy of motion of the turbine becomes electric energy in the generator.

Suppose that you were able to measure the energy at each step of this energy pathway. You would find that you had much less electric energy than the amount of energy from the sun at the start. Some energy was wasted with each change along the way.

Critical Thinking

Why are energy changes not reversible?
Energy is diffused as a result of entropy whenever a transformation takes place. For example, the friction of the bouncing ball disperses some of its concentrated movement energy as heat; the heat will not tend to return to the ball because of entropy.

Teaching suggestion:
Ask students to suggest an energy pathway in which heat energy is changed into motion. Examples include boiling water, rising smoke, and the internal combustion engine.

Main Idea

How does heat from the sun become electricity that we can use?

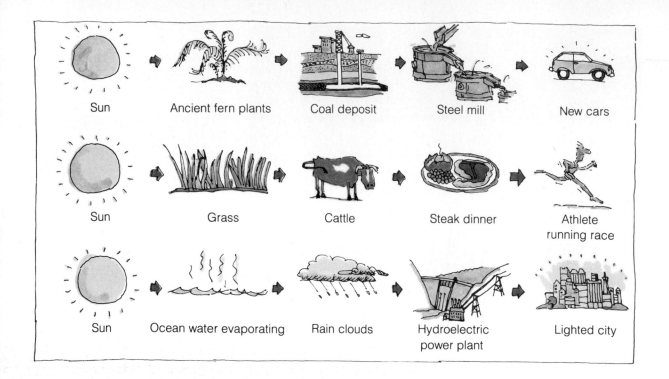

Sun   Ancient fern plants   Coal deposit   Steel mill   New cars

Sun   Grass   Cattle   Steak dinner   Athlete running race

Sun   Ocean water evaporating   Rain clouds   Hydroelectric power plant   Lighted city

Figure 14-5. *What happens to the sun's energy as it travels through these pathways?*
Each time the energy changes form some becomes unusable. Less is available at each step.

Main Idea

What role do green plants play in converting solar energy into another form of energy?

Quick Review answers:

1. The ball has potential energy before it is dropped. The potential energy changes to kinetic energy as the ball falls. When the ball hits the ground, the kinetic energy changes to potential energy and some heat.

2. Green plants use solar energy to produce food used by human beings. Also, green plants use the sun's energy for growth. The energy is stored in the plants as chemical energy. This is converted to heat when the plant remains are used as fuel.

Winds are caused by the heating of air by the sun. A windmill may change the energy in wind motion to energy of motion in a water pump. Or it may operate a generator to produce electricity. Energy is wasted in the change from wind to energy of motion of the water pump and in the change from energy of motion to electric energy. The amount of usable electric energy is less than the energy in the wind motion.

Chlorophyll in green plants traps solar energy. Green plants change the energy into chemical energy in food. Food produced by green plants supplies the internal energy needs for all organisms, or living things. Some of the sun's energy becomes stored in wood in trees. When the wood burns, the energy is released again as heat. Some of this heat may be used by people to keep warm and cook their food.

In some pathways, the sun's energy can be stored for a very long time, then later released and used. Coal, oil, and natural gas are the remains of organisms that lived hundreds of millions of years ago. The chemical energy stored in these **fossil fuels** originally came from the sun.

Quick Review

1. Describe the energy changes that take place when a ball bounces.
2. Describe two energy pathways that include green plants.

Fossil fuel pathways
New vocabulary: anthracite, bituminous, lignite, petroleum, nonrenewable

Coal is the remains of plants that lived hundreds of millions of years ago. Scientists believe that tropical swamps once covered much of the earth's surface. The warm, wet climate was suitable for the growth of fern trees and huge mosses.

When the plants died, they fell into the swamp. Layer upon layer of dead plants built up in the swamp. The shallow water of the swamp prevented oxygen from reaching the dead plants. As a result, the plants were slow to decay.

These plants gradually turned into a spongy material called peat. In time, peat beds became buried under layers of sediments. Pressure and heat caused by the layers of sediment compacted the peat. Hydrogen and oxygen were driven off. Nearly pure carbon, or coal, was left. About 350 million years were needed for this plant matter to change to coal.

Additional information:
Scientists call this time in earth's history the *Carboniferous period.* Carboniferous coal found in Antarctica shows that tropical swamps once existed even there.

Main Idea

When we burn coal today, we are burning a fuel that took how long to form?

Figure 14-6. *Crude oil and natural gas may be trapped in a layer of porous rock that curves up between layers of nonporous rock. The natural gas fills the highest pores of the porous rock. Crude oil fills the next highest pores, while water fills the lowest pores.*

Data Search

What percentage of the energy consumed in the United States in 1980 came from fossil fuels? Search pages 658–661.

Coal, natural gas, and petroleum provided 92.3%. This is calculated by adding the values (which are in terajoules, or 10^{12} J) for these three fuels, dividing by the total fuel consumption for the year, and multiplying by 100%.

$$\frac{16172 + 21502 + 36066}{79916} \times 100\% = 92.3\%$$

Figure 14-7. *The "family tree" of the products made from crude oil. The main branches on the tree are the fuels and the petrochemicals.*

Coal is not all alike. Some types give off more heat when burned than others. Some contain sulfur or other substances which pollute the air when the coal is burned.

Anthracite (AN′-thruh-sīt) coal is a top-grade fuel. It has a high energy content. It contains little sulfur and is considered a clean fuel. **Bituminous** (bī-TEW′-mih-nus) coal has a somewhat lower energy content and contains much sulfur. **Lignite** (LIG′-nīt) has a low energy content but contains little sulfur. Lignite does contain other air pollutants.

Crude oil, or **petroleum** (puh-TRŌ′-lee-um), and natural gas are usually found together. They likely had a similar origin. Scientists believe that they were formed from the remains of sea organisms. Covered by layers of sand and mud, the remains gradually decayed. Heat, pressure, and the action of bacteria changed the remains into oil and natural gas.

Oil and natural gas seep through porous rock layers and sometimes become trapped under domes of nonporous rock. It is from these traps that oil and natural gas are pumped to the surface.

Fossil fuels are **nonrenewable** (non'-ree-NEW'-uh-bul) energy resources. That is, they are being used at much faster rates than they are formed. Most of the energy we use everyday travels through a fossil fuel energy pathway.

The energy pathway for each of the fossil fuels is similar but not identical. The energy in natural gas is most often burned to heat space inside buildings. Oil and oil products are burned in heat engines to produce energy of motion.

Coal, oil, and natural gas are also burned to heat water. Steam from the boiling water turns a turbine. The turbine powers a generator which produces electricity. The energy in petroleum can be found in many fuels and other products we use everyday.

Quick Review

1. Name three different kinds of coal, and explain how they differ.
2. What two kinds of fossil fuel are often found together?
3. How are fossil fuels used to produce electricity?

The fossil fuel dilemma

New vocabulary: exponential

It is possible to read in magazines and newspapers differing views on the energy problem. Some people say there is no shortage and that we will never run out of fossil fuels. Others say that our fossil fuel reserves will be used up within the next century.

In thinking about this conflict, keep in mind these questions:

☐ Are we likely to use more fossil fuels next year than this year?

☐ Is this rate of increase likely to stay the same in the future?

☐ How might continued use of fossil fuels affect the environment?

Coal represents a large percentage of the fossil fuel reserves in North America. Unfortunately, only a very small fraction is clean, high-energy anthracite coal. Look at the

Research Topic

Find out what is meant by the O.P.E.C. countries. What effect have they had on the world supply of petroleum?

Main Idea

What are nonrenewable energy resources?

Quick Review answers:
1. ■ anthracite: clean fuel with high energy content
   ■ bituminous coal: contains much sulfur and has lower energy content
   ■ lignite: low energy content, little sulfur but contains other pollutants
2. Petroleum and natural gas are often found together.
3. Coal, oil, and gas are burned to power steam-driven turbines, which in turn generate electricity.

Main Idea

Since North America's coal reserves are so large, why is there still a need for more fossil fuel?

Activity

14.1a Oil Recovery

Science Processes: Observing, measuring, using numbers, interpreting data, formulating models

Materials 20 minutes Groups of 2 or 3

- plastic bottle with spray pump
- small pebbles (enough to half fill the plastic bottle)
- 100 mL of motor oil
- 30-cm plastic tubing to fit the spray pump nozzle
- graduated cylinder
- cold water
- hot water
- 3 100-mL beakers

Purpose

To determine the difficulty of removing all the oil from a simulated oil well.

Procedure

1. Half fill the plastic bottle with pebbles. Pour 100 mL of motor oil over the pebbles. Make a table like the one shown.
2. Fasten the spray pump to the bottle. Attach a 30-cm length of plastic tubing to the nozzle of the spray pump. Insert the other end of the tubing into one of the beakers as shown in the diagram.
3. Using the spray pump, remove as much oil from the bottle as you can. Record how much oil you recovered into the beaker.

4. Add 70 mL of cold water to the spray bottle. Pump as much liquid as you can into a clean beaker. Record how much oil is floating on top of the water in the beaker.
5. Repeat the procedure using 70 mL of hot water. Record the amount of oil you recovered this time.

Questions

1. What amount of the oil did you recover when you pumped the first time? What percentage of the oil is this amount?
2. How much oil did you recover when you added cold water?
3. How much oil were you able to recover when you added hot water?
4. How much oil was left in the bottle after you pumped out the hot water?
5. What is the total percentage of the oil recovered from the bottle?

Conclusion

Infer from your results why it might be difficult to remove all the oil from an oil well.

Step 2

	Amount of Oil		
	In Plastic Bottle	Recovered into Beaker	Total Amount Recovered
At start			
After first pumping			
After 70 mL of cold water			
After 70 mL of hot water			

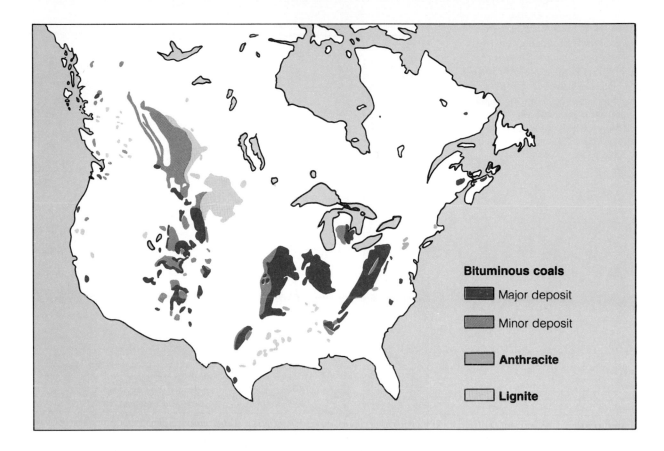

map of major North American coal reserves shown in Figure 14-8. Seventy percent of the coal reserves is in the Great Plains. The coal of this region is mainly lignite, with some bituminous coal. Lignite is low in energy, while bituminous coal is high in sulfur. Most of the remaining coal reserves are in the bituminous coal beds of the central and eastern U.S.

It is more difficult to estimate the size of the oil and natural gas reserves. Since oil and gas are fluids, they often move from the sites where they were formed, and are more difficult to locate than coal. It is likely that new gas and oil fields will be discovered. Much of the oil discovered will be difficult to remove from the earth. At present, for each barrel removed, two are left in the ground.

The demand on our fossil fuel reserves has increased steadily in this century. In part this is due to the increase in the size of the human population. But in the industrialized nations of the world, the demand for energy is increasing even faster than the population.

Energy use is divided among four sectors: residential, commercial, transportation, and industrial. The demand for energy is increasing in each of these sectors.

Figure 14-8. *Principal coal reserves in North America. Are there major coal deposits near where you live?* Answers will vary for different locations, as shown on the map.

Main Idea

What are the four sectors among which energy use is divided?

Figure 14-9. *According to the graph, which is increasing faster— the world population or fossil fuel usage? What do you predict fossil fuel usage will be by the year 2010?*
Fossil fuel usage is increasing faster than the world population is.

By the year 2010, the fossil fuel usage will be 2028 units if it continues to double every 10 years.

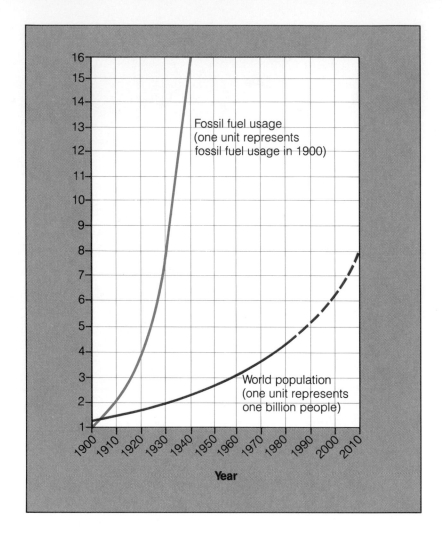

Fossil fuel usage
(one unit represents
fossil fuel usage in 1900)

World population
(one unit represents
one billion people)

Year

Main Idea

What is mainly responsible for the increased energy demand in the transportation sector?

Research Topic

Use an almanac to find estimates of the world population for the latest five years for which data are available. What was the average growth rate per year between each pair of dates? Has the growth rate been increasing?

To find how many years it will take at the present rate for the population to double, divide the latest growth rate into 72.

Air conditioning, central heating, and many new appliances ranging from color TV to electric can openers have increased the demand for energy in the residential sector. The commercial sector is using more energy for lighting, heating, cooking, and the operation of electric office machines.

The automobile has contributed most heavily to the increased demand for energy in the transportation sector. Also, freight is transported more and more by truck or plane rather than by the more energy-efficient railroads.

The industrial sector is the largest user of energy. Part of the increase in this sector is due to the shift to plastics, aluminum, and other manufactured goods which take large amounts of energy to produce.

The largest industrial use of energy is in agriculture. Fifteen percent of the total energy used in North America goes into agriculture. Energy use on the farm is increasing at a rate faster than any other use. It takes an equivalent of 350L of gasoline to run the tractors and other equipment needed to raise an acre of corn.

The demand for energy increases as the human population increases. It took from the beginning of human life on earth until 1850 for the human population to reach one billion. Eighty years later, in 1930, the human population had doubled. By 1975 the human population was four billion. It had doubled again in a period of 45 years. Scientists estimate that the human population will reach 8 billion by the year 2010—a doubling time of 35 years.

Look at the graph of the population growth shown in Figure 14-9. The graph line is not a straight line. It curves upward sharply. The growth rate in the human population is said to be **exponential** (eks-pō-NEN'-shul). The length of time needed for the population to double in size is becoming shorter. In a few doublings, the population grows enormously.

Our use of fossil fuels is growing exponentially. Fossil fuel usage is growing at a rate of about 7% each year. The amount of energy we use doubles every 10 years.

In the 1970s more oil was used than in the previous history of humans. When you read that the amount of electricity used will double in the next 10 years, that means that more electricity will be used in the period than had been used totally before. With a 7% per year increase in fossil fuel use, the amount used each decade is greater than the total previously used.

The exponential growth of population and the energy we use per person is at the heart of the fossil fuel problem. World fuel reserves may be larger than we have used thus far. But in the next 10 years we will need more energy than all we have used in the past.

Quick Review

1. Describe how the human population has grown.
2. How does the need for fossil fuels compare with the human population growth?

Environmental problems

New vocabulary: acid rain

Recovering, processing, and burning fossil fuels have produced many environmental problems. Our ground water and atmosphere have been seriously affected. Yet, even more important, living things have been affected. People and governments are more aware of these problems now than they

The "rule of 72" used at the end of the *Research Topic* can be applied to anything that grows continuously. For example, a bank account that earns 8% interest compounded daily will double in 9 years.

Main Idea

What is true for the length of time needed for the human population to double?

Science background information:
The table below compares the amounts of energy used in the United States in 1960, 1970, and 1980. The numbers represent quadrillions of BTU's (British Thermal Units). One quadrillion equals one million billion. One BTU equals 1053 joules.

	1960	1970	1980
Petroleum products	19.9	29.5	34.3
Natural gas	12.4	21.8	20.4
Coal	10.1	12.7	15.7
Nuclear power	0.0	0.2	2.7

Quick Review answers:
1. The population has been doubling in increasingly shorter periods of time. The latest doubling time is estimated at 35 years.
2. The need for fossil fuels has been increasing faster than the population growth.

Activity

14.1b Exponential Growth

Science Processes: Observing, using numbers, communicating, inferring, predicting, formulating models

Materials   BASIC   20 minutes   Groups of 2 or 3

- **260 pennies or other small objects such as paper clips, toothpicks, etc.**
- **row of 10 squares on tile floor or table top**

Purpose

To determine how things increase exponentially.

Procedure

1. Find a row of 10 squares on a floor or a table top. Place one penny or other small object on the first square. Place two of them on the second square. On each square put double the number of pennies you put on the preceding square.
2. Use a sheet of graph paper to show how the number of pennies increase on each square. On the horizontal axis of the graph, have each section represent the number of a square. Have each section along the vertical axis represent 50 pennies.

Questions

1. What is the total number of pennies on squares 1 through 3?

2. How does the number of pennies on square 4 compare to the total number of pennies on squares 1 through 3?
3. How many pennies are there on square 7?
4. How does the number of pennies on square 7 compare to the total number of pennies on squares 1 through 6?
5. At what square did you run out of pennies?
6. How many pennies would there be on square 10?

Conclusion

Describe the change in the number of objects that occurs with exponential growth.

were years ago. Even though problems have been increasing, people have been doing more to solve them.

Recovering coal from strip mines can cause severe damage problems. Poisonous chemicals seep out of the piles of earth that are dug from the mine. Miners have built drainage beds to help solve this problem. Work of this kind is necessary but costly. It has caused an increase in the price of coal.

Drilling for oil in the ocean has resulted in pollution of the water. On several occasions serious underwater oil leaks have occurred, causing contamination of beaches and death to much wildlife. Governments and oil companies have been working on developing methods of preventing and stopping these leaks. Laws have been passed that restrict off-shore drilling in certain areas.

Oil refineries occasionally catch fire, releasing many contaminating materials into the atmosphere. Sometimes toxic wastes get into the ground from plants where chemicals are made from petroleum. These cause health problems for people who live nearby, and are often carried for long distances in the ground water.

Figure 14-10. *Auto exhaust is still our most serious source of air pollution. Explain why air pollution is most severe in urban areas.*
The high population density and heavy reliance on transportation in urban areas result in more severe air pollution there than elsewhere.

Figure 14-11. *The areas marked on this map are endangered by acid rain. What causes this problem?*
Turn to the next page for the answer to this question.

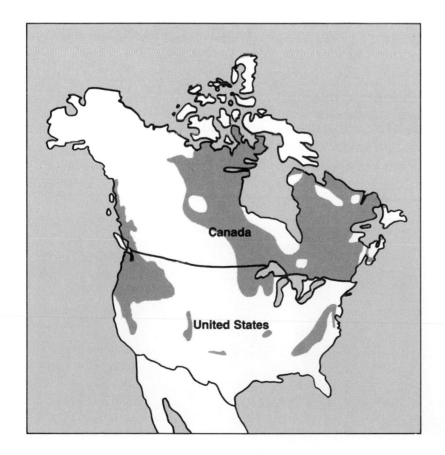

Canada

United States

Quick Review answers:
1. Special construction to drain poisons from strip mines has driven up coal prices.
2. The environmental problems include any one of several examples of air or water pollution.
3. Acid rain seems to be caused by the burning of high-sulfur coal. Acid rain destroys plant and animal life as well as structures.

A nuclear power plant gives off less chemical pollution and uses only small amounts of fuel. Dangers include the waste heat, the radioactive wastes, and the potential release of nuclear radiation.

Figure 14-12. *A fossil-fuel power plant (left) and a nuclear power plant (right). What is the obvious advantage of a nuclear power plant? What are the dangers?*

The use of fossil fuels has caused air and water pollution. The greatest problem of this kind has been auto exhaust. Autos are now equipped with smog-reducing devices that have helped to cut down on air pollution. However, in areas where there are many cars, air pollution from auto exhaust is still a problem.

Another serious problem that seems to be caused by the use of high-sulfur coal is **acid rain.** Rainwater is normally neutral or very slightly acidic. It has been discovered that the rain over the eastern United States and Canada is much more acidic than normal. Many lakes have become so acidic from the acid rain that they have "died." That is, fish and other animal life cannot live in these lakes. Apparently, fumes from the burning of high-sulfur coal react with water vapor in the air. An acid is formed. Winds carry the acid from industrialized areas to the lakes. Rain brings the acid to the ground.

Quick Review

1. How have environmental problems changed the price of coal?
2. Describe an environmental problem that has been caused by petroleum.
3. What is the apparent cause of acid rain? What effect does acid rain have on the environment?

Nuclear pathways

New vocabulary: breeder reactor

Much of our electricity is produced by nuclear fission, which was discussed in Chapter 13, Section 2. Does the pathway for nuclear energy also start with the sun? Scientists are uncer-

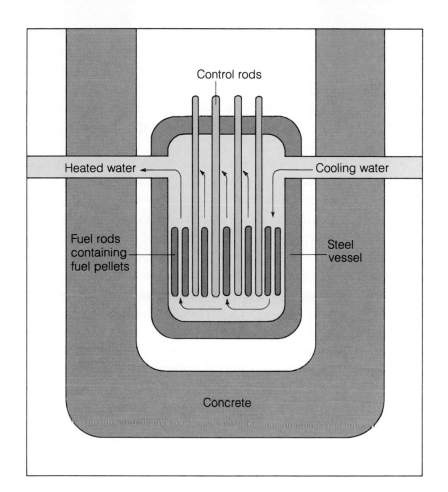

Figure 14-13. *Protection around the nuclear fuel bundles in the core of a reactor.*

Control rods

Heated water ← → Cooling water

Fuel rods containing fuel pellets

Steel vessel

Concrete

tain. This energy has been locked up in matter on earth ever since the earth began.

The known nuclear pathway starts when an atomic nucleus breaks down. The energy given off produces a super-heated water, which causes steam to be produced in a boiler. This steam turns electric generators which produce electricity.

Nuclear power plants give off less chemical pollution than fossil fuel plants. Since only small amounts of fuel are used, there is less of a problem than with strip mining. Yet, nuclear fuel is highly dangerous. Therefore, costly and complex safety systems must be installed and constantly inspected to keep the plant safe.

Many safeguards are built into the system to control nuclear fission within the reactor. Several hundred fuel bundles make up the core of the reactor. Each bundle is made up of uranium oxide ceramic pellets. The arrangement of the bundles and the dilution of the fuel are done to prevent the possibility of a nuclear explosion.

Research Topic

Investigate some actual hazardous events at nuclear power plants, such as the occurrence at Three Mile Island in 1979, or at Chernobyl in 1986. How did these incidents begin? What were the safeguards that took effect? What were the consequences of the accidents? What is happening at these locations today? Has the danger completely passed?

Most of the radioactive byproducts of fission remain in the fuel pellets. The pellets are enclosed in sealed metal tubes. All of the fuel bundles are placed inside a vessel with steel walls 15 to 20 cm thick. Around this is a steel shell and a concrete structure over 1 m thick. Each of these coverings is a barrier to reduce the possibility of the escape of radioactive materials.

Water or another cooling material constantly flows through the core. If this coolant stops flowing, fission should stop immediately. The core, however, would still be very hot. To prevent meltdown and radioactive release, every reactor has safety systems to reflood the vessel and cool the core.

All electric generating plants have a waste heat disposal problem. Nuclear plants have even more waste heat than fossil fuel plants. Too much excess heat released into the air can affect local weather patterns. At present, cooling towers are used to dispose of the heat.

Radioactive wastes are an environmental and health concern. About one third of the fuel rods in a nuclear reactor are replaced each year. Even though the fuel in these rods has been consumed, the removed rods are still radioactive and will remain radioactive for many thousands of years.

At present, spent fuel rods are stored at the reactor site in cooling tanks. Investigations on storing radioactive wastes in underground chambers are being made. Chambers would be mined in stable rock formations almost 1 km below the surface. Another solution is to reprocess spent fuel rods. A fully satisfactory method of waste disposal has not yet been agreed upon.

Uranium is a limited natural resource. The **breeder reactor** could solve this supply problem. The breeder reactor uses uranium and plutonium for fuel. In the fission of plutonium, neutrons strike the nuclei of the uranium. This produces more fuel, including plutonium.

Nuclear fission was once thought to be the ideal solution to the energy problem. Since there have been several near accidents, many people feel that it will always be unsafe. In Section 2 you will investigate other alternative sources of energy.

Quick Review

1. How do nuclear pathways differ from most other energy pathways on earth?
2. How is nuclear energy used to produce usable power?
3. What safeguards are used in nuclear power plants? What do these safeguards protect against?

Main Idea

What advantage does a breeder reactor have over other fission reactors?

Quick Review answers:
1. There is no evidence that nuclear pathways begin with the sun.
2. Heat from fission produces steam, which powers electric generators.
3. Fuel bundles are arranged and diluted to lower chances of an explosion. Steel walls and thick concrete surround the reaction vessel. Automatic shutdown devices are set up to operate in case of problems.

14.1 Section Review

Answers to Understanding the Concepts appear on page T169 in the front of this book. Blackline master test for this section: Section Testsheet 14-1 (TRB page 235)

Vocabulary

2 acid rain
6 anthracite
7 bituminous
9 breeder reactor
5 entropy
10 exponential
1 fossil fuel
8 lignite
4 nonrenewable
3 petroleum

Vocabulary Review

Match each term above with the numbered phrase that best describes it.

1. Coal, oil, and natural gas
2. Seems to be caused by burning high-sulfur coal
3. Oil produced from the remains of sea organisms
4. Refers to anything that is used much faster than it is produced
5. Measure of energy distribution
6. High-energy, low-sulfur coal
7. Medium-energy, high-sulfur coal
8. Low-energy, low-sulfur coal
9. Increases fuel supply
10. Type of growth shown by human population

Review Questions

Multiple Choice: Choose the answer that best completes each of the following sentences.

11. Energy flows from _?_.
    a. heavier objects to lighter objects
    b. places of higher concentration to places of lower concentration
    c. places of lower concentration to places of higher concentration
    d. colder objects to hotter objects
12. When energy is evenly distributed, _?_.
    a. the entropy is low
    b. the entropy is high
    c. much is available
    d. the temperature is high
13. Fossil fuels are _?_ energy resources.
    a. nonrenewable
    b. renewable
    c. recycled
    d. exponential
14. Acid rain is believed to have caused _?_.
    a. lung troubles
    b. disappearance of trees
    c. disappearance of fish
    d. eye irritation
15. Nuclear power plants are an environmental problem because they _?_.
    a. pollute the air
    b. release toxic chemicals
    c. pollute the water
    d. produce dangerous wastes

16. One advantage of the breeder reactor is that it _?_.
    a. does not use uranium as fuel
    b. does not produce radioactive wastes
    c. produces more fuel as a byproduct of the fission of plutonium
    d. produces less waste heat than fossil fuel plants

Understanding the Concepts

17. Describe the energy pathways that would include laundering your clothes.
18. Explain what is happening to the usable energy in the universe.
19. What sort of environmental problems are caused by fossil fuels?

For ideas for classroom demonstration and discussion, see Getting Started on page T170 in the front of this book.

14.2 Alternative Energy Resources

Supplemental materials: Teaching Diagrams 14-2A, 14-2B, and 14-2C (TRB pages 67–69), Reading Checksheet 14-2 (TRB page 116), Skillsheet 14-2 (TRB page 162), Investigation 14-2 (Lab Manual pages 187–188)

Section Preview

- **Alternative fuel sources**
- **Energy directly from the sun**
- **Energy from sun-powered systems**
- **Energy from other natural sources**

Bracketed numbers are Section Review questions correlated to that objective.

Learning Objectives

1. To distinguish between renewable and nonrenewable energy resources. [9, 15, 22]
2. To identify some alternative energy sources that may find use in the immediate future. [1, 2, 3, 14, 15, 16]
3. To describe different ways in which the sun's energy can be put to use. [4, 5, 6, 8, 12, 13, 17, 18, 19, 20, 23, 24]
4. To identify sources of energy that are the result of other natural causes. [7, 10, 11, 21, 24, 25]

Figure 14-14. *The solar panels on the roof of this building absorb energy from the sun. The energy heats air or water inside the panels. The heated air or water is used to heat the space inside the building.*

There are different opinions on how long our fossil fuel supply will last. However, all experts must admit that sooner or later it will be gone. What will happen then? We cannot really go back to living the way we did in earlier times. The present and estimated future world populations are much greater than they were in the days of horses and sailing ships. Modern lifestyles require more energy.

Unfortunately, the world cannot afford to wait to run out of fossil fuels before finding other energy resources. What will those resources be? Two alternative solutions are being studied: 1) finding new, untapped nonrenewable resources; 2) developing new ways to use **renewable** energy resources—those that can be replaced as rapidly as they are used up.

Since all nonrenewable resources will eventually run out, it is probably best to look toward developing renewable resources. However, many of the untapped nonrenewable resources could carry us a long way into the future.

Alternative fuel sources New vocabulary: renewable, synfuel, distill, oil shale, kerogen, biomass

The fuels discussed here probably offer the greatest possibilities for the immediate future. However, other energy sources mentioned later in this section may seem more promising over the long term.

Wood. Some people have changed to a "new" fuel to heat their homes. This "new" fuel is perhaps the oldest fuel in the world, wood.

In colonial times, people heated their homes, cooked their food, and heated their bath water with wood-burning fireplaces. In pictures, those early homes looked cozy and snug. Actually, many accounts of colonial life describe the homes as being quite uncomfortable. It was too hot near the fireplace, and too chilly and drafty away from it.

Today we have wood-burning stoves that are very efficient. Through modern methods, the heated air is circulated throughout a large area. Many people who live where wood is plentiful have switched to this "new" form of heat. People who live near national, state, and provincial forests can often get permission to remove fallen trees free of charge. The improvement of the wood stove is described in *Our Science Heritage* on page 626. Is wood a renewable or nonrenewable resource?

Synfuels. Liquid and gaseous fuels made from other sources are called synthetic fuels, or **synfuels** (SIN'-fyoo-ulz). Two major synfuels are ethanol and methanol. Ethanol and methanol are kinds of alcohol. They are produced from wood and other kinds of vegetation such as corn, grain, sunflowers, and almost any crop that is plentiful. The material is mashed and then fermented by microscopic organisms. It is then purified by **distilling** (dih-STIL'-ing), that is, boiling and condensing the vapors.

One part ethanol and nine parts gasoline have been used to make gasohol. Gasohol can be used as a motor fuel in place of gasoline. Methanol can be used alone as a motor fuel.

Methane is a major part of natural gas. It can be produced synthetically and used like natural gas. Several synfuels, including methane, can be made from coal. Synfuels can also be made from oil shale, tar sands, and biomass. Many synfuel sources are nonrenewable, but methanol and ethanol can be produced from rapidly grown crops. They are fairly easily renewed.

Potbellied stove

Figure 14-15. *Read about the invention of the wood-burning stove in Our Science Heritage. Why is a wood-burning stove more efficient than the fireplace as a source of heat for the home?*
The entire surface of the stove generates heat, using more of the fire's heat energy before it is lost up the chimney. Ask the students how many of them have a wood-burning stove in their home. Also ask how many of them have a wood-burning fireplace.

Research Topic

Find out about the use of synfuels in Brazil. Most autos in that country run on alcohol. Find out how the alcohol is produced. In what other parts of the world are synfuels produced and used?

Oil shale. Ancient Indian legends tell about the rock that burns. When set on fire, the rock would smolder for several days. This rock is known as **oil shale.** Huge deposits are found in Colorado, Wyoming, and Utah.

Oil shales were likely formed from sediments in ancient inland lakes. The remains of many organisms were found in these sediments. Over time these remains formed a solid, waxy substance called **kerogen** (KEH'-ruh-jun).

Oil shale often has a banded appearance. The dark bands contain more organic matter. The bands were likely deposited in winter, the light bands in summer. Examine the photo of oil shale in Figure 14-16.

An oil that can be used like crude oil can be obtained from kerogen. But it is still cheaper to pump crude oil than to get oil from shale. Only recently have scientists studied ways to get oil from shale in large quantities.

Figure 14-16. *What causes banding in oil shale?*
Banding is the result of differing amounts of organic matter present.

Our Science Heritage

Franklin stove

Changes in the Wood Stove

Fireplaces must have large open chimneys to carry out the smoke. Unfortunately, the chimney also carries out a lot of the heat from the fire. Most fireplaces allow about 90% of the heat they produce to go up the chimney. Only 10% of the heat is used to warm the house.

The American statesman and scientist Benjamin Franklin (1706–1790) became aware of this problem. He set about to find a way to put more of the fire in the room with the people. He built a large iron stove in front of the fireplace and ran the flue of the stove back into the chimney. The Franklin stove increased the fire's efficiency to about 40%. Some years later a "pot-bellied" stove was developed that had a round shape and could sit in the middle of a room. This spread the heat much more evenly around the room.

Today, there are modern wood stoves that are much smaller than the "pot-bellied" stove, but they radiate as much heat. Ceiling and floor fans can be made to circulate the heat throughout the house.

Some fireplaces have iron ducts running from top to bottom. The fire heats the air in the ducts. The hot air comes out a vent at the top of the fireplace. Cool air comes in the bottom of the duct and is heated by the fire.

Two methods to process oil shale are being studied. In both methods, the shale is heated to 420°C. At this temperature the kerogen becomes a gas. When cooled, the gas condenses as a thick black oil.

In one method, the shale is heated above ground in a large vessel called a retort. In the second method, the shale is heated below ground. Miners make vertical and horizontal tunnels which divide the underground shale into huge columns. Explosives are used to break up the rock in the underground columns. The shale oil at the top of the column is set on fire. As the surrounding rock is heated, oil is driven from the shale. The oil collects at the bottom of the column and is pumped to the surface.

Large-scale development of oil-shale plants is slow. Keep in mind that oil shale is a nonrenewable resource.

Tar sands. An oil synfuel can be obtained from tar sands. Like oil shale, tar sands also formed from the remains of organisms in the sediments of ancient inland lakes. Scattered deposits of tar sands are found in many places in Canada and the United States.

To recover the oil, tar sands must be heated in a process similar to the one for oil shale. In order to get a sizable amount of oil from tar sands, huge amounts of tar sands must be processed. A large part of the energy obtained is used in getting the oil. This makes oil from tar sands very expensive. Tar sands are also a nonrenewable natural resource.

Main Idea

What happens to oil shale when it is heated to 420°C?

Large amounts of tar sands must be heated, using considerable energy to obtain sizable amounts of oil.

Figure 14-17. *What factors would add to the cost of oil coming from tar sands?*

Main Idea

What are two methods for processing usable fuel from trash and other kinds of biomass?

Kelp is a particularly plentiful form of biomass.

Figure 14-19. *Some scientists think that fuel could be made from ocean kelps. Why would these plants be a good fuel source?*

Biomass. **Biomass** (BĪ'-ō-mas) is the remains, waste, or by-products of living things. Biomass can be changed chemically to produce a liquid or gaseous fuel. Biomass can consist of any kind of vegetation, food-processing wastes, manure, garbage, and certain kinds of trash.

Each year we throw away enormous amounts of biomass. If this biomass could be processed, it would produce fuel and help the solid waste disposal problem at the same time. Unlike oil shale and tar sands, biomass is a renewable energy source.

In a special furnace, trash can be heated at high pressure and temperature to produce fuel oil. But perhaps the easiest way to change biomass to fuel is by fermentation. The biomass is placed in closed containers. Bacteria that can live without oxygen digest the biomass. In the digestion process, the gas methane is given off.

Crops such as sorghum and sugar cane produce a lot of vegetation quickly. These plants convert more solar energy into food than any other plant. Sorghum and sugar cane make a high-energy biomass. Some tropical countries are growing these crops just for their conversion into fuel. Making fuels from farm crops may bring much needed wealth to tropical areas of the world. Another form of biomass that is very plentiful in some places is ocean kelp.

Electrochemical energy. Electric energy can be produced directly from chemical energy. This happens in a battery, but a battery can store only small amounts of energy. Some autos have been made that run on large rows of batteries.

A fuel cell can produce a more constant supply of energy. Recall from Chapter 12, Section 2, that a fuel cell uses hydrogen and oxygen to produce an electric current. At the same time, water is produced from the hydrogen and oxygen.

Fuel cells have several advantages. They are quiet. They are nonpolluting. Tanks of hydrogen and oxygen can be transported easily. The hydrogen and oxygen fuel can be used to produce electricity at the site where it is needed. Fuel cells have been used on space missions, where the water was consumed by the astronauts.

Nuclear fusion. You may recall from the discussion in Chapter 13, Section 2, that nuclear fusion might be an important source of energy in the future. There is an almost unlimited supply of fuel for nuclear fusion.

Successful experiments have been done with controlled nuclear fusion. By the end of this century, fusion reactors may be a reality.

Quick Review

1. Name two fuels discussed here that are renewable. Tell how they can be renewed.
2. What is biomass? What kinds of fuel can be produced from biomass?
3. What kind of fuel is used in a fuel cell? What are the advantages of a fuel cell?

Energy directly from the sun
New vocabulary: passive solar, direct gain, indirect solar, convection loop, active solar

Every day huge quantities of free energy reach the earth from the sun. The amount of solar energy striking the earth's upper atmosphere is thousands of times greater than the world's total energy needs. Year after year the supply remains constant.

Solar energy is a clean energy source. No harmful wastes are produced with its use. With the development of the right technology, solar may be the energy of the future.

The amount of direct solar energy available for use varies at any given time. On a cloudy day as much as 80 percent of the solar energy striking the upper atmosphere never reaches the earth's surface. And of course, at night almost no solar energy reaches even the upper atmosphere of the earth on the side facing away from the sun. In order to be useful, solar energy must be collected and stored in some way.

Main Idea

What are some advantages of fuel cells as energy sources?

Quick Review answers:
1. Wood can be renewed by proper planting and cutting practices. Methanol and ethanol are synfuels that can be renewed by growing crops such as corn and grain.
2. Biomass is the remains, waste, or byproducts of living things. Biomass can be processed into either liquid or gaseous fuels.
3. Hydrogen and oxygen gases are used in a fuel cell. Fuel cells are quiet, nonpolluting, and can be used in remote locations.

Main Idea

What must be done to make solar energy a useful energy source?

Figure 14-20. *(Left) Drums of water are heated by sunlight. (Right) A greenhouse attached to the south side of a home.*

How do design features like these make use of solar energy to heat homes?
The drums are black to absorb the solar energy. Water is used to store the energy because water has such a large capacity to store heat with little effect on its temperature.

The attached greenhouse collects solar energy. The floor absorbs energy and radiates it into the air. Vents allow the heated air to move into the rest of the house.

Research Topic

Investigate some of the latest advancements in home solar heating. Find out what kinds of units are being installed in existing homes. What is being done in new homes?

Passive solar energy.   **Passive solar** energy is used primarily to heat the space inside of buildings. No pumps or motors aid the flow of the heat. Buildings may be designed to use passive solar energy directly, indirectly, or through a convection loop.

To use solar energy directly, buildings are constructed to either let in or keep out sunlight. Large windows on the south side of the building are good solar collectors. A roof overhang will screen sunlight in the summer and let sunlight in during the winter.

In a **direct-gain** solar building, the energy is stored in building materials which make up the floor, walls, and ceiling. Concrete, brick, or stone make good storage materials. Insulated window coverings slow down energy loss at night.

In the **indirect solar** building, massive heat-storage materials are placed behind south-facing windows. Storage materials might be a brick, stone, or concrete wall, or drums of water. The solar energy absorbed by the storage wall is radiated into the living space. Vents in the wall at floor and ceiling level provide natural convection currents.

The passive collection and storage of solar energy may occur outside of the building to be heated. For example, a large collecting surface such as a greenhouse can be attached to the living space. Heat-storage material is built into the floor of the greenhouse. Vents from the greenhouse into the living space control the flow of energy. A reflector on the ground outside of the greenhouse will increase the amount of solar energy collected.

In the **convection loop** building, the living space is enclosed like an envelope by a second building. It is a building within a building. The outer building has a large glass wall facing south. Sunlight shines through the glass and heats the air

See also Activity Record Sheet 14-2A (Lab Manual page 185). Alternate Note, Answers to Questions, and Conclusion appear on page T170 in the front of this book.

Activity

14.2a   A Solar Cooker

Science Processes: Formulating models, experimenting, communicating, observing, measuring, predicting

Materials

- old umbrella
- aluminum foil
- masking tape

- hot dog, luncheon meat, or marshmallow
- pointed stick

BASIC   1 hour   Groups of 4 or teacher demonstration

Purpose

To show how solar energy can be used to cook food.

Procedure

1. Completely line the inside of an old umbrella with pieces of aluminum foil. Try to keep the foil as free of wrinkles as possible. Fasten the pieces of foil to the umbrella with masking tape.
2. Tape small pieces of foil under the support struts around the center pole. The diagram shows how to construct the cooker.
3. On a sunny day, place the umbrella outdoors in a location where there is no wind. Put the top point of the inverted umbrella into the ground so that the open part faces the sun. When aimed properly, the umbrella pole will cast almost no shadow. This experimental model of a curved foil mirror will focus the sun's rays at a point somewhere along the center pole.
4. Place the food you are using on the pointed stick. Hold it close to the umbrella pole about midway. Slowly move it up and down until you find the spot where the food begins to cook.

Questions

1. At what location along the center pole did the food begin to cook?
2. Explain what happened when the stick was moved up and down in the solar cooker.
3. About how long did it take for the food to begin to cook?
4. What improvements would you make if you wanted to construct a permanent solar cooker?

Conclusion

Explain how solar energy can be used to cook food.

Find the focal point along center pole

Sun's rays

What makes active solar energy systems different from passive solar systems?

United States and Soviet scientists have experimented with solar panels as energy sources for satellites, probes, and space stations. Why would outer space be an excellent location for solar panels supplying energy to earth?
If the panels could be put into orbit efficiently, they would collect a far greater percentage of solar energy outside the earth's atmosphere than if they are on the earth's surface. In addition, the panels could be made to rotate so as to receive constant solar exposure. The lack of gravity and air resistance would allow space panels to be constructed to an enormous size.

Figure 14-21. *Solar panels should be placed at a higher angle in more northern areas because the sun is lower in the sky there. What would be the angle of solar panels near the equator, where the sun is almost directly overhead?*
Facing straight up, or 0°.

between the two buildings. Vents control the circulation of this warm air. By changing the vents, a person can make the moving air either give off or take on heat from the living space.

Active solar energy. Like a passive solar system, an **active solar** system requires collection and storage. But it also uses a fan or a pump to circulate the heated air or water.

Most active solar systems use a flat-plate collector, which is placed on the roof or on a slanted platform on the ground. The degree of slant depends on the latitude. The collector is tilted to collect the maximum energy from the sun. Because Miami is much farther south than Chicago, the sun's position in the sky is higher. The solar panel is slanted only a little from the horizon in Miami. In Chicago, where the sun is always lower, the solar panel would have to be at a higher angle.

The hot air or water which has been heated inside the flat-plate collector is pumped into a large insulated storage tank. When needed, it is pumped through a centralized space-heating system. Many family homes and apartment buildings have systems for heating the hot water with solar energy.

It is not necessary that the climate be sunny for solar heating systems to provide comfort and save fuel expense. New advances in solar technology and improved methods of heat storage have made solar heating systems less expensive and more available.

The federal and some state governments are offering tax breaks to homeowners who install solar heating and/or cooling systems. Scientists estimate that if one percent of the buildings in the United States were solar heated, 30 million barrels of oil a year could be saved.

Solar conversion. Solar energy can be changed either directly or indirectly into electric energy. When the sun's rays are concentrated on a single point, intense heat can be produced. This is the principle used in indirect solar conversion.

Experimental stations have been built which heat water in a boiler with solar energy. Mirrors reflect and concentrate the sun's rays onto the boiler, which is located at the top of a tower. Curved or flat mirrors which surround the boiler tower may be used to reflect and concentrate the sun's rays. Computers keep the mirrors properly positioned at all times to reflect the sunlight.

Liquids in the boiler can be heated to over 500°C. The heated liquid is pumped to a steam-powered electric generator. The heated liquid may be stored in specially insulated tanks for about 20 hours. Heated liquid from the storage tank permits the generation of electricity at night and on cloudy days.

Long-term heat storage is a major problem in indirect solar conversion. Also, the method requires large amounts of land. Nevertheless, some scientists predict that by the year 2000 solar energy will be supplying 20 percent of the electricity used.

Solar cells are discussed in Chapter 11, Section 2. With the use of solar cells, solar energy can be converted directly into electric energy. The solar cell is made of materials that release electrons when light strikes them. The flow of electrons into connecting wires sets up a current. The current can be stored in a battery.

Figure 14-22. *What factors should be considered before installing a solar-heated hot-water tank?*
The amount of available sunshine, the best angle for the flat-plate collector, the type of equipment to get, and how long it will take before the cost of the equipment is balanced by the savings in fuel are all factors that should be considered.

Figure 14-23. *In this experimental solar generating plant, solar energy is converted to electric energy. The mirrors reflect the solar energy toward the top of a boiler tower.*

14.2b   Angle for Maximum Solar Energy

Science Processes: Observing, measuring data, inferring, interpreting data

Materials   20 minutes   Groups of 2 or 3

- black construction paper
- cellophane tape
- thermometer
- 2 books, or other adjustable support

Purpose

To determine whether the angle of sunlight affects the amount of energy absorbed by a sunlit surface.

Procedure

1. Make an envelope by folding a piece of black construction paper in half. Fold over about 3 cm of each side, and tape. Place a thermometer inside the envelope bulb end first. SAFETY NOTE: *Use care when handling a glass thermometer around pavement, especially when shaking down the temperature. If possible, shake the thermometer over a lawn. A shattered thermometer is particularly hazardous to clean up.*

2. Set the envelope and thermometer out of direct sunlight for about 5 minutes. Then record the temperature reading.

3. Place a book in direct sunlight. Prop the envelope with the thermometer against the book on the side away from the sun. Adjust the position of the envelope so that only one edge faces the sun, as shown for position 1. The front and back of the envelope should receive as little sun as possible. This is an angle of about 0°. Leave it in place for 4 minutes, then record the angle and the thermometer reading on the table. Shake down the thermometer and replace it in the envelope.

4. Place the envelope and thermometer flat on top of the book for position 2. This position should be an angle of about 45°. Record the angle and the temperature after 4 minutes. Shake down the thermometer and replace it.

5. Finally, adjust the envelope so that one side faces directly into the sun, for position 3. At what angle is the envelope facing the sun now? Use another book as a prop, if needed. After 4 minutes, record the angle and the thermometer reading.

Questions

1. In which of the three positions was the sunlight hitting the face of the envelope at the smallest angle? In which position was the angle greatest?

2. At which angle did the envelope warm up the most? At which angle did it warm up the least?

3. If you had just painted a shelf, how could you arrange it in the sunlight so that it would dry the fastest?

4. Explain how your nose gets sunburned faster than the rest of your face.

Conclusion

Explain how the angle of the sunlight hitting an object affects the amount of solar energy the object receives.

Step 3

Sun's rays

Large quantities of solar cells are needed to produce significant amounts of electricity. At present, electricity produced with solar cells costs 3 to 5 times more than other electricity. Perhaps with new research this cost will drop.

Solar cells are used to make electricity in space vehicles. Solar cells borrowed from the National Aeronautics and Space Administration (NASA) powered the aircraft *Solar Challenger* on a flight across the English Channel in July, 1981. Out at sea, fog horns and buoy lights are powered with solar cells. In remote areas, solar cells provide electricity for runway lights and communications stations.

Quick Review

1. How does passive solar heating compare with active solar heating?
2. How could the angle at which a flat solar collector is placed differ in New Orleans and Toronto?
3. Name two successful uses of solar cells.

Energy from sun-powered systems

New vocabulary: wind farm, solar pond

We can tap the energy of streams, the wind, and sun-warmed water. All these systems receive their energy from the sun. The energy is completely renewable.

Hydroelectric power. The sun provides the energy for water to evaporate. The water returns to the ground as rain or snow. As it flows downhill, the moving water can be used to turn turbines and generate electricity.

About 14 percent of the electric power in North America is hydroelectric, or produced with water. Most of this is produced at dams with large reservoirs.

Generating electricity with water power is efficient. Little heat is lost. No pollutants are produced. On the other hand, most of the desirable dam and reservoir sites have already been developed. Others are too far from regions where the power would be used.

Also, when an entire valley or canyon is flooded, the environment is changed drastically. Some people feel that too many of our wild rivers have been destroyed by hydroelectric projects.

Natural waterfalls such as Niagara have been used as sources of electric power. A column of water flows from the top of the falls. The water passes through a hydroelectric

Figure 14-24. *The wings and top of the* Solar Challenger *were covered with 16 000 solar cells. What are the limitations of solar-powered aircraft?* The number of solar cells needed is very large. Also, this type of plane would have difficulty flying in cloudy weather. Finally, solar cells are expensive.

Quick Review answers:
1. Passive solar energy does not require the use of any motors or outside energy sources to transfer the heat.
2. A solar collector would be much more horizontal in New Orleans than in Toronto.
3. Solar cells are used in remote areas to supply the electricity for lighthouses, aircraft runways, and remote weather stations. Solar cells are also used extensively on spacecraft and communications satellites.

Data Search

Between 1980 and 1983, which provided more energy in the United States—water power or nuclear power plants? Search pages 658–661.

Water power provided more energy in each of the years 1980, 1982, and 1983.

Figure 14-25. *Where does the energy come from to operate the generator in this hydroelectric generating plant?*
The energy comes from the potential energy of the water in the lake. Ultimately, the energy came from the sun, which evaporated the water so that it returned to the ground at an elevation higher than the lake and flowed into it.

Figure 14-26. *Windmills that generate electricity may help people in some areas to become energy self-sufficient.*

plant, where it turns turbines which are connected to electric generators. The water flows back into the river at the bottom of the falls.

Energy from wind. The unequal heating of the earth's surface by the sun causes winds to flow. Since early times, people have used energy from the wind. Sailboats were used very early in history. Dutch windmills were used for grinding grain and pumping water. Windmills have also been used on farms and ranches for bringing up underground water.

Today more and more windmills are being used to generate electricity. Some of these windmills are very large. Other smaller ones are placed in large groups known as **wind farms.** Some power companies have set up wind farms. They are likely to become much more widely used in the future.

In windy areas, some people have set up windmills in their own yards or farms. They generate their own electricity. Sometimes they generate more electricity than they need. A system has been developed that allows these people to send their surplus electric power back through the electric meter into the power company's lines. The meter moves in the opposite direction and records the amount of power they send into the lines. The power company then pays these people for the amount of electricity they supply.

Saltwater systems.   In many parts of the world, the sun shines most of the year, producing great heat. The problem in most of these places has been to find ways of collecting this heat. In areas where there are large deposits of natural salt, there may be an easy answer to this problem.

In most ponds and lakes, energy from the sun is absorbed by the water. But this energy is soon lost by radiation. The heat escapes into the air above. The cooled water at the surface sinks and pushes warmer water up from below.

The **solar pond** uses heavily salted water to prevent the escape of heat. The water at the bottom is kept much saltier than the water at the top. The saltier water is heavier. It will not rise even when it becomes very hot. The heated water is removed from the bottom. It may be allowed to heat a fluid that turns a turbine for an electric generator. Solar ponds were first used to generate electricity in Israel. One in Ohio is being used to heat a swimming pool.

Much of the solar energy which strikes the earth heats the surface water of the oceans. In deep tropical oceans, the difference in temperature between the bottom and surface water can be used to generate electricity.

Ocean heat conversion is a very expensive and inefficient way to generate electricity. However, for tropical islands and mid-ocean factories, it may be an answer to their future energy needs.

Main Idea

How can solar energy absorbed by the oceans be made useful?

Figure 14-27. *In a solar pond, the water with the highest salt content settles to the bottom. There it is heated by energy from the sun. The heated water may flow through a boiler and cause a liquid to become vaporized. The vapors turn a turbine, which turns an electric generator.*

Sun

Vapor

Electric generator

Turbine

Boiler

Cooled water

Heated water

Low-salt-content cool water
(lighter layer; floats on top)

High-salt-content hot water
(heavier layer; sinks to bottom)

Dark heat-absorbing bottom

Quick Review

1. Explain how energy from Niagara Falls could have originally come from the sun.
2. What is meant by a wind farm?
3. In what kind of area would a solar pond be most practical?

Energy from other natural sources

One source of energy we use that does not come directly from the sun is nuclear energy. There are two other sources being tried today that are also not directly traceable to the sun's energy. One is due to underground heat; the other is due to gravitation and the movement of the earth and moon.

Geothermal energy. The earth was formed from a ball of fiery gases, and as it cooled, it took on the form we know today. The inner core, however, is still hot and molten. Natural heat from the earth's molten core is known as **geothermal energy.** Sometimes geothermal energy bursts forth as a volcanic eruption or geyser.

In some places, wells have been drilled into known geothermal energy areas in order to tap the energy. Boiling water and steam come to the surface and turn turbines for electric generators.

Main Idea

What is geothermal energy?

Additional information:
The word *geothermal* comes from the two Greek words for *earth* and *heat.*

Figure 14-28. *A geothermal power plant. What causes the jets of vapor shown here?*
Natural heat from deep inside the earth turns underground water to steam, which erupts under great pressure.

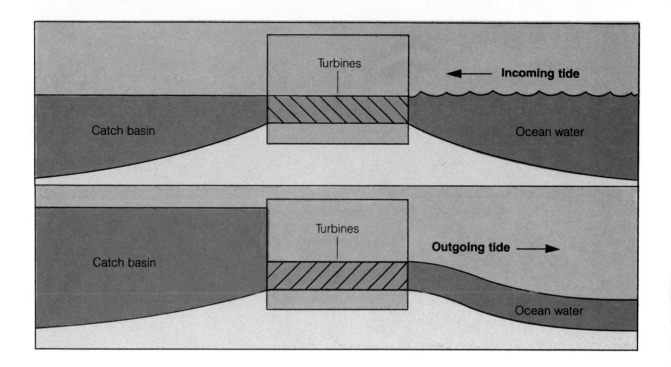

A large geothermal power plant is located in California, north of San Francisco. Several are operating in Iceland, where there is much geothermal activity.

Tidal energy. The water in the earth's oceans becomes higher in certain places than in others. This difference is caused by the gravitational attraction between the earth, moon, and to a lesser extent, the sun. The oceans bulge away from the earth on the side closest to the moon and on the side farthest from the moon. As the earth rotates, the high tides move around the world. In each coastal area, the tides move back and forth roughly twice a day, or about once every 12 hours and 25 minutes. The energy of the moving tides is called **tidal energy.**

As the tidal water moves up and down, the tidal energy can be tapped. This is usually done in a river or canal close to the ocean. As the tide comes in, the water becomes trapped behind a dam. It is allowed to flow out gradually, turning turbines for electric generators as it goes. Figure 14-29 shows how tidal energy can be generated during both cycles of the tide.

Quick Review

1. Describe a possible energy pathway that includes geothermal energy.
2. What natural event causes the tides to come in and out?

Figure 14-29. *A tidal power plant. Water continually turns the turbine blades, whether the tide is coming in or going out.*

Research Topic

Where are tidal power plants now in use? How do they operate? What differences are there between newer and older tidal plants? What conditions are needed in order to construct a tidal plant?

Quick Review answers:
1. Nuclear reactions release heat, which is trapped in the rocks. The rocks transfer the heat to water, which carries it up wells toward the surface. There the hot water is used to turn turbines to generate electric energy.
2. The rotation of the earth causes the tides to move in and out.

14.2 Section Review

Answers to Understanding the Concepts appear on page T171 in the front of this book. Blackline master test for this section: Section Testsheet 14-2 (TRB page 236)

Vocabulary

5 active solar
3 biomass
4 convection loop
12 direct-gain
11 geothermal energy
13 indirect solar
1 oil shale
6 passive solar
9 renewable
8 solar pond
2 synfuel
10 tidal energy
7 wind farm

Vocabulary Review

Match each term above with the numbered phrase that best describes it.

1. Rock containing fuel
2. Liquid or gaseous fuel made from another source
3. Renewable source of methane
4. House in an "envelope"
5. Solar energy system requiring collection and storage
6. Solar energy that is collected without pumps or motors
7. Group of wind generators
8. Contains salt water that becomes very hot
9. Can be replaced quickly
10. Caused by the earth's rotation and the moon's gravity
11. Found in heated regions underground
12. Energy stored in floors, walls, and ceilings
13. Energy stored behind south-facing windows

Review Questions

Multiple choice: Choose the answer that best completes each of the following sentences.

14. Wood, corn, or grain can be mashed, fermented, and distilled to produce ? .
    a. oil
    b. gasoline
    c. kerogen
    d. synfuels

15. A nonrenewable resource that may be used even more in the future is ? .
    a. ethanol
    b. wood
    c. oil shale
    d. methanol

16. One good source of biomass would be ? .
    a. gasohol
    b. sand
    c. garbage
    d. oil shale

17. In buildings heated by passive solar energy, solar energy may be stored in ? .
    a. a concrete floor
    b. glass windows
    c. a roof overhang
    d. vents in the wall

18. Heated water is pumped from roof collectors in ? .
    a. an active solar home
    b. a passive solar home
    c. a convection loop
    d. a direct-gain solar home

19. Solar energy can be converted directly into electric energy with ? .
    a. boilers
    b. solar cells
    c. mirrors
    d. generators

20. Energy from evaporated water is caught in a ? .
    a. fuel cell
    b. hydroelectric plant
    c. tidal plant
    d. solar pond

21. Geothermal energy is produced from ? .
    a. synfuels
    b. solar energy
    c. nuclear decay
    d. tar sands

Understanding the Concepts

22. Explain what the difference is between a renewable and a nonrenewable energy resource.

23. Describe three different kinds of passive solar homes. How do they differ from active solar homes?

24. Tell what alternative energy resource you would recommend for each of the following places.
    a. The coast of Maine
    b. Southern California
    Give your reasons for each recommendation.

25. List the geographic factors that would affect the operation of a tidal power plant.

For ideas for classroom demonstration and discussion, see Getting Started on page T172 in the front of this book.

14.3 Energy Conservation

Supplemental materials: Teaching Diagram 14-3 (TRB page 69), Reading Checksheet 14-3 (TRB page 117), Skillsheet 14-3 (TRB page 163), Investigation 14-3 (Lab Manual pages 191–192)

Section Preview

- **Transportation and energy conservation**
- **Energy conservation in the home**
- **Energy conservation in industry**
- **Future energy usage and conservation**

Bracketed numbers are Section Review questions correlated to that objective.

Learning Objectives

1. To recognize that energy conservation is needed to provide time to develop alternative energy sources. [13]
2. To identify ways in which energy can be conserved. [1–16]
3. To describe needs and practices for the future that would assist in conserving energy. [1–3, 6, 9, 10, 14, 15]

Figure 14-30. *This house is built into the ground. How does this construction feature help conserve energy in both cold and hot weather?* The ground tends to vary in temperature less than the air does. On cold days, the ground helps keep the house from losing heat. On hot days, it helps keep it cool so that air-conditioning is not needed.

Most scientists agree that if we use fossil fuels at the projected rate, we will eventually run out. Alternative fuel sources need to be developed. This will take a lot of time, because most of our present heating units and machines are designed to work on fossil fuels.

One way that we can buy the time we need for this great shift is by conserving the fuels we are now using. Using less energy and building more energy-efficient machines could greatly reduce the quantity of fuels consumed each year. Some people feel that the demand for fuels could be reduced by as much as 40%. The more energy we save now, the longer our present energy supply will last.

What is your energy conservation I.Q.? Which of the following save energy?

☐ Driving at a speed of 55 mi/h (88 km/h) instead of 65 mi/h (105 km/h)

☐ Removal of snow tires during summer months

☐ Keeping tires underinflated

☐ Taking a tub-bath instead of a shower

Data Search

From 1978 to 1983, by how much did total energy consumption in the United States drop? Search pages 658–661.

It dropped by 7786×10^{12} J (or 7.786×10^{15} J), which is 9.5% of the 1978 value.

Research Topic

Search through back copies of consumer magazines. Make a comparison of different kinds of cars and how efficiently they use energy.

☐ Filling the washing machine half full when a half load is being washed

☐ Painting walls and ceilings a dark color

☐ Dusting bulbs and light fixtures regularly

☐ Lighting with one ceiling light rather than several lamps

☐ Covering pans when cooking

In this section you will find out if your answers are correct. You will also discover many other ways to save energy.

Transportation and energy conservation

Over one fourth of all the energy consumed in North America is used in transportation. Over one half of the energy used for transportation is consumed by the private automobile. In a typical family, the automobile is the single largest consumer of energy. By driving less and practicing fuel-efficient driving, people can save large amounts of energy.

As the speed of a car increases, friction between the tires and the road increases. To overcome friction, energy is needed. The higher the speed, the more fuel is used. Driving at 88 km/h (55 mi/h) instead of 112 km/h (70 mi/h) will increase gas mileage by more than 20 percent. Gasoline is used most efficiently at speeds between 56 and 64 km/h (35 and 40 mi/h).

The heavier the car, the more fuel it consumes. For better gas mileage, remove baggage that is not needed. Remove snow tires and luggage racks when they are not needed. Anything attached to your car that increases friction or air resistance wastes fuel.

Air conditioners reduce gasoline mileage. Use them only when it is absolutely necessary. Reduce the need by parking the car in the shade. Air conditioners are most wasteful when the car is driving on local streets. On the highway, an air conditioner does not use more fuel than driving with the car windows open. Why do you suppose this is true? See at left.

Carburetors, spark plugs, and air filters should be checked regularly. Properly tuned engines save fuel. So do tires that are properly balanced, aligned, and inflated.

The best way to conserve auto fuel is to use a car less often. This need not cause you inconvenience if you plan your travel. For example, you can walk or take public transportation whenever possible. Buses, subways, and streetcars are heavy and use much energy. But they are worthwhile because they

Main Idea

What uses over one eighth of all the energy consumed in North America?

Answer to question in text:
Air blowing through the windows when a car is moving at high speed causes as much resistance to the engine as an air conditioning unit when the windows are closed.

Figure 14-31. *The pressure on the gas pedal should never be enough to break an egg between your foot and the pedal.*

14.3a   Surveying Your Car Usage

Science Processes: Measuring, using numbers, communicating, inferring, interpreting data
Materials   2 weeks   Individual work

- **family car**
- **note book**

Purpose

To find out if your family's driving habits are wasteful.

Procedure

1. In a note book, make a chart like the one shown in the Activity Record Sheet. Record the date. Give the size and the weight (if available) of the family car. Estimate the amount and the cost of the gas already in the car. Record the odometer reading of your family car. Do this for each car you study.

2. Each day for two weeks, record on the chart the kind of trips that were taken, if the car was used for city or freeway driving, and whether or not the air-conditioner was used. Each time fuel is put into the car, record the amount and the cost.

3. Each week, calculate the fuel cost per kilometer or mile for each car. To do this, divide the total cost of the fuel used by the total number of kilometers or miles driven for the week. Record this data on the chart.

4. Each week, calculate the fuel-efficiency of each car. To do this, divide the total number of kilometers or miles driven by the total number of liters or gallons of fuel consumed for the week by each car. Record the data.

Questions

1. Which car surveyed by the class uses the least amount of fuel for the miles driven?
2. Is the most fuel-efficient car large or small? How much was this car driven compared to the other cars that were studied?
3. What is the difference in fuel-efficiency between the cars that did mostly freeway driving and those cars that did mostly city driving? Be sure to take into consideration the weight and the size of the cars you compare.
4. Which trips made by your family were not essential? Which trips could be combined?
5. List some incentives that might be used to encourage your family to stick to a plan that reduces car usage.

Conclusion

How can you determine if your family's driving habits are wasteful?

Car Model:				Weight or Mass:			
	Odometer Reading	Distance Driven	Amount of Fuel in Tank	Total Fuel Used	Distance Driven per L or gal	Cost of Fuel Used	Cost per km or mi
Start							
End of Wk 1							
End of Wk 2							

Trip Date	Purpose of Trip	Odometer Reading		Distance Driven	Amount of Fuel Added	Cost of Fuel Added	City or Freeway?	Air-Cond. Used?
		Start	End					

Figure 14-32. *In what ways could you use carpools to save energy?* Carpools reduce the number of cars used by factors of two, three, or even four.

If a bus carries 40 people and a car carries 5, then 8 cars would be needed for a busload of people.

Main Idea

What are some ways to save fuel when going shopping by car?

Quick Review answers:
1. Between 56 and 64 km/h (35 to 40 mi/h)
2. The automobile.
3. Buses carry many people and eliminate the need for separate trips by private car.

carry so many people. How many private cars would be needed to carry the same number of people as one bus? If it is necessary for you to commute to school by car, perhaps you can share rides by joining a carpool.

Try to do several things on each shopping trip you take. Organize trips to avoid rush-hour traffic. Stops and starts waste fuel. Shop at centers where several of your errands can be done in the same area. Invite friends to do their errands with you.

The telephone can eliminate unnecessary travel. Call to make sure a store has the special item you want in stock. When taking a vacation, it helps to make motel or campsite reservations by phone. This will save hunting for a place to stay. If you are visiting a place for the first time, call to find out its location or use a map.

Quick Review

1. At what speed do we get the most efficient use of auto fuel?
2. What is the single, largest consumer of energy in most families?
3. How does the use of buses help conserve energy?

Energy conservation in the home
New vocabulary: humidity, R value, aerator, flow regulator, fluorescent

Space heating and cooling account for 60% of the energy use in the home. Another 13% is used in heating water. Over

20% is used in cooking and preserving food. The remainder is used for lighting and small appliances.

The most obvious way to save energy is to turn the thermostat down in the winter and up in the summer, if you use air conditioning. Don't heat or cool the entire house. Close off unoccupied rooms. Insulate ducts into these rooms. Make sure all vents in the foundation and attic are properly sealed during the cold season.

You can make a house more comfortable at a lower temperature by increasing the **humidity** (hyoo-MID′-ih-tee), or amount of water vapor in the air. To do this, use a humidifier or pans of water in front of hot air ducts. A properly humidified room at 18°C is as comfortable as a dry one at 20°C. You can make yourself more comfortable at a lower temperature by wearing warming clothes. Sweaters over several layers of clothing help to hold in your body heat.

Properly insulating a home results in a great energy savings. All outside doors should have weather stripping. If a quarter slips easily under a door, so will a lot of warm air. Storm windows prevent heat loss in the winter. By putting on another window, you make an air space in between the two windows. Air spaces are good heat insulators.

Walls, attic floors, and basement ceilings should be properly insulated. Insulation comes in rolls, sheets, loose pellets, and foam. All of these work because they contain many trapped air spaces. The amount of wall and ceiling insulation needed in a home depends on climate. Insulation is measured in units called **R values.** The higher the R value is, the greater the insulation. A map of recommended R values for the United States and Canada is shown in Figure 14-35.

Insulating a hot-water heater saves energy. It is also a good idea to insulate hot-water pipes and heat ducts. The oven and refrigerator doors should seal tightly.

Proper care of a home heating or cooling unit can save energy. All vents should be cleaned regularly. Filters in forced-air furnaces should be replaced often. The entire system should be cleaned regularly. Vents should not be covered by furniture, nor should the air flow be blocked.

Proper use of windows and drapes can save energy. In the winter, keep drapes open on sunny days and closed at night. In the summer, draw drapes on sunny windows. Keep windows and doors closed during the hottest parts of the day.

In what other ways could you help conserve energy and help reduce your family's heating or cooling bill?

Figure 14-33. *Which kind of clothing allows you to save more energy at home during winter?* Several layers of clothing, including sweaters, help hold in body heat.

Main Idea

What can be done to a home heating or cooling unit to save energy?

14.3b   Your Shower Usage

Science Processes: Using numbers, measuring, interpreting data, experimenting, formulating hypotheses
Materials   2 days   Individual work

- home shower with a tub (if available)
- thermometer
- masking tape
- metric ruler
- plastic foam cup

Purpose

To determine if a shower uses less hot water than a tub bath.

Procedure

1. On the first day, take a tub bath. Let the cold tap water run for a few minutes. Catch some of the cold tap water in a plastic cup. Immediately measure the temperature of the cold water. Fill the tub with enough warm water to take a bath, making sure the water is at the preferred temperature and level. Before you get into the tub, mark the water level with a piece of masking tape. Measure the water level in the center of the tub with a metric ruler. Measure the temperature of the warm water. Do not add more water after you take these measurements. Use a table like the one shown to record all your data.
2. The next day, take a shower with the tub drain closed. Catch some of the warm water in a plastic foam cup. Measure the temperature of the warm water immediately. After you finish showering, mark the side of the tub with masking tape at the water level. Measure the depth of the water in the center of the tub with the metric ruler. Drain the tub. Record the data.
3. Measure the difference between the tape marking the water level of the tub bath and the tape marking the water level of the shower. Record the data.

Questions

1. What is the difference in the temperature of the water you use for a tub bath and the water you use for a shower?
2. What is the difference between the temperature of the cold tap water and the temperature of the water you use for a tub bath?
3. What is the difference, in cm, in the water depths at the center of the tub?
4. What is the difference, in cm, between the two tapes on the side of the tub?
5. Which method of bathing uses the most hot water?
6. Name some things you can do to conserve some of the hot water used for bathing.

Conclusion

Does a shower use less hot water than a tub bath?

	Tub Bath	Shower
Warm water temperature	°C	°C
Cold tap water temperature	°C	°C
Depth of water at tub center	cm	cm
Measured differences between tapes		cm

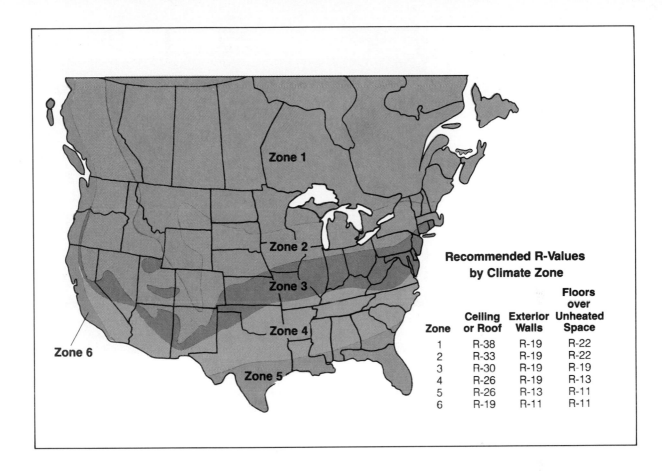

Recommended R-Values
by Climate Zone

Zone	Ceiling or Roof	Exterior Walls	Floors over Unheated Space
1	R-38	R-19	R-22
2	R-33	R-19	R-22
3	R-30	R-19	R-19
4	R-26	R-19	R-13
5	R-26	R-13	R-11
6	R-19	R-11	R-11

Could you heat less water in your home than you do? Many household tasks, including washing clothes, can be done with cold water instead of hot. Faucet **aerators** (AYR'-ray-terz) mix water with air. The amount of water used is reduced. Yet the pressure is strong enough for washing. Special shower heads that cut down on water usage can be bought. **Flow regulators,** which limit the amount of water that comes out, can be installed in existing shower heads.

Any time less hot water is used, energy is conserved. <u>Energy can also be conserved by adjusting the thermostat of the hot water heater. Reducing the temperature 15°C will result in a saving of 20% on the hot water heating bill.</u>

Energy conservation means planning ahead. This is true for food preparation also. Whenever possible, thaw frozen food in the refrigerator before cooking. If the oven is used, it is a good idea to plan to bake several things at the same time. Try to plan foods that will bake in about the same amount of time. Opening the oven door allows much heat to escape. Also, studies have shown that energy is wasted when the oven is preheated.

Figure 14-34. *What is the suggested insulation R value for the region where you live?*
Answers will vary for different locations, as shown on the map.

Main Idea

How can you save 20% on the cost of heating your hot water?

Figure 14-35. *When you use the oven, plan to cook everything in the oven at the same time. What other energy-saving methods can you use in cooking?*
See this page of text for several suggestions.

Research Topic

Find out how people in China have adapted their cooking techniques to the fact that cooking fuel is very expensive. What techniques do they use to reduce the amount of cooking fuel needed?

■ **Safety Note**
If your family uses a gas range, make sure the stove and oven are always turned completely off after use.

One-pot meals cooked on top of the stove save energy. All the food is cooked at one time, and only one burner is used. If using an electric range, turn off the burner several minutes before the stated time. The food will continue to cook from the energy stored in the burner. Match the size of your pan to the size of the burner.

When boiling water, cover the pan. The water will come to a boil faster and save energy. Once the water boils, lower the burner so that the water is just barely boiling. A hotter burner cannot make the water any hotter than boiling temperature. The water will simply evaporate faster.

Energy is used in preserving as well as cooking. For preserving food we depend upon refrigerators and freezers. Both use much energy. They cool food by removing the heat from the air around it. Each time the refrigerator or freezer door is opened, heated air gets inside. More energy must be used to remove the heat. Conserve energy by opening the door as few times as possible. Leave the door open only as long as necessary.

Perhaps the easiest way to save energy is to turn off lights. When you leave a room unoccupied, turn off the lights. You save energy even if you return to the room in just a few minutes.

In areas that need to be brightly lit, use one bright light instead of several small ones. A 150-watt bulb produces more light than two 75-watt bulbs. The long or circular tubes known as **fluorescent** (flor-ES'-unt) lights are more energy-efficient than incandescent bulbs. Dimmers and 3-way switches can save electricity. More light is given off when bulbs, globes, and lamp shades are clean. Walls and ceilings painted white reflect light. Reflected light may reduce the need for additional lamps.

Quick Review

1. In what ways should a home heating system be cared for?
2. What are three ways someone can save energy while cooking?
3. What are three ways someone can save energy in lighting the home?

Energy conservation in industry

New vocabulary: recycle

It takes an enormous amount of energy to manufacture some products. Much energy is used in transporting products. Of course, manufacturers want to save as much energy as possible. Doing so cuts their expenses and allows them to make bigger profits. Cutting energy costs can also mean lower prices on the products you buy.

There is also a way that you can have an effect on the energy used by industry. This can be done by careful consumption. Energy-concerned people will not buy things that are not needed. When they do buy something, they make sure it is durable and will last a long time. Also, taking good care of things will increase the time they last.

Buying habits can save energy. Buy clothes that can be washed in cold water and need little ironing. Compare similar items before buying. In clothing, look for quality of construction and strength of fabric.

A good shopper can save money and energy by reading labels. Laws now require manufacturers to put energy labels on each of their appliances. The federal government has established standard tests to measure the energy used by each type of appliance. The label found on each appliance shows its estimated energy use.

The label can be used to compare the product to others of the same type. The label also gives an estimate of how much it would cost yearly to operate the appliance. Both the selling price and the operating cost must be considered in buying a product.

Figure 14-36. *A fluorescent tube designed for table lamps.*

Quick Review answers:
1. Heating systems should be kept clean and as efficient as possible.
2. Match size of pan to burner, bake several items at the same time in the oven, and cover pans used for heating water. Other answers are acceptable.
3. Turn off lights not used, use single large bulb instead of several small ones, keep fixtures clean, etc.

Research Topic

Review how iron is separated from its ore, and how it is made into steel. Then, find out which parts of the process require high energy. What energy sources are used in the iron and steel industry?

Products that do not get made will not use energy. This does not mean we should buy no products at all. What would that mean in terms of people's jobs and your comfort? It is wise, however, to plan what you purchase. Look for good-quality, long-lasting things that will save energy both when they are used and when they are made.

You can also have an effect by saving and returning materials that can be **recycled**—that is, used again. Energy is saved when things are made from recycled materials.

It takes 70% less energy to make steel from scrap steel than from iron ore. To make an aluminum can from recycled cans takes only 5% of the energy needed to make it from raw ore. There is a 40% savings in energy when paper is made from recycled paper. Recycling glass bottles uses only 25% of the energy needed to make new ones. Find out where the nearest recycling center is. You might volunteer to help out there.

Additional information:

If people did not buy enough products, an economic recession would result. Minimal purchases are required to maintain a comfortable life. Beyond this, much waste of products and energy exists, and could be prevented by more careful consumption.

Quick Review answers:

1. Steel, aluminum, and glass can be recycled.
2. Energy-conserving people look for products that use less energy to operate and/or maintain.
3. Large amounts of energy are saved, along with the raw materials.

Quick Review

1. Name three materials that should be recycled instead of thrown away.
2. What kind of products do energy-conserving people look for?
3. Why is recycling important?

Future energy usage and conservation

Main Idea

How could the need for centralized power plants be reduced in sunny areas?

In the future, we are likely to see a trend toward many different sources of energy in different regions. In New Mexico, homes are now being built with enough solar cells on their roofs to provide more electricity than the residents need. The surplus will be sold to the electric company. Suppose all the houses in a city produced electricity in this manner. The need for centralized power plants would be greatly reduced.

Along the windy North-Atlantic coast and on the Hawaiian Islands, people have put up their own wind generators. In the future there will be many more. Surplus power from wind generators can also be sold to power companies. In many other regions, electricity will be produced by whatever resource is present.

These new regional sources of energy will help us to conserve petroleum. Petroleum is still needed for transportation. Cars, buses, and planes still depend on petroleum products. In the short run, petroleum-based fuel may be replaced by

Labels in figure: Ocean · Wind generators · Lake with hydroelectric dam · Mountains · Desert · Solar ponds · Solar electric plant · Tidal plant · Geothermal plant · Houses with solar collectors · Highway

petroleum substitutes such as synfuels and coal products. Work is also being done on electric cars and steam cars. Experiments have shown that these substitute power sources may soon be practical, if only as substitutes.

However, none of these alternatives is really adequate. Eventually we will need a new form of transportation that runs on renewable fuel. Until such a fuel is perfected, it is wise for people to conserve the fuels we have. We will still be needing them for many years to come.

Quick Review

1. What alternative energy resource is being used in New Mexico?
2. Where are windmill generators being used? What can the people there do with surplus power from their generators?
3. How will the development of alternative regional energy sources be helpful to transportation needs overall?
4. What new sources of energy for transportation are being developed?
5. What kind of transportation is it most important to develop?

Figure 14-37. *What sources of energy will you be using in the future?*
Many different regional sources of energy will probably be in use. Climatic conditions in each region will determine what sources are used.

Quick Review answers:
1. Solar cells (in addition to other sources) are being used in New Mexico.
2. Windmill generators are being used along the North-Atlantic coast and in the Hawaiian Islands (plus other locations). People sell their surplus power to the power companies.
3. Alternative power sources help us conserve petroleum, which is needed especially for transportation.
4. Synfuels, electricity, and steam (plus additional sources) can be developed as sources for transportation.
5. A form that can be powered by renewable fuel.

Environmental Architect

Architects design buildings, homes, and subdivisions. Environmental architects specialize in buildings and community projects that provide a healthy, compatible environment for people. They often use various passive solar features in designing energy-efficient buildings. They consider the existing environment in an area and provide a means by which the people of the community can become a part of this environment rather than make drastic changes in it.

Environmental architects need to understand how to design buildings. They must also be knowledgeable about the effects of buildings and projects on the environment. In addition, they need to be able to communicate well with clients and with people whose lives are affected by building and community projects.

This career requires a college degree. To prepare for a college program in architecture and environmental design you should take high school courses in mathematics, science, art, and mechanical drawing.

For further information, write to: The American Institute of Architects, 1735 New York Avenue N.W., Washington, D.C. 20006.

Environmental architects focus on the energy usage and environments of buildings.

Insulation Worker

The insulation industry has been very busy trying to satisfy the increased need for insulation in homes and buildings. Workers in this industry are involved in the manufacture, sales, and installation of insulating materials.

Modern building codes require that new homes and buildings have much more insulation than in the past. Many existing buildings are being insulated for the first time or are having their insulation increased. It is usually more difficult and more expensive to install insulation in an existing building than in a new building. However, from the standpoint of saving energy, installing insulation is worthwhile.

Many insulation jobs can be learned while working at them. High school courses in industrial arts, general mathematics, and science provide a good background.

For further information, write to: National Insulation Contractors Association, 1025 Vermont Avenue N.W., Suite 410, Washington, D.C. 20005.

Insulation workers wear masks to avoid inhaling small fibers as they install insulation.

14.3 Section Review

Answers to Understanding the Concepts appear on page T173 in the front of this book. Blackline master test for this section: Section Testsheet 14-3 (TRB page.237)

Vocabulary

5 aerator
2 flow regulator
6 fluorescent
4 humidity
3 recycle
1 R value

Vocabulary Review

Match each term above with the numbered phrase that best describes it.

1. Measure of insulation used in the walls and ceilings of buildings
2. Reduces amount of water that can come out of a faucet
3. Use over again
4. Amount of water vapor in the air
5. Mixes water and air
6. Type of light source found in long or circular tubes

Review Questions

Multiple Choice: Choose the answer that best completes each of the following sentences.

7. The best way to conserve auto fuel is to ?.
   a. keep tires soft
   b. warm the engine before starting
   c. use a car less
   d. use snow tires

8. Air conditioners in a car are most efficient when the car is ?.
   a. traveling on a highway
   b. traveling on local streets
   c. stopped in traffic
   d. driven with the windows open

9. In most homes the biggest use of energy is for ?.
   a. heating water
   b. heating and cooling the space
   c. cooking and preserving food
   d. lighting the rooms

10. Energy can be saved in lighting a large room by using ?.
    a. many small bulbs together
    b. incandescent bulbs
    c. fluorescent lights
    d. dark paint on the walls

11. Energy can be saved in cooking by ?.
    a. cooking foods directly from the freezer
    b. baking several things in the oven at once
    c. cooking foods in boiling water at a high boil
    d. preheating the oven for 20 minutes before baking something

12. There are great energy savings when aluminum cans are made from ?.
    a. iron ore
    b. scrap steel
    c. raw aluminum ore
    d. recycled aluminum cans

Understanding the Concepts

13. If alternative energy sources are being developed, why is the conservation of fossil fuels still important?

14. Frozen foods require a greater use of energy from the time they are processed until they are eaten than fresh foods do. Explain why.

15. A 3-way bulb has three different brightnesses. How can lamps that use 3-way bulbs help a person save energy?

16. What alternative energy source might be best for the region where you live?

14 Chapter Review

Vocabulary

acid rain	exponential	passive solar
active solar	flow regulator	petroleum
aerator	fluorescent	recycle
anthracite	fossil fuel	renewable
biomass	geothermal energy	R value
bituminous	humidity	solar pond
breeder reactor	indirect solar	synfuel
convection loop	lignite	tidal energy
direct-gain	nonrenewable	wind farm
entropy	oil shale	

Review of Concepts

Entropy is a measure of the distribution of energy in a system.
- Energy flows from places of high concentration to places of low concentration.
- Entropy increases as energy becomes more evenly distributed.
- When entropy increases, the total amount of energy remains the same, but the energy becomes less available to use.

An **energy pathway** describes the set of changes energy goes through from its source, such as the sun, to its use by humans.
- Each time energy changes form, some of it becomes unusable.
- In a fossil fuel energy pathway, energy from the sun is stored for a very long time in the remains of organisms that slowly turn into coal, oil, and natural gas, the fossil fuels.

A **nonrenewable energy resource** is a source of usable energy that is used much faster than it can be replaced.
- Examples of nonrenewable energy resources are coal, oil, natural gas, oil shale, and tar sands.

- The demand for fossil fuels is increasing at a much higher rate than that at which the world population is growing.
- The supply of fossil fuels will run out sooner or later.

A **renewable energy resource** is a source of usable energy that can be replaced as fast as it is used.
- Examples of renewable energy resources are breeder reactors for nuclear fission, wood, synfuels made from biomass, hydrogen (used in fuel cells as well as in nuclear fusion), solar radiation, flowing and falling water, wind, geothermal energy, and tidal currents.
- Renewable energy resources will have to be used more and more to keep up with the world demand for energy.

Conservation of energy is the saving of energy by eliminating its unnecessary uses and by preventing its waste.
- Conservation of fossil fuels will make them available for a longer time.

- Large amounts of energy can be saved through wiser use of the automobile.
- In the home, energy can be saved by making the heating and cooling of space more efficient.
- Recycling of materials can reduce the energy used in manufacturing.

Critical Thinking

1. Energy cannot be created or destroyed. What is meant when it is said that some energy is lost when it changes form?
2. Why is it that coal is considered a nonrenewable resource while wood is considered a renewable resource?
3. The use of energy in agriculture is increasing at a faster rate than the use of energy for any other purpose. Suggest two or three reasons for this rapid increase.

4. Suppose methane produced from biomass is used to generate electricity. Trace the energy pathway from the sun to the electricity that is produced.
5. How does a roof overhang on the south side of a building with many large windows reduce the amount of energy used?
6. How is conservation of energy almost like finding a new source of energy?

Individual Research

7. Use pH paper to measure the acidity of a local pond or lake. Find out whether the acidity of this pond or lake has been changing and whether the types of plants and animals that live in it have been changing.
8. Focus sunlight on a white piece of paper with a small hand lens that is in a fixed position. Outline the lighted area on the paper. During the next half hour, observe the change in position of the lighted area on the paper. Find out how this movement relates to problems associated with the generation of electricity using solar energy.
9. The amount of light given off by a light bulb is measured in lumens. Look at the packages of several different light bulbs in a store. For the same wattage rating, what kinds of bulbs give off the most light? Why might a person choose to buy a bulb that uses the same amount of energy but gives off less light?

10. Find out approximately how much energy is used each day throughout the entire country. Compare this usage with that of five years ago or even ten years ago. What changes are taking place?

Bibliography

Asimov, Isaac. *How Did We Find Out About Solar Power?* New York: Walker, 1981.
Discusses uses of solar power from ancient times to the present.

Bilstein, Roger E. *Flight in America, 1900–1983: From the Wrights to the Astronauts.* Baltimore: Johns Hopkins University Press, 1984.
The coverage gives a thorough history of flight in America, including public perception of flight achievement.

Deudney, Daniel and Christopher Flavin. *Renewable Energy: The Power to Choose.* New York: Norton, 1983.
The authors survey renewable energy technology including solar, wind, and water power.

Douglas, John H., and the editors of Grolier. *The Future World of Energy.* New York: Watts, 1984.
Describes what energy is, gives a history of its uses, and explains the importance of finding future energy sources.

Goldin, Augusta. *Geothermal Energy; a Hot Prospect.* New York: Harcourt, 1981.
Describes how geothermal energy has been used, from hot springs resorts to power plants in Iceland and New Zealand.

Goldin, Augusta. *Oceans of Energy; Reservoirs of Power for the Future.* New York: Harcourt, 1980.
A nontechnical report on the variety of ways energy can be obtained from the ocean.

Moolman, Valerie, and the editors of Grolier. *The Future World of Transportation.* New York: Watts, 1984.
The history of transportation and future possibilities of transportation of people are discussed in detail.

Morrison, Philip and Phylis, and the office of Charles and Ray Eames. *Powers of Ten: A Book about the Relative Size of Things in the Universe and the Effect of Adding Another Zero.* New York: Scientific American, 1982.
This book is the translation of a film into print; illustrates through photographs the relative sizes and distances of the universe exponentially.

Watson, Jane Werner. *Alternate Energy Sources.* New York: Franklin Watts, 1979.
Discusses renewable sources such as solar radiation, wind, geothermal energy, biomass, and hydroelectric energy.

Watson, Jane Werner. *Conservation of Energy.* New York: Franklin, 1978.
A well-balanced and nontechnical outline of what is being done to reduce energy use, and what individuals can do.

Hydroelectric Power Plants and Wild Rivers

One of the few readily available sources of pollution-free energy lies in the waters of the rivers of our country. This water can be stored in lakes behind dams built across the river valleys. This water is then released over the dam and its energy is used to turn giant turbines which produce electricity. The river, however, is changed forever.

Is this an acceptable method of obtaining energy or is the cost to the environment too high?

PROS

- The energy is produced without adding any pollution to air or water.
- There are not medical hazards associated with the production of energy by hydroelectric plants.
- The lakes which form behind the dam provide water storage for nearby areas.
- The lakes also provide recreational areas for swimming, fishing, boating, and picnicking.

CONS

- The lakes cover many acres of land that were once home to many land plants and animals, and possibly people who lived near the river.
- The damming of the rivers destroys forever the rapids and areas used for recreational white-water rafting and fishing.
- There is the potential for flooding and the loss of lives and property if the dam breaks or overflows.
- The dam prevents the movement of sediments downstream, thereby cutting off the supply to farmlands downriver and ultimately to the beaches at the ocean's edge.
- The build-up of sediments behind the dam must be periodically removed, an expensive process.

Pollution-free energy is certainly desirable but is the cost of it in other environmental consequences too high? How would you design a system that would reduce the problems yet give us the needed energy?

River rafting on "white water" is growing in popularity as stronger, safer rafts become available.

The Gasoline-Powered Car of Tomorrow

Faster than a speeding bullet . . . well, perhaps not faster but the cars of the year 2000 may look like bullets and move down the highway with the same ease. Although attempts are being made to develop an electric or solar-powered car, it appears that the gasoline-powered car will continue as the car of the future. New cars are being designed to use this energy more efficiently, drawing upon a number of high-tech developments from other fields.

Using lasers, designers have been able to improve the aerodynamics of the automobile by obtaining very precise measurements of the car's body. Combining these measurements with computer modeling, designers have come up with new, sleek, and smooth body shapes that reduce the drag as the car moves down the road.

The engine can then be reduced in size and mass and made to be more efficient. Gone will be the large V-8 engines of today. The engines of the future will be four- or three-cylinder, made of aluminum and ceramic materials, with fuel injection and turbo-charging, again drawing on space program technology. The cars of the future will still need to stop at the gas pump to fuel up but probably not as often. The cars of the year 2000 may get as many as 120 km to the gallon.

Finally, computers will do everything but steer in the cars of the year 2000 and beyond. Computers will unlock and open the doors, turn the engine on, monitor the engine's efficiency, adjusting the throttle as needed, and adjust the car's suspension system to meet the road conditions. Computers will also adjust the car's air-conditioning and ventilation and warn the driver of impending problems such as low tire pressure, low oil pressure, or low fuel supply. Cars will be equipped with computer-linked satellite navigation systems to help us find our way. All this information will be projected holographically on the windshield, as in the newest airplanes.

The Probe V, a prototype for future aerodynamic cars, is flanked by an early Ford automobile, in which Edsel Ford is seated. To reduce mass, the new car's body will use lightweight but durable plastics, ceramics, and carbon-fiber materials, some of which have been developed for the space program.

Data Bank

Properties of Common Elements

Element	Symbol	Atomic number	Atomic mass	Melting point (°C)	Boiling point (°C)	Density (g/cm³)	Specific heat capacity
Aluminum	Al	13	26.982	660	2467	2.7	0.215
Arsenic	As	33	74.922	817	613	5.7	0.079
Bromine	Br	35	79.904	−7	59	3.1	0.113
Calcium	Ca	20	40.08	839	1484	1.6	0.156
Carbon	C	6	12.011	3550	4827	2.3	0.170
Chlorine	Cl	17	35.453	−101	−35	.0032	0.114
Chromium	Cr	24	51.996	1857	2672	7.2	0.107
Copper	Cu	29	63.546	1083	2567	8.96	0.092
Fluorine	F	9	18.998	−220	−189	.00179	0.197
Gold	Au	79	196.966	1064	3080	19.3	0.031
Helium	He	2	4.003	−272	−269	.00018	1.24
Hydrogen	H	1	1.008	−259	−253	.00009	3.41
Iodine	I	53	126.904	114	184	4.93	0.102
Iron	Fe	26	55.847	1535	2750	7.87	0.106
Lead	Pb	82	207.2	328	1740	11.35	0.038
Lithium	Li	3	6.941	181	1342	0.53	0.85
Magnesium	Mg	12	24.305	649	1090	1.74	0.243
Mercury	Hg	80	200.59	−39	357	13.55	0.033
Neon	Ne	10	20.179	−249	−246	0.0009	0.246
Nickel	Ni	28	58.71	1453	2732	8.9	0.106
Nitrogen	N	7	14.007	−210	−196	0.0013	0.249
Oxygen	O	8	15.999	−218	−183	0.00143	0.219
Phosphorus	P	15	30.974	44	280	1.82	0.181
Platinum	Pt	78	195.09	1772	3827	21.45	0.0317
Potassium	K	19	39.098	63	760	.862	0.180
Radium	Ra	88	226.025	700	1140	5.5	0.029
Silicon	Si	14	28.086	1410	2355	2.3	0.168
Sodium	Na	11	22.990	98	883	0.97	0.293
Sulfur	S	16	32.06	113	445	2.07	0.175
Tin	Sn	50	118.69	232	2270	7.31	0.051
Tungsten	W	74	183.85	3410	5660	19.3	0.032
Uranium	U	92	238.029	1132	3818	19	0.028
Zinc	Zn	30	65.38	420	907	7.133	0.093

Earthquake Scales

Mercalli Earthquake Scale	Richter Scale	Joules	TNT Equivalent
I. Detected only by seismographs.	> 3.5	1.6×10^7	3.45 kg
II. Detected indoors by a few people.	3.5	1.6×10^7	3.45 kg
III. Rapid earth vibrations similar to a passing truck.	4.2	7.5×10^8	162 kg
IV. Moderate rattling of dishes and windows.	4.5	4.0×10^9	846 kg
V. Buildings tremble. Hanging objects swing.	4.8	2.1×10^{10}	4.5 t
VI. Strong vibrations. Damage to poorly constructed buildings.	5.4	5.7×10^{11}	123 t
VII. Very strong vibrations. Damage to plaster and stucco buildings.	6.1	2.8×10^{13}	6 kt
VIII. Trees shake vigorously. Flow of springs and wells disrupted.	6.5	2.5×10^{14}	54.4 kt
IX. Ground cracks. Buildings are damaged, some collapse.	6.9	2.3×10^{15}	499 kt
X. Considerable landsliding. Dams and houses are damaged.	7.3	2.1×10^{16}	4.54 Mt
XI. Landslides. Broad cracks develop. Sea waves may develop.	8.1	1.7×10^{18}	376.4 Mt
XII. Total damage to most buildings. Disturbed water channels. Rock slides occur.	8.1	1.7×10^{18}	376.4 Mt

Consumption of Major Fuels in the U.S.
($\times$ 1 000 000 000 000 J)

Year	Coal	Natural gas	Petroleum	Water power	Nuclear	Total
1947	16 686	4764	11 987	1398	0	34 835
1960	10 661	13 065	21 006	1740	11	46 483
1970	13 287	22 978	31 129	2794	253	70 441
1975	13 303	21 035	34 515	3394	2004	74 251
1978	14 595	21 090	40 034	3312	3189	82 220
1980	16 172	21 502	36 086	3288	2888	79 916
1982	16 100	19 516	31 880	3772	3285	74 533
1983	16 725	18 491	31 715	4092	3411	74 434

U.S. Environmental Air Pollutant Concentrations

Pollutant	Unit	E.P.A. Air Quality Standard	1975	1979	1983
Carbon monoxide	ppm	9.0	11.9	9.6	7.9
Ozone	ppm	0.12	0.15	0.14	0.14
Sulfur dioxide	ppm	0.13	0.015	0.012	0.01
Nitrogen dioxide	ppm	0.053	0.03	0.03	0.026
Lead	$\mu g/m^3$	1.5	0.69	0.69	0.34
Total suspended particles	$\mu g/m^3$	75.0	60.8	61.1	48.7

ppm—parts per milligram

$\mu g/m^3$—micrograms per cubic meter

The U.S. Environmental Protection Agency sets a standard for the average amount of a pollutant allowable in the air.

World Record Airspeeds

Record holder (year of record)	Aircraft flown	Speed flown (km/h)
P. Tissandier (1909)	Wright biplane	55
J. Vedrines (1912)	Deperdussin monoplane	161
S. Lecointe (1922)	Nieuport-Delage 29	330
H. Stainforth (1931)	Supermarine S6B	655
J. Wilson (1945)	Gloster Meteor F4	976
A. Hanes (1955)	F-100C Super Sabre	1323
P. Twiss (1956)	Fairey Delta 2	1820
B. Robinson (1956)	McDonnell F4H-1F Phantom II	2585
W. Joeisz and G. T. Morgan (1976)	Lockheed SR-71A	3529

Pitch Frequency of Musical Instruments

Instrument	Pitch (in Hertz)
Piano	30–4186 Hz
Harp	30–3136
Bass tuba	55–311
French horn	60–698
Guitar	80–698
Clarinet	150–1568
Trumpet	170–932
Violin	200–2093
Piccolo	600–3729

Nobel Prizes Awarded for Physics and Chemistry

Year	Accomplishment	Winner (country)
1903	For discovering radioactivity and for studying uranium.	A. Henri Becquerel (France) Pierre and Marie Curie (France)
1911	For discovering and working with the elements radium and polonium.	Marie Curie (France)
1922	For studying the structure of atoms and their radiations.	Niels Bohr (Denmark)
1925	For research on the movement of electrons within the atom.	James Franck and Gustav Hertz (Germany)
1947	For discovering the layer of atmosphere that reflects radio short waves.	Sir Edward Appleton (England)
1960	For developing a method of age-dating materials using the carbon-14 isotope.	Willard F. Libby (U.S.A.)
1960	For inventing the bubble chamber to study sub-atomic particles.	Donald A. Glaser (U.S.A.)
1961	For studying the shape and size of the nucleus.	Robert Hofstadter (U.S.A.)
1974	For using small radiotelescopes to probe outer space with great accuracy.	Martin Ryle (England)
1977	For helping to develop solid-state electronic devices.	Philip W. Anderson and John Van Vleck (U.S.A.) Sir Nevill F. Scott (U.K.)

Speed of Sound

Material (temperature)	Speed of sound (m/s)
air (0°C)	331
helium (0°C)	965
ethyl alcohol (25°C)	1207
water (25°C)	1498
copper	3800
glass, pyrex	5170

Boiling Temperatures of Water

Location	Altitude (meters)	Boiling Temperature (°C)
Vancouver, B.C.	Sea level	100
Dead Sea	−389	101
Denver, Colorado	1584	95
Mt. St. Helens	2805	91
Mt. Everest	8700	71

Solar Radiation Reflected from the Earth (Albedo)	
Surface	Percent of radiation reflected
Concrete	17–27
Crops, green	5–25
Forest, green	5–10
Ploughed field, moist	14–17
Road, blacktop	5–10
Sand, white	30–60
Snow, fresh fallen	80–90
Snow, old	45–70
Soil, dark	5–15
Soil, light	25–30

Surface Gravity of Bodies in Solar System	
Body	Surface Gravity
Sun	27.9
Jupiter	2.91
Saturn	1.32
Neptune	1.32
Uranus	1.18
Earth	1.00
Venus	0.90
Mars	0.38
Pluto	0.23
Moon	0.16

The surface gravity of each body is based on the surface gravity of the earth, which is expressed as 1.00.

Electrical Conductivity of Metals at 20°C	
Material	% IACS*
aluminum	65
arsenic	5
copper	100
gold	77
iron	18
lead	8
magnesium	39
nickel	25
platinum	16
silver	108
zinc	29

*International Annealed Copper Standard—a value of 100% is given to copper when it is at a specific conductive state.

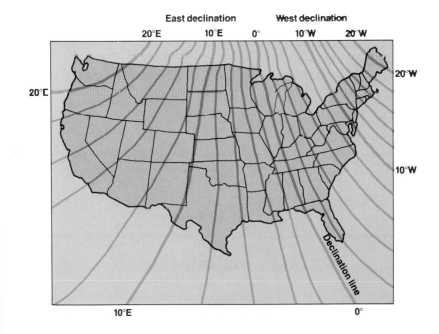

Math Review

Working with Fractions

A **fraction** is one number or quantity divided by another number or quantity. The simple fraction $\frac{1}{2}$ is the number one divided by the number 2. In science, numbers are expressed as decimals, not as fractions. However, fractions are used to express one quantity divided by another quantity. For example, speed is the distance covered divided by the time taken to cover that distance.

$$\text{speed} = \frac{\text{distance}}{\text{time}}$$

In science, the word *per* is often used in place of *divided by*. Speed is said to be the distance per time. Whenever you see the word *per*, think of a fraction.

The top part of a fraction is called the **numerator.** The bottom part of a fraction is called the **denominator.** In the fraction above, distance is the numerator and time is the denominator.

When a fraction is *multiplied* by another number or quantity, the *numerator* is multiplied by the second quantity. In the following examples, different letters stand for different quantities. Note that when two letters are next to each other, the two quantities are being multiplied. That is, ac means the product of a times c.

Examples

1. $\dfrac{4}{5} \times 10 = \dfrac{4 \times 10}{5}$

2. $\dfrac{a}{b} \times c = \dfrac{a \times c}{b} = \dfrac{ac}{b}$

3. $\dfrac{\text{charge}}{\text{time}} \times \text{voltage} = \dfrac{\text{charge} \times \text{voltage}}{\text{time}}$

When a fraction is *divided* by another number or quantity, the *denominator* is multiplied by the second quantity.

Examples

1. $\dfrac{\frac{4}{5}}{2} = \dfrac{4}{5 \times 2}$

2. $\dfrac{\frac{a}{b}}{c} = \dfrac{a}{b \times c}$

3. $\dfrac{\frac{\text{work}}{\text{time}}}{\text{voltage}} = \dfrac{\text{work}}{\text{time} \times \text{voltage}}$

As you can see, the procedure is the same whether you are working with numbers, letters, or quantities from physical science.

Sometimes, as a result of multiplication or division, the same quantity appears in the numerator and the denominator. In this case, that quantity can be canceled.

Examples

1. $\dfrac{a \times \cancel{b}}{\cancel{b}} = a$

2. $\dfrac{\cancel{a}}{\cancel{a} \times b} = \dfrac{1}{b}$

3. $\dfrac{\text{distance} \times \cancel{\text{time}}}{\cancel{\text{time}}} = \text{distance}$

Solving Equations

Many relationships in science can be expressed by equations. An **equation** is a mathematical sentence that uses an equals sign to state that two expressions are equal, or have the same value.

Sometimes you have an equation that relates several quantities, and you want to find the value of a particular quantity. To do this, you must have an equation in which that quantity is by itself on the left side of the equals sign. The other quantities will be on the right side of the equals sign. For example, from the equation

$$\text{distance} = \text{speed} \times \text{time}$$

you can find the distance if you know the speed and the time. However, from the equation

$$\text{speed} = \frac{\text{distance}}{\text{time}}$$

you could not find the distance without first changing the form of the equation.

When you change the form of an equation in order to put one quantity by itself on the left side of the equation, you are **solving** the equation for that quantity. You can solve an equation by doing one of the following.

1. *You may add the same quantity to both sides of an equation.*

$$a = b$$
$$a + c = b + c$$

2. *You may subtract the same quantity from both sides of an equation.*

$$a = b$$
$$a - c = b - c$$

3. *You may multiply both sides of the equation by the same quantity.*

$$a = b$$
$$ac = bc$$

4. *You may divide both sides of the equation by the same quantity, as long as that quantity does not equal zero.*

$$a = b$$

$$\frac{a}{c} = \frac{b}{c}$$

Sample Problem

Solve the following equation for distance.

$$\text{speed} = \frac{\text{distance}}{\text{time}}$$

Solution

1. Multiply both sides of the equation by time. (You do this because time is in the denominator, so you will be able to cancel the denominator and have distance alone.)

$$\text{speed} \times \text{time} = \frac{\text{distance}}{\text{time}} \times \text{time}$$

$$= \frac{\text{distance} \times \cancel{\text{time}}}{\cancel{\text{time}}}$$

$$= \text{distance}$$

2. Since the left and right sides of the equation are equal, they may be replaced by each other.

$$\text{distance} = \text{speed} \times \text{time}$$

The equation has been solved for distance.

Sample Problem

Solve the following equation for mass.

$$\text{force} = \text{mass} \times \text{acceleration}$$

Solution

1. Divide both sides of the equation by acceleration. (You do this because mass is multiplied by acceleration, and you will be able to cancel it and have mass by itself.)

$$\frac{\text{force}}{\text{acceleration}} = \frac{\text{mass} \times \cancel{\text{acceleration}}}{\cancel{\text{acceleration}}}$$

$$= \text{mass}$$

2. Replace the left and right sides by each other.

$$\text{mass} = \frac{\text{force}}{\text{acceleration}}$$

The equation has been solved for mass.

Ratios and Proportion

A **ratio** is a special kind of fraction. In a ratio, both the numerator and denominator are either pure numbers or similar physical quantities (such as length). Thus, the ratio itself is a pure number; it has no units of measurement.

For example, a transformer consists of two coils of wire that are wound on the same piece of iron. Each coil has a different number of turns, or loops of wire. You can talk about the ratio of the number of turns in the first coil to the number of turns in the second coil.

$$\text{ratio of turns} = \frac{\text{turns in first coil}}{\text{turns in second coil}}$$

Note that "the ratio of A to B" means A divided by B. Whenever you see the words *ratio of . . . to,* think of the first quantity divided by the second.

An equation that states that two ratios are equal to each other is a **proportion.** For example, in a transformer the ratio of the voltage drops across the two coils equals the ratio of the turns in the coils.

$$\frac{\text{voltage across 1st coil}}{\text{voltage across 2nd coil}} = \frac{\text{turns in 1st coil}}{\text{turns in 2nd coil}}$$

An equation in this form can be solved for one of the quantities by using the same rules stated earlier. For example, to solve for the number of turns in the first coil, you would multiply both sides by the number of turns in the second coil.

Percentage

A **percentage** is a pure number followed by the symbol %. The symbol %, which is read as **percent,** means "per hundred." For example, 99% means "99 per hundred" or $^{99}/_{100}$. The percentage 100% means "100 per hundred" or $^{100}/_{100}$.

Of course, $^{100}/_{100}$ equals one. You can multiply anything by one without changing its value. So you can multiply anything by 100% without changing its value. When you want to change any pure number (including a ratio, which is a pure number) to a percentage, simply multiply by 100%.

Sample Problem
The efficiency of a certain machine is 0.79. Express the efficiency as a percentage.

Solution
Multiply the value of the efficiency by 100%.

$$0.79 \times 100\% = 79\%$$

The efficiency is 79%.

Graphing

Graphing is a way of looking for possible relationships between two sets of measurements, or data. A graph is a "picture" of the data. You have probably seen different kinds of graphs: circle graphs, bar graphs, picture graphs, and line graphs. In physical science, the line graph is most widely used.

A line graph has two perpendicular straight lines, or **axes,** one for each set of measurements. For example, the vertical (up-and-down) axis might be for distance measurements and the horizontal axis for time measurements. The values of each quantity are marked along each axis, starting with zero at the point where the two axes cross. This point is called the **origin.**

When you label the axes of a graph you are making, consider the following points.

1. If one of the sets of measurements is of the time at which the other measurements were taken, put the time on the *horizontal* axis.

2. Otherwise, determine which set of measurements you had direct control over, and put that quantity on the horizontal axis. For example, if you were changing the length of a pendulum in order to see how the swing rate was affected, put length on the horizontal axis.

3. Your graph paper is divided into small squares. You must decide how much each space along the axes should represent. If your graph paper has heavy and light lines, how many spaces are between each set of heavy lines? (The easiest kind to work with has 5 spaces between heavy lines.)

   Study your measurements, and look at the largest values. You want them to fit on the graph, but you don't want the graph to be too cramped. Choose a scale for each axis where each space represents either one unit of the quantity or a multiple of 2, 5, or 10 units. For example, suppose your largest measurement of time was 30 minutes. On your time axis, each space might represent 2 minutes. You would need 15 spaces to represent the largest value.

Now you are ready to plot your data. Data are plotted by putting a point at the intersection of corresponding values of each pair of measurements. For example, if a person had run 0.7 km in 3 min, the point would be above the value of 3 min on the time axis and to the right of the value of 0.7 km on the distance axis.

Once all the data have been plotted, the points are connected by a smooth curve. This is not the same as "connecting-the-dots," which is an incorrect approach in science. A smooth curve comes as close as possible to the points without having any jagged peaks or valleys. It does not have to go right through every point.

The "smooth curve" can be a straight line, if the data points seem to fit near a straight line. Much of—but not all—the data you will plot in this course will fit near a straight line.

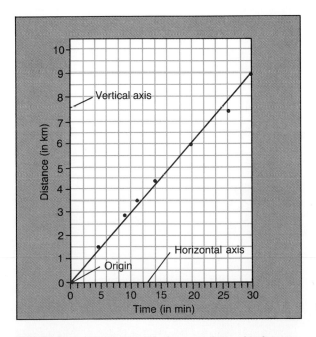

Figure A-1. *This line graph shows a relationship between some distance measurements and some time measurements for a moving object.*

The line drawn through or near the data points can be used to predict data that are not the results of actual measurements. When you predict data by reading the measurements for a point on your line that is *between* two actual data points, you are said to be **interpolating** (in-TER'-puh-lay-ting) data. When you predict data by reading the measurements for a point that is *beyond* any actual data points, you are said to be **extrapolating** (ek-STRAP'-uh-lay-ting) data.

Scientific Notation

Very large numbers are written in a convenient shorthand. This shorthand is based on the fact that each place after the first digit in a number such as 10 000 stands for multiplication by 10. That is,

$$
\begin{aligned}
10 &= 1 \times 10 \\
100 &= 1 \times 10 \times 10 \\
1\,000 &= 1 \times 10 \times 10 \times 10 \\
10\,000 &= 1 \times 10 \times 10 \times 10 \times 10
\end{aligned}
$$

The number 10 000 (which has four zeroes) stands for 1×10 multiplied by itself 4 times. The shorthand way of writing 10 000 is

$$10\,000 = 1 \times 10^4$$

The small number 4 written above and to the right of the 10 is called an **exponent.** The exponent tells how many places are after the first digit.

Similarly, the number 21 435 can be written

$$21\,425 = 2.1425 \times 10^4$$

Just as 10 000 has four places after the 1, the number 21 425 has four places after the first digit. In general, an exponent greater than zero tells how many places there are after the first digit.

Very small numbers are written in a similar shorthand. The number 0.0003 has four places between the decimal point and the first nonzero digit to the *right*. Each place stands for division by 10. That is,

$$0.3 = \frac{3}{10}$$

$$0.03 = \frac{3}{100} = \frac{3}{10 \times 10}$$

$$0.003 = \frac{3}{1000} = \frac{3}{10 \times 10 \times 10}$$

$$0.0003 = \frac{3}{10000} = \frac{3}{10 \times 10 \times 10 \times 10}$$

The number 0.0003 can be written in shorthand as

$$0.0003 = 3 \times 10^{-4}$$

The exponent -4 stands for *division* four times by 10. It also indicates the number of places between the decimal point of the shorthand version and the decimal point of the original form of the number.

In scientific notation, a number is written as a number greater than or equal to 1 but less than 10, followed by "$\times$ 10" with a positive or negative exponent. When the exponent is positive, the original number is greater than 1. When it is negative, the original number is less than 1.

Examples

Radius of the earth = 6 370 000 m
$$= 6.37 \times 10^6 \text{ m}$$

Speed of light = 299 790 000 m/s
$$= 2.9979 \times 10^8 \text{ m/s}$$

Electron
charge = 0.000 000 000 000 000 000 160 2 C
$$= 1.602 \times 10^{-19} \text{ C}$$

Glossary

Pronunciation Guide

A simple, phonetic spelling is given for the words in this book that may be unfamiliar or hard to pronounce.

CAPITAL LETTERS followed by an accent mark (′) indicate the syllable that receives the heaviest stress. An accent mark following a lowercase syllable indicates a syllable that receives secondary stress.

Example: *Acceleration* is phonetically spelled ak-sel′-er-RAY′-shun.

The phonetic spellings are simple enough so that most can be interpreted without referring to the following key, which gives the sound of letters that are commonly used for more than one sound.

Pronunciation Key

a	cat	eer	deer	ng	sing	s	so
ah	father	er	her	o	frog	sh	shine
ar	car	ew	new	ō	hole	th	thick
ay	say	g	grass	oo	moon	u, uh	sun
ayr	air	i, ih	him	or	for	z	zebra
e, eh	hen	ī	kite	ow	now	zh	pleasure
ee	meet	j	jam	oy	boy		

absolute zero The temperature at which the particles of a substance would have no kinetic energy; 0 K or −273°C. (p. 239)

acceleration (ak-sel′-er-RAY′-shun) The changing of the speed and/or direction of an object. (p. 149)

acid (AS′-id) A substance that makes litmus dye turn from blue to red and makes bromthymol blue turn from blue to yellow. (p. 124)

acid indicator A substance that is changed in color by an acid. (p. 124)

acid rain Rain which is much more acidic than normal rain and which has made many lakes so acidic that the fish and other animal life in them have died. (p. 620)

activation energy The energy required to start a chemical reaction. (p. 285)

active solar energy system A system that collects and stores energy from the sun and uses a fan or a pump to circulate heated air or water. (p. 632)

activity The tendency of a metal to give up electrons. (p. 543)

activity series A list of metals ranked in order of the ease with which they give up electrons. (p. 544)

ADP One of the products of the reaction between water and ATP inside a living cell. An ADP molecule has two phosphate groups. (p. 330)

aerator (AYR′-ray-ter) A device that mixes water with air and thus reduces the amount of water coming out of a faucet. (p. 647)

alkali metal (AL′-kuh-lī MET′-ul) Any of the elements in the left-hand column of the periodic table. Examples include lithium and sodium. (p. 103)

alkaline cell (AL′-kuh-lin SEL) A type of dry cell in which the electrolyte is potassium hydroxide. (p. 554)

alkaline earth metals (AL′-kuh-lin ERTH MEH′-tulz) The family of elements immediately to the right of the alkali metals; the family includes magnesium and calcium. (p. 103)

alkane series (AL'-kayn SEER'-eez) The series of hydrocarbons having only single bonds between carbons. (p. 301)

alkene series (AL'-keen SEER'-eez) The series of hydrocarbons having at least one double bond between carbons. (p. 304)

alkyne series (AL'-kīn SEER'-eez) The series of hydrocarbons having at least one triple bond between carbons. (p. 304)

alloy (AL'-oy) A mixture of two or more metals. (p. 94)

alpha particle (AL'-fuh PAR'-tih-kul) A particle having the mass and charge of a helium nucleus. (p. 574)

alpha radiation (AL'-fuh ray'-dee-AY'-shun) Positively charged helium nuclei (alpha particles) given off by the nuclei of certain radioactive atoms. (p. 569)

alternating current An electric current in which electrons move back and forth in a regular repeating cycle. (p. 466)

ammeter (AM'-mee-ter) A device that measures electric current. (p. 468)

ampere (AM'-pihr) The SI unit of electric current. (p. 467)

amplify (AMP'-lif-fī) To make sounds louder. (p. 375)

amplitude (AMP'-lih-tewd) The distance a particle moves from its original position as a compressional wave passes through a substance. (p. 387) Also, the height of a wave's crest above the normal surface. (p. 360)

angle of incidence (AYNG'-ul uv IN'-sih-dens) The angle between an incident light ray and the normal to the reflecting surface. (p. 399)

angle of reflection The angle between a reflected light ray and the normal to the reflecting surface. (p. 399)

anode (AN'-ōd) The positive electrode in a cell. (p. 560)

anthracite (AN'-thruh-sīt) A kind of coal that has a high energy content and little sulfur. (p. 612)

area The amount of space on a surface. (p. 18)

atom (AT'-um) A small particle of matter, derived from the Greek word for *indivisible*. At one time it was believed that an atom was the smallest particle of matter possible and could not be broken up. (p. 85)

atomic mass The mass of one atom of an element. (p. 97)

atomic number The number of protons in one atom of a particular element. In the modern periodic table, elements are arranged in order of atomic number. (p. 101)

ATP A compound which reacts with water inside the cells of living things and releases energy. An ATP molecule has three phosphate groups. (p. 330)

attract To pull toward; said of unlike charges or two unlike poles. (p. 453)

average speed The overall speed by which something or someone moves for a given period of time. Dividing total distance traveled by total time gives average speed. (p. 144)

balanced chemical equation A chemical equation that shows the same number of atoms of each element on both sides of the equation. (p. 114)

balanced forces Forces that oppose each other with equal strength. (p. 155)

base A substance that can neutralize an acid. (p. 124)

battery A series of dry cells. (p. 464)

beta particle (BAY'-tuh PAR'-tih-kul) A particle having the mass and charge of an electron. (p. 577)

beta radiation (BAY'-tuh ray'-dee-AY'-shun) Negatively charged electrons (beta particles) given off by the nuclei of certain radioactive atoms. (p. 569)

binding energy The energy holding the nucleus together. (p. 586)

biochemistry The study of the chemistry of all living things. (p. 328)

biomass (BĪ'-ō-mas) The remains, waste, or by-products of living things which can be changed chemically to produce fuel. (p. 628)

bituminous coal (bī-TEW'-mih-nus KŌL) A fuel containing much sulfur and having a lower energy content than anthracite coal. (p. 612)

block and tackle A combination of pulleys used to provide a large mechanical advantage. (p. 211)

boiling The process in which bubbles of gas form within a liquid that has been heated to a high enough temperature. (p. 68)

boiling point The temperature at which boiling begins. (p. 68)

bond dissociation energy The amount of energy required to break a bond between atoms. (p. 261)

breeder reactor A type of nuclear reactor that uses the fission of plutonium to produce more fuel. (p. 622)

bubble chamber A device using dense liquid to detect the presence of high energy particles; a slight reduction in pressure causes bubbles to appear along the path of the moving particle. (p. 573)

carbohydrate (kar-bō-HĪ-drayt) Any of a group of organic compounds, including sugars, starches, and cellulose, that contain carbon, hydrogen and oxygen only, with the ratio of hydrogen to oxygen usually 2 : 1; many of the first carbohydrates discovered had the general formula $C_n(H_2O)_n$ and hence the name carbohydrate, or hydrate of carbon. (p. 309)

catalyst (KAT′-uh-list)   A substance that can speed up a chemical reaction without being changed itself. (p. 285)

cathode (KATH′-ōd)   The negative electrode in a cell. (p. 559)

cell respiration (SEL res′-per-RAY′-shun)   A series of reactions within a living cell in which glucose combines with oxygen to form carbon dioxide and water. The energy released is used to form ATP from ADP and phosphate. (p. 332)

Celsius   The everyday temperature scale used with SI units. (p. 23)

centimeter   One hundredth of a meter. (p. 18)

centripetal force (sen-TRIH′-pet-ul FORS)   The inward force on an object moving in a curve; "center-seeking" force. (p. 167)

chain reaction   A series of repeated nuclear changes that occur very rapidly. (p. 589)

charged   A word used to describe an object with more of one kind of electric charge than another. (p. 117)

chemical bond   A sort of invisible tie between two atoms that have transferred or shared electrons. (p. 121)

chemical change   A change that produces a new substance. (p. 71)

chemical equation   A summary of a chemical change. Written in terms of formulas, plus signs, and an arrow. In the change, the substances to the left of the arrow react and produce the substances to the right. (p. 114)

chemical formula   A shorthand method used to show the number and type of atoms present in the smallest representative unit of a substance. (p. 61)

chlorophyll (KLOR′-uh-fil)   A green material that enables plants and other green living things to carry on photosynthesis by absorbing energy from the sunlight. (p. 336)

circuit (SER′-kit)   A path of conductors through which electric charges move. (p. 465)

circuit breaker   An electrical safety device that opens a circuit when an electric current becomes too large for safety. (p. 486)

circumference (ser-KUM′-fer-ens)   The distance around a circle. (p. 26)

closed circuit   An unbroken circuit. (p. 465)

coherent (kō-HEER′-ent)   Having wave crests and troughs moving in the same direction at the same time; laser light is coherent, for example. (p. 417)

colorblind   Unable to distinguish one color from another. (p. 426)

color spectrum (KUH′-ler SPEK′-trum)   A band of colors—starting with red and including orange, yellow, green, blue, and violet—into which white light can be split. (p. 423)

combustible (kum-BUS′-tih-bul)   Able to burn. (p. 74)

combustion (kum-BUS′-tyun)   Burning; a chemical change in which a substance combines with oxygen. (p. 74)

complete burning   A burning of a hydrocarbon fuel in which the only products are carbon dioxide and water vapor. (p. 318)

compound (KOM′-pownd)   A combination of two or more elements. A compound has very different properties from those of the elements that make it up and is normally difficult to break down into elements. (p. 61)

compound machine   Any machine made up of two or more simple machines. (p. 209)

compressibility   A property of gases that allows large amounts of them to be forced into a small space. (p. 83)

compression   A squeezing together. (p. 350)

compressional wave   A series of compressions and rarefactions that carries energy through a substance. The wave makes particles of the substance move back and forth as it passes through. (p. 354)

concave lens   A lens thinner in the middle than at the edge. (p. 405)

concentration (kon-sen-TRAY′-shun)   The ratio of the amount of a substance to the volume the substance occupies. (p. 282)

condensation (kon′-den-SAY′-shun)   The change in phase from gas to liquid; the reverse of evaporation or boiling. (p. 68)

conduction (kun-DUK′-shun)   The type of heat transfer in which heat moves through a material without the material itself moving. (p. 226)

conductor   A material through which heat can move in conduction. (p. 226) Also, a material through which electrons can move easily. (p. 455)

cone   One of the cells in the eye's retina that are sensitive to color. (p. 425)

conservation of momentum   Describes the law stating that the total momentum possessed by objects before a collision is equal to the total momentum of the objects after the collision. (p. 166)

constant speed   Unchanging speed. An object traveling equal distances in equal times is traveling at constant speed. (p. 145)

contract   To shorten, as muscle fibers shorten. (p. 327)

control   A standard that has none of its variables manipulated during an experiment; controls are used to guarantee that any effects observed in the experiment are in fact due to the manipulated variable. (p. 11)

controlled experiment   An experiment in which all the factors that influence the outcome are kept the same, except for the one factor whose effect is being investigated. (p. 10)

control rod   Rod made of materials such as cadmium or boron and used to slow down a chain reaction. (p. 591)

convection (kun-VEK′-shun)   The type of heat transfer in which heat moves through a material by actual movement of the material. (p. 226)

convection current   Movement within a liquid or gas due to temperature differences. (p. 226)

convection-loop building   A building in which the living space is enclosed by a second building with a large glass wall facing south. The warm air behind the glass is heated by solar energy, and its circulation in the space between the inner and outer buildings is controlled by vents. (p. 630)

conversion factors   A ratio between two equivalent measurements that can be used to convert between the two; 1 kg/1000 g is a conversion factor for kilograms and grams for instance. (p. 40)

convex lens   A lens thicker in the middle than at the edge. (p. 404)

coolant   A material that is evaporated and condensed to drive the transfer of heat; an example of a coolant is freon which is used in refrigerators. (p. 229)

cooling system   A system designed to remove heat from a space. (p. 227)

corrosion (kuh-RŌ′-zhun)   The combining of a metal with water, air, or other materials in the atmosphere. (p. 541)

coulomb (KOO′-lōm)   The SI unit of electric charge. (p. 464)

covalent bond (kō-VAYL′-unt BOND)   A bond between atoms due to shared electrons. Covalent bonds usually form between atoms of nonmetals. (p. 122)

crest   One of the places in a transverse wave where the surface is highest. (p. 359)

critical angle   Above this angle, light experiences total internal reflection. (p. 414)

critical mass   The amount of atomic fuel needed to sustain a chain reaction. (p. 591)

cubic centimeter   The volume of a cube that is one centimeter on each side. (p. 19)

cubic meter   The volume of a cube that is one meter on each side; the basic SI unit of volume. (p. 19)

cyclic hydrocarbon (SĪ-klik HĪ′-drō-kar-bun)   Hydrocarbon in which the carbons are joined into a ring structure. (p. 306)

data   The collected and recorded observations made during an experiment. (p. 11)

decibel (DES′-uh-bel)   A unit by which noise level is measured. (p. 374)

decomposition reaction   Any reaction in which a compound is broken down into two or more elements or compounds. (p. 264)

density   The mass of a sample divided by the volume of the sample; density = mass/volume. (p. 21)

diameter (dī-AM′-uh-ter)   The straight-line distance through the center of a circle. (p. 26)

diatomic (dī-uh-TOM′-ik)   A word used to describe a molecule with two atoms. (p. 91)

diffraction (dih-FRAK′-shun)   Any spreading out of a wave as a result of its passing through an opening in a barrier. (p. 364)

diffusion (dih-FYOO′-zhun)   The natural movement within gases and liquids that spreads out odors and colors. (p. 233)

dimensional analysis   A problem-solving approach that makes use of the units of measurement stated in the problem. (p. 38)

direct current   An electric current in which the electrons move in only one direction. (p. 465)

direct-gain solar building   A building that uses materials such as concrete, brick, or stone to store solar energy. (p. 630)

direct observation   An observation made using only the senses. (p. 5)

disperse (dis-PERS′)   To split; as a prism splits or "disperses" white light into the color spectrum. (p. 423)

dissolve (duh-ZOLV′)   To form a solution. (p. 59)

Doppler effect   The sudden drop in pitch when the source of a sound and the listener pass each other. (p. 389)

Doppler shift   The apparent change, due to motion of the source or observer, of a wave's frequency. (p. 389)

double replacement reaction A reaction in which an element in one compound is exchanged with an element in another compound. (p. 265)

dry cell An electrochemical cell in which the electrolyte is a paste. (p. 553)

efficiency The work output of a machine divided by the work input, usually described as a percentage. (p. 204)

effort arm The part of the lever between the fulcrum and the point at which the effort force is applied. (p. 206)

effort force The force applied in moving a lever. (p. 206)

electric charge What makes some materials stick together or crackle when pulled apart. Electric charges can be traced to the particles that make up matter: the proton with its positive charge and the electron with its negative charge. (p. 117)

electric current A movement of electric charges, usually due to moving electrons. (p. 463)

electric generator (ih-LEK′-trik JEN′-er-rayt-er) A device that produces electric current by turning a coil through a magnetic field. (p. 507)

electric motor A device that converts electric energy to energy of motion. (p. 521)

electrochemical cell (ih-lek-trō-KEM′-ih-kul SEL) A device that uses a chemical change to produce electric energy. (p. 553)

electrode (ih-LEK′-trōd) A conductor that carries electrons in or out of a cell. (p. 553)

electrolysis (ih-lek-TROL′-uh-sis) The breakdown of a compound by use of an electric current. (p. 558)

electrolyte (ih-LEK′-truh-līt) The liquid or paste in a cell that is made of ions and that conducts electric charges between the two electrodes in the cell. (p. 553)

electromagnet (ih-lek′-trō-MAG′-net) An iron bar inside a wire coil that carries a current and thus sets up a magnetic field. (p. 505)

electromagnetic spectrum The whole range of electromagnetic radiation from highest to lowest frequency. (p. 418)

electromagnetism (ih-lek′-trō-MAG′-neh-tizm) The branch of physics dealing with electric and magnetic effects. (p. 502)

electron (uh-LEK′-tron) A basic particle of an atom. An electron has a negative charge and is in the space outside the nucleus. (p. 99)

electron cloud model A model of atomic structure in which the electrons are not restricted to movement in fixed orbits, but move randomly throughout a definite volume around the nucleus. (p. 107)

electroplating (ih-LEK′-trō-play′-ting) A process in which electric energy is used to deposit a metal on a conducting material. For example, a thin layer of chromium is plated on a steel surface. (p. 560)

electroscope (ih-LEK′-truh-skōp) A device used for detecting electric charge. (p. 572)

element (EL′-uh-ment) A substance that cannot be broken down into other substances. Hydrogen, oxygen, sodium, and chlorine are elements. (p. 61)

endothermic reaction (en′-dō-THER′-mik ree-AK′-shun) Any chemical change that absorbs energy. (p. 259)

energy The ability of an object to cause change. (p. 179)

energy conversion (EN′-er-jee kun-VER′-zhun) The change of energy from one form to another; for example, the change from potential energy to kinetic energy. (p. 184)

energy level The term used to describe the regions around the nucleus in which electrons are found in the electron cloud model of atomic structure; electrons in the lowest energy level are close to the nucleus most of the time, whereas electrons in the higher energy levels are farther away from the nucleus most of the time. (p. 109)

entropy (EN′-truh-pee) A measure of the distribution of energy within a system. Entropy increases when energy becomes more evenly distributed. (p. 608)

escape speed The speed at which an object can escape from the earth's gravity. (p. 174)

estimate (ES′-tuh-mayt) To make a rough measurement by guesswork. (p. 29)

evaporation (ih-vap′-uh-RAY′-shun) The change in phase from liquid to gas at a temperature below the boiling temperature. (p. 68)

exothermic reaction (eks′-ō-THER′-mik ree-AK′-shun) Any chemical change that releases energy. (p. 259)

exponential (eks-pō-NEN′-shul) A term that describes a change that occurs at a rapidly increasing rate. The growth of the human population and usage of fossil fuels have been exponential. (p. 617)

external combustion engine An engine that does work as a result of the burning of fuel outside the engine itself. (p. 321)

family A group of elements with similar properties. (p. 98)

fats   A class of organic compounds made from glycerol and fatty acids; fats have a higher energy content than carbohydrates and serve as a reserve source of fuel in the cell. (p. 311)

fermentation (fer′-men-TAY′-shun)   The breakdown of glucose within a living cell without using oxygen. The energy released is used to form ATP from ADP and phosphate. (p. 335)

filter   A material that can absorb some wavelengths of light and transmit others. (p. 423)

flow regulator   A device which can be installed in a shower head and which limits the amount of water coming out. (p. 647)

fluorescent light (flor-ES′-unt LĪT)   Long or circular light tube that is more energy-efficient than incandescent bulbs. (p. 649)

focal length (FŌ′-kul LAYNGTH)   The distance between the center of a lens and the point where parallel rays of light actually or appear to come together. (p. 404)

force   A push or pull. (p. 154)

fossil fuel   The remains of organisms which lived hundreds of millions of years ago. These remains—such as coal, oil, and natural gas—release energy when they are burned. (p. 610)

fractional distillation (FRAK′-shun-ul dih-stih-LAY′-shun)   The process by which crude oil is separated into useful "fractions" on the basis of different boiling temperatures for the different hydrocarbon components of the crude oil mixture. (p. 315)

freezing   The change in phase from liquid to solid. (p. 68)

frequency (FREE′-kwen-see)   The number of compressions arriving per second as a compressional wave travels. (p. 354) Also, the number of crests that pass a point per second as a transverse wave travels. (p. 361)

friction (FRIK′-shun)   A force that acts to slow down a moving object that is passing through or against a material. Also, a force that prevents an object from moving when it is pushed gently. (p. 157)

fuel   A substance burned to supply energy. (p. 313)

fuel cell   An electrochemical cell for which some of the materials that react are supplied from outside the cell. (p. 555)

fulcrum (FUL′-krum)   The point on a lever that does not turn. (p. 206)

functional group   An atom or group of atoms that replaces one or more hydrogens in a hydrocarbon; the function of the new molecule is often determined by the nature of the added atom or group. (p. 307)

fuse   A safety device designed to prevent short circuits. A fuse melts and breaks a circuit when the current is too large. (p. 485)

galvanometer (gal-vuh-NOM′-uh-ter)   An instrument that can detect small electric currents. (p. 505)

gamma radiation   A kind of electromagnetic radiation, at the high-frequency end of the electromagnetic spectrum. (p. 570)

gas   A kind of matter that has no definite shape or volume and tends to fill whatever space is available to it. (p. 56)

Geiger tube (GĪ′-ger TEWB)   A device for detecting nuclear radiation. (p. 573)

geothermal energy (jee-ō-THER′-mul EN′-er-jee)   Great amounts of heat that are trapped underground and can be tapped to obtain energy. (p. 638)

glucose (GLOO′-kōs)   What sugars and starches are broken down to by the body's digestive system; also called a simple sugar. (p. 330)

gram   A thousandth of a kilogram. (p. 20)

gravitational potential energy (grav′-ih-TAY′-shun-ul pu-TEN′-shul EN′-er-jee)   The potential energy an object has because of its position above the ground. (p. 183)

ground   A conductor that is attached to the earth or to some other large object that can freely accept or give up electrons. (p. 458)

ground-fault interrupter   An electric safety device designed for bathrooms or other places where there is water. (p. 486)

half-life   The time required for half of the nuclei in a sample of a radioactive isotope to decay. (p. 580)

halogen (HAL′-uh-jen)   Any of the elements found just to the left of the inert gases on the periodic table. When a halogen combines with an element from the left side of the table, it forms a compound known as a salt. (p. 106)

heating system   A system used to bring heat into a space. (p. 222)

heat of fusion (HEET uv FYOO′-zhun)   The amount of heat required to melt each gram of a pure solid substance. (p. 222)

heat of vaporization (HEET uv vay-per-uh-ZAY′-shun)   The amount of heat required to turn each gram of a pure substance from a liquid into a gas. (p. 223)

hertz (HERTS)   The SI unit for frequency. (p. 354)

horizontal axis   In a graph, the horizontal line labeled with one of the measured quantities. (p. 26)

humidity (hyoo-MID′-ih-tee)   The amount of water vapor in the air. (p. 645)

hydrocarbon (HĪ-drō-kar-bun)   A compound of two elements, carbon and hydrogen. (p. 297)

hydroelectric (hī′-drō-ih-LEK′-trik)   A term that refers to the generation of electric energy by using falling water. (p. 516)

hydroxide ion (hī-DROK′-sīd Ī′-un)   The negative ion OH⁻, formed when a base is broken up by water into positive and negative ions. (p. 125)

hypothesis (hī-POTH′-uh-sis)   An explanation based on a group of facts or observations. (p. 7)

image   A likeness, such as a reflection in a mirror. (p. 398)

incandescent (in-kun-DES′-ent)   Glowing with intense heat. (p. 552)

incident ray (IN′-sid-ent RAY)   A path of light moving toward something. (p. 398)

inclined plane   A flat surface (plane) that slants; one kind of machine. (p. 200)

incomplete burning   A burning in which carbon monoxide and soot, in addition to carbon dioxide and water vapor, are formed. (p. 310)

index of refraction (IN′-deks uv ree-FRAK′-shun)   The ratio between the speed of light in a vacuum and the speed of light in a particular substance; speed of light (in vacuum)/speed of light (in substance). (p. 113)

indirect observation   An observation made using instruments as well as the senses. (p. 5)

indirect solar   Describes a system in which solar energy is absorbed by a south-facing wall; heat storage material such as brick, stone, concrete, or drums of water; energy absorbed by a wall which is then radiated into living space. (p. 630)

induced charge (in-DEWST′ CHARJ)   A charge on an object that results from the object being close to an object that is strongly charged. (p. 457)

induction (in-DUK′-shun)   The process of charging an object by bringing it near a charged object. (p. 458)

inert gas (ih-NERT′ GAS)   Any of the elements in the far right column of the periodic table. An inert gas is not likely to react with other elements. (p. 106)

inertia (ih-NER′-shuh)   The tendency of an object to remain at rest, if it is at rest, or to continue moving in a straight line at constant speed, if it is in motion. (p. 157)

inference (IN′-fer-uns)   A possible relationship or cause between observations. (p. 12)

infrared radiation (in-fruh-RED′ ray-dee-AY′-shun)   The part of the electromagnetic spectrum between microwaves and visible light; humans detect this radiation as heat. (p. 226)

inhibitor (in-HIB′-it-er)   A substance that blocks the course of a reaction and thereby slows the reaction down. (p. 286)

in parallel   A term that describes the connections of branches of an electric circuit so that the current divides up among the branches. (p. 482)

in series   A term that describes the connection of parts of an electric circuit so that the same current goes through all the parts. (p. 479)

insulator (IN′-suh-lay-ter)   A substance that is a poor conductor of heat. (p. 226) A material through which electrons cannot move. (p. 455)

internal combustion engine   An engine in which fuel is burned inside the engine. (p. 321)

internal energy   The energy inside a substance. (p. 225)

ion (Ī′-un)   An atom, group of atoms, or molecule that has acquired a net electric charge by gaining or losing electrons. (p. 119)

ionic bond (i-ON′-ik BOND)   A sort of invisible tie between oppositely charged atoms (ions), created by the pull between opposite charges. (p. 122)

ionic compound (ī-ON′-ik KOM′-pownd)   A compound held together by bonds between oppositely charged atoms (ions). (p. 121)

isomer (Ī′-suh-mer)   Any of two or more chemical compounds having the same molecular formula but different structures. (p. 301)

isotope (Ī′-suh-tōp)   Any of the atoms of the same element with different numbers of neutrons. (p. 101)

joule (JOOL)   The unit by which force is measured; named after James Joule, a nineteenth-century English scientist. (p. 198)

kelvin   Unit of temperature used in the Kelvin temperature scale; it is equal to a Celsius degree.(p. 240)

kilogram   The basic SI unit for mass. A liter of water has a mass of one kilogram. (p. 20)

kilometer (KIL′-uh-meet′-er)   One thousand meters. (p. 17)

kinetic energy (kih-NET′-ik EN′-er-jee)   The energy of an object in motion. (p. 179)

kinetic theory of matter   A theory that relates the motion of particles of matter to the temperature of a substance. (p. 234)

known   A necessary fact that is stated in a problem. (p. 35)

laser (LAY′-zer)   A device that produces laser light; laser stands for *l*ight *a*mplified by the *s*timulated *e*mission of *r*adiation; laser light is of one wavelength, travels in one direction, and is coherent. (p. 417)

law   A general statement that describes relationships accurately, as tested by many experiments. (p. 13)

law of conservation of energy   The law stating that energy cannot be created or destroyed; it can only be changed from one form to another. (p. 225)

law of reflection   Law that states that the angle of reflection equals the angle of incidence. (p. 399)

lever (LEE′-ver)   A machine that does work by turning around a fulcrum. (p. 206)

lightning rod   A device that protects a building from lightning. (p. 460)

lignite (LIG′-nīt)   A kind of coal that has a low energy content and little sulfur. (p. 612)

liquid   A kind of matter that has a definite volume but takes the shape of the container that holds it. (p. 56)

liter   The volume of a cube that is ten centimeters on each side. (p. 19)

machine   Anything that changes the size or direction of a force used in doing work. (p. 199)

magnetic domain   A cluster of atoms that act together as tiny magnets. (p. 497)

magnetic field   Something that fills a region where magnetic forces can act. (p. 498)

magnetic field lines   Curving lines that represent the direction and strength of a magnetic field. (p. 498)

manipulated variable   The variable that is intentionally changed in an experiment. (p. 10)

mass number   The sum of the numbers of protons and neutrons in one atom. The mass number of an isotope is written after the name of the element, as in carbon-12. (p. 574)

measurement   A description of a property in terms of numbers and units. (p. 16)

mechanical advantage   A comparison of the force needed to do work directly with the force applied to a machine. A machine with a mechanical advantage (M.A.) greater than 1 increases the force applied to the machine. (p. 200)

mechanical energy   The energy due to motion or position; includes kinetic energy and potential energy. (p. 186)

melting   The change in phase from solid to liquid. (p. 68)

melting point   The temperature at which a substance begins to melt. (p. 68)

metallic luster   The shininess that is characteristic of most metals; often revealed by scraping away the coat of rust or tarnish on the surface of the metal. (p. 102)

metalloid (MET′-ul-oyd)   One of a group of elements that have some, but not all, the properties of metals; the group includes boron, silicon, and germanium. (p. 106)

meter   The basic SI unit of length. One meter is about the distance from the floor to the knob of a door. (p. 17)

milligram   One thousandth of a gram. (p. 21)

milliliter   One thousandth of a liter. (p. 20)

millimeter   One thousandth of a meter. (p. 18)

millisecond   One thousandth of a second. (p. 23)

mixture   A substance made of two or more substances that could vary in amount and often are easily separated. For example, sand and water can form a mixture. (p. 58)

model   A description of something unfamiliar in terms of something familiar. A model is used to explain observations and predict behaviors. (p. 12)

moderator (MOD′-er-ray-ter)   A material used to slow down the neutrons released in fission. (p. 591)

mole   The number of atoms in 12.268 g of carbon-12; it is equal to 6.02×10^{23} which is Avogadro's number. (p. 268)

molecule (MOL′-uh-kyool)   A particle of matter with more than one atom. The smallest particle of a compound that has the same formula as the compound. (p. 91)

momentum (mō-MEN′-tum)   A quantity possessed by a moving object that is a function of both the object's mass and its speed; momentum = mass × speed. (p. 166)

monatomic (mon-uh-TOM′-ik)   The term used to describe a molecule consisting of one and only one atom; helium, He, is a monatomic element. (p. 91)

monochromatic (mon′-uh-krō-MAT′-ik)   Having only one color; strictly speaking, of one wavelength. (p. 434)

negative ion (NEG′-ah-tiv Ī′-un)   An atom (or group of atoms) that has accepted one or more extra electrons and thus has a negative electric charge. (p. 119)

negative terminal   The part of a dry cell or battery from which electrons leave. (p. 464)

neutral (NEW'-trul)   A word used to describe an object which seems to have no electric charge. (p. 117) Also, a word that describes a substance which is neither acidic nor basic. (p. 124)

neutralize (NEW'-truh-līze)   To cancel the acidic or basic properties of a substance. (p. 124)

neutron (NEW'-tron)   The neutral particle that is one of the two kinds of particles that make up the nucleus of an atom. (p. 101)

newton   The SI unit of force, named after Isaac Newton (1642–1727). One newton is the amount of force required to speed up a 1-kg mass an additional 1 m/s every second. (p. 101)

Newton's first law of motion   An object at rest remains at rest, and an object in motion continues moving in a straight line at constant speed, unless acted upon by an unbalanced force. (p. 156)

Newton's second law of motion   When an unbalanced force acts on an object, the acceleration caused by the force, times the mass of the object, equals the force: force = mass × acceleration. (p. 160)

Newton's third law of motion   For every force there is an equal and opposite force. (p. 162)

noble gases   Any of the elements in the far right column of the periodic table. An inert gas is not likely to react with other elements. (p. 106)

noise level   The intensity of a sound compared with the intensity of the quietest sound the ear can hear. (p. 374)

nonmetal   A material that does not have all the properties of a metal. (p. 106)

nonrenewable (non'-ree-NEW'-uh-bul)   A term applied to energy sources that are used up at a much faster rate than that at which they are formed. (p. 613)

normal   A line drawn perpendicular to a surface. (p. 399)

nuclear decay   The breakdown of the nucleus of an atom. (p. 580)

nuclear fission (NEW'-klee-er FISH'-un)   The process in which the nucleus of a atom breaks up into two or more smaller nuclei. (p. 589)

nuclear fusion (NEW'-klee-er FYOO'-zhun)   The joining together of two or more atomic nuclei. (p. 593)

nucleon (NEW'-klee-on)   A proton or a neutron. (p. 576)

nucleus (NEW'-klee-us)   The center of an atom, having almost all the mass of an atom. A nucleus is made up of two kinds of particles: protons and neutrons. (p. 100)

observation   What is noticed when one of the five senses is used, perhaps with the aid of instruments. (p. 4)

octave (OK'-tiv)   A group of eight musical notes in which the highest note has double the frequency of the lowest note. (p. 385)

ohm (ŌM)   The SI unit of resistance. (p. 470)

oil shale   Rock that can be set on fire and that contains kerogen, a substance from which oil can be obtained. (p. 626)

opaque (ō-PAYK')   Not capable of being seen through because light is reflected and/or absorbed. (p. 397)

open circuit   An electric circuit in which there is an opening in the path. (p. 465)

ore   A compound or mixture of compounds in which a useful metal is normally found and from which the metal can be extracted. (p. 286)

organic compound   Any compound containing the element carbon. (p. 296)

origin   In a graph, the point where the two axes cross and where both measurements have a value of zero. (p. 26)

overtone   One of the higher frequencies of a musical sound. (p. 387)

oxidation (oks'-ih-DAY'-shun)   The loss of electrons. (p. 535)

oxidation number (oks'-ih-DAY'-shun NUM'-ber)   A number assigned to an atom or ion based on the number of electrons gained, lost, or shared when the atom or ion combines with other atoms or ions. (p. 536)

oxidizing agent (OKS'-ih-dī-zing AY'-junt)   The substance that gains electrons in an oxidation-reduction reaction. (p. 545)

ozone (Ō'-zōn)   A form of oxygen made up of molecules having three oxygen atoms each. (pp. 92, 545)

passive solar energy   Energy obtained from sunlight without the use of pumps or motors to aid the flow of heat. (p. 630)

periodic table   A table in which the elements are arranged in order of increasing atomic number and in which elements with similar properties are in the same column. (p. 98)

permanent magnet   A material in which magnetic domains tend to remain lined up once magnetized initially. (p. 497)

petroleum (puh-TRŌ′-lee-um)   Crude oil. (p. 612)

pH   A measure of the acidity of a substance. (p. 124)

phase (FAYZ)   The property of matter that has three common forms—solid, liquid, and gas—and one rare form—plasma, which exists at high temperatures. (p. 56)

phosphate group   A certain group of atoms, including a phosphorus atom, that can be found in molecules such as ADP and ATP. (p. 330)

photoelectric effect   The release of electrons due to light. (p. 441)

photon (FŌ′-ton)   An energy particle that moves at the speed of light and whose energy is related to the frequency of light in the wave model of light. (p. 442)

photosynthesis (fō′-tō-SIN′-thuh-sis)   The food-making process by which green plants and certain green one-celled organisms change carbon dioxide and water into sugar and oxygen. (p. 336)

physical change   A change in the properties of a substance without a change in the substance itself. For example, ice that melts to become water undergoes a physical change. (p. 64)

pitch   A term that refers to how high or low a sound is. (p. 372)

planetary model   A model of atomic structure in which electrons are said to move in fixed orbits at different distances from the nucleus; first proposed by Niels Bohr in 1913. (p. 107)

plasma (PLAZ′-muh)   Matter, existing at very high temperatures, that consists of bare nuclei and free electrons. (pp. 57, 593)

polarized light (PŌ′-ler-īzd LĪT)   Light having all its vibrations in the same direction. (p. 438)

polarizing filter (PŌ′-ler-ī-zing FIL′-ter)   A material that reduces glare from shiny surfaces. (p. 438)

pole   The term used to describe parts of a magnet where magnetic forces are the strongest. (p. 496)

polyatomic ion (pol′-ee-uh-TOM′-ik Ī′-un)   An ion that is composed of two or more atoms. (p. 299)

positive ion (POZ′-uh-tiv Ī′-un)   An atom (or group of atoms) that has given up one or more electrons and thus has a positive electric charge. (p. 119)

positive terminal   The part of a dry cell or battery toward which electrons move. (p. 464)

potential energy (pu-TEN′-shul EN′-er-jee)   The ability of an object to cause change due to its position. (p. 182)

power   The rate of using energy and the rate of doing work. (p. 211)

precipitate (prih-SIP′-uh-tayt)   A solid formed in a chemical reaction between two liquids. (p. 263)

prism (PRIZ′-um)   A device that splits white light into a color spectrum. (p. 423)

product   A substance that is formed during a chemical change. (p. 113)

property   A quality that can be used to describe something so that it can be distinguished from something else. (p. 48)

protein (PRO′-teen)   Any of a class of large, complex organic molecules serving structural and catalytic functions within the body; these molecules are made up of amino acids. (p. 311)

proton (PRŌ′-ton)   A positively-charged particle in the nucleus; its mass is approximately the same as that of a neutron and almost 2000 times the mass of an electron. (p. 101)

pulley   A simple machine; a type of lever that is a wheel with a groove in its rim. It is turned by a rope or chain that lies against the groove. (p. 210)

quality   The property, other than loudness and pitch, that makes one sound different from another. For example, a note played on a piano has a different quality from the same note played on a violin. (p. 379)

radiant energy (RAY′-dee-unt EN′-er-jee)   Another name for *radiation*. (p. 226)

radiation (ray-dee-AY′-shun)   Pure energy that moves through empty space. (p. 226) Also, the particles and/or energy given off by radioactive nuclei. (p. 569)

radioactivity (ray′-dee-ō-ak-TIV′-uh-tee)   The release of particles and/or energy from the nucleus of an atom. (p. 568)

radioisotope (ray′-dee-ō-Ī′-suh-tōp)   A radioactive isotope. (p. 577)

random   Without pattern. (p. 233)

rarefaction (rayr-uh-FAK′-shun)   A thinning out. (p. 353)

ray   A line that represents the path of a very narrow beam of light. (p. 398)

reactant   In a chemical change, one of the substances that exist before the change. For example, carbon and oxygen are the reactants that change to form carbon dioxide. (p. 113)

reaction speed The ratio of the measure of how far a reaction goes over the time required for the reaction. (p. 279)

real image An image caused by light rays that actually meet. A real image can be focused on a white surface. (p. 401)

recycle To save and return materials so that they can be used again. (p. 650)

reducing agent The substance that loses electrons in an oxidation-reduction reaction. (p. 545)

reduction (ree-DUK'-shun) The gain of electrons. (p. 535)

reference object An apparently stationary object by which motion is judged. (p. 138)

refining The process of removing metals from their ores and other impurities. (p. 286)

reflected ray A line showing the path of light after it has been reflected from a surface. (p. 398)

reflection A change in direction caused by bouncing off a barrier. (p. 363)

refraction (ree-FRAK'-shun) The bending of light as it moves from one substance to another. (p. 364)

reinforce (ree-in-FORS') To increase the effect of a wave because the crests (or troughs) from two different waves are reaching the same point so that the wave is twice as high or low as it would otherwise be. (p. 365)

renewable A term applied to energy sources that can be replaced as rapidly as they are used up. (p. 624)

repel (ree-PEL') To push away. (p. 452)

resistance The measure of how hard it is for an electric charge to move through a conductor. (p. 470)

resistance arm The part of a lever between the fulcrum and the point at which the resistance force is applied. (p. 206)

resistance force The force a lever is used to overcome; this force may be the weight of an object or friction. (p. 206)

resonance (REZ'-uh-nuns) The vibration of a sample of matter due to interaction with a wave having a frequency that is the same as the sample's natural frequency. (p. 388)

ripple tank A device for studying water waves. (p. 357)

rod One of the cells of the eye's retina that are sensitive to low levels of light but not to color. (p. 426)

rusting The corrosion of iron. (p. 541)

R value The unit used in measuring the amount of insulation in a building. (p. 645)

salt A compound formed from the positive ion of a base and the negative ion of an acid. Sodium chloride (table salt) is only one of the many different salts. (p. 127)

saturated hydrocarbon (SACH'-er-ayt-ud HĪ'-drō-kar-bun) Any hydrocarbon in which all the carbon-carbon bonds are single. (p. 299)

saturated solution A solution that contains the maximum amount of solute that will dissolve at a given temperature. (p. 60)

scientific method A system of answering scientific questions by making observations, thinking of hypotheses, conducting experiments, and formulating theories. (p. 9)

second The basic SI unit of time. (p. 23)

series circuit An electric circuit that has a single path with no branches, so that the same current passes through all the conductors in the circuit. (p. 479)

short circuit A dangerous condition that results when the part of an electric circuit with the most resistance is bypassed. A short circuit can cause a fire. (p. 485)

SI The modern metric system of measurement. The letters *SI* come from the French name for *international system*. (p. 17)

simple machine A type of machine that includes inclined planes, including all wedges and screws, and all classes of levers. (p. 209)

simple sugar See *glucose.*

single replacement reaction A reaction in which an element in a compound is replaced with another element. (p. 265)

slope The steepness of a graph line; the greater the slope the steeper the line; in the equation of a line, $y = mx + b$, m represents the slope. (p. 148)

solar cell A device that releases electrons, thus creating a current and producing electric energy, when sunlight strikes it. (p. 516)

solar pond A pond containing heavily salted water from which heat does not escape. The heat can be used to generate electricity or to heat water. (p. 637)

solid A kind of matter that has a definite volume and that keeps its shape when put in a container of another shape. (p. 56)

soluble (SOL'-yoo-bul) A term applied to a substance that is able to dissolve in a particular substance. (p. 69)

solute (SOL'-yoot) The substance that dissolves in another substance. For example, when sugar dissolves in water, sugar is the solute. (p. 59)

solution (suh-LOO′-shun)   A special kind of mixture in which the substances are spread evenly throughout each other. (p. 58)

solvent (SOL′-vent)   The substance in which another substance dissolves. For example, when sugar dissolves in water, water is the solvent. (p. 59)

sound insulator   A material that carries sound poorly. All sound insulators are made of materials that trap air. (p. 368)

special theory of relativity   A theory proposed by Albert Einstein and that has two points: the first being that there is no way to tell the difference between something at rest and something moving at constant velocity (in other words, there is no universal frame of reference), and the second being that the speed of light is constant, regardless of the motion of the light source or the motion of the person making the measurement. (p. 188)

specific heat   The property of a substance that describes the amount of heat that substance will absorb or give up per gram of the substance and per degree Celsius temperature change. (p. 219)

speed   How fast an object is moving in relation to a reference object. (p. 140)

spontaneous (spon-TAYN′-ee-us)   A term applied to chemical changes that do not need any energy to get started. (p. 557)

square centimeter   The area of a square that is one centimeter on each side. (p. 19)

square meter   The area of a square that is one meter on each side; the basic SI unit of area. (p. 19)

static charge   An electric charge that is not moving. (p. 454)

static electricity   The term used to describe the charge that is on a body as the result of an excess or deficiency of electrons; the charge is not moving. (p. 454)

static friction   Friction that tends to keep an object at rest. (p. 157)

steam turbine (STEEM TER′-bin)   A type of steam engine in which entering steam pushes against the engine's blades and causes them and the shaft to rotate. (p. 512)

step-down transformer   A device that lowers voltage. (p. 518)

step-up transformer   A device that increases voltage. (p. 518)

storage battery   A battery of electrochemical cells in which the reaction producing electricity can be easily reversed and the battery easily recharged. (p. 554)

sublimation (sub′-lih-MAY′-shun)   The change from solid to gas or gas to solid without going through the liquid phase. (p. 69)

substance (SUB′-stuns)   A particular kind of matter. Water, wood, and glass are each different kinds of matter and different substances. (p. 48)

synfuels (SIN′-fyoo-ulz)   Synthetic fuels; liquid and gaseous fuels made from other sources, such as oil shale, tar sands, and biomass. (p. 625)

synthesis reaction (SIN′-thuh-sis ree-AK′-shun)   Any chemical reaction in which a single compound is formed from the combination of two or more elements or compounds. (p. 263)

temperature   A measure of how hot or cold something is. (p. 216)

tetrahedron (teh-truh-HEE′-drun)   A polyhedron with four faces; if the faces are equilateral triangles, the tetrahedron is said to be regular; methane and many other carbon compounds have the shape of a regular tetrahedron. (p. 298)

theory   A well-tested model or set of hypotheses about some aspect of the natural world. (p. 13)

thermocouple (THER′-mō-kuh-pul)   A device in which electric current is produced by the contact of two metals at different temperatures. (p. 515)

thermostat   A device to control heating and cooling. (p. 67)

total internal reflection   A phenomenon in which light rays are not refracted as they meet a boundary between two surfaces, but rather, are completely reflected; the light rays do not leave the original medium; the phenomenon occurs when light rays meet the boundary surface at an angle greater than the critical angle. (p. 414)

transformer   A device that raises or lowers voltage. (p. 517)

transition metal   Any of the metals other than alkali and alkaline earth metals; group includes many useful metals including iron, copper, and gold. (p. 103)

translucent (trans-LOO′-sent)   Partly capable of being seen through because some light is transmitted but some light is reflected and absorbed. (p. 397)

transmutation (trans-myoo-TAY′-shun)   A process in which one element is changed into another element. (p. 587)

transparent (trans-PA′-rent)   Capable of being seen through. (p. 397)

transverse wave (trans-VERS' WAYV)   A wave, such as a water wave, in which particles move crosswise to the direction of the wave motion. (p. 356)

trough (TROF)   One of the places in a transverse wave where the surface is lowest. (p. 359)

turbine (TER'-bin)   A type of engine in which a gas pushes against the engine blades and causes them and the shaft to rotate. (pp. 322, 512)

unknown   The term for what is asked for in a problem. (p. 35)

unsaturated hydrocarbon (uh-SACH'-er-ayt-ud HĪ'-drō-kar-bun)   Any hydrocarbon having at least one double or triple bond. (p. 303)

unsaturated solution   A solution that contains less than the maximum amount of solute that will dissolve at a given temperature. (p. 60)

variable (VAYR-ee-uh-bul)   A changeable factor that influences the outcome of an experiment. (p. 10)

velocity (veh-LOS'-it-ee)   The speed and direction of a motion. (p. 140)

vertical axis   In a graph, the vertical line labeled with one of the measured quantities. (p. 26)

vibrate   To move back and forth. (p. 236)

virtual image (VERCH'-uh-wul IH'-muj)   An image caused by light rays that appear to meet but do not actually do so. (p. 399)

vocal cords   What produce vibrations in your throat, and thus sound. (p. 368)

volt   The SI unit of voltage. (p. 464)

voltage (VŌL'-tuj)   The amount of energy supplied per unit of electric charge by a cell or battery. (p. 464)

voltage drop   The energy removed per unit of electric charge passing through a conductor. (p. 470)

voltmeter   A device that measures voltage drop. (p. 470)

volume (VOL'-yoom)   The amount of space taken up by something. (p. 19)

water vapor (WOT'-ter VAY'-per)   Water in the gas phase. (p. 68)

wavelength   The distance between two neighboring crests in a wave. (p. 360)

wave model of sound   The theory that sound is energy that travels in a compressional wave. (p. 381)

wave speed   With respect to water or compressional waves, the speed at which the crests or the compressions travel. (p. 361)

wedge   A form of inclined plane that tapers from a very thick end to a very thin end. (p. 205)

weight   The pull of gravity on an object. Weight is measured in newtons. (p. 168)

wet cell   An electrochemical cell in which the electrolyte is liquid. (p. 553)

wheel and axle   A simple machine that is a type of lever. A steering wheel is an example of a wheel and axle. (p. 209)

wind farm   A large group of windmills used to generate electricity. (p. 636)

work   What is done on an object when two conditions are met: the object must move; a force must be acting on the object partly or entirely in the direction of motion. (p. 196)

work input   The work put into a machine; this quantity is always greater than the work output. (p. 204)

work output   The work done by a machine; this quantity is always less than the work input. (p. 204)

Index

Note: Boldface numerals denote definitions. Italic numerals denote illustrations.

Acknowledgments

Photographs

Unit 1
1	C. B. Firth/Bruce Coleman, Inc.
14	Bureau of Standards
46	Dan McCoy/Rainbow
64	Steve Dahlgren/The Stock Market
69	James McKeen/Taurus Photos
71	Glen A. Knudsen/Tom Stack & Associates
75	Culver Pictures
76B	John Coletti/Stock, Boston
80	John Shaw/Tom Stack & Associates
96	Dan McCoy/Rainbow
100	Culver Pictures
115	Unocal/Larry Lee
133	Chuck O'Rear

Unit 2
134	© Harald Sund
136	Bill Ross/Woodfin Camp & Associates
139B	Craig Aurness/West Light
143	Stephen Krasemann/Peter Arnold, Inc.
154	David Madison
169	Culver Pictures
186	Frank S. Balthis
187	Tim Davis*
189	Chuck O'Rear
194	© 1986 Shirley Burman
203	Raymond A. Mendez/Earth Scenes
211	D. Brewster/Bruce Coleman, Inc.
216	Dan McCoy/Rainbow
232	Ed Bock/Frozen Images
238	Culver Pictures
243	NASA
244	N. de Vore III/Bruce Coleman, Inc.
253	Ken Hammond/Department of Defense

Unit 3
254	Randy Trine/DRK Photo
256	Nathan Benn/Woodfin Camp & Associates
267	Fritz Goro/Life Magazine © 1949, Time Inc.
274	Culver Pictures
276B	Dick Durrance II/Woodfin Camp & Associates
294	Tom Stack/Tom Stack & Associates
297	Diamond Information Center
299	Kenneth Garrett/West Light
305	Chuck Keeler Jr./Frozen Images
313	Gary Randall/Tom Stack & Associates
314	Larry Lee/West Light
315	Dan McCoy/Rainbow
317	Ellis Herwig/Stock, Boston
320	Culver Pictures
327	T. J. Cawley/Tom Stack & Associates
336	Mickey Palmer/Focus On Sports
338B	© 1982 John Elk III
340T	Nelson-Bohart/Tom Stack & Associates
340B	Liane Enkelis/Stock, Boston
344	Larry Lee
345	Ted Spiegel/Black Star

Unit 4
346	Larry Lee/West Light
348	Steve Weinrebe/Stock, Boston
350	James H. Karales/Peter Arnold
371	Smithsonian Institution
378	© 1981 Jane Lidz
381	Barbara Kirk/The Stock Market
394	S. L. Craig, Jr./Bruce Coleman, Inc.
396	Jonathan Selig/Peter Arnold, Inc.
415	Ken Kay/Time-Life Books Inc.
422	Craig Aurness/West Light
424	Runk-Schoenberger/Grant Heilman
426	Bill Kleeman/Tom Stack & Associates
430	Bob McKeever/Tom Stack & Associates
433	Stephen J. Krasemann/DRK Photo

Unit 5
448	Larry Lee
450	Chuck O'Rear/West Light
452	T. Hamburgh/Tom Stack & Associates
473	U.S. Department of Interior/National Park Service Edison National Historic Site
477	John Blaustein/Woodfin Camp & Associates
488	Chuck O'Rear/West Light
494	Paul Chesley/Aspen
503	The Bettman Archive
512	Craig Aurness/Woodfin Camp & Associates
514	Brian Parker/Tom Stack & Associates
517	Dave Spier/Tom Stack & Associates
520	Brian Parker/Tom Stack & Associates
528	Chuck O'Rear/West Light
529	Courtesy Magnavox

Unit 6
530	Dale Jorgensen/Tom Stack & Associates
532	Jim Harrison/Stock, Boston
537	Tom Tracy
541	Richard Pasley/Stock, Boston
543	Roger Ressmeyer/Starlight
544	Chuck Keeler Jr./Frozen Images
547	The Polaroid Corporation
550	John Earle/The Stock Market
559	Alcoa Aluminum
562T	Dick Durrance/Woodfin Camp & Associates
566	James Kilkelly/DOT
568	Chuck O'Rear/Woodfin Camp & Associates
570	Culver Pictures
581	Ray Hunold
584	California Institute of Technology and Carnegie Institute of Washington
591	Tom Tracy
595	NASA
596B	Bernard Gotfryd/Woodfin Camp & Associates
600	Dan McCoy/Rainbow
601	Howard Sochurek/Woodfin Camp & Associates

Unit 7

602   Peter Menzel/Stock, Boston
604   Ron Watts/West Light
606   J. & D. Bartlett/Bruce Coleman, Inc.
607   California Institute of Technology
         and Carnegie Institute of Washington
609   Dr. Harold Edgerton/MIT, Cambridge, Mass.
619   Leonard Nolt/Tom Stack & Associates
620L   Gary Milburn/Tom Stack & Associates
620R   Douglas Kirkland/Contact-Camp
624   Arthur Tress/Woodfin Camp & Associates
626   Dennis Hogan/Tom Stack & Associates
627   Kenneth Garrett/Woodfin Camp & Associates
628B   Ron Church/Tom Stack & Associates
630L   Douglas Kirkland/Contact-Camp
630R   Don & Pat Valenti/Tom Stack & Associates
633   Peter Arnold/Peter Arnold, Inc.
635   Jim Collison/Black Star
638   Gerald A. Corsi/Tom Stack & Associates
641   Jim Brandenburg/Woodfin Camp & Associates
656   Warren Morgan/West Light
657   Courtesy Ford Motor Company

**Other photographs taken
expressly for Addison-Wesley:**

Stephen Frisch
5, 17, 18, 19, 21, 29, 31, 32, 49, 50, 55, 59, 65, 67, 68, 72, 76, 82, 85, 113, 128, 138, 139, 144, 149, 158, 168, 170, 179, 190, 197, 200, 217, 219, 224, 230, 233, 234, 248, 259, 265, 271, 278, 290, 319, 329, 337, 338, 357, 363, 367, 370, 372, 375, 377, 379, 383, 385, 390, 397, 400, 401, 403, 419, 420, 123, 131, 138, 153, 161, 164, 168, 470, 471, 479, 482, 484, 485, 486, 490, 496, 500, 505, 507, 510, 516, 522, 534, 538, 548, 551, 554, 562, 569, 577, 596, 628, 636, 644, 648, 649, 651.

Wayland Lee/Addison-Wesley staff
2, 7, 10, 16, 22, 34, 48, 58, 103, 106, 114, 127, 132, 252, 258, 259, 263, 264, 265, 268, 273, 276, 279, 280, 281, 282, 283, 296, 309, 367, 463, 487, 489, 535, 536, 539, 545.

Illustrations

Barbara Hack Barnett
328, 409

Nanette Biers
25, 142, 146, 164, 172, 176, 180, 358, 369, 384, 386

Don Carlson
446, 447

Valerie Felts
208

Lloyd Goldsmith
40, 111

Eric Joyner
23, 92, 148, 156, 159, 171, 183, 204, 205, 206, 214, 218, 246, 353, 398, 474, 489, 607, 645

Heather King
6, 8, 30, 52, 54, 73, 84, 87, 126, 151, 185, 202, 228, 245, 263, 270, 284, 288, 310, 316, 331, 352, 402, 408, 428, 437, 440, 456, 468, 472, 480, 483, 499, 504, 508, 519, 524, 542, 546, 552, 575, 590, 614, 618, 631, 634

Jane McCreary
41, 323, 334, 373

Yoshi Miyake
157, 163 (bottom), 167, 173, 199

Masami Miyamoto
82, 83, 155, 163 (top), 165, 168, 175, 177, 182, 197, 210, 223, 229, 247, 285, 333, 335, 351, 385, 413, 430, 436, 439, 454, 455, 458, 460, 465, 466, 478, 491, 506, 509, 513, 515, 517, 558, 592, 612, 625, 626, 639

Deborah Morse
56, 93, 97 (bottom), 100, 101, 107 (top), 110, 123, 181, 184, 300, 301, 302, 303, 360 (bottom), 387, 574, 582, 585, 586, 594

Judy Sakaguchi
354, 389

Lois Stanfield
19, 20, 27, 60, 70, 88, 97, 99, 104–105, 122, 125, 145, 147, 148, 152, 153, 207, 236, 240, 242, 262, 321, 332, 339, 359, 363, 364, 365, 382, 399, 400, 401, 403, 404, 410, 418, 427, 429, 481, 497, 498, 501, 555, 556, 571, 573, 580, 589, 608, 611, 615, 616, 619, 621, 632, 633, 636, 637, 647

Ed Taber
610, 642, 651

Carol Verbeeck
491

Tom Wilson
86, 90, 91, 94, 115, 184, 227, 237, 239, 322, 416, 441, 467, 553